HOLLAND PARK SCHOOL

A place of scholarship; determin... ...nding A level and GCSE results.

A place of ambition, endeav... ..., with outstanding success in placing students in top flight universities.

A place of self-effacing confidence.

A place to find oneself and hear the still small voice.

A place where the potency of academic prowess embraces the human beating heart.

A place which believes that lives and futures can be altered and that chance can be marginalised.

An Ofsted outstanding and DfE designated teaching school.

HEAD: Colin Hall | ASSOCIATE HEAD: David Chappell

AIRLIE GARDENS, CAMPDEN HILL ROAD, LONDON W8 7AF

www.hollandparkschool.co.uk | admissions@hollandparkschool.co.uk

THE
GOOD
SCHOOLS
GUIDE

London North

LUCAS
PUBLICATIONS

www.goodschoolsguide.co.uk

The Good Schools Guide is a registered trademark

Still undecided?
Ask the experts today

Our Advice Service works directly with parents to find the ideal state or independent school for your child. So if you need some help and support along the way, then put our specialist knowledge and personal contacts to work for you. Our tailor-made services start at just £120.

Contact the Good Schools Guide Advice Service today
T: 020 3286 6824 E: advice@goodschoolsguide.co.uk

Second Edition published 2016 by Lucas Publishing Ltd
Address Good Schools Guide, 10 Greycoat Place, London SW1P 1SB
Website www.goodschoolsguide.co.uk
ISBN 978-1-909963-05-4 The Good Schools Guide London North 2nd edition
Copyright (c) 2016, Lucas Publications Ltd
Printed by Cambrian Printers Ltd

Acknowledgments

Writers

Amanda Lyath
Beth Noakes
Carolyn Murphy
Denise Roberts
Emma Jones
Emma Lee-Potter
Emma Vickers
Grace Moody-Stuart

Jackie Lixenberg
Janita Clamp
Judith French
Kate Hilpern
Lisa Freedman
Mary-Anne Smillie
Mary Langford
Mary Pegler

Melanie Bloxham
Melanie Sanderson
Nicky Adams
Ralph Lucas
Sophie Irwin
Susan Bailes
Susan Hamlyn

Design: David Preston, Harriet Plyler

Typesetting: Theresa Hare, Optima Information Design

Editorial review by Beth Noakes and team: Janita Clamp, Emma Lee-Potter, Kathryn Berger, Amanda Perkins and Charlotte Phillips

Advertising sales: Charlotte Hollingshead, assisted by Jo Dodds, Publishing Matters

Web manager: Anthony Back

Project management: Katja Lips

Everything held together by: Shari Lord

Junior League of London for excerpts from *Living in London: A Practical Guide*

Photography: Thanks to all the schools who responded to our requests for photographs. Additional photography by Hannah Palmer and Laura Radford
Thanks to these schools for their cover photos:
Westminster School
Orley Farm School
Robert Clack School
Queen Elizabeth's Girls' School
Wetherby School
The Cardinal Vaughan Memorial RC School
St James Junior School

BROMLEY
HIGH
SCHOOL

gdst Girls' Day School Trust

EXCEPTIONAL EDUCATION FOR GIRLS
4-18 YEARS SINCE 1883

Fees assistance & Scholarships available in the Senior School

Leading Independent Schools HMC

Tel: 020 8781 7000

admissions@bro.gdst.net **www.bromleyhigh.gdst.net**

Contents

How to use this book

The age range of a school is indicated by the colour assigned to the title bar.

Junior School

Senior School

The circular symbols found within the title bars indicate the following school characterics:

 Girls' school   State school

 Boys' school   Independent school

 Co-ed school   Boarding available

 Boys' school with co-ed sixth form

 Girls' school with co-ed sixth form

 Co-ed pre-prep, then boys only

 Co-ed pre-prep, then girls only

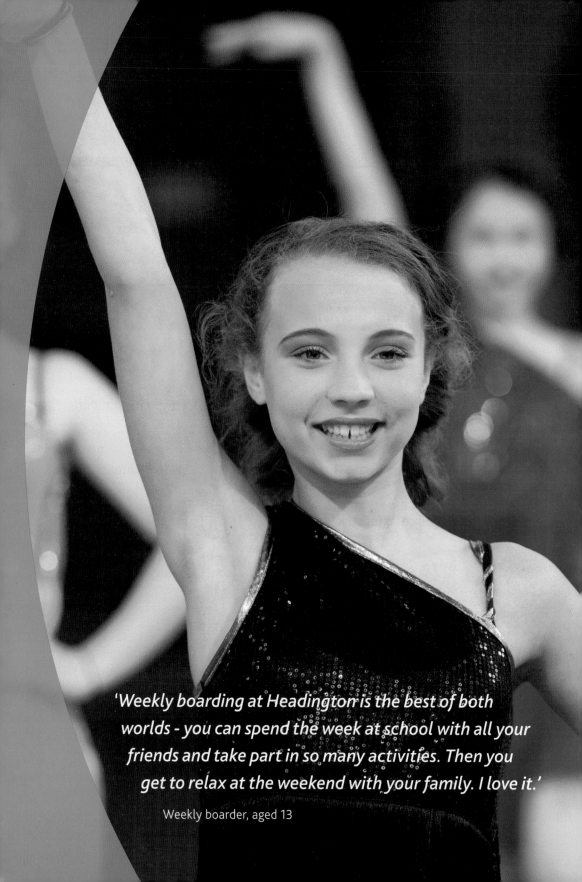

'Weekly boarding at Headington is the best of both worlds - you can spend the week at school with all your friends and take part in so many activities. Then you get to relax at the weekend with your family. I love it.'

Weekly boarder, aged 13

HEADINGTON
SCHOOL · OXFORD

'EXCELLENT' IN ALL CATEGORIES, ISI INSPECTION, MAY 2015

Successful day and boarding school for girls aged 3-18 set in 23 acres in the heart of Oxford

- Dance and Fitness Centre new for 2015
- 240-seat Theatre, Music School and Art School
- All weather sports pitches and swimming pool
- New Library and class room suite for 2016

Termly Open Days and Meet the Head events

www.headington.org/admissions

Headington School is a leading educational charity.
Registered Charity No. 309678 (1942)

   gsa

London North map

Hertfordshire

ENFIELD

BARNET

HARROW

HARINGEY

WALTHAM
FOREST

BRENT

HILLINGDON

ISLINGTON

HACKNEY

CAMDEN

EALING

WESTMINSTER

TOWER
HAMLETS

NEWHAM

CITY

KENSINGTON
& CHELSEA

HAMMERSMITH
& FULHAM

HOUNSLOW

RICHMOND
UPON
THAMES

For schools south of the river see
The Good Schools Guide: London South

Surrey

CENTRAL   45

Camden
City of London
Hackney
Islington
Westminster

CENTRAL WEST   221

Hammersmith & Fulham
Kensington & Chelsea

WEST   373

Brent
Ealing
Harrow
Hillingdon
Hounslow
Richmond-Upon-Thames

NORTH   489

Barnet
Enfield
Harringey

EAST   577

Barking & Dagenham
Havering
Newham
Redbridge
Tower Hamlets
Waltham Forest

University College School
Hampstead

"Renowned for its friendly atmosphere and caring attitude." **The Good Schools Guide**

Bursaries and Music Scholarships are available for Senior School and Sixth Form applicants. Discover more about fee assistance, visiting the school and UCS at **www.ucs.org.uk**

St Margaret's School

AD VITAM PARAMUS

In our 130th Anniversary year, we continue to be committed to providing a secure, caring and challenging learning environment in which girls are encouraged to strive for excellence in all that they do. But don't take our word for it.

"Outstanding GCSE results."
"Strong sense of self worth."
"Outstanding standard of personal development."
"Pupils' attitudes to learning are outstanding."
ISI Inspection Report, 2014

Find out more at
st-margarets.co.uk
or call **020 7435 2439**

130 years, 155 girls, each one outstanding.

Introduction

Welcome to the second edition of the Good Schools Guide to London North. We offer you our knowledge, inside information, experience and opinions on what parents tell us are the capital's best schools north of the Thames.

In the first edition we reported on the shortage of primary school places that affects London probably more than anywhere else in Britain. This year the problem has spread to secondary schools, with fewer than seven in ten families getting their first choice throughout London, whilst some inner London authorities, such as Westminster and Hammersmith and Fulham, offered first choice places to only 60 per cent of applicants. Barking and Dagenham, which already has many multi-form primary schools, has asked all its secondaries to enlarge, including popular Robert Clack, which could grow to 16 forms of entry and 2,500 pupils.

One in four families are reported to have moved house or changed address to get a school place, with London parents paying a high premium for house near a favoured school, and many admitting to buying or renting a second home in a popular catchment area – to the chagrin of those who have lived there for years and find that their child has lost out on a place. Authorities such as Camden are tightening up on their admissions policies, but some inevitably slip through the net.

Certainly many free schools are springing up and new academies opening – but with local authorities being unable to open new schools, despite being responsible for providing places, the match between demand and supply is chequered at best. Less than 20 per cent of free secondary schools open in areas with severe shortages of school places, and overall a quarter of places in free schools are unfilled when they open. In London, particularly, some free schools are cancelled for lack of demand, or difficulty in finding a site: proposed new schools in Walthamstow, Tottenham and Newham have all been scrapped. Others, such as the West London Free School, languish in 'temporary' accommodation for many years.

With the government promising 500 new free schools over the next five years, evidently a vast proportion of education spending – which is liable to shrink in real terms - will be aimed in this direction, with £45 million spent on one central London sixth form. Whilst some free schools contribute a welcome diversity to the local education landscape – offering bi-lingual primary teaching, for example, or a sixth form specialising in maths and physics – others can best be described as niche.

Meanwhile, in the independent sector, four-fold fee rises in the last 20 years or so have resulted in some private schools becoming increasingly the preserve of children of hedge fund managers and the international super-rich. The doctors, accountants and solicitors who would once have sent their children to private school now tend to form queues outside the grammars and successful comprehensives.

The good news? London's schools – both state and independent – have never been so popular. London state schools are some of the best in the country, and although we can review only a small proportion, we give a rundown of the most successful primary and secondary state schools in each London borough.

The increasingly diverse London population is helping to raise standards in its schools, as aspirational parents pass on their ambitions to their children. Pupils who learn and play harmoniously together are a model for the wider world.

This guide celebrates the popularity and achievements of London schools. We describe local areas and their schools, and invite you to let us know about your own experiences. Join us in keeping up the pressure on authorities and educationalists to keep on raising standards, for the future of our children.

GSG Charter

No school can pay to be included in (or choose to be excluded from) The Good Schools Guide, and we do not charge schools for reviews.

In recent years we have helped to defray our costs by selling advertising space and licensing schools to reprint their own reviews for a fee. We make these offers only to schools that are already in the Guide on merit. Whether or not they choose to advertise has no bearing on their inclusion in the Guide nor on the content of their review. Schools we have not chosen for inclusion in the Guide are not allowed to advertise.

The Good Schools Guide Advice Service is a fee paying, personal consultancy service for parents. The Guide and our website also offer other advice on a vast range of education matters, free to subscribers. We receive no commission nor any other payment from any school for these services. We provide information on tutor companies on our website, but they are only included after careful vetting.

We take our independence very seriously and the separation of commercial and editorial content is absolute. If you have any questions or concerns about our commercial policy, please write in the first instance to editor@goodschoolsguide.co.uk.

The British education system

State schools

Many families head for London hoping for a place in a good local state school. There are huge advantages: at primary level in particular, your child's friends will almost all be local, you will soon feel part of the local community and you won't spend hours in a car trying to navigate London traffic or have to squeeze onto a rush hour tube or bus. Many London schools are used to young children arriving without fluent English and have systems in place to help. And of course they are free. At primary level you don't get the specialist teachers that many private preps employ, nor probably the level of facilities, but the quality of teaching at a good state school shouldn't be inferior (see Prep or primary? page 21). With a good comprehensive down the road, you are home and dry. However, state primaries don't prepare children for 11+ entrance exams, so if you are aiming at a selective secondary school you will probably have to rope in a tutor in year 5 or so (see Tutors and tutoring in London page 647).

Admissions

The tricky bit. Many families moving to London want to find a school before they commit to renting or buying a house. However, you won't be offered a state school place without proof of a local address.

Normal primary school admissions are at 3+ into the nursery or 4+ into the reception class (beware: getting a nursery place doesn't usually guarantee a reception class place; you will probably have to reapply). Some are divided into infant and junior schools, the latter starting at 7 years. Most secondary schools start at 11. For a normal application, you will need to apply – with a local address – by around mid-January for primary schools and the end of October of the year before entry for secondary schools, with some leeway for change of address up till mid-December. Apply later, and you become a late applicant, probably joining the queue behind all those who applied on time (see Getting your child into a good state school page 29). NB selective grammar schools now set entrance tests in September, often with a closing date for applications in July of year 5 or even earlier.

Most state schools, primary and secondary, give preference to looked after children, those with specific medical or social needs, then siblings. Some schools have recently (and controversially) abandoned the priority given to siblings so this is something parents should double check. While no state primary school selects by ability or aptitude (except the London Oratory Junior House, which tests all applicants for general academic ability and musical aptitude), faith schools mostly give preference to regular church-goers. Secular primary schools give most of their places to those who live closest (which can, in many areas, mean more-or-less spitting distance).

Secondary schools are a mish-mash of various forms of selection, whether by ability, location or both. Secular comprehensives give most of their places to those who live closest. Academically selective grammar schools (NB many do not have 'grammar' in their name) range from those that offer places to the highest scorers in their entrance tests, regardless of where they live, to those that offer places only to local children. Some schools award a proportion of their places by 'aptitude'; some by church attendance; some use 'fair banding' to get a spread of ability. St Marylebone uses a combination of all three: 60 per cent of places are given to church-goers; it divides applicants into four ability bands, with equal offers to each band; and there are 12 'performing arts' places. For most, distance is the tie-breaker. The local authority will usually tell you how far the cut-off was for the previous year.

Independent schools

Many areas of London are well-equipped with prep schools. These are likely to have small classes, specialist teachers and a relatively biddable intake – if not the sports facilities you find in a country school. They also prepare your child for entrance exams to secondary schools, and advise on which are likely to be most suitable. Don't assume the teaching will be better than at a state school – both sectors include those who would be better off in a different profession.

Prep schools generally don't care where you live, as long as you can pay the fees

A prep school is judged at least partly by its leavers' destinations, so it will do its best to ensure your child moves on to a decent secondary school, even if it has to dampen down your expectations.

A stand-alone pre-prep, that usually goes from age 3 to 7 years, may be a good bet if you are arriving in London at short notice. Some of the children who join at 3 may move on at 4 or 5, so places do come up. The disadvantage is that they are, inevitably, obliged to spend a significant part of the upper years preparing children for 7+ entrance exams.

Independent secondaries range from ferociously selective power-houses such as Westminster and St Paul's to those that provide a gentle haven from hothousing or social integration – with admissions policies to match. A glance at the league tables will give a clue as to the degree of selection they operate.

Admissions

Prep schools generally don't care where you live, as long as you can pay the fees. Many London preps give the illusion, at least, that if you don't sign your child up at birth you are too late. Some selective schools do close their waiting lists early, or have specific dates for registering; others operate on a first-come-first-served basis and do fill up on paper at least. However, it is always worth a phone call. London is a very mobile area and last-minute places come up at the most sought-after schools.

The thought of putting your 3 or 4 year old through a selection session or two may seem round the bend. Indeed, all-through schools (those with a senior school attached) that select this young rarely guarantee that a place at 4 will see you through into the senior school. Even those selected at 7 or 8 are sometimes weeded out at 11 or 13.

Nevertheless, your child may have to go through it. At 3, they may be asked to draw a picture, listen to a story and answer questions, cut out a circle, do a jigsaw, build a tower, match dominoes. Many schools send them out to play together, no doubt with an eye out to see who bites whom.

Selection at this age is not an exact science, and certainly does not mean your child is doomed to failure

Selection at this age is not an exact science, and certainly does not mean your child is doomed to failure because he didn't get a place at 3.

At 7, 8 and 11, most schools set maths and English exams, perhaps combined with reasoning tests. Many have previous papers on their websites. They will generally interview likely candidates and ask their previous school for a report, and may include some sort of group activity. Entry at 13 is getting more complicated, with increasing numbers of London schools setting pre-tests (generally maths, English and reasoning) in year 6 or 7. Those selected usually need to confirm their places by doing well in the Common Entrance exam (in a range of subjects) in year 8. This system is tricky to navigate if you are arriving with a child already in year 7 or 8, and you may need to track down one of the (dwindling number of) schools that don't use the pre-test system.

Many pupils change schools in the sixth form – whether

HIS FUTURE'S
BRIGHTER
AT BEDFORD

GENEROUS SCHOLARSHIPS
NEW AND BURSARIES
AVAILABLE AT 13+ & 16+

BOARDING A LEVEL & IB STUNNING 50 AWARD
& DAY FOR BOYS AT SIXTH FORM ACRE ESTATE WINNING
AGED 13-18 FACILITIES

TO FIND OUT MORE AND BOOK YOUR FAMILY'S PLACE, PLEASE CONTACT
OUR ADMISSIONS TEAM ON **01234 362216** OR VISIT **bedfordschool.org.uk**

Bedford School is part
of The Harpur Trust

from single sex to co-ed, boarding to day, state to private or vice versa. Some single sex schools admit pupils of the opposite gender into the sixth form. Both state and private schools almost always have some sort of entrance requirements at this point, generally involving GCSE grades, interviews and perhaps entrance exams.

Prep or primary?

One of the questions most frequently asked of the Good Schools Guide Advice Service is, 'Should I send my child to a prep school or send him to the local primary and save the money for an independent senior school?'

This question is particular knotty for Londoners. While the standard of state schools in London is improving, the problems facing these schools are becoming more complex. Among them are shrinking budgets, growing pupil numbers and the fact that, increasingly, schools have to fund eg the needs of children with learning difficulties out of their existing budgets.

A primary school should be one to which all the children can walk so that your child's friends will be local

Primary

There are many excellent reasons for sending your child to the local primary – assuming that it really is local. A primary school should be one to which all the children can walk so that your child's friends will be local – people to whose homes he can run round after school when he is old enough. You may find, if your children go to such a school, that your own circle of friends, well into later life, is still largely made up of those parents you met there. If your local school is well-run, the children are happy and the learning that goes on there is evident and interesting, then you are lucky and it would be hard to see why you would consider anything else.

However, not all state primaries offer such a start in life. Many are dilapidated, with transient populations of both pupils and staff. Discipline is lax, often because the parents do not back up the school, aspirations are low and energy levels – amongst the staff, the governors and the parent body – are insufficient to lift the school out of mediocrity. If that is your local school, you may, understandably, be looking for alternatives.

Prep

London prep schools are generally on the small side – though some have as many as 550 children. They always have smaller classes than city primaries and this is a particular draw for many families. They are exactly what they say they are, ie preparatory schools. Their reason for existing is to prepare children for senior schools – in most cases, for academically selective senior schools – and they stand or fall in a highly competitive market by their success in doing just that. A prep school which does not send its leavers in year 6 or year 8 to good selective schools will rapidly lose applicants.

Many people worry that if they don't get their child into a good prep at 4 or 7, they forfeit his chances of getting to a good academically selective – independent or state – senior school at 11 or 13. This is not the case.

The means by which senior schools assess children at 10, 11 or 13 have become very sophisticated. They are increasingly designed to identify children with natural innate ability. The modern computerised reasoning tests cannot be tutored for or even prepared for in any genuinely helpful way. Tutoring a child in English and maths is usually a good idea on educational grounds – all children improve if they have one-to-one time with good teacher – but even this, though it can help, cannot guarantee that a child of average ability will get through stringent entrance tests. Nor should it. Likewise, sending your child to a prep school from the age of 4, while he may have a lovely time in his small, orderly classes with good teaching and lots of sports, cannot guarantee that he will make it to a top London independent school.

Most London independent senior schools will take 50 per cent or more of their year 7 intake from the state sector

Most London independent senior schools will take 50 per cent or more of their year 7 intake from the state sector. These academically selective schools are exactly what they say they are and it is the performance of your child in their subtly constructed tests which will, in the end, determine whether or not he gains a place.

Of course, tutoring or a prep school will help, but only in marginal cases will it tip the balance. And a child is done no favours by putting him into a fast-paced intellectual environment in which he will struggle from his first year and onwards – if he manages to stay. The schools are good at selecting those who will thrive in the academic atmosphere they offer, but we do get the occasional demoralised 13 or 14 year old who is struggling in a school where, through no fault of his own, he was always going to slip further and further behind. This can be demoralising and damaging for years to come.

Of course, tutoring or a prep school will help, but only in marginal cases will it tip the balance

State primary to independent senior

If your child is at a state primary he will not be prepared for entry to independent schools. That is not the job of state primaries – much though many parents wish it were. Consequently, it may well be that your child gets to year 5 or even 6 without ever having done a comprehension exercise to a time limit. To that extent, any state school child is at a disadvantage compared to a prep school child who will have been drilled and tested daily in order to give him the familiarity and practice he needs to tackle entrance tests.

This is when a tutor will help. A state primary child needs that little bit of extra help in doing maths and English tests to a time limit and having the support of an experienced and expert teacher will help to plug gaps, demystify problems and build confidence (see Tutors and tutoring in London page 647).

In general, a bright child from a state primary and with supportive parents like you (you must be or you wouldn't be reading this) has as much chance of gaining a place at an academically selective senior school – state or independent – as any child from a prep school and, quite possibly, more. Prep schools may vaunt the 'special relationships' they have as 'feeder' schools to the seniors, but no decent senior school would turn down the bright and naturally sparky veteran of a good state primary.

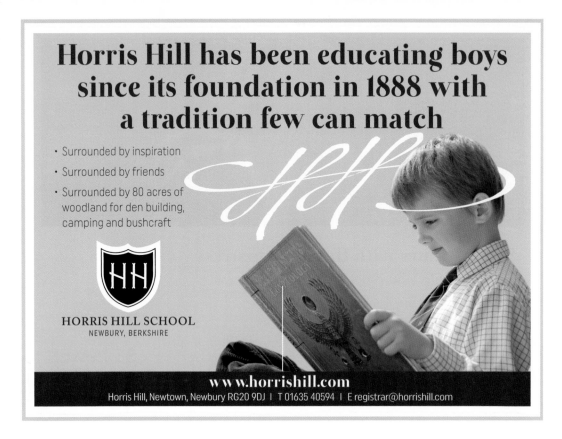
The
Good Schools Guide International

44 countries
50 cities
734 schools listed – the good, the bad and the ghastly
213 schools reviewed – only the good

Local knowledge
of schools around the world.
At your fingertips.

FINE ARTS
COLLEGE

WE OFFER A WIDE RANGE OF SUBJECTS AT A LEVEL AND GCSE

GRADED
OUTSTANDING
BY OFSTED

INDEPENDENT
SCHOOLS
ASSOCIATION
Accredited Member

020 7586 0312

www.hampsteadfinearts.com

Getting your child into a good state school

If you are lucky enough to live in a part of London with flawless state schools that effortlessly accommodate all the local kids, you can skip this section. If not, here are some tactics to consider:

Get moving

Consider moving to a part of London with long-established state school excellence. Generally, but not always, suburbs trump inner city locations when it comes to good-for-ever schools. See our run throughs of the best state schools in each London borough. If you need to know which street to buy or rent in, the Good Schools Guide website features invaluable catchment area maps.

Get God

Failing that, get religion before the birth so your child can be baptised (before 6 months for many Catholic schools) and the family wholesomely engaged in weekly services and voluntary church activities. This will improve your chances of access to an excellent Catholic or Anglican faith school, something that enabled Tony Blair's children to complete their education in one part of London while living somewhere completely different.

Get stuck in

Your local schools may be going through a purple patch or you may be within range of the scattering of selective secondary state schools around London. They're so over-subscribed that getting in is a lottery, but your (bright) child has as much of a chance as anyone else's if you find a good tutor (see Tutors and tutoring in London page 647).

Some secondary schools also admit a small proportion of out-of-catchment pupils based on aptitude – language at Grey Coat Hospital, in Westminster, for instance, or music at

Camden School for Girls – while an increasing number use ballots to prevent parents gaming the system.

Get real

It may come down to helping your child do their best in a less than ideal school environment. This takes time and dedication and is a reason why thousands turn to home education.

Get the information

Research all the schools within your patch. Check to see which are reviewed in the Good Schools Guide. None will be perfect, so look at them from a range of viewpoints, and avoid being over-influenced by reputation and rumour (both can be substantially outdated).

Are the Ofsted reports confidence-inspiring? Are they reasonably up to date? Don't take them as gospel, though: a school may have got its outstanding rating by ticking the right boxes rather than by providing the sort of educational environment that will suit your child. Equally, it may have been rated 'requires improvement' for a failing that does not greatly concern you (and is anyway being dealt with). Do the able get stellar exam results? Do ordinary children do well, too? Do websites suggest a broad and fascinating as well as a successful education? Roughly what does their catchment area look like?

Even if secondary education is a long way off, research secondary schools in the area too. If they are poor, you could face more disruption when your child reaches 11. If good, do they give preference to children in named primaries and are your preferred choices amongst them?

Having arrived at a long list of potential schools, research the admissions process. Though increasingly complex, with every academy and free school entitled to set its own entry criteria, and faith schools providing various numbers of hoops to jump through, your local authority website should round up the lot.

Work your way through the admissions rules. The higher up, the more powerful they are. Find the one that best describes your child. Scrutinise cut-off criteria – often related to distance from the school but calculated in idiosyncratic ways. Note the preference given to siblings, which can benefit families whose younger children are admitted as a matter of right wherever they live, but scupper newcomers' chances in a year with a bumper crop of reception age brothers and sisters.

Don't take it as gospel though: a school may have got its outstanding rating by ticking the right boxes

Get practical

Once you know which good schools you like, might conceivably get into and are in areas you can afford to live in, go and check them out. Schools are individual places with their own styles and cultures. Though a comfortingly large number in London have come good over the last few years, reputation or results alone won't tell you whether they would suit your child. You need to find pupils who match your child in character and ability, and parents who share your outlook on education, and see the school through their eyes.

A visit is essential; being shown round by children during an ordinary school day is best, an open day less so, though it will give you a better chance to chat to teachers, and see everything that school is doing. Talk to locals. Drop into local watering holes and ask what the schools are like or – as a long term measure – consider volunteering to get a unique, in-depth insight.

Get going

At the end of all this work, you should know which schools you would like your children to attend and what you have to do to be sure of getting them there.

Nine times out of 10, at least in London, living in the catchment area is a non-negotiable. Move, live there for at least two years and don't cheat. The penalties if you do can range from cold-shouldering from other parents to the loss of a school place. Some boroughs may even disqualify you if you still own the home you lived in previously. What you do after serving your time is up to you – but you may want to check that siblings get priority over distance if you have younger children.

Move, live there for at least two years and don't cheat

If you need to change school later on, the rules may be different. Once the main process of entry is finished, some schools are individually responsible for filling any 'in year' spaces that may arise through pupils moving elsewhere (and, in London, people are always moving).

Although, nominally, the same entry rules apply, in practice things are much less clear. Schools, or the local authority, keep a waiting list, but the allocation of places can be hard to track. Sound out your favourite school: you are looking at a house nearby, might they have room for your children, if not immediately then over the next year or so? If you get a helpful response, visit them and make good friends. Persistence – and charm – can pay off.

St Lawrence
COLLEGE

Co-educational, day & boarding school for 3-18 years in South East England

With small class sizes and exceptional facilities, St Lawrence College provides outstanding opportunities for all pupils academically, in sport, and in the arts.

Ideally situated on the Kent coast with fast, direct rail link to London.

Day places for 3 to 18 years. Boarding from 7 to 18 years.

For further information or to arrange a visit:

T: 01843 572931   E: admissions@slcuk.com   www.slcuk.com

St Lawrence College, College Road, Ramsgate, Kent CT11 7AE

How to judge a new school

There are many new and newish free schools in London and the Conservative government has promised many more. Whilst some are clearly flourishing, others lose heads and staff at an alarming rate, and sometimes promised premises fail to materialise.

Start a normal business and you can begin with baby footsteps, holding fire on major investment in resources and employees until you are confident you're on to a winner. Founders of new schools, however, don't have that luxury. In addition to substantial premises, other chunky overheads include a head, senior management team (possibly compatible, possibly not) a full pack of teachers (ditto), not to mention the pupils.

With such a potent cocktail, the scope for fast track failure even in an apparently well set up new school is almost limitless. So why should prospective parents be prepared to take the risk?

You, gov...

In an established school, all parents need know about the governors is that they are happy with the head – and vice versa. In a new school, however, the governing body's ability to choose a talented senior team, help get over inevitable initial difficulties and, most important of all, replace people fast if they have made the wrong choices, is vital.

You are looking for governors who are good as individuals and even stronger as a team, leading from the front and putting in the time to observe, listen (to you) and learn. Invisibility on open days or other school presentations is a serious warning sign that all is not well.

If your school has an academy sponsor, they will be involved in the governance. Some, like ARK, have stellar reputations. Others are close to disaster areas. Check out not just your school but the others they run. Their Ofsted reports may say more about them as a group than an individual prospectus ever can.

Heads up?

How confidence-inspiring is the head? With his or her massive extra workload and just one shot at getting things right, 'he'll do' or 'give her a try' just aren't enough. If you doubt the head's ability, give the school a miss.

Top marks for teachers?

Check out the teachers. Do they exude colleague appeal (a good new school will thrive on teamwork)? Do they radiate inspiration? And when you talk to them, do you wish you had been taught by them? Teachers in free schools and academies don't have to be qualified. Unqualified ones may be fabulous – of they may just be cheap to employ.

Parent power?

Observe the attitudes and behaviour of other parents or their children. As a group, you are all important in working together to set the school on the right course. It takes extra energy and commitment and you need to know that other parents will chip in. Do they have what it takes?

Premises

Many new free schools open in uninspiring 'temporary' buildings, with the promise of a move to a fabulous purpose built (but often unspecified) site in a year or two. If the year or two is stretching out indefinitely with no sign of building work finishing (or even starting), beware.

Do your homework

Read every line of the prospectus and then consider what's between those lines. How geared up is the school to deal with 'a touch' of dyslexia? Do the less co-ordinated ever get picked for matches? Is this an 'all work and no play' school? What happens if it becomes successful and oversubscribed and its catchment area shrinks? Will your second child still qualify for a place or will you, and similar other pioneers, be penalised?

Now read on...
For the altruistic, the inner glow that comes with helping improve English education may be enough. For others, the hope that a brand new school will do your child proud is a more tangible benefit. Whatever your reason, good luck!

The Good Schools Guide Advice Service

The Good Schools Guide Advice Service (GSGAS) is a personal service for individual families covering every aspect of schools and education. The advisors are our most experienced and knowledgeable writers and most of them live and work in or near London. They have visited countless schools, quizzed innumerable parents, children, teachers and heads. This vast experience, coupled with the data, inside information and expertise of the entire team, is available to any parents who need assistance with their child's education. Perhaps most importantly, our advisors understand how challenging it can be to be a parent. We are sympathetic and will help in whatever way we can to set you and your child on the right track.

How can we help?

Because The Good Schools Guide Advice Service is a personal service, run on a one-to-one basis, we can help you in whatever way you need us to. You tell us what you require and we tell you how we can help, whether it's advice about places in London schools or something entirely different. Our website: www.gsgexpertschoolsconsultants.co.uk shows you all the services we offer. You can also see details about our advisors and how they can help you. All information is treated in the strictest confidence. Example fees quoted were correct at the time of publication.

London Service

In 2015 we launched our unique London Service, especially to meet the needs of families new to London who need guidance, not just on schools but on areas, family services, nurseries, playgroups, tutors etc in the capital. You will find all details on our website.

Shrewsbury House Preparatory School

Shrewsbury House School is an IAPS Preparatory School for boys aged 7-13

"This is a first class Prep School where academic rigour is balanced by an equally strong offering in arts and sports."

The Good Schools Guide

"Rivals are green about Shrewsbury House's academic record"

The Tatler Schools Guide, 2016

"Extra-curricular activities contribute highly to school life."

ISI Inspection

107 Ditton Road, Surbiton, Surrey, KT6 6RL
Telephone: 020 8399 3066 Fax: 020 8339 9529
office@shspost.co.uk shrewsburyhouse.net

INSPIRATIONAL
Box Hill School
for girls and boys aged 11–18

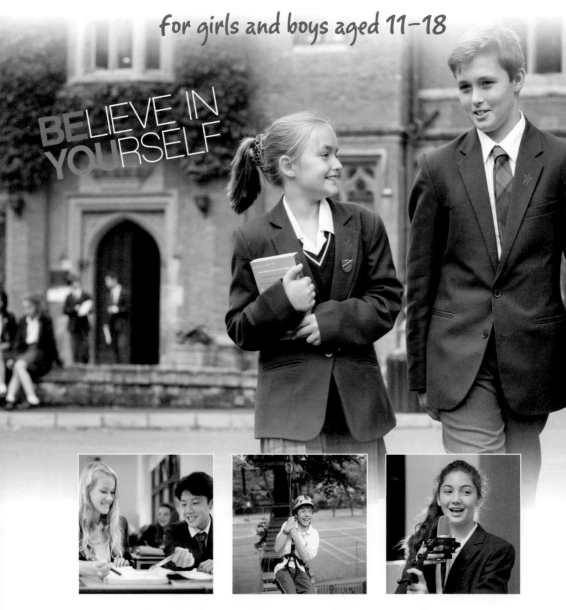

BELIEVE IN YOURSELF

Box Hill School, Mickleham, Dorking, Surrey RH5 6EA
Telephone: +44 (0)1372 373382
Email: enquiries@boxhillschool.com

www.boxhillschool.com

State School Service

In order to meet the needs of increasing numbers of enquirers who are interested in the state sector only, The Good Schools Guide Advice Service now has a new service with its own expert in state school education.

Our aim to be as flexible as possible to meet whatever educational needs parents and children have. In order to keep the fees as low as possible, the State School Service offers parents a choice of consultation packages starting at £50.

Academic assessments

If you're not sure what academic level your child is at, we can undertake academic assessments; we also have a superb team of experts in SEN. Our advisors have professional links with leading experts in fields such as educational psychology and tutoring.

Scholarships and bursaries

The Good Schools Guide Advice Service has amassed information on scholarships and bursaries to create a unique central resource for parents. We now hold information on the fee assistance available at more than 500 schools and the number is growing daily. There is a cost for this service as the search can take some time but we keep our fees as low as possible. For example, if you want a list of ten top senior schools in London which offer, potentially, 100 per cent of fees for a bright child, we would charge around £150.

What should I do?

Phone us on +44 (0)203 286 6824 or send us a brief email to advice@goodschoolsguide.co.uk outlining what you need. Tell us the age of your child and where you live plus your contact details. We will contact you within 48 hours of your initial phone call or email and make sure that we match you with the right advisor. Consultations can be conducted over the phone or email but our advisors are happy to meet you face to face if you prefer. Urgent enquiries are dealt with urgently. We can find an advisor to speak with you within the hour if necessary.

How much?

We provide one of the most competitively priced tailor-made advice services in the UK. Check our website for current fees.

Central

CENTRAL

CAMDEN

An introduction to Central London and its state schools

Today London's state schools are amongst the best in England. This may come as a surprise to those who can remember back to the bad old days of the 1980s and '90s, when many parents were choosing to send children to independent secondary schools or to move out of London altogether to avoid the perils of the local comp.

This turnaround was largely due to the highly effective London Challenge, which operated between 2003 and 2011. This scheme saw strong heads mentoring those in weak schools, zero tolerance of low expectations and the smart use of data to track pupil progress. At its core was a commitment to breaking the link between deprivation and low attainment.

The injection of energetic, new graduates from top universities in the Teach First scheme contributed, as did the success of some of the early sponsored academies. The ethnic composition of London's schools is also important, with typically high pupil aspiration, ambition and engagement amongst recent migrants.

We can review only a small proportion of London's state schools, but here is a brief tour of the boroughs, their characteristics and a selection of notable state primary and secondary schools.

Camden

Camden stretches from the mansion blocks of Holborn and Bloomsbury to Hampstead Heath, with its wooded walks and swimming ponds, and from the council estates of Somerstown to the mansions of Hampstead – which, with its winding, hilly streets, exclusive boutiques and streetside cafes – plus plenty of estate agents – has the ambience of an affluent village.

Camden has long been known to have a good local authority education department – and, most likely in consequence, none of its schools have converted into academies. The only academy in the borough at time of writing is the newish and very popular UCL Academy at Swiss Cottage, which was shocked to receive a tepid judgement from Ofsted in its first report, but has achieved creditable A level results and has seven applicants for every place.

The most famous and popular secondary school is Camden School for Girls qv (which takes boys in the sixth form). It uses banding to select pupils of a range of abilities, and such is its popularity that it will only assess those who live within a mile, whilst offers are generally confined to those living within half that distance (apart from a few music aptitude places). Girls are also well served by Parliament Hill School qv and La Sainte Union qv, the latter with a strictly Catholic intake. These two are part of a sixth form consortium, LaSwap qv, with William Ellis boys' school qv (on the up after some rocky years) and co-ed Acland Burghley (which received a shock downgrading from Ofsted in 2013 but is on the up with a new head teacher). Hampstead School qv on the western edge of the borough is popular too. WAC Arts College is a newish free school in Belsize Park, offering a creative curriculum to disengaged 14 – 19 year olds.

A good range of primary schools, though very much weighted on the faith side – Christ Church C of E, Hampstead Parochial, St Paul's C of E, Emmanuel, Holy Trinity and St Silas qv and The Rosary are amongst the most popular, alongside the free school St Luke's in Hampstead. A secular free school, Abacus Belsize primary, opened in 2013 after much lobbying by parents who wanted to redress the balance. It hopes to move into a permanent home in the vacated police station on Rosslyn Hill in 2017. Non-church-goers may also want to consider Eleanor Palmer (in the news because of some families briefly renting properties close by in order to gain a place), New End, Parliament Hill, Torriano, Fleet, Brookfield, Kingsgate or Christopher Hatton further south.

City of London

City of London, the original Roman settlement that still makes up the square mile of so of one of the world's financial centres, includes the Barbican, some of the Inns of Temple and many financial institutions. Its relatively few inhabitants live amongst medieval street layouts, Wren churches and 21st century skyscrapers, and it throngs with suited and high heeled City workers hulking in packs outside the packed pubs on Friday afternoons, and no place for coffee or a crust of bread on weekends. It also has several independent schools, senior and junior, but no state secondary schools – though the corporation does sponsor city academies in Islington, Hackney and Southwark. Its only state primary school, Sir John Cass qv, is an excellent, multi-ethnic school C of E school, giving priority to regular church-goers.

Hackney

Just north of the City of London and east of Islington, Hackney is an inner city borough that includes trendy Shoreditch and Hoxton as well as the Hackney Marshes and Lea Valley (home of the 2012 Olympic canoeing and kayaking competitions). Its educational landscape is characterised by a high proportion of state and independent schools for the orthodox Jewish community in Stanford Hill. It also has a Muslim free school, the Olive.

Its best known – and very sought-after – secondary school is Mossbourne Community Academy qv, whose founding principal was Sir Michael Wilshaw, now chief inspector of schools. It has complicated admissions criteria involving fair banding and inner and outer zones. The Mossbourne Victoria Park Academy opened in 2014. Clapton Girls' Academy (places allocated by fair banding and distance) is also successful. Popular primary schools include Lauriston, London Fields, Grazebrook, William Patten, Northwold, Queensbridge,

Orchard and Jubilee, and Mossbourne has just opened its own primary school, Mossbourne Riverside Academy.

Islington

Islington is uncompromisingly urban, with little green space but Georgian squares, trendy converted warehouses, Arsenal football club, canal-side walks and street markets, thick on the ground with City workers escaping for lunch or window shopping the antique shops of Camden Passage.

It used to have the reputation of being a black hole for good state schools, with parents commuting en masse to Hampstead, but times are a-changing. Highbury Fields and Highbury Grove are up-and-coming comprehensives, and St Mary Magdalen qv a good all-through school with an international flavour that does IB in the sixth form. City and Islington Sixth Form College qv has links with some of the top universities and often transforms the prospects of students who arrived with uninspiring GCSE results.

Primary schools to move house for include William Tyndale, Yerbury, Grafton and Gillespie, with St John's Highbury Vale C of E, St Joseph's RC and St Peter and St Paul RC attracting parental bums onto pews.

Westminster

Westminster includes Buckingham Palace and the Houses of Parliament, Mayfair and Belgravia (with its streets of garden squares and creamy white stucco terraced houses, painted in the Cadogen colour code of magnolia). It includes Little Venice, the area of large stucco houses round the Grand Union Canal; Soho, famous for its sex industry venues but rapidly undergoing gentrification; the massively redeveloped Paddington Waterside area. Also in Westminster are parts of Knightsbridge, with some streets lined with distinctive and imposing six story red-brick Queen Anne-style townhouses with Dutch and Flemish gables, between high-sided canyons of commercial exuberance. Westminster also includes shabby social housing estates and some very ethnically mixed communities.

It has two of the most popular girls' comprehensives in London, both faith schools with various associated admissions hoops: St Marylebone qv and Grey Coat Hospital qv. St Marylebone has some performing arts places, and Grey Coat Hospital gives some places to girls with a talent for languages; both give a large proportion of places to regular church-goers. Marylebone Boys, due to move to a permanent site in Paddington Basin in 2017, is linked to St Marylebone and with a similar ethos, but without faith places. All of these schools use 'fair banding' to offer places to children from a full range of abilities. Several academies are doing well: Westminster Academy, King Solomon Academy (an all-through school) and Pimlico Academy are all rated as outstanding. A new sixth form college, Harris Westminster, a collaboration between Westminster School and Harris Federation, opened in 2014 at a cost of £45 million, much to the chagrin of other state sixth forms that have suffered massive budget cuts. Students share some lessons with Westminster School sixth formers and it aims to offer a similar level of education.

The church schools tend to be the most sought-after primaries: Hampden Gurney qv, St Peter's Eaton Square qv, St Saviour's C of E qv, St Joseph's RC and St Vincent's RC. Non-church Millbank (beloved of MPs' families), Gateway and Barrow Hill are also well thought of.

The Academy School

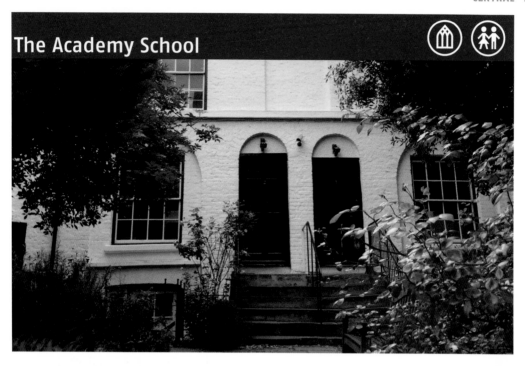

3 Pilgrims Place, Rosslyn Hill, London NW3 1NG

Tel: 020 7435 6621

Independent · Pupils: 95 · Ages: 6–13 · Fees: £17,655 pa

Email: office@academyhampstead.com
Website: www.academyschoolhampstead.com

Principals: Mr Garth Evans (50s) and Ms Chloe Sandars (40s) are joint principals of this small Hampstead school, which they founded in 1997. Chloe studied at the Royal Academy of Music, followed by postgraduate work at Trinity College of Music, then played in a trio while teaching music part-time. Garth, whose great-grandfather accompanied Captain Scott to the Antarctic, was educated at Falkner House, Westminster School and Queen Mary College, London, where he read English. He started tutoring privately at the age of 16 ('to fund my beer money') and went on to work at Trevor-Roberts, where he met Chloe. As private tutors, Garth and Chloe developed quite a following and parents encouraged them to start their own school. 'They liked the way we taught,' says Garth. 'Their children were inspired and given confidence.' The pair are an excellent foil to each other, she calm and organised, he a passionate and reassuring instructor. Chloe has two teenage daughters, both of whom attended the Academy, Garth a teenage son and daughter. Garth's wife Bea (who teaches geography and acts as the school nurse) and Chloe's husband Andrew (ex-City, who runs the finances and also teaches history and maths) are very much part of the four-person leadership team.

Entrance: Though they have occasionally taken a younger sibling, this is essentially a school which begins at 6, once children have learnt to read. 'We start with specialist subject teaching from the word go,' says Chloe. Pupils join at every stage thereafter, including mid year, if a place is available and the school feels it can meet the child's (and the parents') needs. Maximum of 90 pupils, however, and the school tends to be fullest in the summer. Pupils are assessed rather than tested, taking part in a class to see how they fit in. 'We're happy to work with the very strong and the very weak,' says Chloe. 'The questions we ask are: "Do we think we can do a good job?" "Do we like the family?"' Occasional year 7 places for boys after the 11-plus exodus of girls.

Exit: To a wide range of schools but most get their first choice. St Paul's, North London Collegiate, City of London, Westminster, UCS, Highgate, Mill Hill, South Hampstead, Francis Holland, Channing, with several scholarships. 'Sometimes we have to work with parents to adjust their expectations, particularly if they've set their heart on a specific school from an early age, but most parents trust our judgement,' says Garth. Others are just grateful for the help given in pointing them in the right direction. 'My daughter is not at all academic,' said one mother, 'but they did everything to find a school that worked for her and she is now immensely happy.'

Remarks: The Academy is by no means a traditional school and its approach is perhaps defined by the backgrounds of its heads, who spent their early careers mopping up the fall-out from a traditional education elsewhere. The basis of their philosophy is that all learning stems from a happy child. 'It really is true,' says Chloe. 'If children are happy, everything follows from that.' Year groups here are soft-edged ('We're very flexible about birth dates') and so are classes. 'The whole school is planned round the individual and how best to work with their ability. If there's a problem we solve it.' Class sizes of about 14, but pupils are moved up a set in the middle of a term or taken out of a class to be given additional support. A significant part of the process is instilling the essentials. Teaching, particularly in the core subjects, is rock solid and maths and English are thoroughly engrained. Though most pupils can read fluently on arrival, they continue to read aloud two or three times a week. Older children read for 15 minutes at the end of every lunch hour and all have a reading list and a carefully monitored reading record. Maths is unusually strong. 'Children like being good at maths,' says Garth, who believes that any subject, no matter how complex, can be taught well if communication is clear. As proof, on the day the Guide visited, his

'I looked at every church in the area. Then one snowy evening I knocked on the door here and the vicar said, "Step this way"'

class of 11-year-olds had clearly grasped logarithms, a topic normally reserved for sixth formers. The effect lingers into secondary school. 'My daughter has stayed in the top maths set at a competitive school,' said one parent, 'I feel that's down to the teaching at The Academy.'

The Academy started out with just seven children in the premises of a Unitarian Chapel in Hampstead village. 'I looked at every church in the area,' said Chloe. 'Then one snowy evening I knocked on the door here and the vicar said, "Step this way".' The lower years are now housed in two dainty white Georgian cottages, with room sizes that reflect the era, older pupils are taught in the chapel. Facilities are relatively restricted with only a small library and science taught on the move, but pupils are engaged and enthusiastic. 'They give us quite a lot of freedom,' said one, 'but work us very hard.'

The school day starts bright and early with the first lesson at 8. 'We always felt the best part of the day was lost if you started with assembly at 8.30,' says Chloe. There are no 'class' teachers (though the youngest do have one specifically devoted to their needs). The school believes that 'every child is special', but this is not a place that specialises in those with serious learning difficulties. It copes well, however, with those on the margins and a special-needs expert visits weekly. Whatever the child's ability, most parents agree every ounce of potential is fully exploited.

Games are certainly not the raison d'être here and if you had a madly sporty child, whose primary motivation was to be captain of this or that, The Academy would not be an obvious choice. PE is taught on site by a sports teacher and swimming at the nearby Royal Free Leisure Centre, but there's little in the way of team sports. This is more a place where the question is who would like to be in the team – if the answer's yes, you're in. There is, however, a recently established netball squad and matches have been played against other schools in cricket and football, as well as handball, badminton and netball. Music and art are more of a priority. Double art every week, with woodwork on offer and a separate pottery room with its own kiln. Music, too, is taken seriously. 'We do a lot of singing, since it's very inclusive,' says Chloe and the school has a violin teacher and a 19-piece orchestra. 'It's a pretty odd orchestra, with one person on brass and 11 violins, but it's fun and they learn what it's like playing together. Occasionally, an exceptional player will raise the bar for everyone.' The annual school musical, which involves the entire school, is the highlight of the summer term. School food is packed lunch.

Pastoral care is what this school is all about. 'Children are nurtured and encouraged and set very simple objectives,' says Garth. 'We then build it up little by little and make them believe in themselves.' The Academy is inspiration for all, but particularly so for those who've lost their way or lost confidence elsewhere. 'We're good at turning them round,' says Garth, and parents couldn't agree more. 'It's a bit of a cliché,' said one who'd sent two children from two different schools, 'but they do care passionately about the children. In the case of both my children, they were completely transformed both academically and emotionally.' The school has its own visiting counsellor, who teaches PSHE and is available for any pupil who wants to talk. 'They feel it's OK to cross a line with me,' she says. Boundaries here, however, are firm, just further back than might be the case elsewhere. 'We deal furiously with unkindness or making capital at someone else's expense,' says Garth. There is no expulsion. 'We never send them away, we just remove them from society from 8-3.30 unless they behave.' The school has a uniform – a navy sweat top with the school's logo – but it's not strictly imposed. 'We don't really mind as long as they're neat,' said Chloe.

Families are mainly Hampstead locals and the relationship with parents is fundamental. Garth gives out his mobile number and parents can ring whenever they feel the need, a privilege he say they don't abuse. The parents themselves are immensely grateful. 'This is the school we all wish we could have gone to,' said one.

The American School in London

1 Waverley Place, London NW8 0NP

Tel: 020 7449 1220

Independent · Pupils: 1,350 · Ages: K to Grade 12 · Sixth form pupils: 240 · Fees: up to £26,800 pa

Email: admissions@asl.org
Website: www.asl.org

42

Head of School: Since 2007, Coreen R Hester (degrees in English Literature and Education, Stanford University), previously head of Hamlin School in San Francisco. Was ASL's high school principal from 1995-1997, when her children were both pupils there. Early in her career, Mrs Hester taught English at University Liggott in Michigan; she then spent 10 years at the Branson School as teacher, dean, college counsellor, assistant head and interim head of school. Was also previously director of the Western Region Educational Services.

This energetic Californian inherited a well-oiled machine in a newly-renovated campus. She aims to strengthen the already high-qualified teaching staff, is looking at the role of support staff and reviewing the curriculum so that what is taught to 5 year olds makes sense when they are 15. Highly visible, 'larger than life', with 'lots of presence', she gets lots of praise from parents who describe her as 'so smart and insightful', and 'couldn't be more approachable'. 'She's a great communicator'. 'The impact she has had on the school is huge. She has really upped the game for the teachers. We think the world of her!'

Academic matters: ASL's reputation is tops and an expectation of excellence must be pumped in through the air ducts; parents say that ASL aligns itself with the top US independent and public schools. Classes are no larger than 20 (15 is the average in high school) and children are encouraged to take risks and view mistakes as natural learning. To quote a high schooler, 'Being smart is admired here. It's not about showing off, it's about showing what you can do.'

The lower school's project-approach aims to develop attitudes and habits that set up these youngsters for life-long learning, with critical thinking skills and solid foundations. During our stroll through the lower school we saw a full range of teaching contexts – children working one-to-one with teachers and assistants, working in pairs, small groups working collaboratively on projects, whole class groups seated in a big circle on the floor playing a language game, or engaged in teacher-led instruction using an interactive whiteboard. Spanish is introduced from the start, and lower school classes occasionally spend the day at the school's learning centre in Canons Park for outdoor and environmental studies.

They're also building bridges with the nearby comprehensive thanks to a student–led Lego robotics club

The middle school programme is designed to develop independence and organisation. While some parents initially worry that middle school begins at grade 5, a tad younger than the norm in many US and international schools, the structure is well designed so that grades 5 and 6 share one floor, and grades 7 and 8 another, facilitating the transition from primary to secondary education. 'Think of it as lower middle and upper middle school,' parents say. 'It works.'

High school is preparation for higher education with plenty of options in several subject areas, including over 20 AP subjects, making ASL one of the most prolific AP schools outside the US. In 2015, 91 per cent of AP exams taken by ASL students were scored at a grade 3 or higher (out of a possible 5). The school benefits from the work of a K-12 teaching and learning director who has overseen a review of the entire curriculum.

Older students say that this is a school where you need to be motivated and work hard. It's more of an unspoken expectation throughout, but all confirm there is good support in place and teachers willing to put in the extra hours to help. However, it comes a bit easier if you are proactive about seeking that help out. One parent said, 'If a child is highly sensitive, it is not always the kindest and gentlest place to be. But if they can access the education, it is a great experience'. All the departments are strong, improvements to language provision previously noted, although we have spoken to some dual-language families and kids who say they no longer consider themselves to be truly bilingual, having not maintained the other language.

ASL keeps up with US pedagogy, forging strong relations with leading US educationalists, such as Project Zero at Harvard, and not only sends teachers there to learn as part of the school's generous professional development programme but also hosts ASL learning institutes so other educators in the UK and abroad benefit.

Technology is integrated into the classroom beginning in kindergarten. High school students bring their own laptops or can use the many on site.

ASL can handle students with mild learning problems; specialists provide individual support; spaces are limited and there's an additional fee for the programme. One parent we spoke to wanted to dispel the myth that ASL does not deal well with learning problems. Her child's problem, overlooked by previous schools, was diagnosed right away and the SEN team have been 'fabulous'. The English as an Additional Language (EAL) programme helps non-English speakers up to grade 4 come up to speed for better integration in the mainstream. Intermediate and advanced English speakers are integrated up to grade 10. After that, total fluency is required to handle the rigorous academics.

Faculty of 175, average tenure is nine years which is good for international schools. Not only do 75 per cent of the teachers have higher degrees, so do many of the teaching assistants. Despite this longevity of service, a new high school principal, and a new lower school principal and assistant principal joined the staff in 2013. Parents seem happy with the recent arrivals.

Games, options, the arts: Academics are important but so are the arts, sports and other activities, with a growing emphasis on community service. Framed paintings, drawings and photos by former students line the walls, forming part of the school's permanent collection and setting the bar for the arts. New art building under construction. Everyone learns an instrument in the band or orchestra and sings in the choir through middle school. These enthusiastic musicians then take up seats in the bands and orchestras at the high school level. Opportunities available to travel in Europe with the choir and orchestras, or with the drama programme. Photo labs and art studios busy throughout the day. The new auditorium looks like a not-so-mini version of the Barbican, and it's always in use either for concerts and plays or hosting speakers.

Sports are part of the DNA at ASL but, unlike some stateside schools, sports at ASL complement the academics rather than competing with them. At least 85 per cent of high school students play on at least one school team. There are two gyms, 21 acres of playing fields a tube ride away (students are bussed there, though distance means that this is restricted to after-school activities) and a display case filled with trophies leaves no doubt about the school's athletic standing in the international school world.

Special interest clubs too many to mention – all the usual ones and lots of unusual ones, in school and off campus. The PCA funds up to £1,000 for a well-thought-out one-time project put forward by faculty, students or staff. The head also has a fund to support new projects: for example, the school's robotics program began this way.

High school students accompanied by faculty members participate in annual spring Alternatives programme, choosing between recreational, academic or cultural activities done over four days. Community service with new emphasis on local interaction has 270 kids volunteering in charities and projects based within a few miles radius. They're also building bridges with the nearby comprehensive school thanks to a student-led joint-school Lego robotics club initiative. The kids themselves form lots of service-related clubs that do their own independent fundraising for good causes they want to support. Students encouraged to assume leadership roles, challenge themselves and take advantage of London. Field trips, not just in London but all over Europe and Africa, organised to broaden perspectives.

Background and atmosphere: Founded in 1951 as an alternative to the British schools for London's burgeoning American diplomatic, military and corporate community, this London city school uses every inch of its space; through innovative planning and successful fundraising initiatives they continue to embellish that. Compact brick buildings set on a city block encase the 1,350 student

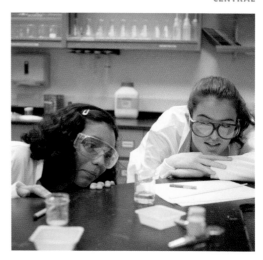

body, which is at capacity. Security fencing surrounds the perimeters and smart security men keep a watchful eye on all comings and goings (no entry without a school pass or photo id). Outdoor spaces adapted to different age groups.

ASL has a strong and proactive board of trustees in the style of US independent schools. They are active and hard-working and take their role very seriously. The last big development project added an extra floor, a gym, new labs and a theatre. The lower school has a pod centre for each grade level; classrooms radiate from a central information space housing computers, reading corners and other teaching resources. The middle school students move around between classes more, and the high school is what you would expect: animated kids rushing around halls, definitely happy to be there. Pupil work is everywhere, for example an impressive student-designed notice board about the US elections conveyed both the US-essence of the school and the calibre of creativity and critical thinking these kids possess.

Middle and high school classes run for 80 minutes with an hour for lunch. Students bring their lunch or buy it in the cafeteria, which is very good, though many in grades 9-12 opt for the off-campus privilege. We hear some grumbles about pressure on lunch facilities; one parent said she was not particularly happy with the early timing of her lower school daughter's lunch sitting. Lower school students eat a packed lunch (from home or purchased from ASL) in their classroom.

Pastoral care and discipline: It seems that students at ASL work hard and play hard. The kids are motivated to try hard to do their best, to try lots of new activities or get better at the ones they excel at. While allowing for individual initiative and responsibility, the organisation and structure is in place to ensure plenty of support so that no one drifts off course.

Parents report few serious disciplinary problems, saying the school plays it 'close to the vest', and that if there are, they're dealt with quietly and confidentially. School rules not onerous but expectation is that they will be followed and the school will take transgressions seriously. When news circulated about a recent (and rare) cheating incident, the head responded swiftly and firmly. Parents say, however, that teachers and principals are not always consistent in doling out the consequences and sanctions which result from misbehaviour.

The school recommends that families abide by US drinking rules – no alcohol for under 21s – which are stricter than those found in Britain, but this is difficult to enforce. If word gets back to the high school dean about a party, he phones the host's parents just to make sure they are aware. At times this makes him more popular with parents than the kids! No dress code, but jeans seem to be the uniform of choice. If you do see the odd shirt and tie, it means a team is off to an away game.

Students arrive at this urban school with different levels of 'street wisdom' and 'stranger danger' awareness. Parents appreciate the way ASL takes pains to speak frankly to parents and kids about the potential problems and equip students with the right skills to protect themselves. A noteworthy issue is that middle schoolers are sometimes targets for muggings in the streets of affluent St John's Wood. Perpetrators are usually other kids

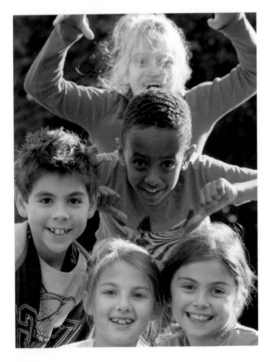

looking for the portable technology now standard kit for many students. Nobody ever gets hurt, but it happens a few times a year. Door-to-door bus service available in the morning and after school and also at the end of the after-school programme, covers central, north and west London.

ASL high schoolers do not have an advisory or home room teacher, a concern for some parents; instead, a dean of year looks after the year group, working in partnership with principals and subject teachers. In grade 11 deans hand over to the university counsellors, each of whom has a light case load so they can give plenty of attention to each of their charges. Daily bulletins and notices are sent by email to all.

Pupils and parents: The school may be in London but the tone is definitely American – let's call it 'global American'. Eighty per cent of the 1,350 students hold US passports, and half of those are multi-passport holders from dual-national families. There are 50 nationalities in the school and the group of great kids who turned up during break to meet the GSG visitor didn't contain a single American! As a rule, ASL students are bright, curious and confident, and willing to express their views about anything you ask them. But, as one middle school pupil observed, 'international passports do not make a place international; the school is pretty American'. The popular award-winning student newspaper The Standard debates this question from time to time. Non-Americans at this school are largely attracted by the academic, social and college counselling preparation for entry into US universities. Lots of 'third culture kids' (professional parents raising children in a country not their own), and expats from the finance world, though the transiency is diminishing as more families stay longer. As one parent said, 'If you are an American coming from another international school, it feels American, but if you are from the suburbs of Chicago or Westchester County, it feels international'.

The school has revised its mission statement to incorporate the 'global perspective', and 'bursting the bubble' is one of Hester's goals for the school, which she describes as 'somewhere in the mid-Atlantic'. After 9/11 the school heightened its security and understandably drew inward but now, Hester explains, 'it's time to bring ASL into London, and London into ASL', with more intentional planning for programming, including emphasis on community service activities.

There is a perception on the part of some parents that it's economic diversity that is lacking, with concerns that 'too many kids are fretting about the right trainers or Prada handbags, and the presence of a few kids so wealthy that their security guards come to school with them, which

If word gets back to the high school dean about a party, he'll phone the host's parents just to make sure

is a bit weird.' This is something the school hopes will change through its diversity statement – and a target to grow the financial aid pot to a level equivalent of 8.5 per cent of the tuition income.

It is worth noting that lots of ASL families are there for the second time. Families sometimes choose London as a posting in part because of ASL; it is regarded by many as one of the key attractions of moving here.

Entrance: Admission is based on school records, teacher recommendations and standardised test results (ERB/ SSATs). Turnover is diminishing, with waiting lists at all grades, which means there may not be space for all family members. Unlike other international schools, ASL will only accept applications a year before admission; the first round of offers is made on 1 February. After that, it's rolling admissions.

Huge praise for the school's support for new arrivals – both parents and kids – including seminars, social events and newsletters. 'It's tremendous how much they reach out to pull you in, because they know you are lost.'

Exit: Most students leaving before graduation do so because of family transfers. For those planning to finish the course, university preparation work begins in grade 11 for students and parents. One parent told us that the rumour that everyone has to go to a 'top 10' is untrue. ASL's US Advanced Placements (APs) are welcomed by British universities, and although more ASL students are getting offers from top UK universities, most still opt for

the USA. Graduates go on to all the big and little Ivy Leagues, as well as the major state universities in the US (Harvard, Yale, Princeton, Stanford, University of Pennsylvania), the major players in Canada (McGill, Toronto) and British Russell Group unis (Cambridge, Bristol, Queen Mary London). A recent graduate entered University of Virginia as a prestigious Jefferson Scholar with full university funding.

Money matters: Tuition covers textbooks, laboratory fees and all required activities except for the music tour for band, orchestra and choir members. There are occasional additional expenses – usually travel – associated with some middle and high school classes. Tuition does not include expenses for trips related to extracurricular activities such as athletics, Model UN or service learning. Needs-based financial aid is available for tuition and also for school-related trips and activities.

Parents say there is a definite expectation that everyone (including staff) will participate in the school's fundraising initiatives; this presents a challenging adjustment for some, particularly families who are less familiar with a US independent school tradition. Besides annual funds, there is a major auction every other year ('Think Sotheby's,' one parent says.) Another parent says that the level of importance attributed to the expectation of significant donations is a lingering legacy of previous heads, and the days when a family's status at school was, albeit subtly, linked to the size of a financial benefaction, are long gone.

Remarks: In her opening letter to the parents the head spoke about 'striving for the best in American education'. Well, this school isn't far from that. The resources and facilities are excellent, attitudes are positive and results are good. Bright, curious, motivated kids do well here and those who are in the middle of the road end up surprising their parents.

Arnold House School

1 Loudoun Road, London NW8 0LH

Independent • Pupils: 260 • Ages: 5–13 • Fees: £17,205 pa

Tel: 020 7266 4840

43

Email: registrar@arnoldhouse.co.uk
Website: www.arnoldhouse.co.uk

Headmaster: Since 2006, Vivien Thomas (50s). A user-friendly, down-to-earth chap with an easy warmth and an unscholarly taste in garish ties (red flowers and giant yellow fish on the day we visited). Makes a point of being accessible on school gate

duty at least twice a week and is generally popular with parents. 'Relaxed, confident, intelligent, and understands how parents feel about their children,' says one. Educated at University College School, Hampstead, followed by St Luke's College, Exeter, where he studied PE and history. Had a trial for QPR aged 17 and dreamt of becoming a professional sportsman but, after failing to make the grade (at football, tennis and rugby), he turned his talents to education. Taught PE and maths at UCS, followed by a spell at an international school in Venezuela. He returned to London to become deputy head at Arnold House, then head of Keble Prep, Winchmore Hill, until 2006. Married to Rowena, he is a man of varied interests, who 'struggles with golf', enjoys travelling and takes guitar lessons with 'a madman in Dollis Hill who used to play with Ginger Baker of Cream'.

Entrance: Application form (plus the usual £100 fee) due before child's second birthday, followed by an open evening held in April/May approximately two and a half years before the intended entry date. Interested parents (roughly 170 families for 38 places) are then invited to meet the head for a 20 minute chat. As always, it is the parents who are being assessed as much as the child. Don't say, 'I need you to get my son into Westminster'. Do say, 'I'd like my child to be happy and enjoy an all-round education'. Prospective pupils then invited for an informal one-to-one assessment and places offered 15 months before entry date. 'I hate the idea that it'll be down to the little boy, that he might be "not good enough",' says the head. 'What I want to know is, will he be a nice little boy to teach? When you open a book, is he able to be engaged? Or is he climbing the walls, unruly and impolite? I don't want it to be a skills-based test, and I find it astonishing that there are tutoring agencies for 3 and 4 year olds.'

Main entry-point is into year 1, with occasional ad-hoc places in other years. Younger siblings and sons of Old Boys looked on favourably. Partial and full means-tested bursaries are available in years 5, 6 and 7.

'What I want to know is, will he be a nice little boy to teach? When you open a book, is he able to be engaged?'

Exit: Strongly 13-plus focused school. A wide intake means a broad exit, but high fliers get into all the top schools, often with scholarships to boot. Two-thirds go on to London day schools, with the remainder heading off to boarding school. Strong links with Westminster, St Paul's, City of London Boys, Highgate, UCS and Mill Hill. Boarders go to Eton, Harrow, Rugby, Marlborough, Winchester and Bradfield, amongst others. Over-ambitious parents are discouraged from entering their son for exams all over the place. 'After 12 years of headship I know the system inside out. I am very honest with parents. What may look like an opportunity to them is in reality a rejection letter on the mat. Granny's all keyed up, everyone is rooting for him, but I know it's just not going to happen. I'll say, "your son is moving along quite happily, do you really want him to get that knock back?"'

Roughly 25 out of 30 boys get their first choice school, the remaining five or six take a bit longer.

'When boys are on the waiting list it's my job to turn that into an offer. We have excellent relations with schools, and that's when the prep school head really earns his corn.'

The school offers excellent results with less of the stressful, hothouse hysteria that so often accompanies the 13-plus experience. 'I offer places to parents who understand the Arnold House ethos,' says the head. 'They should want their son to join knitting club, cooking club, play music and sport, and not be getting anxious if he doesn't get three hours homework a night. We are here for bigger things than getting into a top academic senior school.'

Remarks: While some sniff that it is old fashioned, for others the traditional values of Arnold House are its strongest selling point. 'It's just like the perfect country prep school, but in London,' sighed one happy parent.

In the stressful, results-oriented atmosphere of the London prep school system, Arnold House is an artfully constructed oasis where boys can still be boys. Pupils are even encouraged to have snowball fights and inter-house conker competitions (safely supervised, of course). Admission is non-selective and the school frowns on hothousing, yet year after year leavers gain entry to the holy trinity of Eton, St Paul's and Westminster.

'These boys don't need to be pushed,' claims the head (rather airily). 'It's a question of 'nudging' and bringing a boy nicely, like a fine wine, to the point where he is ready.'

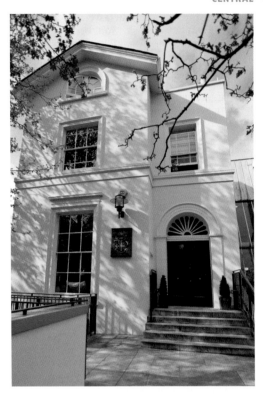

He is a man of varied interests, who 'struggles with golf' and takes guitar lessons with 'a madman in Dollis Hill who used to play with Ginger Baker of Cream'

Arnold House was founded in 1905 with nine pupils by a Miss Hanson, who was keen to prove boys could be prepared for public school entrance by a woman. She was successful, and the school has now expanded to fill three adjoining houses in a quiet St John's Wood side-street. The buildings lack any particular architectural pizzazz, but inside it feels spacious and well laid out, and is probably one of the cleanest schools we've visited. Even the boys' loos were sparkling, and instead of the usual dank, unloved urinals we found modern boutique-style plumbing with glossy lime green and red cubicles.

Entrance is into year 1, with 38 places split into two classes, though classes are smaller at the top

of the school due to natural shrinkage. They are mixed up every couple of years to ensure academic parity and 'social refreshment'. Setting begins in year 3 for maths and English, with subjects taught by specialists from year 5. French from year 1, Latin from year 5, and ancient Greek is an option in year 7. No separate scholarship class, but boys with scholarship potential are identified at the end of year 7 and invited to join specialist lessons.

Lots of examples of creative, value-added education. The Compass Course in years 5 and 6 aims to foster independent thinking, public speaking and IT skills. Pupils work collaboratively to design an EU leaflet, make an animated film, write a play and create a charity PowerPoint presentation. Instead of the bog-standard year 8 battlefields trip, pupils spend time researching Arnold House Old Boys killed in WW1 before visiting France and finding their graves in the war cemeteries to pay their respects. An inspired way to bring history off the page. There is an embarrassment of before-school, after-school and break-time activities ranging from an 8am Quiz Club to Mad Scientist Club, Bug Club, darts, French Fun and Games plus all the usual sport, music and art activities.

Like many London schools has a shortage of outside space. There is an adequate playground, but boys must travel to the school's seven acre sports ground in Canons Park (35 minutes away) for games. The younger boys travel by coach, years 7 and 8 by public transport. ('You'd expect, with the fees we pay, that the boys wouldn't have to get there by tube', mutters one disgruntled parent.) Here there are classrooms, a theatre, tennis courts and pitches for football, cricket, hockey and rugby. Older boys play team games twice a week, younger boys once a week, and there are additional PE and sports sessions at local leisure centres. A busy fixtures list for A, right down to G teams, means that even the most athletically-challenged pupil has an opportunity to represent the school.

Even the boys' loos were sparkling, and instead of the usual dank, unloved urinals we found modern boutique–style plumbing with glossy lime green and red cubicles

The music department is outstanding and has many scholarships under its belt. Some 85 per cent of pupils study at least one instrument and many learn two. Twenty different ensembles on offer, from flute group to jazz and African drums, with lots of opportunity to perform in concerts. Years 7 and 8 can use the whizzy i-music suite for production, recording and pod-casting.

Art is taught to a high standard and doesn't get quietly side-lined as exams loom for older pupils. No need to feign enthusiasm when pupils arrive home clutching yet another art project. We saw wonderful Cubist self-portraits from year 3 and some very accomplished papier-mâché shells that any parent would be proud to put on display.

SEN support is excellent and, with a year of free one-to-one sessions before charges kick in, is more generous than at many comparable schools. One permanent SEN qualified staff member is supported by three visiting specialists for dyspraxia, speech and language and occupational therapy. Pupils who need extra help are identified in years 1 and 2 and either given classroom support by the six teaching assistants, or allotted one-to-one sessions as necessary. Dyslexia screening for every pupil in year 4 as a 'final trawl' to identify those with SEN needs, which can often mean brighter pupils in which dyslexic tendencies are masked.

So what type of child does Arnold House suit? 'My son has been blissfully happy, but there is a certain rough and tumble that goes with a boys' school, and I think if they are very fragile they might find it easier at a co-ed. They don't have to be uber-sporty though, there's drama, singing, art, something for everybody.'

'We take the boys as they are,' says the head. 'We have boys with IQs below 100 all the way up to 140. Once we take a boy on we're looking to be together as a team for eight years.' He admitted that, occasionally, if a boy looks like he is struggling by year 4 or 5, he will have a meeting with parents to decide 'whether or not this is looking like a good plan'.

Behaviour at the school is generally accepted to be good. 'We expect the boys to rise to a certain level of behaviour. I don't know if you can teach kindness, but you can certainly teach consideration,' says the head. There's the usual system of sanctions and rewards with Good Citizenship badges for 'being a good egg' and Industry badges for trying hard. Senior boys get ties for art, music, games and responsibility. 'I'm always pleased to hear how strict the school is,' says one parent. 'My son is well-behaved, but I occasionally hear of other boys being told off, and they are properly told off.'

Bullying is rare but, as in all schools, it happens. Usually nipped in the bud early by class teachers, but suspension has been used when necessary. 'In 7 years I've had only four situations where I've had to step in,' says the head. 'There isn't a parent I've met who thinks their son could actually be the bully, so it always has to be thoroughly investigated.' The head is very hot on cyber bullying. 'If a boy is being talked about in a derogatory way on Facebook on Sunday night, then it's going to cause problems at school on Monday morning. Even if it happens outside school, I will deal with it.' Only one parent we spoke to was unhappy, feeling that a situation had been dealt with 'too late'.

Parents are a mix of multi-national successful professionals, with 50 per cent close enough to walk to school (should they ever choose to leave the 4x4 behind) and others coming from further afield (Notting Hill, Islington, Highgate). Reputed to be a friendly, sociable parent body, though the higher-than-average fees mean there's a lot of wealth sloshing around. 'There are a few amazingly flash cars, but also plenty of beat-up cars like ours. It's an easy, mixed group and I've seen no snobbishness whatsoever.' This is not the place for wags, trophy wives or school gate show-offs. 'It's definitely not a "women who lunch" school,' said one mother. 'All the mothers have, or have had, interesting careers. At my son's nursery I was the only working mum and had nothing in common with anyone, so I find the professional ethos here a relief.'

School lunches would definitely win a triple gold star from Jamie Oliver. A very jolly cook was making roast beef, Yorkshire pud, parsnips and broccoli on the day we visited, and the gravy was even made with a dash of wine.

The Camden School for Girls

Sandall Road, London NW5 2DB

Tel: 020 7485 3414

State • Pupils: 1,010 • Ages: 11–19 • Sixth form pupils: 420 (125 boys)

Email: csg@camdengirls.camden.sch.uk
Website: www.camdengirls.camden.sch.uk

Headteacher: Since 2010, Elizabeth Kitcatt BA MA (Institute of Education). Ms Kitcatt has been at the school for many years, joining from Parliament Hill School, where she was head of English. At Camden, under the previous regime, as well as teaching English, she was deputy head, responsible for 'teachers' professional development' and 'school improvement planning'. Looks a bit like Delia Smith and has the same reassuring, measured presence. Clearly strong on detail, but generally considered rather more cautious and less charismatic than her predecessor. 'She's a bit bland,' said one long-term parent. 'She's quite a lot stricter, but otherwise seems to have made little impact.' Determined to maintain the school's high standards and inclusive approach. Enjoys singing in her spare time.

Academic matters: Camden is one of the country's most successful comprehensives. Latest Ofsted rated it 'outstanding' in every respect (except attendance) and commented that 'it rightly deserves the outstanding reputation it has among parents and in the community'. In 2015, 78 per cent of pupils got 5+ A*-C grades at GCSE, including English and maths, and 43 per cent of grades were A*/A. But the sixth form is the jewel in the crown and A level results are stellar, with 82 per cent A*-B and 48 per cent A*/A grades. 'Top class curriculum,' says Ofsted, and that includes a hard-going compulsory core at GCSE of English, maths, science, philosophy and theology, physical education, French or Spanish and PSHE. Mixed-ability classes of about 28 pre-GCSE, 20 in the sixth form, and work carefully monitored with individual targets set at the beginning of each year. Homework, too, taken seriously, with detentions for slackers.

Looks a bit like Delia Smith, and has the same reassuring, measured presence

The sixth form decidedly less mixed-ability than the lower school, as only those who make the grades make the transfer. The curriculum here is traditional and academic with classical civilisation, history of art, ancient Greek (unfortunately under threat due to government funding cuts), economics and philosophy supplementing the mainstream subjects. ('Softer' options such as media studies and DT are only taught to AS level). Extended Project Qualification (EPQ) also popular. Intellectual stretching taken even further for Oxbridge aspirants with after-school masterclasses covering everything from the Economic Downturn to The Wasteland. Much inspired instruction, particularly in the sixth form. 'It's like an old-fashioned grammar school,' said one parent. 'The teaching is really rigorous.' Lower down, there are those who struggle with more challenging pupils. ('Some teachers just can't control the class,' said one year 9 parent. 'There are subjects where my daughter has completely given up.') Though sciences are well taught with strong results, this is a noticeably arty school – possibly not the ideal place if medicine is your ultimate goal. Special needs well catered for, with sensitive individual support in class or by withdrawal in small groups. After-school homework club for dyslexia and spelling. Middle-class parents, too, tend to pick up the slack when students flag.

Games, options, the arts: 'Art and music are fantastic here,' said one mother with two daughters, one artistic, the other musical. Most parents (many in the media) agree. The school has specialist music status with dedicated music places at both 11 and 16, and this pool of talent forms the core of two orchestras (including a 70-piece symphony orchestra), various chamber music ensembles, three choirs, a wind band, a jazz group, a jazz choir and a recorder group. Both music and music technology offered at A level. Energetic and dedicated head of music. Art, too, is incredibly strong ('Art is really big in this school,' said one student fan) with powerful work on display throughout the halls and a glorious traditional art studio (formerly the gym), with a suitably bohemian skylight, as well as a pottery studio. Textiles equally vibrant. Art is the fourth most popular A level choice (after English, maths and history) with a good number of A*s. The keen also use the EPQ to extend their range (a short film made by a student was recently shown on the South Bank) and about 20 per cent of leavers go on to art-related degrees. Drama too – with the already professional among the sixth form – is strong, with an annual Broadway show and sixth-formers mounting their own production. (Stage management is offered as an enrichment activity and last year one pupil left to take up a recording contract.)

Sport, on the other hand, is probably not the school's forte. An on-site gym, outdoor netball court and attractive dance studio are supplemented by excellent facilities at Cantelowes Park, a few feet from the gates, but play-up, play-up and play the game is not really the ethos here. Plenty of clubs from art, technology and modern languages to specialist make-up and knitting, and sixth formers devote Wednesday afternoons to 'enrichment studies', ranging from creative writing to personal finance and tag rugby. All the more traditional ornaments, too, including a sixth-form newspaper and a debating society. Though there's plenty going on, you do have to be self-motivated to make the most of it. 'My son was supposed to do football as an enrichment activity,' said one mother, 'but no one monitors it. He just has Wednesday afternoons off.' School trips (Austrian tour for musicians, ski trip) and work experience abroad organised annually.

Background and atmosphere: Camden, founded in 1871 by Frances Mary Buss, is an iconic school in the history of education. Buss – and her limerickly-linked counterpart, Dorothea Beale, who founded Cheltenham Ladies' College – were responsible for establishing three of the great landmarks in women's education. Buss founded North London Collegiate in 1850, and then, specifically for girls of more modest means, Camden, which opened in 1879 and until 1920 (when it established its own sixth form) regularly sent scholarship girls on to North London for sixth form. The school went comprehensive in 1977.

Relatively restricted site with a motley collection of buildings, from the high-ceilinged, large-windowed Victorian through 60s concrete to red-brick modern. Good facilities with new science labs, a well-stocked library, modern computer rooms and classrooms and a building which houses design technology, English and music. Socially, the atmosphere is relaxed but purposeful. 'I was at quite a strict girls' independent school before I came to Camden in year 10,' said one sixth former, 'and I much prefer it here. You're treated like an adult.' Good food – pasta and garlic bread, curry – at reasonable cost.

Pastoral care and discipline: Deliberately few rules, but Ms Kitcatt is generally noted for having tightened up on the detail, clamping down on latecomers and absentees. 'Camden Compass' spells out the behaviour code, but generally a strong sense of trust and girls are 'let out into the unknown' from

'Camden girls have a sense of their place within the world that is immediately recognisable,' said one former head girl, and who could dispute her standpoint?

year 9. That doesn't mean, however, their activities remain unobserved. 'The one time my daughter was absent without leave, you knew immediately,' said one parent. 'They really have the girls sussed,' said another, with a daughter who'd encountered considerable difficulties. 'I really feel they listened to my worries.'

Highly praised induction programme eases new pupils into the sixth from, where the approach is definitely 'young adult', with signing in rather than register and no requirement to be on site during study periods. 'We see it as transition between school sixth form and college,' says the head. Loose-rein it may be, but a strong team of tutors oversee 18 students each and offer advice on everything from study skills to gap years. Elected prefects organise the leavers' ball and help out younger girls. Parents in general think the outcome is all that could be desired. 'It's a terrific environment and produces really feisty girls, who are encouraged to think for themselves and question.'

Pupils and parents: 'Camden girls have a sense of their place within the world that is immediately recognisable,' said one former head girl, and who could dispute her standpoint? 'Girls are confident beyond belief,' said one parent with a more ambivalent view. Camden is a cool school, an obvious haven for the daughters of the north London, left-leaning media classes. Current and former parents include the sculpture Antony Gormley, Random House chief Gail Rebuck, and Tate Modern director Sir Nicholas Serota, and old girls in the same style number Sarah Brown (wife of Gordon), Professor of Networking Julia Hobsbawm and actress Emma Thompson. The mainstream here is street-smart and sociable and frequently blessed by names like Hermione, Indiana and Genevieve. But while all participate in the uniform non-uniform of skinny jeans and stylish footwear, this is not a socially homogeneous institution. The school serves a catchment where the proportion of those eligible for free school meals is well above average, and it educates a plentiful sprinkling of refugees and asylum seekers, from Kosovo to Kurdistan. 'It's multi-dimensional and multi-ethnic,' said one mother. 'It's an urban experience, but excellent.' In the sixth form, there's a significant influx – boys and girls – from the independent sector.

Entrance: At 11, everyone sits an assessment test which places them in one of four bands – 28 admitted from each band. Preference within this to those with an SEN statement/EHC plan naming the school; then looked after children; then siblings; then those with exceptional medical or social need. Eight music places: three offered to those scoring highest in musical aptitude test; next 50 invited back for five minute instrumental performance audition to compete for other five places. Distance the tie-break for the remaining places – generally rather less than half a mile. Camden is definitely one of those London schools which people move house for (and sometimes only pretend to move house – a naughtiness the school clamps down on firmly). If that's your plan, living within a few feet of the gates is your only sensible course of action. In the sixth form, Camden goes co-ed, admitting a further 150-170 new pupils (from about 1000 applicants), no more than half of whom can be boys. Once again siblings are given precedence (but only if the sibling is still at the school on the date the applicant starts). Other places are dependent on distance from the gates, academic references and GCSE grades, predicted and actual (documentary proof required for all three). Grade Bs essential in at least five subjects, including maths and English language. At this point, a further 15 music places on offer to those who play 'an orchestral instrument to a high standard.'

Exit: Quite a number leve at 16, either because they don't make the grade or because they prefer a sixth-form college, apprenticeship or employment. Vast majority of leavers at 18 to further or higher education, including 11 to Oxbridge in 2015, and occasional one to Harvard. Sussex particular popular, as are art foundation and music schools.

Money matters: Camden is a voluntary aided school and, as such, has to contribute 10 per cent to its buildings costs. Parents give generously and there is an annual fundraising appeal, with monthly donations from £10. Plenty of further fundraising activities, too, where celebrity watching is the order of the day.

Remarks: One of London's best and coolest schools. Suits the self-motivated, self-assured, creative individualist, particularly those who might find the atmosphere elsewhere pettifogging and unimaginative.

The Charterhouse Square School

40 Charterhouse Square, London EC1M 6EA

Independent • Pupils: 201 • Ages: 3–11 • Fees: £14,565 pa

Tel: 020 7600 3805

Email: life@charterhousesquareschool.co.uk
Website: www.charterhousesquareschool.co.uk

Head: Since 2009, Caroline Lloyd (40s). BEd in geography from Exeter University (although her parents had wanted her to do a 'proper' degree). Her first job as an NQT was at Charterhouse Square School in 1994, straight after leaving university: 'I was young, determined and desperate to be a teacher.' Indeed Caroline (as she is known to staff and pupils), knew she wanted to teach since the age of 7 and 'used to line up my teddies, pretending they were in class.' However, she had a very specific idea for the school where she wanted to teach which included being co-ed and prep. Only five schools matched her criteria – Charterhouse Square being one of them.

During her 15 years at the school and prior to becoming head, Caroline experienced teaching in all year groups from nursery through to year 6. After leaving to start a family she returned six months later on a part-time basis as she 'missed teaching so much'. In 2008, the school was purchased by Cognita and the position of head was advertised. Caroline says: 'It was never my intention to become a head, but I was worried that someone new would come in and not see how special the school was' – so she applied for the post. After so many years at the school, Caroline's application was seen as a natural progression by both parents and children. One parent told us: 'The school was good before with the previous head, but it's great now. The children have just blossomed under Caroline.'

Tall, immaculately turned out and very feminine – this attractive head could easily have been separated at birth from the Middleton family and would look equally at home sipping Pimms at a polo match. Her boundless enthusiasm for her job and life in general is infectious, and we had some good old girly banter (as well as serious talk of course). However, be not fooled, this head is no pushover and knows that some people would call her a control freak: 'I'm on the school door every morning and most afternoons. I feel that if communication is strong, we can get things sorted before they escalate out of control.'

One can't imagine too many things getting out of control at this genteel, independent school, which has had no permanent exclusions in its 25 year history – the main challenge being 'managing over-aspiring parents.' Caroline says: 'I've often had to remind parents that I'm actually on the side of the child, when they get pushed too hard to get in to certain secondary schools.'

This head could easily have been separated at birth from the Middleton family and would look equally at home sipping Pimms at a polo match

Entrance: Completely non-selective, this school selection is entirely lottery based – except, of course, if you have a sibling who already attends. Parents come from far and wide, but predominantly City based. Twenty-six 3+ places offered each year and roughly 70 on the waiting list. No point putting names down at birth: you can register up till the end of June the year before entry and a ballot is drawn on 1 July – much to the chagrin of many parents. The head says: 'For some parents who have been used to pulling out a cheque book to buy their way in – this is one time they can't, which can make me pretty unpopular.' However, £4,000 non-returnable deposit payable when accepting a place. The odd celeb parent (more of the academic kind), has been known to send their child to Charterhouse Square, as well as 'pretty big movers and shakers in the City.'

Exit: Fierce competition for nearby City of London Girls' and City of London boys' schools. Some pupils even pulled out earlier from Charterhouse (age 7 or 10), to increase their chances of getting in, which school says is a shame and 'can be disruptive.' Out of the 2015 cohort nine places offered to one of the two schools as well as a sports scholarship. Thereafter, a good chunk goes to Channing, Francis Holland, Forest School, Portland Place and Queen's College, with a smattering travelling further north – eg Highgate and North Bridge House. One pupil offered a place at St Paul's Girls' School and another pupil a scholarship to Roedean.

Remarks: The name alone suggests something grand, and indeed Charterhouse Square is a historic square in Smithfield, central London. In 1371 a Carthusian monastery was situated on what is now the north side of the square. It was established near a 1348 plague pit, which formed the largest mass grave in London during the Black Death. The monastery was eventually dissolved and is now used as an almshouse and chapel. Charterhouse Square School is located on the south side of Charterhouse Square.

We had high expectations of this school with its enviable location near the Barbican and the extraordinary (if slightly morbid) history of the surrounding area. So we were a little underwhelmed on first impressions. Founded in 1985 and occupying a five-storey Victorian building overlooking Charterhouse Square, the exterior of the school, a smart enough brick building, is easily missable with no identifying features to stand it alone from the other neighbouring offices and apartment blocks. Perhaps this was its intention – but because of its £15k odd fees a year, and if compared to other independent schools we've visited (with sweeping driveways and enviable grounds), maybe we expected a tad more.

Having said that, this is of course a City school and parents know exactly what they're buying into when they make the decision to send their children here. One parent told us: 'I work in the City so I am able to drop my kids off on the way to work, which is one reason I chose this school. The other reason is that I often saw happy and well-mannered children when they were out and about. I know some people initially think it looks more confined than other schools, but it works for us and my children are very happy here.' Also, as we've learnt from experience, a school is not simply bricks and mortar, but the quality of education, the pastoral care, the vision of the head, the atmosphere of school and the attitude of its pupils. And in all of these areas, Charterhouse Square most definitely ticks all the right boxes.

This is a non-selective school which can cater for up to 200 pupils aged from 3 to 11. Entry is by ballot only and not on a first come first served basis, as this would raise 'serious concerns' for Caroline: 'I know of a couple of schools which are completely oversubscribed and as a result, mums are planning their Caesareans to ensure that their child is born in the correct month for entry.' Parents seem to welcome the non-selective element of the school as they say you get a 'range of abilities' and it caters for 'all sorts.' This is quite an unusual independent school in many ways, including a no uniform policy and all teachers including the head being addressed on first name terms. One parent told us: 'I love this school for being individual with very individual ideas.' Another parent said: 'Coming from a convent school background, I was initially horrified about the idea of first name terms, but I have to say it works very well and makes the teachers far more approachable to the children, without diluting any respect.'

'Charterhouse Square School provides an outstanding education for its pupils. It very successfully meets its aims.' Ofsted. This is not a one size fits all school and definitely not a hothouse, although prior to Caroline's tenure, it had tendencies this way: 'When I came on board, early years was very formal and a bit of a hothouse. Drama was only every other week and there were no school trips. I think it's about broadening the curriculum so that we can make sure that all pupils can excel at something.'

Parents whole heartedly agree, and one parent told us: 'I have one son who is extremely academic and probably one of the best in his year at maths. I have another son who is less academic and is encouraged to work on what he is good at.' Curriculum planning meets pupils' different learning needs so the pupils receive a tailored education. There is a very high emphasis on developing literacy and numeracy skills, as well as skills and understanding in a wealth of other subjects, so pupils develop an extensive portfolio of knowledge – highly aspirational with spelling tests being given to children as early as reception in the summer term.

One-to-one booster groups offered for children with SEN, which accounts for a handful of the school's intake. Designated SENCo – but no officially statemented pupils on the register. The nature of the school building means it is not designed for pupils with a physical disability.

We had high expectations of this school with its enviable location near the Barbican and the extraordinary (if slightly morbid) history of the surrounding area

Academic success is proven in the destination of leavers to high calibre, selective secondary schools. For a non-selective school, this is pretty good going, and could, in part, be attributed to the splitting up of year groups in years 4 and 5 (something we still don't hugely understand the mechanics of). To make it more complicated, classes are named not numbered, so there is the red room, green room, balloon room, upper and lower kite rooms etc. What we think happens, is that years 4 and 5 are taught together, allowing them to have the same teacher for two years before the all important year 6. 'Year 6 pupils have one whole year to be exam focused to prepare them for secondary school entrance exams.' Years 4 and 5 work on a two year curriculum with the exception of

homework, and English and maths text books. They are also ability grouped. One parent told us, 'I'm not really sure how it works – but the kids seem to understand it, so that's the main thing.'

It was 'animal dress up day' so we were greeted by a colourful vision of tigers, bears and monkeys

Pastorally, this school is second to none and uses a number of highly effective strategies to help pupils feel safe. Older pupils can make use of classroom 'feelings boxes' to share concerns privately with teachers, and the 'buddy' system supports pupils new to the school. Every parent we spoke to raved about the buddy system: 'It's a great system as it makes new children feel less intimidated and gives older children a buy in to look after the younger ones.' Teaching was highly praised as being exceptional and passionate and instilling a love of learning in all pupils (very low turnover of staff), and the head was praised for being such a consistently visible presence; 'She knows every pupil by name and is very natural at being great with children. The school just seems to run seamlessly.'

Our tour started in the early years foundation stage classes, nursery and reception, which contain 54 children in total. Whilst we were there nursery was having its annual 'animal dress up day', so we were greeted by a colourful vision of tigers, bears, monkeys and a couple of unidentifiable animals that were unconventional and imaginative in their attire. It was a happy, bright and colourful space with engaged children and smiley teachers. There was a sweet little add-on area designed for role play which was effectively outside, but covered by a canopy and surrounded by a high wall. This, we were told, was to prevent anything landing on the tracks of the Barbican train station, which would carry a huge fine (on an hourly rate!). Thankfully, this has not happened so far.

Small but well stocked library from where children are encouraged to take books home nightly, and a carpeted school hall in which proudly sat a beautiful white piano and an interesting and colourful wall display of ukuleles – just two of the features which stuck out. All extracurricular activities such as judo and table tennis take place here and all children are offered the opportunity to learn a musical instrument. 'Informal' Spanish also offered in the early years. One parent said: 'I was amazed when we went on holiday to Spain last year, that my 5 year old daughter was able to communicate with a local in pigeon Spanish.'

Bright, neat, colourful classrooms full of interested, happy and very polite children. The atmosphere of the school is extremely warm and friendly with a harmonious air. Pupils who were moving on to other schools told us how much they'll miss Charterhouse 'sooo much' and how accommodating the teachers are. One told us: 'What I really like about the teachers is that they are all so friendly. Also, we are often asked to tick a box privately at the end of a lesson about whether we found the classes easy or difficult. If we are really struggling, we can sometimes get an extra private lesson.'

Despite the limited indoor space of this tall and narrow school ('I often had to walk up five flights of stairs when I was pregnant,' the head told us), children don't seem to lack breathing space and outdoor air. Every lunch time during the warmer months, children can have their lunch break across the road in the private Charterhouse Square gardens, and every Wednesday they are taken to charming Coram Fields for sports and a run around or the nearby Golden Lane Leisure Centre, for swimming, rounders, netball and tennis nearly every day. Pupils do take part in inter-school sporting events, but no regular fixtures because of the issue of 'bussing children around.' One parent did say that this school is perhaps not the right option

for the 'extremely sporty child', although another said that her two boys 'are extremely sporty and it meets their needs.' A highlight in the calendar is sports day: 'It's just such a joy, well handled and fun.' During the colder and wetter months, pupils can play in the 'jungle' downstairs.

It was lunchtime whilst we were there and (this is a first for us), because of limited space and no designated canteen area, until recently the only option for lunch was a packed lunch brought in by individuals. However, in the last year or so, the school have commissioned a company to bring in hot food in thermos containers, if the parents require. The head says: 'This system works very well and the advantage is that parents know what their children like and can order accordingly.' We are told the quality is great and there is a veritable mix of meatballs, pasta, wraps, soups and stews on offer.

A successful school and a happy environment, although its limited space means it won't be for everyone. Definitely a wonderful option if you either live in the area or commute there. Plenty of opportunity for pupils of varying abilities to thrive, and with comments such as: 'My child loves every day of her school life!' who could ask for more?

The Children's House School

King Henry's Walk, Islington, London N1 4PB

Independent · Pupils: 68 · Ages: 2–8 · Fees: up to £13,545 pa

Tel: 020 7249 6273

Email: upper@childrenshouseschool.co.uk
Website: www.childrenshouseschool.co.uk

Head: Jill Rothwell BA PGCE (50s). Mrs Rothwell (Jill to all) took her first degree in English and drama (at Manchester), then a PGCE at the Institute of Education, followed by two years teaching in the state sector. She became a parent at the Children's House in 1985 and a member of the parent's committee, but it was only when she came to register her third child in 1995 that she was invited in to teach. 'When I rang up, they said, "We'd like to offer you a place"; that's when I discovered my vocation.' She took over as head of the nursery in 2003, then, in 2005, oversaw the launch of the pre-prep. Retired temporarily in 2011 but, after a brief interlude, was back. Parents confirm both her commitment to the school and her devotion to the children. ('She's the most child-centred person; whatever else is going on, she never loses that perspective.')

Entrance: Register for nursery as soon as possible after birth and (crucially) register separately for

nursery and pre-prep (deposits of £1500 and £2000 respectively). Places offered by date of registration and sibling priority. Most places in the pre-prep are filled from the nursery, but 'one or two' spaces available in reception, again based on date of registration.

Exit: Some leave at the formal entry points to other schools at 4 and 5. 'Parents ask if we mind,' says the head, 'but our advice is always to do what's best for the child.' Twenty-eight start out in two reception classes, but numbers generally reduce to a manageable 20 by year 2. Boys at all stages to the main north London preps (The Hall, St Anthony's, Hereward House, etc) and, at 7 plus, to the junior schools of major senior schools (Highgate, UCS). Girls to South Hampstead and nearby City of London School for Girls. Significant numbers, too, to St Paul's Cathedral School, Forest and The Cavendish.

Remarks: Founded as a nursery in someone's front room in 1973, when 'there was little in the way of Early Years provision and nothing in the way of policies and procedures', the nursery is now a fully-formed school, housed independently in a converted chapel in central Islington and headed by Emma Berou. Here children from 2 enjoy a rich

---

In break children wander in and out of the school office. ('We're doing plaits,' confided one pair, 'can you help us?')

---

and dynamic offering (including conversational French, dance and sport) taught by fully qualified teachers. 'It's a lovely, friendly place,' said one parent. 'They really care about each child.'

The pre-prep came into being when a former parent spotted a school to let in the local newspaper. 'Our nursery parents always felt it was a pity children had to move on at 4 and 5.' Now they can remain in the fold, housed in a petite and picturesque Victorian schoolhouse nestled in the shelter of its big brother church. 'It's idyllic, like Enid Blyton,' said one parent.

Mornings are devoted to the three Rs, with much of the work 'topic based'. 'We take an overarching theme and help children make links across the curriculum,' says Jill. (Typical subject matter, for example, is Ourselves, in which children might explore the senses in science, study old toys in history, make a toy in design technology, and visit the Bethnal Green Museum of Childhood.) Often children work in groups. 'We like them to work collaboratively, one child supporting another.' A very creative school; arts and crafts is central to learning. Children might make shoebox interiors as a part of a home topic, create tetrahedron mobiles in maths, and paint and embroider textiles to study printmaking. Homework introduced gently in reception and year 1, with a more significant push towards 7+.

Specialist teachers extend the core. French and ICT, with a dedicated teacher and a full-class supply of laptops, throughout. Singing and rhythm taught by a music teacher, plus a weekly half-hour violin lesson from a professional violinist. 'I want the children to be at the end of passionate teaching,' says Jill. Dance, too, taught by an external expert.

The school prides itself on being 'very inclusive' and a hard-working SENCo addresses both minor and significant difficulties. Good support, too, for those with English as an additional language, addressing the requirements of an increasing number of bilingual children.

Not the school for those looking for an early introduction to competitive team games, but a specialist teaches PE and ball skills (relay races, running, pitching) in one of the two large adjoining church halls. Well-equipped playground provides further scope for fresh air, exercise and, most importantly, play. 'We have a lot of play resources and use them to extend their learning with carefully planned activities,' says the head. Working the nearby community garden provides further time out of doors and educational avenues.

Plenty of 'enrichment'. 'The school is fantastic at making lovely things happen for the children,' said one parent. Two visits a term, a least one in the form of 'entertainment', plus numerous themed days (dressing-up day, book day, etc). All stay for after-school clubs (sewing, fencing, cookery, drama, football, arts and crafts and yoga).

School uniform minimal and practical (navy and white sweatshirt with logo). No hot food; children bring in lunch boxes, supplemented by a snack and fruit in the morning.

Traditional values of courtesy and consideration central to the ethos. 'Being kind is paramount,' said a mother. Monitors chosen weekly, with top-of-the school year 2 given increased responsibility. 'They're so helpful and dependable,' says the head. 'If you ask them to do something, they'll get it done.'

One of the things parents like most about the The Children's House is its home-away-from-home atmosphere. In break, for example, children wander in and out of the school office. ('We're doing plaits,' confided one pair, 'can you help us?') 'There's no such thing as a closed door,' said one happy parent.

Families form a tight bond, regularly arriving to read, organising the summer fair

---

Founded by parents, The Children's House remains a parent-driven operation, with active participation from its Parent Committee. 'No one owns it,' says the head. 'It's a collective.' All vote for the Council of Management, which administers the school. Unsurprisingly, families (Hackney and Islington media, City, lawyers and artisans) form a tight bond both with each other and the school, regularly arriving to read, organising the summer fair, quiz night, etc. 'I couldn't do it without the parents,' says the head. 'They're amazing.' 'We're always made to feel welcome,' said one.

About 10 per cent of children are on means-tested bursary places, covering up to 100 per cent of fees.

City and Islington College

283–309 Goswell Road, London EC1V 7LA

State · Pupils: 1,350 · Ages: 16–19

Tel: 020 7700 9333

Email: courseinfo@candi.ac.uk
Website: www.candi.ac.uk

38

Director: Since September 2015, Peter Murray, previously deputy director of sixth form.

Academic matters: Takes students from a wide ability range but most come here with reasonably high grades. 'We would let someone do three A levels with five A* to Cs; to do four subjects they have to have four Bs at GCSE.' Requirement is lower than Woodhouse College or Camden School for Girls, but the college also attracts 'some with all A grades.' Many come from abroad with EAL needs and do very well – 'although not all are capable of maintaining the high grades expected here, the majority do'.

Results have been pretty consistent since 2010. A level results for 2015 show 40 per cent A*-B grades. Strongest subjects include further maths, French, geography, film studies, Italian, media studies, Spanish and Turkish.

Teacher/pupil ratio of 10:1. Teachers are A level specialists, many of them examiners or IVs (internationally recognised certificate that allows teachers to evaluate other teachers). Others come with vocational or industry experience and do in-service training with other teachers. 'We are one of the biggest providers of A levels, if not the biggest in the country, so we have expertise about teaching

A levels, what kids need to do to progress and the ability to tailor everything to that.' The wide range of subjects attracts many. 'I wanted to go to George Moneaux but they didn't have the courses – I came here for the range,' said one student. The college also offers the IB, which college is keen to grow.

While the past has been about helping those who have under-achieved to reach their full potential, college says the present is about 'finding a way to stretch the ablest,' without neglecting the mission to enable past under-achievers to progress to higher education, if not necessarily to a Russell Group university. College is noted for its strong support for students with learning difficulties and disabilities. The school's self-assessment report notes that success rates for those with learning difficulties have been increasing, especially those with Asperger's and hearing and mobility impairments. Learning support team provides literacy, numeracy, dyslexia, ESOL, examination and disability support to learners at all levels. Support is provided in class, in one-to-one sessions, workshops and in small groups.

Games, options, the arts: Sport is not huge here although there is a football team and a basketball court. Plenty of enrichment activities though, and visits to theatres and galleries. Joint projects between different years and partner schools are common. 'We did an art exhibition with year 11s from a partner school and primary schools have been coming to use it for inspiration for work,' said one pupil. Performing arts centre, comprising studio and theatre space, teaches drama, dance and music and benefits from partnerships with Sadler's Wells, Almeida, Welsh National Opera and Islington Community Theatre. Productions often have a political, cultural or campaigning focus – for example World Mental Health Day and a Dance 4 Life production to promote sexual health. Political awareness also drives the agenda for a wide number of talks and debates, on subjects like the London riots, conflict in Serbia, responsibility and justice and 'the nature of female rebellion.'

Political awareness drives the agenda for a number of talks and debates, on subjects like the London riots and conflict in Serbia

Enrichment activities are tailored to helping students develop employability skills and are backed up by a very good careers department. 'I don't think (other places) have as much as we do in terms of help with employment,' a student told us.

Students are introduced to the careers service from the start and can visit at any time to talk about future plans or concerns about subject choices or to get help with writing a CV or university applications. Well-equipped careers centre (interview rooms, library resource areas, dedicated staff team and plenty of information) organises talks by different universities and employers, including UCL and Cambridge. 'We put an enormous amount of effort into building links with universities and employers and stretching kids,' explained the student careers adviser.

Ready, Steady, Job is a programme comprising self-directed study, tutor-led activities and careers talks, for those seeking employment rather than university. Moodle site provides detailed information and advice on jobs and employment and training fair takes place in the autumn. Law support group arranges visits to the Old Bailey, magistrates' courts, supreme court and law firms.

Students attend masterclasses, taster courses, open days and summer schools. The Lloyds scheme is run at the bank's HQ near St Paul's and provides an employment gateway for 40 students 'who want to work somewhere in finance or law and want to apply for a degree maths or economics'. Similar partnership with Barclays Capital. The college is

upfront about the aim behind these partnerships: 'We are lucky as we're just down the road from many of these centres. We are such a big provider so teachers can use that to create relationships with outsiders.'

Background and atmosphere: The college is located in Islington – the 14th most deprived borough in England. It is housed in a modern, four-storey building with subject departments on the upper levels, and careers centre, student support office, cafeteria and resource study centre on the ground floor. Students say, 'whenever a book isn't in the library they order it from another library. All you have to do is to ask.' Glass building has a bright, corporate feel against its city landscape – it is walking distance from the Angel, St Paul's and King's Cross.

Walls are decorated with pictures of influential thinkers as well as student council members, anti-bullying stance ('It's not big to make others feel small'), learning agreement in full and tips on completing AS level portfolios. Students' fine art, painting and photography work on show in the general administration office. Accolades like outstanding Ofsted in all categories, Queen's Anniversary Prize for Education (second time), Silver Investor in People Award, STEM Assured status (reflecting excellence in science, technology, engineering and maths) and reaccreditation

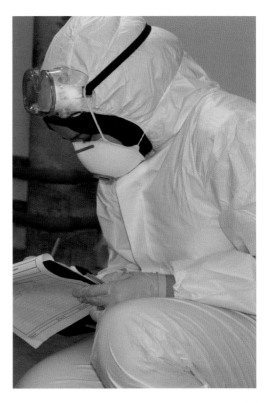

by MATRIX all help create a sense of achievement and pride here.

The site was purpose built as a sixth form college for 1,100 students, so there are works to extend toilets, administration blocks and meeting areas. It is an 'exciting place to work,' where 'teachers end up staying a long time.' Students say, 'everyone in the college is nice, so you settle into your work straight away,' although one or two commented on the 'cliques that gather around in groups in the cafeteria' and said, 'you have to walk through to go to lessons and it can feel intimidating.'

Pastoral care and discipline: In this college environment students are expected to develop independence in their approach to study. However, there is a very strong tutorial/pastoral system in place to help them make the transition from school. Tutors are supported by more experienced lead tutors who operate like heads of year and manage any 'at risk' students referred to them. 'We try to move them from dependency on teacher and home as a lot will go to university so will have to become independent in more ways,' says the college. 'There are rules and structures in place to "frighten" the student into arriving promptly. You have to be in your lessons and do all your work otherwise you don't need to be here. You cannot come here and just do nothing.'

'Parents want them to do well, so you can find higher aspirations here than you would have in many suburbs'

Each student has an individual learning plan, used to set 'challenging but realistic long and short term academic and personal goals.' These are monitored through regular one-to-one tutorials and course team reviews and can be tracked online via the college intranet – 'so we can see where we are any time,' say pupils. Lots of support for students who are struggling, like A2 buddies, mentoring, one-to-one support and drop-in workshops.

Punctuality is good on the whole and bullying rarely happens. 'Not that we're well behaved,' a student told us. 'We're just too busy and there's so much work you don't have time to do anything else.' Parents say: 'It's not like school, where if your child misses a day they give you a call.' Some felt there could be more contact, adding that 'here it's a bit like just turn up and get on with it.'

Pupils and parents: Students from ethnic minorities predominate, with many from abroad.

'Challenging but realistic long and short term academic and personal goals'

Twenty-eight different languages spoken here. Students come from 200 schools across London. College says: 'All aspire high. We have the inner London characteristic of lots of kids from immigrant communities. Parents want them to do well, so you can find higher aspirations here than you would have in many suburbs.' Parents are largely a mix of first and second-generation immigrants, professionals and semi-skilled workers.

Despite lamentations from parents about 'not much contact with the college,' they are kept updated by a newsletter, emails, annual report and parents' evenings. There are also HE information for parents of A2 students, giving information about university application process and finance. Annual bus trip to Cambridge for parents – to educate them about what is on offer. 'We have a large number of students whose parents have never been to university or to university in this country. We try to demystify that.'

Past pupils include actress Zawe Ashton, presenter Reggie Yates and singer Paloma Faith.

Entrance: Open day in November. Applications must be received before end of January, with interviews held in March. Enrolment dependent on GCSE grades meeting entry requirements and on places being available. A local school partnership with five Islington schools (Elizabeth Garrett Anderson, Holloway, Islington Arts and Media and Mount Carmel) means pupils from these school get priority.

Exit: Eighty per cent of students go to university, including four to Oxbridge in 2015. Many students also take advantage of the other courses on offer at other centres at the college, choosing apprenticeships, BTec courses, and/or employment rather than university and a degree.

Remarks: Careers advice is exceptional, with a good range of choice and information given to students on university, training, employment, gap years and other post-sixth form options. Clearly offers a good range of opportunity to develop political and social awareness through the wide cultural mix and unusual blend of enrichment activities. To get the most out of all that this college has to offer students need to be pretty outgoing, independent and open-minded, or they may find the environment too much of a harsh contrast to school sixth form. That said, it does very well by most of its pupils.

City of London School

Queen Victoria Street, London EC4V 3AL

Independent · Pupils: 920 · Ages: 10–18 · Sixth form pupils: 250 · Fees: £14,886 pa

Tel: 020 7489 0291

Email: admissions@clsb.org.uk
Website: www.clsb.org.uk

30

Head: Since April 2014, Mrs Sarah Fletcher MA PGCE NPQH, an Oxford historian (early 50s). Previously head of Kingston Grammar School, where her regime was creative, modernising and human. Before that, a deputy head at Rugby and she has taught at, among others, Wycombe Abbey, St George's Montreux, Habs Girls' and Lawrence Sheriff Boys' Grammar in Rugby – a diverse and venturesome academic career. And an excellent preparation for one of the top jobs in the independent day school sector.

An inspired appointment. It put some noses – and a few other organs – out of joint. Her headship followed the long reign of an exceptionally popular predecessor. It raised eyebrows and, in some minds, the alarm; and her first term or two were not easy, involving, as they did, the sudden departure of two senior members of staff, which went down less than well with some older boys and their parents.

Mrs Fletcher – soft-spoken, pretty, candid, sensitive and determined – has the unreserved backing of her governors – The City of London Corporation. She has the vision, eloquence and, when needed, steel to make an excellent head of this venerable school and we are confident that the school itself,

once it absorbs what she brings to it, will continue to warm to her and celebrate the many opportunities her intelligent and enabling approach will provide. 'The best results come,' she told us, 'from trusting people and giving them the space to develop their own thinking.' Sound advice.

Academic matters: Offers A levels – but a move to Pre-U (NB Mrs Fletcher's brainchild some years back) is on the way, initially with biology, history and RS. Others may well follow. All in the sixth can opt to take the Extended Project Qualification in addition to three or four main subjects. Mrs Fletcher is keen to develop computing – already exceptionally well provided for – throughout the school and is on the look-out for a replacement for the ECDL – something with programming built in, a cry we hear everywhere. Links with IT companies being developed to further upgrade the offering. No weak subjects or depts – results at A level and GCSE uniformly impressive. Columns of A*s, As, a few Bs and very little in the lower order columns (90 per cent A*/A grades at I/GCSE and 72 per cent at A level in 2015).

Maths much the most popular A level but modern languages hold up and Latin and Greek battle on. Mandarin compulsory in first two years and, seemingly, catching on here rather more than elsewhere. Links being forged with schools and organisations in China. Economics and drama the only concessions to the more 'modern' subjects – no psychology, business or other 'studies'. Lots of academic prizes eg recent successes in Olympiads, the prestigious Erasmus Essay Prize and the international Juvenes Translatores prize. 'My son's teachers have all been wonderful – especially in maths and the arts,' a parent enthused. A second felt, 'My sons are always stretched to be the best they can be but never pushed. They don't let you become so obsessed with work so you can't do other things. The teachers plainly want the best for each boy.' Another was concerned: 'There seems to be a drive to climb the league tables. We don't want that. It's not why we chose the school.' But head assures us there is no shift in the school's aims in that respect. She teaches all year 9s (we do like that!) and sees everyone with their UCAS form. Around 60 on the school's SEN register – mostly dyslexic or needing help with organisation. Not a prominent feature of the school's mix.

Good library – rather like a top notch public library in design and atmosphere but with 50,000 books, periodicals, CDs and PCs galore plus cases

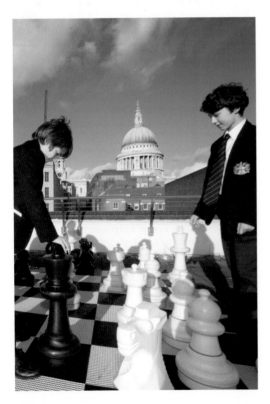

Overall impression is of a varied, creative and quirky programme with plenty for everyone from sports stars to unashamed geeks

housing the more venerable volumes for show. Unique, in our experience, is the school bookshop – a real one. Super 'science lecture theatre' but memorable lectures seem to be on anything but science.

Games, options, the arts: Sports and arts praised unreservedly by parents despite the trek to the school's main sports centre at Eltham. 'They do fantastic things with them. The music tours are amazing.' More than half learn an instrument; many take LAMDA exams; much-praised joint productions with the Girls' School in eg choral concerts with a choir of 200+. Music tech facilities of a high order. Lively drama – productions at all age levels. Smallish, pretty basic, studio theatre but excellent main, flexible 150-seater theatre would do credit to an upmarket fringe venue. Weekly school publication The Citizen produced by students. Four high-ceilinged art studios – all do art and music to year 9 – and much varied and vigorous portraiture on display. We enjoyed the ceramics – especially the satisfying crunch of some material or other underfoot. DT on the bottom floor also lively and fun and more DT and to a higher level (as yet no GCSE) on the cards, to boys' delight.

Football is main winter game and the school is a powerful presence in inter-school tournaments. Basketball, cricket, water polo, swimming and athletics all strong. Current National Water Polo champs and champs in London basketball and football tournaments – no narrow academic focus here. On-site huge sports hall, weights room and pool. Sizeable Astros marked out as pitches. Rest happens 25 minutes' away at sports clubs around the metropolis. Some 200+ on D of E Award programmes; CCF surprisingly lively for a city school but offering mouth-watering, subsidised opportunities – 'I did a powerboat course and got my licence from it,' said one young man.

Excellent range of trips and tours with a focus on educational value and enrichment rather than the extravagance one sees elsewhere. Good use made of London and its riches – a three-weekly trip to somewhere in the capital made by all year 9s. Good range of clubs with a bent towards to the literary and the philosophical – we like The Diaspora Club, The Comedy Society and Modern Language Society, in particular. Many have their own sizeable domains – we passed The Railway Society room

– 'thousands of pounds worth of kit in there,' we learned. Debating is popular and lively as is Model United Nations. Lots of outreach and charity work done out of conviction more than duty. Overall impression is of a varied, creative and quirky programme with plenty for everyone from sports stars to unashamed geeks.

Background and atmosphere: A school with a long, complex and obscure history. Its original benefactor, John Carpenter, and his executor intended his legacy to be for 'the finding and bringing up of four poor men's children with meat, drink, apparel, learning at the schools, in the universities, etc, until they be preferred, and then others in their places for ever'. The school as we know it today was finally established four centuries later, in 1837, first just off Cheapside, moving, in 1883, to Blackfriars and finally, in 1986, to a purpose-built, magnificently-sited, establishment between the Thames and St Paul's Cathedral. While it can no longer claim the nobly charitable purpose intended by Carpenter, it retains a liberal, progressive ethos, not least in its determinedly ecumenical attitude to religion and its generous bursary scheme, and, under its new head, much is being done in 'outreach' – eg working with The City of London Corporation's three academies, charitable ventures, multiple imaginative and beneficial links.

Wherever you are, great city buildings look in at you through many windows. And the river light is likewise inescapable. The building – which seemed over-warm and airless to us on a mild spring day – is wearing well. It's a little municipal – the signing, wide corridors and atria are reminiscent of an NHS hospital – but the whole is softened by relics from its previous home (we appreciated especially the row of Victorian leaded lights lining the dining room celebrating school luminaries), trophy cabinets, miles of red lockers – and the arts and crafts about the place. Displays stay up for rather too long, we gather, so that people stop looking. Extraordinary things like the fragment of a second century AD limestone Roman head of Mars found as part of an old riverside wall. Large 'concourse' used for events, adorned by plaques and statues to more school luminaries. Also, seemingly, hundreds of PCs everywhere. School houses are named for great figures in the school's history.

Pastoral care and discipline: Houses are 'important but not that important', we were told, ie sports, chess, intellectual competitions etc run on house lines but 'being in a different house never separates friends'. Sixth formers are grouped by shared subject teacher rather than houses. Every parent stressed how happy their son(s) were at the school. 'The boys in his class are so lovely – friendly, happy and always polite and nice to each other,' one told

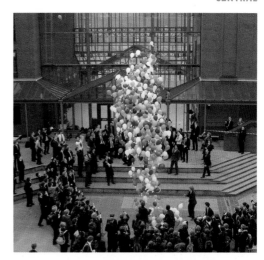

us, while a second said, 'it's a nurturing environment – they offer help, they set him up with a mentor and try to nip problems in the bud'. A third felt that the boys were 'very respectful of the teachers – it's a liberal ethos and it works'. And a fourth, 'The boys help each other in all kinds of ways'. Few discipline problems, though we heard one class giving a language assistant a bit of a rough time.

Pupils and parents: From all over London and the Home Counties. Mostly native English speakers, but a great diversity of home languages spoken including Chinese, Hindi, Russian and Tamil. Very few need EAL support. Brains the only common denominator – parents, who like the social mix in the school, are mostly professional, bright, urban and appreciative of broad and liberal educational values. 'They learn to respect everyone,' said one, 'and realise that not everyone can afford parties in limousines.' Formidable list of notable former pupils (known as Old Citizens) includes HH Asquith (PM 1908-16), Arthur Rackham, Ernest (Oh for the Wings of a Dove) Lough, Denis Norden, Julian Barnes, Daniel Radcliffe, Mike Brearley, Anthony Julius, Steven Isserlis, umpteen brainbox academics, legal eagles, cleverclogses of all sorts, among them three winners of the Nobel Prize.

Entrance: Highly selective. By competitive exam in English, maths and verbal reasoning for 10+ (40-50 places for which around 160 apply), 11+ (60 places for which around 550 apply) and 13+ (40 places – pre-test at 10, followed by conditional offer based on CE – perhaps 350 apply) plus interview and report from current school. At 11+, two distinct competitions, with those after 100 per cent bursaries sifted by taking an online reasoning test in December. Around half of all entrants come from preps, the rest from state primaries. At 16, applicants are tested in their two top subjects – 20 available places for which 75 apply. The school courts the primary/prep sector early – admission in year 6 is unusual and they clearly steal a march on the rest.

Exit: Around 12-15 leave after GCSEs, almost all to state sixth forms. All leavers go on to heavyweight subjects at good universities – around 15 per cent to Oxbridge annually (34 in 2015 plus 12 medics) and the rest to eg UCL, Bristol, Durham etc.

Money matters: Around 10 per cent of current pupils on 100 per cent fee remission via 'sponsored awards' available at 11+ and 16+ for bright candidates whose family finances would not stretch to fee-paying school without assistance. All applicants sifted via reasoning tests. Gross parental income to be below £45,000. Around 30 academic scholarships available at all entry points, worth up to 25 per cent of fees. Candidates invited to a 'demanding interview for which no preparation is helpful'. Sports scholarships – good footballers especially welcome. Music scholarships and choral bursaries – these for those who become choristers at The Temple Church and The Chapel Royal.

Remarks: 'A very down-to-earth school,' asserted a parent and we agree. An inspiring yet grounded school with solid values, providing vision, opportunities and a wonderfully civilised start in life for its lucky students. A jewel in London's crown.

City of London School for Girls (Prep School)

Linked school: City of London School for Girls, 78

St Giles' Terrace, Barbican, London EC2Y 8BB

Independent • Pupils: 90 • Ages: 7–11 • Fees: £14,976 pa

Tel: 020 7847 5500

Email: admissions@clsg.org.uk
Website: www.clsg.org.uk

31

Headmistress: Since 2010, Miss Jane Rogers MPhil BA (London). Worked for 10 years in the state sector before moving to the Institute of Education as a science lecturer and educational researcher. Moved back into education when she took a post of senior teacher at the Lyceum School, after which she came to the prep, because 'I'm interested in academic excellence'. Educated at Chelmsford County High School for Girls, University College London (geography) and Institute of Education. Has two teenage children.

Entrance: Twenty-four hotly contested places at 7+, sitting nationally standardised tests in English, maths and verbal reasoning plus some spelling and writing tests of the prep's own authorship. Register your daughter early to be sure of her being seen: the school assesses a maximum of 150 girls, and is always oversubscribed. Of those 150, the top 50 are called back for a further day's appraisal, during which they're examined in English, maths, science and DT – this last because it allows the girls to be observed in practical activities and working as a team. The 24 places are then offered to those 'with academic ability and the potential to become independent, happy learners.' Girls are seen in the November of the year preceding entry; closing date for accepting or declining offers is mid-February.

Exit: Parents take note: entry to the senior school is not automatic. By Easter of year 5, reserved places (ie places that are guaranteed) are offered only to those girls 'who continue to develop'. Any child who joined the school later than year 3 doesn't get one at all, and must sit for a place along with the external candidates. Head insists that 'the vast majority go through' (all but one in 2015). Some parents' perceptions are different; see below. Destinations of those who do go elsewhere include St Paul's Girls', North London Collegiate, Francis Holland, Channing and Queen's College London. 'We've been hugely successful in placing girls at other schools,' says head. 'Schools like City Prep girls, and they don't get them that often.'

Remarks: Broad curriculum, with specialist teachers from the senior school coming in to teach music, art, DT, PE, Latin (years 5 and 6) and modern languages. The girls learn a different language each year: Spanish in year 3, French in year 4, German in year 5 and Mandarin in year 6. The idea is that the girls acquire an enthusiasm for languages which then helps them to choose the right ones when they go on to senior school, which is certainly commendable. It struck us as odd, however, that they only studied each language for a year before having to drop it and move onto the next one; a year 5 girl

'The girls are incredibly competitive, but also very supportive of each other, and have a strong sense of loyalty'

we spoke to admitted that she'd now forgotten the Spanish she'd learned in year 3.

As well as benefiting from the senior school teaching expertise, the excellent senior school facilities – swimming pool, sports hall, library, Astroturf, tennis courts – are all available to the prep school, which doubtless explains why there's no difference in fees between the two (though prep fees do include lunch). Sports and gymnastics are strong, and music likewise, with the Y6s doing a Prep Opera every year. Impressive LAMDA results in 2014, with virtually everyone getting distinction. There are also lots of residential trips which are perennially popular. Wide variety of clubs, and after-school care provides an opportunity for girls to do their homework as well as have fun. ('They have a register to make sure you don't wander off,' said one of our tour guides, earnestly.) Sixth formers from the senior school run clubs for the prep girls, which, says head, creates 'a big sister culture. They're great role models for the younger girls.'

Other than some worrying reports which we outline below, it took a long while for parental feedback to reach us about this school. Our first invitation was met with complete silence, and even a second appeal didn't yield very much. (This was in contrast to the parents of girls in the senior school, who were quick to tell us how happy they were.) Those who did eventually contact us agreed that the girls are worked hard but achieve highly. A couple remarked on the school's competitive nature: 'The girls are incredibly competitive, but also very supportive of each other, and have a strong sense of loyalty to their school,' said one. Another observed, 'If you're prepared to buy into the idea of City and have a daughter capable of swimming in its often competitive seas, it will be a worthwhile experience for her and for your family.' These parents emphasized that their daughters were enjoying their time at the prep, had made friends and embraced the opportunities on offer there.

However, some of these same parents expressed disquiet about the entry process to the senior school. 'The goal posts seem to have been moved,' said one couple, 'The message about not everyone getting reserved places is stronger now than it was when our daughter got in.' The same worried mother continued, 'Choosing to put a child through an entrance exam when they're 6 is not an easy decision; in our case we hoped to avoid the stress at 11+, which we now find we may not do. I suspect the feeling of rejection and the dent to self-confidence is higher if you don't get a reserved place from the prep and can't stay with your friends, than if you apply and fail as an external candidate.' Miss Rogers told us that an average of four girls leave City Prep's year 6 every year: two out of choice, and two who were 'advised to go elsewhere.' School figures show an average of three girls a year recently have not been given reserved places. This figure seems high to us, given both the stringent nature of the admissions process and the acknowledged high workload put upon the girls during their time here; and we did ask the head to comment on it. 'Not all girls develop the same,' was her comment. 'Some go upwards and some go downwards,' adding, 'sometimes things happen in families to disturb girls.'

Parents and former parents are divided in their feelings about the school. On one side of the argument, accounts have been passed to us of recent City Prep girls whose confidence, and even health, had been so undermined by the school's approach that their parents voted with their feet and took them out. These parents write with angry eloquence about the school's 'complete lack of nurture and care' and claim that it 'values malleability and obedience over originality and sparky intellect.' They allege that there is poor support for special needs such as dyslexia, and that some of the teaching is sub-standard ('After we moved her, we discovered that she had been so poorly taught that she needed to relearn a year's worth of maths,'

said one mother, and another mother reported an identical experience.)

The head insists that the school works closely with parents, and that the girls' happiness is paramount to her. 'We love quirky individuals. We've got lots and lots of those. Girls are allowed to be themselves here.' And indeed, other parents told us that their daughters loved coming to school. One, whose child had excelled there academically, spoke of the school's 'really good pastoral side.' 'The prep is a nurturing and non-threatening environment,' said one mother whose child was now at CLSG senior, 'and I would have no hesitation in recommending it.'

Picking our way through such contradictory accounts was difficult. We can only conclude by suggesting that, since entry to CLSG senior school isn't guaranteed, parents should think closely about whether City Prep is the right choice for their daughter; or whether a prep school not linked to any senior school, but with a proven record of getting its leavers into the destination of their choice, might suit their family better.

City of London School for Girls

Linked school: City of London School for Girls (Prep School), 76

St Giles' Terrace, London EC2Y 8BB

Tel: 020 7847 5500

Independent • Pupils: 730 • Ages: 11–18 • Sixth form pupils: 160 • Fees: £14,976 pa

Email: admissions@clsg.org.uk
Website: www.clsg.org.uk

32

Headmistress: Since April 2014, Mrs Ena (pronounced Enna) Harrop BA MA MA MPhil PGCE (one of the longest list of degrees in The Guide!) (early 40s), a modern linguist, originally from Spain. Her previous incarnations include head of Spanish at Royal Russell and head of modern languages at Royal Grammar, Guildford. She joined City Girls as director of studies in 2010 and – unusually and remarkably – was appointed internally to the headship, clearly to the delight of the entire school. One of the most popular heads we have encountered.

You can, instantly, see why. She is the real deal. Formidably intelligent, chic, softly spoken, charming and beautifully articulate, her credo is the centrality of gender equality and the necessity of the modern world being gender-blind. And, as a head and the mother of three daughters, she lives the dream. Her (teacher) husband took her maternity leave when their last daughter was born. In the words of her pupils: 'She was – before she became head – a kind of figurehead.' 'The message

of feminism she promotes in the school is so inspiring.' 'She is likeable, approachable.. collaborative, efficient.' One admitted, 'I was scared when she came on our school trip but she was so relaxed it wasn't daunting at all.' And another, 'When she became head we just thought it'd be great to have more of her.' And every parent we spoke to concurred.

'Independent learning' is a phrase you meet a lot here and, again, the head – with her list of degrees – walks the talk. 'I feel tempted,' she told us, 'to take at least two A levels at this school – economics and art.. and then there's..' A very modern head: a recent assembly was on 'All you need to know about pregnancy and childbirth' and she refers to 'the nappy barrier' to women's achievement. Behind her desk sits a text: 'Feel the fear but still do it.' With Mrs Harrop as role model, a City student will leave as well-equipped to take on and challenge the world – while remaining her essential self – as any young woman could.

Academic matters: Maths rules. As elsewhere with clever students, this has become the most popular – and successful – A level subject, and recent takers outnumbered those who take languages all put together. 'My girls are strategic,' explains Mrs Harrop, 'and they know that if they take a language they are less likely to get an A*/A than if they take maths.' The girls say: 'People really like maths – they see the use of it.' Other popular subjects – in an, admittedly, conservative range as befits the preferences here – are history, chemistry and English. Mandarin, after a very successful course to GCSE, now offered at Pre-U, and should markedly boost the number of language takers which, has, in any case, increased since Mrs Harrop took over. Overall, A level results included a remarkable 79 per cent at A*/A and 97 per cent at A*/B in 2015. GCSE results no less impressive with 94 per cent A*/ As. However, although results are obviously a key factor in the school's success, the school itself puts the emphasis elsewhere – on, for example, independent learning and thinking.

She was appointed internally to the headship, clearly to the delight of the entire school

Lots of computers and library has a bank of borrowable laptops. Librarian seen as 'wonderful', though library itself, possibly, not the most impressive feature – we were bemused by some strange cataloguing and location of books and it felt a bit tired. Although a third of the pupils speak a language other than English at home, almost none need EAL help. Around 12 per cent with a mild SEN of some kind, all supported as needed on an 'as and when' basis but no-one with major learning difficulties here. School not easy for those with mobility difficulties.

Games, options, the arts: Art is, according to all, wonderful. We saw some terrific painting and the results at A level and GCSE are phenomenal. Good hall for display of work and three studios, all richly and messily busy – the colour and variety of the top floor a refreshing relief. DT taken by all years 7-9 in good sized studio with 3D printer and laser cutter plus all else you'd expect. We enjoyed some lively work including inventive year 7 torches. Lots of music – individual, large and small groups, pursued with excellence and enthusiasm. New director of music joined in September 2015 – two good sized teaching rooms at top of the building plus numerous practice rooms. Drama in huge hall and Black Box Theatre at the top of the building. Well-designed literature for shows is evidence of classy production values all through. Draughty outdoor theatre a splendidly imaginative recent innovation – a bit like a Greek theatre, only colder.

Games, remarkably, mostly take place on site – planners found flat spaces, inside and out, for two tennis courts, a large Astro pitch, various other big enough spaces for a gym, 25 yard pool, table tennis, new dance studio (2015). Outside space overlooked by flats – the girls must get used to it. Non-selective approach to some teams gives all enthusiasts opportunities and it works. They do cross-country round the high level walkways. Many representatives in borough games and several notable individual successes on local and grander levels.

But perhaps the most exciting aspect of the extracurricular offering is London itself. 'There are all the galleries and museums – they are so easy to go to from here – you can get there in a double art lesson. It's one of the reasons I came here,' typifies the response. Young Enterprise, likewise, outside speakers, visits, lectures at UCL, the Royal Institution etc, trips and tours – all add to the stimulating mix and the avid seizing of a rich variety of opportunities here.

Background and atmosphere: One of the more surprising school locations in the UK. Navigating the Barbican complex is notoriously tricky, but if you negotiate the grey concrete and glass mini-village to its heart, you will find the school. You get there via brick-paved walkways and the school sits between the ancient church of St Giles, Cripplegate one way, with glass office blocks behind, while the other way are the Guildhall Conservatory, the Barbican arts venue and the city flats with their valiant window boxes – and a large, flagged and lilied, ornamental pond between. Also surprising the eye and breaking up the harshness are the gallant trees and the improbable wodge of ancient London wall which squats defiantly opposite the school's main entrance. The school opened here in 1969 – the first, pretty much, of the reincarnations of venerable educational institutions needing new and purpose-built homes. A bold conception and it wears well. The inside is as stark and workful as Gradgrind could have wished, though lively displays and lots of big windows help relieve the Spartan architecture. 2008 sixth form centre cleverly bolted on. You go in and out a lot as you negotiate the five storeys and we were glad we were not there on a cold wet day. Good-sized dining hall

Perhaps the most exciting aspect of the extracurricular offering is London itself. 'There are all the galleries and museums – they are so easy to go to from here'

and jolly good menu – Wok Theatre, Italian/Indian Fusion and Big Bowl Salad looked tempting.

The original school began life in 1894. William Ward, who believed in giving girls a broad and liberal education with an emphasis on scholarship, left a third of his fortune – £20,000 – to the City of London Corporation for the foundation of a girls' school. Livery companies, banks and city firms continue to give financial support. The Corporation still administers this and numerous other schools and the board of governors is appointed by the Court of Common Council. The Corporation has an education strategy and its portfolio of schools gives rise to mutually beneficial links between City Girls' and state primaries eg for sixth form community service.

Famously diverse mix of pupils and staff as befits the school's situation in the heart of the city. 'Diversity' is a word you hear a lot here, in numerous contexts. Not least the effect of coalescing people from so huge an area. Likewise, we heard 'exciting' a lot. The girls say, 'It's always busy here – but in a good way, and being in the Barbican is so exciting!' Pupils are bright-faced, smiley, articulate and confident – with no trace of arrogance. They have a sense of their responsibilities to the wider world alongside their own personal ambitions.

Pastoral care and discipline: Light but 'tightly run' discipline. 'The teachers really care that the girls are happy,' a parent told us, 'and they deal quickly with problems.' 'No-one gets thrown out if they haven't had loads of warnings first,' girls told us. 'They bring in parents. It's mostly just poor behaviour over a long period but it hardly ever happens.' And most pay tribute to the excellence of pastoral care and their 'lovely' teachers.

Pupils and parents: They come from a vast circumference around the city – Chigwell to the north east, Harrow to the north, Shepherd's Bush and Fulham to the west – even as far away as Cambridge. 'It's helped me become a lot more independent and the school gives us "travel buddies" when we join so that we can get used to the journey with someone experienced.' Parents say: 'The mix of girls is wonderful. They're not a flashy lot and they not tarted-up either.'

Entrance: Numbers of applicants, as at other academically selective London schools, now hitting heights of absurdity and severely straining schools' resources, especially where, as here, physical space needed on assessment days is limited. School is part of the North London Consortium so exams in English and maths and what is graphically described as 'an interview with teeth'. Around 900 now applying for the 100 places at 11+ (or 850 for 75 places excl those applying from City's own on-site prep). Around 70 applicants for the 10-15 places at sixth form. Sixth form places conditional on school's own exams taken in potential A level subjects and on A*/As at GCSE in all subjects.

Exit: Around 15 leave post-GCSE to board or go co-ed or to sixth form colleges. Early warning – sometimes as early as year 9 – given to those who are unlikely to make it into the sixth form. Some parental criticism of the less than gentle manner in which this has taken place in the past but the Harrop regime is softening the approach, though the criterion for staying – ie no more than three Bs and all else at A*/A at GCSE if you want to stay on – remains in force. Sixth form leavers are starry – 15 to Oxbridge in 2015; the London University colleges also take a good number. Great range of serious courses and number of linguists now rising. Notable former pupils include Claire Rayner, Hermione Lee, Alison Weir, Elizabeth Emanuel, Romola Garai, Winklemans – Claudia and Sophie – and Daisy Christodoulou. Also Anna Blundy and Dido Armstrong, who both did their sixth forms at Westminster. One wonders whether they still would now.

Money matters: Around 20 per cent on some kind of fee assistance and head keen to up that to 25

per cent when possible. Few scholarships and those worth 10 per cent of fees. Means-tested bursaries – as elsewhere – the way it's going.

Remarks: By any standards, a top school for girls, with an edge of excitement, modernity and realism. Makes the most of what it is, where it is. Says a parent: 'My daughter is incredibly happy there. She has blossomed. Her friends and the head are amazing. I've only ever heard good things.'

Collège Française Bilingue de Londres – Junior Section

Linked school: Collège Française Bilingue De Londres, 83

87 Holmes Road, Kentish Town, London NW5 3AX

Tel: 020 7993 7400

Independent · Pupils: 340 · Ages: 5–11 · Fees: up to £8,627 pa

Email: info@cfbl.org.uk
Website: www.cfbl.org.uk

Headteacher: Since 2011, François-Xavier Gabet (50s). He has degrees in teaching French and French as a second language from University of Lille. Has taught in French schools in France, Saudi Arabia, USA and Australia and was a French language adviser to the US state of Louisiana. Set up the first bilingual French/English school in Melbourne (while also teaching at Monash University). Leaving in June 2016.

Head of primary is David Gassian, and Cerian Maraviglia is the deputy head of primary.

Entrance: This school is highly over-subscribed, with some 800 applications for 140 places. We have heard that a maximum of 30 per cent of places are allocated to children whose parents work for the consortium of French companies that helped to secure the school building. The school says that the list of partner companies is available for inspection if required. As with the other French homologue schools, entry is not easy and some families start out at other schools. Getting one sibling in helps boost the chances of the others. The priorities are: siblings (both primary and secondary), children from another official French school (locally or abroad), including students following the CNED (the French distance-learning programme), then any miscellany of Francophones fortunate enough to get in. It seems there are some last minute surprises. The nearby La Petite École is a popular feeder and others opt for local British independent schools while they wait for the coveted place at CFBL.

Exit: The good news is that upon completion of their primary education at CFBL, children continue to secondary at CFBL. At this point some move to British independent or state schools but the vast majority stay on. No testing, no interviews, no worries.

Remarks: The French primary model has two divisions – maternelle (reception and year 1) and primaire (years 2 to 6). At the junior section of the CFBL 50 per cent of children have French and English language instruction and 50 per cent follow the French national curriculum. Half the staff are UK qualified and half are French. The teachers are timetabled in such a way that when classes are being taught by French teachers, the English-speaking staff are freed up to support students whose English language skills need bolstering and to ensure that English literacy standards are of a high level.

The refurbishment is brilliant, with high ceilings, large windows drawing in masses of light

There are two forms of 25 students each for the youngest classes, 30 per class from the age of 7+. Classes are of mixed ability but the combination of French and English teachers means that they are able to differentiate the curriculum. English and French as a foreign language taught up to four

A real mix of families, including expat corporates on international assignment, entrepreneurs, local business owners

times per week. Other specialists include teachers of PE, music and ICT (interactive whiteboards in all classrooms), while the bilingual French librarian works closely with the teachers in developing the literacy scheme and creating class libraries. No specialist SEN support but class teachers are able to provide some support and there is a part-time educational psychologist too. Parents pay for diagnostic testing. A speech therapist is available.

Though 'curricular extras' do not traditionally loom large on the French educational landscape, they do make an effort at CFBL. We heard lots of talk about a Camden-based project called the English Pocket Opera Company, where 700 children participated in a production of Orphée. Judging from the parents we spoke to, this involved the whole community. The school is working on developing a choir and activities for instrumental music and there are hopes that the school's new sports facility will mean some new sporting activities.

The CFBL was established with a mission to offer a French curriculum in a bilingual context to 700 students. The school was at one time known as L'Île aux Enfants and was located in a nearby building that now houses Le Petite École, a French primary school that also feeds the CFBL. Now housed in a Victorian school building in Kentish Town, the school backs on to attractive residential streets but its front sits on a street that is less so. Step inside, however, and it's another story. The refurbishment is brilliant, with high ceilings, large windows drawing in masses of light and parquet wooden floors, plus modern touches like internal stairways with lots of glass. Cosy primary library in its own little building on the playground – most of the resources are French, although they are developing the English language collection.

A small portion of the central playground has been forfeited for the sake of a new cafeteria. Bright and airy, it provides an attractive place to serve equally attractive lunch menus for the youngsters. (Lunches are compulsory, with meat and fish served daily, or vegetarian options available for non-meat eaters or those observing kosher or halal diets).

Parents are happy with the level of attention given to their children, particularly when they first arrive at the school. There were no disciplinary concerns expressed by parents, who said the children are very accepting and welcoming. Deputy head of primary appears to have the confidence of the parents who speak highly of him and were happy when they heard he had been appointed in this role after several years as a teacher.

A real mix of families at CFBL, including expat corporates on international assignment in London, entrepreneurs, local business owners and French nationals whose marriages have created bicultural families. CFBL families suggest that the socio-economic atmosphere at CFBL is 'less rarified' than the more salubrious environs of the Lycée Charles de Gaulle in South Ken. Some end up at CFBL by default (no room at the Lycée) while others genuinely prefer this school. The size is another factor – it is much smaller than the Lycée and this is something that parents of primary pupils particularly like.

Collège Française Bilingue De Londres

Linked school: Collège Française Bilingue de Londres – Junior Section, 81

87 Holmes Road, London NW5 3AX

Tel: 020 7993 7400

Independent · Pupils: 355 · Ages: 11–15 · Fees: £7,801 pa

Email: info@cfbl.org.uk
Website: www.cfbl.org.uk/en

Headteacher: Since 2011, François-Xavier Gabet (50s). He has degrees from University of Lille – in teaching French and French as a second language. Has taught in French schools in France, Saudi Arabia, USA and Australia and was a French language adviser to the US state of Louisiana. Set up the first bilingual French/English school in Melbourne (while also teaching at Monash University).

He was the ideal founding head for this newish London school and arrived a year before it opened – to plan every facet. Despite his traditional website photo, when we met him he was fashionably turned out in jeans, turtleneck jumper and blazer – looking more like a high-tech dot-com CEO on London's Silicone Roundabout than what one might expect for the head of a prestigious French school.

Steeped in the high standards associated with French educational tradition, he is refreshingly internationally-minded and aims to help his multilingual students recognise the advantages of being part of a global network of schools. While well aware of the rigorous demands of the French system, he asks teachers to be flexible, creative and generous in their approach. He cares about the school's relations with the local Kentish Town community (he does not want CFBL to be a 'French bubble') and works closely with the board (whom he describes as 'capable, professionally-accomplished and yet humble') to find ways to improve this full-to-capacity school.

Fit, energetic and quite the coolest head this Good Schools Guide editor has met, he is married with a daughter at university in Belgium and a son at CFBL. His 'tour of duty' is up in 2016 and he will leave a big pair of shoes to fill.

Academic matters: The French secondary model has two divisions – collège (years 7 to 10) and lycée (years 11 to 13). CFBL offers collège, following on from the school's primary section.

Students (already working in French and English) now have the option to join the Anglais Renforcé section, where 45 per cent of the curriculum is delivered in English, preparing them nicely for the new international diploma (DNBI) section at the Lycée Charles de Gaulle. Others can opt for the Plurilingue stream, where they begin a third language (German or Spanish). Music, sport, IT and art are taught in English. Parents have mixed views – some feel the bilingual programme gives their (French-speaking) children lots of good exposure and immersion in English while others say the level of English is not as challenging as they'd like and that it's essentially French with a few English classes. Bilingual school models are never straightforward, with different perceptions about what exactly it means. IT is taught weekly – some parents would like to see a bit more, but concede that with the extra time already devoted to languages, this would be challenging.

The pupils work long hours – the additional English language means more hours than usual – so parents should be clear on this before they enrol their children. This is in addition to the homework load. The French educational system is regarded as one of the best in the world and academic standards are not an issue here. It's deciding if you want to do this with the added challenge of a bilingual or trilingual programme.

Games, options, the arts: Though extracurricular activities don't traditionally loom large on the

French educational landscape, they do make an effort at CFBL. We've heard lots of buzz about the English Pocket Opera Company, when 700 youngsters participated in a production of Orphée which seems to have involved the whole community. More sports on tap here than is the norm for French schools – the football team practises locally and took part in a tournament in Paris. Netball is popular with girls. The school is working on launching a choir and developing interest in instrumental music activities. Sixième students (first year secondary) go on a residential trip with outdoor pursuits activities aimed at integrating new students and team building.

CFBL has an exchange programme with schools in Uruguay and Berlin for students studying Spanish or German, and strong links with a school in Spain. Mandarin club recently introduced. The head hopes that these experiences will help students and parents value the importance of learning languages and about other cultures.

Background and atmosphere: The Collège Français Bilingue de Londres was born out of the recent French ambassador's call for increased capacity to meet the growing demand for French education in London. With funding from the French government and from French companies (we're guessing banks and perhaps Eurostar, whose London base is conveniently nearby), who formed a charity to acquire the school property, the school's mission is to offer a French curriculum in a bilingual context to 700 students. The school was at one time known as L'Île aux Enfants and located in a nearby building that now houses Le Petite École, a feeder primary school.

More sports on tap here than is the norm for French schools – the football team took part in a tournament in Paris

Housed in a Victorian school building in Kentish Town. The head is aware of the impact that the mass arrival of a French community in the heart of this traditionally working-class area of north London has had and is working to win over the hearts and minds of locals. Most families living in the area were attracted to the Victorian terraced properties and the 'gentrification' of the area is thought to be partly thanks to the school (as well, of course, as the long-standing local Camden School for Girls). Part of the neighbourhood charm offensive was the introduction of French language classes for the local community.

He was fashionably turned out in jeans, turtleneck jumper and blazer – looking more like a high-tech dot-com CEO on London's Silicon Roundabout

The school backs on to some picturesque residential streets, though it fronts onto a street that is less so, and a bit of planting and tidying of the outside pavements and garden patches would improve the first impression. Step inside, however, and it's another story. The refurbishment is brilliant, taking full advantage of the Victorian features, with high ceilings, large windows drawing in masses of light, brick and glazed tile walls and parquet wooden floors, while incorporating modern touches. The upper school library – with high ceilings and huge windows – is fully equipped with impressive French and English collections, loads of computers and armchairs.

A small portion of the central playground has been forfeited to create a bright and airy cafeteria. Lunches compulsory, with meat and fish served daily and vegetarian options available for those observing kosher or halal diets.

The school has recently acquired an outdoor space a five-minute walk away. This will feature a massive inflatable structure for sports and other activities and will be available to the local community too.

Part of the AEFE (Agency for Teaching of French Education Abroad), CFBL is one of an international network of schools directed by the French ministry of education. The school is managed by a 12-member board – six representing the companies that helped fund the acquisition of the building and six elected by the parents. Its goals are to provide continuity of education to the French expat community in London, but also to prepare students to go to the best French universities. In fact 80 per cent of students who graduate from the Lycée Charles de Gaulle head to British or US universities. The head feels that the internationally-minded, multi-lingual emphasis of the school serves to provide good preparation for these options later on.

Pastoral care and discipline: Parents are very pleased with the school, many jumping through hoops to secure places. A parent of a child with SEN described it as particularly caring and attentive to her child. Classes are smaller than most French schools – a maximum of 30 in a class, with a two or three form intake. Discipline is not a worry for parents – one parent speculated that the presence of more UK-trained teachers (there to deliver the bilingual programme) strengthens the pastoral care perspective of the teaching faculty (not always as high on the French teachers' radar). The school runs careers counselling through a jobs forum that parents help to organise.

Pupils and parents: The community is a blend of expat corporate types on international assignments and more permanent French families who have found themselves in London for other reasons, including entrepreneurs, local business owners, French nationals whose marriages have created bi-cultural families. Parents suggest that the socio-economic atmosphere at CFBL is less 'rarified' than one finds in the more salubrious environs of the Lycée Charles de Gaulle in South Ken. While some end up at CFBL by default (no room at the Lycée), others prefer this school. The size is another factor – even with its capacity of 700, it is much smaller than the Lycée. French families who find the Eurostar terminal at St Pancras convenient are increasingly moving into neighbourhoods that are handy for the train journey through the tunnel to France and for the school.

The community is about two-thirds French. Some parents feel the school is less international than they would like, while others who come from France find it very international by comparison. There is obviously an underlying French cultural and educational foundation, but it seems that with a school community consisting of many dual national families, they seek to honour all cultures and traditions. Parents are happy that the children integrate easily, although some say teachers don't make as much of this diversity as they might. A parents' association provides lots of volunteer opportunities for those who want to get involved.

Entrance: Highly over-subscribed with some 800 applications for 140 places. We hear that a maximum of 30 per cent of the places are allocated to children whose parents work for the consortium of French companies that helped to secure the school building. The list of partner companies is available for inspection if required.

As with the other over-subscribed French homologue schools, some children start out at other schools. Getting one sibling in helps boost the chances of the others. Admissions priorities are: siblings (both primary and secondary), children from another official French school (local or abroad), including students following the CNED (the French distance-learning programme), then any miscellany of Francophones fortunate enough to get in. It seems there are some last minute surprises. The nearby La Petite École is a popular feeder, while others opt for local British independent schools while they wait for the coveted place at CFBL.

Exit: Some expat families move abroad and continue their education in the French system. Others, finding the fees an issue (though remarkably good value when compared to most London independent schools), enter local state schools. Students who are less confident about their French language skills may leave after quatrième to do GCSEs in the local British sector, although the English section at the Lycée Charles de Gaulle is an option for them. Many head to the Lycée Charles de Gaulle to enter their Baccalauréat programme, others to the new Lycée International Winston Churchill in Wembley.

Remarks: An interesting school that embodies all of the academic rigour associated with the French tradition, but with a strong emphasis on languages and English. A sparkling little gem in the heart of Kentish Town, it is a bilingual environment with a truly international mindset.

Connaught House School

47 Connaught Square, London W2 2HL

Independent • Pupils: 85 • Ages: 4–11 • Fees: up to £16,500 pa

Tel: 020 7262 8830

Email: office@connaughthouseschool.co.uk
Website: www.connaughthouseschool.co.uk

Joint principals: Since 1991, Mrs Jacqueline Hampton (60s) and her husband, Mr Frederick Hampton MA RCA; both studied at art school. Mrs Hampton, aged 19, came here to lend a hand to her mother, Mrs Nancy Keane, who founded the school in 1952 with just six pupils, and never left.

An intimate, cosy, family-run school, refreshing in this age of private equity backed independent schools. Mr and Mrs Hampton are very hands on and complement each other in their skills and strengths. She is form teacher for year 5 and he teaches English and art. Mrs Hampton describes herself as a 'big picture' person. She wants to see the children having fun while they learn and is determined to withstand the pressure, that faces all London schools, to turn into an exam sausage factory. However, she recognises that there has to be a balance and there needs to be some push to enable them to move on to good schools. The couple have two grown-up sons (both of whom were here).

One of their daughters-in-law, Mrs Victoria Hampton (30s), who runs the early years part of the school and has taught here for more than six years, is being groomed to take on the reins of headship. Not that she needs much training. She comes with a wealth of experience of young children, having started and run her own nursery in Oxfordshire, been deputy head of a nursery in Clapham, as well as having a host of qualifications for teaching young children – Montessori diploma, Early Years foundation degree, Hornsby diploma (dyslexia). She has two young boys of her own who will come here and loves being part of the fabric of the school. Gentle, pretty, with a mellifluous voice and perfect diction (which we suspect matches her handwriting), the children clearly love her as do the staff. She knows them all, is actively involved in observing and participating in lessons throughout the school and has already initiated and implemented changes and improvements. One of these was to bring the reception class (known at Junior One) up from the ground floor so that they can have plenty of space, free flowing between two large, high ceilinged rooms.

Although this is an independent, privately owned school, it has none of the trappings of a profit-motivated business. 'We are a school first that happens to have to run as a business,' say Mr and Mrs Hampton in unison. Phew – such schools do still exist. The Hamptons are wonderfully down to earth and direct. No kow-towing to demanding high net worth parents goes on here (and some parents do feel their concerns aren't listened to). The children are their focus. They know the children, enjoy the children, and put their interests above all else. They are proper educationalists, in the more traditional mould, and despite the competitive pressures common to all London day schools, are ensuring that music, art and drama are as central as the academics. They are firm believers in the theory that a happy child will be a successful child.

Entrance: At age 4 into reception (here called Junior One). Sixteen places for girls and boys. 'Very gentle assessments' take place when the child is 3 to ensure that they will get as much out of the school as possible. Children are assessed by two teachers and also have some one-to-one time. Absolutely no preparation is necessary. Priority is given to siblings and second and third generations. After that, proximity to school. 'The local community ethos is something we value very highly and would not like to lose,' says Victoria Hampton. Applications can also be made for entry into the upper end of the school. Academic and music bursaries are available to those applying at 7 or 8. Many come from local nurseries, including Great Beginnings and Paint Pots, and there is some liaison with nurseries after places have been offered.

Exit: All boys leave at 7 or 8 and tend to go to local prep schools such as Westminster Under School,

She wants to see children having fun while they learn and is determined to withstand the London schools' pressure to turn into an exam sausage factory

Sussex House or Wetherby, the odd one going north to UCS junior school. The girls stay until 11 and generally opt for London day schools – Francis Holland, Clarence Gate, is currently the most popular, but many also to Godolphin and Latymer, City of London, More House, Latymer Upper, Queen's Gate and South Hampstead High. Those wishing to board generally choose Wycombe Abbey or St Mary's, Ascot. Despite leaving a very small school to go on to these much larger establishments, none of the pupils seems to be fazed – the confidence they acquire at CHS gives them the ability to cope in a broader environment.

Remarks: There is no danger of the slightly old-fashioned, wonderfully personal and child-centred ethos of this tiny school changing. The school has not expanded at all since it was first founded. It still occupies the same building, and is very small; you will know quite quickly if you love it or not, but if you don't, be careful not to write it off too soon. This is a rare little boutique in the increasingly branded, competitive world of London day schools and it offers a uniquely personal touch that many similar schools are in danger of losing. Despite its small size, good use is made of the environs. Hyde Park is only a short walk away, and children enjoy lots of outdoor activities there all the year round, including parachute games, obstacle races, rounders and football. Fencing, dance, and martial arts all take place at Little Venice Sports Centre. Tennis, football, hockey, basketball and the annual sports day happen at Paddington Recreation Ground. Swimming is at Queen Mother's Sports Centre in Victoria. There is sport every day of one kind or another. Although we heard some whispering from former parents of boys here – that the boys didn't get to run around enough and there were insufficient sporting opportunities – we could see no evidence of this. The Hamptons clearly understand boys well, with two sons and at least two small grandsons of their own.

Art and music are the main extracurricular strengths of the school. Plenty of music assemblies and lots of performances. Everyone takes part, and the large, high-ceilinged room in the middle of the building is a comfortable and intimate place to perform. We were treated to a mini concert, which included violin and recorder players as well as piano and singing – impromptu concerts of this kind are not unusual, we were told, and you can see how much confidence is imbued into these tiny performers as a result. The art room is a relatively dark, pokey room in the basement, but the quality of art that is produced defies the facilities. Perhaps to be expected, since both heads are trained artists. We saw small children beavering away at covering balloons in newspaper to create hot air balloons. We were shown wonderful wooden red buses and fire engines, built by the children, and split-pin dolls clothed in fabulous petite Victorian dresses and hats. Colourful displays adorn the walls – work obviously done by the children rather than touched up by the teachers (what a relief), and bright Chinese lanterns and colourful fish were bobbing from almost every ceiling.

Plenty of drama; each junior form does its own play once a year (these have included the Gruffalo's Christmas and Charlie Cook's Favourite Book), and years 4, 5 and 6 have performed Sleeping Beauty. Drama productions and concerts take place at the Carisbrooke Hall down the road or the Steiner Theatre close to Baker Street. Although this is very much a mixed community school with no particular religious bias, there is an annual carol concert in St John's Church, Hyde Park Crescent, which everyone is expected to attend. 'We would rather it were inclusive,' says Mrs Hampton.

'The local community ethos is something we value very highly and would not like to lose'

Clubs are varied and numerous. The Hamptons make a huge effort to ensure that everyone from years 2-6 try everything. There is lots to try, from embroidery, pottery, board games and mini beasts to any kind of dance from country to zumba as well as chess and music. Full advantage is made of the school's cosmopolitan location – recent trips have included to the Globe Theatre, the Courtauld and the Tate Modern, the Celtic Harmony Camp, London Zoo and to the obvious museums – Science, Horniman and Transport.

You need not worry about little Freddie not getting enough attention either. There are only 16 pupils in a class – they try to keep an equal number of girls and boys in the early years. Junior One (reception) has two teachers and a qualified teaching assistant. Forms 1, 2 and 3 have both a form teacher and qualified teaching assistant in each class. All children use personal Fizz books (little laptops, as far as we could tell), there are MacBooks in every classroom and the Hamptons pride themselves on recruiting excellent teachers with 'diverse interests'. There is a competitive fives player on the staff at the moment. With such a small school, and class sizes, it is relatively easy to pick up any learning difficulties, we were told. They have a few cases of children with glue ear who may need speech and language therapy. Specialist therapists, for, eg, dyslexia are brought in at extra expense for parents but Victoria Hampton herself is a dyslexia therapist, and they prefer to keep as much support in school as possible. We were told that there is usually only one child in each year group who needs any kind of help at all. There are a high number of children with English as a second language, and although they need a reasonably good grasp of English at assessment, because of the high level of teacher support (and a recently introduced EAL club) they usually progress very quickly.

All in all, a very special little school which is loved by parents and pupils alike, where the children feel challenged every day and their parents are constantly amazed by what they know. 'The closest you can get to home schooling,' declares one. If that sounds appealing, take a little trip to Marble Arch now.

Eaton House Belgravia

Linked schools: Eaton House The Vale, 251; Eaton House The Manor Girls' School; Eaton House the Manor Preparatory and Pre-Preparatory Schools, see *The Good Schools Guide: London South*

3–5 Eaton Gate, Eaton Square, London SW1W 9BA

Independent • Pupils: 235 • Ages: 4–8 • Fees: £14,670 pa

Tel: 020 7730 9343

45

Email: admin@eatonhouseschools.com
Website: www.eatonhouseschools.com

Headmistress: Since September 2015, Annabel Abbott (30s), previously deputy head. History with primary education degree from the University of the West of England; spent nine months in Australia as a gap student teacher before joining Queen's Gate School. Moved to Eaton House in 2000, taught throughout the age range and was promoted to deputy head four years later.

Entrance: At 4+ non-selective – places are allocated on a first come first served basis with priority given to siblings, children of staff, ex-staff and old boys. Put your son's name down early – £50 for a confirmed place and £30 for a waiting list place. Deposit of a term's fees, two terms before the child starts, which is credited against your final term's fees.

Exit: At 7+ and 8+ mainly to London day schools – Sussex House, Westminster Under, Westminster Cathedral Choir School, Colet Court, St Philip's, Eaton House The Manor Prep and Wetherby. A few head off to board at Summer Fields, The Dragon, Ludgrove and the like.

Remarks: Traditional 3Rs curriculum with lots of added extras, particularly in the arts and science – the school boasts its own lab, boys enjoy potion and crystal making amongst their many experiments and discoveries. Pupils are divided into small classes, no streaming but informal sets for maths to ensure that everybody is meeting their potential and able to go at their own pace. As in the past, the school's aim is to give boys a good grounding and a full understanding in all maths and English topics, rather than rushing ahead.

An actor visits the school to help train the boys for junior debating club

No outdoor space so school days are very structured – boys are bussed to Hyde or Battersea Park every day to let off steam and play sports. Swimming takes place at the Queen Mother's sports centre. Good choice of after-school and optional weekend sports clubs encourage boys to choose and try out different activities. Chess lessons for years 2 and 3.

An actor visits the school to help train the boys for junior debating club. Lots of spirited music and drama, which is reflected in the many assemblies, plays and themed days, which often see teachers dressing up too. Excellent choir for ones so young, performs at a local charity events and is thought to be adorable by parents and anyone lucky enough to catch one of their performances. Five small practice rooms in the basement for young instrumentalists – boys can learn piano, flute, violin, recorder and guitar.

Well-organised SEN supports children with specific learning differences; Move Fit group is run by physiotherapists for anyone who needs to improve coordination, and touch typing tuition for year 2 upwards.

Mainly local clientele with many parents working in the City as bankers and lawyers, although much more international than in the past. Staff and parents have high expectations for the boys as the majority move onto academically selective prep schools. Boys are set numerous challenges, both physical and intellectual, and well trained so they become familiar with class exams in preparation for the formal 7+ and 8+ entry examinations. Head and her staff are always on hand to advise parents about suitable choice of prep schools.

Bustling kitchen runs two lunch sittings a day; where possible the food is fresh and cooked on-site. Birthdays are special days, with boys bringing cakes or biscuits to share with friends and staff. Boys present as cheerful little chaps. School remains a popular and successful recipe for pre-preppers as ever.

Eaton Square School

79 Eccleston Square, London SW1V 1PP

Tel: 02079 319 469

Independent • Pupils: 395 • Ages: Ages 4–13 C of E • Fees: up to £19,050 pa

Email: admissions@eatonsquareschool.com
Website: www.eatonsquareschool.com

46

Headmaster: Since 2010, Sebastian Hepher BEd (early 50s). Educated at Alleyn's and University of Greenwich. Began teaching career in state sector, at Hurstmere Boys' in Kent, followed by The London Nautical School. Joined Eaton House Pre-Prep in 1990, before being asked to lead Eaton House The Manor in 1993. Under his headship, the school grew from the initial embryonic phase to a thriving prep school. Married, with four children currently at four different schools, with the youngest here. Swims in his local lido every day of the year, come rain or shine. Avid reader of Russian literature. Warm and charismatic, with a good sense

of humour. Every parent we spoke to described him in glowing terms. 'He is the reason people gravitate towards the school,' according to one mother. Teaches reasoning.

Entrance: Main intake is at 4+ via assessment. The school runs several nurseries for children from 2.5 to 4 and these pupils are assessed by head of nurseries and head of pre-prep. They are given priority over other candidates and make up well over half the intake. 'It's not automatic but very rare not to accept a child from one of our nurseries,' explains head. Assessments, in November for external candidates, involve phonic and numerical activities, as well as colouring, cutting and talking to teachers. Between 100 and 150 external children compete for 30 places. Sibling policy, 'as we truly are a family school.'

Occasional vacancies further up the school are quickly filled from the school's waiting list, after the child has successfully completed a series of online tests and spent a day at the school in a classroom setting.

Exit: Most girls leave at 11 and boys at 13. Very few girls stay on for the 13+, usually those heading for co-ed boarding. Pupils progress onto a wide range of senior schools, both boarding and day. Rare to send more than a couple of children to any one school in any given year. Recent girl leavers have headed for Francis Holland, Godolphin & Latymer, JAGS, Benenden and Downe House; boys to Tonbridge, King's Canterbury, Harrow, KCS Wimbledon, St Paul's and Dulwich College. Impressive number of sports, drama and music scholarships, though school does not prepare pupils specifically for academic scholarships, 'so if one is awarded, it's done so retrospectively.'

Head starts dialogue about senior schools in year 5, often encouraging parents look at boarding too even if previously dismissed out of hand by international clientele. Head acknowledges that 'London schools are not the place for the average boy' and that some need to cast their net further. Numbers of boys heading to boarding has increased noticeably and is 'beginning to bubble for the girls.'

Remarks: Situated in three large town houses in the heart of Belgravia. Separate buildings for senior prep, junior prep and pre-prep. One parent likened the children to mountain goats, as they make their way up and down the steep stairs.

Vibrant, colourful classrooms where the emphasis is on practical work, consolidated by written work

Founded in 1981. Recently became part of the Minerva Education Group. Teething problems have left some parents feeling a little raw. One mother we spoke to said, 'The transition to the new ownership has been pretty bumpy, especially as it coincided with an escalation in fees'. Head feels some parental perception has been inaccurate and that school fees have not actually increased more than usual. Indeed, the second year of ownership has actually seen a reduction to the usual increase. On the positive side, Minerva has enabled the school recently to buy a new building and will also make it financially possible to open up a senior school soon which will go up to 16.

Current head is credited with having pulled the school up by its bootstraps academically. It has grown both in size and standing on his watch. One parent commented, 'It used to just be a sweet, local school before Mr Hepher took over. He is much more ambitious and has taken it to another level'. Pupils now follow a more academically rigorous and broader curriculum. Excellent language provision. Spanish being introduced. Extra French classes for fluent speakers. Mandarin offered as a two year course from year 4, though pupils must commit to it for the duration and take a CE exam at the end. Latin for all from year 5.

Head abhors the culture of tutoring and believes 'we need to educate parents.' He has addressed the matter of intense competition for senior places with intelligence and worries that increasing number of schools using pre-tests works against late-developers. School prepares pupils well for senior school entry without being a hothouse.

Typically five reception classes and four year 1 classes. Class size fairly small, with a maximum of 16 up to year 5 and a maximum of 18 in final years. Currently only eight pupils in each year 8 class and 11 in year 7, giving plenty of scope for individual attention. Pupils are placed in sets for maths and English at start of year 2 but these are fluid, with 'plenty of room for manoeuvre'.

Parents feel pupils are well prepared for transition to senior school, partly because the curriculum is kept broad throughout. Once 11+ exams are over, girls 'latch onto boys' CE syllabus.' No time wasting allowed here, as can often happen elsewhere post 11+, much to the parents' delight.

From the start, all pupils are encouraged to be articulate and confident citizens. Head believes that good manners are essential. Each class has its own official greeter who comes to the front, shakes hands firmly and welcomes visitors on behalf of the rest of the class. A charming touch.

Thriving pre-prep department. Vibrant, colourful classrooms where emphasis is on practical work, consolidated by written work. 'It's hands on, creative learning here.' Impressive writing on display up the stairs. Everything is beautifully presented, from the work crafted by the children to displays produced by teachers. Charming library area where children can be found earnestly recommending books to each other.

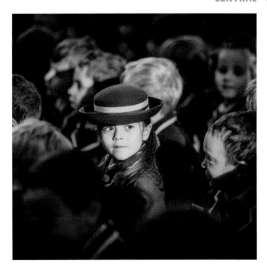

Each class has its own official greeter who comes to the front, shakes hands firmly and welcomes visitors on behalf of the rest of the class. A charming touch

As school is non-selective, there is a huge ability range. Full-time SENCo, supported by highly experienced learning enrichment team. Approximately 30 pupils currently having SEN support (mostly dyslexia, dyspraxia and dyscalculia), either one-to-one or small group sessions. Two children with statements. More able pupils extended through challenging extracurricular activities.

Pastoral care is well structured. Head worries about life being stressful for these children. 'We have a duty of care to shield children from excessive pressure which London and the system place on them. Parents who are anxious tend to pass that on to their children. I worry that we're causing a very anxious society. We want to make sure that children are happy when they are here.' Whole school comes together once a week for a reflective and celebratory reflective assembly at St Michael's Church, Chester Square.

Charity is an important part of school life. Huge amounts raised by parents and children. Head is aware of how privileged pupils are here and is hoping to get older pupils involved with visiting elderly residents who live on their own in the Square.

Teachers mostly in late 20s and early 30s; some 10 members of staff have been here a decade. One parent described them as being 'friendly, energetic and good at communicating with the parents. Just what you want'. 'We haven't had a bad teacher yet!' said another, whose children are currently in the middle of the school. Parents demonstrate their gratitude to the staff with a 'parent appreciation breakfast' once a year.

Sensational drama. Huge annual musical performed by year 5 and 6 children at Unicorn theatre in the West End. Professional theatre director hired for the occasion. Years 7 and 8 perform something more challenging such as a Greek play. Younger children perform on stage twice a year. Music also a central part of the school with over 100 pupils learning an instrument. Performances in abundance, from carol services to rock concerts. One parent felt that 'music is certainly more organised than it has been in the past.' Art taught to a high standard. Extra scholarship classes offered to the most artistic; the standard of portfolios is considered exceptional.

Despite its lack of outside space, school takes sport very seriously and coaching is excellent. Mainstream sports all offered as well as ballet, climbing, fencing and kayaking on the Thames. Pupils compete strongly in prep school ski-ing championships, recently bringing back a clutch of gold medals. Legendary swimming squad currently on a four year unbeaten streak. Unusually, pupils swim here from day one. Football also strong, with plenty of practice taking place in Battersea Park. All children make a team of some description. 'The problem is finding enough other schools who can field C and D teams,' laments head.

Extracurricular activity viewed as important. Sensational residential trips. Year 3 heads off to Sussex for a four day adventure. Years 4 and 5 go on a ski-ing and cultural trip to France where pupils practise speaking the language in context and also have daily French lessons. Snowball fights with the teachers apparently one of the highlights. One mother was delighted that the children were made to 'carry their own skis and make their own beds.' A novel experience for some, apparently. Pupils in year 6 go on a classical tour of Rome and Naples. Year 7 spend a week at a château in Normandy. At the end of year 8, pupils go on outdoor pursuits trip to Scotland to celebrate the end of common entrance. Head now setting his sights on a residential trip for year 2. Thirty-four clubs currently offered, at extra cost, including numerous sports, chess, story-telling and cookery.

One mother was delighted that the children were made to 'carry their own skis and make their own beds'. A novel experience for some, apparently

Pupil composition is predominantly expat, with more than half the pupils from overseas. Americans, Australians, Italians, French, Spanish mostly, with a sprinkling from Germany, Russia and Asia. One mother observed that there had been 'a thick crust of oligarchs' children in the past, but not any more.' Significant proportion does not have English as their first language. School is committed to its international families and has an EAL system in place which supports every child who joins with no, basic or limited English. Currently 14 per cent of pupils require targeted EAL lessons, which are intended to 'help speed up the process of full inclusion in the classroom.' Many of the parents we spoke to felt that its international feel was an advantage. 'It is a British school in terms of manners, etiquette and uniform but feels international in terms of its welcoming and warm approach.' Rare for mothers to work. A sea of nannies at the school gate on the day we visited. Pupils mainly come from local area but radius extends as far as 'Kensington in the North, Fulham in the West, Battersea and Kennington in the South and Marylebone in the East.' School bus service in operation to and from west and south-west London for those who live further afield.

Parents are encouraged to become involved, from hearing children read to giving career talks. Strong sense of community here and very active PTA. 'When you go into the school, there is a smile on the staff's faces. It's not the sort of school where you drop your child at the door and never get to venture across the threshold,' explained one mother. Head feels parent body is caring and empathetic, 'partly because of the huge mix of nationalities. Parents who come here are quite open, as they have often changed city and country themselves. You need to be outward looking to do that and this feeds into their children. It creates a lovely atmosphere.' One-upmanship, so prevalent elsewhere in London, is refreshingly lacking here.

Heady mix of traditional British education with an international flavour. Children are happy here as they have the freedom to be themselves. Judging by stampede to get into the building at the start of the day, Eaton Square offers its pupils an joyful start in life.

Fine Arts College Hampstead

Centre Studios 41–43 Englands Lane, London NW3 4YD

Tel: 020 7586 0312

Independent · Pupils: 160 · Ages: 14–19 · Sixth form pupils: 140 · Fees: £18,900 pa

Email: mail@hampsteadfinearts.com
Website: www.hampsteadfinearts.com

Joint principals: Nicholas Cochrane and Candida Cave (50s). Both studied at the Ruskin School of Drawing and Fine Art, Oxford. Cochrane then went on to work for the Old Masters Department at Christies. The pair started teaching at a tutorial college and found 'we were quite good at inspiring people'. The decision to set up a college of their own was something that just 'came about', but clearly had a market, and has grown steadily ever since. Nicholas Cochrane teaches fine art, while continuing to exhibit with The Royal Society of Portrait Painters. (Has won the Prince of Wales's Award for Portrait Drawing.) Candida Cave, too, remains a practising painter and playwright, while teaching art history. Parents and pupils are great fans of their warm and relaxed approach. 'Candida Cave is what all parents dream of in a teacher, but think they'll never meet,' said one. 'She's imaginative and nurturing, but not a pushover. My daughter just fell in love with her.'

Academic matters: A very broad, almost exclusively, arts-based curriculum (no science in the sixth form, though a few mathematicians). The visual arts remain, as one might expect, exceptionally popular. Photography is the number one subject choice (80 students this year) but also large numbers for fine art and art history, English literature, textiles, graphic design, film studies and media studies. The fine arts approach provides a strong traditional grounding (from classical busts and life models), which leaves many students with strong enough technical skills to bypass foundation courses. (The college also runs a two-term post A level portfolio course, to ensure preparation for art degrees and art college is tip-top). An extensive curriculum (29 subjects in all) of liberal arts, social sciences, modern languages (French, Spanish and Italian), and classical studies (Latin, Greek, ancient history and classical civilisation), can be taken in virtually any combination. Strong results overall (32 per cent A*/A and 56 per cent A*-B in 2015), with English and fine art particularly stellar. Exceptionally high 'valued added' between GCSE and A level (fourth highest in the country) produced by caring teaching in small groups (classes never exceed nine).

'My daughter had failed spectacularly at two fee-paying schools,' said one appreciative mother of a daughter now at a Russell Group university. 'She thought she was a dunce until they took her under their wing. They produced an incredible turn around and she went from Cs to As.' Also offers GCSEs, with two year groups of about 20 in all. 'We find there's a real need in year 10,' says Candida Cave, 'particularly when schools start saying, you should drop this or that.' GCSE subjects include biology and some physics but probably not the place for nascent medics. In 2015, 22 per cent A*/A grades. Staff long-serving and enthusiastic (including three ex-students and Candida Cave's daughter), with a fair proportion who also have alternative lives as professional artists, film makers, etc. Teaching style relaxed but enthusiastic; student style, co-operative competition. 'It's very much teaching in discussion, they want to impress each other in a nice way,' says Candida Cave. Good information given to parents and pupils about progress, with fortnightly reports and two parents' evenings. Rated outstanding by Ofsted in latest report.

The teaching style is relaxed but enthusiastic; student style, co-operative competition

Games, options, the arts: Plenty of opportunity to display talent, with an annual art exhibition, music and drama recital, and short films shown at the local Everyman Cinema. (One girl was recently runner-up for the Young Film Critic Award at Bafta). Loads of outside speakers and cultural outings, with annual study trips to Florence, Paris and Venice. Not at all a hierarchical place, and students organise their own entertainment – 'a certain number tend to take the lead each year' – including charitable fundraising (for Breast Cancer awareness, the Red Cross, a local hospice) and other social events. Certainly not the ideal environment for the sporty (and few here care) but GCSE students have fencing lessons plus PE at a local sports centre and the college's long-standing football team plays against other sixth-form colleges. Popular table tennis, too, on site.

Background and atmosphere: Started in 1978 in the YMCA in Tottenham Court Road, teaching art and art history. 'We started because there wasn't anyone else specialising in the arts,' says Candida Cave. Moved to Belsize Park in 1982, started offering GCSEs in 1994, and then, in 2002, added a converted Victorian dairy, which now forms the hub of the school, providing rambling lateral space around a cobbled courtyard. A good mix of classrooms (some more spacious than others) and excellent studio space, for art, drama, photography (with its own darkroom for traditional-style printing) and media studies. The atmosphere is intentionally informal and teachers are called by their first names. 'The college was very much founded as a bridge between school and university. Many students come here because they're looking for something more flexible.' Students congregate in the common room, where free coffee is on offer, but no food supplied on site. Some bring sandwiches, the majority visit the multitude of local eateries. Dress code vaguely artistic and bohemian (the odd fur gilet and extreme make up, the majority in UGGs and tracksuits), but kept well within limits. 'If it offends, we tell them to dress properly. It's just common sense.'

Pastoral care and discipline: 'What we liked about the college', said one parent, 'is the industrious informality. They take the job seriously, but don't wear it too formally.' Pupils' work and well-being is immaculately monitored. Everyone has a personal tutor, whom they see for an hour and a half each week. The tutor goes through reports, helps with essay-writing and advises on university applications. All GCSE pupils sign in at 9am and again at 1.30pm. If pupils are not in class an email is sent to parents within half an hour. 'Pupils turn up because they want to,' said one parent. 'But,

Families tend to be relieved that their children have found such a civilised and creative niche

equally, they know that if they can't be bothered to turn up, the attitude will be, don't bother to come back.' Most have no problems with this. 'I've never been to a school before where all the other pupils want to learn,' said one boy. Students sign a contract of behaviour, so know exactly what is expected, and misbehaviour, social or academic, is followed by an oral warning, a written warning, and then a parental meeting. 'We've not excluded anyone for eight to nine years, and not even suspended anyone for a long time,' says Candida Cave. 'We're run here on mutual respect and they do

'We started because there wasn't anyone else specialising in the arts,' says Candida Cave

seem to rise to that.' Most see the college as a place where they can be confident concerns will be dealt with quickly and in confidence. Definitely a haven for those for whom more boisterous or insensitive environments have just not worked. 'The college made my daughter believe in herself. I feel I owe them,' said one parent.

Pupils and parents: A mix of mostly local professional/artistic families, who tend to be profoundly relieved that their children have found such a civilised and creative niche. Some of those who come to do GCSEs have previously been educated abroad. Others have had enough of boarding school, or failed to fit into more conventional schools. Alumni include Orlando Bloom and Helena Bonham-Carter.

Entrance: All applicants are interviewed with their parents and the college makes offers based on two criteria: candidates 'really want to be here' and 'they intend to go on to higher education'. Minimum five GCSEs with C or above, but this liberal benchmark is generally well exceeded, not a few arriving garlanded with a multitude of A*s. Most from local independents and leading boarding schools, a few from the state sector and schools further afield.

Exit: Around 30 per cent leave after GCSEs. For the rest, a generous sprinkling into every permutation of arts and media – from film studies and fine art to fashion retailing and creative writing – but also to history, psychology and sociology. Sussex, Falmouth, Nottingham Trent and Leeds currently popular.

Money matters: One scholarship of 100 per cent (based on academic merit, a statement of why they deserve a scholarship, and an interview). Two of 25 per cent may be given for outstanding exam performance at GCSE ('We wanted to show we appreciated their intelligence.') A limited number of bursaries awarded to students who have previously been educated in the state system who would not otherwise be able to afford private education.

Remarks: A low-key, calm and friendly place, with strong teaching and results, particularly in the arts. Ideal for the 'arty, urban misfit' who has wilted in a more conventional environment.

Francis Holland Junior School, Sloane Square

Linked school: Francis Holland School, Sloane Square, 96

Graham Terrace, London SW1W 8JF

Independent • Pupils: 165 • Ages: 4–11 • C of E • Fees: up to £18,450 pa

Tel: 020 7730 2971

Email: education@fhs–sw1.org.uk
Website: www.fhs–sw1.org.uk

Headteacher: Since 2015, Caroline Spencer-Kruger, previously deputy head.

Entrance: Assessments at 3. Some 150 girls tested in January for 24 places. School assesses 'girls' potential and readiness to learn.' School was horrified when a parent asked about tutoring for their 3 year old and advises, 'Parents need to read to their children, take them to the park and talk to them. That's the best preparation for these tests.' Places occasionally available further up the school and prospective pupils are then assessed in the classroom setting. Barely a spare seat in the house.

Exit: Fairly evenly split: one third to the senior school, one third to other London day schools and another third boarding. One parent remarked that she thought it would be 'a hard jump to go from Francis Holland Junior School to a large co-ed. Girls are protected here and can be quite gentle. I'm not sure they are always ready for the hurly burly of senior school.' Popular day destinations are St Paul's, Godolphin and Latymer, Latymer Upper, JAGS, North London Collegiate and City of London

Girls. Current boarding favourites are Wycombe Abbey, Downe House and Cheltenham Ladies'.

Remarks: A small, academic school, tucked away behind Sloane Square. One form per year of 24 maximum. Shares a site with senior school. 'Low pressure in the early years,' says school. Reception children have naps after lunch in first term when sleepy. From year 4 it hots up, with summer exams in maths, English and science from then on. No setting but plenty of differentiation. The consensus among parents we spoke to was 'You need to be academically robust to cope here. There are so many projects and tests, and parents are expected to be able to support their offspring massively. It feels almost relentless at times.' More academic than senior school: 'The girls here are clever and motivated,' said one parent. 'Strong foundations are laid but the girls work hard for it,' according to another. The standard of work on display was astonishingly high. The girls themselves feel that they are well prepared for the 11+, but 'we don't feel too much pressure.' Year 6 pupils kept working to proper timetables once 11+ exams are over; no coasting here. Teaching is superb and staff considered by the parents to be high quality. Teachers come over from senior school to teach PE, science, French (from 8) and some art. Well motivated staff. 'We're a strong team'.

Bright classrooms, inventive displays, beanbags and colour everywhere. Wonderful library, shared with senior school, and huge numbers of books at every turn.

Girls have beautiful manners and stand up with military discipline when adults enter the room. Highly articulate and fluent. Very keen to show their projects to us when we visited and tell us what they had learnt. Highly engaged in lessons, from early years upwards. Pretty tartan uniform. One girl in top year thought it would be worth staying at the school just so she could get to wear the new kit.

Plenty of time for fun, with highly-anticipated trips to Cornwall in year 6 and Canterbury in year 5. Sport is a real strength. Ballet taken seriously: compulsory in the first years, fabulous ballet studio. Highly anticipated Princess Margaret ballet competition every summer term – her daughter is an old girl. Lots of music and drama, including impressive end of year 6 musical. Girls take the initiative by providing the costumes, designing the posters and rehearsing on their own at break times. Great emphasis placed on creativity throughout the school. Junior choir from year 3 and a very select chamber choir for the most talented singers. Significant numbers learn Instruments from year 1 onwards. 'Girls need time to be bored. They should not have every moment of their lives timetabled.'

Highly anticipated Princess Margaret ballet competition every summer term – her daughter is an old girl

Wants them to discover what interests them for themselves. Plenty of clubs on offer including chess, speech and drama, pottery, art and French.

A very caring school in which older girls are expected to, and do, look after the younger ones. Year 6 pupils write and illustrate books for year 1 pupils. Lots of raising money for charity. All year 6 girls are prefects, though badges confiscated for poor behaviour.

Families are 'more and more international'. 'A bewildering number of languages spoken in the playground at pick up time,' according to one mother. Children come from nearby Westminster, Chelsea, Knightsbridge and Pimlico.

'A happy school,' is the general consensus amongst parents. Bullying very rare. School feels girls are 'traditional and polite'. One pupil acknowledges, 'It will be the saddest day of my life when I leave Francis Holland to go to my next school.' School described as 'vibrant', and it was certainly buzzing on the day we visited. A real energy about the place. Francis Holland girls have a wonderfully stimulating start to life here, with devoted care and attention from outstanding teachers. No wonder there's a queue to come here.

Francis Holland School, Sloane Square

Linked school: Francis Holland Junior School, Sloane Square, 95

39 Graham Terrace, London SW1W 8JF

Independent • Pupils: 335 • Ages: 11–18 • Sixth form pupils: 70 • C of E • Fees: £18,450 pa

Tel: 020 7730 2971

Email: registrar@fhs-sw1.org.uk
Website: www.fhs-sw1.org.uk

48

Headmistress: Since September 2012, Mrs Lucy Elphinstone MA PGCE MEd FRSA (50s). Educated at Barnstaple Grammar School, Devon, and Newnham College, Cambridge (English). Very varied career, including stints in publishing, bookselling, catering, property and ghost-writing. Wide teaching experience from 3 to 18 years, and countless leadership roles including head of a pre-school, head of English at King's Taunton, director of studies in two prep schools, director of drama and resident tutor

at Fettes College. Came here from Downe House where she was head of sixth form, senior leader and Oxbridge co-ordinator. Four highly successful adult children. Living in London for the first time since her 20s and loving the culture. Hobbies include ski-ing, watercolour painting, Scottish reeling and Victorian children's literature. Acknowledges she is very different from her long-serving predecessor, who was 'a mathematician with very different strengths from mine.'

Keen to build up girls' resilience to help them deal with the challenges ahead, including multiple changes of career. Wants pupils to be confident risk-takers. In her assembly on the day we visited, she encouraged girls to take on board Christopher Robin's advice to Winnie the Pooh: 'You are braver than you believe, stronger than you seem, and smarter than you think.' One parent described her as 'ambitious for the school and highly visionary'. Another claimed, 'She's shaken the school up. It was good before but she has lifted our spirits.' Girls consider her to be 'a great role model.' Dynamic, vivacious and engaging.

Academic matters: In 2015, 43 per cent A*/A at A level; 76 per cent A*-B. History of art and English currently popular, with ever-increasing numbers taking maths and science. Compulsory extended project qualification in sixth form, introduced by head to develop girls' research skills and to prepare them for the next stage. Photography, business studies and music technology recently introduced at A level. Seventy-three per cent A*/A at GCSE. Spanish, chemistry and history results impressive. Setting in English, science and maths by year 9. 'Not onerous amounts of homework in first couple of years,' said one parent.

Excellent reports about provision now on offer to pupils with special needs: 'no longer just lip service,' said one parent. All screened for dyslexia on arrival. A handful of pupils have EAL requirements and are seen on a one-to-one basis by specialist staff. Extra support continues to sixth form.

Some teaching described as 'fantastic', but one parent we spoke to felt there were 'still some members of staff who need weeding out. They aren't inspiring the girls and aren't getting the results.' Approximately a third of staff has been there at least 10 years. Recent appointments, particularly of younger members of staff, seen as very positive. Staff feel 'empowered' by newish head.

She encouraged girls to take on board Christopher Robin's advice to Winnie the Pooh: 'You are braver than you believe, stronger than you seem, and smarter than you think'

Academic success is recognised with flamboyant prize giving at nearby Cadogan Hall, with performances by talented dancers and musicians. The girls were hugely excited to see staff wearing their graduation gowns and 'felt proud' to be part of Francis Holland. A great success, recently introduced by head, who is clearly keen to celebrate success in all fields.

Two parallel classes throughout senior school. Classes start at 16 on average and rarely go above 20 in lower years, diminishing to six to eight in sixth form. Would split sixth form classes if they exceeded 10 pupils. From year 11, all girls have an academic mentor, so everyone is fully supported and no one is left floundering. Girls genuinely feel that staff are keeping a close eye on them and that they are guided through university entrance 'incredibly well'.

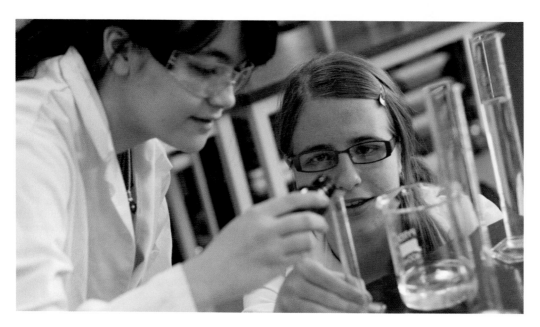

Games, options, the arts: Sport now taken very seriously, at all levels, and is compulsory for all. Head believes, 'Sport is important as it teaches you that you can't always win, but you can pick yourself up and carry on'. Newly appointed head of sport who everyone is raving about. Well-equipped gym and netball/tennis court on site. Outdoor sports in Battersea Park, including tennis, hockey, athletics and rounders. Top years can try pilates, yoga, squash and boxercise as well as more traditional team sports. Most parents are delighted that fixtures are now arranged on Saturday mornings and the school wins the majority of matches.

Music is flourishing. Nearly 60 per cent learn an instrument. Choirs, orchestras, chamber groups and jazz groups galore. Two choir tours to Europe each year. Head wants creative and enterprising pupils and girls recently set up own theatre company. Highly successful theatrical collaborations with boys from nearby Cardinal Vaughan School, with minimal adult input. Parents consider drama to be a real strength. Speech and drama very popular with many reaching top grades in exams. Princess Margaret Ballet Competition held annually, culminating in a final attended by governors and prestigious figures from the ballet world. Many take ballet exams, and talented pupils have auditioned to attend the Royal Ballet School Associate Programme.

Impressive selection of clubs including debating and philosophy, as well as animal club for younger girls. School has a renowned menagerie of animals, from gerbils and snakes to chinchillas, and younger girls get to take home animals for the weekend. Girls encouraged to become proficient in public speaking: debating club from year 10, and mock elections and English Speaking Union events arranged. Broad horizons and an informed awareness of current affairs expected.

Background and atmosphere: Set up by the Rev Francis Holland, Canon of Canterbury, in 1881 as a C of E foundation but all faiths welcome. Sister school to Francis Holland Regent's Park: the schools share a governing body, staff training days and have the same ethos. Same site as junior school, in a Tardis-like building behind Sloane Square. Head aware that being in the same place from 4-18 years has its disadvantages and is keeping her eye out for property nearby. Beautiful interior decorating: stunning new entrance hall lifts morale on arrival and upper sixth common room seriously plush.

Pastoral care and discipline: Described by parents as being 'nurturing'. Lower sixth girls are paired with year 7 girls in 'Big Sister' programme, to make sure they settle on arrival at the school. Head concerned that 'high performing parents have high expectations of their children.' Aware that girls can feel pressurised to perform and a wellbeing programme, including mindfulness, has been set up to help girls to cope, when it all becomes too much. Head is a trained counsellor and pastoral care is high on the agenda.

Strong ethos of service fostered, whether fundraising for school in Uganda or organising tea parties for elderly in Battersea. Girls are expected to give something back.

Head would expel a girl for drug taking; those caught smoking pay money to a cancer charity, phone their parents from head's office and do community service within the school grounds. Won't tolerate unkindness or rudeness and girls we met were fantastically polite. Sixth formers allowed out for lunch but 'school food is delicious so we prefer to stay at school for lunch and just go out for a coffee,' said one.

Pupils and parents: Happy, confident and charming girls who seem ready to take on the world. Well-heeled and polished with ready smiles. Couldn't wait to tell us how lucky they felt to be here. High octane, international families: mainly French, Spanish, Italian, Russian and American. Most live within a three mile radius of school. Communication with parents now greatly improved with regular newsletters and reports. 'We are delighted that we finally know what is going on,' said one.

School has a renowned menagerie of animals, from gerbils and snakes to chinchillas, and younger girls get to take home animals for the weekend

Notable former pupils include Vanessa Mae, Sienna Miller, Cara Delevingne and Rose Tremain.

Entrance: At 11+, exams in English and maths, as well as half a day spent at school consisting of interview and taster lesson. Part of the North London Consortium Group One. Some 500 girls sit for 50 places. Bar raised each year. At 13+, exams in English, maths, science and French. For sixth form, by entrance or scholarship exams in proposed A level subjects.

Exit: A trickle leave after GCSE. Most sixth formers to university. Occasionally one or two Oxbridge places. As one girl put it, 'I have applied to Oxford, but it's just one of my choices. It's not made into a big deal here. My other choices are great too.' Art foundation courses also popular. Medicine, economics, history and psychology are favoured courses; Leeds, Bristol and Nottingham regular destinations. Increasing numbers to US universities, especially for liberal arts degrees, and not only those with a direct American link; others to Spain, France and Canada. Head of careers is a very successful recent appointment; she asks girls at beginning of sixth form, 'What is your dream?', and then helps them to chase it. Higher education fair organised by school. Girls well supported once they leave, throughout university and beyond if needed. Relations with alumnae now actively fostered.

Money matters: At 11, four academic scholarships, as well as music, art and drama scholarships. Bursaries at 11+, 14+ and four in sixth form. Daughters of clergy offered remission on a third of fees.

Remarks: This school is undergoing a transformation and the excitement is palpable. Expectations are high and challenges are being set, but the girls and staff know they have a strong leader and are following her willingly. 'An excellent appointment,' said one parent. 'We feel seriously lucky to have our girls here on Mrs Elphinstone's watch,' said another. Though small, this school is now punching above its weight. An exciting and exhilarating place to be.

Francis Holland School, Regent's Park

Clarence Gate, Ivor Place, London NW1 6XR

Independent · Pupils: 465 · Ages: 11–18 · Sixth form pupils: 120 · C of E · Fees: £17,700 pa

Tel: 020 7723 0176

Email: admin@fhs–nw1.org.uk
Website: www.fhs–nw1.org.uk

Head: From January 2016, Charles Fillingham, currently deputy head at City of London School, who will be this school's first male head. French degree from the University of Wales, with a PGCE in French and German from Bristol University and an MA with distinction in education management from King's College, London. He has taught in both the independent and state sectors, in single sex girls' and boys' schools and in a co-educational school. He is also a trained independent schools' inspector and sits on the governing council of the ACSL (secondary heads' association). He is married with a son and a daughter.

Head since 2004, Mrs Vivienne Durham MA (50s). Prior to her arrival at Francis Holland, much-loved deputy head at South Hampstead High and had taught at Guildford High and Haberdashers' Girls, where she headed the English department. Deservedly one of the most popular heads in the business, loquacious, enthusiastic, fervent in her belief in 'education' rather than in specifically 'girls' education', highly articulate and jolly good fun. She is a people person writ large, but also a clever strategist and manager of resources. You want to give her your daughters and we spoke to no-one who regretted having done so. 'Mrs Durham is very caring, very switched-on and really nice to deal with,' vouchsafed one grateful mother, who spoke for many. The staff clearly love her too and the girls plainly see her as a role model. We could quote much of what she says but will settle for: 'I've never seen an online facility which could replace a good human being in the classroom'. She is infuriatingly svelte and chic and married to the ex-head of University College School. Awarded Tatler's Best Head of a Public School award in 2014.

Retiring in December 2015.

Academic matters: Small classes – especially at A level – are an almost USP here. No class is bigger than 25 and, in the sixth, 14 max – many are far smaller. For a relatively small sixth form offers a creditable range of subjects including economics, history of art and psychology. Most popular subjects tend to be art, biology, English, history and maths; the best results in RS, politics, geography, history of art and art. Economics less strong. Theatre studies offered at A level though not at GCSE. Outstanding results in many subjects – 60 per cent A*/A in 2015. Extended project (worth half an A level) can be taken in addition to A levels and challenges the most able.

GCSEs and, increasingly, IGCSEs (76 per cent A*/A) also include a good number of options – most popular are history, art and geography. Wisely, allows girls to take either three separate sciences or double science – we approve.

SEN support is generally by withdrawal or out-of-lesson individual support. Most of those who receive help are mildly dyslexic/dyspraxic but additional support also for those perceived as G and T. Three-strong 'learning enhancement' team. 'We give girls extra support the entire time – it's simply part of what we offer,' says head, and parents concur, 'The girls can refer themselves for support and there's excellent liaison between the subject staff and the team'.

But the academic input here is far more than just good teaching. Weekly lectures by outside speakers open to all from year 9 up. Lots of trips hither and yon and good use made of privileged location and the proximity of the odd museum, Houses of Parliament, Bank of England or three.

Games, options, the arts: Minutes from Regent's Park, where most sports take place. Onsite is a tiny Astro playground – good for netball shooting practice but no more – but a good sized gym, fitness suite and, surprisingly, basement swimming pool, opened 1996 by, somewhat improbably, Old Girl Joan Collins – swimming one of the more competitive sports. Plans for a

---

Basement swimming pool, opened in 1996 by, somewhat improbably, Old Girl Joan Collins. Plans for new swimming pool in time for centenary of school's move to Ivor Place

---

new swimming pool in time for centenary of school's move to Ivor Place, at the end of 2015. Sport compulsory for all, but lots of choice by the time you're in the sixth and zumba is a recent, popular addition – along with yoga and the use of the fitness suite.

Art is exceptional here – lots of it lines the corridors and we felt inclined to snaffle some of the best pieces to hang at home: really attractive, skilful, imaginative work. Top floor now houses the two studios, plus kiln, dark room, and printing press; views over the grey slate, Georgian rooftops and grey, steel satellite dishes must inspire artistic freedom, as it clearly burns bright.

Music also housed up here, though you'd not imagine the few small rooms result in the level of skill and performance managed by the girls here. Seventy per cent learn at least one instrument. Orchestras, choirs – large and chamber – and other ensembles thrive and surprise. Annual concert with the boys of Harrow School is a highlight. Music and drama combine to produce major annual show, plus drama competition – these draw in most, one way or another, though more drama – especially in the upper years – would be appreciated by many. Young Enterprise and Duke of Edinburgh Award scheme both thrive, along with more than 70 clubs and activities.

Background and atmosphere: Founded by Canon Francis Holland in 1878 at the instigation of his wife, Mary Sibylla, an interesting woman, mother of six, who pushed for the education of 'girls from the middle and upper classes' and later converted to Roman Catholicism. Moved from Baker Street to Ivor Place in 1915. The second school with Canon Holland's name was founded shortly afterwards just off Sloane Square; the two schools are run by the same foundation. Sibylla's letters were published by her children and make for touching reading.

Minutes from Baker Street and Regent's Park, the main building is a classic 1900s redbrick school – smallish classrooms, corridors, lots of floors and a wonderful hexagonal hall with three galleries and lots of polished wood. But the Tardis cliché really applies here. From the unassuming outside, you can't imagine how the school could accommodate more than a few dozen girls, but inside it goes on and on and has some surprisingly spacious areas. The library is also a decent size and has acquired a new area for computers in addition to the trad bookshelves and table space. Sofas and armchairs – we approve of that too. The stock is good, but some updating might inspire more to use books along with Google.

'They are so kind – they bring us up hot chocolate and muffins,' and that really is kind, as four flights of stairs are involved

---

The hall – used for all major events – is not an ideal performance space but has extendable staging and clearly works. The acquisition of the adjacent Gloucester Arms pub and its consequent reopening as the Gloucester Wing was a major advance – Mrs Durham is on the lookout for a further property to enable further expansion, not in numbers but in facilities. Now possesses two good

art studios, seminar rooms and a splendid, well-used lecture theatre. The old saloon bar is a useful space for drama work, charity activities and talks. School is an admirable mix of traditional and up to the minute – computer system recently renewed and everyone now wired in and up, as you'd expect.

Right at the top is the sixth form area and it's super – lots of space, though it can get crowded at breaks – with a roof top garden, a workroom, silent study area and common room with cooking area, sofas and lockers. Staff allowed in to pop marked work etc into sensible pigeon holes. School is accessible – lift enables wheelchair-users to get almost everywhere, though some corridors and steps make odd corners impossible.

The food is 'the best in London' – certainly the salads were lusciously inviting, as were the plates of fruit – pomegranates, passion fruit and melon slices: drool! Kitchen staff clearly popular with sixth formers – 'They are so kind – they bring us up hot chocolate and muffins,' we were told, and that really is kind, as four flights of stairs are involved.

Pastoral care and discipline: Universal praise for the pastoral care – 'the school could not be more supportive'; 'The staff are incredibly sensitive and caring. They are firm when it's needed, but you are always supported,' parents told us again and again. 'The staff are inspiring – they are more than just academic: they look after the whole child,' is another theme. Heads of year have overall responsibility and a counsellor visits weekly. Home and social difficulties – as anywhere – but few discipline problems; Mrs Durham the ultimate arbiter.

Back-up for practical as well as emotional needs: 'The UCAS support here is amazingly impressive,' an Oxbridge hopeful told us. 'The school has been so on top of everything – you get at least three teachers helping, loads of sessions; our head of sixth is amazing and she makes us feel completely secure in how we approach our applications.'

'I want them to be confident and self-possessed but not trumpet about it,' asserts the head. 'We are absolutely about nurture. We are kind and academic. Kind is central.'

Pupils and parents: Interesting mix. Professional families from all over – hence the higher than usual incidence of relocating ins and outs that results in places appearing at odd stages: academics, medics, thesps and financiers, as you'd expect. The very rich – 'There are a few "princesses" in the sixth form,' muttered one or two parents – along with those who struggle to find the fees.

Notable Old Girls include Theresa Villiers, Joan and Jackie Collins, Tamara and Petra Ecclestone, Emilia Fox and Holly Branson.

Entrance: From over 170 preps and primaries. Majority from Pembridge House, Bute House, Sarum Hall, St Mary's, Hampstead, St Christopher's, Hampstead, St Christina's. Applications via the North London Consortium – exams in English and maths plus interviews. Oversubscribed of course, but as for many parents whose daughters also apply to the other powerhouses in the area the school, for all its virtues, is not always the first choice, a good chance of a place at 11+ if your daughter is able and would fit in. Location in central London means that relocating families come and go more than elsewhere and places often occur in other years – it is always worth a call.

> *'I want them to be confident and self-possessed but not trumpet about it. We are absolutely about nurture. Kind is central'*

At 16+ very few are taken – Mrs Durham has a sizeable sixth form and is not straining nerves to cram in more. Perhaps two to three places awarded to, perhaps, 20-30 applicants. A/Bs needed at GCSE.

Exit: Around 10 leave after GCSE and head for mixed sixth forms, notably Highgate – some come back. Mrs Durham is not the head to throw you out if you have problems or your GCSEs disappoint – 'We take them in at 11: we'll stick with them till 18'; also several families whose daughters have found refuge here from unhappiness elsewhere.

No identikit FH leaver – fledglings go everywhere including New York University, Durham, Warwick and Imperial College. Three to Oxbridge in 2015.

Money matters: A few bursaries and scholarships and worth enquiring, but, like most girls' day schools, not munificently endowed.

Remarks: Your clever daughter will be well taught and will do as well here as anywhere. Your shy and gentle soul will be loved and encouraged. Definitely no hothouse but a school that warms and nurtures. A gem in the heart of the metropolis.

Grafton Primary School

Eburne Road, Holloway, London N7 6AR

State • Pupils: 564 boys and girls • Ages: 3-11

Tel: 020 7272 3284

Email: graftonschool@grafton.islington.sch.uk
Website: www.graftonschool.co.uk

39

Head: Since 1993, Mrs Nitsa Sergides OBE (awarded in 2012 for services to education), (60s). Qualified as a teacher in 1973, followed by 19 years of teaching at a local school. Became deputy head of Grafton Primary in 1991, and head two years later.

Cypriot born Nitsa (as everyone calls her), is the embodiment of Mediterranean warmth. Her pupils adore her, 'lovely to all of us, talks to us like family.' Her teachers are loyal (incredibly low turnover of staff) and parents marvel at her dedication: 'She's quite amazing, her enthusiasm never wanes and

she genuinely wants the best for everybody.' Another parent told us, 'She is truly exceptional. Apart from her incredibly nurturing side, she has a gift of being able to get hold of every resource going for the school.'

Nitsa came to the UK at the age of 13 with teaching firmly on her radar, 'I think I was 7 when I realised that's what I wanted to be.' Now in her third decade at Grafton School, she still wants to make a difference. 'I believe that children must be given every chance to succeed regardless of background or ethnicity. We try to create opportunities some pupils may not otherwise have.' This could be a yearly trip to the coast (which for some pupils is their first experience of the sea), or the chance to learn a musical instrument.

One of Nitsa's proudest achievements is that she hasn't had to exclude a child for 11 years, 'I always believe more in preventative measures rather than reactive measures.' She also believes that, given the correct guidance, inner-city schools can be as good as any: 'My three children are all products of Islington comprehensives. My son is now a neurosurgeon and both my daughters are barristers.' Married for 40 years to an engineer, 'my bouncing board', she loves visiting art galleries and museums and spending time with her grandchildren. Such is her infectious enthusiasm that we left her office grinning.

Entrance: Standard local authority criteria of siblings, proximity to school and children in care etc. Competition for places is fierce – most recently 354 applicants for 60 places. As word spreads about this school there is concern about wealthier parents buying property in now trendy Holloway to get their kids a place, with predictable consequences for Grafton's rich diversity.

Exit: Mixed bag on offer for secondary schools in the Islington area. Most go on to Acland Burghley (if they live close enough), Highbury Fields, Highbury Grove, Mount Carmel school for girls, St Mary Magdalene and others including Islington Arts school, Central Foundation Boys' School, Camden School for Girls, Highgate Wood, Parliament Hill and William Ellis. A few try for grammars like Latymer or Dame Alice Owen and independents such as City of London.

Remarks: A tricky one to find, Grafton Primary sits adjacent to the Holloway Road, off Seven Sisters Road, accessible by car via a tiny slip road. Most pupils walk to school thereby avoiding the perils of Holloway's one-way system.

Rarely have we seen so much artwork (including a wonderful tree of life installation which ran the length of the lobby and through the school's office)

We were expecting great things and we weren't disappointed. Rated outstanding by Ofsted for the past 10 years and awarded the title of Beacon School, Grafton defies its demographics. A staggering 55-60 per cent of its pupils would qualify for free school meals (although in Islington, these are fully funded for all pupils), 25 per cent of children have SEN, 12 per cent with statements. Grafton is genuinely inclusive – big on equal opps for pupils with disabilities and a vast ethnic mix. One pupil told us, 'I have friends from so many different cultures and we are like a big family.' We heard the word 'family' used frequently and there is definitely a sense of unity and loyalty as well as pride in this school.

103

Grafton has recently become a teaching school, meaning that they now train teachers and support staff from other primaries. It is also one of only a few pioneering schools to have been chosen to introduce the CAME maths programme (Cognitive Acceleration through Mathematics Education), which promises to have a significant impact on both pupil and teacher development. Maths is already a very strong subject at Grafton. Up to 20 per cent of year 6 achieve a level 6 in maths Sats.

On entering one is immediately struck by the spectacularly colourful lobby. Rarely have we seen so much artwork, sculpture, ceiling displays (including a wonderful tree of life installation which ran the length of the lobby and through the school's office). Grafton has partnerships with art professionals, a specialist art and design teacher and an artist in residence, believing that time given to creative subjects helps children achieve in other areas.

The interior of the school is charming, if a little cramped (could be because every inch of space is covered with student displays). The Victorian building is DDA compliant and has a lift for wheelchair users. A 3.5m refurb means all classrooms are now up to spec and there's a new sports hall and reception play area. Library is still a work in progress but promises to be a great space.

Outside is an oasis of calm – amazing, considering proximity to the very urban and not very pretty Seven Sisters Road. Grounds are fairly large for an inner-city school and in addition to the playground there is a quiet formal garden with benches for students to have lunch and read (undergoing a refurb during our visit) and a wildlife garden. This mini eco system with pond and bug hotel feels a million miles from the city. 'Many parents volunteer their time in the garden and elsewhere', we are told. At the end of the wildlife garden is a glass building that we thought was a greenhouse; it's actually the art room, a quirky space crammed with creative materials.

In the assembly hall we were treated to a music assembly in Swahili, just one of the 34 languages spoken here. On site translators assist parents from the three main non-English speaking groups – Somalian, Turkish and Bangladeshi, and the school told us, 'We do what we can to make parents from all sectors of society feel included.'

'If they're not hopping on a bus to St Paul's Cathedral, visiting the zoo or going to art galleries and museums, they are doing a walking tour around London'

The pupils we met were a highly articulate bunch – happy, confident and engaging. They loved their school and the opportunities it offers. One told us, 'Julia Donaldson has visited the school and some Paralympians came to talk to us, which was amazing and inspiring.' Another said he loved the cricket and football 'and we've won many tournaments.' A few negative comments about the lunches (free of charge for all pupils) and we thought that some of the food did look pretty unappetising. It seems almost churlish to mention this when for some pupils it may be the only cooked meal they get in a day.

Parents and pupils generally seemed extremely happy with their school. One parent did mention that she would like more sporting activities within the school day as opposed to just afternoon clubs, although she added that the Grafton school day is such a busy one, she's not sure where they would fit it in. Another told us, 'The school is amazing at being pro-active, especially with day trips. If they're not hopping on the bus to St Paul's Cathedral, visiting the zoo or going to art galleries and museums, they're doing a walking tour around London. That's the benefit of being so inner city with free bus travel.' The quality of teaching came in for particular praise. One mother told us, 'My older children go to private schools and I know that the teaching my youngest is getting here is better than they received at her age.' She also said that there is a very high ratio of staff to pupils – 1:6 in the first two years – again, as good, as if not better than at some independent schools.

The Grey Coat Hospital

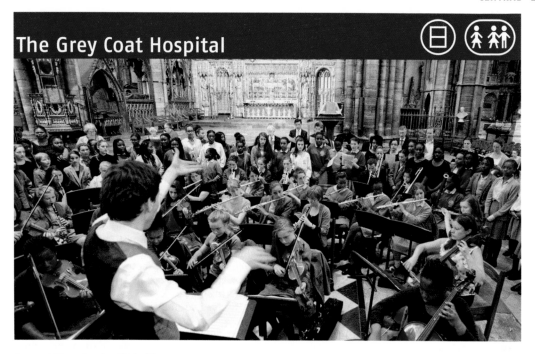

Greycoat Place, London SW1P 2DY

State • Pupils: 1,034 • Ages: 11–18 • Sixth form pupils: 267 (32 boys) • C of E

Tel: 020 7969 1998

Email: info@gch.org.uk
Website: www.gch.org.uk

Headteacher: Since 2011, Ms Siân Maddrell BA (40s). Educated at Surbiton High, followed by a degree in French at Durham. After gaining her PGCE at Oxford, she began her teaching career at Grey Coat in 1992, soon becoming head of modern languages and one of the first advanced skills teachers in the country. Left Grey Coat in 2000 and later became the first vice principal of Pimlico Academy. Friendly, thoughtful, efficient and clearly devoted to her school. Takes great pride in her pupils and their achievements. Not above picking up stray litter in the playground.

'We want to enable girls to take charge of their learning, make decisions based on Christian values, live in the world as independent women and meet the challenges of the 21st century,' she told us. 'We just try to focus on our pupils. It's a very ambitious school and the students will tell you that the expectations and aspirations are really high for everybody. It's about empowering the pupils to do their best. We want girls to be confident enough to be able to seize every opportunity.'

Enjoys sport, theatre and travel – 'I'm very interested in other countries and cultures.' Married with two sons, so 'most of my free time is spent with my family.'

Academic matters: School is regularly rated outstanding by Ofsted. Recently received congratulatory letter from local MP and schools minister praising pupils and staff for position in the performance tables and saying 'it is clear that your school has equipped its pupils to be successful hereafter, both in terms of their readiness for further study and in terms of their readiness to enter the world of work in due course.'

'Students will tell you that the expectations and aspirations are really high for everybody'

In 2015, 85 per cent of students gained five or more A*-C GCSEs including English and maths, and 43 per cent of grades were A*/A. Girls take between nine and 13 GCSEs. At A level, 57 per cent A*/B and 25 per cent A*/A grades. Grey Coat has recently been in the top 100 non-selective schools in the country in terms of GCSE results and progress. Good range of subjects on offer to GCSE, including Latin, business studies and computing. Pre-U offered in Latin, Greek and art history, all of which are taught at neighbouring Westminster School. 'The pupils love their lessons at Westminster,' the head told us. A level subjects include film studies and sociology as well as more traditional fare. Biology, English, history, maths, psychology and religious studies currently very popular. EPQ is becoming increasingly fashionable.

Grey Coat is a specialist language college and has an outward looking, global focus. 'We encourage an international outlook as well as strong grades,' says the head. 'It is important for our students to gain an understanding of other countries and cultures and to have an open and inclusive approach, as well as to develop their linguistic skills.' All students study Spanish and a second modern language (French or German). Most continue with two foreign languages to GCSE. Opportunities to study Mandarin, Japanese and ancient Greek out of school hours. Japanese exchange offered to girls in year 10; other exchange trips to France and Germany, as well as opportunities for work experience in Germany.

International May Fair for younger pupils is an annual highlight. Students are encouraged to represent a country – through fashion, food, dance, ecology and culture. The competition is judged by staff and the prize, awarded to the most impressive tutor group, is a trip to Paris. School is excellent at offering incentives to pupils; girls are encouraged

> ### 'We are the Westminster sports champions in practically everything and we provide a rich variety of sports,' says the head

to be competitive. Pupils regularly win local and national science and maths competitions.

Grey Coat prides itself on being an inclusive school. SEN pupils make good progress academically and are fully involved in school life. All year 7 girls are screened for learning difficulties on entry to school. Small support groups for literacy, numeracy and social skills run at lunchtime for younger girls. Five per cent have a statement of special educational needs. Gifted and talented extension programmes in place for more able.

Average class size is 26, with a maximum of 30. No setting in year 7. Year 8 pupils setted for English, maths, science and languages.

Games, options, the arts: Good level of participation in wide variety of sport. 'We are the Westminster sports champions in practically everything and we provide a rich variety of sports,' says the head. Opportunities for fencing, squash, ice-skating and athletics as well as team sports. Currently Westminster netball champions. 'We've struggled a bit with athletics as we have to bus the pupils over to Battersea Park,' admits bursar. Massive sports hall at Regency Street site. Annual gym and dance display.

Creative subjects taken seriously. Excellent facilities in art and design; these remain very popular subjects and the quality of art displays is very high. 'The standard of art work is mind-blowing,' according to one parent. Music and drama both strong. Instrumental and singing lessons are subsidised by school's foundation. Good range of choirs, bands, string and jazz groups and orchestra. Several concerts every year. Successful gospel choir recently reached semi-finals of BBC's School Choir of the Year competition.

Roughly 15 pupils a year achieve D of E gold award. Good spread of clubs, including maths challenge, debating, football, trampolining and creative writing. External inspirational speakers come in regularly to motivate and encourage the girls. Workshops led by outsiders a regular feature of the education offered here. School takes part in BBC News School Report, enabling pupils to make their own news reports for a live audience. Students develop their journalistic skills and have a ball.

Lots of time for fun here too. Talent show at the end of the Easter term is eagerly anticipated while staff pantomime is apparently 'the best day' of the school year. 'It's absolutely hilarious watching the teachers,' said one pupil. Post-GCSE celebration for year 11s includes a fashion show of their textiles work.

Background and atmosphere: Originally founded for boys – by eight merchants of Westminster on St Andrew's day in 1698. In 1706, Queen Anne granted the Grey Coat Hospital Foundation a royal charter and her portrait hangs in pride of place in the Great Hall. Original wooden boards detailing the names and donations of 18th century benefactors line the stairs. In 1874 Grey Coat Hospital became a girls' school, under church management. Whole school was evacuated during the war and its buildings suffered significant bomb damage.

A C of E school – head says 'Christian values play a key part in what we aim to do here.' Church services held each term either in Westminster Abbey or St Margaret's, including a service on Ash Wednesday and a July celebration to which new pupils (and their parents) are invited. 'It's a lovely event – beautifully done,' said a parent. Confirmation services take place at Westminster Abbey and school has its own chaplain.

School occupies two fabulous buildings in the heart of Westminster. Huge quantity of traffic and people encircling it on the streets outside. Strikingly beautiful building in Greycoat Place, freshly painted and well polished. Statuettes of Grey Coat boy and girl adorn the front façade of the school. Wonderful entrance hall, glistening with trophies and artwork. School celebrates the achievements of the girls at every opportunity. In 1998 the school celebrated its 300th anniversary by opening a new upper school building on Regency Street, having sold another site on Sloane Square.

Original building at Greycoat Place is used by the younger pupils (years 7 to 9) but lots of coming and going of pupils from one site to another. Fantastic new arts block, includes swish drama studios where recent productions have included Shakespearean plays and The Madness of George III. 'Drama is one of those things that is taken very seriously at Grey Coat and the performances are very professional,' we were told. Facilities hired out to National Youth Theatre in holidays.

Welcoming staff. Healthy female/male ratio and mix of long-servers and newly qualified teachers. 'A positive balance,' says the head. Turnover of staff can be high, with up to 20 per cent a year leaving, but 'there's no clear pattern.'

Symbiotic relationship with Westminster School. Grey Coats go there for lectures, some lessons and Oxbridge preparation, while graduate trainee teachers from Westminster come here to gain experience of teaching in a state school. 'It's wonderful for our students that they have these opportunities,' says the head.

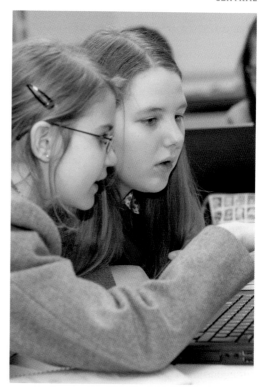

Pastoral care and discipline: Pastoral care is a major strength of the school. 'Each girl is part of a tutor group family and a year group family, so each feels looked after here,' says the head. Strict code of conduct, but relatively few behavioural issues here. Older girls are given plenty of responsibility, with 40 prefects in final year. Girls can become ambassadors for their year group, having successfully explained at interview why they should be chosen. 'There is a strong sense of community here,' says the head. 'We have counsellors, student counsellors, and older students working with younger pupils. It's about creating a sense that we're all in this together.' It certainly seems to be working well. A learning mentor is on hand to help girls organise themselves if needed, as well as a drop-in school nurse.

Girls start off in smaller, lower school – helps them cope better with the progression to upper school. 'It's rare to hear of anyone being miserable here,' a parent told us. 'The school keeps a close eye on its pupils and intervenes quickly if things are going awry.'

Food thought to be 'very good, with lots of choice' according to one pupil. Vast quantities of pizzas being eaten at break on the day we visited. Oyster card system in place so girls don't need to carry money and the canteen is open from breakfast onwards. School is confident that 'we'd know if a girl wasn't eating.'

Head is justifiably proud of the excellent attendance record of 98 per cent throughout the year – rating it the third highest in the UK. 'All our pupils came in when the recent tube strike was on,' says the head. Pupils with 100 per cent attendance and punctuality for a year get a trip to the theatre.

Pupils and parents: 'A real mix,' the head told us. Twenty-eight per cent of pupils eligible for pupil premium. Two-thirds from minority ethnic groups. A quarter whose first language is not English – more than 50 languages spoken at home, including Yoruba, Swahili, Spanish, French and Dutch.

Big inner-city blend of families, including daughters of politicians and education professionals. School recently hit the headlines with the news that prominent politicians are sending their daughters here. Old Greys include TV presenter Sarah Greene and Tamsin Dunwoody MP. Recent leaver is Ebony-Jewel Rainford-Brent, the first female black cricketer to play for the England team (she presented awards at last prize-giving). Many old girls remain loyal to the school and return to the annual school celebration service in Westminster Abbey each year.

Entrance: Huge catchment area from the dioceses of London and Southwark. Pupils travel from as far away as Essex and Kent and are rarely local. Total of 151 places offered in year 7. Fifteen language places (following an aptitude test which 450 sit); 88 C of E places; 28 other church places; 20 open places.

Priority given to looked-after children, then siblings, church attendance for church places and a distance tie-breaker. The comprehensive intake is placed into bands following an assessment test – 25 per cent places to band 1, 50 per cent places to band 2 and 25 per cent to band 3. Offers sent out in March.

Open events for year 6 pupils in September and early October each year. Sixth form open events in November. Relatively little movement of pupils. 'We are a very stable population,' says the bursar. Once pupils are here, they tend to stay put, even if it means travelling long distances. In-year admissions are dealt with by the local authority. Forty boys in sixth form, all 'charming,' according to one member of staff.

Exit: Around a quarter leave after GCSEs, usually for schools closer to home or offering subjects not available here. Their places are taken by a fresh intake – the head says 'it's a fresh start for all.' Around 90 per cent go on to higher education. School encourages pupils to aim for top universities and some 40 per cent go to Russell Group universities. Popular destinations include Oxbridge (three places in 2015), Exeter, St Andrews, Leeds, Durham, Nottingham, Bristol and Manchester. Popular subjects include medicine, sciences, maths, English, religious studies and classics.

Money matters: Parents' Guild raises money each year for both the school and charity. Recently paid for a beautiful stained glass window by Michael Coles. Parents are asked to contribute a small amount of money on a monthly or annual basis.

Remarks: A sensational mix of high academic standards strongly supported by caring and devoted staff. No wonder they are prepared to travel for hours each day to be part of this buzzing school. The girls we met were charming, articulate, interesting and purposeful. Their pride in the school was striking. Not only are they ambitious and successful but they're also happy. On the day we visited, groups of girls were sitting cross-legged on the tarmac playground at break time, chatting and laughing as though they didn't have a care in the world.

The Hall School

23 Crossfield Road, London NW3 4NU

Independent • Pupils: 460 • Ages: 4–13 • C of E • Fees: up to £17,427 pa

Tel: 020 7722 1700

Email: office@hallschool.co.uk
Website: www.hallschool.co.uk

Headmaster: Since September 2013, Christopher Godwin, previously head of Bedford Prep. Read geography at Loughborough, then masters in Middle Eastern studies at Durham. Joined Bedford in 1993 as second master and director of studies before taking over the headship four years later.

With no experience of London schools, his post came as a surprise to some parents, although he quickly won hearts and minds with his keenness to maintain the ethos and values of the school, along with his gentle and unassuming nature and fresh pair of eyes. 'There's a track record of people taking this job who are greying and in their early 50s,' he laughs, 'but I hope I've brought a new energy to the school.' Parents and pupils concur, praising his emphasis on 'positive psychology rather than rules, rules and more rules,' as one parent put it. 'There's a strong pastoral element to his thinking,' said another. Sees the next phase as making the school even more responsive to 'the world we now live in', with a growing focus on preparing boys for what their next schools require and embedding ever more IT into an already technology-heavy curriculum. Known for being open and available to parents and a great team builder among staff. Often seen out and about in school and is not precious about his office, whose conference table is often used by boys themselves. Teaches current affairs to year 5s upwards, geography to year 8s and frequently reads stories in junior school. Heavily involved in the assessment of boys. Keen and active sportsman, particularly rugby – now as coach rather than player.

Entrance: This is the top north London prep school for those looking towards the country's top academic secondary schools, so competition for entrance is hotter than hot, with applications restricted to those registering before their first birthday – and even so, the school is three times over-subscribed. At 3, parents are invited in to discuss whether a child will apply to enter at 4 or 5 (32 places at 4, 22 at 5). 'This can be down to issues such as birth date, speed of development, grasp of English if they come from a bi-lingual family and, of course, the parents have a say too,' says head, although he stresses that it all comes down to the individual boy, rather than any set guidelines. All applicants are tested in the same year – 4+ entrants in January for September, 5+ entrants in late April/May for the following September – for which parents have been known to tutor their offspring at as young as 3 (although the school says it frowns upon this). Boys are assessed in groups of six. 'We are looking for a hunch about their potential, as well as how interactive, sociable and curious they are and their ability to concentrate,' says head. 'It's very detailed, with lots of personal attention, so that we get boys who are right for the school and who we can take right through the school.' Inevitably, there wind up being strugglers and – as the head puts it – 'those who feel adrift from their year group', and these boys have been known to be guided elsewhere, although school insists this is rare and it's clear that increasing effort is made to help every boy keep up. Favours siblings, but no guarantees and many haven't got places in recent years. Occasional places arise higher up the school, with a formal registration process for the waiting list. 'They do a good job of picking the right boys,' said one parent. 'Those that don't get in shouldn't get in and those that do are generally a good fit.'

Exit: Seventy per cent to top London day schools, particularly Westminster and St Paul's, but also largish contingents to UCS, City of London, Highgate, Merchant Taylors' and Mill Hill. Sizeable minority to traditional single-sex boarding schools – Eton, Harrow, Winchester, Tonbridge, with others going to St Edward's Oxford, Aldenham and Uppingham. Co-ed boarding schools becoming more popular (and increasingly encouraged by the school), including King's School Canterbury and Arundel.

Exceptional guidance in secondary school choices. 'We encourage parents of boys in year 4 upwards to start looking widely. We don't leave it with a year to go,' says head. The match is made by a meticulously planned programme of assessments, which include annual verbal and non-verbal reasoning and day-to-day performance, and which are all tracked on a graph for each boy. Scholarship form in year 8 for those completing the demanding exams of Eton and Westminster, but not all scholarships derive from this form.

Remarks: Prep schools don't come more ambitious than this. Catering to the needs of boys who are intellectually curious, academic and highly motivated, this is a school that stretches them in every direction, the result of which is a cohort of fiercely intelligent and extremely articulate boys. Yet there's nothing precocious about them and we found the school environment to be surprisingly relaxed.

Two classes of 16 in reception, reshuffled to three of 18 in year 1. By year 8, four classes of 12 to 14, with a scholarship form and three fast common entrance forms. Staff are a broad age range, including at the senior end, and have notable experience and oodles of enthusiasm. 'They're strict, but you can have a real joke with them too,' said one boy, and we certainly found humour abundant in the classrooms and corridors, with a refreshing ease of communication between pupils and staff. 'The lessons are unbelievably interactive. You never just sit and listen,' said another pupil.

> *'Even if you're in set 3, you're still really smart, so there's never a feeling of being bottom of anything,' said one pupil*

Specialist French, science, music, sport and ICT more or less from the word go. Latin added in year 5, Greek in year 7 for scholarship candidates. Setting in core subjects from year 5 and Latin from year 6. 'But even if you're in set 3, you're still really smart, so there's never a feeling of being bottom of anything,' said one pupil. Three sciences, taught in a more combined way than in the past. ICT provision has long been outstanding, with digital learning embedded into just about every subject and clearly apparent when we visited, with plenty of tablets being used across the board. Advanced coding and programming is praised, as is the collaborative work using shared computer files. Head still not resting on his laurels, though, with £250,000 about to be spent on further ICT, including a new virtual learning environment when we visited. Homework starts gently, then builds up and peaks at two preps of 45 minutes for years 7 and 8. No Sats but exams taken very seriously, with all subjects examined twice yearly in the upper forms. 'The teaching is so good that you actually don't need to revise for exams,' said one boy, 'although most of us do anyway.' Does well in national competitions, such as the Townsend Warner History Prize and national Maths Challenges.

The school itself is divided up, with junior school (reception to year 3), middle (years 4 and 5) and senior school (years 6-8) on separate sites all within a short walk of this upmarket residential area. Junior school is made up of two well-ordered Victorian buildings, with the head living in a flat above. Middle school is a 1970s building that was probably cutting-edge at the time, but could do with a rethink in terms of use of good space now. Senior school is the original red-brick school building, with lots of quirky design features, including split level classrooms, which make for a cosy learning environment.

Classrooms generally on the small side, especially in the middle school, but well-ordered, and many are innovatively designed (especially the history room, with its very own upstairs library and historically decorated walls) and welcoming. Even the DT room, where boys were making splurge guns ready for their production of Bugsy Malone when we visited, is carpeted. Lovely, bright art room, with separate pottery room that boasts two kilns. Wathen Hall, which is the main hall, feels a bit past its use-by date and would benefit from something more airy and with better use of space. Well-stocked, two-story, library with library sessions once a week. Stand-out common room, known as the Pit, with a focal snooker table and split level, contemporary and airy environment.

Like most north London preps, outside space is limited, although the junior school has a colourful and imaginative playground, whilst the older boys use one all-weather pitch, which school admits 'can get crowded' at playtimes. Sport, however, is prioritised, with £2m recently invested in the sports field at East Finchley, which the boys are transported to by coach two afternoons a week, and where they play football, rugby, hockey, cricket and tennis. Gymnastics and fencing in Wathen Hall. Every boy gets a chance to represent the school at some point in a team game (nine football teams) and the school is currently looking to extend its fixture list outside London. Some parents concerned that sport generally favours the best boys, however. 'All boys get to play, but if you're good, you get much better training,' said one. 'If the boys aren't sporty, they're not really bothered with them,' said another. County and national representatives at chess, fencing, skiing and tennis. Annual skiing trips to France and biannual cricket tour of Sri Lanka. 'We competed against teams that got 1000 runs in 10 games in the last tour. The quality of cricket was amazing,' said one boy.

Boys were making splurge guns ready for their production of Bugsy Malone when we visited

Over 80 per cent of boys play an instrument, with an army of peripatetic teachers made available, on top of which there are two specialist music lessons a week for all. 'It's not unusual to find boys playing three instruments,' said one boy. Plenty of encouragement to join the large orchestra, string quartets, jazz group and choir, all of which regularly win music awards. 'You get to sing in some amazing places if you're in the choir,' said one boy, listing Southwark Cathedral, St Albans Cathedral and Eton Chapel. 'There are some great music trips too,' said another, citing a year 7 trip to South Africa. The annual bands night is popular and boys rave about the new recording studio. Drama taken seriously, with boys of all ages encouraged to perform in plays, concerts, public speaking and most notably debating. When we visited, an actor in residence (an MA student from the nearby Royal Central School of Speech and Drama) was about to begin his year-long post.

This isn't the kind of school where every boy knows each other (not helped by the lack of single campus) but school does what it can to encourage peer support, with older boys helping out in the junior school and becoming ambassadors for subjects, such as geography. From year 5 upwards, the four houses have so-called 'bungalows', which comprise cross-year groups of eight boys who meet regularly and are led by a year 8 boy to discuss topics such as new ideas for activities or views on the rewards system for good work. In addition, there's a lively school council, that makes a lot of recommendations around meals ('I really don't like the food,' admitted one pupil) and equipment for the playground, as well as decisions about various charity fundraising. Boys say the atmosphere is highly supportive. 'Everyone is really friendly here,' said one.

School accommodates all the usual SEN free-of-charge, including dyslexia and Asperger's, and is open minded about discussing pretty much any difference, provided the underlying intellect is there. 'My son is dyslexic and the school just took it in their stride, which had a hugely positive effect on his confidence,' said one parent. Learning support department, which is run by a full-time staff member (BEd and certificate in dyslexia), involved in identifying issues, as well as monitoring and supporting them either in the short or long term, bringing in outside expertise where necessary. Only one statemented child when we visited. Huge range of clubs, including cookery, Mandarin, model making, computer maths games etc.

Lots of links with the local community, with teachers offering services at other local schools, whilst boys join forces with other schools to do everything from enrichment maths to drumming workshops. Boys are also encouraged to help out at the community centre 100 yards away. More religious than many nominally Christian schools, but it's a culture that's easily accessible by boys of other faiths or indeed of none, with some assemblies more spiritual or modern or even focusing on current affairs, although expect daily hymns and grace before meals.

The jury remains out on how nurturing the school is. A strong reputation persists that it has a competitive atmosphere, with a focus on academics at the cost of emotional support. But the school itself, along with the parents and pupils we spoke to, made convincing arguments that problems are nipped in the bud, with good pastoral care from teachers, two matrons and the part-time school counsellor, who has links with the Tavistock Clinic. In consultation with parents, the school undertakes a pastoral review every three years, with clear recommendations made. 'Despite its reputation, I've found it to be an incredibly child-centred school, with a caring and supportive environment,' insists one parent. 'I think people see academic success and believe it must be down to a harsh environment, but actually the environment is genuinely caring and warm,' says another.

School doesn't promote rules as such, but there are clear expectations (many of which are dotted on posters around the school), and sanctions to back them up, most commonly detentions. But boys say punishment can be inconsistent. 'You can wind up with a worse punishment for running to pass a boy a book in the corridor than being really rude,' said one. 'And sometimes you turn up for detention, but the teacher has forgotten all about it.' Parents told us there's far less bullying under the new head, who has made the message loud and clear to both pupils and parents that it won't be tolerated.

Parents mostly high-flyers – bankers, media types, lawyers etc – many of whom have extremely high aspirations for their boys, which can mean the head has his work cut out. Mainly local, but some travel from Notting Hill, Holland Park and Islington. Very active PA and parents socialise regularly, although some years are rather cliquey, with very strong personalities, according to the parents we spoke to.

This is a school that offers boys with high academic potential a dazzling start in life. Most leave not only with great academic results, but excellent general knowledge, huge intellectual curiosity and an appreciation of all things cultural. Myths abound that these are boffins that are hothoused, but in fact we found they are boys with a great sense of fun and who are highly motivated, genuinely enjoying being stretched. For the right boy, this school is hard to fault, but boys who wind up struggling could feel left out in the drive to achieve. As one parent put it, 'The school does all it can to help such boys, but if you don't have a particularly bright son, the bottom line is he's better off somewhere else.'

Hampden Gurney CofE Primary School

13 Nutford Place, London W1H 5HA

Tel: 020 7641 4195

51

State • Pupils: 240 • Ages: 3–11 • C of E

Email: office@hampdengurney.co.uk
Website: www.hampdengurneyschool.org.uk

Headteacher: Mrs Evelyn Chua (40s). A firm and fashionably-dressed visionary, originates from Malaysia and has worked immensely hard to transform this inner-city C of E primary to a school with beacon status, recently ranked third in the country. A formidable figure, the children certainly respect her, the punishment of last resort for the naughty, but those who've experienced her teaching also find her an inspiration. No British embarrassment about supporting the gifted and talented, but equally determined that every child in this exceptional school will come out a winner.

Entrance: School is affiliated to the High Anglican Church of the Annunciation in Bryanston Street near Marble Arch, and gives priority to church-going applicants, so if sung mass and ample evidence of the Virgin are not part of your belief system, not the school for you. Don't relax your church attendance either once your eldest has secured a place – sibling priority only as a tie-break. Heavily oversubscribed. No automatic transfer from nursery to reception.

Exit: Results to make many a prep school head weep. Plenty of academic, music and art scholarships, as well as bursaries. 'We don't give specific preparation, but we just teach them very well,' says the head, and clearly 'very well' is very well indeed. Recent awards have taken pupils to Latymer Upper, City of London Boys and Girls, Notting Hill and Ealing, St Benedict's, Westminster Under, St Paul's Girls, Cardinal Vaughan and Colet Court, with others to eg Highgate, Queen's College, St Marylebone, Holland Park and Chelsea Academy.

Results to make many a prep school head weep. Plenty of academic, music and art scholarships

Remarks: Long-serving head is clearly able to stretch and enthuse young minds and the busy, well-organised classrooms and dedicated staff (three male teachers) are testament to her management skills. Clearly no area of the curriculum here where good is good enough. Half the pupils come in speaking little English; the rest are prosperous middle class, many from international backgrounds, but nearly all those moving on to secondary school attain top marks in maths, English and science. Specialist teaching in PE, art, DT and music, with a rotation system of teachers two afternoons a week.

Particularly noted for its gifted and talented programme – this is definitely a school where it is cool to be clever. Mrs Chua has high standards and many students reach or exceed them – 'In year 6, some of the children are doing GCSE maths,' said one mother. But also strong (individual and group) out-of-class support for every child who needs it.

A fairly hefty homework diary, particularly for a state primary: 30-45 minutes a night in years 3-5, one hour in year 6, with English, maths and science set nightly and other subjects once a week. Optional holiday homework as well. Well-equipped ICT suite with digital cameras and laptops. Interactive whiteboards in every classroom. ICT taught creatively with an annual ICT week, where even the youngest gets a chance to demonstrate their Spielberg potential. Light and well-equipped rooftop science 'pod'.

Despite its restricted playground space, the school performs sporting miracles with daily sport clubs and specialists provided by the local authority to teach PE, netball, cricket, tennis, tag rugby. Young footballers play for Westminster and regular football competitions with other local schools. Swimming at nearby Seymour Leisure Centre.

Several years ago the school decided to rebuild its worn-out classrooms to match its league-table-topping position and, working with architects Building Design Partnership, sold off part of its land to fund a new building. Now The Beehive, a six-storey dome of steel and glass, has become both a local landmark and an inspiring place to learn, with nursery pupils starting out on the ground floor and progressing to the tent-covered roof as they rise through the curriculum.

Neat and practical red and grey uniform. Strong house system with houses named after eminent Brits and points for everything. Ample extracurricular activity, ranging from sewing and gardening to writing and publishing the school newspaper. Strong emphasis, too, on charitable fundraising. Residential trips to the countryside.

Heavy emphasis on attendance and punctuality (head firmly warns prospective parents against sinful thoughts of mid-term breaks). Escalating punishment system (warning, missing play time, time out, Mrs Chua) but minimum behavioural problems. Indeed classrooms are a model of well-ordered enthusiasm.

Founded in 1863 by Reverend Hampden Gurney, Rector of St Mary's Bryanston Square, the school's ethos is still strongly High Anglican, with compulsory attendance at weekly sung Eucharist and RE teaching firmly rooted in the Church of England.

Mrs Chua has collected many awards, everything from the National Association for Able Children Award to Service Excellence Award. Not unnaturally, most parents are immensely positive: 'You couldn't find a better education in the state system,' said one mother, who'd taken her children out of the private sector. And the articulate, confident and happy pupils are the school's best advertisement. One boy, asked about what he liked about the school, replied, 'Everything.'

Hampstead School

Westbere Road, London NW2 3RT

Tel: 020 7794 8133

State • Pupils: 1,245 • Ages: 11–19 • Sixth form pupils: 230

Email: enquiries@hampsteadschool.org.uk
Website: www.hampsteadschool.org.uk

7

Headteacher: Since 2006, Mr Jacques Szemalikowski MA BSc PGCE NPQH CPhys MInstP (50s). This head needs no Red Bull! Positively explodes with energy, a dynamo. Five minutes in his company and you are left exhausted. With four young children of his own, this guy is driven. He is here to make a difference, and in his tenure as headmaster of Hampstead School, he has.

A graduate in astrophysics, and a teacher for 25 years before his first headship at The Warwick

School, Redhill, Mr Szemalikowski is somewhat old school in his principles and discipline. A misbehaving student can find themselves holed away for the day in the exclusion zone, 'our naughty step' – a small building situated at the back of the playing fields. He makes no apologies for his rigorous approach to education, both for his students and staff members alike. His mantra is 'Every child can achieve, every child will achieve, whatever it takes' – and he does what he can to ensure this is not just hot air. He organises trips to Oxford so that his students can be aspirational: 'I want them to know this can be for them too. I want them to be the movers and shakers of the modern world.'

His staff are not allowed to rest on their laurels either. He doesn't do 'good' – he wants outstanding from his staff and they are expected to attend weekly regular after-school workshops in order to achieve this (the latest Ofsted report commented that there 'wasn't yet enough outstanding teaching.') A recent high turnover of staff, he says, was testimony to their 'tremendous training' which secured them promotional posts in other schools. Like him, don't like him, 'I'm not here to be popular, I'm here to get the job done.'

Hit the headlines recently for reporting the student author of a blog critical of the school to the police and to the universities where he hoped to study.

Academic matters: 2015 saw 54 per cent of pupils achieve 5+ A*-C grades at GCSE including English and maths. Consider that nearly half the pupils are bilingual (63 different nationalities), five per cent are statemented and nearly 40 per cent are on free school meals. Seventeen per cent of grades were A*/A.

A level results 28 per cent A*/B and 10 per cent A*/A. In the top 20 UK state schools for continuing into science A levels after GCSE. Big emphasis on science, and there is the option of triple rather than double science for students who attain at least a level 6 at the end of key stage 3. Maths, too, is strong and the school is very involved in maths challenges with students achieving above national average numbers of gold, silver and bronze certificates. The school also offers free Saturday school

He organises trips to Oxford so that his students can be aspirational. 'I want them to know this can be for them too, to be the movers and shakers of the modern world'

maths masterclasses for gifted mathematicians from years 5 and 6 of local primary schools.

English and media are popular subjects, and students also have the option of learning Arabic and Italian (as well as French and Spanish). Bilingual homework support is offered. Pupils have six BTECs to choose from including catering and hospitality, and a wide variety of A levels including three new ones in philosophy, creative writing and culture and communication. No subject is offered at GCSE level which can't be carried through to A level. 'We don't stream, we set, so there is movement', the head points out. Maths, English and science setted from year 7. Every faculty in the school has a remunerated teacher responsible for gifted and talented children. There is a clear focus on standards and students are tracked from the moment they arrive. They have individual charts and are monitored six times a year. As soon as a student starts to slip, staff want to know why. An appreciative parent commented that the school is 'quick to congratulate children if they've done well – very good at praising.' Strong curriculum support and SEN help, notably those who arrive with little English, and catch up is rapid: 'Assessors couldn't tell the difference between SEN students and non-SEN students', we were told.

Archaic-looking but well-equipped classrooms, most notably the music department, where a large cash injection has meant up-to-date technology. Through their status as a technology college they have been able to implement a £0.5 million upgrade to the library, creating an independent learning centre combining traditional library resources with new technologies. (That said, the library is actually quite scant on books itself.) Masses of extracurricular activity perhaps also reflects the academic ethos of the school: the school's debating society has had spectacular success in Model United Nations – with ongoing victories both as a delegation and individuals. Involved in Jack Petchey Speak Out Challenge and has a Youth Parliament.

Games, options, the arts: Fizzes with activity – plenty to do. Music is popular and heavy investment in this department has meant that each of the school's 1,300 students is offered the opportunity to learn a musical instrument. Pupils can choose to join a wide variety of musical activities, including senior or junior orchestra, guitar orchestra, jazz band, junior choir and many more.

Enthusiastic drama – great on-site replica fringe theatre, partnerships with the Hampstead Theatre Club, Royal Court and Tricycle all help to inspire; a few students had extras parts in the Dustin Hoffman movie Quartet.

Strong sport, particularly football, basketball and table tennis. The football team recently won the Bliss Inner London Cup, becoming the first Camden school to win the trophy; the girls' basketball team won the Under 15 Championships recently. A team of students and staff also recently completed the 56-mile London to Brighton bike ride. Limited playing fields, but somewhat redeemed by its other on-site facilities including a basketball/netball court, a dance studio, a fitness suite, a multi-use Astroturf and an on-site pool (that could do with some love).

The plethora of extracurricular activities includes gardening (they have an allotment which grows produce for the catering department), poetry, rugby, dance and aikido clubs, plus several music ensembles. For the more dedicated student, those who lack quiet space at home and those who need extra help, there are after-school homework sessions.

Background and atmosphere: Hampstead Schmampstead – this school is no more in Hampstead than Arsenal (FC) is in Arsenal! Situated in between colourful but definitely not posh Cricklewood, Kilburn and semi-posh West Hampstead, you can see the flag before you see the school. Red and emblazoned with the school logo, the flag waves proudly high above this impressive large red-brick building. The main building, formerly the old Haberdashers' Boys' school, was built in 1908, and indeed on first appearance promises great things.

One is immediately struck by the amount of banners displayed on the building's facade: 'Best ever GCSE results', 'Read more, earn more, learn more', 'Leaders of tomorrow' and so on. Mr Szemalikowski, who has been on three trips to the USA (Chicago, Boston and DC), says it's very much an American thing to do: 'It reinforces key aspirations at all times.' Tear your eyes away, walk up the ramped approach, through a plate glass entrance into a fairly modern foyer and see more slogans – this time on a wall-mounted flat screen TV, and from the wisdom of Galileo: 'Measure what is measurable,' the theme of the week.

Mosey on through the foyer to a vast concrete, central open air atrium faced by a modern teaching block and broken only by a dark and reedy pond – 'there are fish in there.' Mr Szemalikowski smiles brightly on our tour. The school was due for a substantial rebuild in 2011, but sadly the national school redevelopment scheme was axed by the coalition government. Refurbishment started and ended on new loos – £125,000 spent on giving them a spruce up as 'the test of any state school is its loos', says the head. (Although why the staff room is right next to them – the mind boggles).

A well-equipped ICT and catering block (with industrial spec kitchens) looks in stark contrast to the rest of the school. Good sixth form centre with huge common room overlooking the central atrium. Lucky sixth formers can feast their eyes on yet more banners – this time displayed on the walls around the central atrium – (did we mention Big Brother?) Wheelchair access throughout – the school is completely DDA compliant. There is a disability resource which can cater for up to seven students with complex needs. These students are fully integrated into mainstream lessons.

This is a big, sprawling campus, and easy to lose your bearings, especially for new pupils coming from little primaries. Lest you forget where you are, fear not, everything is logoed – from school water bottles to the dustbins, another of the head's ideas of constant reinforcement of group identity. Pupils are a mixed and diverse bunch, but all seem to share a common loyalty towards the school and enjoy being there. One 13-year-old pupil told us: 'I love the responsibility they give us. I was on a panel to help elect the last deputy head of the school.'

Badges are awarded to students who meet standards and display good behaviour – bronze through to platinum. Get platinum, you can have lunch with the head! Students' pride in their school is evident in the total lack of graffiti, vandalism and litter.

Commendable efforts to involve the outside world and lots of whole school charity work. An appreciation of the diversity of the school is prevalent – Black History Month, Gay/Transgender Month, a recent trip to Auschwitz, to name but a few. The school culture involves loads of celebration and reward of achievement and improvement.

Pastoral care and discipline: If punctuality and attendance ain't your bag, this ain't your school. Mr Szemalikowski and the entire senior management team are at the gates to greet pupils from 8.40am, after which sluggards have to report individually. (Early risers' club offered from 7.30am onwards for an extra cost of 50p). Attendance has improved dramatically since Mr Szemalikowski came on board. He is completely intolerant of any absence during term time (other than illness) and allows pupils two days a year for religious holidays. 'Every day counts' is one of the school's many slogans.

He is the head that reintroduced uniform to the school, and according to an ex-student, it has made a huge change – 'now everyone is on a level playing field.' Different ties denote whether or not a student has been trained in peer mentoring, and any student feeling vulnerable can approach those who have. Automatic exclusion for fighting, drugs, alcohol or carrying a weapon (as was recently the case with a student found to be carrying a knife). The head walks around daily to keep in touch, and lo and behold, if a student is wandering aimlessly in the grounds, they are stopped and questioned – and only when Mr Szemalikowski is entirely satisfied with their response are they sent on their way. Good level of security – brings to bear the stark reality that you are in an inner-city school.

However, despite Mr Szemalikowski's robust attitude to discipline, one parent says, 'it doesn't go far enough'. She feels that students are given too many chances, although she does acknowledge that the exclusion zone is a good deterrent – 'my daughter was in there once, and has said she won't be going there again.' (It is a small outhouse building, which can hold up to six students at any one time, with no contact with their peers for the whole day). Classes seemed to be well behaved for the most part – with the exception of the odd class joker – and a good level of concentration in what they were doing. PE, however, was on the very raucous side.

Non-teaching heads of year are one of Mr Szemalikowski's brainchilds. The idea is that the heads of year are there solely for the pupils' welfare needs and not to be distracted with marking homework. It works brilliantly, one parent enthused. 'It means that if I have any concerns about my child I know I can contact the head of year, and they are always available to speak to, no matter what time of day.' Year common rooms are 'exclusive to Hampstead School' – the idea being that year groups can eat together at lunchtimes and the heads of year have their offices in there and are always available at lunchtime too.

One 13-year-old told us: 'I was on the panel to help elect the last deputy head'

Buddying, mentoring and restorative justice schemes all bolster pupils' sense of security, and bullying is rigorously kept in check. 'The House', situated a stone's throw from the Exclusion Zone, is a cuboid block on the perimeter where you go if you are troubled – or troubling – and is well staffed with welfare workers, counsellors and other supportive types.

Recent school awards include: British Council International Award at outstanding level; The Prince's Teaching Institute English kite mark; UNICEF Rights Respecting School (Level 1) Award; Pupils' and Parents' Achievement for All Quality Mark (first school to achieve this and now a national roll-out school); International School Award; School Games (Silver) Award; Gold TfL Sustainable Travel award; Safe School Award.

Pupils and parents: From moneyed West Hampstead, to recent refugees in temporary housing, the demographic is diverse – all the more admirable when one considers how far the school has come. One pupil told us: 'I love the fact that one of my best friends is black, the other wears a hijab'. A real feature of the school, we were told, is that no ethnic groups predominate. Nineteen per cent is white British – the largest group.

Former pupils include Sadie Frost, Rachel Yankey, ex-MP Julia Drown, Alec Bogdanovic, Jake Lensen, Tobias Hill, Zadie Smith.

Entrance: From up to 71 primary schools (no named feeders; totally non-selective), and covering three boroughs – Camden, Brent and Barnet (admissions managed by Camden) – the school is now oversubscribed in every year. One parent, a born and bred Cricklewood local, remarked how the school used to have a 'terrible reputation', and no right-thinking parent, given the choice, would have sent their kids there – but she said, 'that's changed since Mr Szemalikowski came on board'. Oversubscribed sixth form both from internal and external candidates. Twenty year 12 places are available to external applicants that meet the entry requirements – which vary according to the level of course they want to pursue.

Exit: About 70 per cent stay for the sixth form, the remainder go to other colleges and sixth forms. Some 70 per cent of sixth formers move on to an impressive range of higher education – from chemistry at King's College, law at Bristol and maths at Leeds to a paid apprenticeship in aerospace engineering with Airbus, at University of Surrey (which was big news because the student beat a large number of applicants for the prestigious placement). One former student has become an international DJ and producer as a result of studying A level music at the school.

Remarks: The head's energy and vision has already worked wonders on this school. A melting pot of culture and diversity, and a whole host of activities to keep even the most apathetic child interested. However, this school ain't for the faint hearted – large and imposing, and big on discipline and punctuality. In need of a massive cosmetic makeover (DfE!).

Heathside Preparatory School

16 New End, London NW3 1JA

Independent · Pupils: 370 · Ages: 2–13 · Fees: up to £14,250 pa

Tel: 020 7794 5857

Email: info@heathside.net
Website: www.heathside.net

8

Headmistress: Since the school's foundation in 1993, Ms Melissa Remus Elliot MA PG Dip (40s), who is also joint owner. She grew up all over the US, following her father's work, and attended Duke University and The American University, Washington. She worked as a Washington intern and on several Broadway shows before moving to the UK and becoming a teacher. During three years' teaching she formulated an idea of her ideal school and set up Heathside with her business partner and co-head (now retired), Jill White, becoming the youngest head teacher in the country in her 20s. She also got an MA in Counselling Aspects of Education at The Tavistock Clinic.

'Science teaching brilliant – really hands–on and fun. And my daughter is very excited about being allowed to chop wood'

Married with four children, all at or graduated from Heathside, 'which gives me a good insight into what actually goes on in the classrooms'. Over-flowing praise from parents: 'a very open-minded and dynamic person, relentlessly striving to find ways to make the school better'; 'open and honest in a very refreshing way'; 'both pragmatic and inspirational'; 'extraordinary ability to retain a thorough portrait of each child'; 'unbelievably energetic and gung-ho'.

Entrance: Takes 2 and 3-year-olds into the nursery class. Most places go to siblings and those who sign up very early, though it's worth trying for an afternoon place if you have been less well organised. More join to form three reception classes of 15 each. Children visit for a day to ensure they and the school are a good match. 'If there is any question mark we may ask them to come in for several days. We try to be careful to make sure that the school suits the child. We don't take children with behavioural difficulties or serious special needs, and if we have any concerns about academic ability, we would speak in detail with the parents and teachers about whether we could create a special programme to support the child.'

Exit: Most move on at 11, the vast majority to the local independents: Highgate, UCS, North Bridge House and Belmont; also Haberdashers, South Hampstead, Francis Holland and Channing. Some to City Boys' or Girls', some very bright children to Westminster, St Paul's or North London Collegiate, and some who prefer a less intense environment to Aldenham. A few to local state schools, eg Camden School for Girls and St Marylebone. Generally a good haul of scholarships. Parents comment on 'Melissa's dogged commitment to find places for all her pupils. She reads children exceptionally well'.

The school has now added years 7 and 8. The first year 7 class (fully co-ed) has pupils who have already gained places at Westminster, St Paul's and City of London in year 9.

Remarks: Started in 1993 on the site – and with much of the equipment and quite a few of the staff and pupils – of a former prep school that had come to a rocky end. Occupies six buildings in the middle of Hampstead. Aims to let every child follow their strengths and interests, with plenty of extracurricular activities and fun, practical lessons.

The lower school is housed in a converted and extended church hall, which includes a music practice room, a hall used for gym, yoga, music and drama as well as assemblies, a nursery room with comfortable sofas, and art and science rooms. 'Science teaching brilliant – really hands-on and fun,' said a parent. 'And my daughter is very excited to be allowed to chop wood and use a glue gun in DT.' 'Can't imagine my kids being more stimulated or jolly,' said another.

Since the school is non-selective it includes a fair ability range, but teaching groups are small and the lower school has plenty of teaching assistants. 'Learning is really celebrated,' said a parent. Several ability groups for maths from year 1 upwards. 'Children have different ways of learning, and we group them accordingly. Some need lots of reinforcement, but we never assume that a child is no good at maths. We work in a way that helps them to understand, and once the building blocks are firm, they can fly.' When we visited, a group of children who found times tables challenging were learning them through pictures and stories, whilst another group (of year 4 pupils) were working on secondary level problems.

Several literacy groups – 'they are all good readers, but some have difficulty with writing'. These get intensive tuition in years 3 and 4, ready for the lead-up to year 6 exams. 'Because we don't have to prepare them for 7+ exams, it doesn't matter if they take longer to come through.'

French is taught throughout the school, with plenty of songs and games, by a teacher who talks entirely in French from the start. 'They think she only speaks French, and they learn amazingly quickly.' Latin is a 'massive hit,' said a parent; also a Mandarin club.

Inevitably the pressure rises as the 11+ approaches, but parents praise the imaginative approach. 'They're pushed in their ability to write essays and do comprehensions, but it's not a brutal régime,' said one. 'In a typical Heathside move, an ex-parent who is a literature professor comes in twice a week and encourages them to read and enjoy sophisticated texts. They're worked incredibly hard, but it's very exciting.' Has now added year 7 and 8 classes.

The full-time identified needs coordinator is renowned for helping with dyslexia and dyspraxia. One-to-one help costs extra, but most learn in compatible groups. The school would not suit an autistic child – 'We're too busy and active' – and would hesitate to take one with other behavioural difficulties – 'We have to think about the rest of the class.' However, a girl who came into year 4 with limited experience of maths 'blossomed, and got into all the secondary schools she tried'.

Small groups work at their own pace in various nooks and crannies. 'You may find your child having a lesson in what looks like a broom cupboard – but they are learning,' said a parent. Prose and poetry competitions, with everyone writing

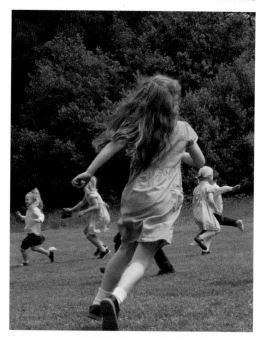

poems and learning a piece to recite, and plenty of drama from Macbeth to Pirates of Penzance. 'We do really challenging stuff, but in a fun way.'

The full-time music director is 'amazingly inspirational' – everyone learns the ocarina and recorder and many play the piano and other instruments too. Several instrumental groups and choirs, and termly formal and informal concerts 'spur them on'.

Chess is a big deal here – teams go off for weekend tournaments, and Heathside has been the English Primary Schools Chess Association National Small Schools champion for eight years. 'It's a big social scene,' said a parent, 'and they're very good at encouraging girls to play.' A 'huge variety' of other clubs including gym, art and science. Parents talk of 'amazing trips', including ice skating at the Tower of London and 'going to France for the day to meet pen-pals'.

The school's only outside space is a small playground with climbing frame alongside the lower school. However, nearly everyone from year 1 upwards goes to Hampstead Heath for an hour at lunchtime most days – the younger ones go three times a week – to climb trees, run around, build dens, play in the snow. The children also play sport every day, at UCS and Swiss Cottage; on Friday morning they have a swimming and multi-sports programme – ranging from rock climbing to judo – at Swiss Cottage leisure centre. Specialist coaches include an ex-international Sri Lankan cricketer and an ex-professional footballer, and the football, swimming and cricket teams are rarely beaten. Many teams are co-ed – 'Our best footballer is a girl' – and girls' sport was boosted by the arrival of a coach specialising in rounders, field hockey and netball. Sports day includes 'proper races' at Parliament Hill Fields running track.

Parents praise the family atmosphere, with friendships across the year groups. 'There's a real relationship between teachers and children,' said a parent. 'They are strict about talking and noise, because they have to be in a building that size, but then you see a child hurtling downstairs with no shoes on to do some photocopying for their teacher. It's an adventurous, common-sense and human approach.' Another parent commented that she is delighted with the 'close and intimate, nurturing atmosphere which generates a real appetite to learn. It's very warm, very flexible'. We have however had reports of a lack of response to parents whose child was experiencing difficulties. Organic lunches served daily.

Huge mix of families including some wealthy, famous parents and quite a few international families. But it tends to attract those who are not happy with the more traditional private sector ethos; quite a few have moved their children (often reluctantly) from state primaries. Parents tend to become closely involved: one dad runs a gifted maths club, another comes in to talk about astronomy, many parents help with festivals such as Chinese New Year and Halloween, others help run the library or become class reps. 'We're an interesting mix,' said a mother. 'Most people are very friendly and very engaged with the school.' 'We absolutely love it here,' said a father, 'and so does every other parent we've met.'

Hereward House School

14 Strathray Gardens, London NW3 4NY

Tel: 020 7794 4820

Independent • Pupils: 176 • Ages: 4–13 • Fees: up to £15,600 pa

Email: headmaster@herewardhouse.co.uk
Website: www.herewardhouse.co.uk

Headmaster: Since January 2015, Pascal Evans, previously director of studies, and before that head of French, at Westminster Under School. A keen runner, he is married to Akiyo.

Entrance: Register by the time your son is a year old at the latest. Head sees all parents and boys, when boys are 3. 'We make a significant commitment to finding the right boy.' Siblings guaranteed a place, the rest chosen on 'suitability' rather than ability. 'We could test to find the most academic, but we're not going down that route. What we're really looking for is a good chap to have in the place, a player rather than spectator.' Offers – conditional

'We could find the most academic, but what we're really looking for is a good chap to have in the place, a player rather than a spectator'

on staying till the age of 13 – are made one year before entry at 4+. Occasional places thereafter due to relocation, but those on the waiting list get first dibs. Occasional places at end of year 6.

Exit: The school won't prepare for entrance tests at 7 or 8. 'Our record at 13 is so strong, there's no need to exit early.'

Highgate perhaps losing favour, with a fairly even split between between UCS, Westminster, St Paul's and others eg City, with regular scholarships. 'Our scholarship record is broadly comparable per head to the best schools in the area.' Regular places also at Eton, Harrow, Rugby and Winchester.

Careful guidance given in the run up to CE. 'Parents here will typically ask: "What is the right school for my son?" rather than saying "which school can you get him into?" They really do want the best fit.'

Remarks: The school was founded in 1951 in its current red-brick Hampstead house. In essence it's still a family business, though now governed by a trust made up of members of the Sampson family, the owners.

Though not a school in which selection is made on academic grounds, almost every boy here is above average, with 'the top third as bright as anywhere'. Generally no setting until year 8 (occasionally from year 7), then only in English, maths and Latin. Specialist teaching, in part from year 4, entirely from year 5. Latin from the start, Latin from year 5, Greek from year 8 (potentially from year 7). Teachers know boys well and respond quickly to their needs. ('Teachers are often outside during pick-up time,' said one parent, 'and will seek you out to talk about your child.') Learning support also fine-tuned, with two specialists to help the struggling ('in the majority of cases, boys come out the other end without a problem,' says the school.) A former barrister provides the stretch needed for the most demanding scholarship papers. Parents feel the school works well for all abilities. 'Our older son is very academic and remains challenged with lots of extra work,' said one, 'while our younger son is smart, but playful, and the school uses a very different approach to stimulate him.' Homework at manageable levels. 'It should be do-able in an hour if working at a steady pace.'

Sport is 'central to the school life'. Two afternoons of games a week, one on Hampstead Heath, the other in Brondesbury. Cricket and soccer particularly strong and every boy gets to play, with a first, second and third team. 'This is simply too small a school for a boy to be sitting on the sidelines handing out oranges. They love to represent the school.' Punches above its weight – the Colts remain unbeaten for nearly two years – but can struggle against the largest schools. Cross-country also taken seriously, with weekly lessons in the spring term. Fencing, tennis and hockey on offer as clubs, plus timetabled swimming at Swiss Cottage baths just down the road. Smallish playground with an intricate system of who uses what bit when – seems to work like a well-rehearsed ballet.

Almost every boy plays an instrument, half play two or more (the orchestra has nearly 60 members). Form concerts every term. Art, too, highly valued. Boys' work now hangs around the school ('we wanted to take art out of the art room') and a cricket-themed display now ornaments head's study. Pottery and DT also popular (though a cleverly crafted crossbow did have to be confiscated). Drama taught until the final two years, when academic works takes precedence. Major drama production every other year, with every boy involved.

Loads of clubs, including photography, fencing, tennis, typing, art, music theory, chess, Spanish and science. 'If boys want something else we make it happen.' Handy prep club, too, nightly from 4pm to 5pm (with flexibility to stay till 6pm). Popular annual ski trip, accompanied by head and parents, where card playing is often a focus of evening activity. 'We believe in cards. We don't see why they shouldn't learn to play whist and basic bridge.' First school disco held recently, so boys can 'learn how to treat a lady.'

'We believe in cards. We don't see why they shouldn't learn to play whist and basic bridge'

Bright, high-ceilinged classrooms, originally the living quarters of an affluent turn-of-the-century family, complemented by relatively flimsy science and music space, which are top of the school's agenda for a make-over.

This small school revels in its size. It wants a family atmosphere and does its utmost to make this happen. 'Academic performance is based on the foundation that the school is happy.' All boys are known by name and all are given a position of 'meaningful' responsibility at the top of the school, with eight prefects, four house captains, and further captains for music, drama and games. 'Every boy must have his moment in the sun.' Parents definitely approve: 'Senior boys thrive on the responsibility and have the confidence to display a fair amount of individuality in how they fill their role.' Two senior boys, for example, are at the door each morning to greet each boy by name. There are merit prizes, with bronze, silver and gold awards, form prizes for effort and contribution to the community and school colours for non-academic achievements. Elected school council has considerable sway. 'They wanted more pasta and sweet and sour chicken and that was delivered.'

Rules kept to a minimum. Beyond the basics, the main principle is that boys should treat one another well and make the most of what's on offer. 'Hopefully boys have a sense they are part of the system, not ruled by it. We're looking for good chaps, gentlemen with a general sense of decency.' Parents

remark on how considerate boys are to each other – even out of school. Disciplinary problems only of the extremely minor variety like tipping chairs and talking in line. Staff eat lunch with boys every day to engage boys in friendly conversation. 'It's a great time to find out how things are going.' The head also meets with prefects weekly to discuss concerns they may have about younger boys. 'Everyone knows everyone else; older boys look out for younger ones; the more confident encourage the less so.'

Parents are typical north London professionals, with a cosmopolitan range of nationalities, generally reasonably local. Newly founded PTA, very much part of the school's drive for a sense of community. 'Everyone is very welcoming to newcomers,' says one recent arrival. 'My two boys, who joined higher up the school, have had plenty of invitations.'

Holy Trinity and Saint Silas CofE Primary School

Hartland Road, London NW1 8DE

Tel: 020 7267 0771

10

State • Pupils: 210 • Ages: 4–11 • C of E

Email: admin@holytrinitynw1.camden.sch.uk
Website: camden.schooljotter.com/holytrinitynw1

Head: Since 2013, Lorraine Dolan (40s) BEd and masters in education, both from the University of North London. Her first job as an NQT in 1996 was at Holy Trinity and St Silas; 'My plan was never to stay at the same school for long but to have an open mind.' However, when Annie Williams took over as head of the school in 2001, Ms Dolan, who respected her greatly, found it difficult to move on. Fourteen years later Ms Dolan started to get 'itchy feet', and when Annie Williams took a sabbatical Ms Dolan became acting deputy head and from there decided to move into leadership. She subsequently left Holy Trinity to take up the post as deputy head at St Paul's Catholic school in Wood Green. Although she says her time there was a 'great experience', she couldn't achieve what she wanted as a deputy head. When Ms Williams died in 2012, Ms Dolan had begun looking at headship and when the post was advertised, she applied, believing that she had the skills, understanding and experience to drive the school forward.

Tall, with waist-long fair hair, Ms Dolan looks on first impression like someone who might be in the world of media rather than a primary school head teacher. Although softly spoken and friendly, this ex-convent school girl is definitely no pushover

and hides a steely determination. It is a prerequisite for this job. Any weaker souls would not survive the legacy of the former head teacher, who changed the fortunes of a not particularly good school to an 'exceptional school' (in the words of Ofsted) and was a woman who had edited the word 'compromise' from her vocabulary. Ms Dolan says, 'Annie was a force to be reckoned with.' Ms Dolan offers a more 'open door policy' than her predecessor and welcomes parent inclusion in the school. One pupil told us, 'she's very approachable and a great role model.'

She has been described by a parent as being 'very old school, in a good way.' She is very intent on bringing traditional values back into the school and has particularly clamped down on the school uniform, which was a bit hit and miss prior to her headship. As she points out, 'You either have a uniform policy or you don't; you can't have a bit of a uniform.' Another parent told us that Ms Dolan 'doesn't rest on the laurels of Ms Williams and wants to make her own mark. She is around most of the time and is often chatting to parents in the playground.'

Ms Dolan has a 24 year old son, whom she had in her early 20s, and who, she says, 'has been the making of me in many ways.' The product of Irish Catholic parents, Ms Dolan went to a convent

'The school just feels amazing when you walk in. There is the sound of laughter and always someone playing the piano'

school, where she says she was 'often challenging the system'. Her son forced her to be responsible, and although she wasn't thinking of a career in education at that time, was accepted onto a Montessori teaching course, 'which was perfect as I could take my son with me and leave him at the nursery'. Little did she suspect then where that first rung up the ladder would eventually lead. She and her long term partner are both members of a cycling club, and she also enjoys running: 'Keeping fit is a great outlet for stress.'

Entrance: After the customary priority for looked-after children, the primary admissions criterion is church attendance, either at The Most Holy Trinity Church across the road or at St Silas the Martyr in Kentish Town. Approx 60 per cent come via this route; the remaining 40 per cent of admissions are catchment based. When Ms Williams became head, the school was very much bottom of the parental-choice agenda, but the intake has altered and now gets more professional parents – particularly in creative and media related fields. Not too many, school hopes – 'we have a good social mix and want to keep it that way'. At the moment, remains a class and ethnic melting pot, with the largest minority being Bangladeshi.

Exit: Mainly to the local comprehensives – Haverstock, William Ellis, Parliament Hill, St Marylebone and Camden School for Girls – but school has also developed a relationship with The Hall, one of north London's leading prep schools, and some year 6 boys go there with bursaries before proceeding to leading London independent day schools.

Remarks: Housed in a typical Victorian schoolhouse, a meander from tourist-packed Camden Lock; one has to enter two heavy duty doors to reach the main reception – the first to the playground and the second to the main building: 'We qualified for extra security', the head told us (part of their recent funding programme). However, once inside with its pristine, soothing interior, you'd never guess where you were – fresh flowers, polished parquet and a big red school bell are all from another era.

Teaching at the school is strong; a number of parents have pointed this out and cited a couple of exceptional teachers, one of whom – Kirsty Mccreadie, the current deputy head – held the school together after the previous head's departure and is described by parents as 'simply the most exceptional, passionate teacher – the cornerstone of the school'. Ms Dolan herself has been very successful in turning the maths results around – something she has been working hard to address. When she first came on board, results had been dipping, but her close monitoring seems to have worked – more or less everyone gets at least level 4 Sats, with around two-thirds now reaching level 5+.

The teaching staff are generally well qualified, with two MAs, one law degree, three teachers who speak fluent French (so French is taught convincingly from reception to year 2), and a couple of graduate teaching assistants who, according to Ms Dolan, arrived with 'passion and drive'. The excellent teaching is partly the legacy of Ms Williams, who had said: 'I'm very snobbish about teachers – they have to have been to a good university and to have travelled. It gives them a cultural understanding', and partly due to the current head who adds: 'All the teachers are clear about my expectations. It's not OK for one child to slip through the net.'

Despite the fact that the majority of pupils arrive at Holy Trinity with well below average attainment, the school is at the pinnacle of the league tables, with results in English in the top one per cent nationally. Literacy is taught for two hours a day, primarily through poetry and prose. This again, we are told, is largely down to another inspirational teacher – Luke Williams, a specialist drama teacher who teaches English and drama from reception to year 6, through the works of Shakespeare. Every year the school puts on a whole-school Shakespeare play, including every pupil and member of staff, and has now helped found a borough-wide Shakespeare festival with five neighbouring primaries. Hardly surprising then that, according to Ofsted: 'Pupils' empathy with the works of Shakespeare is quite remarkable'.

All the arts are fundamental to the curriculum. Music is central to the school and one parent told us that music largely formed her decision to send her daughter there: 'The school just feels amazing when you walk in. There is the sound of laughter and always someone playing the piano or another instrument.' Pupils can choose to join the jazz band or one of two choirs, or learn an instrument from a long list of specialist music teachers. However, drop-ins on any of the music groups have been abolished in favour of auditioning for them, as the head firmly believes, 'if you make that sort of commitment, you need to stick to it.'

Art is equally important, and despite limited square footage, has its own department; pupils' work is hung boldly throughout the building. Painting even spills out into the large urban playground (underneath the rattling of the Camden overground train), where one inner-city wall has been reborn as a rural, summer scene (with a 3D vegetable plot to extend the experience). We were particularly struck by an astonishing ceiling display in the upper school hall of famous London landmarks – the London Eye, St Paul's Cathedral etc, all made from paper mâché. The idea for this came from a walk around London with year 6 pupils, who were learning about architecture (from a parent architect) inspired by the imminent development works to the school. One parent told us: 'We're so lucky at this school, there is such a pool of talented and creative parents who can come in and share their skills.' Trips are very much part of the education. Visits to the theatre, opera, ballet and museums are planned on a regular basis.

Though about 40 per cent of pupils are not Anglicans, the Christian message is strong, with a thoroughly involved parish priest (Father Graham), regular church attendance and class mass held half termly. Grace is said before lunch. Lunch itself is entirely healthy, and mealtimes, too, are considered a development opportunity. Music is played and, on Fridays, tablecloths laid. A firm emphasis on good manners. The 'golden rules' dictate: don't talk with your mouth full; learn to use your knife and fork correctly. Rules elsewhere are equally clear cut. Attentive good behaviour is the norm, but for those who stray, the first offence means displacement to another class; further disruption means an encounter with the head.

Although standards may be firmly upheld, one parent complained that the pastoral care system is not great and there isn't much of a structure in place. However, the head says that whilst historically issues were not dealt with, she 'has worked very hard to get parents to trust that when they raise a concern about their child, whether emotional or academic, it will be dealt with and monitored.' The children are supported by the class teachers. They have weekly circle time sessions and are encouraged to share their concerns as well as develop their understanding about relationships with their peers.

The school takes a proactive approach to its parents, and offers core subject curriculum evenings to support parents with home learning. Parents respond with energetic fundraising – the PTA raises on average £4,000-£5,000 a year which goes towards buying new computers. Ms Williams herself was no ingénue when it came to fundraising and won considerable support from charities – a legacy continued after her death, with the Annie Williams Education Trust, set up by her husband, which has already received many donations.

Plans are currently under way to expand the school building and make it more accessible, the school being one of 10 schools in Camden identified as in need of updating. This will include a three storey extension at the side to house a new office, reception area and staff room and will allow the hall downstairs to be opened up into a large performance space. Classrooms will be increased in size (as they are rather on the snug side) and a lift will be installed, as this old Victorian building is currently unsuitable for anyone with a disability.

'Superb' is Ofsted's summary of the Holy Trinity and St Silas experience, and pupils agree: 'We love it here, we don't want to leave,' said one year 6 pupil. And a parent added: 'I just love the mixed demographic and the fact that everyone talks to everyone. I once saw David Miliband [a former parent], in the playground chatting to a mother in flip flops and pyjama bottoms, about the best pirate parties for boys.'

La Sainte Union Catholic Secondary School

Linked school: LaSwap Sixth Form Consortium, 130

Highgate Road, London NW5 1RP	Tel: 020 7428 4600
State • Pupils: 1,220 • Ages: 11–18 • Sixth form pupils: 305 (55 boys) • RC	Email: general@lsu.camden.sch.uk Website: www.lasainteunion.org.uk

Headteacher: Since 2008, Mrs Maureen Williams (40s). Educated at a convent school in Hampshire, read English and medieval literature at Exeter University before taking her PGCE at Digby Stuart College, Roehampton. Taught English at St Joseph's College, Croydon and La Retraite Roman Catholic Girls' School in Lambeth, before taking over from long-serving head Sister Teresa and becoming the school's first lay principal, charged with a mission to gently modernise while maintaining the traditions of La Sainte Union. A calm and competent presence; no doubt the school's illustrious tradition remains in safe hands. Married to a senior

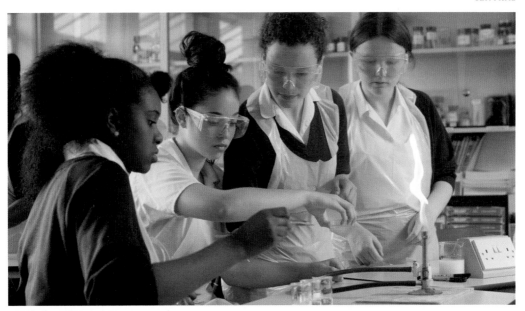

probation officer, she enjoys running, walking and good food in her spare time.

Academic matters: One of Camden's top-performing comprehensive schools. In 2015, 77 per cent of pupils achieved 5+ A*-C grades at GCSE including English and maths, with 34 per cent A*/A grades – a significant achievement for a school with no academic selection, and not reached by any fudging of the exam system. Pupils here take a demanding curriculum, with nine and half subjects kept going until GCSE, including a compulsory modern language, ICT and RE. Has specialist status in science and maths and 25 girls a year take all three sciences. Everyone, however, benefits from the science enrichment programme, with a multitude of speakers from UCL and Imperial College (both of which offer work placements). 'Many of the girls come from backgrounds where there is limited experience of higher education,' says the head. 'The programme raises their aspirations.' Science results have improved significantly, though A level physicists are still a relative rarity. Setting in maths from year 7, broad banding in science, English and languages (French and Spanish) from year 8. The gifted and talented are led along at a brisk pace, taking some subjects early and adding to the basic diet with astronomy, geography, Italian and statistics. 'The school has some really clever girls,' said one mother, 'and they really nurture them.'

All abilities and interests, however, are well catered for, with young apprenticeships and diplomas increasingly popular. 'Not everyone has to be brilliant, but everyone has to achieve what they can,' commented a parent. 'They say, this is your goal, go for it – but not everyone's goal is the same.' About 70 per cent proceed to the sixth form, which forms part of the popular local consortium of four comprehensives, LaSwap. A commendable 44 per cent A*/B grades and 15 per cent A*/A at A level in 2015, though results post-16 are not quite as starry as at GCSE. 'We could raise the entry requirements,' says the head, 'and attract a higher ability cohort, but we know we can achieve these results without doing so.' Some 20 pupils have statements of special needs, wheelchair access by means of lifts. 'They try to help everyone,' commented one parent.

Games, options, the arts: Music is a particular strength ('super,' says Ofsted) and is based here for the entire consortium sixth form. The standard of singing is unusually high with a 'talented' voice coach in residence. Whole school enthusiasm manifested in a 130-strong gospel choir. A year 11 jazz band and a strong chamber choir. About a third of pupils take individual instrumental or voice tuition.

Definitely not a 9am-4pm place – 50 clubs operating, before, during and after lessons, everything from rowing and trampolining to keep fit and cookery. For hard-pressed working parents, the homework club, with supervised study before and after school, is a real boon – as it often is for girls. Thriving art department. The spacious walled grounds include a decent range of pitches, made full use of for two hours' compulsory weekly sports, including rounders, netball, athletics, basketball, trampolining, football and aerobics. 'There's no sitting on the side here,' says the head.

Background and atmosphere: One of a number of schools founded by the Sisters of La Sainte Union de Sacre Coeur, a teaching order founded in the early 19th century. The Camden school has now been in the borough for the past 150 years. Housed in a gracious Victorian building (with later additions), maintains the stately and soothing presence of the former convent boarding school it once was. The classrooms in the main block are light and high-ceilinged, the floors polished to a mirror sheen, the gardens to the rear are elegantly laid out with a small orchard and an ample stock of summer roses (sensibly, girls are required to keep to the path and admire from a distance).

Though now very much a modern comprehensive, with a broad intake of practising Catholics from across the capital, still has the purposeful air of calm you might expect from its history. The last teaching sister departed in 2010, but the tradition of the founding order and those of the Catholic faith are well maintained. 'We see our mission as promoting the values of the gospel and spirituality, preparing children for a life centred on Christ, celebrating the sacrament and providing links with other parishes and the international LSU community,' says the head. Has its own pretty chapel and pupils attend mass on a weekly rota. Founder's Day is marked with mass – and ice cream.

Pupils wear the distinctive uniform of tartan kilts and white stockings with pride and recently voted to retain this particular tradition. Strong sense of community, both local and international,

The gardens to the rear are elegantly laid out with a small orchard and an ample stock of summer roses

including its sister school in Tanzania. Vocal school council (with elections for president and vice president) has its say on bullying and school food as well as uniform.

Pastoral care and discipline: Despite its affluent north London location on the lower slopes of Highgate, intake is anything but indulged – 65 per cent of pupils from low income families, 10 per cent on free school meals. The student population reflects the Catholic population of London – a third speak English as an additional language; a sizeable percentage are first and second generation immigrants from Nigeria, Ghana, the Congo, Poland, South America and southern Europe. Parents are active in their own churches and in the school. 'There is a real sense of community,' said one. No linked parish but many families attend nearby St Joseph's, Highgate and St Dominic's in Kentish Town.

Pupils and parents: 'This is an inner-city comp,' insists the head, though anyone dropping in from outside might be excused for thinking the term doesn't match the orderly space within. Behaviour is generally exemplary but, for those who stray, bad marks and detentions, as well as fixed-term exclusions. Girls with difficulties are certainly not left to fend for themselves. 'Some girls are from families with real problems and they would rather be at school on weekends and holidays than at home,' says one mother. 'This is a safe place to be.' Offers both parental support and additional help with behaviour management and conflict resolution. Teaches about the temptations of drugs and alcohol but drugs are not a significant issue, at least on-site. Problems mainly concern friendship disputes that change social boundaries. Good induction day in year 7 brings pupils from disparate locations and homes together. 'My daughter has really blossomed here,' says one happy parent.

Entrance: 180 girls admitted to the heavily oversubscribed year 7, mainly from Catholic primary schools. No selection on ability but must be practising Catholics baptised in the first year, then able to demonstrate regular church attendance for at least three years. Pupils arrive from seven boroughs (from Walthamstow to Barnet) as distance is measured by public transport rather than metres from the gates. Eighteen places offered on musical aptitude, with an aural test and a small audition. Entry to La Swap sixth form requires mostly Bs for A level. All girls who enter between 11 and 16 base themselves at the school for the sixth form.

Exit: About a fifth to Russell Group universities, with UCL a favourite option. Popular subjects include English, history, business studies and art foundation. Medics get specialist coaching for BMAT tests. One or two to Oxbridge each year, including medicine.

Money matters: Despite the fact that two-thirds of parents here are on a joint family income of £30,000 or less, most manage the £100 a year voluntary contribution. 'Parents are very generous' and very active, constantly raising funds with second-hand uniform sales etc. 'This is not a rich school,' said one, 'but the school and parents make every effort to give the girls the opportunities that others might take as a given.'

Remarks: A calm and orderly universe, demanding (and getting) high standards of achievement from girls who might not always be expected to reach this high.

Lansdowne College

40–44 Bark Place, London W2 4AT

Tel: 020 7616 4400

Independent • Pupils: 220 • Ages: 14–19 • Sixth form pupils: 200 • Fees: up to £20,950

Email: info@lansdownecollege.com
Website: www.lansdownecollege.com

52

Principal: Since September 2014, Mark Love BEd PGCLME (50s). Educated at Bristol Polytechnic and Sheffield Hallam University. Twenty-three years' experience of working in post-16 education sector, the majority with independent sector organisations. Taught A level economics, business and accounting and spent seven years as principal of Abbey College before becoming principal of CATS College London.

A former GCSE and A level examiner, he lists his main interests as team building and leadership,

general management, curriculum development and pastoral care. His wife is an interior designer and they have two daughters. In his spare time he is interested in politics, rugby, football, film, reading, current affairs and travelling.

Academic matters: There is a small GCSE cohort of some 40 pupils, but this is essentially a sixth form college offering one and two year A level courses, plus short retake courses. With the demise of January retakes, it now offers February to June courses. 'They can come to us in September to sort out UCAS, then go off for a gap few months before getting down to work. We hope they'll come back with renewed vigour.'

Colleges like this stand or fall by the value they add, and Lansdowne claims an average one to two grade increase at A level on its short courses. 'We're expert at getting people with Cs up to A/Bs. And at getting Cs for people who were predicted to fail.' In 2015, two-thirds of A levels were A*/B. Classes are tiny: six is average, with one or two not unusual, especially for more esoteric subjects such as Russian, Japanese or geology. Around half are retake students and half do their entire A level course here. Maths is the most popular subject, with large cohorts also for biology, chemistry, English, psychology and economics. Courses range from accounting to graphics to philosophy.

The college starts in year 10, teaching core GCSE subjects plus a carousel of options, but the GCSE course runs over one year and most join in year 11.

Passing exams is the raison d'être here – students are 'very focused on achieving examination success', said Ofsted, mentioning 'interesting and challenging lessons' – and tutors make sure the foundations are in place. 'They went back to basics, and kept repeating them, but they did make her enjoy her subject again,' said a parent. Teaching

'They went back to basics, and kept repeating them, but they did make her enjoy her subject again,' said a parent

focuses on exam technique. 'Because time is so short, we have to concentrate on ensuring they know how to get the best results – to understand what examiners want,' says the college. 'They have to know how to tick the boxes.' Students have weekly exam practices in the hall where they will sit the real thing. 'If they do it once a week they don't panic when the time comes.' GCSE and lower sixth students have at least three hours a week of supervised study periods. No exam study leave or June half term: 'We run our own revision programme. We teach right up to the last exam in the last subject.'

Abilities range from those who have failed first time round to those who need top results for competitive courses. 'But in a small class this range doesn't matter. Stronger students tend to pull up the weaker ones. If you put all the C grade students together they tend to stay at that grade. However, if we find we have a particularly weak group we may add on extra lessons.'

The college rarely accepts students with statements – 'we don't have the facilities or staff' – but has improving learning support, with a third of students on the register. 'We've just bought 25 new laptops for those who need them.'

Very flexible timetabling – organised by the principal – means the college can offer any combination of its 47 A level and 27 GCSE subjects. It also enables sports stars or those with medical problems to fit in lessons round other commitments. 'Every single timetable is written for an individual. And they are organised for the convenience of the students, not the teachers.'

Many of the teachers have higher degrees. 'This sector attracts highly qualified staff, because every class is an exam class.' Ofsted rated the college outstanding, commenting on the 'very wide and flexible range of courses' and the teachers' 'excellent knowledge of their subjects'.

Runs a medics' programme for those aiming at medicine, dentistry, pharmacy or veterinary degrees, and Easter revision courses, with plenty of individual careers advice and help with UCAS applications.

Games, options, the arts: Plenty of creativity going on, with GCSE drama students rehearsing their devised piece during our visit, photography and artwork adorning the corridor walls, a bright north-facing art studio, graphics room and 'fantastic' photography department with its own dark room.

GCSE students have one PE lesson a week, the football team plays in a league, and there are ad hoc rugby and netball teams. There's an annual ski trip, a chance to do the Duke of Edinburgh Award, and a post-exam activities week that includes paintballing and a trip to Thorpe Park, 'to say thanks for working so hard'. In the autumn term, GCSE and AS students spend Friday afternoons visiting museums, galleries and other London sites or listening to outside speakers. They go ice skating, bowling and to the cinema together. There's a Christmas party and a summer ball, organised by the student council. However, it is fair to say that these students' main focus is on their studies, and no-one joins the college for its extracurricular offerings. As a parent said, 'you're not going to go there for the night life.'

Background and atmosphere: In a quiet back street between Notting Hill and Queensway, the 60s building could be an anonymous block of flats. Inside is a maze of classrooms, science and language labs, art and photography rooms. Noticeably, whilst there is a study centre with plenty of computers, magazines, reference material and past exam papers, there is no library. It is bright, but one parent commented, 'You have to fight the look. There's not a frill to be had.'

Very flexible timetabling – organised by the principal – enables sports stars or those with medical problems to fit in lessons around other commitments

Originally a primary school and community centre for the neighbouring synagogue, it became a college in the late '70s. Once individually owned, it is now part of Astrum Education, which also includes Duff Miller and Chelsea Independent Colleges, and is owned by private equity firm Sovereign Capital. Happily, the firm is prepared to invest in the infrastructure, and building work has create more classroom space and freshened up the fabric. No common room but students socialise in the canteen and on the small outdoor patio area.

Pastoral care and discipline: Relaxed atmosphere – 'having no uniform breaks down a lot of barriers' – but a stringent approach to punctuality and attendance, with a register taken at the beginning of each lesson. The college has a full time attendance officer who will phone or text any missing student, then their parents. Each student has a personal tutor who keeps an eye on their well-being and progression. 'Because our groups are so small we can keep tabs on things and deal with any problems quickly.'

Post-exam activities week that includes paint-balling and a trip to Thorpe Park

The college will expel for smoking drugs repeatedly. 'If they're caught once they're suspended; if they're caught again they're expelled. I can't pretend it doesn't happen – we are in central London. It's the worst day of my life, but I do have that ultimate sanction, and there's no shying away from it.'

Pupils and parents: A mix of backgrounds, including around 13 per cent international students from countries ranging from Kazakhstan to Libya, a percentage liable to increase over the next few years. Some pupils come from state schools in year 11 for intensive small-group GCSE tuition, others are recent arrivals in London. Some have been ill or been asked to leave their previous school. Most join the sixth form to improve on previous grades.

Entrance: All applicants are given a tour and interviewed by the principal or vice principal. 'We ask about their background and how we can help them.' The college is not selective, but will look at previous exam results.

'It was the tutors who convinced us when we looked round,' said a parent. 'They told us it would be hard work for our daughter, and could be lonely, but they thought they could get her through. And they did.'

Exit: Of the GCSE students, around 50–60 per cent stay on for A levels. A level students nearly all to university: occasional one or two to Oxbridge; around half to top universities ranging from Durham to Sussex to SOAS, for subjects ranging from medicine to anthropology and aeronautical engineering.

Money matters: Several means-tested bursaries and academic scholarships up to 40 per cent of fees awarded each year, the latter via the autumn scholarship exam.

Remarks: Extremely good at its job, which is concentrated and detailed preparation for passing exams. Few frills or frivolities. 'It's a sleeves rolled up place,' said a satisfied parent.

LaSwap Sixth Form Consortium

Linked schools: La Sainte Union Catholic Secondary School, 124; Parliament Hill School, 145; William Ellis School, 217

William Ellis School, Highgate Road, London NW5 1RN

Tel: 020 7692 4157

State · Pupils: 1,000 · Ages: 16–19

Email: laswap@williamellis.camden.sch.uk
Website: www.laswap.camden.sch.uk

Joint Heads: LaSwap is a sixth-form consortium composed of four neighbouring comprehensives – Parliament Hill, La Sainte Union, Acland Burghley and William Ellis, and the heads of the four schools share the headship. They meet monthly to plan a strategic overview.

Academic matters: These four comprehensives, geographically within a few hundred metres of each other, created an amalgamated sixth form to provide the widest possible subject variety and range of qualifications. Lucky sixth formers here have a choice of a remarkable 39 A levels, as well as BTecs, NVQs, a certificate in childcare and GCSEs (for those who need further preparation before going on to A levels). About 80 per cent of students follow a purely academic course, the rest sit vocational exams, but those who want to can mix and match. In 2015, 40 per cent A*/B grades at A level. The consortium's strengths lie in vocational subjects, the visual arts (with consistently outstanding results) and arts subjects, like RE, media studies and English. Still possibly not the ideal location for scientists.

Each school retains its distinctive ethos and pupils generally enjoy the change of pace

Teaching (with over 300 teachers) is enthusiastic, knowledgeable and well prepared. 'We've generally found the teaching to be very good,' said one parent, 'though, as always, you'll get the odd dud.' Some criticism for not always taking into account the wide range of ability in this relatively unselective sixth form, but not all would agree – 'In my classes, some people have 10 A*s and others mainly Cs, but I haven't found that a problem,' said one boy. All students are allocated a base school but most study on a number of sites. Some subjects are taught on all the sites, the more rarefied – philosophy, textiles and dance, for example – on only one.

Each pupil is given target grades on entry based on GCSE results and is carefully tracked thereafter, with good exam preparation and help with study skills, as well as twice yearly reports. 'The communication with home is excellent,' says one parent. 'If my son has done something well they email me. Equally, if he's not doing his homework, they'll let me know.' The academic side is clearly complex, but well organised. 'I wanted to change one of my subjects early on,' said a pupil. 'I went to see the head of year and it was sorted by the end of lunch hour.'

Games, options, the arts: The extracurricular here is a significant part of what LaSwap has to offer, being as varied and extensive as the academic range. The generous enrichment programme, which largely takes place on Wednesday and Thursday afternoons, provides 35 options, from ballet and debating to theatrical make-up, DJ-ing and maths masterclasses. Off-site sports include sailing and climbing. The programme is not compulsory, but everyone is encouraged to have a go, regardless of previous knowledge or expertise.

Background and atmosphere: The four schools (La Sainte Union, an all-girls' Catholic school, William Ellis, an all-boys' former grammar school, Acland Burghley, a co-ed comprehensive, and Parliament Hill, an all-girls' comprehensive) decided to unite their sixth form offering 25 years ago. Each school retains its distinctive ethos and pupils generally enjoy the change of pace. 'I really like the different atmosphere in each school,' said one. Parliament Hill and William Ellis combine to form a joint co-ed sixth form, the other schools retain the pupils they take in at 11, and each has its own director of sixth form and heads of year.

One great plus of the model is the halfway house it offers between school and sixth-form college. 'My daughter originally wanted to leave and go to college,' said one mother, 'but once she'd started at LaSwap, she found the teachers treated her with more respect and she was given much more responsibility for her assignments.' The advantage for students who opt for continuity is that they remain in familiar surroundings while meeting new people and conquering new horizons. 'In the earlier years, my daughter's friends were all local,' said one parent. 'In the sixth form, she suddenly had a whole new set of friends from all over London.' New students, however, don't feel excluded – 'I felt everybody was in the same position as I was,' said one. 'People had friends from their original school, but they didn't know anyone from the other schools.'

LaSwap is careful about taking both existing students and recent arrivals to a more independent level of study, with a well-planned induction programme, including a thorough briefing on the outline of each course and relevant dates and department procedures. Students like the friendly, laid-back but organised approach and strong sense of community.

Pastoral care and discipline: All students register at their base school, where they take most of their lessons. Here they have a head of year and a tutor who monitors their work and well-being, with regular interviews to discuss problems and set appropriate targets. Also a confidential professional counselling service and regular PSHE, with outside speakers, group work and discussions.

Pupils and parents: Students, from a huge range of ethnic and social backgrounds, apply from a vast swathe of north London. Despite the consortium's leafy surroundings on the eastern edge of Hampstead Heath, all four schools are inner-city comprehensives with a socio-economic intake reflective of the term. Generally, pupils are confident and mature and get on well.

Entrance: LaSwap has about 1,300 places on offer. Eight hundred of these generally go to existing students; a further 300 are available for students from schools outside the consortium. The entrance procedure is intricate and careful attention must be

'In the sixth form, she suddenly had a whole new set of friends from all over London'

paid to every step and date. First step is to register interest online by the end of the autumn term. Then, armed with a ticket and a parent, prospective candidates attend the open evening in January. Applications must be submitted by post or by hand in early February – those who miss the deadline are immediately put on the waiting list. All applicants who meet the deadline are offered an interview at the school in February or March to discuss subject choice and given conditional offers based on GCSE grades. Those with offers must attend the one-day induction course held before the start of the summer holidays, when summer assignments are set. Post GCSE results, further interviews and places are confirmed. Now asks for mostly B grades at GCSE (rather than C grades, as previously) to study A levels.

Exit: About 400 students go on to 60 universities to study 50 different subjects, from medicine and accountancy to drama and international relations. About 20 per cent to Russell Group universities. A large contingent to leading art colleges, mostly to the University of the Arts, London (Central St Martin's, Chelsea, Camberwell and London College of Fashion etc). Four to Oxbridge in 2015.

Remarks: A good compromise between school and a sixth form college, with an extraordinary range of subjects on offer. Tends to suit the motivated and the self starter, but not ideal for those who will be distracted by studying on a number of sites or who require the disciplined parameters of a school sixth form to function at their peak.

L'École Bilingue Elementaire

St David's Welsh Church, St Mary's Terrace, London
W2 1SJ

Independent • Pupils: 120 • Ages: 3–11 • Fees: Maternelle
£8,665 (ages 3–5) Elementaire £9,345 (ages 6–11) pa

Tel: 0207 224 8427

53

Email: admin@lecolebilingue.com
Website: www.lecolebilingue.com/html/pages/
pagesuk/introuk.htm

Headteacher: Veronique Ferreira studied Biochemistry at the University of Paris and after obtaining her teaching license in 1999 began her

career as a primary school teacher in the suburbs of Paris, working with children with behavioural and academic difficulties. This gave her a lot of insights into the different learning styles of children, something that has shaped a lot of the teaching approach she has established at L'École Bilingue. Moving to London, she started in a French nursery school, but as parents continued to speak of their interest in a more bilingual programme, she pondered on how she might introduce a different sort of French primary school model in London. She focused on child development theories, looking Canadian, UK (including EYFS), French Breton bilingual educational models. Youthful yet wise beyond her years, her confidence is drawn from her solid foundation in pedagogical studies and the popularity of the school which was her brainchild. Her partner and the father of her daughter, Franck Laurans (head of administration), has provided the business knowledge needed to help her realise her vision for a school that is small, personalised and less rigid that the traditional French models where her students can 'find pleasure in learning'.

Entrance: There are no particular feeder schools. L'École Bilingue is non-selective, but with only 15 places at the 3-year-old entry class, places are highly sought. Parents like the fact that, unlike other French schools, this is a transparent process. Priority is given to siblings (in 2014, 12 of the entry places were allocated to siblings), but after that it is first-come, first-served, so sign up early – from birth if you wish. (Nationality/passport are not a factor as in other French homologue schools). Vacancies for children older than 3 are subject to space; worth a call but most classes are wait-listed, so as soon as someone leaves (and with many expats, children do leave) there is someone to fill the spot. Note that if you miss out on the first round you need to proactively let them know you remain interested.

Exit: Many leavers are headed for the French schools – some to the Lycée in South Kensington, though others prefer the Collège Français Bilingue de Londres in Kentish Town, which ensures some continuity in the French/English bilingual model. The new Lycée Winston Churchill in Wembley is another option.

The library is brimming with French and English children's books, a cheerful space

The head meets parents individually to discuss the options, and some non-native French speakers may at this point opt for 11+ exams (a very few leave at age 7 or 8) and a move away from the French system. Recent examples include Francis Holland, City of London Girls' School, Lady Margaret

They are particularly proud to have been invited to participate in the French Parliament des Enfants (a sort of 'junior parliament')

(Fulham) and South Hampstead High. While moving from L'École to the ginormous French Lycée is a big change, the Lycée tries to place two L'École students in the same year form group, so that helps a bit. The school has noted that French students repatriating to Paris often seek out bilingual schools there to keep their English language strong.

Remarks: The curriculum is bilingual French and English, and although the French curriculum model is predominant, the head says that she has looked in depth at other curricula, including the national curriculum, the IB primary years and the international primary curriculum, and drawn on elements of all these. Some subjects are taught in French (French, maths, history), some in English (science, English, geography) and some are taught in both languages simultaneously (arts, ICT, drama, music). Children move between English- and French-medium classrooms so that they are immersed in the relevant language for that part of the day.

Though a small school, the limited space is used to good effect and is immaculately tidy. The compact library is brimming with French and English children's books, a cheerful space where we saw some one-to-one learning taking place; walls lined with colourful boards neatly display creative work by students of all ages; we noticed some tailors' mannequins with student-designed fashions – part of a broader project including all the London French homologue schools in celebration of the centenary of the Lycée Charles de Gaulle. Some special needs support (French and English) available; some children with statements in the school receive individual support either in-class or on a withdrawal basis. Teachers (19 in total, average age early 30s) are a mixture of French and English, all suitably trained and qualified. Staff turnover is higher amongst the French teachers than the English as they may be here as accompanying spouses or may move on to other French medium schools in London or abroad.

By all accounts, the pupils are busy and engaged in a wide range of activities. They are especially proud to have been invited – by recommendation of the French education inspector – to participate in the French Parliament des Enfants (a sort of 'junior parliament'). This event has influenced some of the themes and topics that have been studied by pupils in all the year groups. Other academic extras sometimes include a French mathematics competition for French schools in the north of Europe. French assessments are given in year 3 and year 6 to measure attainment against French standards; the school is inspected by Ofsted as well as the IEN French Inspector for the northern European region.

Year 3 goes to Brighton for two nights, year 5 spends three days in East Sussex and year 6 goes to Brittany for a week. The music programme is strong and some children do extra Suzuki violin and piano. Parents sang the praises (no pun intended) of the innovative music teacher who had recently done a 'bilingual Beatles' unit. As with other London French schools, many of the extra-curricular activities are organised by the parents' association, and parents run some of the clubs, which include fencing, dance, art, choir and football. There are no competitive sports on offer; they use the local sports centre – where many students do tae kwon do after school – from year 2 they swim at Imperial College pool. There are two major shows – the annual Christmas carol service and an end-of-year show. We saw the former in final rehearsal – joyful voices, silver tinsel halos and red Santa hats.

An enclosed garden features a vegetable garden, an eco-pond (with resident creepy crawlies), and an area for messy hands-on learning with sand and water

Though the school is secular, the some of the ecclesiastical architectural features in the former Welsh church nestled in a quiet back street in Maida Vale have been put to effective use, making this a most unusual school building. An enclosed garden behind the school features a vegetable garden for pupils, an eco-pond (with resident creepy crawlies), and an area for messy hands-on learning with sand and water. There is an outdoor play area at the front of the school. A small multi-purpose hall is used for assemblies. Four-course lunches (optional) are prepared and served at school by cooks who know each child by name, chivvy those with picky palates to eat their vegetables and then report to parents on how many ate their carrots. Too much chatter is discouraged during lunches to encourage eating; an adult may read stories aloud instead.

There is a big emphasis on developing the 'soft skills' and the small size means that there is no anonymity in the school. Everyone contributes; everyone has a role to play. The appeal, parents say, is that at L'École they have found a near-perfect balance of strong (French) academic foundations in a very caring environment where everyone knows everyone. The intimacy of the school ensures that behaviour standards are high, and parents subtly suggest that the presence of several English teachers means that discipline is managed differently than in traditional French schools. Parents describe the children as 'kind' and very welcoming of new students. It's also highly inclusive. 'Birthday parties usually involve all of the siblings.'

Parents are big fans of this school, so much so that when they heard of the Good Schools Guide interest in meeting them, they organised a coffee morning (mostly mums, though one dad came) to share frankly their opinions about the school. The small size is an attraction – 'it's digestible for young children'. Another says, 'it's like comparing a mom and pop shop with B&Q'. One recent arrival accustomed to French schools voiced a concern that L'École may lack rigour; others from elsewhere in Europe and the US were delighted with the academic standards. Despite its small size, it appears that communication is patchy; some people seem to be in the know; others (particularly those new to the school) felt they were out of the loop. The school gate is definitely the place to find out what's happening. It seems that parents who are not fluent French speakers can find other parents willing to help and explain things.

Some 40 per cent of families are French (expat and local), 25 per cent are dual French/other nationals, 18 per cent are French/British, and some eight per cent represent other nationalities (including French speaking north Africans, Canadians and others). Some international families also speak Arabic, Spanish, Italian, etc. Most families live nearby and walk to school, though some are drawn from as far as Fulham, Kentish Town, South Kensington and Hampstead. Because of the school's South Kensington origins, a bus that comes from the Brompton Road area serving families who joined the school in the early days.

The school is owned by founders Franck Laurans and Veronique Ferreira. Parents like the fact that this couple, who 'live above the shop', are firmly at the helm; they feel they provide continuity and sustainable leadership that secures the school's future – at least for the time being. Some subsidies come from the French government for French national students,

Described by one parent as small, friendly 'village' school that draws on the best of French academics and English pastoral education, this bite-size school in the centre of London is worth a visit by parents who want something a bit different.

The Lyceum School

6 Paul Street, London EC2A 4JH

Tel: 020 7247 1588

Independent • Pupils: 100 • Ages: 3–11 • Fees: £14,550 pa

Email: admin@lyceumschool.co.uk
Website: www.lyceumschool.co.uk

35

Interim Headteacher: Mrs Vanessa Bingham is in charge during the 2015/16 year. She took over following the abrupt departure of previous head Edwin Brown in July 2015. Mr Brown had been appointed in 2014 when the founding heads sold the school to Minerva Education. Mrs Bingham is an experienced head, who has led schools in the UK and China, including managing the three schools in the Rego group. For the past two years she has been interim head at several primary schools in England.

Entrance: Places at 3 and 4 are offered on a first-come first-served basis with priority to siblings. Plans to increase to two form entry from 2016. A few places for 7 year olds and the odd vacancy later on, awarded after assessment. The school does not set out to cater for special needs and one parent with older children at the Lyceum told us she chose not to send her youngest child because she required more specialist support. Nevertheless, in recent years, the school has employed a SENCo and part-time speech and language therapist, which has helped as the needs of individual children have become apparent. Before parents accept a place, they are invited to meet the head to ensure they

fully understand what the school is about before making a commitment. Many families use public transport from Hackney or Islington but the demographics have altered in recent years, as more mothers are working or living close by in the City and several families live in the Barbican.

Exit: The majority stay until 11, with a few leaving earlier for schools like City Girls' Prep. The school does not specifically prepare pupils for 7+ examinations; however, the top year is skilfully prepared with plenty of 11+ examination technique and care. Definitely not a hothouse, the Lyceum offers an alternative to hothouses on the one hand and very laid-back schools on the other. One parent said, 'I chose The Lyceum deliberately because I didn't want my child stressed out going to school'. Another remarked, 'The school doesn't come across as overly academic, however, it should promote its achievement in getting children into good quality schools.' Destinations have widened over the years to include City of London, Highgate, Channing, North Bridge House, Dulwich College, Queen's Gate, Forest School, South Hampstead, Frances Holland Clarence Gate and Portland Place, as well as a few boarding schools like Headington and Cheltenham Ladies', with several academic, art and music scholarships. The variety of destinations reflects the mixed ability of the pupils.

Remarks: A short walk from Liverpool Street and Moorgate, the building which houses the school was originally a distribution warehouse for the Radio Times. Parents find the packed lunches a chore but accept the location of the school and lack of space cannot be helped. Throughout the building there are massive silver pipes for filtering air. The school is sure they have 'less asthma as a result' but it is utilitarian – if post-modernist.

Apart from the nursery, the classrooms are semi-open plan and grouped together chronologically with a shared library and cloakroom in the centre. The bright strip lights in the hall are functional, whilst central pink chandeliers in the open plan classroom area are quirky and fun. We saw teachers working and sharing, encouraged to support one another, with plenty of resources. 'The relationship with the teachers is very important,' commented one parent of three, 'as the pupils see them as allies, friendly, someone to help them, rather than adversarial'. Another praised the fact that 'the children come out very comfortable with themselves, not brash', and another added, 'They develop interpersonal skills, are comfortable talking to adults' – as we experienced in our conversations with a group during our visit. There is a good balance of staff age with some long-serving teachers and energetic young ones. Some of the teaching assistants we met are old pupils, who loved the school so much they wanted to return. Each day begins gently with music playing as a signal for parents to depart. Specialists teach French (from reception), and music; afternoons are devoted to creativity and sports.

Parents appreciate that their children 'are learning to love the City and all there is on offer'

Year groups are paired for trips and non-academic lessons, or to make up the numbers for games. This results in the children knowing each other and looking after one another, taking responsibility without the need for houses or prefects. We saw small classes, 16 on average, each with a teaching assistant (including one man), thoroughly enjoying their learning. In small classes friendships can become an issue, but parents remark: 'The school deals well with this and talks through any situation quickly and effectively. There is zero tolerance of bad behaviour.'

Some of the teaching assistants we met are old pupils, who loved the school so much they wanted to return

Despite the urban location, the children all have plenty of physical activity and play on a daily basis. There is a reasonably large, indoor courtyard, which works well for breaks and small sports, as well as a gallery/hall for drama, dance, music and gym, plays and assemblies. For half the year they use the local Broadgate Centre ice rink for skating and parents really appreciate the use of local facilities such as the vast Honourable Artillery Ground, Bunhill Fields and Golden Lane Sports Centre for tennis, swimming and netball. Clubs include judo, run by ex-Olympic athlete. One parent commented on the disadvantage that the children are taught the basic sports skills but do not have much experience of team fixtures and matches, but they quickly learn when they move on to secondary school. Another parent appreciated the fact that 'the children are learning to love the City and all there is on offer'. They come and go in their navy and white uniform, with smart caps for boys and felt hats/boaters for girls. All the pupils we spoke to said they like the uniform and feel comfortable in it.

We saw a good mix of artwork in lively topic displays and a developmental whole school (nursery to year 6) set of colourful paintings of poinsettias in the hall. The school is keen to stress the many opportunities to perform, with regular plays, assemblies and concerts. The majority learn instruments and take examinations, and they reach a high standard of performance. We watched an impressive big band rehearsal and a chamber choir practice. As one boy proudly stated, 'It's great fun. For a small school, we can play loads of instruments'. Charlotte Barbour-Condini, an ex-pupil, was runner up in the BBC Young Musician of the Year playing the recorder.

Recently-introduced Mandarin clubs, plus an IT consultant, who has been working alongside the staff. The school is keen for children to be 'producers of content, not just consumers', and we saw children producing sophisticated animations, websites, mobile apps and even their own ebook. Much of this work is related to the Living History topics and annual year 5 and 6 residential trips to eg Edinburgh, Paris and Amsterdam. Parents praised these as being 'vivid and memorable', though one emphasised the need for careful budgeting, as they are in addition to the annual fees.

The emphasis is not on cramming and there are no end of year examinations, but parents feel that pupils are successfully prepared for secondary schools. Working parents can drop off their children, pop back for an assembly or attend sports day in the knowledge a nanny or grandparent would be equally welcome. 'The Lyceum produces well rounded children who are happy,' say parents, and

'It manages to strike a good balance between creativity and very good results,' no mean feat.

New owner, equity-backed Minerva Education, has agreed to maintain the school's ethos: parents will be anxious to ensure this is a reality, particularly in view of the previous head's short tenure.

Mossbourne Community Academy

100 Downs Park Road, London E5 8JY

Tel: 020 8525 5200

State · Pupils: 1,350 · Ages: 11–18 · Sixth form pupils: 350

Email: enquiries@mca.mossbourne.org
Website: www.mossbourne.hackney.sch.uk/

Principal: Since 2012, Mr Peter Hughes (30s), who took over when founding principal Sir Michael Wilshaw left to lead Ofsted. An Australian, he came to Mossbourne as part of the Future Leaders programme, which identifies, supports and trains potential head teachers. He has taught at Pimlico and Highgate Wood, and was an advanced skills teacher. He can be seen out running at 6am with rowers (the school has a liaison with London Youth Rowers and is close to the River Lee).

Academic matters: Truly outstanding results: in 2015, 84 per cent of pupils got 5+ A*-C grades at GCSE including maths and English. More than 32 per cent A*/A grades. At A level, 65 per cent of grades were A*/B. Not only are these some of the best state school results in the capital, they are also all the more extraordinary given the fact that a significant proportion of the pupils arrive in year 7 hardly able to read.

The country's highest ranking school for 'value added' – how is it done? Well, a formula that bears no relationship to wishy-washy liberalism – a tough-love approach with a strict uniform policy, ferocious discipline, meticulous monitoring with weekly target setting and a 'can-do' culture. Young and enthusiastic teaching staff (who receive performance-related bonuses) have no official office hours and parents universally praise their dedication. 'My kids never complain about their teachers,' said one mother. 'They seem to be in school at 7 every morning. They recognise that not everyone is going to be a rocket scientist, but still manage to make every child feel relevant, included and loved.'

The banded intake is set on entry in all the main curriculum subjects (English, maths, science, humanities, ICT and modern languages), though considerable movement between sets. Music, drama, dance, PE, art and design technology are not setted. Three languages on offer at GCSE – French,

German, Spanish – as part of the core curriculum, but students also have the opportunity to take public exams in Turkish, Latin, Bengali, Swedish and Italian. Both vocational and academic exams on offer post-GCSE (though considerably more academic than vocational), with a BTec in business studies and level 3 ICT. Homework is set in abundance. Interactive whiteboards in all classrooms and all students offered access to the internet and laptops. What really makes the school excel academically, however, is the minutely monitored assessment – the 'personalised learning agenda' is certainly not just government jargon at this school.

The SEN provision is particularly remarkable, with its own well-resourced teaching centre and well-qualified specialists who cope with the full range of difficulties from autistic spectrum to dyslexia. All pupils with academic, social, emotional or behavioural difficulties have a learning mentor and those who require learning support work with a teaching assistant (in class or outside), receive specialist teaching and the support of external specialists if required. Handwriting club and homework club. Additional English classes, too, for non-native speakers on Saturday mornings. Strategies to suit all, including the brightest. The head quickly followed up on one parent's suggestion that Latin might be a desirable addition and equally quickly found himself with 30 students, who went on to take GCSE.

Games, options, the arts: Extracurricular here is part of the curriculum, with an additional, compulsory, off-piste period every afternoon from 3.10 to 4.10pm. This time is used to help strugglers, and also to broaden horizons, with more than 70 activities on offer. All pupils required to take a minimum of two extension classes, which include everything from journalism to marathon running. Saturday morning school provides a safe place to have fun and weekend activities include the City explorers club, to discover the joys of London. Sports include football, netball, basketball, cricket and even rowing, and 'best in Hackney' for athletics. Wonderful head of sport, reports one mother – 'my son had no problem getting up at 6am three mornings a week to be at cricket practice at 7'. Clearly buzzing on all fronts – annual junior concert, dance and drama production; trips to Edinburgh, Belgium, the Isle of Wight, language trips to Spain and Germany; Spanish play, poetry competition, debating, links with London College of Fashion.

Music is a specialism, and over 250 pupils have subsidised instrumental lessons. Bands, choirs, ensembles and individuals perform at eg the Lord Mayor's Show.

Background and atmosphere: Founded on the site of Hackney Downs School, once a successful local grammar school, whose alumnae include Sir Michael Caine and Harold Pinter. By the 1990s, however, it had become notorious as 'the worst in Britain' and was eventually demolished. Mossbourne was rebuilt on the same site, a tricky triangle bounded on two sides by railway lines. Founding principal Sir Michael Wilshaw worked alongside architects, Richard Rogers and Partners, to design a school (costing £32.5 million) which met his requirements. Now one of the largest wooden structures in England, it was created in a V shape, which holds in its arms a triangular social area. Wilshaw believed that pupils need to be kept under constant observation, so the head's office and the classrooms all overlook the grounds. No corridors – hotspots for bullying – and no staffroom, since Wilshaw felt teachers need to be involved at break times and after school, when most trouble occurs. Indoors, the triple-height space is light and airy and learning takes place in 'learning areas'. Sparkling new sixth form centre added in 2009.

'They still manage to make every child feel relevant, included and loved'

Pupils' aspirations always focused upwards. Rather than the Lord's Prayer, students recite the Mossbourne reflection: 'Throughout this lesson I aspire to maintain an inquiring mind, a calm disposition and an attentive ear, so that in this class and in all classes I can fulfil my true potential'. Parents without hesitation describe the school as 'absolutely amazing' – 'the kids are plainly very well cared for, polite, helpful and considerate. You feel that they are looked after and they are looking out for each other'. An incredible loyalty between kids from completely different ethnic and social backgrounds. Perhaps the greatest compliment any parent can pay is: 'You walk into the school during the day and there is an air of studiousness and control. I don't think about it any more – I know the teachers are in charge'.

Pastoral care and discipline: As celebrated for its discipline as for its academic success – little opportunity to slip up here. Particularly in the early years, pupils are drilled in army-like expectations. Detentions commonplace, for lost homework, left-at-home games kit, being more than 10 seconds late when the morning whistles goes at 8.40am, and students stand when a teacher enters the room. Wherever the potential for rule breaking, staff are on hand – stairwells manned between lessons and students monitored after school. Pre-GCSE pupils wear smart grey and red school blazers and neatly knotted ties, sixth formers graduate to business-like suits and skirts (at or below the knee). No piercings allowed, except for ears, hair must be kept to an acceptable norm (those indulging in the shaven look work in isolation until locks re-grow). Mobiles banned and students not allowed to enter shops on their way home or loiter outside the gates in groups. 'Structure sets a child free,' says the head. And it certainly seems to – a 96 per cent attendance rate.

Pastoral care is as strong as the discipline. Few personal problems go unnoticed, whether bullying or self-harm. At the first sign, parents are invited to come and speak to the staff. One grateful mother has nothing but praise for their intervention. 'They made it very easy for my children to speak to a counsellor. Mossbourne is a place where you can talk and get support when you can't always get that at home'. Food healthy and delicious.

Pupils and parents: A large percentage of the intake comes from the adjacent Pembury estate, an urban sprawl which tends to hit the headlines for its shootings and drugs rather than its high educational aspirations. Four-fifths of pupils are from minority ethnic groups (many Turkish Kurds), two-fifths speak English as a second language, 50 per cent are on free school meals. But also a fair number of clued-up, middle-class parents – the kind who used to go private or bus their children out of the borough – who fight from a great distance to get their children the superb education the school offers.

Entrance: Total of 200 places – now one of the country's most over-subscribed schools. The head is looking for a balanced intake: 'We want a comprehensive – we don't want a secondary modern'. Won't take pupils who have been excluded from two other schools. Applicants sit reasoning tests to divide into four equal ability bands. Fifty per cent of places in each band are given to those who live within the inner zone (up to 1km from the gates); 30 per cent of places go to those in the middle zone (1-2km) and 20 per cent to those in the outer zone (2-3km). Priority is given to looked after children, those with a child protection plan, siblings, those with medical needs and children of staff. Further places by lottery. Now offers an additional 10 percent of year 9 places to those with the potential to become elite rowers (zoning does not apply to this group).

The lower sixth form has 170 places and generally about 100 places are filled by pupils already in the school. Applicants must meet the demanding criteria of seven A*-C GCSEs, including English and maths. Successful external candidates are frequently, but not exclusively, from other Hackney comprehensives.

Exit: Most proceed to the sixth form. Four to Oxbridge in 2015. Many others to Russell Group and other top unis, including the US.

Money matters: Money is not a problem at this well-resourced school – everything from the buildings to the technology is of the highest standard and whatever the head wants to get done he has the means to achieve.

Remarks: Proof that with sufficient resources and the right direction, the kids who life intended to fail can succeed. Parents rightly fight to get into its safe, inspiring and eco-friendly classrooms.

North Bridge House Pre-Preparatory School

Linked schools: North Bridge House Preparatory School, 140; North Bridge House Senior School, 142

8 Netherhall Gardens, London NW3 5RR	Tel: 020 7435 2884
Independent • Pupils: 410 • Ages: 2.75–7 • Fees: up to £15,285 pa	Email: preprep@northbridgehouse.com Website: www.northbridgehouse.com

13

Interim Headteacher: Mrs Christine McLelland is in charge for the first two terms of the 2015/16 academic year, following previous head Joanna Hockley's departure due to 'sad personal reasons' after a short tenure.

Entrance: Life begins at playgroup level and children are mostly siblings of current pupils. Then the nursery takes around 30 children out of the 120 applicants. Reception, the following year, takes the same number out of a similar number of applicants. Occasional places thereafter, but around 10 children out of 40-odd are taken into year 3.

Criteria are refreshing – first come siblings, then children of former pupils, then families who live closest and finally, those who fit the age

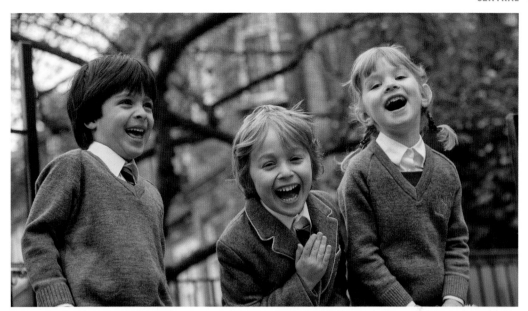

bracket the school wants to fill. Makes a point of covering the entire chronological year in any class year group.

That doesn't mean no assessment. All applicants visit and parent and child are interviewed. So the emphasis is more on whether the child – and family – fit the school's ethos rather than on academic potential. The result is a spread of ability, ethnicity and just about everything other than location – most live within three miles of the school, many near enough to walk. Equal split of boys/girls. Runs a good coach service to obvious areas.

Exit: Virtually all move on from the junior school to the prep school in year 3, despite the different location. Those who leave at this stage mostly do so for single sex education.

Remarks: Highly confusing for outsiders. The nursery and junior school are housed in two buildings moments from each other in Hampstead. The preparatory school lives off Regent's Park, whilst North Bridge House Senior School amalgamated with the Royal School in Hampstead in 2012 resulting in NBH Senior School moving to the Royal's central Hampstead site. Another NBH senior school, covering years 9 – 13, opened in Canonbury in September 2014.

Life begins in the nursery building – a splendid Victorian house on Fitzjohn's Avenue. Classrooms are full of happily absorbed children. We saw year 1s engaged in water play while the parallel class had a friendly 'show and tell session'. Art was fun – we enjoyed Mondrian-inspired collages on the walls and appreciated the principle that 'everyone's work goes

up – not just the best'. It's well-equipped – a music room doubles as an eating room, a good gym/hall for concerts and shows – and does not feel as crowded as some similar schools, though we found some of the rooms uncomfortably hot. Everyone learns French from reception and PE is four days a week. Outside space, again, compares well with comparable schools – some safe surfaces, a lovely wooden play train and caterpillar, with some covered nooks for secret conversations and conspiracies.

We enjoyed Mondrian-inspired collages on the walls and appreciated that 'everyone's work goes up – not just the best'

The Fitzjohn's site houses the playgroup, nursery and reception. The building on Netherhall Gardens is the main site for the junior school and has the year 1 and 2 classes. This is a quieter corner – a cul de sac overlooking the Finchley Road; the house is a five-storey red-brickery, interestingly sited between the British College of Osteopathic Medicine and the former home of Sidney and Beatrice Webb. It's a corner favoured by independent schools – South Hampstead Junior School is opposite and nearby, Southbank International (also owned by Cognita, the owners of North Bridge) is up the road, and others not more than a rubber's throw away. Efforts are made to stagger drop-offs and pick-ups. From the top of the main building splendid views – over to Harrow-on-the-Hill one way and to the North Downs the other.

As in the nursery building, every inch is covered in displayed work – much to intrigue and delight the eye. Classrooms are occupied by quiet and relaxed children, clearly engaged and interested. Music, French and PE are said to be the school's specialties – everyone learns music and a third or more learn piano, guitar or violin in school; choirs and bands. Outside space is less impressive, though. A marked out chess board and a climbing frame on the tarmac. Sports mostly at the Talacre Centre in Kentish Town. More could be done to make this a livelier area.

A full-time learning support teacher sees around 25 pupils regularly – up to three times a week – for varying types of support. Despite the manner of entry, nothing more than mild dyslexia/dyspraxia surfaces here. All children are monitored twice-yearly to check progress.

Junior and nursery school parents praise the friendliness and welcome they find here and feel what is offered at this level hardly differs from what the overtly academic neighbours do.

North Bridge House Preparatory School

Linked schools: North Bridge House Pre-Preparatory School, 138; North Bridge House Senior School, 142

---

1 Gloucester Avenue, London NW1 7AB

Tel: 020 7267 6266

Independent · Pupils: 470 · Ages: 7–13 · Fees: £15,585 pa

Email: prep@northbridgehouse.com
Website: www.northbridgehouse.com

14

Headteacher: Since 2005, Mr Brodie Bibby BA PGCE MEd (40s). Took his first degree in archaeology and ancient history at Exeter, followed by a PGCE at Roehampton, then taught in state and independent schools, including time at The Banda School, Kenya and as deputy head of Westminster Under School. Still teaches history, drama and games.

Energetic and efficient, he's a man who gets things done, but wants what's done to combine high achievement for all with happy kids protected as much as possible from the early pressure of the modern exam system. Parents rate him highly. 'He's really involved in all areas,' said one, 'and knows and welcomes every parent. You feel he's really proud of the school.' Has recently run the senior school during the previous head's maternity leave, but is now happily back on his own stomping ground, with more room to move around and year 3 now under his wing. His own son and daughter attended the school, always a recommendation.

Entrance: Most come up from junior school. For year 3 entry from outside – around 20 places – assessment in January in English, maths and reasoning. Open mornings held throughout the year.

Exit: Plenty of guidance about appropriate secondary school starting in year 5. 'It's important to be honest with parents and make sure the school is the right fit,' says the head.

Excellent results at 11 for girls. Good chunk each year to Channing and South Hampstead, but to a wide range of state and private, including impressive numbers to Henrietta Barnett. Boys, too, go everywhere, with impressive results at 13+ and common entrance. A solid handful to Westminster and St Paul's and significant numbers to City, as well as all the usual north London suspects. Those who wish to continue to North Bridge House Senior School in Hampstead are now more or less guaranteed a smooth passage, though occasionally someone may be asked to look elsewhere. Girls can now stay till 13, if they want to go on to North Bridge House Canonbury or take common entrance.

Remarks: North Bridge, one of the largest standalone prep schools in London, opened in 1939 in St John's Wood and is now part of the growing stable of schools run by the Cognita group. It is a school that has undoubtedly benefited from the recent relocation of its senior school to a new home. Now years 3 to 8 are grouped together on the same site, with considerably more elbow room.

Formerly a convent chapel, then a Japanese school, the site has gradually been updated to provide a spacious welcoming reception and good playground space. Still a bit of a rabbit warren (younger children are carefully guided round), but some impressive features, such as the lofty pillared and gilded assembly hall, two newly equipped science labs and music rooms.

Teaching – by friendly, well-qualified staff in classes of about 20 – is lively and fun, with the national curriculum followed in the early years, then stretched well beyond later on. 'My son is looked after really well,' said one mother. 'His teachers completely understand his strengths and weaknesses and seem to catch his imagination.' Pupils' progress is meticulously tracked on a database. Specialist subject teaching in ICT, French, music and games. French, taught by native speakers, from reception; Spanish added in years 3, 4 and 5; Latin and Greek from year 6. Plenty of 'professional development,' too, so teachers are kept on their toes. Classroom style is relaxed but orderly.

Children with special needs are given group work in class plus one-to-one attention outside if necessary. In years 3, 4 and 5, teachers are supported by assistants who help out with reading and group activities.

Girl-boy balance kept as even as possible in the younger years then in year 6 boys are hived off into a separate all-boys prep on the top floor to prepare for common entrance. The school prides itself on its support for those taking 11+ and 13+ entrance tests. 'The exams can be quite ruthless and it's important pupils feel good about themselves,' says the head.

Prides itself on its support for those taking entrance tests. 'The exams can be quite ruthless and it's important pupils feel good about themselves'

Strong emphasis on art, music, drama and sport. The art room (home to art club and regular exhibitions) has now been freed up for use by all pupils. Music – with an orchestra, a number of choirs and plenty of informal concerts – is vibrant. Annual school play (recently The Pied Piper) attracts enthusiastic auditioning. Sport, played twice a week, offers a good choice for both boys and girls (kayaking, rock climbing, basketball, dance and table tennis in addition to the standard fare) and regular matches against other local schools. Two well-equipped playgrounds and afternoon break in the open spaces of Regent's Park, just across the road. The school is non-denominational, but pupils receive education in all major faiths.

Exciting range of out-of-class activities (at lunch and after-school) includes flamenco, yoga and cookery, as well as arts, sport and drama. Chess particularly popular, with a coach training potential grandmasters for national competition. Reorganisation has allowed space for a purpose-built library, with bean bags, newspapers and library lessons. Plenty of trips, including abroad (Rouen, Vienna). Energetic charitable involvement (recent fundraisers include a Readathon and cross-country run). Lunch, featuring traditional favourites like fish and chips and jelly with ice cream, is served in the assembly hall and eaten alongside the teachers.

Excellent communication with parents, with an informative handbook distributed at annual info evening and email access to teachers. 'They send you an email if they have any concerns and you can email them with anything that worries you.' Pastoral care, too, comes in for high praise. 'Problems are picked up immediately and dealt with sensibly and sensitively,' said one parent, whose daughter had experienced some low-level bullying.

Families live fairly locally (mainly Hampstead, Islington and Queen's Park), but are metropolitan and cosmopolitan (Russian, American, Chinese, Japanese, African), often in the arts and media. The approach certainly appeals to those who might find other local schools too formal. 'I like it because it's unpretentious,' said one father of three. 'It doesn't take itself too seriously.'

A successful school (which received 'outstanding' in every category in its last Ofsted report), but also a happy and friendly place which seems to find room for everyone to thrive. 'We get very good results, but we don't want to pressure someone into getting into a school. We let children be children,' says the head. A philosophy which clearly works. 'I really like coming to school in the morning,' said one girl in her final year.

North Bridge House Senior School

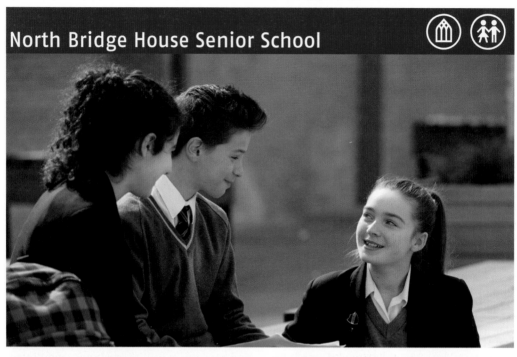

Linked schools: North Bridge House Pre-Preparatory School, 138; North Bridge House Preparatory School, 140

---

65 Rosslyn Hill, London NW3 5UD

Independent · Pupils: 300 · Ages: 11–16 · Fees: up to £16,860 pa

Tel: 020 7267 6266

Email: seniorschool@northbridgehouse.com
Website: www.nbhseniorschool.co.uk

Head: Georgina Masefield BA MA PGCE (40s). Australian by birth, Mrs Masefield grew up in north London, where she attended Channing School. Then to UCL to do a BA in English literature and linguistics, followed by an MA in medieval literature. She also holds a PGCE and is currently completing a masters of education from Buckingham University (where she has worked as a mentor and tutor). Started at North Bridge in 1998 as a supply teacher, moving quickly up the ranks from form teacher and head of art to head of English in the senior school. 'She's a fantastic teacher,' says one former pupil. 'Everyone she taught used to get A*.'

In 2010, she left (temporarily) to become an adviser and then education officer for the school's owners, Cognita, helping to develop curriculum and standards across the group. ('I loved it, but in the end, I felt I wanted to shape and drive my own school.') Remains passionate about teaching. 'I still observe lessons, sitting where the children sit and doing the activities.' Glamorous and ebullient, she's also clearly effective, and the rate of change since she took over has been rapid and decisive. Married to an archaeologist, she has one son at university.

Academic matters: North Bridge has never been (and has no desire to become) a hothouse, but there's definitely a sense that academic outcome has now been put higher up the agenda (with a considerable exodus of old staff and influx of new). In 2015, 91 per cent of pupils achieved 5+ A*-C grades at GCSE, with 49 per cent of grades A*/A. Don't be surprised, however, if these statistics improve in the coming years. 'We're very keen to retain diversity,' says the head, 'but we also want pupils to leave with the best possible grades.' (Some parents feel the shift is entirely positive, 'She's really pushing the school in the right direction'; others are less convinced, 'I preferred it when it was a bit quirkier.')

'There's no stigma attached to children with special needs here. Children want to come'

Since taking over, Mrs Masefield has made a number of significant alterations, introducing specialist subject teaching in year 7 and increasing the academic content. All pupils take nine GCSEs, including English lang and lit, maths, double or triple science (about half do triple) a social science (history or geography) and a modern foreign language (those with dyslexia can be absolved). French from year 7, German and Spanish in year 8. Latin now compulsory in year 7 ('It's not only helpful for understanding English linguistics, but useful in terms of developing modern language skills,' says the head). A rich GCSE offering beyond the core includes textiles, photography, media studies, food technology, art, music, classical civilisation and (newly added) computer programming to complement the existing offering of IT.

North Bridge has always done well by those with mild learning difficulties, and about 10 per cent of pupils here need some sort of support (usually able dyslexics and dyspraxics). Lovely, large, bright dedicated room (with its own sofa), overseen by a full-time SENCo and a medley of part-timers (all with specialist dyslexia qualifications). 'There's no stigma attached to special needs here,' says the head of learning support. 'Children want to come.' Regular assessment for all and informal support with study skills, revision techniques and exam strategies available at break and after school on a drop-in basis. The school also has a lift, and can provide additional support for those with English as a second language.

Games, options, the arts: Always a creative place, particularly in the visual arts and drama, the new building has extended the range, with well-designed, dedicated space for textiles, ceramics and DT, as well as a new media suite (fully equipped with Macs), dark room and de-luxe food technology department.

Music teaching provided entirely in-house, with more music in the curriculum and a carousel of additional opportunities. Compulsory choir in year 7, musical theatre in year 8 and plenty of performance, including Battle of the Bands and clubs for close harmony singing, grade 5 theory and jazz.

For a small school, a very decent amount of sport, with a multitude of teams and access for everyone. Pupils already participate regularly in out-of-school competitions and sports trips and the new sports hall and newly landscaped grounds (with market garden and netball court) have undoubtedly improved on-site possibilities.

Perhaps the most popular innovation is the enrichment programme, a weekly 50-minute slot embedding in the timetable activities generally considered add-ons. 'If extracurricular activities just take place in clubs,' says the head, 'they tend to fall off the radar.' Now the whole school mingles in a choice of 26 varieties (changed termly), encompassing a broad and imaginative sweep, from archaeology and cheerobics to origami and animation.

Background and atmosphere: First established as a junior school in 1939, the senior school was set up in 1987. In 2004, the entire outfit (junior school, prep, and senior school) was bought by Cognita. The group runs 64 schools across three continents, but encourages each to retain its founding ethos. 'Here, it's to celebrate the individual in a caring way, to offer a wide breath of experience, to aim high and push pupils a little bit further so they exceed their potential,' says Mrs Masefield. North Bridge is Cognita's flagship and the association comes with undoubted benefits – centralised services and long-term planning – but some feel it's also accompanied by just a whiff of the corporate.

In 2012, the senior school separated physically from the prep school, moving out of the cramped site in Camden Town to take over the premises (and pupils) of the Royal School in Hampstead. The 60s building has now been entirely refurbished, combining all the positives of the era (acres of windows, light and spacious classrooms, outstanding views) with all mod cons. Comfortable, well-stocked library, with enthusiastic librarian who arranges tantalising displays of 'banned books' and interesting guest speakers. Delicious food (freshly baked bread, minted pea and quinoa soup, vegetarian option) provided by outside caterers. Free inter-school shuttle bus aids parents needing to pick up from the prep or pre-prep, plus a reasonably priced school coach taking in a broad sweep of north London.

Pastoral care and discipline: School prides itself on its family atmosphere and this, all agree, is one of its chief strengths. 'Kids really look out for one another,' said one happy parent. 'What I love about the school,' says another, 'is the way that everyone from the oldest to the youngest gets on. There's a real sense of camaraderie'. Others are upbeat about the individual, confidence-boosting attention. 'My son came home from a residential trip declaring, "Now, I'm not afraid of anything any more." He's really flourished at the school.'

Transition to secondary carefully managed, with the entire year contained on one floor and newcomers linked with year 11 'buddies'. Twice daily form periods make sure no pastoral (or disciplinary) issue is overlooked and head holds weekly open house ('Masefield Mondays') when pupils can come and 'tell me anything'.

An unpretentious and civilised place, where good behaviour and good manners are paramount. 'This is a nurturing school, but we have clear expectations and firm boundaries,' says the head. (The latter are now being made more explicit, with detention for uniform lapses, for example). Usual disciplinary ladder, starting out with discussion in form time. Good behaviour and achievement acknowledged by 'head's tea' and activities like ice skating and bowling.

New World of Work initiative, targeted at year 10, has upped the careers offering. Older pupils now do a week of work experience and gain a wider understanding of a range of professions (from local government officials to astronauts) through

Enthusiastic librarian who arranges tantalising displays of 'banned books' and interesting guest speakers

weekly speakers interviewed by the head or groups of students.

Three houses compete throughout the year (in maths, poetry and cake baking, amongst other activities), with winners rewarded with a trip. All of year 10 invited to apply for positions of leadership and responsibility. Prefects, house captains and head boy and girl appointed in year 11. Student voice throughout loud and clear. 'We want children to run things.'

Pupils and parents: Families generally local, many within walking distance, then trickling out to Highgate, Muswell Hill, Finchley. A few from further afield. Quite a cosmopolitan bunch, often less intensely exam focused than parents elsewhere in north London. 'They want a happy, stimulating, wide-ranging education for their children that won't turn them into nervous wrecks,' says the head. Pupils are often those who flourish in a more intimate, less pressured environment. 'When we looked at some of the bigger secondary school options, my son just hated the idea of them,' said one parent.

Entrance: Entrance is selective, but not unduly so. ('Pupils are admitted who are performing at or above the national average'). At 11+, considerable numbers from the state sector. Apply one year prior to entry, with a (flexible) closing date in December of year 6. A number of assessment days held in the spring, with applicants invited in in groups of about 20 for a two-hour assessment in English, maths and an informal interview with the head or deputy. 'It's quite relaxed. We want to find out how much they know and whether they'll fit in here and do well.' Those with 'scholarship potential' invited back to sit further papers or demonstrate skills in sport, music, art or drama. School does its best to balance the girl-boy mix, but still tilted 60:40 in favour of boys. Pupils at North Bridge House prep guaranteed entry at 11, but not at 13 (though they still get priority). Siblings, too, are favoured.

Exit: All leave after GCSEs, with plenty of advice and preparation (including interview practice) from year 10. Significant numbers to Camden School for Girls, Highgate, UCS, City, as well as to a range of sixth form and tutorial colleges (eg Woodhouse, DLD). In 2015, 15 per cent moved on to the new 13+ North Bridge senior school in Canonbury.

Money matters: Range of scholarships, academic, creative (art, music, performing arts) and sport. Limited number of bursaries, but schools does its best to support existing parents.

Remarks: An inclusive, nurturing school, which gets the best out of many children who would struggle in a larger pond.

Parliament Hill School

Linked school: LaSwap Sixth Form Consortium, 130

Highgate Road, London NW5 1RL

State • Pupils: 900 • Ages: 11–19 • Sixth form pupils: 550 in joint sixth form with William Ellis, part of LaSwap consortium

Tel: 020 7485 7077

Email: headteacher@parliamenthill.camden.sch.uk
Website: www.parliamenthill.camden.sch.uk

Headteacher: Since 2005, Ms Susan Higgins MA (Cantab) MA (Ed) (50s), previously head of Brentford School for Girls for five years. She studied English at New Hall (now Murray Edwards) College, Cambridge, after a peripatetic school career, as her family moved around the country. The first Oxbridge student from her Bradford comprehensive, she was enthused by 'an inspirational English teacher'. She was head of English at Walthamstow School for Girls for much of her career, taking time out to become deputy head at Skinners' Company's School for Girls in Hackney and spending time as a school-based PGCE tutor for the Institute of Education before returning to Walthamstow as deputy head. She has two children.

A strong and capable leader with a good back-up team. Parents say: 'I'm very impressed by her.... She's personable and engaging, with great people skills. She has a firm grasp of what needs to be done....The girls love hearing about her experience of going to Cambridge as a working class girl...She's a great role model for them.'

Academic matters: A huge ability range here, with lots of bright girls and also plenty in need of extra support, whether educational or emotional. Accordingly, the school offers a range of options. Everyone studies for a core of GCSE subjects which includes maths, English, core science, RE, and short courses in PE and citizenship. They can add on more GCSE subjects, or choose a vocational BTec from a range that includes business, art and design, ICT and health and social care, or go for a young apprenticeship. Most of the latter two options are taught elsewhere in Camden. Everyone is allocated to either French or Spanish classes for the first three years, and can start the other language in year 9; about a third take a modern language GCSE. Other popular options at KS4 include additional AS maths and triple science; ICT AS and photography GCSE are taught after school as twilight classes.

In 2015, 67 per cent of girls got 5+ A*-C grades including English and maths at GCSE; 35 per cent of grades were A*/A.. English has been very strong, maths and science historically rather weaker. However, maths now taught in ability sets from the second term in year 7, and the curriculum has been redesigned substantially. Girls arrive at the school with, on average, much higher verbal than non-verbal aptitude scores – 'but as a technology college we focus on building up their confidence and aptitude in maths and science'. The science department has appointed some very highly qualified teachers over the last few years. Triple science courses very popular, with excellent results. 'They're very good at assessing strengths and weaknesses,' said a parent, 'and throwing lots of energy at weaknesses.'

The head is reviewing all the schemes of work in key stage 3, including building in greater differentiation for ranges of ability –'in a comprehensive you have to keep revisiting this and doing it better'. Homework and marking – aspects raised by parents as sometimes inconsistent – are other key priorities. 'Every department has produced its own guidelines with clear expectations. Parents need to know these'. The latest Ofsted report, under the new, harsher regime, downgraded the school from outstanding to good, citing the gap in achievement between poorer

A scheme targets very able scientists, who take part in work experience and masterclasses

students and the rest. However, parents generally feel it still deserves an outstanding rating.

SEN provision has been 'transformed', with an assistant head leading the way on SEN and inclusion. Consultants brought in recently to review the provision were 'very positive'. Few state schools feel that they have sufficient funds to provide all the help every child needs, but 'we feel we've made substantial progress'. The Extra Mile project targets under-achieving year 10 girls, who are mostly from white low-income families.

Gifted and talented provision focuses on what goes on in lessons. 'In a comprehensive you've got to make sure you're providing stretch in the classroom. We get professionals in to make sure we're getting it right'. Also masterclasses and mentoring, and year 7 girls recently visited Murray Edwards College, Cambridge, to meet undergraduates and visit the zoology department. 'Many of our girls wouldn't naturally consider applying to a university like this. It's essential they have their aspirations raised'.

Joint sixth form with next-door William Ellis School, with co-ed tutor groups. It is also part of LaSwap, which includes La Sainte Union and Acland Burghley schools too, and has over 1,500 students. Each school teaches the core sixth form subjects, but students visit other schools in the group for more minority subjects eg film studies and further maths. The ability range encompasses those aspiring to read medicine at Cambridge and those working for an introductory BTec diploma in health and social care, with appropriate entry requirements. A scheme in conjunction with La Sainte Union targets very able scientists, who study together and take part in organised work experience and masterclasses. English is the most popular A level subject at Parliament Hill, with psychology second. In 2015, 16 per cent of grades were A*/A and 74 per cent A*-C.

Full programme of work experience, mentoring, higher education visits, workshops and presentations in collaboration with eg Matrix Chambers, Deloitte, Sky Broadcasting, British Library and Oxbridge.

Games, options, the arts: Everyone takes DT GCSE, with a choice of four options – year 7s were busy cooking muffins during our visit. The single storey DT block was built to an environmentally-friendly design with a green roof, and forms the fourth side of a grassy courtyard, twisting up to meet the original Edwardian building. On another corner of the building is the performing arts block, clad in green glass, which provides music rooms and dance and drama studios. The top floor corridors are lined with expressive GCSE and A level photography and artwork, and textile designs hang in the stairwells.

Music probably not the highest profile subject here, but many girls have instrumental lessons and play in the orchestra or in the jazz, string or brass ensembles, or sing in the choir. Those on free school meals get free music lessons. Two hours' timetabled PE a week for everyone. Two tennis/netball courts at the front of the school and a grassy area at the back where the football teams practise, plus a rather ageing hall for gym and badminton with a fitness suite. On the wish-list is a new sports hall. All year 7s learn to swim at Swiss Cottage baths and the head hopes in future to make more use of the Lido, which is more or less next door. Sports teams play successful matches against other Camden schools.

Is at last – hooray – in receipt of £19.2m to rebuild the well-past-its-sell-by-date Heath Building ('we're all going to lean against it until it falls over,' promised head)

A breakfast club every morning at 8am and plenty more activities ranging from Italian and chess clubs to basketball and rounders. Plenty of opportunities to perform, in musicals such as the 'excellent and ambitious' production of The Wiz, dance shows and music concerts. They visit museums, theatres and galleries, travel to China and go on physics trips to Switzerland. D of E very popular, as is debating – many students have competed passionately in the Urban Debating League and the Debate Mate Cup.

Background and atmosphere: Opened in 1906, has an idyllic site on the edge of Hampstead Heath. Plenty of grassy space, including a sculpture park and kick-around area. Buildings range from solid Edwardiana to the 21st century award-winning DT and performing arts blocks. Is at last – hooray – in receipt of £19.2 million to rebuild the well-past-its-sell-by-date Heath Building ('we're all going to lean against it until it falls over,' promised head when we visited) which houses maths, English, science, canteen and library.

Harmonious atmosphere. Despite the huge range of pupils, both ethnically and socially, girls tend to get on well together, with few reports of bullying. Recently one of six in the country to win a Diamond quality mark for cultural diversity. 'They manage the mix very well,' said a parent.

Pastoral care and discipline: Many vulnerable pupils here, including refugees and those with learning difficulties, who get 'excellent' support, says Ofsted. Liaises with its feeder primary school to identify girls likely to be in need of extra help with making the transition to senior school. It works with outside agencies that provide therapy or counselling to those in need, including Kids Company, with a designated key worker in school. It also runs many programmes to motivate disaffected pupils, stretch the aspirations of bright girls and ensure everyone gets a chance to broaden their horizons. Assertive classroom management keeps most lessons running without disruptions.

Older girls are allowed to go out onto Hampstead Heath at lunchtimes, together with pupils from nearby schools, William Ellis and La Sainte Union, and locals have complained about litter problems. 'We're very concerned. The girls regard the Heath as very special to them, and we're doing work on social responsibility to educate them that it's for everyone in the community'.

Pastoral care is very good, report parents. 'I've always felt they know my daughter very well,' said one. 'They've contacted me whenever they've had concerns, and they've dealt with any problems quickly and well.'

Pupils and parents: 'Amazingly diverse' student population speaks some 50 different languages at home, though few are at early stages of learning English. Over 200 refugees. Nearly half of the girls are on free school meals, but also good support from some local middle-class families. OGs include actress Katrin Cartlidge, BBC journalist Laura Trevelyan and Lola Young, Baroness Young of Hornsey.

Entrance: Takes 180 girls into year 7, with admissions organised by the LA. Priority for particular SEN, siblings, children in care and those with exceptional social needs. Then by distance – generally within a mile and a half. Those joining LaSwap sixth form to do A levels must have at least eight GCSE passes including three C and two B grades; various vocational courses available for those with lower grades.

Exit: Between two-thirds and three-quarters of pupils move on to joint sixth form with William Ellis school, part of LaSwap sixth form consortium. Some join other sixth forms, eg Camden School for Girls or Woodhouse College, others go to colleges such as City and Islington or Westminster Kingsway to do vocational courses.

One or two a year to Oxbridge, one in 2015. Around a quarter to Russell Group universities, London universities, Sussex, Nottingham and Leeds popular for a range of subjects – eg biomedical science, pharmacy, physics, languages, history, English, architecture and psychology. Quite a few to art foundation courses.

Remarks: Popular girls' comprehensive in idyllic situation on the borders of Hampstead Heath, with a diverse but harmonious student population. Strong, popular head who is a driving force in building on strengths and tackling weaknesses. 'My daughter has been so happy there that she has become an ambassador for her school,' said a parent.

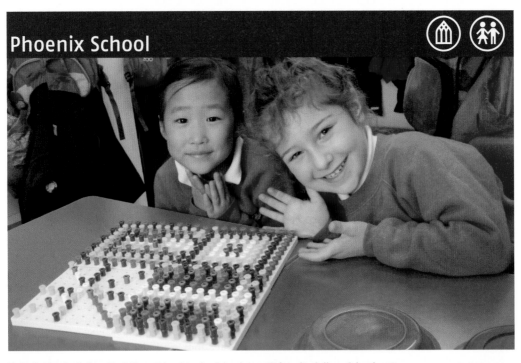

Phoenix School

Linked schools: University College School Junior School, 197; University College School, 198

36 College Crescent, London NW3 5LF

Independent · Pupils: 130 · Ages: 3–7 · Fees: £13,935 pa

Tel: 020 7722 4433

Email: thephoenix@ucs.org.uk
Website: www.ucs.org.uk/the-phoenix-school

17

Headmistress: Since September 2015, Dr Zoe Dunn, previously founding head of the Rimon Jewish Free Primary School. BEd from Homerton College Cambridge, PhD, NPHQ.

Entrance: Two main entries, each taking a balance of boys and girls. The afternoon nursery class takes children whose 3rd birthday falls between September and December. Approximately 20 places are offered for the nursery classes, attending for five mornings and two afternoon sessions. Register in January 18 months before admission. Most places go to siblings or to those with University College School (UCS) connections. Occasional vacancies at

4+, 5+ or 6+; prospective pupils are invited for a half-day assessment.

Exit: Most boys go to UCS Junior School at 7, subject to passing the entrance exam. Girls are also expected to stay till they are 7 and most move on to South Hampstead High's or Highgate's junior departments. A few pupils to eg Westminster Under School, North London Collegiate, North Bridge House, Academy School.

Remarks: Was purchased by the UCS foundation in 2002 as its pre-prep and benefits from sharing the funding and facilities. Compact site up above the Finchley Road near Swiss Cottage, which nevertheless includes a hall, art room, music room, library and playgrounds with sandpits, climbing frame and Wendy house, as well as classrooms. Children also use the UCS junior branch ICT suite and the senior school swimming pool and theatre, and spend an afternoon a week at the UCS playing fields in West Hampstead.

Specialist music, art and PE teachers. Before and after-school clubs include ballet, yoga, taekwondo, Mandarin and art. Plenty of visitors and trips to eg museums and art galleries.

Can cope with mild special needs, eg dyslexia. Though not a hothouse – 'we don't do never-ending practice exam papers' – it has a strong academic focus and prepares well for the next stage.

Portland Place School

56–58 Portland Place, London W1B 1NJ

Tel: 020 7307 8700

Independent • Pupils: 429 • Ages: 9–18 • Sixth form pupils: 100 • Fees: £18,990 pa

Email: admin@portland-place.co.uk
Website: www.portland-place.co.uk

Headmaster: Since January 2015, Mr David Hyman, previously academic deputy head. BSc mathematics and management studies from the Royal Holloway College; PGCE in secondary mathematics education from Bath University. Has also been joint head of maths at Tomlinscote Secondary School in Camberley, deputy head of maths at Epsom and Ewell High School and assistant headteacher at Hinchley Wood Secondary School. Enjoys playing and watching sport, theatre and experiencing different countries and cultures on various family holidays.

Academic matters: A broader band of ability than in most of the fiercely competitive London day schools

– something the school takes pride in and, together with its small class sizes, sees as a 'unique selling point.' Only 12 in a class in years 5 and 6, an average of 15 in years 7 to 11 (we saw several smaller ones) and smaller still in the sixth form means that attention can be given to each child – you can be sure that there will be both stretching and confidence building. A godsend for the discerning parent who can see through the merry-go-round nature of 11+ and wants to ensure their child is educated rather than exam-processed. Hence the increasing demand for places lower down the school; there is now one class in year 5 as well as two in year 6. Piles on the value added – 'We're always near the top of the value added tables' is the boast.

No Latin or Greek at GCSE ('there isn't the demand from our parents,' we were told). Economics, computing, sport studies and media are offered, along with the traditional subjects. All pupils take at least one of French, Italian or Spanish, not much enthusiasm for taking up a second modern language. If your daughter speaks Italian at home, she is encouraged to do Spanish as her GCSE option. If you want your child to take a GCSE in, for example, Arabic, the school will facilitate it within the timetable, but the onus of paying and finding the teacher is on you.

At GCSE, 85 per cent achieved five or more A*-C including English and maths, 35 per cent of grades A*/A in 2015. The value added shows at A level, where the results are more impressive, most being in the B-D bracket, with a decent sprinkling of As (19 per cent A*/A grades and 48 per cent A*/B in 2015). We saw small tutor groups of as few as five – notably these were in science subjects. Clever ones, with offers from Oxbridge as well other Russell Group universities. Arts subjects tend to be busier (up to 15 in a group). Library manned by full-time librarian and a nice place to sit and read. Lots of fiction, used for competitions, book club and quiet study. As an academic resource it is risible (school prefers 'needs developing' and reminds us that the individual heads of departments keep library resources in their offices). Good IT suites and resources for the popular media and film options.

Setting in maths, science and English from year 7. Plenty of movement between sets, we were

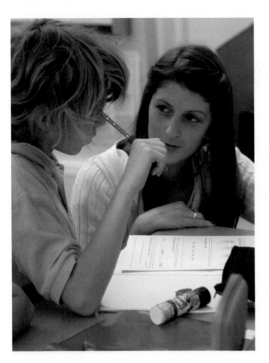

A second building has a breathtaking eyeball-to-eyeball view of the BT Tower, seemingly within grabbing distance

assured. Sizeable number of mild dyslexics but no additional support in lessons apart from general support from class teacher. Staunch policy of no withdrawals from classes (except once weekly for children who have EAL). School employs four specialist learning support teachers who will arrange to see children outside lesson time in groups of two or three to devise strategies to help them access the mainstream curriculum. No screening on admission. However SENCo oversees general provision and monitoring – 80 to 90 children perceived as having some kind of mild learning disability or difficulty and some have IEPs. Most with more than the mildest difficulties seek support outside school. Inside school, the attitude is healthy – 'I'm not treated as if dyslexia is a crime, unlike at my last school,' we were told. Two of the three buildings have lifts but school will be helpful if someone breaks a leg and move lessons to the ground floor.

Games, options, the arts: Well known for sporting prowess despite there being virtually no facilities on site. Pupils are bussed or walk everywhere – mostly to Regent's Park, with pitches and courts of all kinds, Seymour Place for swimming – and the results and achievements, given the conditions, are impressive. Years 7 to 9 have sport timetabled four times a week (one of the advantages of no canteen and shorter lunch breaks: time can be reallocated to sport). Football and netball tours of Barbados, swimming teams win competitions (Westminster champions five years in a row), masses of medals in cross-country and local honours in athletics and team sports. Pervasive pride in school sports, helped, no doubt, by classy Olympians on staff. However most really keen sportsmen and women do their serious sport outside school – girls' football a particular highpoint. Sport now compulsory to year 12 – one afternoon a week minimum of netball or football.

Music and drama similarly 'massive.' Music mostly means pop and jazz (we saw lots of ukulele enthusiasts). There are also a few violinists and woodwinders amongst the jazz pianists, guitarists, drummers and bassists who predominate, but eclectic range of music taken seriously. We were shown round by a budding actor in year 10 who enthused about the opportunities he has been given to develop his talent. Wholehearted, whole school productions annually – West Side Story, Singing in the

Rain, The Producers and Annie are recent offerings; not on-site as no suitable space but venues include The RADA Studios in WC1. Upper school recently performed a resoundingly successful Richard III – which was then a sell-out at the Edinburgh Fringe. Lower school (up to year 9) most recently performed Skellig as their annual production. Good-sized on-site drama studio can accommodate smaller productions (we were impressed with the assortment of costumes and props).

Art in the lower school is lively and inventive. We saw ink portraits in the style of Peter Howson, as well as Pop Art-style Creme Eggs. Fewer than 10 do art A level – facilities limited, though there is a textiles room and school excels in photography. DT similarly energetic – resistant materials, pewter casting, CAD and CAM, though all in rather small and poky rooms in basement. Lots of extracurricular stuff – when we visited a stress management workshop was being delivered to all GCSE students. Trips galore – we have seldom seen such a full programme. Much use made of London's galleries, museums and exhibitions, plus the nearby wider world and the opportunities it offers for field, sporting and other educational exercises, both here and abroad.

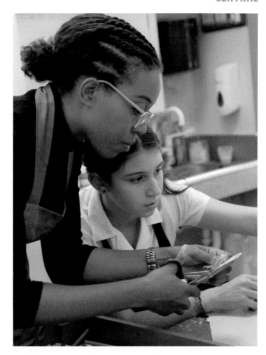

Background and atmosphere: This is a young school, founded only 20 or so years ago by the visionary head of science at St Paul's Girls', Richard Walker. His aim was to create a smaller independent co-ed senior school that wasn't super selective. Part of the Alpha Plus group, it forms one of their 19 UK schools and colleges, bringing the advantages of the economies of scale. Portland Place – the road – is a broad, straight thoroughfare in the heart of regency London, two minutes from Oxford Circus to the south, two minutes to Regent's Park to the north. It is lined by august embassies (China, Kenya, Poland, Portugal) and the HQs of royal and learned institutions (architects, physicists, radiologists, anaesthetists). The main school building – Portland Place – identifies itself with a modest brass plate and is elegantly splendid. It is rare for us to compliment a school on its decor but a pleasure to do so here. Eye-catching blue carpet up and down the stairs (not just on the ground floor for show as elsewhere), magnificent ceilings, cornices, columns, capitals and fireplaces: nowhere more so than in the old ballroom, rescued from its carapace of false ceiling and fluorescent tubes and very much in use. All in tip-top nick. This building houses the lower years, the hall (used for gym and dance) and the top floors (formerly the servants' quarters) accommodate music and languages.

A second building in Great Portland Street, five minutes away, houses the upper years and has a breathtaking eyeball-to-eyeball view of the BT Tower, seemingly within grabbing distance.

Harford House, also in Great Portland Street and with a facade resembling that of a corporate HQ, is home to art, drama and science. It's a logistical nightmare – five or seven storeys to be up and down all day, three buildings and it all has to be timetabled, supervised and navigated. We suppose everyone to be very fit – a real bonus for children who need lots of movement and exercise if they are to perform well mentally.

No school kitchen. Pupils bring packed lunches or order in from local cafés (which deliver dozens of paninis etc in little brown carriers). Years 10 and 11 and the sixth hang out in the many cafés in or around Great Portland Street and just love the privilege of this kind of freedom.

Pastoral care and discipline: Definitely an informal feel to the place. Although not quite on first name terms with teachers, one can sense an equality in the relationships not seen in more traditional establishments. Good use of sixth form mentors for years 7 and 8 – really fosters inter-age group understanding and friendships, especially helpful in so small a school. Solidly structured pastoral care hierarchy picks up and deals with problems. but there's a pervasive sense of everyone looking out for everyone else. People seem to know each other's little brothers and sisters here. Parents praise the home-school communications and especially the termly parents' evenings. 'The teachers are mostly young and energetic,' enthused a parent, 'and you really get to know them.'

Pupils and parents: More boys than girls (about 60:40 in lower years) – simply because there are so many more girls' and co-ed schools in London. Mixed, as befits its location – trad, moneyed independent education veterans alongside newbies and newcomers from here, there and everywhere, blended with those who couldn't get into the 'academic' schools and for whom PP has been a jolly lucky find. From the whole urban sprawl – no longer just the north and west but around 30 per cent from east and south too. Mostly UK born and based but also from pretty much the rest of the globe, solar system and beyond, in a great undivided family. Brains? Yes, though common denominator more palpably pleasure, pride and enthusiasm for the place.

Entrance: There are 9+ and 10+ intakes – partly to steal a march on the competition and partly to meet the needs of those who dread the 11+ circus and will do anything to avoid it (wise move). 'Informal tests' in English and maths with deputy/head of year. Year 7 has tests in English and maths and a chat with a teacher. For places at 12+, 13+ and 14+ – same format plus additional test in science. School keen to dispel image that it's the go-to place for a child

on the dys-strata. Child has to be able to cope and pupils who can't will be turned down. A few join at year 12, on flexible terms. They come, at 11, from a large number of schools – state and independent.

Exit: Wide range of post-A level destinations and courses, including sports and exercise science, mechanical engineering and forensic investigations at the newer universities. The odd one to study music and to art college; London and Sussex universities particularly popular. About 30 per cent leave after GCSE (mostly to non-fee paying sixth form colleges).

Money matters: Five scholarships for academic, music, drama, sports and art. All worth 25 per cent of fees. No bursaries.

Remarks: Small, nurturing and refreshingly relaxed. A haven of creativity in the pushy academically competitive world of London day schools. A place for engaged, lively, normal kids – privileged, yes, but Sloanes, no. Becoming ever more popular as more and more people discover it. The challenge will be to maintain its ethos of 'broader academic intake' in the face of increasing demand.

Queen's College Prep School

Linked school: Queen's College London, 155

61 Portland Place, London W1B 1QP

Independent • Pupils: 210 • Ages: 4–11 • C of E • Fees: up to £15,690 pa

Tel: 020 7291 0660

Email: info@qcps.org.uk
Website: www.qcps.org.uk/

55

Headmistress: Since 2008, Mrs Annie Dempsey BA Cert Ed. A history graduate and specialist English teacher, she has wide experience in preparatory and secondary education. Previously head of St Dunstan's College Junior School, a co-ed independent which she took from 'good' to 'outstanding.' Her own two daughters have been through the London day school system and now work in the City. Parents describe her as 'efficient, very clear and empathetic' and are full of praise for her achievements, 'Under her guidance the school has gone from strength to strength,' we were told.

Smart and engaging, with a gentle manner, head is well established and fully committed to her role. She is proud of the school and cares deeply that her charges become 'well-grounded, well-mannered, with the ability to make relationships.' She is keen that whilst pupils are at school they learn 'how to

think and what not to think.' Has created a very strong management team, including male deputy head (academic), and male assistant head (pastoral care and administration). 'Head greets every child daily by name,' said an appreciative parent, valuing how well she knows each girl. Parents feel pupils are thoroughly prepared for the entrance examination procedure. 'We have received excellent guidance – spot on,' said another. 'We had regular meetings and if we needed more detail there has been flexibility and an open door.' Head said: 'It's about finding where her soul's going to sing.'

Entrance: Most children join in the September after their 4th birthday. No formal assessment but entry to reception involves a parental interview with the headmistress. Two forms in every year, with an average of 16 in a class. Entry to all other year groups (if places become available) involves an assessment of the child's academic achievement and potential, an evaluation of social skills and school reports, plus a parental interview. Two open mornings, by appointment only, are held each term and parents who have registered are invited to attend.

There is no one main feeder as pupils come from a wide range of nurseries in north London. They include Broadhurst, the Liberal Jewish Synagogue Nursery School, Hope Montessori, Marylebone Village Nursery, Great Beginnings and the Windmill Montessori Nursery School. The catchment area includes Marylebone, Regent's Park, St John's Wood, Maida Vale, Mayfair, Fitzrovia, Little Venice, Hampstead and Islington. Pupils are international, multi-cultural, multi-faith, with majority living locally and with English as their first language. 'We love a family,' says the head.

Exit: 'We prepare for choice,' says the head – and the results show a variety of destinations, with around 40 per cent choosing the senior school (all by competitive entrance examination so the Queen's College Prep candidates on a level playing field with outsiders). Girls regularly win academic, art and music scholarships. London girls' day schools are popular choices, including both Francis Hollands, Channing, City of London School for Girls, South Hampstead High, Godolphin and Latymer, North London Collegiate and St Paul's Girls' School. A few head for boarding at Cheltenham Ladies' College and Downe House.

Remarks: This small, traditional girls' day school is well situated, very close to Regent's Park. 'Surroundings really matter,' the head told us and her study with its soothing, grey and cream décor provides a calm setting for dealing with parents

and daily concerns. School is housed in two tall Adam buildings – ornate ceilings and ground floor classrooms with columns and fireplaces. All attractively light and bright.

Her study provides a calm setting for dealing with parents and daily concerns

The imaginative use of space and excellent modern resources work well, from the ICT suite to the transformed first floor drawing room (with sprung floor for dance, drama and fencing). Basement has a well-lit music room, dining room and gym. It was good to see girls enjoying reading in the well-stocked library (with part-time librarian). Older pupils can bring Kindles in for leisure reading. Something of an Aladdin's cave when you climb up past the big, bright science room to art studio on the top floor. Large windows, with great views of nearby roof-tops, fill the room with light. Good to see younger pupils creating colourful Elmer-inspired elephants – freely drawn rather than using templates. No kiln, but girls produce batiks in the senior school. Senior school theatre used for top year productions and All Souls Church at Langham Place for harvest and carol services.

School offers a broad curriculum. Each day begins and ends with form teachers – to help pupils organise themselves and their homework. Mornings are dedicated to English and maths and the timetable has been constructed to build in time for travel to various sports facilities nearby. Older pupils have longer days on Tuesdays, Wednesdays and Thursdays. Specialists from reception up for music, French, PE, ballet and musical theatre. Specialist art from year 1, Latin from year 5 and study skills in year 6.

Rather than girls going out of class for individual learning support lessons, the emphasis is placed on differentiation in small classes. Recently appointed male SENCo manages the department, reporting to the deputy head, and there is a clear policy with procedures in place to identify girls with SEN as early as possible. Outside specialists for speech therapy, occupational therapy and dyslexia – by arrangement with parents. Head informs parents on entry that girls must be able to access the curriculum on offer and told us: 'This is the right school as long as we can meet their needs.'

Parents are full of praise for the high standard of teaching and care taken to cater for individuals. The small class sizes help, along with the use of teaching assistants (unusually up to year 4). Underpinning it all, however, is an effective, carefully honed monitoring system for pupils' progress – implemented by the management team and used to share information at regular meetings. Parents told us: 'The girls are happy as they are treated as individuals and there is an excellent balance between academic and life experiences.'

Vibrant displays, and imaginative artwork act as a stimulus for learning and celebrate the pupils'

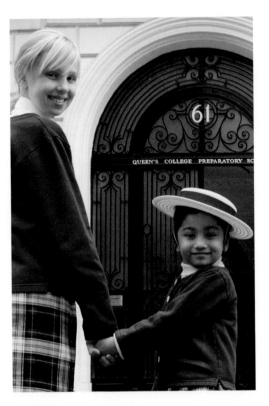

We loved the walk-in mermaid's cave for an 'under the sea' topic in year 1

achievements. We loved the walk-in mermaid's cave for an 'under the sea' topic in year 1, complete with relevant books on display. 'The teachers really take trouble,' a parent said, adding that teachers dressed up as astronauts during a recent project about space.

The pupils we spoke to felt very well supported and encouraged by the reward system (includes head's commendations and house points). Setting in maths and, where appropriate, English from year 3. This works well. We saw enthusiastic teaching, with girls focused, challenged and thoroughly enjoying their learning.

School takes full advantage of cultural opportunities and there are two class trips every half term. A parent told us: 'For me this makes up for other areas as like other inner London prep schools, there are limitations to sports provision.' Having said that, the girls get a very wide and varied diet of sports, including tag rugby and football. They also use nearby Regent's Park and other sports venues across London (some form of physical activity timetabled each day for the older children). Younger pupils enjoy a lovely private garden across the way. Tennis is not in the curriculum. Enthusiastic PE staff run sessions at weekends and are willing to try out new ventures (trampolining when we visited). Head wants the girls to work hard and play hard. Music and dance are very popular, with vast numbers seizing opportunities to learn instruments, sing and attend the dance academy that operates after school and in the holidays.

At morning break older girls socialise in the dining room, and at lunch times there are organised activities to enable them to relax, have fun and mix. We watched a lunchtime marimba ensemble rehearsal. Girls concentrated hard and produced delightful syncopated African rhythms alongside their enthusiastic teacher. The energetic dance teacher runs a variety of classes from ballet and jazz to street dancing and tap and the girls love it. The performing arts are a real strength of this school.

Confidence is a key word and is nurtured and developed throughout girls' time here. All the pupils we spoke to during our visit were polite, well mannered and happy. In lessons they readily explained what they were doing and were eager to throw themselves into activities, finding mathematics fun as they devised and budgeted for their own theme park or discussed performance poetry and how to communicate with an audience. They understand the importance of being kind, showing mutual respect to their teachers and each other. They are mindful of the code of conduct (present in every classroom and emphasised in assemblies taken by the head).

Active parents' circle for fundraising and social events. Parents are encouraged to be involved, with two form representatives for each year. Communication with parents is excellent. Alongside the usual there's a general weekly newsletter. The school has also introduced specific year group newsletters with valuable curriculum information, key dates, details of pupils' achievements and splendid photographs.

Food is prepared in the senior school and parents complimentary about the weekly menu. The parent of a daughter with allergies felt very supported by the school. Smart uniform; only niggle expressed by parents was that they'd like winter hats to be reintroduced (girls love their summer boaters).

Parents told us that this is a school 'that raises the bar.' They praised 'the quality of education, staff retention, creativity and happy children' and said that above all it's a place 'that takes genuine pride in its charges and allows each individual to flourish.'

Queen's College London

Linked school: Queen's College Prep School, 152

43–49 Harley Street, London W1G 8BT

Independent • Pupils: 360 • Ages: 11–18 • Sixth form pupils: 65 • C of E • Fees: £16,860 pa

Tel: 020 7291 7000

Email: admissions@qcl.org.uk
Website: www.qcl.org.uk

56

Principal: Since 2009, Dr Frances Ramsey MA DPhil (Oxon) (40s). Completed doctorate in medieval history before starting teaching. Taught at Westminster School, where she was head of history and director of studies. Discovered the importance of the pastoral side when she became Master of the Queen's Scholars. Cerebral and professional, she is determined to lead the school onwards and

upwards. Says it has the same feel and ethos as Westminster and parents and staff feel familiar. All the latter have full lives beyond day-to-day teaching, which she thinks is important. Very much likes the all girl set up – 'no distraction in the classroom'.

'The school has a certain quirkiness and it is important that this is not ironed out,' say parents. They are impressed with 'the buzz of the school and the direction it is going in'. There were mixed reactions from parents to the introduction of uniform for years 7 to 9, mainly because they didn't want general informality of the school to change. But, as Dr Ramsey is a firm believer in 'evolution not revolution', we don't feel they need to worry and the change was enthusiastically welcomed by prospective parents. She misses having the time to teach but makes sure that she is as visible as possible, taking assembly twice a week, having coffee/tea meetings with the senior girls and congratulating younger ones who bring her their 'show principal' reward cards. Is also seen at all school performances. She interviews all the parents of new applicants and the school maintains a continuous open door policy (parents tell us that they can go in and go anywhere any time they like), so she is not inaccessible.

Married to an Oxford academic, with two children in central London schools. We think that Queen's College is lucky to have her.

Academic matters: Excellent results across the board, with a curriculum that covers a broad range of subjects and is as strong on the creative side as the academic. Parents say: 'Well structured, but girls don't feel it is rigid and therefore thrive on it. Art is taken as seriously as maths.' Dr Ramsey has upped the academic ante, increasing the number of subjects taken as IGCSE and bringing in triple science for the top set. She says that despite the school not being super selective, the girls are all

Parents say: 'Well structured, but girls don't feel it is rigid and therefore thrive. Art taken as seriously as maths'

able and ambitious. In 2015, 74 per cent of GCSE grades were A*/A. Parents say the school 'embraces a girl's whole brain'; is 'sympathetic, understanding and supportive'. All agree that the school is not a hothouse, the atmosphere is relaxed, yet it manages to bring out the potential in all girls, academic or artistic.

Teachers praised for their dedication and support. The director of studies, one of the good proportion of males on the staff, is bright and approachable and was appointed to oversee academic developments. Appears to cater well for different types of children, guiding them towards opportunities. No EFL tuition but will give support for EAL if necessary. Small classes in the sixth form (average eight) are, a parent said, 'the jewel in the crown'. A huge range of subjects available to be studied, including several languages. Maths, English literature, history and biology seem the most popular. In 2015, 47 per cent A*/A grades at A level.

Popular, fully trained and experienced SENCo four days a week. Can cope with the milder end of the spectrum. All children assessed in year 7 and extra tuition given where necessary. Deputy head says head of English superb at finding any problems – in fact, all teachers good at spotting and communicating concerns: 'Nobody gets through the net'. Classroom assistants not needed as class sizes small (15-20 in years 7-11) and varied. Parents kept fully in the picture – communication lines are good.

Games, options, the arts: As in many town schools, physical activity an ongoing problem, but one they do seem to have cracked here. Head of PE has completely reorganised the system and all girls have at least one sport-type session four days a week. Could be gymnastics, in a beautifully refurbished, fully-equipped hall, ballet, seasonal games in Regent's Park, swimming or anything else that demands physical activity. In fact, when we were discussing the school uniform issue, one parent suggested that they didn't really need to bother as 'my daughter seems to wear her sports kit most days!' Lots of matches played against other schools and the Duke of Edinburgh award is a popular option. Senior girls can go to the University of Westminster gym for exercise or pilates and yoga type classes. Very grown-up.

Wonderful pictures on display everywhere. Well-equipped art room up in the eaves (north lit, of course), showing coverage of all aspects of the subject. We were fascinated by a huge sculpture made of wire coat hangers. Talented head of art develops ability and encourages imagination, as is evidenced by their results. Music from beginner to grade 8. About 50 per cent learn an individual instrument or have voice tuition. Several concerts, formal and informal, and musical ensembles each year, as well as musical theatre productions and opera. Enthusiastic head of drama finds many different ways to stimulate and stretch her students such as The Crucible being performed in the round – an exciting first. This school is not scared of experiment or innovation.

Wouldn't those early Victorian students be amazed to see the glass computer room, 'the goldfish bowl', so cleverly integrated, science and language laboratories

Clubs abound and take place in the middle of the day as well as at the end. Each day is jam-packed with activity. Lots of girls stay late on Tuesdays to attend the thriving running club. No excuse for any girl ever to sit twiddling her thumbs. Plenty of outings making use of all London has to offer. Regular trips home and abroad, both educational and social. Lots of charitable involvement and fundraising activities.

Background and atmosphere: Founded in 1848 and given a royal charter in 1853, a pioneer in education for women, this was the first institution in Great Britain to give academic qualifications to girls. Still on its original site in four elegant, well-proportioned Georgian houses, internally it has often been altered through the years in order to provide the best modern education possible. Wouldn't those early Victorian students be amazed to see the glass computer room, 'the goldfish bowl', so cleverly integrated, science and language laboratories beyond their imaginations, the wonderful libraries and the great hall, where modern lighting and sound equipment helps to enhance perhaps almost recognisable costume dramas? They would certainly enjoy the more relaxed atmosphere and the idea of learning through discovery rather than rote. Teachers who really care and want to help their pupils to learn and discover in an informal way. A happy atmosphere in the school today that gives girls confidence and helps them find their own way forward.

Two of the earliest students, Miss Buss and Miss Beale, went on to found the North London Collegiate School and Camden School for Girls, and St Hilda's College Oxford, respectively. Katherine Mansfield and Jacqueline du Pré also stand amongst the long list of distinguished old girls as well as, more recently, writers Daisy Goodwin and Imogen Lloyd Webber. A distinguished tradition and history in the making.

Pastoral care and discipline: Dr Ramsey has added a layer of pastoral staff, giving, she believes, better co-ordination and consistency. Girls have a year tutor as well as a form tutor, so should always have someone to talk to if necessary and should not slip through the net if difficulties arise. Has also introduced mid-term mini reports in every subject, 'a quick reality check', as she calls them, which should help highlight potential academic problems. Apparently the girls have responded well to this idea. Strong anti-bullying policy – would not hesitate to exclude an offender.

Pupils and parents: The usual cosmopolitan London mix of nationalities and backgrounds. About 10 per cent don't speak English at home.

Entrance: Mainly at 11+ via the North London consortium exam. Must also have reference from previous school and be interviewed by the principal or a senior member of staff. A good percentage from Queen's College Prep, about 25 per cent from local state primaries, the rest from other private preps. Another intake at 16+ subject to GCSE results and letters of recommendation from their previous schools. All prospective entrants at this level interviewed by the head of sixth form.

Exit: Around 30 per cent leave after GCSEs, mostly for co-ed sixth forms. A levels leavers to top universities (one to Oxbridge in 2015) eg Edinburgh, Leeds, Manchester, Nottingham, UCL, York, to study everything from art and design to science subjects.

Money matters: Several means-tested bursaries available at 11+ and 16+, funded by the Old Queen's bursary trust fund. Academic, music and art scholarships, for up to 25 per cent of fees, for both internal and external candidates. Would hope always to be able to find a way of keeping a pupil in need.

Remarks: A happy, rounded school where girls are encouraged to be individuals in an informal, unstressful environment; where nurturing teachers bring out the best in them and help them to find their own paths; where they develop confidence and a desire to succeed. Where being yourself is respected and really matters.

St Anthony's Preparatory School

90 Fitzjohn's Avenue, London NW3 6NP

Tel: 020 7431 1066

Independent • Pupils: 295 • Ages: 4–13 • RC • Fees: up to £17,160 pa

Email: gill.hooper@stanthonysprep.co.uk
Website: www.stanthonysprep.org.uk

Headmaster: Since 2010, Paul Keyte MA. Educated at Bloxham and Oriel College, Oxford, where he read philosophy and theology, graduating with a first. Fell into teaching during his postgraduate research (on Wittgenstein and Kierkegaard). 'I thought I'd teach for a couple of years before going back,' he says, but, instead, became hooked. Started out at Dulwich, where he taught philosophy and RE, before becoming head of liberal studies. Then to King's College Wimbledon, where he set up the philosophy and RE department and was under master (pastoral). 'You have to understand the shadow side, the theft and the bullying.' Then, senior master academic at Winchester and director of studies, deputy head at Highgate and at South Hampstead.

St Anthony's is his first prep school. ('I was attracted to the job because it was big enough to be interesting yet small enough for me to be a father.') An undoubted enthusiast, he remains passionate about teaching ('I feel anchored in the classroom'), and continues to teach RS to year 8 and 'learning enrichment' to all. Knows virtually all his pupils by name. A convert to Catholicism and married to a Catholic (who teaches at South Hampstead), he has one son (now at the school). Outside (and often imported) interests include singing, Schubert ('I learnt German to understand it

better'), musicals and Leeds United (much to his pupils' amusement). Energetic, enthusiastic and intellectual, yet accessible, parents feel fortunate to have him. 'He's incredibly supportive and gracious,' said one parent. 'He's the reason we chose the school,' said another.

Entrance: Two form entry at reception. Tour, then register, as early as possible. Some assessment places reserved for Catholics, who also get priority on waiting lists. All boys are interviewed. 'I'm looking for teachability and sociability,' says Mr Keyte. 'They have to be able to cope with the pace and adapt to our style of teaching. We're not competitive, but we're famous for creating independent learners.' Boys from about 25 feeder nurseries, but Catholics have often attended nearby St Mary's and St Christina's in St John's Wood.

Exit: In large numbers to UCS, City and Mill Hill, then everywhere with chunks to Highgate, Haberdashers' and Merchant Taylors', a solid sprinkling to Westminster and St Paul's, as well as to leading boarding schools (Eton, Oundle and Ampleforth). Plenty of scholarships, including for sport and music. No one is ever asked to leave. 'That's our duty, once they're here,' says the head. Occasionally, some may decide that the academic pace is not for them and are 'gently helped' to find somewhere else.

Remarks: The head's heavyweight presence sets the tone and is a good match with the school's highly qualified staff (many with Oxbridge degrees and interesting first careers).The school is split into two sites across the road from each other, each with its own spacious Victorian building. In the junior school (reception to year 3), you'll find a sweeping staircase, turn-of-the-century tiling, large light classrooms and a good-sized dining room (which doubles as an assembly and concert hall). Class size is kept to a maximum of 16-20. Specialist subject teaching in French and music from reception. Mandarin from year 1. 'We aim to send them from the junior school happy and well adjusted, able to cope with the demands of exams,' says the head. 'We're building the personality rather than drilling.' But skills are thoroughly inculcated. 'In the junior years,' said one mother of two, 'the teaching is very precise. They really get the handwriting and spelling under control, which reaps benefits as they get older.'

The head has tripled the number of music lessons and managed to acquire a baby grand

---

In year 4, a move to the senior school (years 4-8) is accompanied by greater subject specialisation, more male teachers and recently renovated premises. Some setting in maths, flexible setting elsewhere. No scholarship set, but plenty of 'learning enrichment.' 'Exams require sophisticated skills and we introduce enrichment early on,' says the head. Philosophy, Latin, Greek and Arabic all on offer. The head also runs lunch-hour discussion groups which any boy can attend. Parents feel he has got a firm grip on the rapidly changing exam landscape. 'The school used to be not quite as rigorous,' said one mother, 'but now the head is really on top of it.'

Good support for SEN with two specialists, one with expertise in dyscalculia. Sophisticated early screening identifies those who may require additional support. Discreet withdrawal to two small bright dedicated classrooms for those who struggle as well as those who need stretch.

The arts, now as always, remain core to what this school is about. The head has tripled the number of music lessons and managed to acquire a baby grand as well as introduce a music studio. 'My head of music says, "No boy leaves here who couldn't do grade 5 theory",' he says happily. A fair

number are gifted musicians, one carrying off a recent Eton music scholarship, another singing with the ENO. Outside school hours, boys are given plenty of encouragement with the school providing the weekend venue for Trinity Laban's by-audition-only classes. Other art forms not neglected, with a big annual Shakespeare production and two weeks of film-making post common entrance. A wide range of hobbies and clubs – logic and puzzle, general knowledge, chess, dance, touch typing – cover a range of enthusiasms (the lunch-time chess players packed out one classroom on our visit).

Not traditionally known as a 'sporty school', but the head is keen to give sport an increasingly important role. 'This is one area I'm working on developing. I'm passionate about what sport brings to children.' Traditional carousel of rugby, football, hockey, cricket, played twice weekly at Brondesbury, a 10-minute coach ride away. On site, the school has its own pool and two good-sized playgrounds. At St Anthony's, however, sport is as much about taking part as winning, with as many boys as possible participating. 'I'd rather the boys lost nobly and honourably than win for the sake of it. But there's nothing wrong with really nice sportsmen who get gold medals.'

As a family-owned prep school founded in the 19th century, St Anthony's was run in its own highly individual way, with a famously alternative 'vibe', creative and quirky, underpinned by a strong Catholic ethos. Parents felt concern when the school was taken over by the efficient operator Alpha Plus, but have found that a professional distance has been kept, while judicious investment has brought the infrastructure into tip-top shape.

The only all-boys Catholic prep school in north London (with an 'outstanding' Diocesan report), this remains very much a Catholic school (about 80 per cent of families are practising Catholics).

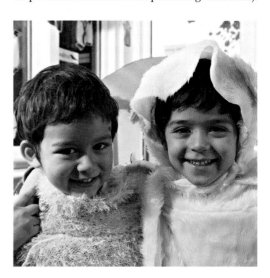

'Faith is part of the heartbeat of the school,' says the head. Prayers said morning and afternoon, as well as grace at lunch, and you'll find a crucifix in every classroom as well as the Catholic RE syllabus at common entrance. The head, however, feels the function of religion is not to exclude. 'We have a mission to provide for the Catholic community, but inclusivity is important.' And most feel included. 'Families with other beliefs get incredible respect,' said one Jewish parent.

Despite its slightly bohemian reputation, good manners and ethics remain key. Discipline here is done with the lightest of hands, but the boundaries are clearly in place. All teachers known by their first name and learning very much a cooperative enterprise. There's a golden toffee for those who've done something special (such as sing a song in the style of Johnny Cash), but those who break the Code of Conduct are entered into a 'green book' and parents are brought in to discuss anyone who's managed to rack up a third offence. Higher up the school, boys discuss what they've done wrong and what they've learned from it. 'I've only given one detention since I got here,' says the head. 'It never gets to that point. I try to give them a dignified exit.' Strong anti-bullying policies. 'The teachers are exceptionally kind and nurturing,' said one parent. 'They'll always do their best to help, whether it's finding a lost rugby kit or providing interview preparation for senior school tests.'

Parents usual north London lawyers, bankers and advertisers, but Catholic purpose means plenty of Italians, Germans and Spanish. Media parents often come with useful benefits. 'One allowed us to preview films, another offered tickets to the Wigmore Hall.' Boys are not necessarily the neatest, but are undoubtedly enthusiastic and individual. 'St Anthony's boys are never the same. There's no stamp.'

St Christopher's School

32 Belsize Lane, London NW3 5AE

Independent · Pupils: 244 · Ages: 4–11 · Fees: £13,500 pa

Tel: 020 7435 1521

Email: admissions@st-christophers.hampstead.sch.uk

Website: www.st-christophers.hampstead.sch.uk

Head: Since 2003, Mrs Susan (Susie) West (60s), BA PGCE MA Educational Management. Educated at Howells, University of Newcastle, Oxford (PGCE) and the OU. Then taught extensively in the private sector in England and abroad, at Oakham, at St Bede's, Eastbourne (where she was head of the pre-prep school), at Sherborne (where she was a housemistress), in Kuala Lumpur (where she was head of English), and at Sussex House, before becoming deputy head of Kensington Prep. An energetic figure who cycles to Hampstead every day from Pimlico, Mrs West is divorced with a grown-up son and daughter. She continues to teach some English to years 4 and 5, feeling that not only is this the best way to get to know the children but also the ideal means to understand the issues faced by her staff. Down to earth, positive and straight talking, with a clear passion for educating and a genuine empathy with her pupils.

Standing down in July 2016.

Entrance: St Christopher's is one of London's highest-achieving academic prep schools, with results at 11 the envy of many of its neighbours. This, however, is a school which selects primarily on ability. Part of the selection procedure is standardised tests, so summer birthdays don't lose out. 'It is not an academic assessment,' says the head. 'We observe how they play together and how they interact with other children.' The school operates a split entry and successful candidates are allocated a place either for reception or for year 1, depending primarily on 'school readiness'. Tests dates and results are co-ordinated with other leading selective north London prep schools. Early registration is essential (as near birth as possible) for those already resident in London. Entry lists are closed at about 300 to be assessed for 38 available places. The head, however, is always willing to be flexible for those who've just arrived. Siblings are given an automatic offer, unless it is considered 'they will not flourish'. Not flourishing, however, is fairly loosely interpreted. 'If you have two clever daughters and the third is not as bright,' says the head, 'some parents think she'll upset the exit poll, but that's not the way we work.' Parents confirm that year groups cover a (relatively) wide spread of ability. Occasional vacancies after entry. One 100 per cent means-tested scholarship available per annum and other support available as necessary.

Exit: 'We're fortunate in London that there are so many great schools,' says the head, 'and we are proud of the achievement of all our girls. There's no scholarship board here. We don't want to make some pupils feel instantly diminished.' That said, this is generally a school of bright sparks and ambitious parents and the majority proceed to the highest performing London day schools. City of London, North London Collegiate and South Hampstead top the list, with St Paul's Girls and Highgate close behind. Quite a number of scholarships amongst them. A handful to board and a few to Henrietta Barnett.

Remarks: St Christopher's was founded in 1883 by two local literary lesbians, but established in its current form in 1950 by the writer Rosemary Manning. It became a charitable trust in the 1970s. Housed in a large Victorian family house (with modern additions) in fashionable Belsize Park, this is a top-flight prep school for top-flight north London parents and the ethos and atmosphere are reflective of that. The education the pupils receive here is thoughtful and exciting. It concentrates on the fundamentals, but only after the fundamentals have been carefully considered. 'We have to ask the question "what are we educating children for?"' says the head. 'It's a world we know nothing about, a world very different from our own.' The school has carefully analysed the impact of technology. 'The girls think technologically and it can be much more difficult to get them to listen to a story and concentrate.' The issue is addressed by concentrated focus on the task of reading and understanding and girls read aloud every day from reception to year 3 and regularly thereafter. 'If you can't read, you can't do maths,' says the head. No concessions are made when it comes to literature ('We don't use abridged texts') and Dickens and Lewis Carroll are digested in the original. An excellent library underlines the school's priorities.

This is media land, and there is a thriving film club, where girls learn to make their own

Much of the timetable follows the national curriculum ('It would be foolish not to, there are some very interesting things, but we cut away the trivia. We don't reject it, we tweak it.') and the approach is based on 'child-initiated learning' with pupils taught to question and take responsibility for what they learn. Work is then tailored to the needs of each pupil, with maths books, for example, customised to the age and stage. (Though those in need of learning support are in the minority – mainly younger siblings – parents consider this tailoring, too, to be strong.) Spanish ('one of the most

'We're proud of all our girls. There's no scholarship board here. We don't want some pupils to feel instantly diminished'

widely spoken languages in the world') is taught throughout, Latin from year 5 and French as a club from year 3. Specialist subject teaching from year 4, with drama added to the curricular mix, joined by history of art in year 5. Flexibility of mind is encouraged by the inclusion of chess. ('It's a brilliant thinking exercise.')

Hard-working, well-qualified staff, particularly in the final two years. 'I cannot imagine better teachers than the maths and English teachers in years 5 and 6,' said one parent. 'They are really transformative.'

Despite the school's outstanding scholarship record, there is no scholarship class and no setting, except in maths in the final two years. Nor is this a school that crams for exams; preparation lasts just one term, when practice papers are given weekly. 'They're not missing core subjects from year 5, they still have time for all the extracurricular, they're not pressured and processed,' says the head. The approach here is enriching and the head believes there is as much value in creativity as in the core subjects.

Music is generally considered strong and enthusiastic, with two music classes plus a singing class each week. What's learnt here is put into practice with a junior orchestra, a wind group, a string group, piano club, junior and senior choirs and a chamber choir. This is media land, too, and there is also a thriving film club, where girls learn to make their own. Cultural outings are very much part of the offering, with regular visits to theatres and museums and a young writers' workshop.

Sport is perhaps less important than it might be elsewhere (some parents complain that unless you're in a team, this can be a rather neglected area). Netball court and gym on site and regular matches against other schools in netball and rounders. Short tennis is also taught in the summer term and senior girls play lacrosse. Swimming lessons only in year 3 at nearby Swiss Cottage baths, sports day held at Hampstead Cricket Club. Though the outdoor space here is not unduly extensive, it is used very effectively, with an outdoor classroom, an Alice Garden and a science-themed garden. 'Children today have a very boring existence, chauffeured here and there,' says the head, 'and we wanted to create an environment where they were allowed to be imaginative.' Indeed, the thread that runs throughout St Christopher's is that a good education is stimulating, interesting and exciting. The extracurricular is therefore addressed as energetically, with everything from public speaking to self-defence and Indian dance and, while there may be a Florence Nightingale workshop, the message that banking is as worthwhile a career for girls as nursing is instilled with visits to the Bank of England and a mock Dragons' Den. All staff are required to run two clubs a year and the offering is extensive.

Four houses, Bronte, Nightingale, North and Pankhurst, provide the basis for inter-house competition. The school has a strong family feel, sheltered and relaxed. There are no school rules ('We just ask for respect in the classroom and for them to be polite to teachers.') Good behaviour is instilled by discussion. ('Why did you do that? How do you imagine that would look?') Occasionally parents feel that emotional difficulties are not picked up as quickly as they might be. ('If you mention a problem, they take it seriously, but it's not always spotted,' said one.) Assembly every Friday is non-denominational. School meals exclude pork, shellfish, ham and nuts in order to cater for all.

The facilities here have been brought thoroughly up to date, too, with a smart extension providing additional classrooms and impressive IT. The uniform of green Aertex shirts and blue trousers is practical and durable.

Over a third of pupils live within walking distance and the rest travel from affluent nearby postcodes like St Johns Wood, Maida Vale, Islington and Highgate. Parents are often intellectual, professional, international and Jewish – and occasionally celebrities. 'They are interesting and incredibly well-informed,' says the head. 'They are very involved and desperately keen to support their children's education.' ('Sometimes too keenly involved,' remarked one father. 'There are a lot of non-working mothers who once had high-powered careers and are now directing their energies on their children.') Occasionally expectations have to be gently adjusted.

A high-octane education producing confident, well-informed and articulate girls. 'The nice thing about St Christopher's is that it provides an excellent education without trying to breed a master race,' says one happy customer.

St Margaret's School (London)

18 Kidderpore Gardens, London NW3 7SR

Independent • Pupils: 158 • Ages: 4–16 • C of E • Fees: up to £12,723 pa

Tel: 020 7435 2439

Email: enquiry@st-margarets.co.uk
Website: www.st-margarets.co.uk

20

Principal: Since 2008, Mr Mark Webster BSc (40s). Educated at Highgate School and University College London (where he read psychology), PGCE at Cambridge. Spent 15 years at the Royal School, Hampstead (first in primary, then IT, psychology and maths, before becoming deputy and acting head). Never planned to become a teacher – 'If you'd asked me early on what job I wanted to do, I'd have said teaching was 999th out of 1000'. A chance encounter changed his mind. 'I was working in publishing, when I met someone who said their job in teaching was fantastic. I'd never met anyone who felt that way about work.' Now equally enthusiastic about his chosen profession, Mr Webster continues to be hands on in his approach, teaching mathematics and '125' (see below). Particularly positive about working in a small school – 'I like the proximity and enjoy seeing the children grow up. You feel you can make a significant difference'. Operates an open-door policy and is constantly updating and improving what's on offer. Fundamental to his approach is the view that education is about

instilling a sense of curiosity – 'Qualifications are a passport to the next stage, but if you remain curious you will never be bored'. He himself retains a passionate interest in art, history and reading. Also plays football for Highgate Old Boys. A tactful, sympathetic enthusiast, Webster is a good fit for this family-like school. 'It's unusual to have a man,' said one mother, 'but I think he really cares.' Married to a teacher with two young sons.

Academic matters: GCSE options include Spanish, French, psychology, drama and music. An unusual addition is the head's own invention, '125' – a tribute to the school's 125th anniversary – which provides pupils with a list of activities to attempt at some point in their schooldays. 'There are, in fact, 158 options, so they do have some choice.' The range includes the practical, the cultural and the altruistic ('Do a nice thing for something who can do nothing in return'). In years 7, 8 and 9, 125 is a designated lesson.

'Qualifications are a passport, but if you remain curious you will never be bored'

In 2015, 42 per cent of GCSEs were A* or A grades. The majority take additional science (taught in a compact, but efficient, lab), enabling them to go on to science A levels, which many do. A modern language is compulsory (enthusiastic chatter about letters from French pen pals on the day we visited). The school is relatively non-selective and the ability range always includes the very able and those with more modest aspirations: in mathematics in year 11 there will be at least one girl taking the Foundation paper, whilst another achieves A* at A level. The plus side of a small school is class size (between 11-15 in the junior school, 11-19 thereafter) and personal attention – 'You don't get excellent results without teachers having spare time to help'. Setting introduced when necessary but, with limited space, teaching is usually differentiated rather than physically separated.

Outsiders have been known to view the school as a haven for the struggling, but it is only the right school for those with up to moderate special needs. 'We don't have the depth of resources for learning support that a larger school would have,' says the head. SENCo, plus a couple of teachers trained in dyslexia and dyscalculia, but the main support comes from classroom teachers. All abilities equally well catered for – 'We aren't results-driven and we exhaust every avenue'.

Games, options, the arts: The head's view is that education is a 'can-do', 'must try' matter and, inspired by the celebrated art historian Sir Ernst Gombrich's attitude – 'You don't have to like it, but it's important to understand why other people do. We compel them to try lots of things. They may moan, but we make them give it a go'. Drama is taken seriously. Performance is compulsory – 'We don't do Hamlet and let some people end up as third tree on the left. We make them write their own script and perform on a series of nights'. Music, too, is important – 'We have a super-motivated music teacher' – with a variety of traditional and less traditional extra-lesson options ('Handbells are very popular'). A number of choirs, plus a junior school orchestra. Some 80 per cent of girls have private instrument lessons at the school. Art immensely popular, with excellent results at GCSE: two studios, one reasonably spacious, the other definitely petite.

Outside space, too, is relatively restricted, with a largish garden transformed into an Astroturf playground. A local hall is used for gym and the school now has a sports area for netball, tennis and other sports two minutes' walk away. Minibus takes girls to Hampstead Heath for rounders or running, to Hendon Leisure Centre for aerobics, rock climbing and badminton and the Welsh Harp for rowing. Inter-house and inter-school matches from year 4 upwards. In David and Goliath mode, the school is unafraid to compete with much larger north London schools like Highgate and Channing – 'We often lose' – but succeed when more evenly matched. Plenty of clubs (fencing, theatre, cookery, bicycle maintenance, knitting, philosophy, book club, tennis) and trips, local and international, from walks on Hampstead Heath to Spain and Iceland.

Background and atmosphere: Founded in 1884, it moved to its present site in a quiet, suburban Hampstead road in 1943. Senior and junior schools both occupy the same building and have the same head, with different uniforms but little separation between them. The school has three houses, where pupils of all ages work together to raise funds for charities of their own choice and compete at sports. It is small, cosy and friendly; a parent commented: 'It allows the girls to achieve whatever they can – but in a safe, non-confrontational environment'. Red and white uniform in the junior school, black and white in the senior. 'The head has changed the uniform and it's much more flattering,' said one mother. 'These things matter to teenage girls.'

Pastoral care and discipline: Discipline not a significant issue. Though head insists this is not the garden of Eden, disciplinary issues tend to be confined to infringements of uniform – 'We can live with earrings if there's no drink or drugs'. Bullying – 'We get a case every year' – is dealt with promptly. 'Parents tend to be very supportive. They come to this school for its caring environment and they're quick to back us up.' Parents couldn't agree more – 'You get ups and downs with some of the girls, but if you ever get a problem it's dealt with straight away,' said one. Most parents feel one of the school's greatest strengths is its pastoral side, allowing girls to fulfil their potential and know exactly who they are. 'It's too small a school not to be a community. Girls, for example, will discuss a problem on Facebook and say, let's resolve this.' The school has its own head of pastoral care but also relies on a school counsellor when needed and pro-actively encourages 'bonding' with a variety of trips. 'The

In David and Goliath mode, the school is unafraid to compete with much larger schools

girls mix across the years and are often close to girls in the year above and below,' said a parent.

Pupils and parents: Nice, well-behaved, confident girls from a cosmopolitan range of backgrounds reflecting the school's north London location. A sizeable chunk come from within walking distance, then in an arc stretching from Wembley to Islington (school minibus on offer for those who require it). Very much a family school in every sense – 45 per cent of pupils are sisters or relatives of current or ex-pupils. 'A lot of people like the sense of support and nurturing.' Most newcomers hear about the school by word of mouth, though the internet (and favourable newspaper coverage) have slightly altered the traditional intake. Those relocating can find it a particularly valuable resource. 'I like it because there is more of a mix than usual in north London,' said one mother.

Entrance: From reception to year 2 assessment involves girls coming in for the morning and working with the class teacher. From year 3 upwards they take a standard set of English and maths assessments. Guaranteed transition from within at 11. 'Once we've made the commitment, unless there are particular special needs we can't support, we stick to it.' External candidates take English, maths and verbal reasoning exams.

Exit: About 80 per cent of junior school girls stay on to the senior school, though a small number move to more selective senior schools such as North London Collegiate or City of London School for Girls.

School has no intention of opening a sixth form despite parental requests. 'By then it really is time to move on.' Notably successful with applications at 16. Most popular choices at that point are local co-ed sixth forms like Highgate and UCS, and similar atmosphere girls' schools like Channing. A reasonable number to the state sector (St Marylebone particularly popular). Good guidance on offer at both 11 and 16 – 'It's really important to make an informed choice. Not every school will suit every girl and they are used to being supported here'. School also works with them on interview practice and personal statements. Girls generally get their first-choice sixth form – 'My daughter got in everywhere she applied,' said one parent.

Money matters: Not an expensive school by any means, but not much scope for additional funding. One 50 per cent scholarship at 11, about five per cent get some sort of bursary.

Remarks: A gentle, nurturing school with a strong and secure family atmosphere providing a stimulating, tailor-made education. 'A little gem,' to quote one parent, though possibly not the ideal venue for the child that needs plenty of space to run around or one who requires the challenge of a big stage.

St Mary Magdalene Academy Primary School

Linked school: St Mary Magdalene Academy, 166

Liverpool Road, London N7 8PG

Tel: 020 7697 0123

State • Pupils: 210 • Ages: 4–11 • C of E

Website: www.smmacademy.org

Headteacher: Since 2008, Joy Parke (50s), BEd (Hons) University of North London, NPQH National College of School Leadership. She's impressed with the inquiry-based International Baccalaureate Primary Years Programme (IBPYP) which was introduced at the same time she joined the school, saying it fits well with the school's Christian values, and suits the mixture of faiths represented in the school community. Her school is physically 'attached' to the SMMA Secondary School, and she works closely with SMMA Trust Executive Director Paul Hollingum. While she independently manages the day-to-day activity of the primary school, she acknowledges the advantages and support that secondary students, staff and her fellow SMMA Secondary head teacher offer. Blond, slender and smartly-attired, parents describe her as 'reserved', but say that they are confident she is on top of everything going on in the school. 'She runs a tight ship.' Mindful of this school's legacy, Parke brings a 21st century approach that is compatible with Saint Mary Magdalene's 300-year-old history.

Entrance: The school has one-form entry with classes numbering 30 pupils, boys and girls evenly mixed. 'It's quite cosy', one parent tells us. Because of admissions criteria, all the students are local Islington residents and represent a wide socio-economic mix; from children of affluent professionals to the children of immigrants and asylum-seekers residing in assisted housing. Siblings are given priority and as it is a C of E school, church attendance is also taken into consideration. Full details are given on the school website.

Exit: Majority move on to the senior school where they will study for GCSEs and then the International Baccalaureate Diploma programme.

Remarks: This is the only state school in Greater London to offer the International Baccalaureate Primary Years Programme (IBPYP), and families familiar with this programme, found in schools worldwide, will feel at home here. Ms. Parke speaks positively of the clarity and direction of the curriculum and how this covers and at times exceeds National Curriculum requirements. She is confident in the ability of her teachers, who themselves represent a variety of nationalities, to deliver the programme. Parents are complimentary about Ms. Parke's talent for recruiting good teachers, though there have been the usual challenges of dealing with staff absence and turnover due to maternity leave, relocation, etc., sometimes causing a break in continuity for the children. Specialist teachers offer music, PE and languages; class teachers do the art. The EYFS, and Key Stage 1 and 2 Sats are used to assess how SMMA students are measuring up to their peers nationwide, and the end of Key Stage Two results exceed both local and national averages with children regularly achieving up to level 6.

An annual Shakespeare project culminates in performances, both dance and drama

In keeping with the IBPYP philosophy and the school's own global education priorities, pupils study French (years 1 and 2), Spanish (years 3 and 4), and Mandarin (years 5 and 6); Latin is an after-school option. Students take lots of trips around London to see museums or take part in workshops linked to their units of inquiry (sometimes incurring a modest cost). Years 5 and 6 take residential trips into the countryside. A parent told us: 'I love the varied and engaging approach to learning, and there is consistency across the subjects that helps children explore things in a more holistic way.'

Lots of after-school sports (including competitive teams) and other activities on offer – such as Japanese art, chess, book club and gardening. Some of these activities are run by SMMA secondary school teachers and coaches and even sixth form students (earning D of E points) and make use of SMMA's impressive sports facilities – one of the advantages of being a through-school. An annual school-wide Shakespeare project supported by the Young Shakespeare Company culminates in performances, both dance and drama, by the students. Dance is popular, SMMA students excel at table tennis and were National Champions in 2014.

Although parents say there is a good range of activities on offer, one remarked that the school had not been particularly flexible about approving a student absence in order to participate in special activity outside the school during term time. The

school responds that they have authorised term time absences for children attending both sports activities and activities related to the arts, eg TV, film and stage work.

The primary and secondary schools share the same site but are quite separate so that the primary students have their own space while benefiting from use of the secondary school facilities. Lots of windows throughout make for bright classrooms and many have access to outdoor areas – either to the garden or balconies. The library is welcoming and well-stocked.

The IBPYP features a built-in 'character education' element through the IB Learner Profile which is amplified by the school's Christian values (Commitment, Empathy, Forgiveness, Hope, Independence, Integrity, Thankfulness and Tolerance). Golden Values are highlighted throughout the year, and school fundraising events support causes such as the Nepal earthquake and other good causes.

St Mary Magdalene Academy

Linked school: St Mary Magdalene Academy Primary School, 165

Liverpool Road, London N7 8PG

State • Pupils: 963 • Ages: 11–18 • Sixth form pupils: 150
• C of E

Tel: 020 7697 0123

Email: firstcontact@smmacademy.org
Website: www.smmacademy.org

Founding Executive Director: Since 2005, Paul Hollingum has been director of the trust that governs the four SMMA institutions including the early years centre, the primary and secondary schools and the specialist school for SEN. BA (economics) Wolverhampton Polytechnic; PGCE, Birmingham University, MA (Education) Institute of Education, University of London; previously taught economics, business studies and law in selective and independent schools, deputy head of Wilson's School, Surrey, head of Raine's Foundation School, London. This is his first experience of an IB school.

Fair hair and complexion, sparkling blue eyes, he appears approachable and steady; he speaks with humility about what has been achieved in a few short years at SMMA. He attributes this to a collaborative team effort on the part of supportive governors and his headteachers, who are all committed to high academic standards, well-rounded education with enrichment activities and global citizenship. Describes SMMA as a 'new breed of church school', the international dimension of the

IB and the notion of service to the whole community links nicely to the Christian ethos of service. Mr Hollingum's long-standing involvement with China through the British Council has had an impact on SMMA and he continues to work as an advisor to schools there on behalf of the School's Trust. He manages this thanks to the strong leadership of head teacher Victoria Linsley, to whom he leaves the day-to-day running of the secondary school. Partner school The Courtyard serves 14-18 year old students with autism and/or speech, language and communication needs, who share some enrichment activities with SMMA students. A parent tells us he is often on the school gate greeting everyone; he's 'visible to all'.

Headteacher Victoria Linsley is founding head teacher; BA (history) Nottingham, MSc (history) and PGCE from Oxford. A Lancastrian educated in public schools, for 20 years she has worked in London comprehensive schools, and as a consultant with failing and special measures schools. She has previous experience as a deputy head at

Broomfield School. This slim, petite, youthful head teacher is an energetic dynamo who notices everything and does not miss a trick as she roams through the school giving stern looks to students who may be pushing the uniform boundaries, while generously doling out affirmative 'well-done's to beaming students in classrooms and corridors. A few approach, eager to share something with her. Proud of the school, its facilities, resources and especially students, she does not shy away from talking about areas for improvement. It seems the Hollingum-Linsley chemistry has created magic at SMMA.

Academic matters: SMMA describes its specialties as humanities and global citizenship, and this involves eight key concepts: citizenship, social justice, sustainable development, diversity, values and perceptions, inter-dependence, conflict resolution and human rights. For the 11-16 year olds, this is essentially a non-selective inner-city comprehensive preparing locals for GCSEs using the national curriculum, but aligning it with common entrance assessment standards at the end of year 8 so they can track progress. A good range of GCSEs are on offer and the school sets the bar high. Parents say that the kids know they are expected to achieve; students appear to be serious and committed at school and parents confirm that there is an expectation that pupils will work hard and to the best of their ability – whatever that is.

'They work hard at setting a high standard; they go beyond the call of duty. They will give kids – even the bright kids – a bit of a kick up the backside'

At sixth form, which offers the IB and A levels, the profile changes; more students come for the final two years and there are admissions criteria (preference to those who want to do the IB, which is the more popular option). Parents credit the school leaders with working hard to help local families understand the advantages of the IB. Limited A level subjects offered: economics, English lit, government and politics, history, maths and sociology, but will offer a full A level range from 2016. There is an expectation of high achievement that is underpinned by what parents and students describe as a strong programme of pastoral care and sense of community. Pupils know they will be supported. Class sizes are 30 for years 7-8; for GCSE classes they are limited to 25 (streamed for core subject areas), and at IB class sizes are limited to 15 but

often much smaller. In 2015, 75 per cent got 5+ A*-C grades at GCSE including English and maths; 25 per cent of grades were A*/A. Average IB point score: 34, with eight students getting 40+ points out of 45.

An energetic dynamo who notices everything and does not miss a trick as she roams through the school

The school's emphasis on global citizenship is demonstrated in a variety of ways, perhaps most notably, according to the parents and students that we spoke to, through the language programme. Most take French, Spanish or German and many also do Mandarin: year 7 students who have scored well on the school's language aptitude tests are invited to study Mandarin and sometimes Latin through the Inspire Programme in addition to a modern European language. There are several overseas travel opportunities and a special emphasis on Mandarin and China. These global dimensions are also enhanced by partnerships with schools in places such as Finland, China, Senegal, and Jerusalem.

SMMA is one of the few UK Confucius Classroom Schools – thanks to Mr Hollingum's links with the Institute of Education. Funding from the Chinese government promotes the study of Chinese culture and languages through teacher exchange; two teachers from China also help to plan visits to sister schools in China, and help with cultural studies and festivals within the school. 'Chinese New Year is really something here,' we hear. All the students taking GCSE Mandarin Chinese achieved A*-C grades in 2015. It's also on offer at IB level.

Another important partnership is with Deloitte, which supports the school and students in many ways as part of its corporate social responsibility programme. Deloitte staff work with students and provide expertise to help prepare them for life after secondary school.

It seems that the teaching staff are a real strength of the school. The parents can't praise them enough and the pupils agree. They are described as hard-working, committed, quick to respond to parents, and they motivate students to learn and to work to their full potential. Most are local, but some have international experience, a few from European countries. It seems that it is a satisfying place to work; the turnover is quite low. Two young Oxbridge grad tutors are based in the library to help students with essays, maths or any other academic challenges. Parents say the teachers are good role models for the youngsters and help instil a sense of pride. 'They work hard at setting a high standard; they go beyond the call of duty.

They will give kids – even the bright kids – a bit of a kick up the backside and say, "We can do better than this".'

This is offered within the context of a C of E Christian perspective, but it is an inclusive school with students of all faiths, and parents say the religious aspect is subtle and low-key. Good support for SEN.

Games, options, the arts: Parents and pupils are excited by all the extracurricular opportunities on offer here. The school has a roof eco garden with a pond, tall grasses for insects, chickens, an aviary and bird feeders with cameras installed by students for filming and observing the hungry visitors, all making the place a mini wildlife haven in the heart of urban Islington. On another part of the building are rooftop sports facilities. D of E from year 10 upwards counts toward the IB Creativity, Action and Service (CAS) section. Pupils recently worked on a community project creating drawings of the local area to inspire a colourful mural on permanent display at a local train station. An extended school day on Mondays and Tuesdays offers sports, Mandarin language and culture, arts, community involvement and cooking. Parents talk enthusiastically about this programme and the variety of opportunities it affords.

The school makes good use of its networks – sometimes through its partner schools around the globe, or through parents – to invite all sorts of guest teachers and performers to work with students. They also take advantage of 'virtual networks', having Skype conferences with students in other countries. Younger classes go on camping trips, sixth formers have an activities week in Cornwall; on alternate years there are trips to partner schools in China – parents and students rave about these; they have travelled to Berlin, to Mexico and also to Senegal, where they volunteered in a local school and learned about African music.

Perhaps because of Chinese links, pupils have won national table tennis competitions

The school has impressive sports facilities considering its urban setting, including a sports hall. Netball, basketball and football teams are all in training; and perhaps because of the Chinese links, pupils have won national table tennis competitions.

Music is popular and all year 7 and 8s learn musical instruments – we walked in on a group listening to a just-finished recording of a pupil playing her own composition. World music features highly here, and rather than full scale orchestras,

Chickens, an aviary and bird feeders with cameras installed by students for filming and observing the hungry visitors

the school features numerous small instrumental ensembles.

Pupils were keen to talk about the school's twice-yearly drama productions, which can involve everyone interested. 'If you are in year 7, you may not get the lead, but there is a part for you!' all sixth formers encouraged to volunteer, not just IB students with their 150 hours of CAS.

One student told us about Chapel Club, led by the full-time chaplain, which she had enjoyed earlier in the day: they had read and discussed biblical proverbs, which she said 'was something refreshing in the middle of day.' The school definitely has a C of E ethos, but there is no pressure to conform.

Background and atmosphere: While there has been a Saint Mary Magdalene School here for 300 years, the development of a 21st century 3-19 academy offering the IB programmes was an initiative of the church in partnership with Islington council and opened in 2007. The facilities are truly dazzling. Modern, minimalist, pale-coloured wood, carpeted throughout with lots of light pouring through windows throughout the building. The design and layout ingeniously mask the school's vast size. There are two floors largely reserved for sixth form, and all the floors overlook a large open courtyard area where the canteen and dining area is based, a gathering space effectively at the heart of the school. On the ground floor is the theatre, along with the 'noisier' specialist teaching rooms. The school is immaculately tidy without feeling sanitised; beautiful displays throughout celebrate student classwork and art, and most of the classrooms have lots of internal windows so that pupils at work are easily observed from the walkways. 'Open and transparent' is the feel.

Ms Linsley believes in the importance of maintaining an orderly, organised environment for her pupils. Rising above the central communal area is the two-floor library (one level reserved for sixth form) with chapel (more of a quiet room) above – imagine it as a structure built on 'stilts' at the first floor level – so they are easily accessible by crossover walkways all from all floors. Classrooms are spacious and more than ample for the class sizes – nowhere did we see students crowded and cramped – and there are copious specialist teaching rooms: the art quad even has a built-in large kiln studio and an IB art studio, so that students can leave their partially-completed projects out without worrying about accidental disturbance by others. There are music rooms with practice spaces, recording facilities, etc there are ICT suites; and there's a spacious classroom for the school's high achieving autistic and Asperger's pupils, who also intermingle with the other pupils.

Pastoral care and discipline: Rather than traditional form tutors SMMA has teacher 'academy guardians' who manage multi-age groups of lower secondary student 'families'. They stay in the same groups as they rise through the years, and everyone likes this pastoral continuity. In sixth form they become part of a new 'family' of combined first and second year IB diploma and A level students, who meet with their guardian regularly. They also serve as mentors to younger groups of pupils, enabling them to learn from their older peers about what lies ahead in the sixth form. The family groups are named after continents, emphasising the school's global outlook. Guardians are the first port of call for any concern and it seems they are quick to return phone calls or emails. Communication is a strong suit, according to the parents.

They have travelled to Senegal, where they learned about African music

Though we gather there are definitely some pupils who are more motivated to learn than others, behaviour, as such, is not an issue. The school is non-selective and has a highly diverse socio-economic student community, but there are expectations and consequences for absence; pupils who arrive more than seven minutes late to lessons may be refused entry by the teachers. This sets the standard. One parent told us, 'There is a very rigorous code of discipline; they don't kick them out, there's a sort of "3-step programme". Kids who don't want to fit in with the standards of behaviour tend to move on.'

It is also interesting to note in the 'tips from sixth formers' that pupils 'should not use up too many hours working in a part-time job', suggesting that this is a community where pupils need to earn their pocket money.

Younger pupils wear uniforms, and on the day we visited were immaculately turned out – impressive! Sixth form has a sensible dress code.

Pupils and parents: The students we met were a multicultural mix – both 'home bred' and recently arrived. They speak of the strong community feel; the continuity of the mixed-age 'family' groups is

reassuring. One previously home-schooled student said she chose SMMA over an independent London IB school because she was so impressed by the 'great' teachers she met during the open day taster sessions. 'They are so supportive and really helped me adjust to the system here'. She said that she felt there was less pressure at SMMA than she sensed at some of the independent schools she visited. Another said that the sixth form is enhanced by the international perspectives gained by having classmates from all over the world. 'You get a glimpse into all sorts of cultures here. That is very motivating and makes you want to know more about those people and places.'

Entrance: Year 7: 180 pupils admitted on the basis of strict criteria. after looked after children and siblings, and those coming up from the primary department, 70 per cent Open Places (by proximity) and 30 per cent Foundation Places (children attending an Islington C of E primary school, with proximity as a tie-break); 18 places (no catchment criteria) based on literacy aptitude tests; smaller intake at year 9. For IB, a minimum of seven grade B GCSEs, including English and maths, with A grades to study science and/or maths at higher level; for A level, a minimum of five grade C GCSEs including English and maths, with B grades in A level subjects.

Exit: Some 70 per cent leave after GCSEs; even SMMA students applying to sixth form must go through an admissions process (see above). University and career counselling is good, and this is one of the areas where the Deloitte partnership is helpful. Destinations include one to Oxford in 2015, St Andrews, Durham, London, Leeds, Nottingham, York, Exeter, Southampton, Courtauld Institute of Art; plus a soccer scholarship at North West Texas.

Money matters: Most parents happy to pay for school trips, though there is support for those who find this a challenge. ParentPay cards also serve as ID cards and enable parents to replenish student accounts for lunch money.

Remarks: Students say: 'There's something for everyone here. Even if you don't like a subject, you can learn to enjoy it. They don't give up on kids here and you develop a lot of independence.' The students we met were gorgeous – perhaps a bit too smart, ethically-minded and work-focused to be uber-cool, they were a memorably impressive bunch and the sort any parent would be proud to boast about. Kudos to the C of E and Islington on this impressive success story.

The St Marylebone C of E School

64 Marylebone High Street, London W1U 5BA

Tel: 020 7935 4704

State • Pupils: 1080 • Ages: 11–18 • Sixth form pupils: 330 (110 boys) • C of E

Email: info@stmaryleboneschool.com
Website: frog.stmaryleboneschool.com/index.phtml?d=552073

57

Headteacher: Since January 2014, Ms Kathryn Pugh MA (Cantab), PBCE, NPQH (mid 30s). A Cambridge graduate with first class honours in English, she joined St Marylebone in 2005 as an English teacher and learning co-ordinator, and was promoted to assistant head in 2008, before succeeding the long-serving and legendary Elizabeth Phillips OBE. This is only the second school she has worked at. She arrived here after cutting her teeth (as she puts it) at Riddlesdown Collegiate, a large co-ed comprehensive in Surrey, where she taught English and drama. Straight after leaving Cambridge she spent four years working in business and media, and worked in theatre and communication for 18 months in Malawi, as well as working for The Teacher Support Network, an educational charity.

Tall and willowy, Miss Pugh looks more like a Chanel model than headmistress. She cycles to work each day and is described by her pupils as 'inspirational', 'accessible', and 'empathetic'. We were regaled with tales of her contorting herself into yogic positions during English lessons as well as her passionate encouragement of 'complete randomness in lessons'. Said to be a fruitarian, she is described as looking strikingly beautiful in her red

cape, while standing in the midst of girls in green cartwheeling and cavorting. She 'mucks in – not afraid to get her hands dirty during the fairs'; and 'She's so dynamic,' enthused one parent, 'everyone wants to do their best for her, both her pupils and her staff...the school is lucky that it has so many years of someone so ambitious and committed.'

We spoke to her surrounded by her senior management team. This is a woman who clearly prefers to see herself as prima inter pares. Her predecessor, the legendary Elizabeth Phillips, was a great delegator, and responsibility continues to be very much shared. She wants to talk about the school and its achievements and defer to her colleagues. She is deeply uncomfortable when the questions focus on her. Appreciative of a strong and supportive team, Ms Pugh is doing sterling work channelling the goodwill of both her staff and a diverse parent body.

Academic matters: Results are excellent. At A level, 71 per cent A*-B with 33 per cent A*/A in 2015. School keen to point out that girls who take further maths and chemistry perform brilliantly. While English is the most popular subject, school does have 10 STEM ambassadors, and offers two sixth form maths/ICT scholarships to students likely to go on to study STEM subjects at university. Psychology, sociology and economics among the options – the first much the favourite, with a spread of results. German now phased out in favour of Spanish. High take-up; French and Spanish students achieved excellent results with a high percentage of top grades – a great improvement since our last visit.. Supervised study periods during year 12 help the less-disciplined with their homework. Relatively good teacher:pupil ratio, with setting from the start, and school invests in retaining good staff. Our student guides were keen to tell us how many of their teachers had doctorates and were specialists in their fields.

We were regaled with tales of her contorting herself into yogic positions during English lessons as well as her encouragement of 'complete randomness'

Offers a good choice of subject options – 'an amazing variety,' enthused one parent. A future skills award and child development have replaced health and social care; dance, Latin (now compulsory in years 7 and 8) and business studies canter alongside the front runners at GCSE and all are in the ribbons. Eighty-three per cent 5+ A*-C grades in 2015 including maths and English with some outstanding performances (45 per cent A*/A grades). RS results are knock-out and the curriculum is praised for its earnest inclusiveness. The Englishes are good, so are the single sciences. One full class takes triple science each year, though most take the double award. Maths more than respectable. School does, after all, have a maths and computing specialism as well as performing arts. All students study both French and Spanish in key stage 3 and over 75 per cent take at least one language at GCSE. Art and history strong and popular. School has policy of taking some subjects – ICT, RS – early to excellent effect.

Gifted and talented programme now called Aspiration and Challenge, with the idea of achieving excellence for everyone. High Achievers' programme for those with high academic ability; Scholarship programmes those talented at dance, music or drama. Two SENCos, a full-time SEN teacher, learning support assistants and specialist centres for students with learning difficulties. It is a centre of excellence for severe emotional and behavioural difficulties. Can provide for moderate physical difficulties too. EAL is an important area also (about half of the cohort speak a language other than English at home) and this department plays a vibrant part in celebrating cultural diversity.

Games, options, the arts: This has a performing arts specialism – with 14 places awarded to those talented in dance, drama or music. It is perhaps not surprising, then, that sport takes a lower profile. That is not to say that there are not opportunities available, and there are a surprising number of athletically ambitious girls. Our guide was a penthathlete, excelling at high jump, long jump, shot put, 800 metres and hurdles, participating in clubs both in and out of school. Cross-country is also popular. Grey Coat Hospital School is the big rival at netball; they also play Portland Place and Holland Park. Plenty of inter-house sports competitions too (five houses across the year groups – Hardwick, Dickens, Barrett, Nightingale and Wesley). Annual sports day at Willesden Green. Other sports on offer include footballing, trampolining, rugby and tennis as well as the D of E awards scheme. They have managed to fit an underground sports hall into this already over-filled space. Sport very much available even if not always enthusiastically taken up.

Dance, drama and music are outstanding and production values are high. 'The girls take huge pride in their performances,' we were told, 'even if not everyone can take part. It is inspirational.' The inspiration is further fuelled by the innovative and outstanding three storey building that incorporates the visual and performing arts space, with dance studio and gym in the basement. This makes a huge difference – not least to the amount of space it frees for other curricular activities. In all respects the arts reign here. You can make everything from jewellery to ceramics and print your own photos. Up-to-date laser cutters in the well-equipped DT workshops. Graphics also well regarded. Debating, dance and musical performance of all kinds thrive. Scholars' concert happens in the Wigmore Hall; some musicals, eg sixth form production of Chicago, performed at the Rudolf Steiner Theatre; whole school production of Grease in the old-fashioned, polished-wood-smelling school hall.

Some disagreement among parents as to whether there is an opportunity for everyone to get involved in these productions and performances. Grumblings in some quarters that only the best are given roles – and here, there are a lot of girls considered to be glittering. So your aspiring Milly who doesn't quite make the grade may well end up sitting on the sidelines for much of her school years. School quick to point out that over 150 pupils across the school took part in whole school production at Christmas. We, like Ofsted, were impressed with range of other co-curricular activities which don't necessarily require high-confidence performance skills: book clubs, green committee, Young Entrepreneurs, Fair Trade group etc. However, opportunities like GCSE photography work in the highly professional Metro Studios only available to the three or four girls whose applications to take the course are considered sufficiently impressive. This is the reality of a state-funded school, but it must be trying for the also-rans and would-bes.

Background and atmosphere: Tucked between Princess Grace Hospital and Marylebone High Street and close to the teeming runway that is the

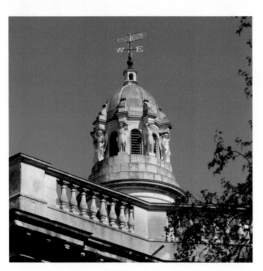

Old-fashioned termly reports which don't just parrot what the class has done but actually talk about your own daughter

Marylebone Road, the school is a leafy, contained oasis of calm and purpose. St Marylebone Parish Church is a focus point and contributes to the peacefulness. This is where assemblies and concerts happen as well as religious services. A closely-knit jungle of buildings from red-brick Victorian, complete with heavily green gloss painted corridors, to modern glass and concrete are packed onto this one compact site. Further down the High Street on Blandford Street is the sixth form building, which is modern, purpose-built, and feels more like a tiny university campus than a school.

Five forms per year, and with only 750 in the main school with 330 in the sixth form, St Marylebone is a relatively small inner London comprehensive – and this shows. As intimate as it can be, spread over two sites, it is an unintimidating place, with plenty of smiles and polite greetings between staff and pupils as well as between the pupils themselves. No space for lockers, so girls have to learn to be adept at carting their lives around with them and being organised about what they need for each lesson. Lunch is eaten in form rooms, though year 10 examinees and upwards are mercifully allowed out to settle in the numerous cafés round about at lunchtime. Sixth formers have their own canteen in Blandford Street.

Pastoral care and discipline: Pastoral care is very strong, affirm several parents. As well as there being systems of support in place among the staff and pupils, there is a strong mentoring facility between the older and younger pupils. This is an intense time of life for any teenager, but one senses that in this school the experience can perhaps become more intense than elsewhere. School says that the intensity is 'offset by a very caring community feeling which identifies and helps deal with problems' – and denies that this is a school of 'precious princesses'. Maybe it is part of the performing arts culture.

Girls, on the whole, very supportive of each other, though there is a lot of competition and this has to be managed. Behaviour is good. Cases of bullying rare, we were told. A smell of smoke doesn't linger in lavatories here, and a zero tolerance approach means that your child may well end up with detention just from talking in class. The bar is high, girls feel lucky to be here and want to behave well. Parents commend the fluid communication lines whenever a problem arrives. Lots of positive feedback when a struggling girl starts to perform well as well, as the more obvious commending of high performance. Much appreciated are the proper, old-fashioned termly reports which don't just parrot at you what the class has done but actually talk about your own daughter. Good, realistic and collaborative target-setting also works.

Pupils and parents: Broad social mix, made up of the heady variety of backgrounds and cultures that you would expect in an inner London comprehensive. Much more middle class than many of its kind, however, because this is the golden apple if you are after an excellent education for your creative daughter who also likes to perform. A higher proportion than usual of parents are actors, barristers, artists and, yes, even bankers, than you would find at just any ordinary central London comprehensive, many of whom may have been privately educated themselves.

The gritty detail is there are approximately 65 per cent from ethnic minority backgrounds and from 90 different countries. Over 50 per cent of pupils are bilingual. More than 60 languages spoken at home. Sixty per cent C of E members; the largest second religious group is Muslim. School clearly tries hard to integrate the social mix – has an annual World Culture Day among many other initiatives – and attracts fierce loyalty. Girls travel some distances to get here – from as far as Hackney in the East to Ealing and Shepherds Bush in the West, Kilburn, Kentish Town and Islington in the north as well as Wandsworth and Southwark in the south.

Entrance: As maddeningly oversubscribed as you would expect – something like 1,000 applicants for 150 places. Looked after children and those with statements have priority. Sixty per cent C of E places, 30 per cent 'open', with distance the only criterion. Fourteen places annually given to those with outstanding aptitude in an aspect of performing arts (music, choral, dance or drama). Applicants divided into four ability bands with equal numbers accepted from each band. Tie breaker of how near to the school you live. In the sixth, 330 places – priority to existing students, though they have to fulfil requirements (minimum of five A*-B GCSEs, with at least C grade in maths and English). Boys are taken into the sixth and, again, more apply than there are places for. Performing arts and maths/ICT scholarships for sixth formers. School receives five applications a week for occasional places.

Exit: One-quarter leave after GCSE and go to sixth form colleges, the independents, eg Latymer Upper, or other state schools, eg Camden, largely for a greater range of A level subjects. Most stay, though entrance to the school's own sixth form is not a given, even for their own. Sixth form leavers to good universities and a range of courses; five to Oxford and Cambridge in 2015 and three medics. Students go on to study a decent mix of arts and science subjects, from bio-medicine at Edinburgh to Spanish and Hispanic studies at Bristol to criminology at Manchester. A few each year to read music, usually several to art foundation, dance foundation and drama school - immediately or after a gap year.

Money matters: National funding programmes largely cut so bidding for extra money from various sources takes up a lot of time. The result, however, is a school that is well-staffed and well-equipped, if not to lavish private school standards.

Remarks: If your daughter is outgoing, confident and creative this is an excellent choice. St Marylebone is an exceptional school. It has the benefits of the moral ethos of a Church of England school but is ethnically diverse and serves many different communities. With a bright young head at the helm, its future looks as rosy as its history.

St Mary's School, Hampstead

47 Fitzjohn's Avenue, London NW3 6PG

Tel: 020 7435 1868

Independent • Pupils: 300 (20 boys) • Ages: 2y 9m–11 • RC • Fees: up to £12,915 pa

Email: enquiries@stmh.co.uk
Website: www.stmh.co.uk

21

Headmistress: Since 2003, Miss Angela Rawlinson BA MA (50s). A New Zealander, she did a degree in education and psychology at Auckland University, then trained as a teacher at Auckland Teachers' College. Taught in NZ for seven years, before arriving in the UK in 1989 to 'stay for a year'. After research at Cambridge (on drama in the curriculum), she worked in the state sector (as deputy head at the Servite RC Primary in Fulham and head at the Marlborough School, Kensington), before taking over at St Mary's.

Immensely professional, enthusiastic and energetic, she loves her work: 'In what other job would you find 300 people coming in and saying "I love you" every day?' Weekends are spent on the south coast reading, playing tennis and golf. 'She's amazing,' said one mother. 'You'll come in in the morning and find her skipping with the children. My daughter always rushes in to give her a big cuddle'.

Entrance: Names down at birth, but even delivery-room efficiency will not guarantee a place. These go first to siblings, then to Catholics, then to non-Catholics. Parents generally tour the school nine months before entry, sign the acceptance form and pay a deposit. Nursery arrangements are particularly parent friendly. Children are admitted from 2 years and 9 months and can stay to lunch or all afternoon with minimum notice. Boys make up a third of nursery entrants. A few further places for girls often become available in year 3.

Exit: About 85 per cent to leading academic secondary schools – South Hampstead, City of London, Channing, North London Collegiate, Highgate, Haberdashers' etc – quite a number with scholarships. Also to selective state schools (St Michael's Catholic Grammar, Henrietta Barnett). Secondary school advice is a strength, starting with individual parent meetings in year 5. 'Most trust us and listen to what we recommend', says the head. Boys leave by the age of 6, many to neighbouring Catholic prep St Anthony's.

Remarks: Founded in 1871, by the Congregation of Jesus, the school moved from Belsize Park in 1926 to its present building, a turn-of-the century mansion with polished mosaic floors and vast country-like gardens. Against this gracious period backdrop, facilities are thoroughly up to date, with a super, Mac-filled IT suite, large, new assembly hall and well-stocked library located in the panelled former billiards room. In 1992, when there were too few teaching nuns to manage the school, a charitable trust was formed to continue the good work under lay management.

A non-selective school, it still manages to pull off high-flying results at 11. Teaching (as described in the recent ISI report) is 'excellent' – sharp, lively and very pupil focused. 'The teacher worked out my daughter in three minutes', said one parent. Praise is appropriate and immediate. 'My daughter had been struggling to write a longer essay. On the day she did so, the head immediately called her in and gave her two merit points. It encouraged her so much'.

The brightest are stretched through a curriculum enriched with plenty of arts-related activities and sport. 'We wanted to make it more relevant', says the head, 'and incorporate risk taking and thinking independently'. Interesting extra work for those who need stretch (lunch-time puzzle club, for example, is a big hit).

Fluid ability grouping throughout, then setting in maths and English in year 6 in the run up to 11 plus. Excellent support for strugglers, too, with three special needs teachers providing help in class and out of it (in lovely, bright teaching space). 'The learning support is fantastic', said one mother with a daughter finding maths a mountain. 'Very

'You'll come in in the morning and find her skipping with the children. My daughter always rushes to give her a big cuddle'

few independent schools are non-selective, but St Mary's does very well by all'. Another told us: 'You really feel they care about every single girl. If someone is not up to scratch, the response is "what can we do to help them shine?"' External specialists are invited in to keep absence to a minimum.

Strong sport, with a double court for netball and a well-equipped gym. All the usual team games (rounders, netball, hockey, football), plus swimming at Swiss Cottage baths (for years 3 to 6) and athletics in Regent's Park. Gymnastics particularly popular, with pupils competing at regional and national level. High achievement too, in music and excellent dance and drama (including an all-encompassing production in year 6). Heaps of clubs (Latin, Spanish, needlework, craft, lingua franca) and plenty of trips (year 5 to an adventure camp in Devon, year 6 on a five-day break in France to meet pen pals and make croissants, little ones to a farm and the seaside).

Boys are well integrated and given appropriate scope in the Big Boys Club, in which football is played and steam let off on imaginary motor bikes. 'It lets them be boys in this all-girls environment', said one mother.

Very much a Catholic school, with about 70 per cent Catholic parents. 'I think one of the most wonderful things about it is that the Catholic ethos permeates every aspect of the children's life', said one. Those who wish can be prepared for First Holy Communion by much-loved Father Chris on his twice-weekly visits to the school chapel. Pupils participate in mass and study Catholic Christianity. 'Many of our parents have had a Catholic education themselves and want that for their children', says the head – but even those who haven't feel included. 'As a non-Catholic', said one parent, 'I was quite concerned at the outset, but Father Chris is so lovely and gives such interesting talks. They really teach the children how to be good and loving members of a community'.

Pupils are beaming and notably well-behaved (not a peep was heard when our guide was chatting to one teacher as children queued to leave the room). 'We really work hard at being positive. We want to catch children doing the right thing', says the head. Plenty of rewards for those who are caught doing things 'the St Mary's Way'; those who slip up are gently reminded of 'expectations'. 'We want pupils to do their best, to be their best,' says the head. Most pupils adore the school ('my daughter can't wait to get back after the holidays') and parents are equally appreciative. 'You're never made to feel unwelcome, you never feel you shouldn't be there', we were told.

Mostly professional families from Hampstead and the surrounding areas, with a wide range of backgrounds (from Europe, the US, Asia and the Far East). About half speak at least one other language at home (with good in-school support for newcomers on the foothills of English). Mums 'really involved' (with reading, bazaars, the library, uniform sale). Despite its Hampstead location, this is a fairly understated place and, unusually for a prep school, offers a number of full bursaries.

St Paul's Cathedral School

2 New Change, London EC4M 9AD

Independent • Pupils: 250; 35 boarders (boy choristers) • Ages: 4–13 • Fees: Day up to £13,932 pa; Boarding £21,989 pa

Tel: 020 7248 5156

Email: admissions@spcs.london.sch.uk
Website: www.spcslondon.com

33

Headmaster: Since 2009, Mr Neil Chippington MA (Cantab) FRCO (40s). Music scholar at Cranleigh, organ scholar at Cambridge, Fellow of the Royal College of Organists, music is certainly in his blood. Came from Winchester College where he was a housemaster for eight years and, having himself been a quirister (chorister) at Winchester Cathedral, seems to be the ideal person to have taken the responsibility of 30 boarding choristers and a school bursting with music. Says he wants to make sure that all children reach their academic potential and are stretched to the limit of their abilities without the school becoming a hothouse. Feels it is crucial to get the balance right so that both choristers and day children get a wide breadth of educational experience and benefit from each other's talents.

Currently reviewing the curriculum, looking at different ways of approaching CE. Open minded and not afraid of change. Says 'the bottom line is to instil a love of learning'. Has introduced a more significant staff appraisal system. Communication apparently an issue when he arrived but believes he has opened up the lines. Responds quickly to emails and maintains an open door policy. Parents acknowledge this improvement. Married with two small sons, the elder of whom is at the school.

Entrance: Seventy on list for 20 available places at 4+, so best to put children down early. Informal assessment in November before year of entry. More places at 7+ when boarding choristers also start. January assessment and short test for day children (also taken by those in pre-prep); informal audition with director of music for choristers, followed by formal audition and same academic test as day children. More places for choristers at 8+ and occasionally 9+. Choristers' fees paid by Dean and Chapter of St Paul's Cathedral with parents paying boarding fee. This will carry on even if a boy's voice breaks early. If in need, bursaries available for day children also. Head is keen to build up a fund and expand this.

Exit: At 11+ and 13+ to a mixture of London day schools and top boarding schools. Majority of girls at 11+ though head eager to keep girls and maintain balance. Choristers mostly to boarding schools at 13+. An impressive number of music and the occasional academic scholarships. Westminster appears high among day schools, with Alleyn's, City of London (girls and boys), Dulwich College, Highgate, Forest School and JAGS also featuring. King's Canterbury popular amongst a wide selection of good boarding schools. Recently, Eton, Stowe, Uppingham and Oundle have all offered academic and music scholarships. Famous ex pupils include Alastair Cooke (England cricket captain) and Simon Russell Beale (actor).

Remarks: A small school, nestling in the precincts of St Paul's Cathedral, providing an excellent all round education in a traditional setting with a formal, spiritual context to everything it does. In amongst the hustle and bustle of the City of London, an oasis of orderliness and calm. Boy choristers have been around since 1123, originally linked to a grammar school which became St Paul's School, London, about 400 years later. Only tenuous links remain. In 1989, the Dean and Chapter decided to expand the tiny choristers' only school to include day boys as well. Girls arrived in 1998 and the school grew to the size it is today.

In amongst the hustle and bustle of the city of London, an oasis of orderliness and calm. Boy choristers have been around since 1123

Two low concrete towers house the classrooms and are linked by the school hall, the gym, the library and various other communal activity areas. We seemed to wander up and down and across as enthusiastic pupils showed us their school but 'once you know the two towers it's easy,' they assured us. Three lovely bright classrooms for the pre-prep years, two each for years 3 and 4, then subject-based doubling up as home rooms from year 5 onwards.

Broad-based curriculum with all subjects well taught. Parents praise 'inspirational teachers' who are 'passionate about everything they do'. Average age 39 seems about right. Our guides also spoke enthusiastically about their teachers, singling out science and Latin/Greek as exceptional. Certainly pupils did look happy and absorbed in the excellent science lab, however the French class we looked in on appeared chaotic. Mixed ability classes throughout with some discreet setting, particularly in years 7 and 8. Previously some complaints about lack of preparation for 11+ entrance exams but head is driving this forward and has made important changes, revamping part of the curriculum and timetabling non-verbal reasoning, study skills etc into earlier years. Parents very happy about this. Creative writing, apparently, a great strength. Latin compulsory from year 5. Modern languages not the strongest point, though French taught from the beginning and Spanish available as an extra. Head's wife a linguist, so change could be in the air. Interactive white boards in classrooms and new IT suite. All special needs problems dealt with by head of learning support. Teachers flag up concerns and he is immediately involved. Any necessary help is provided, mostly free of charge. Additional staff available for one-to-one and in-class support when necessary. Parents kept fully in the picture and involved from the beginning.

Reasonable art. Studio also contains a printing press (given by the Stationers' Company) and a kiln for firing imaginative clay models. Location excellent for visiting Tate Modern as part of extended art lesson. Drama strongish and everyone gets a chance to take part in a production. As one of our guides said, 'if you're not particularly musical, you can still do drama and have fun'. LAMDA exam course available.

Inevitably the greatest strength is music, huge both instrumentally and vocally. Virtually every child in the school learns an instrument of his or her choice (no bagpipes!). Choristers learn two, piano being compulsory. Over 300 music lessons given each week, beginners all the way to grade 8. At least six different choirs plus 15 orchestras and ensembles from classic to rock band. Something for everyone you might say. For musical, creative children it is a great place to be. Opportunities abound. Choristers are in the minority but it is their talent that is the backbone of the school. Head feels that one of the most crucial things he needs to do is clarify the way they are perceived. The day school exists because of them and they are getting a wider breadth of education because of the day school. Thus both sides are gaining a huge amount and it is important to maintain the balance. Choristers are acquiring an excellent academic education and day pupils are seeing, hearing and being involved in music of an exceptionally high standard. All of

them are equally at home in the cathedral, which they treat as an extension of the school. Assemblies and occasional special services held and the majority get the chance to sing there. A parent told us, 'the Christmas service was something to behold.. about six or seven different choirs were fielded, including a combined one which seemed to involve most of the school'.

Virtually every child in the school learns an instrument of his or her choice (no bagpipes!). Choristers learn two

Choristers have a pretty heavy schedule with singing practice before school every morning, evensong on Tuesdays, Wednesdays, Fridays and Saturdays plus Saturday morning rehearsals and Sunday services – alongside a multitude of other occasions when they have to perform. One of the first things the head did for them was to negotiate Monday evenings off as well as Thursdays. Seems only fair after an action-packed weekend. He also stresses the importance of watching the development of their voices and becoming more aware of change – necessary with the earlier physical growth that now occurs. Thirteen-year-old trebles are rarer. Both the cathedral's director of music and organist are also committed to their personal development and nurture.

Separate boarding house with two resident qualified nurses; common room with snooker, table football etc. Many choristers live relatively close by and are allowed out with their families during free time in between services at weekends, including Sunday evenings (though they must be back in time for before-school Monday rehearsals). Those without nearby families are taken out by staff on duty at weekends.

A father said, 'Sport at the school is active, fun and inclusive'. Despite its inner city site, it is well catered for. Pupils are bused to Coram's Fields and Regent's Park for seasonal activities. Matches fielded against other schools in hockey, football, cricket, rounders, fencing and netball. Have been runners up in U12 London Schools' Cricket Association Cup, winners of the Girls' Football South London Tournament and pupils have been selected for the U10 National Fencing Squad and the U11 Surrey County Cricket squad. Also swim at local baths recreationally and competitively. Rubber surfaced playground, marked up for ball games, for the prep where teachers also arrange impromptu games and sports practice. Brand new, larger, grass and woodchip playground with climbing equipment for the pre-prep. Older children allowed to play quiet games here but not allowed to climb.

A variety of after-school clubs, mainly on Thursdays to enable choristers to join in, but on other days too. Range from cookery to dance to computing etc. Bound to be something for everyone. Also children may stay to do supervised prep at school, charged as an extra but useful for working parents. Plenty of outings and expeditions, academic, cultural and sporty. Home and occasionally abroad. A lot to see within walking distance as well.

Parents stress the happy atmosphere – 'it has been the making of our little boy' – (of a chorister) and 'our unsettled, troublemaker has been transformed' – (of a day boy). 'Very good discipline, they don't tolerate bad behaviour'. General feeling that children are treated as individuals, academically stretched and made to work to their own levels; that the school is 'well managed and well ordered'. Much of this appears to lie in the vertical tutor system. Pupils are assigned to a tutor from day one and, in normal circumstances, remain with him/her until they leave the school. Thus tutor groups mixed in both ability and age and there is easy rapport between all children across the school. The older ones love helping the younger ones.

According to parents, excellent pastoral care, particularly for the boarders. 'They get well cared for, individual treatment and feel they are part of a family'. Several raved about the deputy head (pastoral) who, they say, really carried the school through recent difficult times. Definitely feel there's a good team in place now.

Effective and active PTA. General feeling is that head is in tune with all pupils and ideal person to be running the boarding section as well. Watch this spot for further developments.

St Peter's Eaton Square CofE Primary School

Lower Belgrave Street, London SW1W 0NL

State • Pupils: 310 (plus 30 in nursery) • Ages: 3–11 • C of E

Tel: 020 7641 4230

58

Email: office@stpeaton.org.uk
Website: www.stpeaton.org.uk

Head: Since 2010, Ms Nicola Cottier BEd Cantab (40s). Previously head of St Matthew's, Westminster, since 1996. Educated at Sutton High, her first job was at Moira House, an independent girls' school in Sussex. She has worked in the Bahamas, United States, Canada and Wales, but most recently in London schools with church links. She is married with two children, and lives in Kew. She revolutionised the music provision at St Matthew's, where she was described as an 'inspirational headteacher' who 'created the most wonderful spirit in the school'. She is hugely enthusiastic, rhapsodising about the 'fantastic' ethos and supportive community at St Peter's.

Entrance: Ten part-time nursery places. No automatic transfer to reception – must re-apply and meet criteria. Nearly all of the nursery places go to baptised children whose families worship regularly at St Peter's Church Eaton Square; preference after that to siblings, then to baptised children who attend other churches without their own church school. Families come from a wide area and a huge range of backgrounds – 'duchesses to dustmen'. Apply through the local authority, with supplementary school form, during autumn term a year before entry. Takes 50 children into reception, again according to criteria.

Exit: Girls to Grey Coat Hospital, St Marylebone, Lady Margaret's; boys to London Nautical, Pimlico

Academy etc. Over half to independent schools: Westminster Under School, JAGS, City of London, St Paul's, Godolphin and Latymer, Emanuel, Streatham & Clapham High etc. Children not encouraged to move on to independents at 7 or 8: 'We won't go out of our way to support it. It is disruptive, and our children do very well getting the places they want at 11.' A parent commented: 'Why would you want to move earlier when they all do so well here?'

There is a strong community of parents, many of whom also meet at church events, and including those who attended the school themselves

Remarks: Very popular and over-subscribed central London primary school, tucked away in a side street just round the corner from Victoria Station. Consistently excellent, lively teaching, with each child's progress closely tracked. The majority of pupils reach level 5 in year 6: a huge achievement. Languages strong: Latin from year 3 upwards. Dedicated IT suite with 30 computers. Inclusion Manager has responsibility for EAL and G&T as well as those with SEN. Teaching assistants deployed to support children as needed. Parents also pitch in as eg volunteer readers. Good at spotting problems with vulnerable children and liaising with outside agencies where necessary. 'We always cater for a wide range of needs.' Two reception classes of 25; higher up, the children in each of years 1/2, 3/4 and 4/5 are divided by age into three classes over two year groups.

'We are blessed that we have really fabulous music.' No orchestra, but peripatetic teachers for recorder, violin, drums, guitar, piano and brass, as well as class music lessons, trips to concerts at the Barbican etc, singing at the Royal Albert Hall and at Friday's Sung Eucharist service. Very little space for sport on site – the hall is used for gym and PE and the small, soft-surface playground has a climbing wall along one side. However, they swim at the Queen Mother Sports Centre (notable successes in galas), play sports in Battersea Park and Hyde Park (year 1 were off for a multi-skills session when we visited) and borrow Westminster School's Vincent Square sports site. Professional sports coaches run twice-weekly sessions, and football, cricket and tennis teams play in inter-school matches. 'It's such a cramped site that we try to get them out as much as possible.'

Enrichment is a buzz word here and there are plenty of outings – 'It's a fabulous situation: everything is on our doorstep' – to eg the V&A, National Gallery, London Zoo. Year 6 visits Sayers Croft field centre in Surrey. Girls from Grey Coat Hospital do work experience at St Peter's, and pupils visit Westminster City School for their science week. Strong tradition of raising funds for charity.

St Peter's was first mentioned in an 1860s survey as an infants' school in Ecclestone Square. Moved to its present site, donated by the Marquess of Westminster, in 1872; became an infant and junior school in 1949. Building and site compact, but even the basement nursery classrooms are light, bright and cheerful; youngest classes have their own indoor/outdoor partly-covered play area. The upper floor classrooms, carved from the top half of a hall, have beautiful large, round windows. Airy feel but very cramped for space: every nook and cranny has at least three different uses. A major building project in 2012 remodelled the school to create sufficient classrooms to introduce two forms incrementally into each year group.

School follows Anglo-Catholic tradition and there are services at school and in Westminster Abbey as well as in the strongly-linked namesake church: clergy pop in and out and are available for counselling. The church interior, redesigned after an anti-Catholic arson attack 20 years ago, is a beautiful, simple, open space which 'lends itself to our nativity plays' and is also the setting for year 6 productions, concerts and speech days as well as services.

Professional sports coaches run twice-weekly sessions, and football, cricket and tennis teams play in inter-school matches

A tightly-run ship: children are neat and tidy, with tucked-in shirts and tied-back hair. They are orderly in class and move quietly around the building. The atmosphere is welcoming, friendly and purposeful. Parents appreciate the combination of excellent behaviour, kind ethos and inspiring teaching. 'It is a warm and safe place,' said one.

Active PTA which organises social events such as Burns Night and helps with eg Easter Fair. This is not a local school – families come from a wide area – but there is a strong community of parents, many of whom also meet at church events, and including those who attended the school themselves. Children who have moved on to secondary school come back to do work experience and spread their news. 'We know they do well wherever they go.'

St Saviour's CofE Primary School

Shirland Road, Maida Vale, London W9 2JD

State • Pupils: 240 • Ages: 3–11 • C of E

Tel: 020 7641 6414

Email: office@stsavioursprimary.co.uk
Website: www.stsavioursprimary.co.uk/

59

Headteacher: Since 1994, Ms Lindsey Woodford, BA in education from London University. A warm, humorous, approachable woman with none of the lofty airs that waft around some heads. 'She's fun and she's ballsy, but she's strict. It's a winning combination.' Happy to muck in, she even joined a team of parents in a sponsored swim to raise £12k to Astroturf the playground. 'I don't know many other headteachers who'd don a wetsuit and swim 3.5km in the Thames. She's pretty game.' Her office, far from being a scary place, is crammed with 100-200 soft toys which have colonised every available surface. She is ably assisted by Ripley, her border terrier, who is adored by the children. Pupils who have done well (or are perhaps just feeling a bit glum) are occasionally awarded 'Ripley Time', which means being allowed to sit in her office for a supervised stroking session.

In her spare time Ms Woodford enjoys embroidery, crime novels, antiques and baking. We can vouch for her excellent homemade biscuits (gooey peanut butter flavour the day we visited). Very much hands on – small children approach her for a hug as we walk through the playground (and you can't fake that). Previously deputy head at St Michael's in Highgate, following stints at schools in Bucks, Brent, Haringey and Ealing, so oodles of experience. A local girl, she was born at nearby St Mary's Hospital and attended Parliament Hill School in North London. She is married to the contractor who created the nursery in 2000. The ultimate accolade comes from a grateful mother. 'I'm proud of how my daughters have turned out and I feel they have been formed by Ms Woodford as much as they have by me. I owe her a lot.'

Entrance: Heavily over-subscribed one form entry school. Over 90 applicants for nursery and 140 for 30 reception places. Nursery is mornings only, though afternoons are available for a fee. No catchment area; pupils come from as far afield as Camden, Kentish Town, Kensal Rise and Harlesden. After the customary preference given to looked-after children, admission boils down to enthusiastic worship at one of two affiliated churches, St Saviour's and St Mary on Paddington Green. This means 'at least three Sundays every month for at least a year before application'. Prospective parents might want to reconsider that sneaky lie-in every fourth Sunday, as admission is uncompromisingly awarded to the 'most frequent worshippers'. And don't even think of slacking off once you've got your foot in the door as progress from nursery to reception depends on continued regular worship – a rule that is enforced. 'We hate to lose children but it does happen,' admits the head.

Admission for siblings languishes way down at no 8 on the list of criteria, though occasional places in later years are well worth applying for as later places are awarded 'on need'.

Exit: Pupils progress to a wide variety of schools. Favourite state schools include Greycoats, St Marylebone and Twyford High School, plus Paddington Academy, Holland Park and St George's. The head is also very open to the independent sector ('We love a good badge') with pupils winning places at Highgate, St Paul's Girls', Latymer Upper, City of London, UCS, Merchant Taylors', Channing plus boarding schools like Christ's Hospital and Wycombe Abbey. It's enough to turn an expensive prep school head green with envy.

'For the last two years we've got a child into Colet Court [junior school for St Paul's] at 11 plus. They only take 10 children a year, so we're very proud of that.'

'I don't know many headteachers who'd don a wetsuit and swim 3.5km in the Thames'

Secondary transfer meeting in September where both state and independent school admissions are explained and various bursaries and scholarship options discussed. 'It's never too early to come and talk to me.' Parents who are considering the independent sector are given advice from year 2 onwards, plus suggestions for specific tutors. Ms Woodford is brutally honest about a child's chances of success. 'I don't mind where children go on to as long as it's the right school for that child'.

Remarks: Nestling in a quiet side street amongst the tall wedding cake mansions of Maida Vale, this Ofsted outstanding state primary has won more awards than you can shake a stick at. But, despite the wealthy area, this is no middle class ghetto school.

'It's truly comprehensive,' said one parent. 'You've got people who live in million pound houses and families who live in local authority housing by the canal. Everybody just gets on with it and befriends each other.'

Here the classrooms are large and light-drenched with walls of vast windows

Broad international mix with 35 languages spoken (the largest groups being white British, followed by Eritrean and other African). A tranche of bankers, diplomats and media types alongside a large number of low income families just above the free meals threshold. Twenty-four children on free school meals (approx 10 per cent) when we visited, though the number waxes and wanes. Winner of Boris Johnson's Gold Club Award for succeeding against the odds in improving pupils' achievements. 'It doesn't matter to us that we get a badge for it, what matters is our free school meal pupils do at least as well, if not better, than other pupils. We buck the trend,' says the head.

The socially and culturally diverse mix makes the school's outstanding results all the more impressive. Over 60 per cent of pupils regularly achieve level 5 in Sats, and they are top of the Westminster league table for pupils achieving level 6 (expected level for 14 year olds). 'They really encourage each child to discover something they can excel in, whether it's art, English, maths or anything else,' said one happy parent. 'It's not just about sitting exams, it's about becoming a well rounded, caring, bright little person who wants to learn.'

Our immediate first impressions were that St Saviour's is an exceptionally smiley school. We got eye contact and a friendly grin from pupils and adults alike as we waited in reception, and the smiles kept on coming throughout our tour. In an age when so many children look down and mumble when addressed by an adult, the confidence of these pupils shines out. Clearly, the social graces are given the same importance at this state primary as they are in the private sector.

Bog-standard Victorian school building, but preferable to the cramped conditions so often seen in converted premises used by some London independents. Here the classrooms are large and light-drenched with walls of vast windows. Trad architecture could feel forbidding in dark stairwells, but they've done their best to create a bright, cosy and well cared-for learning space. Walls covered in excellent artwork. Comfortable sofas, toys and a multi-sensory room in the early years section. Pupil loos are clean and colourful (no smells) and only one wet tissue apologetically stuck to the ceiling.

Separate junior and senior playgrounds. Outside space is limited, typical of most inner city primaries, but they've made the most of what could have been a rather dank concrete area. Good range of outdoor toys including space hoppers, a climbing wall and some rather grand-looking trees in pots. Small side garden growing potatoes, rhubarb and herbs and we even spotted the head's mum who had popped in to tend the plants. Truly a family-oriented school.

Setting starts in reception, with four groups per class. Some groups might have just two pupils, while others are much larger, depending on the needs of each individual year group. Teaching assistants work with higher ability as well as lower ability pupils. 'We focus on what each child needs.' Weekly Spanish lessons from reception onwards with a linguist Star of the Week award.

Regular pupil progress meetings to identify and keep track of underperforming pupils. Each child on the SEN register has a target sheet so progress can be tracked in lessons and support groups, and to ensure no child slips through the net. A qualified SEN specialist working part time is ably supported by battalions of TAs trained in many different types of strategies and interventions. Success of the school's support safety net self-evident in outstanding results for all pupils, regardless of background. 'I have a dyslexic daughter and they are very clever with their thinking,' said one mother. 'If you can't learn your times tables they'll come up with another way to teach them to you. They teach each individual child, rather than sticking to a formula.'

Lessons are suspended and every corner of the school given over to creative activities

Provision in sports and the arts is a huge strength at St Saviour's. Thriving PTA holds monthly fundraisers to generate over £65k a year, most of which is used to fund three specialist teachers for art, music and sport. This means, in addition to the standard PE hour with class teachers, all pupils have a weekly session with a professional sports coach. There are also dance lessons with a West End choreographer, covering fun stuff like Bollywood, musicals and Strictly Come Dancing.

Then there's swimming in year 4, cycle training in year 5 and the year 6 pupils do a course of horse riding lessons in Hyde Park. Opportunities to try tennis, golf, cricket and tag-rugby and to compete in teams against other schools.

Art is taken seriously here and is of a high standard. The PTA-funded Artist in Residence works with each year group on a project relating to subjects they are studying in class, for example year 3 pupils made a giant sarcophagus when they were studying the Egyptians. We saw excellent William Morris designs done by year 5 while studying the Victorians, screen prints of the Tudors by year 4, and some awesome studies of real fish done by gifted and talented pupils. Pupils identified as G&T in art are given additional opportunities to work on projects with visiting artists (such as designing the 3D climbing wall), plus there are regular drama and music workshops run by outside experts.

For working parents there's an (oversubscribed) wrap-around care scheme running up to 6pm and a two week summer holiday camp. All staff members (including the headteacher) are responsible for an extracurricular club running from 3.30-4.30pm. Pupils can choose from horticulture, ICT, arts and crafts, media, football, website, cooking, construction, choir and many other options. More innovatively, there's a coding club, and coding is also taught as part of the curriculum in years 3 and 4. 'Coding is a big buzz in education at the moment and we're right at the forefront of that,' says Ms Woodford.

What sets St Saviour's apart is the head's boundless enthusiasm and creativity. 'What we do here is we don't say no. We consider all ideas and are willing to try new things'. STEAMco was a concept some parents had seen at a festival. It's now an annual day when lessons are suspended and every corner of the school is given over to different creative activities such 3D printing, learning the ukulele, an apothecary's garden, dance, sculpture, making furniture out of newspaper, launching home-made rockets, cooking and much more. Pupils are free to browse at will – some try everything, others stick with one experience all day. Year 6 pupils built an electric goblin eco-car designed to spark an interest in engineering, which they subsequently raced at Goodwood. Then there's Maths Week. Every class pitches a business idea to Ms Woodford and she decides whether to 'lend' them £20. The class must turn a profit and pay her back, plus one per cent interest, by the end of the week. Business pitches mostly involve making and selling various sweets and cakes but pupils have fun and grasp the idea of profit, loss and interest.

Pastoral provision is outstanding. Each child selects two staff 'listening partners' that they can talk to about any fears or worries. Some staff members are chosen by 20 children, others just a handful, but even the catering staff and site manager have their listenees. Then there is a Buddy System in which each year 6 pupil is paired up with a reception 'buddy'. The buddies read and play together, go on trips and can be invited to tea by the respective parents. There is a daytime 'sleepover' where pupils bring a pillow, toy and sleeping bag and lie in the art room reading stories to each other.

Few behavioural problems. A general policy of positive behavioural reinforcement, high expectations and aspiration seems to work well. Much ado is made of the Star of The Week system, with postcards sent home, a mention in the newsletter and announcements at school. Four houses (named after planets) and team points awarded for a variety of endeavours. 'The school is strict and that's what I love about it. They will not tolerate any bullying and they don't like cliques either. Pupils are encouraged to be friends with everyone, so nobody is left out,' said a satisfied parent.

St Vincent de Paul RC Primary School

Morpeth Terrace, London SW1P 1EP

Tel: 020 7641 5990

State • Pupils: 250 • Ages: 3–11 • RC

Email: office@svpschool.co.uk
Website: www.svpschool-primary.org.uk

Head: Since September 2015, Mr Nathaniel Scott-Cree, previously deputy head at St Vincent's Primary School in Marylebone.

Entrance: Always oversubscribed. Nursery children are not guaranteed entry into the main school at 4+. Priority given to practising Roman Catholics, with distance from the school used as a tiebreaker. First priority goes to looked after Catholic children, then baptised, practising siblings, then baptised Catholics. A waiting list is kept for occasional places.

Exit: Most pupils get their first choice secondary school. Popular choices include Sacred Heart, London Oratory, Cardinal Vaughan and St Thomas More as well as others further afield including Westminster Cathedral Choir School.

Remarks: School was founded in 1859 by the Sisters of Charity of St Vincent de Paul to enable them to work with the poor of Westminster. Moved to current premises in the shadows of Westminster Cathedral, conveniently next door to St Paul's bookshop, in 1974.

Pupils come from a wide variety of backgrounds. Around three-quarters speak English as an additional language. Fairly compact site – outdoor space has been redeveloped to create three separate play areas for nursery children, infants and juniors. Cleverly designed, with lots of greenery and modern play equipment. Pupils also use the playgrounds and local sports facilities for team sports and have a dedicated sports coach for all PE lessons. Inside, school is light, modern and well designed. Peaceful chapel is very much at the heart of this friendly and well-disciplined school.

While this is a Catholic school, pupils are taught to understand other faiths and cultures. Good behaviour, thinking of others and cooperation goes without saying. Pupils are monitored regularly to assess their progress and there are plenty of parents' evenings, giving everyone the opportunity to discuss their children. Written reports at the end of each year.

Alongside the national curriculum, the arts and sports, pupils benefit from being taught Spanish from the age of 7. Latin is introduced in year 4. Academic results are exceptional. Staff have high expectations and have created a good learning ethos. The SENCo coordinates additional needs and runs a Units of Sound action programme. There is also a school counsellor.

Multi-coloured and multimedia displays of artwork adorn classrooms and corridors. Large,

Peaceful chapel is very much at the heart of this friendly and well-disciplined school

multi-purpose hall where children practise for termly concerts and plays and musical performances. School is part of the Westminster Cathedral Choir School outreach programme and the choir performs at Westminster Cathedral as well as singing regularly at family mass. Well-stocked music room with an impressive selection of instruments – from glockenspiels to bongo drums. All have singing and music lessons, provided by a dedicated music teacher. Pupils talk excitedly about how they are encouraged to create their own music. Small charge is made for individual lessons on a wide range of instruments.

Sixth formers from neighbouring Westminster School work as volunteers, acting as classroom assistants and helping to run school clubs. ICT room doubles up as a cinema for film club.

Not a place for those who wish to sit on their laurels. Energetic PTA meets regularly to discuss the organisation of numerous fundraising events for the school. Each family is asked to make a small annual contribution towards the maintenance and building fund – for the benefit of the present community and to ensure continuation for future generations. Pupils are active fundraisers and run regular charity events. The school also works with Mission Together, a charity that encourages children to care about mission through prayer, learning and fundraising.

A lively and impressive school that produces caring and thoughtful individuals. Recently downgraded by Ofsted to 'requires improvement', largely due to lack of challenge at KS1. However, parents praise it to the rafters and pupils say they look forward to going to school.

Sarum Hall School

15 Eton Avenue, London NW3 3EL

Independent · Pupils: 180 · Ages: 3–11 · C of E · Fees: up to £13,500 pa

Tel: 020 7794 2261

22

Email: admissions@sarumhallschool.co.uk
Website: www.sarumhallschool.co.uk

Headmistress: Since 2008, Mrs Christine Smith BA Cert Ed RSH (SpLD) (50s). Previously at Lochinver Prep in Potter's Bar, where she is now governor. Originally taught home economics and textiles at

Edmonton County School, which she left to bring up her two daughters. Subsequently returned to teach deaf children, later becoming director of studies at Lochinver and setting up their learning support unit. When her children left home, she wanted a new challenge and 'fell in love' with Sarum Hall the moment she visited. Believes she's known for being kind, fair, calm, trustworthy, experienced and well connected in the educational world and, on the whole, parents agree, adding that she's 'lovely', 'nice,' 'always smiling' and a 'great listener.' 'Whether it's staff, food or sports day, if you have something to suggest, she'll seriously consider it,' said one parent. Mostly office bound, although she does greet the girls, teaches SRE, and dines with them, daily, along with all the usual lesson observations, assemblies etc. Not a captain that socialises with her crew, we feel, although the head points out that she has an open door policy and provides a long list of ways she supports her staff including organising end of term meals out. Married to an actuary, with interests including tai chi, cooking, theatre and martial arts (she spent time in Beijing learning about swords).

Entrance: Main intake in September after 3rd birthday, with parents invited to register as soon after birth as possible, with a non-refundable registration fee of £100. Parents invited to visit the school on a working day two years before entry, then write to confirm their continued interest. Non-selective, although priority given to siblings and children and grandchildren of former pupils (of whom there are many). The rest of the 23-24 nursery places are based on the head's decision. 'I meet with all parents and am looking for those who understand

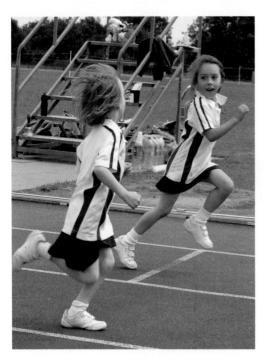

> *This very much sets the mood of the school, which parents repeatedly refer to as turning out 'very well-mannered young ladies'*

that the arts, and indeed play, are as important as academic learning for children's development,' she says, although presumably that's all of them, unless they failed to research the school before applying. It's all a bit vague for our liking; we feel that fitting in probably plays a vital part.

Exit: Almost all to their first choice of school at 11: Channing, City Girls, Francis Holland, Godolphin & Latymer, Highgate, Immanuel, North London Collegiate, South Hampstead, St Helen's and St Paul's. Unusually for a north London prep, a fair number go on to board too, at the likes of Cheltenham, Queenswood and Wycombe Abbey. Recommendations as to the next school very much the head's own, for which she uses her 'first-hand knowledge of the girls, together with the teachers' recommendations, results, tracking data, and my knowledge of the families, which the teachers are not always privy to.'

Remarks: Nestling among the opulent period homes of this leafy north London street is a contemporary, RIBA-lauded, purpose-built building, with no less than three secured doors to get inside the learning environment ('Safeguarding means a lot to our girls' parents,' explains the head). Inside the building, which was completed in 1995 (although the school itself dates back to 1928), the combination of high design standards, light oak floors, high ceilings, masses of natural light and (recently) air conditioning makes for a welcoming, airy space in which to work, move about and play. White walls are tastefully decorated with displays of the girls' work from across the curriculum and there's no shortage of colour, ranging from the odd single fuchsia wall here and there to groups of pastel colour chairs. If anything, there's over-use of pink, but this very much sets the mood of the school, which parents repeatedly refer to as turning out 'very well-mannered young ladies.' These are girls that will hold the door for you even if you're still half way down the hall and who, from year 2, leap to their feet when the head enters and chorus 'Good morning, Mrs Smith.'

Not that there's any compromise on academic learning. The head's unwavering vision of the school focuses on being both academic (with an expectation that girls go onto further education and huge praise from parents about girls being superbly prepared for 11+), as well as having a strong emphasis on the arts.

New national curriculum forms the cornerstone of learning, but without the dreaded Sats and with embellishment of other subjects, including French from reception, Mandarin in years 4 and 5 and Spanish for one term in year 6. Specialist subject teaching in music, IT and French from nursery, science from year 3, English, maths and humanities in years 5 and 6. Some setting in maths. Big emphasis on cross-curricular teaching, with girls preparing for a performance of Frozen when we visited, having made the characters (art), in preparation to perform the play (drama) in French (languages). Great attention to tailored learning, with plenty of classroom assistance and additional work, for instance, for those sitting boarding school entrance exams.

Music, art and drama all thriving. Music facilities include a spacious ground-floor room, with no shortage of instruments, while the rooftop extension, completed in 2000, provides three practice rooms and the so-called Rainbow room, which is used for rehearsals, workshops, fencing, the wellbeing programme (relaxation, yoga etc) and a resting place for girls in nursery after lunch. Majority of girls study one or more instruments after year 2, with plenty of opportunity to perform in assemblies, recital evenings and frequent concerts. Junior and senior choirs, open to everyone. 'My daughter does 8 music-related things a week including choir, music theory, music lessons and two instruments,' lauds one parent.

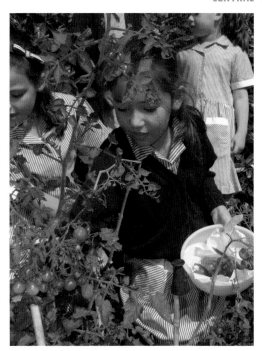

Girls particularly love the five colourful beach–huts. Surrounding this are wormeries, raised beds and an environmental pond

Drama taught in the Rainbow room, school hall and upstairs in the new playhouse, with performances generally including double year groups, and including recent examples of A Midsummer Night's Dream and Olivia the Musical. Also sit the English Speaking Board exams (and LAMDA if requested) to build up communication skills. Fabulous high-ceilinged studio art room, with girls studying sculpture, textiles, woodwork and more. Facilities include a printing press and kiln. Plenty of outings to exhibitions, including the Royal Academy, with which the school has close links.

IT suite has 16 computers organised on round tables, with half the class using it at any one time. Chrome books and iPads also used in the classroom, although not to any great extent. Well-equipped science lab, with a teacher having

introduced sustainability in a big way to the school. Sunlit, well-stocked library, with soft beige carpet and big wooden table in the middle, with 12 colourful chairs and plenty of visits from authors, such as Helen Peters and James Mayhew.

Nursery and reception areas nurturing, with a good mix of tables and chairs and dedicated play areas, including an (again pink) indoor wigwam and freeflow outdoor space on the balcony, with two stylish 'SH' embossed canopies to keep the sun off young skin. Plenty of mingling with older girls, thanks to buddying and monitor opportunities, along with a shared play time once every half-term.

Outdoor space had been recently refurbished when we visited and although by no means vast, it's exceptionally well-planned and welcoming, with a new two-storey playhouse in the middle of the play area to provide more surface area of play (and welcome shade on hot days). Girls are free to use the lower level during breaks, whilst the upper level is used for drama, small group workshops and exhibitions. Girls particularly love the five colourful beach-huts. 'With the middle three, each of the houses chooses what goes in them,' explains one girl. 'Our one has sporty things, and the other two are for crafts or being creative.' Surrounding this and the adjacent sports court are wormeries, raised beds and an environmental pond, allowing children grow vegetables and herbs and do gardening club, all of which have helped the school achieve Green Flag status. 'In terms of being green, they've achieved a lot, even by Camden standards,' says one parent.

Daily sport (netball, hockey, rounders, soccer, cricket and tennis) takes place on the court or in the assembly hall, which doubles as a gym for both dance and gymnastics, and triples as a theatre. Swimming once more part of the curriculum, at nearby Swiss Cottage Baths one afternoon a week for one term for year 4. Cross-country at Primrose Hill. Annual sports day becoming more competitive and challenging, after parents complained it was too gentle.

Pupil voice much improved in recent years, with eco team and school council having made changes to snacks, lunch menus, uniforms and are regularly involved in décor decisions.

'We go to church three times a year and the vicar comes in for some assemblies. But I recently invited a rabbi too'

Breakfast club from 7.30am, and homework club until 4.30pm, included at no extra cost. Over 40 after-school clubs (photography, chess and draughts, yoga, board games among them), also included in the fees, unless outside staff need to be brought in. Plenty of outings, particularly to London museums and galleries. Residential trips to Norfolk for year 5 and a château in France for year 6. Homework introduced gently in year 2, rising to around an hour a night in year 6.

The girls themselves 'aren't the most savvy and streetwise,' as one parent puts it. 'But all the parents I know like it that way,' she adds. 'It can make the transition to senior school a bigger deal, but having nice, polite girls is a good trade-off,' says another. Behavioural problems minimal and nipped in the bud, with strict use of policies and procedures. 'Positive rewards for good behaviour and our constant emphasis on Golden Rules help,' adds the head. 'These are different to school rules because they're about how we should behave, rather than what we mustn't do. We are gentle, kind and helpful. We listen and are honest and work hard. We look after property. We don't hurt anybody's feelings' etc. If a girl doesn't work hard, or indeed underperforms for any other reason, her case gets taken to the weekly curriculum meeting and a plan put in place, with full parental involvement.

Great food (all clean plates when we visited and we cleared our own too) prepared daily on site, with vegetarian option and great excitement about puddings such as Arctic roll and sponge and custard. Served in dining room, with pastel spotty tablecloths to brighten up the four rows of long tables with benches, where staff eat with girls after grace has been said.

Christian background, but head quick to point out that they support other faiths. 'We say the Lord's Prayer daily, go to church three times a year and the vicar comes in for some assemblies. But I recently invited a rabbi too.' Big on charitable fundraising, with each house choosing a children's charity each term, then arranging activities to raise money for it.

Parents and pupils reasonably multicultural, but mainly affluent, white, middle-class. Plenty of bankers, lawyers, solicitors and barristers. Many girls have brothers at The Hall and Arnold House (and head tries to coordinate term dates). Bursary fund, which is means-tested. One girl on it when we visited, with another about to join. Many of the governors have a connection to the school and have been there for many years, with (unusually) no set system of election or removal.

Learning support unit has one dedicated member of staff (trained to RSA level 7) who comes in four days a week. Copes with mild dyslexia, dyspraxia (five children in total when we visited) and the 'gifted and talented' at no extra cost. Support is mainly in the large dedicated room, but some classroom assistance too. Two deaf children when we visited ('The school has been incredible with meeting her additional needs and going the extra mile,' says the parent of one) and one child had just been offered a place with a visual impairment. But whilst school is well laid out for wheelchair access, no child has ever attended who uses one. Won't take children with serious behavioural difficulties, although never had to turn anyone away or asked a child to leave. Outside help brought in for speech and language when required. School nurse recently brought in, who doubles up as school counsellor. 'Both my kids were flagged as needing extra help,' says one parent. 'The school kept me informed, had meetings and they made innovative suggestions, all of which has meant the children are now on the right path. I can't fault it.'

This is a small, intimate, highly structured and extremely traditional girls' prep in a stunning modern setting that gets children of a broad range of ability to reach their full potential, without too much pressure. 'I've got three girls at the school – one very academic, one shy and musical and the other in between, and they all shine,' says one parent. 'The school has a knack of fostering natural talent,' says another. Its emphasis on the arts and play, alongside academic learning, means it's not for the tiger parent and and its preciousness, emphasis on authority and very high expectations around manners means it's probably not for the non-conformist child either. 'But if you toe the line, this is a lovely, fun school that you see girls skipping into.'

Sir John Cass's Foundation Primary School

St James's Passage, 27 Duke's Place, London EC3A 5DE

Tel: 020 7283 1147

State · Pupils: 249 · Ages: 3m–11 · C of E

Email: office@sirjohncassprimary.org
Website: www.sirjohncassprimary.org

Headteacher: Since September 2014, Mr T Wilson.

Entrance: At 3+, oversubscribed (75 applications for 30 places) and priority given to families/children in need in the City of London, then those who attend St Botolph's or neighbouring churches and live in the area, then siblings. Worth ringing, since places do open up when families move out of the area. If your child gets a place in the nursery, the school will do its utmost to keep them throughout the school. The school is currently developing a proposal to expand to admit two forms of entry each year from 2016.

Exit: To full range of secondary schools – church, community, independent and residential eg City of London Girls, City of London Boys, Christ's Hospital, City Academy in Southwark. Since performing arts and music are so strong here parents are advised to look for opportunities for their children to continue.

Remarks: Founded in 1710, the only voluntary aided school in the City of London (so not short of resources); this Georgian mass is open 50 weeks a year and is so much more than just a school. An oasis in the traffic that is Aldgate (the pollution monitor in the playground registers remarkably low readings), pedestrians can peer down at the little ones in the courtyard of the Cass Child and Family Centre – 90 reading and language partners from surrounding offices volunteer at lunchtime. The main entrance is opposite a café, and visitors walk directly into the playground. The day we did, there was a line of helmeted children ready, with their trusty steeds, for their cycle safety test.

Between them pupils and parents speak 36 languages, and backgrounds range from two families sharing a flat to one with a Barbican pad and a house in the country. A teacher and a nursery officer work alongside class teachers to support those with English as a second language (50 per cent of the kids are Bangladeshi). A SENCo liaises with children, four LSAs and nine TAs for reading development, and school is also in touch with CAMHs. Snoezelen room in the nursery section is fully equipped with sensory equipment to calm children (and staff!). The school is totally inclusive of those with relevant support – at present three with statements and one with Down's Syndrome.

A key worker is assigned to four or five families and they are visited before children's entrance. The centre also offers an extended school service to the community with health and social visitors, Jobcentre Plus and lots of advice and support sessions for parents in the family learning room and The Sp@ce: computer lessons, volunteering at your school, child development classes, first aid, ESL and getting back to work training. Many social functions for parent and community group (eg summer market, international food night) and art projects have led to work exhibited in the V&A and the Bethnal Green Museum of Childhood.

The teaching team is stable and ranges from the newly qualified to those with 30 years of experience. RE is popular, with two terms on Christianity, the other on another world faith and, as with sex education, parents can withdraw their children from these lessons but none do. The curriculum is made real in all manner of ways: artist and poet residencies, a roof garden with class planters and greenhouse overlooked by Norman Foster's Gherkin, maths linked to musical notation and vice versa, the home beat police officer in class to talk about peer pressure and avoidance of gangs, after-school clubs (including knitting with senior citizens who provide tales of the war years to those kids with no extended family). Key stage 2 go on two school trips of a week each to experience life with their friends outside London.

A roof garden with planters and greenhouse overlooked by Norman Foster's Gherkin

A musicianship teacher begins strings project with the little ones (nursery to year 3) and by years 4, 5 and 6 all play a violin, cello etc of their own – groups have performed for the Lord Mayor, Prince Phillip, Bill Clinton and Tony Blair. The choir has sung on the Queen's Christmas broadcast and at the Royal Albert Hall (three-part harmony!).

The school coach runs relays to St George's Pool on the Highway or a crocodile of children snakes to the one in Golden Lane. The annual sports day takes place at Mile End stadium, the school competes as the City's team for the London Heathrow Games and occasionally plays rugby against other schools but, since it is the only one in the borough, there is not much competition. There's a traditionally equipped sports hall (huge windows and high ceilings) on the second floor, in addition to the lines of different courts painted in the playground.

The basement (a secure area in case of bomb threat) houses the computer suite with 15 workstations networked to a couple in each class and an interactive whiteboard. This technology doesn't come without an awareness of the environment: the school received an award for work on recycling paper, printer cartridges, composting and installing timers on light switches.

Food is cooked on the premises and served in what is now called The Restaurant on the top floor;

there are themed days with the menu scribed up on a whiteboard (tropical fruit, bread), and a comments book for the children. Some 35 per cent get free school meals. Manners are incredibly important here (one child says a prayer before everyone tucks in) and everyone learns to behave politely according to their surroundings, whether it is lunch at the Mansion House or breakfast club.

The Behaviour for Learning Policy is applied positively; however, a series of sanction slips is given out for ignoring the school code of conduct (respect, cooperation, truth and honesty, trying your best etc) – four of these mean the child will be excluded but this hardly ever happens. Fire drills and bomb alerts are necessarily slick with the head's bleeper linked directly to the City of London police.

South Hampstead High School Junior Department

Linked school: South Hampstead High School, 190

5 Netherhall Gardens, London NW3 5RN

Tel: 020 7794 7198

23

Independent • Pupils: 264 • Ages: 4–11 • Fees: £12,972 pa

Email: junior@shhs.gdst.net
Website: www.shhs.gdst.net/junior–school

Headmistress: Since September 2013, Mrs Gabrielle Solti BA PGCE (40s), previously head of Notting Hill and Ealing Junior School for 10 years. A welcome home-coming – she commuted from Hampstead while working in Ealing and previously taught at Trevor-Roberts, after which she was deputy head of Primrose Hill Primary. A highly experienced and much-admired head whose tenure here began simultaneously with that of the senior school head, Helen Pike – providing a significant injection of energy, inspiration and ability across both schools. Mrs Solti is that ideal junior school head – highly professional but intensely and personally committed to her school, her charges and to educational values. She is articulate, voluble and manages to be warm and vehement all at once. Realistic about her 'market', in this most aspirational part of the capital, she says, 'We are competing against other very good schools. People in this part of town are prepared to drive their children to wherever they think is best.' Mrs Solti's pupils may be thought the best judge of where – and who – is best. 'She's not like normal teachers who may just say, "oh, get on with it",' one seasoned year 6 child explained. 'Mrs Solti has children herself so she knows what

we're going through.' Whatever it is that they are going through, one would wish that all children had some of it.

Entrance: Some 250 apply for the 24 reception places (so, you have to see it as taking pot luck) and around 130 apply for 24 more places in year 3. Immense care is taken over the assessment at both stages and, clearly, the school would love to be able to take more of the able and sparky little girls who apply. Reception assessment is play-based. All are seen in the November prior to entry in age-based groups of 12-13 with four or five staff observing and interacting. Mrs Solti sees all applicants herself. A hundred of the 250 return in January when the school 'looks for a range of personality types' and aims at a balanced year group. No shying away from summer birthdays – 'we expect a little less of them' – which is good to know. Year 3 applicants tested in maths and English and interviewed. 'We take it seriously and take a lot of pride in it,' says Mrs Solti, while acknowledging that the process, of course, is a something of a lottery. She understands entirely the anguish and anxiety of parents. 'All we can do is be as understanding as we can.'

'The art displays change regularly and it's not always the best artists whose work goes up but people who try really hard'

Exit: Virtually all to the senior school, round the corner. And why ever not?

Remarks: Sited in two handsome Victorian red-brick buildings surrounded by lots more of a similar kind in lovely, quiet, tree-lined, similar Hampstead streets. If your junior school has to be in London, what could be nicer? In number 12 you will find reception to year 4. Number 5 houses years 5 and 6. Outside, reception tots have a new safe surface with play equipment and, inside, we observed happily absorbed groups of children involved in all kinds of educational play. Year 4 were all researching 'rivers' in all manner of interesting and exploratory ways. Everywhere we met the quiet buzz of happy learning. Every face was thoughtful.

Cross-curricular learning is embedded here and our guides stared when we told them about the rigid subject boundaries we met elsewhere. 'Oh no, we used Excel, Word and Paint for our geography project research on families – there was a lot of maths, especially geometry, when we made graphs when we used the census data,' we learned. Unusually, the girls are very aware of the school's approach to learning: 'They try to get us to have an open mind,' one told us. 'So they set us homework like 'Black or White' or 'Seven' and we can explore it any way we like.' We loved the big display board on Animal Arguments, on which were posted many questions eg 'Do we underestimate animals?' and 'Should products be tested on animals?' and 'Is it right to breed different species in captivity?'

'Learnpads' and laptops are there for the borrowing. Very good library in each building. Lots of trips out of school to support subject learning eg the Kew Steam Museum and the Henry Moore Foundation, Vikings in York, French battlefields etc. No slacking but no-one seems to want to slack. 'We're pushed hard in reading,' one girl told us. 'The librarian tells us that we can read harder books so we try and we really like it!' Good identification of those with special needs – mostly the occasional dyslexic, dyspraxic or ASD child. 'We enable them to go on and have a very successful time here whenever possible,' says Mrs Solti.

Excellent relationships between girls and staff and girls and girls. 'No-one is mean,' it was explained to us. 'We're all very independent but we do encourage each other.' Much praise from parents and girls for the new house system brought in by Mrs Solti. 'It has brought us all together,' we were, somewhat paradoxically, told. And other Solti innovations also appreciated. 'We are smarter and more sophisticated now,' a worldly-wise year 4 child confided and a year 6 friend concurred. 'The school felt a bit wobbly before but it feels more steady now.' Wobbliness certainly not felt by parent body – this school has been solid and stable for yonks. Much praise too for the School Council and girls clearly feel their views are taken seriously. 'They got the new playground equipment because of what we said.' And girls acknowledge the

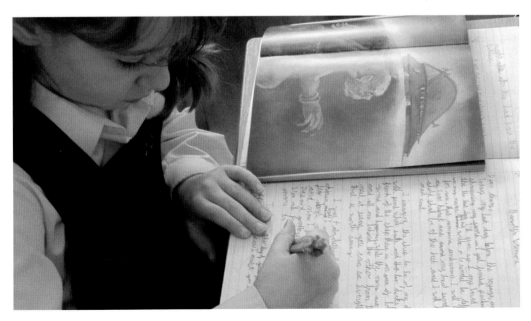

fairness of the regime in other ways. 'The art displays change regularly and it's not always the best artists whose work goes up but people who try really hard.' Huge array of extracurricular opportunities – much goes on before and after the school day and is there for those who want it. PTA and parental involvement across the board.

This junior school offers robust, stimulating and creative learning in a secure, warm and nurturing environment. It's ambitious without being pressurising, cosy without being lax. For your bright, energetic, creative daughter, a perfect start. We would wish them more space to be able offer this start in life to a lot more deserving girls.

South Hampstead High School

Linked school: South Hampstead High School Junior Department, 188

3 Maresfield Gardens, London NW3 5SS

Tel: 020 7435 2899

Independent • Pupils: 916 • Ages: 11–18 • Sixth form pupils: 144 • Fees: £16,119 pa

Email: admissions@shhs.gdst.net
Website: www.shhs.gdst.net

Headmistress: Since September 2013, Ms Helen Pike MA x 3 (40s), statuesque and dead glam. Formerly a teacher of history/politics with a pedigree to intimidate all-comers – her previous schools include St Paul's Boys (head of politics), Westminster (history) and City of London Boys (dep head of sixth). She is a novelist (The Harlot's Press – a Georgian, political bodice-ripper which, of course, all the girls have rushed to read) and an academic editor. And she is a very modern, dynamic head.

Ms Pike took over the school after a prolonged period of planning, negotiation, local diplomacy and, finally, permission from the LA to demolish the old school building and to build a new one. So her job, from day one, involved responsibility for the day-to-day oversight of this immense project and the fun of decision-making on decor etc – see below. Her relish of every stage has infected everyone and helped the school through a complex year of relocation and compromised space. 'It has been immensely well-done,' parents agree.

You might think that this, plus working in two halves of a school a mile apart, would delay Ms Pike's ability to engage with girls throughout the school. Not so. She teaches the year 7s and, 'she reads everyone's Personal Statements and takes a personal interest in everyone,' one year 13 girl told us. 'She seems quite formidable and she is sharpening up the girls who were quite scruffy before,' said one parent. All were aware of her drive to redesign the uniform. 'She has brought something new to the school.' 'She is very good,' said another, 'and she has brought in a lot more good new staff'. 'Her door,' a sixth former told us, 'is literally always open and if you have an "issue" she'd be the person you'd want to see.' She is impressive to meet but she also knows how to enjoy herself and relax. She is

clearly thrilled with the job, the new building and the opportunities it presents for the entire school community. A sixth former summed up the general impression. 'She's very human. She gets it.'

Academic matters: Outstanding. And, with a few historic glitches, has been so since its venerable inception. Results at both GCSE and A level are hard to beat. 2015 GCSEs totalled 92 per cent at A*/A. A levels also impressive – 75 per cent A*/A in 2015 – though one feels that they will soar higher with the stability the school now enjoys. Tiny numbers get lower than a B in anything. Surprisingly few linguists – modern, especially. Overall, the results speak for themselves and Ms Pike is uncompromising. 'People need to be absolutely confident about the results in all subjects,' she says. But she is not running a cramming operation. 'We can get the results and we can have fun doing it.' And there is vastly more on offer here than work. Bucketfuls of Science Olympiad and Maths Challenge medals at all levels. Masses of activities – intellectual, artistic, cultural – to stimulate the intellect, and all is characterised by a spirit of enquiry and exploration. Much is done to facilitate it by way of cross-curricular programmes, a constant questioning and a valuing of independent learning. A seriously-hard-working school, but one which feels friendly, collaborative and focused.

EAL and SEN support given unstintingly where needed but the truth, of course, is that if your needs in these areas are more than minimal you are unlikely to be here in the first place. The new building is blissfully accessible. The new sports and multi-purpose games area also means that those with mobility difficulties no longer have to leave the building in order to exercise.

There is every reason now to expect South Hampstead to regain its pre-eminence – academic and cultural – amongst the elite London girls' schools.

Games, options, the arts: Sports have never been South Hampstead's selling point but things are changing fast under the new regime. Well-resourced sports facilities at the Cumberland site provide for more than 20 sports and the new sports hall is now revolutionising opportunities on site. More sports now on offer and more teams to join. Football, cricket and rugby on the timetable. Much individual success including several in national teams. Gym, dance, netball, hockey, tennis and athletics especially strong. Sensitivities of sixth form girls, so long and carefully catered for since the days of compulsory hockey in freezing mud, now, ironically, need attention again. We cackled when some told us, 'It's very nice that they put on all these things like zumba and yoga and rock climbing but actually what we really like is old-fashioned team games like netball!'

> *'It's very nice that they put on all these things like zumba and yoga and rock climbing but actually what we like is old-fashioned team games like netball'*

Art and DT block to the left of central atrium provides ample space for all kinds of artistic efforts including ceramics room and kiln. Art, drama and music – always strong here – now in golden age of creative energy – witness excellent displays of independent-minded work and fabulous musical performances. Year 9 pupil became GDST Musician of the Year in 2014. Writers' groups, experimental drama and exploring in every field of creative intellectual life. Girls pay tribute to the excellent extracurricular provision – especially the programme of outside speakers which would do credit to a university. Beautiful school publications, many worked on by girls, and one elegantly produced by Condé Nast. Over 50 clubs each week and lots of trips. Vast take up of the Duke of Edinburgh Scheme. It is hard to see how a day school manages to do so much.

Background and atmosphere: One of the most prestigious and venerable of the Girls' Day School Trust's schools. South Hampstead's senior school had been housed in a single imposing Victorian red-brick mansion for most of its 140-odd years. Various more modest buildings were added but all except the latest science block, the Waterlow building, and the sumptuously decorative Oakwood, were crushed beneath the bulldozers in 2013. And a magnificent phoenix rose steadily from the ashes over the following 18 months. The new build – opened in a gloriously celebratory evening in January 2015 by Old Girl Helena Bonham-Carter – is breath-taking – not least because of how much space has been found in what seemed a cramped site. From the immense sports hall deep in the core of the Hampstead hillock on which the whole stands to the sedum roof garden overlooking much of north west London, all has been finished to a fine sustainability spec – Douglas fir louvres, solar shading, photovoltaic roof cells, energy efficient glazing and air cooling, motion-sensored lighting – not that any of this obtrudes when you wander the spacious teaching areas, wide corridors, subject rooms, library, recital room and studios to meet every modern scholastic need.

The older buildings are connected to the new one by bridge or corridor. All the new classrooms are good sizes, smaller ones for sixth form teaching. Plentiful loos on each floor. And changing rooms have hairdryers! Plasma screens and whiteboards all over the place. Music and DT well-equipped. The building is perforce long and relatively narrow and some rooms, mostly the departmental offices, have no natural light or ventilation, but light and space prevail everywhere else. All is finished in subtle light blues and white. And devastated Old Girls seeking their physical alma mater might be consoled by knowing that bricks from the old building were cleaned and used where possible. A remarkable achievement.

Pastoral care and discipline: 'We have very few rules,' says the head. 'Those we have are to keep you safe, secure and harmonious. If there are any others, we shouldn't have them.' Acronym is TORCH: -Toleration, Open-heartedness, Respect, Care and Helpfulness. 'We talk to them a lot about friendships. We are tough on bullying – especially cyber-bullying.' But incidents are few and all girls we spoke to – all ages – remarked on the friendliness and supportiveness of their peer groups. Much parental praise for the pastoral care: eg 'My daughter's form teacher was on the case even before I was'; 'The girls and staff are mutually friendly and respectful – there's no 'them and us'"; 'The way the teachers know the girls is very impressive'; and 'My daughter's teachers are wonderful mentors'. Praise from the girls for Ms Pike's approach to difficult matters. 'If there's a problem, she confronts it, head on.' Some mild chafing over the emphasis on uniform and dress code and a sense that this is a 'tough' school ie one in which 'you learn social skills you wouldn't learn in a gentler environment – it doesn't have a small, cosy feel'. But a consensus that the girls here have fun and learn through fun. As one mother told us, 'The school has the idea that the girls have to be happy first'.

Pupils and parents: High proportion lives locally, even close enough to walk, though others live an hour or more away. From both state and independent sectors and from diverse backgrounds. Around 30 different home languages spoken. This is the premiere girls' school in leafy, classy, intellectual, arty and moneyed Hampstead with the clientele to suit. Parents have high expectations of the school and the school meets them with a high degree of pre- and post-school provision. Parents are heavily involved with the school at all levels and the head and staff need experience and confidence to work with such a demanding but rewarding clientele. Girls are committed, energetic, clever, articulate, creative, independent and delightful.

Entrance: Fifty-five places at 11+ for which 450 apply via the North London Consortium. Two classes (about 40) come up from the junior school. A few in after GCSE if there are spaces in their subject classes. Entrance exam in two subjects plus general paper.

Exit: Very few leave after GCSE – why would they? A couple to, perhaps, state sixth forms and a couple more to join their brothers at UCS up the road but, otherwise, about 95 per cent sensibly stay put. Sixth form leavers to everywhere good to do everything interesting. A good handful now to US universities and the rest to eg Oxbridge (nine in 2015) and other well-established universities/colleges. Impressive number of engineers and economists but a sad dearth of linguists, despite exemplary results. Notable Old Girls include Helena Bonham-Carter, Lynne Featherstone MP, Suzy Klein, Angela Lansbury, Joanna McGregor, Rabbi Julia Neuberger, the late Lynsey de Paul, Fay Weldon, Olivia Williams.

Money matters: Academic scholarships worth up to 50 per cent of fees awarded based on performance in entrance exam. Music scholarships also worth up to 50 per cent. Bursaries also awarded on academic merit and financial need.

Remarks: 'This will be the most interesting school in London,' says the head. The others are now on their mettle to prove her wrong.

Sylvia Young Theatre School

1 Nutford Place, London W1H 5YZ

Tel: 020 7258 2330

61

Independent • Pupils: 239 (25 boarders stay with host families). • Ages: 10–16 • Fees: up to £13,500 pa

Email: info@sylviayoungtheatreschool.co.uk
Website: www.syts.co.uk

Principal: Since 1981, Sylvia Young OBE (70s). The founding principal, she is something of a legend in London's theatreland and has been supplying junior talent to the West End stage for over 30 years. With some early training, she decided 'performance was not for me', but soon realised she had a knack for spotting and inspiring talent in others. She started on a small scale, working with local children at a youth club in east London, then launched a full-time school at the suggestion of one of the parents. The school is her passion and she now lives on the site with her husband. Two grown-up daughters have both entered the profession, one (Frances Ruffelle) as a Tony-winning actress and singer, the other (Alison) as a theatrical agent. Her granddaughter is the pop singer Eliza Doolittle. Sylvia Young is a sympathetic soul, whose persistence and drive has developed the school from a walk-on role to full stardom. 'It's the Oxbridge of theatre schools', said one parent. She was appointed OBE in 2005 for services to the arts.

Since 2005, Ms Frances Chave BSc PGCE (40s) has been the academic and pastoral head. Ms Chave read maths at Exeter University, followed by a PGCE at Southampton, then taught at two large comprehensives (Cranford Community College and Feltham Community College), before helping to set up a third, Overton Grange School in Sutton, where she was deputy head. 'When I decided to move on, I wanted something completely different,' she says. Sylvia Young is about as different as it gets and Ms Chave has steadily improved the academic offering, particularly on the science side. A strong and sensible presence, she enjoys theatre, 'but only as a spectator', and in her spare time plays golf and other sports.

Academic matters: The school has long been known for the high standard of tuition in the performing arts, and has put increasing emphasis on the more academic side of the curriculum. 'We decided early on we didn't want our pupils to lose out by coming

'You have to learn that you may not get picked because you're not right for the part, no matter now talented you are'

to a theatre school', says the founder. The school is unusual in that it hives off academic lessons into three hard-working days on Mondays, Tuesdays and Wednesdays, leaving Thursdays and Fridays free for professional studies. The subdivision is reasonably demanding. 'Both staff and students have to be very focused,' says Ms Chave. Unsurprisingly, the academic curriculum is more compact than you'd find in a mainstream school – so no PE (no need with all that dancing), geography or DT – and the emphasis is definitely on the arts. All pupils study English lang and lit, maths, science (core and additional), expressive arts and drama to GCSE, when other options include music, art, media studies, history and Spanish. English, drama and theatre studies are the most successful GCSEs, but the head has worked hard to bring up attainment in science and maths (both of which are set).

Results are respectable, and 2015 saw a big improvement in the percentage of pupils getting five or more GCSEs at A*-C including English and maths, from 52 to 74, with the percentage of A*/A grades back up to 33. 'Most of our pupils do better than expected', says Ms Chave. 'If you're somewhere you really want to be, it does have a knock-on effect'. Parents agree: 'My daughter was at a mainstream academic school before. Here she's achieved because she wants to, not because she's being pushed'.

The school, which is non-selective academically, tests all pupils for learning difficulties on entry and copes well with moderate problems, from dyslexia to Asperger's. 'We have two children here on the autistic spectrum, one's a great dancer, the other a great actor'. Well-qualified SENCo oversees help in class and out, with teachers kept well in the loop. Inevitably, lessons here are interrupted by professional work, but no one is allowed to lag behind. 'We have very good systems in place to catch up,' says Ms Chave. 'Every week staff write out what has been covered in class and what has been set for homework and everyone gets a copy'. Students are expected to make up what they've missed in their own time. 'They're amazingly adaptable, they just fit straight back in'. When a professional engagement is protracted, staff liaise directly with on-set tutors.

Games, options, the arts: The performing arts are of course the raison d'être of this all-singing,

all-dancing institution and Thursdays and Fridays are devoted to the training needs of aspiring stars. Many of the performing arts staff are themselves working professionals and don't spare their students from the profession's harder knocks. (At one lesson the Guide attended, the class was asked to vote on the best singer.) Students are set by ability across the age range in all the performing disciplines – so, for example, a talented year 7 may be in the same ballet class as a less nimble year 11. Everyone studies all aspects of drama, music and dance, with classes ranging from voice production to recording technique, and all take annual LAMDA exams in speech and drama. All pupils, too, are represented by the in-house Sylvia Young Agency and put forward for professional work, ranging from West End musicals (the school regularly supplies cast members for Matilda and Billy Elliot) to advertising voice-overs and language tapes. 'You have to understand what a real performance is like', says Sylvia Young, 'and you have to learn that you may not get picked because you're not right for the part, no matter how talented you are. It's part of the training'. The school takes care, however, to ensure work doesn't interfere with academic priorities. 'My daughter has GCSEs coming up and they don't allow her to go off every five minutes', said one parent. 'School work comes first'.

The school works equally well for those who might want more self-effacing roles

Background and atmosphere: The school started out by running part-time classes in the 1970s, then opened full-time in Drury Lane in 1981. In 1983 it moved to Marylebone and in 2010 transferred into spacious premises in a converted Christian Science church just behind Marble Arch. The refurbished building provides excellent facilities for both the vocational and academic, with 10 purpose-built studios, two computer rooms, two science labs, two bright art rooms and a small library (mainly used for catching up with homework). Priorities, now as always, remain the family atmosphere and care of and attention to children, whether they're constantly in work or destined for a civilian career ('we do sometimes have to tell parents a child doesn't have what it takes for performance'). Regardless of the eventual outcome, all are equipped with valuable 'transferable skills' – confidence and the ability to communicate well and work with adults: 'The aim is to ensure they're secure in themselves', says Sylvia Young. Parents say pupils take on board the virtue of industry. 'They know the world they're contemplating is fiercely competitive', said one mother, 'and it's not going to be an easy ride. They learn a very strong work ethic'. Though clearly those who've gotta dance or act or sing (or all three) are ideally served here, the school works equally well for those who might want to enter the profession in more self-effacing roles. 'They teach you about every aspect from choreography to TV'. Twenty or so pupils board with London host families (generally present or past parents), often in groups of two or three. 'The woman my son boards with is marvellous', says one mother. 'She picks him up from the theatre at night, makes sure he does his homework, and arranges fun evenings of singing or games'.

Pastoral care and discipline: This is a school which is essentially about self-discipline, and disciplinary problems of the mainstream sort are rare. 'We don't have bullying', says Sylvia Young firmly, 'just children being silly sometimes'. The school monitors each child carefully, with an individual log kept on each. 'The children know they can come to us and we'll listen'. Parents feel confident their children are happy. 'My son feels so lucky. He is doing what he wants to do every day and there aren't many adults who can say that'.

They're all here because they want to be. 'My son, who'd been at a local primary school, said when he first saw Sylvia Young, "Mum, it's amazing. I just fit in there"'

The school has a strong disciplinary structure. 'We're very firm about the basics,' says Ms Young. Rules are clearly spelled out – no make-up, no micro skirts, no uploading of photographs onto the internet (a serious danger in a school where celebrity is a daily fact of life) – and consistently enforced. 'Other schools have these rules, but at Sylvia Young they really impose them', said one parent. 'It's quite old fashioned'. Two uniforms, one for academic work (white shirts, blazers, jumpers and ties), another for vocational days (tracksuits and unitards). Both are neatly worn.

Pupils and parents: Parents cover the full range. 'They're not pushy stage-school parents at all', says Ms Young. 'They're a very normal group, from all backgrounds'. Though certainly some are affluent, many really struggle to send their children here and travel considerable distances to do so. The children, of course, are as diverse as the parents, but significantly more talented than the average. They're all here because they really want to be. One parent told us: 'My son, who'd been at a local primary school, said when he first saw Sylvia Young, "Mum, it's amazing. I just fit in there".' Others who fitted in equally well include Billie Piper, Denise van Outen, former Spice Girl Emma Bunton, Jade Ewen from The Sugababes, Nathan Sykes of The Wanted and the late Amy Winehouse, whose father has set up a scholarship in her memory.

Entrance: The first entry point is year 6. 'Year 6 is a good time to come', says Sylvia Young, 'because either pupils can continue into year 7 or they have time to go elsewhere. A few decide it's not what they want'. Most enter at year 7, with the occasional place at other times. At all ages, the audition is the most important part of the process. The school offers a preliminary audition, with low-key workshops. Those with most potential are invited back to perform two drama pieces (one from Shakespeare and a modern work), a song and a dance. Candidates also sit academic tests in English and maths. 'But we're not a grammar school. We just need to feel happy they'll cope with the pace and be able to get done in three days what most do in five'. That said, the stronger an applicant is on the professional side, the more leeway is given academically. Motivation, too, is carefully examined. 'There's a lot of discussion about what the child wants and what the parents are looking for'. The school sees up to 500 applicants for 40 places at 11.

Exit: Pupils are assessed at the end of years 8 and 9, which provides an opportunity for families to reassess their child's career path. Currently all move on at 16 (though the school is contemplating a sixth form). About half (mainly dancers) go on to specialist colleges, the rest to traditional academic sixth forms to do A levels and then frequently to study drama at university. Destinations include The Arts Educational School, Hurtwood House and Elstree UTC, which offers technical training in the visual and creative arts. School has close links with central London tutorial colleges (Lansdowne, Duff Miller etc) and some pupils move on to these.

Money matters: Three official scholarships (one full and two half), and many more get some sort of help. Quite a number put their theatrical earnings towards the fees.

Remarks: A school which combines a sound academic background with outstanding vocational training and professional opportunity. Hard work, but hard work undertaken with purposeful pleasure.

Trevor-Roberts School

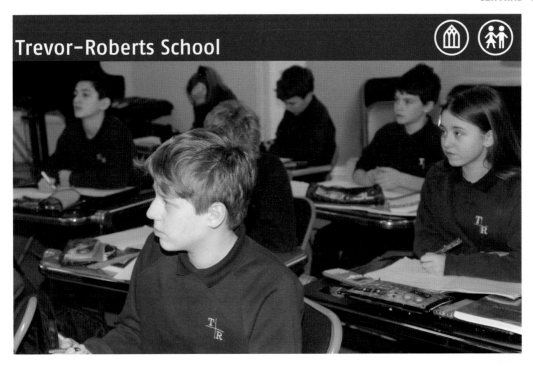

55–57 Eton Avenue, London NW3 3ET

Tel: 020 7586 1444

Independent • Pupils: 180 • Ages: 5–13 • C of E • Fees: up to £15,060 pa

Email: trseniorweb@trevor-robertsschool.co.uk
Website: trevor-robertsschool.co.uk

Headmaster: Since 1999, Simon Trevor-Roberts BA (50s). Son of the founder, Trevor-Roberts studied at Westminster School before reading English at Aberystwyth. In 1983, he joined his father Christopher in the family firm, where he learnt his trade by example. (He has since been joined by his sister Amanda, who heads up the Junior School). Mild mannered and reflective, he has a very clear sense of what the school is about: 'We try to get children to enjoy the process of learning.' Continues to teach maths to the 13 plus candidates, because he's found he, too, now has the knack of putting things across clearly. 'I shadowed my father for a long time and learnt how to do it by osmosis.' Parents find him immensely approachable and engaged. 'You always have complete access to the head and he knows all the kids incredibly well.' Married with two grown children, both of whom attended the school.

Entrance: Register as soon after birth as possible. About 80 sets of parents are contacted when their child is 1 and offered a tour. Those who wish to proceed confirm this in writing, and the school assesses the first 50 children on their list in the September prior to the calendar year in which they turn 5. 'We're not expecting any preparation, but

we want to make sure it will be a happy transition,' says the registrar. 'We're looking for inquisitive children who want to learn. Getting that is more a dark art than a science.' The school generally tries to give priority to siblings, 'but only if it's the right school'. Often takes in one or two more in year 4, when the year group divides into two classes.

Exit: Girls mainly – though not exclusively – at 11, generally to Francis Holland, South Hampstead and other north London favourites. Most boys (and some girls) at 13, to a wide range of day and boarding schools, including regular placements at City of London, Eton, Harrow, Highgate, Latymer Upper, Merchant Taylors', UCS and Westminster. 'The head is very good at managing parental expectations,' says one former parent.

Remarks: This is a family-run school with a very distinctive ethos, deriving in large part from its origins. Founded by the current heads' father in the 1950s with just 14 boys, it was originally seen as a refuge for the 'unteachable'. 'My father had a reputation for taking those whom other schools had given up on and getting them through entrance exams to leading public schools,' says Simon Trevor-Roberts.

Today, the school can takes its pick of north London's brightest, but continues to select a mixed-ability (now co-educational) intake and provide a tailor-made education for all. 'They want every child to work to his or her potential and really do treat every child as an individual,' said one parent.

Children start in year 1 in a class grouped according to the calendar year of their birth. In year 4, this is re-arranged to allow everyone to be in place for secondary school entrance. One class of 16-18 in the early years, two classes in years 4 to 6, then a single form again for the final two years. 'We like to move children around so they're not in the same group for eight years,' says the head. 'It give us the flexibility to allow those who require it a bit more time and accelerate those who need it.' Parents confirm this is skilfully managed. 'They're constantly re-adjusting their approach for different levels of learning, but not in a way that disturbs the children.'

Specialist subject teaching from the word go, with a classroom teacher for the core subjects, but music, history, geography, science and art all taught in their own space. 'It keeps the week fresh.'

Plenty of imaginative teaching by intelligent (including many Oxbridge), though not always qualified, staff. French from year 1, Latin from year 5, some Greek in year 8, Mandarin taught as a club. Special needs addressed by weekly sessions with the learning support coordinator and outside specialists.

No truck with overly formalised exam training. 'Non-verbal reasoning is not a subject'

Everyone staying for the final two years sits common entrance. 'We take it very seriously,' says the head. 'Eleven plus is about flexible problem solving; by 13, it's more structure on the page.' Senior schools praise the 'structure on the page' received.

Very good at ensuring the basics are in place. 'Sometimes you have to be a bit tough,' says the head. 'We insist that children use a pen rather than touch type. If you have to write an essay under exam conditions, you have to be able to discipline your thoughts.' No truck with overly formalised exam training. 'Non-verbal reasoning is not a subject,' he says crisply.

Formal homework from year 3, starting out with 20 minutes in English or maths ('It shows them how to work by themselves and for themselves'), up to two hours a night for the top forms. 'They do work very hard, but the atmosphere still manages to be reasonably relaxed,' says one mother.

Good relationships with staff are fundamental, as is the view that effort should be lauded over achievement. 'Children are perfectly aware there's competition elsewhere, they don't need it reinforced. We want them to be in competition with themselves.' Good work is rewarded with a 'digniora', with recipients queuing in the lunch hour to have their accolade verified and registered. Three merits win a £4 token to be spent at independent local shops.

Breadth well beyond the exam curriculum is given enormous emphasis. Outstanding music – 'We love music' – with a dynamic head. Taught in the classroom from years 1 to 6, with the addition of numerous ensembles (brass, jazz, string, woodwind, chamber choir, rock band) and much external participation (at the Royal Festival Hall, St John's Smith Square, etc.) Twice weekly art lessons (one in year 7) in a bright art department at the top of school, with its own kiln. Extra art and DT on offer for enthusiasts on Wednesday afternoons.

Cultural values that have largely been submerged elsewhere – 'Everyone is encouraged to have a novel on the go' – with half an hour of silent reading daily after lunch. Poetry and drama matter and prove great confidence builders. 'My son almost died of nerves the first time he had to read out a poem,' said one mother, 'but now he loves drama and performing.' '

Plenty of fresh air and exercise, with a good-sized, well-equipped playground, including popular table tennis, miniature railway and chicken coop ('the chickens are a great comfort to quieter, shyer children.'). Primrose Hill, a few hundred yards from the door, enables twice weekly games. Definitely not a school, however, where 'go-fight-win' is on the agenda. 'Children love sport, but I don't want a First Eleven ethos, with the captain of games strutting around,' says the head. 'We do play matches against other schools, but everyone has a go.'

The senior school building, a fine example of the Arts and Crafts, was the founder's own home and still offers delightful domestic interiors with William Morris wallpaper in the front hall and mid-century classic tables used instead of desks in the top forms. The juniors are housed in their own building with a separate dining room and science lab.

The atmosphere is civilised but structured ('It's a nice mix of the very strict and the nurturing and kind – teachers are always willing to talk things through.'). Pupils sit down to eat their biscuits at break before rushing off to the playground. Everyone has a hot lunch, served through an open hatch, 'so they can see where it is made.' Staff share the dining hall with pupils. 'Eating is socialising.' Food is freshly prepared on site using local produce.

Manners and uniform are both reasonably relaxed (no backs against the wall here). Light blue polo shirt for younger children, dark blue for older ones. Trousers and skirts, 'something reasonable'. 'Jeans are fine, jeans hanging off the hips are not.'

Often the school of choice for the liberal, media intelligentsia (including some famous names), the type of parent who genuinely believes in the well-rounded education, not the rush to the top of the league tables. (Competition here, though it undoubtedly exists, tends to be on the level of how many operas your child has seen rather than where the family went skiing.) Mainly local, some from Notting Hill, Queen's Park, Islington. The head feels 'there's no typical child, but I've heard people say our children are very kind.'

University College School Junior School

Linked schools: Phoenix School, 148; University College School, 198

11 Holly Hill, London NW3 6QN

Independent · Pupils: 252 · Ages: 7–11 · Fees: £17,028 pa

Tel: 020 7435 3068

Email: juniorbranch@ucs.org.uk
Website: www.ucs.org.uk

Headmaster of Junior: Since July 2014, Lewis Hayward (40s), previously deputy principal of Highgate School. He has an MA in classics from Oxford and one in educational leadership and management from the Open University. He started his teaching career in Nairobi, moving to Saudi

Arabia as an EFL teacher at the Saudi Aramco Oil Company before returning to Nairobi as co-founder and editor of a newspaper there. The newspaper folded following the bombing of the US embassy, and he came back to the UK. Has since taught classics at Holmewood House and Highfield Prep, joining Highgate in 2009. He is married with two children, one a dancer.

Entrance: Some 170 applicants for 60 places at 7. At the initial assessment, in the autumn term, staff hear boys read – 'we're looking for two years above chronological age' – then read them a story and ask them questions in groups. Meanwhile, the head takes parents on a tour of the school, 'to make sure they want us'. Confident readers are asked back for English, maths and non-verbal reasoning tests in the spring term, with attention also paid to how they interact in groups.

The main feeder pre-preps tend to be The Phoenix, Mulberry House, Golders Hill School and Hampstead Hill School. Although The Phoenix is the UCS pre-prep, applicants take the same entrance test as everyone else. 'All things being equal they'll get a place. But they must be able to cope.'

Exit: Virtually all to the senior school, without taking the entrance exam. 'If a boy is really struggling we'll talk to his parents – but that has only happened once whilst I've been here.'

Remarks: Compact site tucked away at the top of Hampstead behind the Everyman cinema with views across London from every classroom. Nice boy-friendly science lab with tarantulas and poisonous frogs, which doubles as recording studios where boys can come in to write and record songs at lunchtime (an apprenticeship, no doubt, for the rock band culture of the senior school).

Art, woodwork and cookery rooms, all well-used: plenty of time here for creative activities. Some impressive photography displayed: came third in the Prep School Photographer of the Year competition. Smallish rubber surface playground/football pitch; boys play rugby, football, cricket and hockey at the senior school grounds in West Hampstead. Also use the senior school swimming pool and thea-

Nice boy–friendly science lab with tarantulas and poisonous frogs, which doubles as recording studios

tre and have concerts in the great hall. Giant chess set in the playground; the under 11 team recently won the National Schools gold award.

Does not have to prepare boys for common entrance, so no huge academic pressure – can spend less time on maths and English and more on other activities. Relaxed pace. Undoubtedly some parents feel that their children are not stretched academically and some complain of lack of homework, though the latest Independent Schools Inspectorate report (following a bad inspection previously) praised standards. 'I think we've turned it round'.

Happy to accept able boys with physical disabilities. 'If they're bright and can cope we'll take anyone.' 'They've been amazing helping with all his needs,' said the parent of one disabled boy. Full-time school nurse who 'knows all the boys and is involved in their personal development'. Two part-time SEN teachers.

Warm, friendly atmosphere. 'It's a very happy school,' said a parent.

University College School

Linked schools: Phoenix School, 148; University College School Junior School, 197

Frognal, London NW3 6XH

Tel: 020 7435 2215

Independent • Pupils: 850 • Ages: 11–18 • Sixth form pupils: 305 (60 girls) • Fees: £18,423 pa

Email: ssadmissions@ucs.org.uk
Website: www.ucs.org.uk

27

Headmaster: Since September 2013, Mr Mark Beard BSc MEd (early 40s), a chemist. Mr Beard came from Brighton College where he'd been deputy head with a period as acting head between the redoubtable Seldon and the remarkable Cairns – a good place

to cut headmagisterial teeth. He is credited with this school's greatly increased number of Oxbridge entrants. He began his career at King Edward's School, Birmingham, where he is remembered as 'a jolly good chap', thence to St Paul's School, as head of chemistry. Mr Beard is married with two young children and enjoys squash, reading and ancient history.

He is energetic, open, likeable, relaxed and clear-sighted. He follows a loved and warmly respected head, Ken Durham, and big shoes can be hard to fill. However, 'I came in to be myself,' he asserted when we met. 'I set out my stall openly and clearly from the start.' Mr Beard's appointment to this major school as a first headship is a considerable vote of confidence. He flustered some in the school community when, in his first term, he cracked down on aspects of this traditionally 'liberal' school – notably its somewhat relaxed attitude to uniform. 'I have been keen to explain..that liberal scholarship is not the same as liberal attitudes.. There is a school uniform and it is to be worn properly at formal occasions; you should be punctual to lessons, mind your manners and if you have homework, you do your homework.' Many parents applaud. 'Things needed tightening up,' one told us. 'I think he'll make it stricter, smarter and tidier – but within the ethos of the school,' thought another. 'It's early days,' said another, long-term, parent. 'He's less overtly charismatic than Ken – more cautious and considered. He will be a very good influence but it's a slow burn.' Sixth formers concur: 'He's growing on us. He'll do interesting things over time.'

Academic matters: Mr Beard's charges did not let him down. His second year saw the some of the best results in the school's history with 64 per cent of A levels graded A*/A, 87 per cent A*-B, and almost half achieving at least three A grades. At GCSE, 86 per cent of exams got A*/A and 59 per cent were A*s. Over a quarter of the cohort of 121 pupils secured nine A*s or higher and 16 pupils received 10 straight A* grades. Impressive by any standards.

Far freer choice of GCSE and A level subjects than elsewhere including no blinkered – in our view – insistence on the holy trinity of sciences. Twenty plus A level options. Much teaching material tailor-made by school's own staff – that's proper teaching. Universal praise for the English dept. 'It's phenomenal,' drooled a parent. Very good languages dept and exchange system. Mandarin is growing seriously now and a new short course in Italian is on its way to the sixth. School has switched to the Pre-U for languages, DT and English since 2015. We approve. But teaching praised across the board. A sense of academic work being serious but also offering infinite opportunities for thought, exploration and discovery.

He cracked down on aspects of this traditionally 'liberal' school – notably on its somewhat relaxed attitude to uniform

Parental approval of Mr Beard's instant moving of A level mocks from March to January. Much appreciation of staff dedication. 'They're always there if you need help. There's a young bunch of teachers and many run extra classes for those who need them,' we were told. There are also support mechanisms such as regular tracking and reporting back to parents, to help boys who need pushing.

All are screened in general literacy, numeracy and reasoning on entry. Mild SEN seen as no problem here. Two full-time and one part-time learning support specialists. Individual support either by withdrawal or classes before and after school – also for those with mild EAL needs.

Games, options, the arts: The school has traditionally focused on inclusivity over winning – an excellent principle but one which can elicit grumbles. 'They don't put the money into it,' a parent told us. 'If your son is motivated and competitive and wants extra coaching etc I'd look elsewhere,' opined another. Boys concur. 'There are lots of talented boys here,' one said, 'but they don't get the opportunities.' However, this is clearly changing now. Regular Saturday fixtures for up to 18 teams including C and D teams and many extracurricular clubs/practices in eight key sports taking place before school, after school and lunchtimes. School enthusiastic about recent sporting triumphs, which include the 1st XI football team lifting the cherished London Schools Cup. Under Beard, there is greater emphasis on performance. There is now an 'elite sportspersons' programme', additional soccer and cricket coaches, increased games options and other initiatives to allow pupils to reach their potential. Recent results in several sports including some individual triumphs suggest that, indeed, a fuse is burning here and may start

crackling soon. Mr Beard wisely reminds us that the school motto is 'Paulatim sed Firmiter' ie Steadily but Surely. They have county/academy rugby players, hockey players and cricketers, England (ISFA) footballers, tennis players very high in the national rankings, international swimmers as well as individual rowers and fencers. Plans are afoot for a new pavilion to be built on their 28 acres of playing fields in West Hampstead.

'The music and drama are simply brilliant,' a parent enthused. Music has long been exceptional here and we noted the number and quality of ensembles eg the symphony orchestra, chamber orchestra, several chamber groups, umpteen bands of all kinds including jazz and swing and excellent choirs. Well-provided for. Many pupils take LAMDA exams to high levels. Students write and direct their own plays and performance values are high. DT and art are outstanding. Evident creativity, freedom and experimental ethos and the dept has more the air of an art college than a school. Many media, some wonderfully bizarre and arresting work and all good stimulating stuff.

Music has long been exceptional here and we noted the number and quality of ensembles

Far more interesting sounding clubs and extracurricular activities than we meet in most schools. Friday afternoons are given over to sixth form enrichment and staff follow their own enthusiasms in running classes such as Latin American film culture, wine tasting, life drawing, rock climbing, Literary London. Pupils set up clubs to pursue their own interests so we found a medical ethics society, a law and justice society, an eco-friendly club and bee-keeping among many others. We wanted to sign up to them all.

Far from being a crammer in atmosphere, independence in all things is key. 'If your kids are self-starters, motivated and organised there is so much on offer, but they have to make the effort to get it. They don't come after you,' an appreciative parent explained. 'There is so much on offer even for the less academic child,' said another.

Exceptional outreach activities include collaboration at all levels with several state schools and pupil volunteering with eg Kids Company.

Background and atmosphere: The main buildings, dating back to 1907, are solid and imposing but rest comfortably on the southern slopes of the Hampstead hill. An unusual history. Founded by the University of London and various interested liberal intellectuals in 1830, it was designed to give

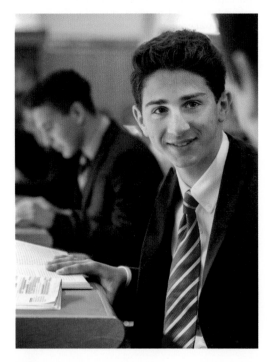

an education to boys from dissenting (ie not conformist C of E) families and, initially, had no form of communal worship – unique at the time. Also no corporal punishment and no boarding. Its earliest incarnation was in Gower Street, hence the designation of Old Gower for an alumnus. So, from the off, it was regarded as 'liberal', and the tradition has been proudly maintained. What does it mean? 'It means, "no rules just for rules' sake",' ventured one parent, and that's at least part of it. Another parent quoted a prep school head: 'It's a school for mavericks.' While we like this observation, we feel it's a bit off the mark and UCS suggests that, while the great majority of pupils are far from being mavericks, the school is inclusive and can certainly accommodate them. Perhaps best summed up by a veteran parent: 'It's a wonderful, liberal, free-thinking school – you can look however you want to look, whether whacky or entirely traditional. They are accommodating and accepting and they celebrate difference.' It also still means no RE or religious assembly and a spirit of tolerance and inclusiveness.

A terrible fire in 1978 destroyed the huge Great Hall but the rebuilt version is almost overwhelming in its size and gravitas – wood panelling, stucco ceiling, huge organ and brass chandeliers. All eat in the handsome panelled refectory – all refectory tables and forms – with a strangely monastic feel. Droolly enthusiasm for the school food. 'No-one complains here,' we were told, and the menu was about the most varied, tempting and creative we can remember.

Girls arrived in the sixth form in 2008 to both trepidation and excitement from staff and boys. But it has worked, and not too much to the detriment of relationships between the school and its all-girl neighbours. 'The boys love the girls coming in the sixth form – it works very well,' one veteran parent assured us. 'They take very confident girls – the multi-tasking, vibrant, feisty ones – and they settle well.' The girls we spoke to bore this out, but they also paid tribute to the efforts made to integrate them before term and to help them quickly make friends once the year begins.

'They take very confident girls – the multi-tasking, vibrant, feisty ones – and they settle well'

Later buildings include: the 2006 sports centre with excellent pool – also used by the local community; the sixth form centre with large and well-appointed common room, study areas – with and without PCs – and an excellent all-day café; the Lund theatre – a large and flexible space in which most productions happen and which is constantly in use; a 1993 block with well-designed and well-stocked library – with carpet; plus music dept etc. Site now feeling a touch full (head prefers 'compact') although space still for super vegetable garden and bee hives, three Astro pitches/courts and little green nooks for sitting and relaxing. Some smartening up needed hither and yon – a little paint and patching will do wonders and a rolling refurbishment programme is under way. The emphasis here is not on every kind of here-today-obsolete-tomorrow IT gizmo but on rock solid teaching.

Pastoral care and discipline: Houses are called 'demes' here and matter, but not too much. Praise for the Beard tightened-up regime. 'Some of the younger boys were getting lippy and needed reining in.' But equally, parents, pupils and OGs keen that the school's treasured 'liberalism' is maintained. 'It isn't a school for those who need a highly regulated, organised system,' explained a devotee. Another parent concurred, 'It's very friendly and informal. It's warm and family-like.' Much praise for the home-school communications. 'I have mobile numbers for all my son's teachers and they reply to emails almost before you've sent them.' Even warmer praise for the 'deme' wardens: 'They are phenomenally good on the pastoral side.' Mr Beard has a light touch but a firm view. 'We want them to be the problem solvers of the future, not the problem causers. That's partly what a liberal education should be about.' Few discipline problems. Leavers reflect thoughtfully on their schooling: 'You learn to manage your time. They cultivate you into someone who can deal with a high level of intensity in your work. They build it up so that you don't really feel how much more deeply you are thinking. You become very independent and self-reliant in this school.'

Pupils and parents: From all over north and central London. Pupils are as diverse as the capital itself. They are articulate, thoughtful, independent. Parents are achievers, ambitious, cultured, moneyed – for the most part – and involved. 'Increasing numbers of middle class parents have to work hard to find the fees,' acknowledges Mr Beard.

Entrance: About two-thirds of 11-year-olds come from the junior school in Holly Hill. They move up without needing to take an entrance exam. At 11+, 350+ boys, mostly from local primaries, try for 30 places. Exams in maths, English and reasoning in January. Around 40 per cent of applicants thereafter invited for interview. NB part of a group of independent co-ed/boys' schools that coordinate 11+ results, but forbid those who have accepted a place at one school from taking up a subsequent waiting list offer from another.

At 13+, 300 boys – mainly from local preps, eg Arnold House, Devonshire House, The Hall, Hereward House, North Bridge House, St Anthony's and Trevor-Roberts, but also Notting Hill and Westminster Cathedral Choir School. Pre-test in year 6 in maths, English and reasoning. About 150 return for an activity morning and interview in the October of year 7. Offers extended to fill about 30 places conditional on performance at CE.

At 16+, some 200 apply for around 40 places. Most entrants at this stage are girls, but no actual quota – entry on merit. Girls come from eg City of London, Francis Holland, North London Collegiate, Channing, South Hampstead. Some from Highgate School. Also from St Marylebone School, Hampstead and William Ellis. Selection via November assessment and about 50 per cent of applicants interviewed. Assessment is an objective test of thinking, reasoning and problem-solving. All offers conditional on GCSEs.

Exit: Everyone goes off to a good university to read a proper subject. London University is a favourite; many also to Durham, Manchester, Leeds, Bristol, Nottingham. Impressive numbers annually to Oxbridge (19 in 2015). A few to the US. The vast range of subjects they pursue is testament to the individuality fostered here.

Notable Old Gowers include: Tristram Hunt, actors Hugh Dennis, David McCallum and Bertie Carvel, journalists Ian Katz and Jonathan Freedland, Thomas Adès, Members of Bombay Bicycle Club, Will Self, Justin Stebbing, Chris Bonington, Roger Bannister, John Barrett, Paul Dacre.

Money matters: Around £1m a year disbursed to pupils who would not otherwise be able to afford UCS. At the time of our visit, 52 pupils were on 100 per cent bursaries – one of the most generous provisions in the UK. Most of this funded by the letting of school facilities to the community, charitable work and donations. No academic scholarships but music schols worth up to 25 per cent.

Remarks: A very good school and set to rise even higher under energetic and confident head.

Westminster Abbey Choir School

Dean's Yard, London SW1P 3NY

Tel: 020 7222 6151

62

Independent · Pupils: 34 (all boarders) · Ages: 8–13 · C of E · Fees: (after subsidy) £7,848 pa

Email: headmaster@westminster-abbey.org
Website: www.westminster-abbey.org/choir-school

Headmaster: Since 2002, Mr Jonathan Milton BEd (50s), married, formerly head of The Abbey School in Tewkesbury. Bred, if not born, into the choir school tradition – he was a choral scholar at York. Music was his degree subject, though he now teaches geography. A gentle man, whose quiet, friendly manner betrays a profound love of his unique school, the tradition it enshrines and the community of boys and staff which gives it ever-fresh life. Clearly, an inspired appointment. Mr Milton is, at once, a traditionalist and a moderniser – exactly the right balance for the place. 'When I came, there were no carpets or curtains and it felt tense – that's now completely gone. It was dark too. We've tried to make it gentler.' He showed us the little IT room next to the dormitories: 'a marvellous way for boys to stay in touch – much simpler than writing a letter. And the staff communicate with parents every week electronically.' Gentler the school may well be but he has also tightened the academics, keeping step with the outside world in which senior school places are no longer assigned in little chats between heads of 'big' schools and trusted prep heads. Mr Milton's openness, thoughtfulness and warmth are mirrored in his boys. Those we talked to were similarly relaxed, candid and

'They have to enjoy being part of a close-knit team and they must have personality and character,' says Mr Milton

friendly. Head and boys share their view of life here, 'it's tough, you get very tired but.. it's fabulous.'

Entrance: No formal entrance test day or the like. Over the year, school will see around 25 boys for voice trials – usually in ones and twos – and usually in year 3. The Master of the Choristers will hear them and the head will chat to the boy and parents and, if the lad looks promising, he will be invited back to spend a day in the school. This will include a more formal voice trial, a chance to play their instruments and testing in maths and English. What is looked for is not grade 8 in six instruments but musical aptitude and the kind of attitude to music, community and learning that make for a happy and successful Westminster Abbey chorister. 'They have to enjoy being part of a close-knit team and they must have personality and character,' says Mr Milton. Academic brilliance is less important though, clearly, the boy must enjoy learning. Of the 25 they see, places may be offered to between four and six, on average, though one or two may be invited to come back some months later.

These days, more than half come from state primaries and can be caught up and supported where necessary. 'With year groups of six or seven, we can tailor-make classes,' says head. School fees are subsidised by the Abbey and no-one, however impecunious, should be put off applying if their boy is a natural chorister. Funds will be found. 'Some pay nothing at all,' says Mr Milton. Boys now come from further afield – Yorkshire and even overseas. Quite tough for an 8-year-old, you might think. 'And,' says Mr Milton, 'few of our parents would have chosen a boarding school – when they see it, they realise it's a way of life.' Yes. This represents the most amazing opportunity for the right child and a peerless preparation for life.

Exit: An astonishing list of leavers' destinations over the last three years. Many win music scholarships to prestigious schools and many win academic and/or art scholarships too. Most popular senior schools are King's Canterbury, Eton and Winchester with the rest hither and yon, and doing very well wherever they end up.

Remarks: This is the only choir school in the country which is only a choir school – no day pupils, no girls, no non-choristers. Average class size six, maximum is nine. In a way, that says it all. The place hums with quiet activity – mental, physical and musical. It all happens in a tall, unobtrusive building in Dean's Yard – right under Big Ben, the Houses of Parliament and Westminster Abbey. Dean's Yard is a grassy square lined by augustly solid houses. Opposite is the modest arch which leads to Westminster School – no connection with the choir school except that the large pupils and the little choristers see each other passing all day which makes the business of scholarship and growing up in this – the heart of the great centre of London – seem quite the normal thing.

Five floors accommodate all learning, admin and living space. All is freshly-painted and feels light, comfortable and well-cared for. There's a super ground floor 'music room' used for assemblies and the like – a splendid stained glass window commemorating Purcell and the other Masters of the Choristers who between them make up a history of English choral music – Gibbons, Blow, Simon Preston et al. Classrooms are small with conventional desks, whiteboards and it all looks a bit dolls' house in scale – enhanced, when we visited (during exam week) by the very cuddly teddies (for good luck) sitting reassuringly on desks. More teddies in the dorms which – it is a boys' school – are, if not Spartan, certainly not prettified. Bunk beds with integral cupboards in airy rooms. Good shower rooms, good ICT provision and a very nice sitting room with sofas, piano, TV, books and games and feeling really snug.

Boys enjoy textile work, DT – they make fan-powered vehicles for racing – and knitting

Everyone does standard prep school curriculum but flexibility can be built into the system with such small classes and so small a school. Individual help is the norm. No boys with SENs, we are told, though the odd mild dyslexic may creep in. A boy with dyslexia would find chorister-life tough, says Mr Milton – what with having to read music and a foreign language at speed and so on. 'It wouldn't be fair.' Yes. Sports take place via buses to Battersea Park, The Queen Mother Sports centre in Victoria and water sports in Docklands – Mr Milton is a keen sailor. They kayak, rock climb and sail and Mr Milton sees this – and the opportunity to get away from the closed chorister world – as essential for good relations.

Evidence of boy-life and wit abounds. 'WACS Lyrical' – the boys' own noticeboard – details competitions, initiatives, jokes and notices – full of fun and ideas. The art room, open in the evenings, similarly lively – we were terrified by the huge multi-tusked cardboard, paper and paint beast which 'would be tamed by listening to Palestrina'. Boys enjoy textile work, DT – they make fan-powered vehicles for racing – and knitting: 'very popular', we were told. Obviously, music is central to life. Singing practice in the song school happens each morning and each afternoon before evensong – except on Weds and alternate Mons. Instrumental practice is timetabled and very much a normal part of everyday life. Musical guests and ensembles visit, there is a composer in residence – a real privilege for such boys – and school takes full advantage of the concert halls and galleries roundabout. Likewise, the school goes into local primaries – boys take their instruments – to inspire others, 'just to give music a boost'.

What do the boys say – and their parents? 'You have to be very independent and organised,' a seasoned 12-year-old told us. 'You can't rely on your parents to pack your bag and find your pencil case – you have to do it all yourself. You have to manage your own revision and music practice.' (Sounds like a course in choristership might be handy all round!) 'It is very tiring – I'd like to have more of a rest after concerts.' On the other hand – 'singing all the special services we do is brilliant. We did a special service for the spies! (100 years of MI5.) They just looked normal. They don't wear T-shirts saying "I'm a spy".' And 'We're on TV, we go on tours and make CDs.' 'It can be exhausting,' said a parent, 'but they bounce back. It's unbelievably rewarding.' And they clearly enjoy the abbey community with whom they share Christmas and Easter meals and so on. A choristership here is a treasure. A huge commitment for boys and family while it lasts, but a gift for life.

Westminster Cathedral Choir School

Ambrosden Avenue, London SW1P 1QH

Independent • Pupils: 172; 25 boarders (choristers) • Ages: 7–13 • RC • Fees: Day £16,854 pa; Choristers (boarding) £8,841

Tel: 020 7798 9081

Email: office@choirschool.com
Website: www.choirschool.com

63

Headmaster: Since 2007, Mr Neil McLaughlan (40s). Married with a young son and daughter, and a man who radiates humour, decency and charm in equal measure. Read philosophy and politics at Durham and spent a few years with Andersen Consulting in London before embarking on a teaching career in 1997. After spells at Stonyhurst and Worth, he took up a post as head of English and director of development at Downside School, before joining WCCS as headmaster. He hopes to be there 'for the duration.' Parents hope so too. 'Lovely guy!' said one. 'So easy to approach!' said another. 'An extremely dedicated head and a great promoter of the school,' said a third. Typically modest, he hopes to do 'lots and lots of small things right.' We think he's doing lots of big things right too. Under his visionary yet kindly leadership, this has become an inspiring school that is going from strength to strength.

Entrance: Main entry points for day boys are at 7+, where 14-15 places are available, and 8+ (a further eight or so places – mostly for choristers). Applicants sit tests in English, maths and non-verbal reasoning in January of the year before entry. Occasional places in other year groups, notably at 11+. The school is always oversubscribed, and, once boys have met the required academic standard, will give preference where possible to practising Roman Catholics and to boys with a brother at the school.

Choristers, who must be Catholic and boarders, join at 8+. Would-be probationers have to pass informal and formal tests with the cathedral's master of music, as well as succeeding at the academic assessment; and if they manage all that, they spend two nights at the school to see whether chorister life will suit them. Only then will they be offered one of the six available places. As the school's popularity grows, so inevitably does the competition; there are now half a dozen serious candidates for each choristership, and for the first time in over a decade, the school has not had to go recruiting for them.

We didn't try the football, but we can confirm that the food is splendid

Up to full fees assistance for choristers; none for day pupils, whose families just have to fork out. As a result, there is more cultural than social diversity here. Boys come from a wide range of nationalities, among them France, Spain, Italy, Russia, Ghana and Korea, making this a truly international school. With some 80 per cent of the boys now from Catholic families, the school is less religiously diverse than it was, but remains open to day boys of all faiths provided their families are happy to support the school's Catholic ethos.

Exit: The head has worked tirelessly to raise the school's profile, and WCCS's exit record is superb. Boys regularly leave for boarding schools like Eton, Harrow, Winchester, Uppingham, Stonyhurst and Ampleforth, and for a raft of top London schools, including Westminster, St Paul's, City of London, KCS Wimbledon, Latymer Upper, Dulwich College and the new Wetherby senior school, often with music scholarships. Others to Cardinal Vaughan

and the London Oratory. 'The school is much more linked into the senior schools than it was a few years ago,' reported one satisfied parent. 'Oh yes, the head's always going on about schools,' confirmed one of the boys, equably.

Remarks: The school was endearingly shabby once, but not any more. A five-year programme of refurbishment has just finished, and everything is now bang up to date. Visitors are welcomed in the beautiful glass-fronted foyer, where handwritten Music for Mass schedules from 1905 are hung beside huge photos of current pupils radiating health and cheeriness. Throughout the building, ceilings, floors and lighting are all new, and all the classrooms are gleaming and well-resourced, with interactive whiteboards in each one. Large and much-loved playground, covered with Astroturf, where boys play 'crazy games' on the climbing apparatus. 'That was a real selling point for me,' said one parent. 'The boys have a chance to be boys.' 'The way to the heart of little boys is good food and football at playtime, and WCCS excels in both,' confirmed another. We didn't try the football, but we can confirm that the food is splendid, a delicious combination of tasty and healthy. Boarding facilities have also been upgraded. We can't comment on the refurbished boarders' common room, because a curmudgeonly old trumpet teacher therein told us we were interrupting his lesson and to get out, but we did manage to see the sleeping accommodation, which was cheerful, light and airy. The rigours of chorister life notwithstanding, feedback on the boarding experience from both parents and boys was uniformly positive. 'The key thing,' says head, 'is to have good, kind people around the boys, good accommodation and excellent food. An army marches on its stomach.'

Years ago, parents had disquiets about aspects of WCCS. Nowadays, they cannot find enough superlatives with which to express their delight. 'We have been thrilled by both the teaching and pastoral care provided by the school.' 'The staff generate a wonderfully positive energy.' 'It's an amazing school, the teachers are so kind!' 'You couldn't choose a better school, I recommend it to everyone.' 'A wonderful warmth and care is present everywhere.'

'The only problem I have had is to find a way to drag my boys out of the playground'

A father of a new chorister told us, 'My son absolutely loves it. He's thrilled to pieces. The first weekend they were eligible to go home, he didn't want to come.' (Poor mum!) And a mother of two day pupils wrote, 'Happiness is guaranteed at this school; it is such a nurturing, caring and stimulating environment. I can honestly say that the only problem I have ever had is to find a way to drag my boys out of the playground and back home at the end of the day.' What's behind this remarkable success? 'The one ingredient a Catholic school should have is joy,' said the head, simply and without any side, when we asked him,.

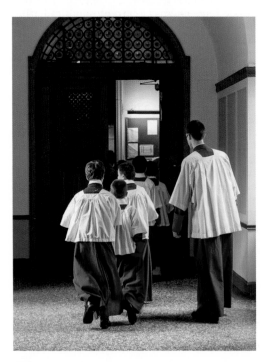

There is joy in the teaching here, that's for sure. A quiet revolution is taking place in the WCCS curriculum that made this reviewer go all excited and wobbly at the knees. Schemes of work have been painstakingly redesigned, with scholarship and a genuine love of learning at their heart. 'The idea is to present knowledge as a unified whole,' explained the head, 'so for instance, whilst they're studying Adam and Eve in RS, they'll be doing CS Lewis's The Magician's Nephew in English. Likewise, we use geometry and graph-plotting in maths to support map skills in geography, and they'll draw antique maps in art at the same time. If the boys are doing the human body in science, they'll look at what the Greeks and Romans discovered about it in history.' The boys we spoke to praised the lessons as 'really good fun,' adding, 'The work's challenging, but in a good way'.

Much emphasis on poetry, with poems studied every week, as well as learnt by heart and declaimed. 'We want them to know the great poets of the English language,' said the deputy head, and to further this, the school has produced its own wonderful anthologies, where the selection is 'unashamedly classic.' In addition to regular English lessons, boys receive two lessons a week on formal grammar and punctuation, and Latin is compulsory from the off – 'Latin is crucial for grammar, it's not an academic luxury,' insisted the deputy head. 'As an international school, the story of the world's great civilisations interests us. But children of this age also need connections, and they need the basics.' All those who have wrung their hands at the disjointed, shallow content of so many modern lessons, lift up your hearts and hope.

This is clearly a scholarly yet joyful environment, and the quality of student work we saw reflected that. We read, misty-eyed, a set of poems by the year 7s about Westminster Bridge (inspired by Wordsworth's sonnet) that were outstandingly creative and well-written; likewise, a history essay on Thomas Becket was not only mature and insightful, but skilful and lucid in its use of language. But mightn't this approach favour only the brightest? WCCS's SENCo emphatically denied it, asserting that boys at the school with SEN benefited from understanding how language works. We were impressed with the support the school gives to those with dyslexia and dyspraxia, as well as to ESL students, such as the two grave and courteous Russian boys we saw having extra English tutorials. And all the staff we met were purposeful, well-bred (curmudgeon excepted), cultivated, devoted to what they do, and, according to parents, 'incredibly dedicated.'

As you'd expect, the standard of music here is outstanding. The choristers are completely immersed in music-making at the highest level (listen to the downloads on the website, and

My son is neither Catholic nor musical, but has been recognised for other things he has to contribute to the school'

marvel), and the day boys, swimming in the same element, also achieve great things. We saw year 8 boys composing their entries for the school's Christmas carol competition, and heard much excellent instrumental playing as we went round the school. 'The music programme is amazing,' enthused one parent. 'My son's piano playing has come on by leaps and bounds in just a few weeks.' Many pupils achieve grades 7 or 8 in their chosen instrument(s) by the time they leave.

Football, rugby and cricket are the main sports here, played at local pitches, and swimming and PE are held at the nearby Queen Mother Sports Centre. Lots of extracurricular activities, including debating, philosophy, chess, scrabble, code-breaking, the Airfix model club, current affairs, and cross-country running. 'But where do you run?' we asked, glancing with some surprise at the surrounding streets. 'Oh!' said our tour guide, 'Green Park, Hyde Park, St James's..'

Lucky lads, you might think. And they are, of course. But what struck us most about this lovely little school was how considerate, well-mannered and sanguine about life its pupils seemed to be. They are achieving great things, while remaining likeable and happy boys. As one mother wrote, 'My son is neither Catholic nor musical, but has been recognised for other things he has to contribute to the school. They're grounded children with good values. It's a perfect place for my son to grow into a confident young man.' We agree with her. For boys fortunate enough to come here, this is as near perfect as it gets.

Westminster Under School

Linked school: Westminster School, 210

Adrian House, 27 Vincent Square, London SW1P 2NN

Independent • Pupils: 288 • Ages: 7–13 • C of E
• Fees: £17,034 pa

Tel: 020 7821 5788

Email: under.school@westminster.org.uk
Website: www.westminster.org.uk

64

Interim Master: Philip Lough, previously head of The Hall, Hampstead and Windlesham House, is holding the reins until September 2016, following the sudden departure of Elizabeth Hill. A solid, dependable and experienced head who should enable the school to ride out any turbulence.

Entrance: Academically selective (very) at 7, 8 and 11. Some successful applicants are merely 'well above the national average', about a third 'far above'. All candidates need to read fluently well beyond their chronological age and approach the unexpected logically and imaginatively. No obvious feeders, though all the usual central London pre-preps represented.

At 11+, a reasonable chunk from state primaries, most of the rest from schools which end at year 6. (The school encourages entrants from 'those leaving at a natural point.') Twenty-two places at 7 (175 applying), a further 22 at 8 (175 applying), then 28 places at 11 (250 applying). At 11+, now uses computerised pre-tests in December before written exams for call-back candidates. About 40 invited at each stage for interview and further testing. 'We want to understand each child and decide if this is the right school for them.' What makes the fit? 'The school is about passion, enthusiasm, determination and a hunger for achievement. We're looking for boys who are independent, intellectual and individual. Everybody here loves learning.'

Exit: About 90 per cent go on to the senior school (including all those who come in at 11), with a good number of scholarships (seven in 2015), but the school is equally happy to prepare for entrance and scholarships elsewhere. About a dozen each year to Eton (often those with family connections), quite a few with major scholarships (three King's Scholars, two Oppidans in 2015). Generally a couple to Winchester, and sometimes a sprinkling to City, Dulwich, Alleyn's, etc.

Remarks: Academically top of the tree. Well-qualified staff (a number with PhDs) provides teaching that is mostly strong, lively and challenging. 'We're looking for boys who will think and problem solve. We want them to work things out, not be spoon-fed.' Most boys seem to relish the offering. 'I really like all my lessons,' said one. 'The teachers are very enthusiastic and if you have a problem they just want to help,' said another. However, the pressure to be high in the rankings comes as a shock to some.

Specialist teaching in all subjects from year 5. In English, boys are encouraged to 'develop their own voice'. Books are seminal, with even the smallest scouring the library shelves in their lunch hour. Reading lists updated termly and topped up with an in-house bookshop and regular swapshop. Weekly maths competitions hone skills both for lessons and the Intermediate and Senior Maths Challenge, where plenty achieve gold and beyond. Maths and science extension club. Programming from year 3. French throughout, taught by native speakers. Classical studies combined with Latin from year 5, stand-alone Latin from year 6, Greek in year 8. Annual Latin play competition. 'There's a real sense of intellectual endeavour,' says one parent.

Thorough monitoring, with internal exams November and June, plus mocks in the Lent term of year 8, as well as regular subject testing. Lots of rewards for achievement with cups and shields for virtually everything. 'They really ram home competition,' said one parent. Homework load significant at all levels. An hour a night in years 3-5, an hour and a half in years 7 and 8. Some parents have voiced the view that supportive homes are essential. The school says this shouldn't be necessary: 'We don't require parental support and you absolutely don't need a tutor. If you need a tutor, you shouldn't be at

Weekly maths competitions hone skills both for lessons and the Intermediate and Senior Maths Challenge, where plenty achieve gold and beyond

Westminster.' We have, however, heard rumours of unhappiness in both staffroom and parental circles, with one parent commenting that tutoring is 'rife'.

New arrivals at 11 – two forms of 12-14 boys – are given Saturday morning lessons from the moment they're accepted, then segregated for lessons (but not other activities) in year 7. 'We give them lots of attention, before dividing up the whole year group into scholarship and CE forms in year 8.' Those from state primaries can find the transition taxing. 'Catching up to common entrance in two years was difficult,' said one parent. 'There was an enormous amount of work and my son found it stressful.'

Few struggle in the conventional sense, but an experienced SENCo provides support with study skills, exam technique and organisation, arranging clinics where help from peer mentors is particularly productive. Plenty of 'enhancement', too, through debating, history of art etc.

Music of an exceptionally high standard (many boys with grade 8 and beyond and plenty of music scholarships to senior schools). Head of music (also musical director of National Youth Music Theatre) oversees over 500 lessons a week, an outstanding choir and biannual music trips.

Not everyone's idea of a sporty school, but the athletic ante has been raised recently with the addition of a number of well-qualified coaches. ('One boy attends the Chelsea football academy one day a week, but still manages his academic work.') For a central London prep, notably well-endowed with playing fields, and the expansive garden square opposite the front gates provides an ample supply of pitches and courts as well as an adventure playground. Games twice a week, with regular inter-house and inter-school tournaments in football, hockey, cricket, tennis and basketball. Recently-acquired sports hall just down the road (also able to accommodate mass gatherings of parents) offers further scope for indoor games, including judo, fencing, karate, wall climbing and nets.

Exciting theatrical tradition maintained by an 'inspirational' head of drama, with three productions annually (recent highlights include Lord of the Flies, School for Scandal) and a new performing arts centre. Art now housed in its own light and lovely double studio, with a self-contained art history library. Clubs every night (history, Mandarin, debating, etc). Chess (taught by a Grand Master) particularly popular, with 90 members and England players. Competitions galore, including hotly contested Scrabble tournament. (Some find the atmosphere slightly too competitive. 'They don't just have a Scrabble club or a chess club, they have a Scrabble competition or a chess competition.')

Plenty of external speakers and trips in London and further afield. (Recent adventures include classics to Sorrento, cricket to South Africa, geography to the Grand Canyon.) Philanthropy a core value. 'They learn to enjoy giving and love raising money for disadvantaged children.' (Parents and boys raised £45,000 last year, £18,000 in the popular Readathon.)

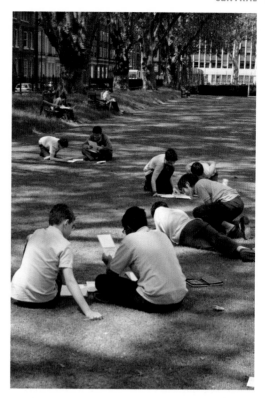

Head of music (also musical director of National Youth Music Theatre) oversees 500 lessons a week, an outstanding choir and biannual music trips

Founded in 1943 as a class of 17 boys located in the senior school, then decanted to Ecclestone Square, the school took up residence in its current spacious premises in Adrian House – a red-brick Victorian former hospital – in 1981. The Under School continues to share both governors and outlook with the senior school, allowing the same careful planning over future development. A large new building, directly opposite the existing school, opened in 2013, providing a loft dining hall and indulgent stretches of well-equipped teaching space.

Discipline not an issue. 'You don't have to shout at Westminster; we encourage good behaviour through positive behaviour management and high expectations.' Certainly, one boy unbidden held open a door, all answered questions readily and politely. Immaculate uniform, perhaps, not a priority. In PSHE, 'they learn about emotional intelligence and empathy for others. We talk about life. We want them to be able to talk with us about anything and it will be OK.'

At 7 and 8, parents primarily prime-central-London (often City) high achievers. At 11+, more diverse, with pupils coming from as far afield as Dagenham and Guildford. Plenty of bilingual, multicultural homes. Parents tend to be proud (and occasionally pushy). Boys are extremely articulate (one 8 year old, asked how he'd cope with a broken arm, responded, 'I will just have to become ambidextrous') and can undoubtedly be boffiny ('Thus, you can see,' explained one 11 year old).

No scholarships, but a few means-tested bursaries of up to 100 per cent at 11 (which take the recipient through the senior school). 'Our philosophy is that the children who can come here should not be prevented from doing so for financial reasons.'

An exciting, demanding education for the intellectual, industrious child.

Westminster School

Linked school: Westminster Under School, 207

17 Dean's Yard, London SW1P 3PB

Independent • Pupils: 741; 144 boy, 42 girl boarders
• Ages: 13–18 • Sixth form pupils: 385 (128 girls) • C of E
• Fees: Day: up to £26,322 pa; Boarding: £35,058 pa;
Queen's Scholars £17,529 pa

Tel: 020 7963 1003

Email: registrar@westminster.org.uk
Website: www.westminster.org.uk

65

Head Master: Since September 2014, Patrick Derham MA (50s), previously head of Rugby School. At 12, he was sent to live and study on the naval training ship Arethusa, run by the children's charity Shaftesbury Homes to prepare young men for the navy. Two years later the ship was abruptly sold due to financial difficulties and, with a day's notice and little idea what a public school was, he arrived at Pangbourne College on a bursary. He eventually became head of school and read history at Cambridge (first class degree), and feels 'my life was transformed by education.'

Taught at Cheam School and then Radley, where he was head of history and a housemaster for '12 very happy years' before being advised by the warden there to go straight for a headship. Five years as head of Solihull were followed by 13 at Rugby, before landing the headship of 'the home of liberal education – the perfect culmination of my career.'

His background ('my mum still lives in a council house in Scotland') has clearly been a powerful motivating force in his commitment to widening access to a good education – as he points out, 'all the great schools were founded with that intention.' At Rugby, he set up the Arnold Foundation to provide bursaries for children who need the stability of a boarding education ('we didn't just cream off the brightest middle class kids'). He is a trustee of the SpringBoard Bursary Foundation, a national charity modelled on the same lines, and vice chair of IntoUniversity, which gives disadvantaged children academic support and mentoring to raise their aspirations.

'He did an amazing job here and will be brilliant at Westminster,' said a Rugby insider. Very down to earth, personable, fantastic speaker, say Westminster parents. 'You feel like you can trust him'... 'He really cares about getting to know everyone'... 'I like it that he already knows who I am and who my children are'… 'Very responsive to comments'… 'My daughter thinks he's great'.

Clearly no ivory tower head, he loves interaction with pupils and teaches A level history. Parents watching their sons compete in the recent National Schools Rowing Regatta were delighted to see Derham there cheering on the teams (they won the championship eights' title for the first time in the school's history).

Married to Alison, a teacher, with two grown up children. Westminster seems to be in very steady, to say nothing of inspiring, hands.

Academic matters: With these very bright pupils, 'you can teach for the love of the subject and focus on the exam when need be,' says the head. 'It's a breath of fresh air,' said a parent. 'Intellectual risk taking is encouraged. They're never not challenged.' 'It's incredibly inspiring,' said another. Many of the teachers are experts in their fields, encouraged to follow their interests. 'I cannot believe there is a more stimulating place to teach in the country,' said a teacher. 'It is so much more liberal than at my previous school,' said a sixth form student. 'It's not constrained by the syllabus – it's learning for the sake of learning. It really allows you to get a proper understanding outside the exam baselines.' Pupils tend to internalise that love of learning. 'They read and they question and they challenge,' says the head. 'In my first lesson one asked me, "Where is the evidence?" I'd never been asked that before.'

'They read and they question and they challenge,' says the head. 'In my first lesson one asked me, "Where is the evidence?" I'd never been asked that before'

Everyone encouraged to include a practical subject, eg art, electronics, drama, music, at GCSE. Huge range of languages includes Dutch, Arabic and Portuguese. Several parents commented that inspirational teachers had sparked their sons' interest in subjects they had previously hated. 'He'd always been a bit of a maths boy but now he is flying at English and languages too. They've understood how to teach in a way that suits him and developed all these new interests.'

Top exam results are, nonetheless, part of the package, with 84 per cent A* and 96 per cent A*/A at GCSE in 2015. At A level/Pre-U, 55 per cent of subjects were graded A* or the Pre-U equivalent (D1/D2) and 86 per cent A*/A. New thinking skills course – designed as a more challenging alternative to critical thinking A level – introduces sixth formers to the elements of informal logic, and helps prepare for university entrance skills tests such as the Oxbridge Thinking Skills Assessment.

His background ('my mum still lives in a council house in Scotland') has clearly been a powerful motivating force in his commitment to widening access to a good education

High academic ability is obviously a pre-requisite, but study skills coordinator works with all those who need support for eg mild dyslexia, dyspraxia or Asperger's, or just lack of organisation, helping them with the skills needed to cope with learning at different levels as they move up the school.

Links with local state schools Grey Coat Hospital and Harris Westminster Sixth Form – the latter sponsored by Westminster School – see sixth formers from these schools joining in German, Latin, music, art history and drama lessons with Westminster students. 'They've done a really good job at integrating us,' said a Westminster sixth former. 'I'm as good friends with students from outside as anyone else in the class.' Joint senior management meetings with Harris Westminster staff: 'We are going to learn from each other.'

Games, options, the arts: An almost overwhelming range of extracurricular opportunities. Societies often stem from the particular passions of both staff and students, ranging from feminist to secular to geography. English society may see Simon Russell Beale answering questions on playing King Lear at the National, whilst Piyush Goyal, national treasurer of the Indian Bharatiya Janata Party (BYP) party tells the political society about Indian public affairs. 'I set up a society and had an ambassador from Panama come to talk,' said one student. 'Staff are really supportive when you want to set up new things.' Huge range of journalists and politicians, scientists and thinkers drop in to give talks; poet in residence inspires creativity. Trips everywhere: climbing in Cataluña, Beijing exchange, art history in Venice. Years 9-11 go off for a week's climbing, sailing, hill walking or camping at home or abroad.

'Phenomenal' music, with professional standard orchestral concerts at St John's Smith Square and the Barbican, carol service in Westminster Abbey, masterclasses, eminent musicians from Nicola Benedetti to Ian Bostridge giving evening concerts. One parent felt that 'unless you are excellent you won't get a look in,' whilst staff point out there are house concerts and ensembles for the less stratospherically talented. 'We like to think there is room for everyone.' Drama equally high performing – Guys and Dolls a recent sell-out but much cerebral fare too, plus house drama and GCSE/A level pieces – and again huge talent required to bag a role in the large scale school productions.

Art, too, 'wonderful', with much emphasis on traditional drawing and painting skills, life classes, film making facilities and a darkroom. Plus, of course, easy access to all of London's galleries and museums. 'My son had no artistic ambition when he arrived, but is now doing art A level. They have totally inspired him,' said one parent, whilst another commented: 'They let these academic boys be so creative – they feel free to explore.'

Sports – known as 'Station' – take place on Tuesday and Thursday afternoons, mostly on the enviably large playing fields in nearby St Vincent Square plus adjacent sports centre (in a previous life one of the Royal Horticultural Halls). In Westminster liberal fashion, no particular sport is compulsory, with a huge range of choices from sailing to judo to golf to girls' football. 'You wouldn't send a very sporty boy to Westminster,' thought a parent, who was grateful that her keen but not-particularly-athletic son had been in teams which he would have been unlikely to make at a more overtly sporty school. However, particularly

successful at rowing (and was basking in glow of recent success at National Schools' Regatta when we visited), fields nine football teams with 'at least respectable' results, and 'we do very well at niche sports such as rock climbing [third in the Independent Schools' Championships] and fencing [bronze medal in U15 Foil]'. Often dominates the London School Cross-Country Championships and the Westminster Secondary Schools Swimming Gala, with pupils representing Westminster in the London Youth Games, and is successful at fives and real tennis. 'You are encouraged to try lots of things and find something you are passionate about,' said a student.

Delete pull out quote and insert: 'My son had no artistic ambition when he arrived, but is now doing art A level. They have totally inspired him. They let these academic boys be so creative – they feel free to explore'

Volunteering taking on increasing importance with new head's passion for outreach, with nearly all Westminsters teaching music or setting up debating societies in local primary schools, working on Hampstead Heath, learning sign language to communicate with deaf children. 'People are really involved and really making a difference,' said a student. 'Staff have the time, passion and faith in us to let us get on with things.' Phab week – where year 12 Westminster students host young people with physical and/or mental challenges, taking part in creative activities and seeing London together – is a 'life changing experience'. 'With privilege comes enormous responsibility to give back,' says the head.

Background and atmosphere: Whilst some other great public schools overshadow their environs, Westminster is an integral but discreet part of central London, largely located in the walled precincts of the former medieval monastery of Westminster Abbey. Its main buildings surround the square of Little Dean's Yard, known as Yard, where pupils spill out after lessons to chat or kick a football or practise basketball. The Abbey, next door and with its own private entrance, is used as the school chapel, used for twice weekly services plus carol and other concerts.

The last Anglican monastery in London now houses Purcell's, a girls' boarding and boys' day house with attached chapel. Five other boarding houses, all in or near Little Dean's Yard and all of which include some day pupils.

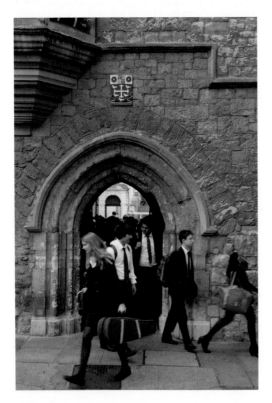

Westminster had become a school by 1179, with pupils taught by monks of the Abbey at Westminster. It survived Henry VIII's dissolution of the monasteries in 1540 and has been in continuous existence since the 14th century, with Elizabeth I celebrated as the school's official foundress.

'It is an incredibly tolerant and civilised atmosphere,' said a parent. 'Unlike other schools, they don't try to mould pupils into a particular product. They are quite laissez-faire.' Parents of quirky students are relieved to find a school that is very kind and accepting of eccentricities. 'If he was at any other school he'd be toast,' said one. 'Some schools can be so unforgiving: Westminster is the complete opposite.' Another reported that it has 'catered brilliantly' for each of her very different children. 'It's so wonderful to see these kids spark off each other.'

Pastoral care and discipline: Tutors attached to each house oversee the academic side, whilst housemasters look after all else. One parent felt that both have too many charges to know her son well. 'I feel his well-being is my responsibility, not the school's. I don't think anyone there knows him well in the round.' Others, however, described the pastoral care as 'exceptional', and a student said, 'I have always found the school really responsive. Your housemaster is always there and will take care of everything from not feeling well to having too much work.'

Pupils expected to be proactive, motivated and organised, with very full timetables but no compulsion to take part in organised activities. 'But anything you want to try, there's some way of doing it,' said a student.

Old Westminsters of her acquaintance have gone into a far wider range of careers than those from other schools

The only full boarders are sixth formers, and Saturday evenings tend to be quiet. There are supervised prep sessions during the week, and evening activities in the sports and music centre, but those after a full-on boarding experience jammed full of organised activities may want to look elsewhere. 'He likes it for the independence and to be with his mates,' said a boarder parent, whilst another said, 'It feels like a convenient b&b. Much better than having to pick him up at late after a rehearsal or lecture.' However, a sixth form boarder commented on the 'serious sense of community you can only get from living with others. The people in your own house become quite special to you.'

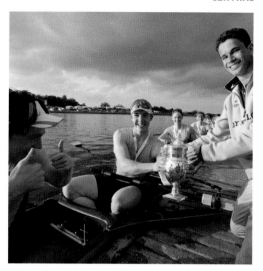

Pupils and parents: 'Lots of people said I wouldn't like Westminster,' reports the head. 'They told me the pupils were arrogant, staff unmanageable, parents difficult. None of this is true.' Westminster families undoubtedly tend to be wealthy, intellectual, metropolitan, cosmopolitan and no doubt demanding, but most parents are extremely supportive of the school. 'It is very hard to withstand this full on praise and delight.' 'I am a real believer.' 'Fantastic on every front.' And from an initial sceptic: 'I am increasingly fond of it.'

Girls entering the sixth form report a much easier ride than they might have expected. 'I had heard rumours about the boys being awful and arrogant – but they weren't,' said one. 'Some would show off in lessons to begin with, but they calmed down pretty quickly.' 'I suspect they look for a certain confidence,' said another. 'If you were insecure you might find it intimidating.' 'It was quite a shock to the system at first,' said a third, 'but we can hold our own.'

'Westminster imbues in you a sense that it is fine to talk to anyone on equal terms,' said an ex-student. 'You have a real feeling of being special.'

Parents – nearly all are Londoners, with even boarders mostly coming from within the M25 – offered a cornucopia of outings to Dulwich Picture Gallery, tours of Westminster Abbey and the Houses of Parliament, plus quiz nights, drinks parties, concerts in the Abbey, and the opportunity to attend expert lectures with their children. 'Parents very friendly and there's a good sense of community and involvement,' said one.

Old Westminsters span the centuries and the professions: the massive list ranges from Ben Jonson, John Dryden, Robert Hooke, Lord Lucan, Kim Philby, AA Milne, John Gielgud, Tony Benn,

Corin Redgrave, Helena Bonham-Carter and Imogen Stubbs to Dido and Mika.

Entrance: Register by the end of year 5 for 13+ entry (boys at state primary and other schools that finish at 11 may apply to Westminster Under School). Computer pre-tests in English, maths and reasoning in year 6; high performers who also have a good report from current school called for interview, which includes short maths and English tests. Those with conditional places sit either the Challenge scholarship exam or CE (pass mark 70 per cent) in year 8.

For 16+ places, register between summer and October of the year before entry. Applicants – boys and girls – take exams in their four most likely A level subjects, and are interviewed.

Exit: Excellent and detailed preparation not only for Oxbridge but for American university entrance, with school trips to visit east coast universities. 'The school has been very supportive from an early age,' said a student, 'keeping us up to date with when to take subject tests and when to visit colleges.' Good preparation too for medicine, which is amongst the most popular degree subjects alongside liberal arts.

Up to half of sixth formers do, indeed, go to Oxbridge (68 in 2015, with 14 taking up places at leading American universities), most of the rest to London universities, Edinburgh, Durham and Bristol.

Money matters: A number of means-tested bursaries of up to 100 per cent of fees available at 13+ and 16+; applicants must live in London. Bursaries also available at 11+; boys spend two years at the Under School before moving on automatically to the Great School. Eight Queen's Scholarships awarded at 13+; recipients must board, and the scholarship covers half the boarding fee. This can be topped up by a bursary in case of need. Five exhibitions at this level. Up to six music scholarships at 13+ worth 25 per cent of day or boarding fee, plus free instrumental tuition. No 16+ scholarships.

Remarks: One ex-student commented that Old Westminsters of her acquaintance have gone into a far wider range of careers than those from other schools. 'They seem to be following their passion. Westminster instils a belief that you can do whatever you want to do.'

Wetherby Preparatory School

Linked school: Wetherby School, 369

48 Bryanston Square, London W1H 2EA

Independent · Pupils: 305 · Ages: 7–13 · Fees: £19,350 pa

Tel: 020 7535 3520

Email: admin@wetherbyprep.co.uk
Website: www.wetherbyprep.co.uk

66

Head: Since 2008, Nick Baker BA PGCE (early 40s). A grammar school boy, he hails from Bucks, was educated at Dr Challoner's and University College London, where he read geography, before qualifying as a teacher at Newcastle University. He has taught geography in a range of schools, including Holloway Boys comprehensive, head of year at Borehamwood, a former state middle school, and head of geography at Chesham Prep school (where he went as a boy, is now a governor, and where his two sons currently are). He has taught at Wetherby Prep since it first started in 2004, initially as a senior master before becoming deputy head, and his brief continues to expand as he is now head of the new Wetherby Senior School, since September 2015, as well as continuing to run the prep.

Tall, broad-shouldered and youthful, with a reassuring laugh that echoes from his belly, Nick

Baker is hugely popular, with parents, pupils and staff as well as colleagues in the wider prep school world. A keen supporter of Watford Football Club, he celebrates their victories at whole prize-giving events as well as in his blog and emails, and even the many Chelsea supporters among the families here share in his delight and enthusiasm. Open and affable, his weekly newsletters in Wetherbuzz frequently include anecdotes about his two boys and what his family is getting up to. Hot on values and manners, one of the many 'challenges' he initiated is the Politeness Challenge. 'Much the best news is hearing that Wetherby boys are good house guests,' he says. Parents like the fact that he is so present both around the school and at the many social events organised for teachers and parents, the Headmaster's Ball, or 'pub nights with dads', for example, as well as the Come Dine with Me event where teachers cook and wait on the parents. The adjectives that we heard most often were 'very professional', 'excellent communicator' and 'very driven and opinionated', but what is most apparent and consistent is that they trust him.

Entrance: At 7 and 8 into year 3 (when about 100 sit for 20 places) and year 4 (when 200 sit for 40 places). Boys from the pre-prep have automatic entry and arrive in year 4, so year 3 might be the safer bet for applicants from elsewhere. Everyone else (including from other Alpha Plus schools like Chepstow House, but apart from siblings who also enter automatically) sit papers in English, maths and reasoning during an assessment day at the school and also take part in group activities.

Exit: An impressive number to top academic schools, especially considering the range of ability in each year. In recent years a handful (three or more) to Eton, St Paul's and Westminster, as well as the odd one to Winchester College and King's Wimbledon. Harrow, Bradfield, Wellington and Charterhouse are other popular boarding destinations. The day pupils go to a range of other schools from Dulwich and City of London to Kew House and the Harrodian, and increasingly, since September 2015, to the new Wetherby Senior School.

Remarks: Wetherby Prep, and its brother, pre-prep Wetherby School, are currently riding high and widely regarded by parents across London as the jewel in the Alpha Plus crown. Slick as a well-oiled machine, Wetherby delivers precisely what its parents demand: high quality teaching, a broad and

Parents and children cram into every corner and, after singing a hymn, prizes are distributed. These can be for anything from the history prize to the prize for the best joke

extensive choice of activities and sports and exceptional communication. Many of the parents are bankers and Wetherby is the prep school equivalent of a well-resourced City institution. Boys here are polite (everyone stands up when you enter a room – 'our parents like that,' says Mr Baker) but sparkling and not squashed. One occasion which captures the spirit of the school is the prize-giving assembly which takes place every Friday in the Church of Annunciation behind Marble Arch. Parents and children cram into every corner and, after singing a hymn, prizes are distributed. These can be anything from the history prize to the prize for the best joke – let alone for sporting achievements (like running the marathon). Mr Baker conducts the whole occasion with warmth and humour. He clearly knows every child well and there is a lot of boyish banter. A cauldron of competitiveness, when house points are read out there are huge whoops and cheers. These boys really care if their house is ahead – especially if it's about the amount of food waste they are managing to avoid. We also witnessed a charming joy in their peers' achievements. The best kind of competitive spirit. We were most impressed when boys not only moved aside to let us sit down but also folded and cleared our chairs for us amid the chaos of cricket bats, violins, hockey sticks and trumpets at the close of proceedings.

Situated behind Marble Arch in leafy Bryanston Square, the Georgian building is grand and spacious. The signature red painted front door welcomes you into a smart, light, high ceilinged entrance hall, complete with wood panelled, gold leaf scholarship boards and lists of head boys, prefects and house captains of the school. Boys pile past heaving musical instruments and sports equipment, looking smart but tousled in cricket gear, grey and red blazers and caps. A sweeping staircase takes traffic up the several flights, a small back staircase channels them down. All the classrooms are large, light and airy, well-equipped and organised. The basement not only houses a couple of very well-equipped science labs, a fitness suite with rowing and running machines, and the dining room, but also a pet snake which boys can stand and stare at to while away any spare minutes in their busy day. Every boy has his own red locker – no need to lug every book and file around with him the whole time. School laptops seem to be littered at strategic points around the school and are available for anyone to use. There are also 20 desktop PCs in the library, which doubles up as an ICT suite where the boys learn coding, touch-typing and animation.

Lots of well-heeled bankers and lawyers, and a smattering of celebrities – what else would you expect in this part of London?

From year 4, boys are setted in maths and English and have specialist subject teachers; most other subjects are setted in year 6, when they also start Latin. Three classes per year, with about 20 in each class. With automatic entry for siblings and boys from Wetherby School, alongside selective entry for others, the school is mixed ability but, Mr Baker observes, 'the academic demographic gets stronger year by year. The average CAT score used to be 112 and is now 120.' Full-time SENCo, assisted by one other person, gives support to children with mild learning difficulties, including dyslexia, dyspraxia and mild autism. Support provided ranges from touch-typing to reading groups as well as one-to-one session in maths and literacy outside the classroom. Approximately 16 in the school are getting support at any one time. Lots of prizes and rewards including a meeting with the head – the Headmaster's Good Show – to commend outstanding work. One young 9 year old told us proudly that

he was 'very good friends with Mr Baker' as a result of his regular chats with him.

Sport is strong and getting better and better each year, both in terms of what is offered, the facilities and the teams' performances against other schools. The Park Club, in Acton, is now their home ground, and although some parents complain of traffic and the length of time it gets to bus them there, most were very enthusiastic about the excellent facilities, the space and the fact that they no longer need to box and cox in various places around central London. Boys play rugby and football in the winter, athletics, tennis and cricket in the summer. Their annual sports day is a major fixture in the calendar. There are plenty of other sports on offer too – hockey (including roller hockey), horse riding, fencing, rowing, rock climbing and badminton. One gets the impression that when Mr Baker goes to his Alpha Plus governors to ask that the tap be turned on (to make provision for another club for example), it will be done. Lots of popular 'fathers and staff' fixtures too, in cricket and football.

Parents enthuse about the 'excellent' music. 'Despite the fact that my son is sporty, his favourite club is choir,' observed one father. Dynamic head of music has a modern and innovative approach. Plenty of public performances, impromptu as well as more formal. Breakfast concerts happen twice a term, there is a junior and senior school recital and a band as well as an orchestra and a chamber choir. Art is well organised and cross-curricular. We saw lots of lino cuttings and Mac books in the art room as well as impressive pieces of work around the school. In DT they were building clocks, and there is a dark room for photography, but the 'backbone of the department is printing,' we were told. Drama could be better, Mr Baker acknowledges; some parents, more brutally, described it as 'almost non-existent.' They use the Rudolf Steiner theatre up the road for productions, 'but it's so difficult to get good drama teachers/directors,' explains the head.

Parents here are slightly more diverse than those at the pre-prep. The numerous school buses run like clockwork and depart and arrive when they are meant to, enabling many parents to entrust their boys to the school transport, so they come from as far as Islington in the north east to Hammersmith in the west. Lots of well-heeled bankers and lawyers, and a smattering of celebrities – what would you expect in this part of London? – but a refreshing mixture of cultures and backgrounds. Nick Baker's openness and inclusivity – both in the weekly Wetherbuzz newsletters as well as in his public addresses – helps to contribute to a real family and community feel. An outstanding school, polished and professional, and an excellent foundation for your all-rounder son.

William Ellis School

Linked school: LaSwap Sixth Form Consortium, 130

Highgate Road, London NW5 1RN

Tel: 020 7267 9346

State • Pupils: 884 • Ages: 11–18 • Sixth form pupils: 1,250 in LaSwap, a consortium of four schools

Email: info@williamellis.camden.sch.uk
Website: www.williamellis.camden.sch.uk

Head: Since 2011, Mr Sam White, chemistry graduate and previously deputy head of the London Oratory. Good news, say parents: 'He has an exceptionally good manner with boys and parents.' 'The boys like and respect him.' 'Whenever I go in I see him chatting with a boy, and he seems to be genuinely interested in them.' A pupil concurred. 'He has been really keen to get to know us all. He is a good influence on us.'

He was appointed during the interim headship of Jill Hislop, who took over after the school had suffered a budget deficit, got through two heads in quick succession and been slated by Ofsted. Ms Hislop, who still has strong links with the school as its 'professional partner', started the upward trajectory that Sam White has continued. Ofsted returned and pronounced the school 'good', quoting a teacher's remark that 'The headteacher is leading and pulling everyone here along.'

He felt that he was taking on 'a challenge, but manageable... it was a school that desperately wanted to improve'. His first job was tackling

behaviour – 'we needed to re-establish clear boundaries' – and his first two years saw a high rate of temporary exclusions, which has now dropped significantly. He has also continued the work on improving the quality of teaching and, despite some initial staff turnover, maintained teacher morale and encouraged staff to work collaboratively to produce good schemes of work.

'They will take time and patience with those who are bright but not pulling their finger out'

Camden is one of the few areas of the country where no schools have converted to academies, and the local schools (which collaborate as a joint sixth form, LaSwap) work closely together. 'I get lots of support from Sue next door [at Parliament Hill], Maureen across the road [at La Sainte Union]...'

Academic matters: Huge ability range, with year 7 reading ages ranging from 8 to 17. In 2015, 55 per cent of pupils got 5+ A*-C grades including English and maths, with 20 per cent A*/A grades. Parents report that English, once a weak point, has been turned round by the 'very impressive' new HoD. The school now teaches the IGCSE English language, and those who took the exam early achieved 'brilliant results'.

The school has a language specialism, and everyone starts French in year 7, with around half studying it to GCSE. School has links with the nearby Collège Français Bilingue de Londres. Most take up either Spanish or German in year 8 (offered in alternate years), but this is no longer compulsory, and some spend extra time on English fluency instead. Latin and Mandarin are taught in clubs, and fundraising has enabled a sixth form Mandarin and geography trip to China in 2014 – the first for three years.

Around a quarter of boys take single sciences to GCSE. Those with a more vocational bent can take OCR science, and choose from various other courses with a large coursework element such as business studies, travel and tourism, and ICT. Some spend a day a week in years 10 and 11 at Westminster Kingsway College studying eg catering, construction or motor mechanics.

Fluid grouping rather than setting across the curriculum from year 8 (school hopes to group maths and science from year 7 in future) at the discretion of each faculty head. 'If a set of boys has a particular weakness in a subject we may put them together for a term, but there's plenty of movement.' Some parents would prefer more rigorous setting, but praise the willingness of staff to go the extra mile for boys at all levels. 'They will take time and a lot of patience with those who are bright but not pulling their finger out. I don't feel

'He has a sense of belonging and pride in the school. It fosters a nice attitude and spirit in the boys'

they are just settling for the easiest way of getting them through exams.'

Parents are mostly optimistic, though one complained about a lack of homework. 'We've found the teaching really good so far,' said another. 'My son is very happy here and seems to be doing well.' 'My son, who is very academic, is being well supported,' said another. 'I had severe reservations about some of the teaching during my son's early years here,' said a long-standing parent, 'but I don't now. I've never felt I had to get a tutor in.'

Teaching assistants are increasingly being trained to help with particular subjects, or with behavioural or language difficulties, rather than being velcroed to a particular child. The school uses some of its pupil premium funding (alongside sponsorship) on its City Year team of volunteers, who act as mentors, support teachers in class, run breakfast and homework clubs and supervise in the playground. The funding also helps with small group and one-to-one teaching, particularly in English, as well as counselling and interventions to improve attendance.

Joint sixth form with Parliament Hill School, which is part of the LaSwap consortium that also includes La Sainte Union and Acland Burghley. This enables a wide range of courses for a wide range of abilities, from a BTec in health and social care to further maths A level. In 2015, 14 per cent A*/A grades and 41 per cent A*-B. Students stay in their base school (which for William Ellis boys will be their own school or Parliament Hill) for the majority of lessons, but may go elsewhere for minority subjects.

As well as working with Camden to provide one-to-one careers advice, school uses Future First, set up by old Elysians, to help it keep in touch with alumni and get them involved in giving careers advice, work experience and mentoring. It organises career sessions here and brings back old boys to talk about their work.

Games, options, the arts: A large trophy on the head's table when we visited is the new house cup. Houses (named after local historic buildings: Lauderdale, Burgh, Willow, Keats and Fenton) have been reintroduced and are run by 'young, enthusiastic staff'. Pupils gain house points by competing at sports and taking part in talent shows, spelling bees, chess, model building, cake sales et al.

Year 7 and year 9 have a week camping at the school's field centre, The Mill, in Surrey. Boys also go on ski trips, language exchanges and field trips.

'The extracurricular activities have improved markedly over the past few years,' said a parent, citing her son's sessions at the Royal College of Music, playwriting with professionals, theatre and concert trips, Model UN.

Football and basketball are the most popular team sports, but rugby is up and coming – the RFU provides coaching and talented players are encouraged to join local clubs. The eight table tennis tables get enthusiastic use. Takes part in the annual Camden Shield boys' competition, which sees teams from six Camden secondary schools compete in football, table tennis, basketball, badminton, athletics and cricket. Pupils report that team sports peter out in the higher years: 'The teachers do try, but we tend to get a bit lazy in years 10 and 11.' The school has a newish sports hall, with facilities for PE and basketball and a multi-gym, and the playground doubles up as five-a-side football pitches. Sadly, the school cannot afford to hire the field next door, groomed for cricket when we visited, but it does play games on other parts of Parliament Hill Fields and uses the athletics track there. Clubs include cricket, running and trampoline.

Light top floor art rooms display impressive work; a sixth former was recently a finalist in the Camden Art Competition, and students have exhibited their work at the local Lauderdale House. Some parents find the music provision underwhelming, but there are choirs, ensembles and a range of concerts for all, from beginners to advanced musicians, often in conjunction with Parliament Hill School and La Sainte Union, which form a joint orchestra with WE. There are also workshops and masterclasses run by professional musicians. The head of music 'has been very supportive of my son writing and performing his own music,' said a parent, and a school group recently reached the finals of the Roundhouse Band Slam competition. School subsidises instrumental lessons for boys on free school meals.

'Whenever I've emailed to ask questions, I've had an immediate and pleased reply'

Not a school that goes in for full-scale musicals, but there are many smaller drama performances, such as the recent drama club interpretations of the Ancient Mariner and Christmas Eve in the Trenches at the Winter Concert. Pupils work with outside organisations such as the Donmar Warehouse, and take part in the Shakespeare Schools Festival. 'They do it thoroughly and well,' said a parent.

Background and atmosphere: William Ellis was a public-spirited businessman who founded several schools in the mid-nineteenth century, believing children should be taught 'useful' subjects such as science and to develop their reasoning faculties, rather than rote-learning religious tracts and ancient languages. William Ellis School, the only one of his schools that still exists, was founded in Gospel Oak in 1862 and recognised as a boy's secondary school in 1889. It moved to its present site, on the edge of Parliament Hill Fields, in 1937. Originally a grammar school, it turned comprehensive in 1978; the red-brick vine-clad buildings still have a grammar school feel.

'My son has had a very happy time here,' said a parent. 'He has a sense of belonging and pride in his school. It fosters a nice attitude and spirit in the boys – confident but not arrogant.'

Pastoral care and discipline: As mentioned, one of the head's first actions was to tighten up on discipline, with plenty of fixed term exclusions in his first couple of years. He also appointed a new and effective head of pastoral care. This has helped to cut down on the low level disruption that once marred many lessons, and has made boys feel safer inside and out. 'They are much stricter on uniform than they used to be, and you no longer have to hack your way through a posse of boys smoking round the gate,' said a parent. Year 7 has its own quad, with table tennis and picnic tables. The year 7 head has links with most of the feeder primary schools, and boys are invited to summer school before they start.

One parent commented: 'The pastoral care is very good. A few years ago I went through a difficult divorce and they were brilliant at supporting my son.' Another said, 'Whenever I've emailed to ask questions, I've had an immediate and pleased reply. They are extremely responsive to an interested/meddling parent.'

Increasing emphasis on carrots rather than sticks, with boys earning house praise points for good work and good attitudes, from persistence to creativity. 'Relationships can be much more relaxed once ground rules are established,' says the head. Deep Learning Days, part of the PHSE curriculum, see timetables dropped for a day in favour of discussions on relationships, including peer pressure and bullying, careers and the world of work, with plenty of outside speakers. 'We try to make it circular – get the boys to present back to their peers what they have learned. Recently 25 year 9 boys did a play for the rest of the school.' One parent commented on her despondence at a lack of creativity in the PHSE teaching, but another said, 'They are very good at raising the boys' social and political awareness. They don't shy away from issues that can be sensitive, such as homophobia and religion.'

Pupils and parents: Huge ethnic mix, with fewer than a third of pupils from white British background, and others ranging from Irish to Turkish to Somalian. Huge social mix too, from the large social housing estates of Gospel Oak to the multi-million pound houses of Dartmouth Park. 'There were cliques lower down the school, but in years 10 and 11 everyone hangs out together and we all get on,' said a pupil. 'The fact that the boys come from a huge range of backgrounds doesn't seem to matter one bit, which is a very impressive trick for a school to pull off,' said a parent. Old Elysians include Toby Young, Robert Elms, Sean French, Andrew Sachs and Len Deighton.

Entrance: Usual admissions criteria for 125 year 7 places: looked after children, medical and social need, siblings, up to 12 musical aptitude places, then by distance (usually up to about two miles). Generally around 300 outside places for LaSwap sixth form consortium, with an intricate admissions system and a range of entry requirements for different levels of courses.

Exit: Around 70 per cent move on to LaSwap sixth form. Some go off to eg Camden School for Girls, Woodhouse College, St Marylebone, Fortismere or FE colleges. Around 20 per cent of LaSwap leavers to Russell Group universities, including several a year to Oxbridge (one in 2015).

Money matters: Voluntary aided by the William Ellis and Birkbeck Schools Trust, but otherwise is as hard up as most other state schools.

Remarks: Small boys' comprehensive in idyllic situation on the borders of Hampstead Heath, now emerging rapidly from the doldrums under strong, popular and enthusiastic head. 'It can only get better and better,' said a satisfied parent.

Central West

Hammersmith & Fulham
Kensington & Chelsea

Kilburn

Camde

St John's
Wood

Regents
Park

rlesden

Maida
Vale

HAMMERSMITH & FULHAM

KENSINGTON & CHELSEA

47

41

51

24

54

43

Hyde
Park

St

29

33

12

35

20

Notting Hill

Shepherd's
Bush

40

23

Kensington

27

34 39

5

2

16
17

52

44
45

37

31

36

14

1

26

42

38

53

50

4

18

28

We

9

15

46

21

48

32

25

Chiswick

8

3

6

10
11

7

19

13

30

22

Chelsea

49

Fulham

Battersea

Barnes

Wandsworth

1   2   3 Miles

CENTRAL WEST

An introduction to Central West London and its state schools

Hammersmith & Fulham

A long borough that travels from north to south, albeit with numerous bus routes linking the two ends. Just west of Chelsea, this is a hard borough to pin down, with Fulham's pockets of large mansion flats near the river and Victorian terraced houses within sound of gentle thwonk of tennis balls at the Queens Club – cheek by jowl with council housing and some fairly mean streets. But some of the harder areas are on an upward trend, particularly near the recently gentrified Fulham Broadway and in Hammersmith with bustling King Street, ever improving pubs and new development spreading out from the huge Westfield shopping centre.

A high percentage of children used to attend secondary schools outside the borough, but the arrival in 2011 of two very different schools has changed the face of secondary school provision here. The Hammersmith Academy had a wobbly start in the face of the sudden and fierce competition from the much publicised and surprisingly popular West London Free School. The latter, with its public-school-like stipulation that Latin be learnt by all and that boys play hockey and rugby, not football, was a London middle class magnet. However, as the years roll on and its pupils are still nowhere near being housed in the premises they were promised (the elegant and spacious Palingswick House on King Street), and reeling from losing two heads in three years, the West London Free School is starting to lose some ground to its more established, well-resourced rival. The Hammersmith Academy is modelled on the highly successful Thomas Telford Academy in the Midlands. It has three hour lessons conducted in the splendid circular premises between the Goldhawk and Uxbridge Roads, and the Mercers (the Guild that is behind St Paul's boys and girls, among others) as sponsors.

Burlington Danes Academy – towards North Kensington – is one of the ARK academies, with the associated financial and expert support. The school has become a serious contender – results are good and becoming better, and Ofsted judges it to be outstanding across the board. Phoenix Canberra, in Shepherds Bush, benefitted enormously from the tight control and charismatic headship of Sir William Atkinson. While he has gone now, academic performance remains reasonably steady with some improvement. A good choice of vocational subjects as well as academic, but probably not the place to sit A levels.

Sacred Heart High qv in Hammersmith is a reason for parents of girls to convert to Catholicism and choose a local Catholic primary school (siblings are quite low on the priority list).

In the south of the borough, Fulham Cross Boys' School (once called Henry Compton) and Fulham College Girls' School (both 11 – 16 years) are now in a federation with the new Fulham Enterprise Studio. This is a vocational 'studio school' for 14 – 19 year olds, specialising in construction and performing arts (production). Free schoolers are at work here too, setting up The Fulham Boys' School (C of E but welcoming all faiths and none) in West Kensington. The school is currently housed in temporary premises on Mund Street where they will stay for the next couple of years.

Lady Margaret qv in Parsons Green, an all-girls, Church of England school with over 50 per cent church-goer places, feels more like Wycombe Abbey than a London comprehensive. This end of the borough is also home to the highly prestigious London Oratory qv – the holy grail for Catholic parents with sons. Boys are accepted from across London, the admission requirements stringent, but the lucky parents who have succeeded in jumping through those precarious hoops (including Blairs and Cleggs) are satisfied customers.

Popular primary schools include John Betts qv, traditional and small, lots of parents opining that it reminds them of their own primary school, Brackenbury, and Greenside (the latter despite a string of highly disappointing Ofsted reports). The West London Free School primary school has made a promising start, say parents cautiously, with automatic entry into the senior school. The Ark Conway Primary School in the far north of the borough, part of the ARK group of academies, is in a relatively deprived area but is well managed and in a splendidly characterful building (the old library).

There is a plethora of good church schools, most notably the outstanding St Stephen's on the Uxbridge Road, which sends large numbers to Twyford C of E high school in Acton as well as the West London Free School (its founder's children go there), and the ever-popular St Peter's in the leafy Hammersmith square of that name off King Street. For the Catholics, Larmenier & Sacred Heart in Brook Green and The Good Shepherd off Askew Road feed boys to Cardinal Vaughan and the London Oratory, girls to the ever-outstanding Sacred Heart.

Kensington & Chelsea

The Royal Borough of Kensington and Chelsea is one of London's smallest boroughs geographically and yet one of the most densely populated areas in Europe. It includes Holland Park, the area named for the eponymous park, which features leafy streets and some of the largest detached and semi-detached houses in London. Notting Hill of Hugh Grant fame is home to the Portobello Market and hosts the largest annual street party and carnival in Europe, held over the August bank holiday weekend.

The borough houses some of London's wealthiest as well as its poorest. Half the residents educate their children privately, half of the state school pupils receive free school meals, and half of the borough's children go to secondary school in another borough. It is also, on DfE statistics, the best performing area in England for GCSE results.

There are only five mainstream secondaries and of these only one, Holland Park qv, is a community school. It is rated outstanding and is hideously oversubscribed, but gives up to 10 per cent of places to students who show an 'aptitude in art and design.'

The rest have a religious requirement as part of the admissions process. Three are Catholic (St Thomas More – co-ed – in SW3, Sion-Manning – girls – in North Kensington and Cardinal Vaughan qv – boys – in Holland Park) and one, co-ed Chelsea Academy (Fulham), is C of E (50 per cent faith and 50 per cent open places, with some preference for children from K&C primary schools). Cardinal Vaughan, with its tight entrance rules and tight discipline, is the number one choice of school for the children of a number of prominent political figures.

Fox qv, with its tiny catchment tightly focused primarily on and around Kensington Church Street and south of Notting Hill Gate, is a very vibrant and a reliable primary school choice. Half of the 27 primary schools are either Catholic or C of E, St Barnabas and St Philips and St Mary Abbots – the latter attracting leading lights in the parliament – perhaps the most coveted. Further south towards Chelsea, the Oratory is a popular choice for Catholics and Christ Church for the Anglicans. If you're not religious and live close to a salubrious area that incorporates, inter alia, The Boltons, then Bousfield qv is likely to be your number one choice. Other less well known schools that have a good reputation in the (slightly) darker corners of the borough include Barlby and Thomas Jones qv.

Ashbourne Independent School

17 Old Court Place, London W8 4PL

Tel: 020 7937 3858

Independent • Pupils: 270 • Ages: 16–19; plus small GCSE stream • Sixth form pupils: 210 • Fees: up to £24,000 pa

Email: admin@ashbournecollege.co.uk
Website: www.ashbournecollege.co.uk

20

Principal: Since 1981, Michael (Mike) Kirby BApSc MSC (60s), who founded the college. Mr Kirby read aerospace engineering in Toronto (he retains a soft Canadian burr) and Birkbeck where he did a masters in statistics. Very tall, laconic and seemingly inscrutable, but a warmth and a smile escape him occasionally and the man is momentarily revealed. After 32 years, unsurprisingly, he and his school mirror each other. Focused and clear-sighted, he has made a place where little distracts from work but where the work ethic is underpinned by the sense of support felt by the students. His involvement with the students is integral to the day-to-day running but the touch is light. 'I know a lot of them personally – they can be a bit wide-eyed and innocent but they're just nice kids and they're great fun.' He still teaches maths revision classes – as ever, we applaud – and, unlike many in his position, sees the students very much in their own home context. 'We positively encourage parents to get involved.'

Prominent member of CIFE (the Conference for Independent Further Education) and the British Council Education Counselling Service, he is the owner and proprietor of Ashbourne. This and the length of his tenure make him unique. He is keen that Ashbourne be recognised as a 'bona fide part of the independent school system', hence his resolve

not to be the first resort for resit students – though they do come in penny numbers. He launched and continues to steer a pretty effective school.

'It's way beyond the A level syllabus so you learn about Marx and Freud and feminism and then apply the theories to film and literature'

Academic matters: Most students come for the two-year A level course, although one year and 18 month A level programmes also on offer – these popular with, mostly, overseas students. Separate classes for those AS students who want to improve their grades – a growing trend. However, AS students who significantly 'underperform' – having been warned that they are in danger of doing so – are shown the door. No embarrassment at this – 'We filter,' says Mr Kirby. 'That's how we get the results'. A small middle school offers two year (years 10 and 11) and one year (year 11) GCSE programmes However, refuses to divulge up to date exam results.

At A level, 37 subjects on offer and all taught in small classes – seven is average, 10 is max and even ones and twos for some subjects. Maths much the most popular subject and with the most impressive results – almost all A*-B. Similarly with further maths. The sciences also taken by many – again with a decent crop of results. We witnessed one Eng lit class – all girls. Languages holding up well and business here, as everywhere, gaining a more

Art is legendary here and the art room – where we were glad to see some mess – was full of concentrating artists and makers of textiles when we visited. Lots of colour and art seemingly derived from diverse influences

mixed bunch of results. Unsurprisingly, no Latin, no Greek. All language teachers are native speakers. Lunchtime critical theory seminar much-praised and very popular: 'It's way beyond the A level syllabus so you learn about Marx and Freud and feminism and then apply the theories to film and literature. I learned so much from doing it that way,' an A2 student enthused. All lessons are two hours long. Teachers much praised for their enthusiasm and care. Many are long-serving.

Few SEN students with anything other than mild dyslexia/dycalculia/ADHD and neither building any good for those with mobility difficulties. No SENCo though SEN overseen by affable head of middle school. Mr Kirby says: 'The school is happy to accept those with SEN but makes no special provision beyond arrangements for exams.' A few here have extra exam time, a laptop in exams or a scribe.

Games, options, the arts: Some variance between the college, which claims to offer 'a very wide extra-curricular programme', and the students, some of whom seem to know little about it – mostly, apparently, the Brits who don't live locally. However, much enthusiasm from those who do partake and especially from those who have gone on overseas subject-related trips with the college. We are told that the college has now appointed an officer who is specifically responsible for student activities and for ensuring that everyone knows about them.

Art is legendary here and the art room – where we were glad to see some mess – was full of concentrating artists and makers of textiles when we visited. Lots of colour and art seemingly derived from diverse influences. College runs a choir but no orchestra/ensembles. Lots of societies – held in

lunchtime and after college; good college newspaper written by students. No sport to speak of and some join gyms etc (there's one next door) but, as everyone agreed, it's the price you pay. Very popular Christmas Revue in which virtually all take part – local fringe theatres are hired for these and other performance events.

Background and atmosphere: Principally in two buildings, separated by Ken High Street. 'Old Building' (in Old Court Place) is tucked down a side road – helpfully guarded by two policemen holding rifles (actually outside the Israeli Consulate) – and so discreet, it's very easily missed. Most sixth form classes take place here. 'Young Street Building' in – you couldn't make it up – Young Street opposite houses the middle school and the rest of the sixth form classes including a huge art room – by far the biggest of the school's rooms. Internally, both buildings are pristine – white walls relieved by stylish and undistracting prints and some larger artwork made on site. Plain carpet, bare wood stairs. Sofas only in one common room and the two staff rooms which are as severely workful as the rest of the establishment. There's nowhere to doss, nowhere to hide. You come here, you work. If you want to mess about, you go out. And they do. Ken High Street, the park, cafés and shops – it's all on the doorstep and, if the inside of the school is cramped, up close London is huge, spacious and full of things to do. Students would welcome kitchen space – somewhere to warm up lunch brought from home (daily eating out is expensive) – but every inch counts here and the common rooms are small. Lockers only for GCSE, art and photography students.

School has recently bought the upper floor of a period building at 47 Kensington Court, which provides, alongside extra classrooms, a new dedicated drama space with elegant top-lighting.

Little sense of 'them and us'. Everyone has a personal tutor – the same throughout their time

Can accommodate up to 250 students. Teaching rooms are definitely small. Interactive whiteboards in use everywhere and Mac PCs everywhere too. The library is all Macs and the shelves have text books and uni guides. Good music room – again, all tech, as far as we could see though there is, apparently, a piano and a guitar. Good film/media room and photography studio has dark room. A pervasive air of relaxed purposefulness. And a fantastic location.

Pastoral care and discipline: The parents we spoke to paid tribute to the excellence of home-school communications and this is true equally of local or UK-based families and the overseas ones. Few such colleges offer the community feel and nurturing to be found here – strengthened by everyone being on first name terms and easy exchanges of emails between parents and staff. Staff room doors are glazed and usually open – little sense of 'them and us'. Everyone has a personal tutor – the same throughout their time – 20 tutees to a tutor. This is not the place if all you want is processing to achieve results. The staff gain much praise for being on top of their game educationally but also for 'really caring' and being very approachable. Drug use would lead to immediate expulsion but this sanction very rarely used. Probably not your first shot if you've been ejected elsewhere.

Pupils and parents: Students come from state and independent schools in the UK, as well as from private schools abroad. Around half the students from around 40 different countries – the rest from the UK. Fewer Chinese than hitherto – more now from Vietnam and Malaysia but college recruits from Russia, Botswana, Ukraine and Kazakhstan and elsewhere. All students have to speak good English and must speak English during the school day – even when with compatriots. About 40 per cent of the students have dedicated English-language classes (no extra cost) – up to six per week – however, best not to choose Ashbourne if you need substantial EAL reinforcement. Of the UK students, around third to a half from the state sector. No boarding though college has halls shared with other educational bodies close by and in Hampstead. Some international students' families find their own more local accommodation. Slightly more girls than boys overall and girls vastly outnumber boys in the humanities. Students here don't look like rebels, dropouts or rejects but wholesome and focused – much as at any academic, independent school's sixth form. All relish the social mix and the internationalism. Students on bursaries complement the loaded with no discernible difference. 'It's a bit cliquey,' we were told, 'especially if you're not into smoking and drinking,' but that's what they do at this age – it's part of being a teenager and drugs seem not to feature here, unlike elsewhere. The principal notes that Ashbourne appeals particularly to 'pupils from good local girls' independents who want something different at A level'.

Entrance: January and September intakes makes for flexibility and a great help to those who need time to re-group after, perhaps, mind-numbing GCSE results. Entry via interview – telephone or face-to-face with either principal or director of studies plus a subject-related entrance test. Auditions for drama/music applicants and portfolio for those who wish to pursue fine art – in which the college

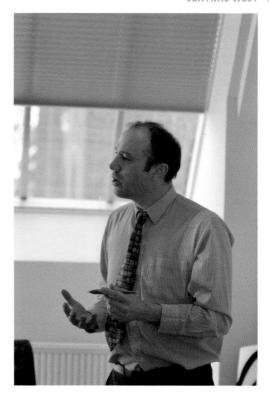

has a distinguished tradition. Also, most recent school report/grades/predictions and a personal statement. Bs expected for entry to A level courses – though some flexibility. International students must have minimum 5.5 IELTS or equivalent.

Exit: To a diverse list of colleges and universities – no processed clones leave here. Oxbridge places and unis abroad not uncommon. Perhaps predictably, London universities figure prominently, along with eg Edinburgh University. Courses taken mostly point to solid professions and vocations. Many ultimately into law and finance but this is no mere spawning ground for the suited professions. Creatives include artist and photographer Marion Sosa, fashion designer Chau Nguyen, actors Calum Witney and Vicky Pasion, and the writer Dane Weatherman (founder of the literary periodical Black and Blue).

Money matters: Some bursarial help for students of exceptional ability, especially in drama, art and music, which offer a very few full scholarships. Candidates assessed on the basis of academic and (where relevant) performance or artistic ability. Also a rigorous, wide-ranging interview.

Remarks: Solid, reliable and effective place to study. Not for socialites, smack-heads or slackers.

Bousfield Primary School

South Bolton Gardens, Old Brompton Road, London
SW5 0DJ

State • Pupils: 430 • Ages: 3–11

Tel: 020 7373 6544

Email: info@bousfield.rbkc.sch.uk
Website: www.bousfieldprimaryschool.rbkc.sch.uk

21

Headteacher: Since September 2014, Helen Swain BEd MA, deputy head for last eight years. Has been in teaching for 26 years and joined Bousfield as a year 6 teacher nearly 20 years ago.

Entrance: Due to cuts in funding there are now 60 part-time places in the nursery on offer, rather than the previous 30 full-time places. Two parallel classes from reception to year 6, each with 30 pupils. Applications for the nursery are done through the school; applications to the main school are done via Royal Borough of Kensington and Chelsea.

No automatic transfer from the nursery to the main school – parents must reapply. Children who are in care or have an SEN statement are considered first, followed by siblings and then proximity to school (currently approximately 0.5 of a mile and shrinking). Distance measured as the crow flies. Places do become available further up the school, due to high mobility rates of pupils, so worth persevering. Hugely over-subscribed. As one current parent puts it: 'If you get offered a place here, you'd be mad to turn it down.'

Exit: Most popular secondary schools are Holland Park, Chelsea Academy and Lady Margaret's. Over a third go on to independent senior schools, including Latymer, City of London, The Harrodian, Putney High and Francis Holland. No special preparation given for those doing 11+ exams. School knows a large amount of tutoring probably goes on, but says pupils get plenty of exam practice anyway. Much parental advice and support given when it comes to choosing next school.

> *When we visited, children were beautifully behaved and all engaged. A sense of calm pervaded the school*

Remarks: Strikingly international, with 41 different first languages currently spoken at home. Sixty per cent have English as an additional language. After English, the most prominent languages are French and Arabic. School sees this cosmopolitan element as a real strength and the high level of harmony being something to celebrate. A significant number arrive with very limited English. It is 'sink or swim, but usually swim.' Much language teaching on offer, including Italian classes laid on by the Italian

Strong parental involvement, with school questionnaires showing overwhelming parental support and high levels of satisfaction. Numerous opportunities for parents to attend curriculum workshops

Consulate and French to all KS2 pupils. Bilingual pupils tend to outperform monolingual ones. Much coming and going due to large expat intake. Lots of French families have departed recently due to job losses in the City. Only about half the class in year 6 have been there from reception.

Superb academic results, particularly given the huge EAL contingent, though school always looking to 'up the ante.' English, maths and science Sats results well above national average. There are plans afoot to introduce some setting for maths and reading in year 6, though lack of space means separating children into groups is a challenge. Pupils' progress is tracked carefully.

When we visited, children were beautifully behaved and all engaged. A sense of calm pervaded the school. Manners and presentation clearly high on the agenda. No uniform. Packed lunch or school lunch. Fruit given to the younger years, funded by School Fruit and Vegetable Scheme.

One full-time teacher and one teaching assistant in each class, as well as extra support staff for pupils with statements and EAL pupils in the early stages of learning English. A great team of dedicated staff, who 'put the hours in.' Many loyal, long-serving teachers (20 members of staff have been there more than 10 years), as well as newer ones. A strong team – 'no prima donnas.'

Bright, vivid displays throughout the school. Some classrooms smallish; every iota of space used. School is a 1950s listed building which makes expansion and development problematic.

Arts are very strong in the school, though not at the expense of academics. Lots of music, dance and drama going on. School believes performance helps to build children's self-esteem. Pupils are offered a rich curriculum, full of workshops, plays and concerts. More than 90 learn a musical instrument. Guitar and strings ensembles, two choirs but no orchestra. Parents attend practice workshops so they know what a good music practice at home should involve.

Plenty of sport – gym and games as well as after-school clubs offering tennis, football, cricket and even cheerleading. Swimming for years 3 and 4. Pupils take part in borough events (including athletics) in the summer term.

Quantity of homework has been reduced – parents were completing too much of the pupils' project work ('you can always spot the hand of a parent,' we were told) and copious amounts were being downloaded unthinkingly from the internet. Homework now more focused on the basics, with reading, spelling and maths given from early on.

Some children with SEN statements. More on the SEN register, receiving support of some kind. No specially trained teachers but school feels they have strategies and experience to help those in need. Has experience of pupils with Asperger's syndrome, autism, ADHD, emotional/behavioural difficulties and moderate/severe learning difficulties, as well as dyslexia, dyspraxia and hearing and visual impairment. School is not a centre of excellence for all of these – very occasionally pupils move to special schools, either when Bousfield can no longer adequately support them or when they move to secondary school. Staff say Bousfield is 'an inclusive school' that does its best to accommodate those with difficulties.

Strong parental involvement, with school questionnaires showing overwhelming parental support and high levels of satisfaction. Numerous opportunities for parents to attend curriculum workshops and 'book looks' (when they visit to look at children's books). Parents welcomed in at the beginning of the day.

Arts are very strong in the school, though not at the expense of academics. Lots of music, dance and drama going on. School believes performance helps to build children's self-esteem

Some wrap-around care available, albeit not all on-site. Breakfast club on offer and pupils can be escorted to a neighbouring school (with more provision) at the end of the day if required.

Bousfield has close connections with artist Quentin Blake, who attends prize-givings and pops in regularly. All leavers receive a prize at the final assembly and Blake says his spirits are raised as each leaver is celebrated. 'After the ceremony, I go away feeling that at this point in their lives perhaps they really have all won,' he adds.

A great sense of purpose permeates this thriving school, with pupils bright-eyed and focused, offered a lively, dynamic and interesting education. As one satisfied parent lamented: 'I just wish it could go on into secondary school.'

Bute House Preparatory School for Girls

Luxemburg Gardens, London W6 7EA

Tel: 020 7603 7381

Independent • Pupils: 310 • Ages: 4–11 • Fees: £13,962 pa

Email: mail@butehouse.co.uk
Website: www.butehouse.co.uk

Head: Since September 2012, Mrs Helen Lowe (50s), BA Oxford Brookes, LGSM Guildhall School of Music and Drama. Married to Phil, whom she met at drama school. They have two grown up children. Having 'got acting out of my system' she started her teaching career in big Essex comprehensives, where she taught drama. She is verging on the evangelical about the profoundly positive benefits a background in drama can have – 'everyone should go to drama school because it's all about people and understanding other people's point of view'. She then went on to teach at primary schools in Richmond and became the literacy consultant for the whole of the borough. Her experience in the independent sector includes being a drama teacher at St Paul's Girls' in the 1990s, curriculum coordinator at Lady Eleanor Holles junior department and head of juniors at King's House in Richmond, where she taught for three years. Bute House is her first 'stand alone' headship, ending the 20 year tenure of the formidable Sallie Salvidant.

Bright and bubbly, Mrs Lowe likes to make an impact. Never one to be seen without her pink lipstick, snazzy glasses and white blonde hair well coiffed. Her confident manner ('I'm very bossy,' she admits with a twinkle) could be overbearing were it not delivered with such warmth and humour. Parents remark on her ability to make changes without a fuss. Good changes – a whole school Christmas celebration at a local church for example. 'I am a great communicator,' she says. Parents agree. She holds open house appointment sessions where parents can discuss any concerns about the school. She not only puts her point across impressively but listens too. What's more, the parents listen to her, even when it might be news they don't enjoy hearing – that their daughter won't suit a school they have set their hearts on, for example.

She knows the girls properly, and by the time the 11+ process kicks in, she is well-equipped to write their reports for senior schools and advise the parents on the best school for each one, having taught all girls in their second half of year 5 and first half of year 6. 'I have the best interests of the child at heart,' she avers. This may not always coincide with pleasing the parents but it doesn't faze her. When it comes to decisions about boarding school, however, she is sensitive to the fact that this

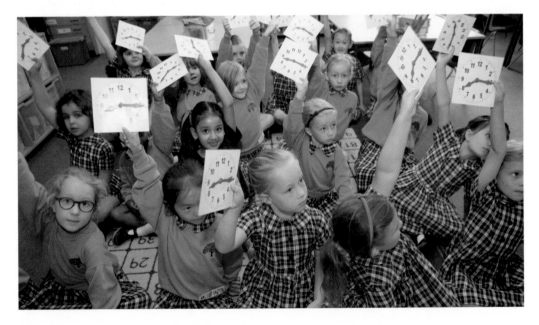

is a decision that affects the whole family, not just the girl. A refreshingly modern and human touch from a prep school that sends a fair few to the top girls' boarding schools.

Entrance: There are two entrance points: reception – a one form entry where 22 places are allotted by ballot (after taking into account siblings, which could mean that the number is easily halved), and year 3, when girls are selected after sitting the 7+ exam (in the January of year 2). About 400 girls are entered into the ballot, two years before entrance, which is then scrupulously and rigorously drawn – by the chair of governors, with the head, the bursar, the school secretary and a lawyer in attendance. No question of rigging, and absolutely no point in ensuring that little Emily can recite her 10 times table.

For year 3, about 200 register for 38 places. Assessments in English, maths and non-verbal reasoning are carried out in a relaxed way along with various activities which focus on team work and social interaction. The girls are carefully observed by a number of teachers and Mrs Lowe said, 'hand on heart', they weren't just looking for the most academically able and – don't choke on your skinny flat white – they have turned down girls despite their marks being among the highest. They are looking for girls who respond well to learning, with a positive and enthusiastic attitude. This is a school determined to maintain its mixed ability, academically non-competitive ethos (this and the ballot were the two non-negotiables in her interview, Mrs Lowe tells us).

No sibling preference at 7+ assessment, but school 'looks very carefully at sisters'. Occasional places thereafter are competed for by test, and the school has a waiting list for each year. Girls come from the local boroughs and as far as Barnes, Ealing, Kew, Putney, Wimbledon and north London. Vast diversity of backgrounds; the US and Asian contingent is fairly significant and a number are bilingual in combinations of French/Mandarin/Italian/German, to name but a few.

Exit: Over half each year go either to St Paul's or Godolphin & Latymer. Even if they don't go there, these are the two schools that most parents aspire to. The rest either board – Wycombe Abbey, Downe House, St Swithun's the current favourites – or go to other all girls' day schools eg Putney High, Lady Eleanor Holles, the Francis Hollands. Recently greater interest among parents in co-ed – Latymer Upper is becoming increasingly popular. Interestingly, around the same proportion of those who enter at 4+ as those who come at 7+ go on to the most academic schools. Bute girls trail scholarships: in 2015, the leavers were offered, between them, 36 scholarships (including plenty for music and two for PE).

Remarks: One can be forgiven for thinking that this is the prep school for St Paul's Girls' School; it used to be years ago, but hasn't been since the 1950s, and it's a dangerous mistake to make. Although Bute is lucky enough to share the St Paul's swimming pool and some games pitches, and is only a stone's throw away, it is an entirely separate and distinct institution. You may have won the jackpot to get your daughter in here in that she will have a fabulous education during her early years, but you haven't been granted a stepping stone into the hallowed halls of St Paul's Girls. There are no friendly ears to be bent. Iris will have as great a chance of getting in there from any of the good London preps as she does from Bute House.

An outstanding prep school, Bute House manages to combine solid substance with flair and panache. There is lots going on: the academics are excellent despite – or probably because of – its non-competitive ethos, but this is one of the most passionately competitive about sports of any of the girls' day schools we have seen. In the classroom, however, there is no setting, streaming or ranking, and marking is all done by comment: 'That's what contributes to the girls being so good and kind to each other – and makes it such an amazingly warm, happy and friendly place,' comments Mrs Lowe.

Learning support is known as 'learning enrichment' here – SEN and G&T girls occasionally removed from their lesson in order that their learning be 'enriched'. The head of the learning enrichment department is an SEN specialist, as are the other members of staff who both support those girls needing extra help and extend the more able girls. Teachers from the LED work in class alongside class teachers as well as sometimes taking groups of girls out of the classroom. The teaching is clearly, for the most part, inspired, and this is true of the learning enrichment programme too. Fifty-two girls are on the LE register, many needing only minimal support. This support is free. Those who don't speak English at home have one weekly support session. Some see the SENCo on a one-to-one basis and some in small groups. Ninety on the G&T register. School says that any difficulties are diagnosed early and dealt with as soon as possible.

We detected some sensitivity around the issue of special needs. The school says that it 'makes it clear in its parents' contract that girls with specific learning difficulties who need a great deal of additional support may be encouraged to look for another school that can meet their needs better'. A few parents, albeit under the old regime, felt that their daughters with learning difficulties were not getting sufficient attention compared with those who were 'gifted'. School is keen to point out that this is changing. A dynamic SEN teacher coupled with a change in priority and ethos from the top means that everyone here gets the attention they need. However, there does appear to be some tension between the non-competitive academic ethos and the fact that ultimately this is an academic school with parents who have academic aspirations. Mrs Lowe asserts that early identification of any issues should enable all the girls to achieve highly, and she is especially keen to ensure that every girl achieves to the best of her ability. She says she also looks carefully at the transition from year 2 to 3, since this can cause anxiety for parents who

perceive that the new intake may well be more academically able, and the flood of new girls will result in their daughter becoming 'lost'. The strong non-competitive academic ethos comes as a shock to a lot of parents who are attracted to the idea of Bute House as a top prep school with a history of a relationship with St Paul's – often in competitive professions themselves, they find themselves feeling frustrated not knowing whether Molly is top of the class or not.

The Bute building itself is a surprise – a somewhat futuristic 1950s neo-greenhouse farrago with add-ons in pine, pink render, louvred glass and warm-toned brickwork

Any competitive instincts can find an outlet in the sports programme, however. Bute girls are known in the prep school world to be formidable netball players and there is a D team as well as an A so everyone should get a chance to play. Some mutterings among mothers that this is not the case – but we suspect that the kudos of playing in the A team is such that both daughter and parents aspire for that. Gymnastics is also very popular and of a high standard. Although gym squad, run by external coaches, is only for the most talented, school says that those not in the squad have plenty of opportunity to be involved in gymnastics. Excellent sports facilities, especially considering its inner urban site, with use of St Paul's pool next door, and swimming is strong – plenty of squads and galas so that everyone gets a chance. Mrs Lowe attributes the excellent team spirit among the girls to the lack of competition in the classroom.

Very young, innovative head of drama (complete with red glasses and severe fringe) injecting some exploratory imaginative work into the drama curriculum; the class we saw were all lying on the floor with their feet in their air waving their arms. Head of music also young and energetic – a benign 'Jack Black school of rock' type, he arranges lots of different groups, bands and orchestras ('smiley strings', 'string fever', 'jammy jazzers' to name a few). Girls have class music twice a week from reception through to year 6 and most learn at least one instrument, from the double bass through to the bassoon.

Rich curriculum – everyone does French from reception, Spanish from year 5 but no Latin at all. Specialist teaching from reception in drama, music, sport and art (and DT) as well as French. Specialist science teaching from year 4 and proper DT facilities – saws, work benches, as well as a well-equipped art room – first class and unusual in a London prep school. Huge superbly-equipped science lab and lots of outside space – netball courts as well as playgrounds, comfortable sitting areas and plenty of greenery. Every floor has stairwell storage for laptops, which are available for the girls to use when needed. Excellent library, well-stocked, well-organised (there are two librarians) and most importantly well-used. Lots of music rooms for lessons and practice. All the girls do one drama performance once a year. The show at the end of year 6 is a highlight, with the most recent being Annie.

The Bute building itself is a surprise – a somewhat futuristic 1950s neo-greenhouse farrago with add-ons in pine, pink render, louvred glass and warm-toned brickwork in a quiet Victorian terraced street just off fashionable Brook Green, five minutes from the Hammersmith jungle. It has a splendid atrium with the reception and offices and big screens with the news of the day, timetable changes etc; even the day's birthdays – rather nice. One eye catching and charming tradition is the corridor outside the hall, the walls of which are covered by little ceramic tiles, each one made by a Bute pupil as a record of their time at the school. The school, thereafter, in the head's words, 'is a bit of a Tardis' and one is not prepared by the hotch-potch exterior for the spaciousness – of each classroom, the immense hall and outside space as well as of the airiness and uncluttered feel of the whole.

The classrooms are a feast. Reception is big and there is plenty of space for everyone at the little tables and around the many activities. Everything is beautifully laid out – pencils in pots, a discovery table with 'new life in spring' exhibits – most remarkable – a canopied and cushioned book corner and lots of lovely dressing-up stuff including some pretty cool shoes. All the children use the garden, complete with lots of climbing things and a real – not a bouncy – castle and sandpit. Reception children have their own times when they also use large wheely toys. This is perhaps the most colourful school we know – everywhere are displays, pictures and models – all bursting with vitality, wit and fun. Many rooms, including the hall, are flexible, and divisible into two. All classrooms have smartboards and, oh joy! – all are air-conditioned. The girls eat in one half of the hall and drool over the food. 'It's just the best'..'it's cooked to perfection!' Free cucumber and carrot wedges are served at break and there are water-fountains inside and outside school.

If your daughter is lucky enough to get a place here she will have stimulating and exciting time, making good friends and building excellent foundations for her future. Your aspirations and ambitions need to be tempered, however; the school she ends up going to next will be right for her, but it may not necessarily be the one you had in mind when you set out on this odyssey.

Cameron House School

4 The Vale, London SW3 6AH

Tel: 020 7352 4040

Independent · Pupils: 120 · Ages: 4–11 · Fees: £16,875 pa

Email: info@cameronhouseschool.org
Website: www.cameronhouseschool.org

Headmistress: Since 2007, Mrs Lucie Moore BEd. School founded in 1980 by Josie Cameron Ashcroft, who is the proprietor and, as Mrs Moore puts it, 'is her one and only governor'. A member of the IAPS, Ms Ashcroft taught at Thomas's and coached children privately before setting up her own school in St Luke's Church, Sydney Street. She remains principal and still keeps a close eye on the ongoing vision and image of the school and knows all the parents as well as the staff.

Mrs Moore, as headmistress, is in charge of the day-to-day running of the school. She started her teaching career in a state primary in Winchester, then in international schools in Italy and Bangkok, before settling into the hurly burly of London day schools. She spent seven years at the Hampshire

School, where her career took a meteoric rise under the paternal guidance of Arthur Bray: 'He was like a mentor to me'. He soon identified her talents and she swiftly became head of prep and vice principal of the Hampshire Schools before he encouraged her to apply for the post here.

Her husband, the finance director at City Airport, is always by her side at school events. A young headmistress (she was 36 when she started), Lucie (as she is known to everyone, pupils, staff and parents) is attractive and bubbly. She has a huge sense of fun and clearly adores the children. Each sentence is peppered with 'Aren't they just so sweet?' She's got a point – children here are very cute: girls clad in fresh blue and white striped summer dresses with cherry jumpers and cardis, boys bumbling, adorable in blue cord shorts.

Parents enthuse about her smiling enthusiasm, warmth, excellent communication and understanding of each child. We heard reports of her firm but sensitive approach to the big issues that arise in a child's life, whether it's an instance of unkindness – difficult to conceive of a child being actually bullied here – or problems at home. She also has enormous reserves of energy and is very driven. As well as teaching every class in the school once a week ('It's important that I keep my feet on the ground for the sake of the children and the staff'), coordinating the SEN, and working on the weekly newsletter, she is at the front door every afternoon and morning greeting each child.

If any parent expresses an interest in a senior school she doesn't know, she will make sure she spends plenty of time there – not only to establish important links with the head but also to make sure in her own mind that the school would suit that child. Highly efficient ('I'm a Virgo,' she says. 'I need to be organised and to plan ahead') and not at all concerned about getting her hands dirty, she describes the job as 'fitting like a glove'.

Entrance: All children are assessed at 3, so no need to rush to get your baby onto a list; register up till a year before entry. A popular school – over 200 applicants for 20 places and Mrs Moore acknowledges how difficult it is to choose – 'It's heartbreaking to reject anyone,' she says. Ultimately they look to create a class with a balance of the confident and the shy and some happily in between. They work closely with nurseries and rely on their reports (children come from a wide range including Pippa Poppins, Paint Pots, and Miss Daisy's). Putting school down as a genuine first choice always helps.

In Book Week everyone dresses up, even Mrs Moore, who is not at all fazed when she greets prospective parents dressed as Captain Hook

Exit: A few boys at 7+ or 8+ to, eg, boarding or Catholic schools (Ludgrove, St Philip's), but head actively discourages year 3 leavers so fewer and fewer now. Mrs Moore has fine tuned the 'stepping stones' options for boys who want to do 13+ common entrance and sends them for two years at 11 to, eg, Newton Prep, Fulham Prep, Sussex House, Wetherby or the Hampshire School Chelsea. Lots of advice given to parents from year 5 onwards.

At 11 girls and boys go to a broad range of schools each year – current favourites are Latymer

---

Major dramatic productions – The Lion King, A Midsummer Night's Dream among them – take place in a closely guarded secret venue

Upper, St Paul's Girls, City of London Girls' and Boys', Dulwich, Alleyn's, Emanuel, Godolphin & Latymer, Queen's Gate and Francis Holland. They nearly always get their first choice school, we're told (due in large part to Mrs Moore's determination that parents choose the school that suits their child, whatever they themselves might prefer). 'And they interview beautifully because they're so confident,' she gloats. One or two girls every year board at, eg, Wycombe Abbey or Downe House.

Remarks: A tiny (one class per year of about 20), cosy, pretty school, but don't be misled into thinking it's just chocolate boxy – Cameron House is a serious player in getting children into sought-after London schools. Wide range of ability, but what all children have in common is that they are confident and very, very smiley.

They are given a lot of preparation in the final year. In year 6, class sizes shrink so everyone gets more attention, compulsory homework club gives all children an extra hour at school and removes the pressure from the parents. 'We shoulder the worry,' says Mrs Moore, 'and the last thing I want is to see 10 year olds being counselled for stress.' A lot of staff channelled into year 6, when they do group work, prepare for scholarships, have mock interviews and confidence-building workshops. The formula clearly works – they get results, but no-one could describe this as a hothouse.

Approximately 15 children are helped with mild to moderate SEN – dyspraxia, dyscalculia, dysgraphia etc. The school takes a holistic approach. Learning support is timetabled and structured with clear IEPs drawn up – parents pay extra. Programme for the gifted and talented run within the class. In addition a select few are invited to join the Discovery Club and Explorers Club. Mrs Moore explains the cautious approach to the gifted and talented programme. Children are identified towards the end of year 1 – 'We wouldn't want to have to say, "You weren't gifted after all!"' she says.

A town house with not a great deal of space, but the soft plush tartan carpet throughout the stairwell, lavatories with pretty wallpaper, water filters, attractive blue furnishings and every teacher referred to by their first names – without even a Miss or Mister attached – give the school a homely, uninstitutional feel.

Children have fun here, whether it's enjoying music, drama or sport, watching caterpillars trans-morph into butterflies or playing giant magnetic chess in the playground (a good excuse to see the lovely Lucie, to get the chess pieces). Even maths can be made to be an excuse to dress up and laugh – Bubbles the maths clown visited, the hall was filled with balloons and children came to school dressed as shapes. In Book Week everyone dresses up, even Mrs Moore, who is not at all fazed when she greets prospective parents dressed as Captain Hook. 'If they don't like to see their future headmistress being able to laugh at herself, then we're clearly not the right school for them nor them for us,' she says.

Nearly everyone plays an instrument or has sing-ing lessons – the lessons happen in a little Wendy house type hut in the playground. Major dramatic productions – The Lion King, A Midsummer Night's Dream among them – take place in a closely guarded secret venue – 'Let's just say a theatre off Kensington High Street,' is as far as Mrs Moore will be drawn. 'We aim high,' she says proudly, as she lists the impressive artistic accomplishments for such a small school, which include getting to the final for young choir of the year at the Royal Festival Hall. They have an orchestra, string quartet and three choirs.

One of Mrs Moore's challenges has been to stop the boys leaving at 7+ or 8+ – signs of suc-cess. Although previous year 6 classes have had few boys, some none at all, when we visited there were an equal number of both sexes. 'Parents are starting to realise that they can get their boys into Westminster Under, Colet Court or Latymer at 11,' she says, 'and there are plenty of stepping stone options between 11 and 13.' Children are kept a lot more active here than at many similar schools. Games takes place three times a week – children can do cricket, football, hockey and netball as well as martial arts in the huge loft space at the Boudokwai centre. Lots of matches (most of which they lose, comments one parent) but the advantage of being a small school is everyone gets to have a go – it's not just the sporty types who do everything.

A lot of expat families, mainly from the US, Canada and Australia, reflecting the cosmopoli-tan area. We saw masses of glamorous long-haired mothers off to the gym after drop off. Lots of city types, but also more than the usual number of crea-tives – artists and actors, as well as doctors and art dealers. All parents are very involved and enjoy the open door policy of the school.

A charming school that will discover your child's strengths, nurture and support them.

The Cardinal Vaughan Memorial RC School

89 Addison Road, London W14 8BZ

State · Pupils: 945 · Ages: 11–18 · Sixth form pupils: 350 (131 girls) · RC

Tel: 020 7603 8478

Email: mail@cvms.co.uk
Website: www.cvms.co.uk

Headmaster: Since 2011, Mr Paul Stubbings MA. Educated at Worcester Grammar school and Durham University, where he read classics. His conversation is littered with his experiences of 'damascene' moments – his love of Latin and Greek, his vocational calling to become a teacher. One wonders (though he didn't say it) whether it was a similar enlightened moment that drove him to fight for the headship and steer the school away from the dangerous rocks of conflict between the Westminster diocese and a section of the governing board. He certainly stepped into the breach when horns were locked over a tussle between whether the school should be a 'pan London Catholic school' or whether priority should be given to local residents of the borough. He was promoted from deputy head, pastoral – aka the enforcer, and feared by many in the role. He refers to himself in that incarnation as 'the chief chastiser – good at scaring

kids, but not nastily'. One former parent described him at this time as a sergeant major, famous for issuing multiple detentions as snowballs flew on one of those rare fun-filled winter days. A smooth negotiator is certainly not the role one would immediately assume for him, but since he has taken the reins the school has been running with-out much jolting, and both parents and staff are delighted with his appointment. He is completely 'home grown', and has taught here in various roles since his teaching practice placement in 1988. He officially started as a classics teacher in 1989 and still teaches Latin to year 7.

Since morphing into the top man, he sees himself as more of an avuncular figure to the stu-dents and confesses that he misses the on going day-to-day bustle. However, he embraces having to articulate the direction of the school and describes his vision as the replication of qualities of Cardinal

Vaughan himself – namely his energy and foresight-edness, firmly rooted in a Catholic foundation. He regards the school as embodying the best of tradition and 'the old', whether is be the traditional hierarchy or the gowns the teachers still wear. 'The only times hierarchies don't work,' he says, 'is when they cease to be benevolent'. However, he acknowledges that change cannot be avoided: 'I have to row this school forward in order for it to stay the same'.

As we left his large modern study, he with a flourish of his gown, two boys were waiting outside whom he confided he was about to exclude. The lines here are straight and inflexible, and if you cross them you can be in no doubt of the consequences.

Academic matters: Consistently impressive results and school makes no bones about aiming for academic excellence in its comprehensive intake. Sunday Times continues to rate it as the highest attaining comprehensive school in the country. School has specialist status in mathematics and IT and computing is BIG here – computer science is now part of the curriculum – an innovation that puts paid to the any suspicion that the school might be stuck in the past. A level results 87 per cent A*-B grades in 2015 and 53 per cent A*/A. Range of subjects offered not immense but includes economics, music tech, Latin, philosophy and sociology. It has to be said that the 'newer' subjects do not attract vast numbers. School also offers applied A level in business – Bs for most. Most popular – and successful – A level subjects are maths and Eng lit, both astonishingly good. GCSEs: again not a huge range of options – French and Spanish now the only modern langs, though Latin thrives and

Greek is available at GCSE. Most popular subjects are engineering – a double qualification – French and ICT. Everyone takes RS. 2015, 40 per cent per cent A*/A grades overall - and remember this is a comprehensive school..

This degree of success is not achieved by having independent school sized classes. In the lower school class sizes are 28-30, though music, DT, art and IT groups have 20 pupils. At KS4, class sizes vary but core subjects are taught in groups of 25-30. Most sixth form classes are under 20. Girls and boys seem to achieve similarly though there are some mutterings about AS candidates being 'encouraged' to drop subjects rather than continuing to A2 if it is felt they are unlikely to do well. Accolades abound – the Vaughan is in the top 20 of just about every league table – often near the top. It is regularly named 'top Catholic comp in the country' by those who have such plaudits to give away. Parents and pupils, for the most part, add to the encomia. No-one could eulogise the school's shiny new facilities – apart from all the IT stuff – or accommodation. The level of achievement here is down to the quality of the teaching and the staff and pupils' pride in the place. We heard of 'lovely teachers', the good monitoring of progress and much high praise, especially of the music dept. Bright pupils speak warmly of their 'inspiring' teachers – 'they are amazing – best in the business' – and they mean it.

All applicants are tested – to ensure that school takes across the ability range and to better enable banding once they arrive. School takes 'more than our fair share of statemented children' and it is a beacon of hope for those parents of children with significant difficulties, seeming, as it does, to offer

The level of achievement here is down to the quality of the teaching and the staff and pupils' pride in the place. We heard of 'lovely teachers', the good monitoring of progress and much high praise

real education in a compassionate community. Majority with SEN, though, are mild dyslexics and dyspraxics. Who goes where is decided, of course, by the LA but school is concerned about the sheer additional physical space taken by extra LSAs who accompany some of the children with more severe SEN. And this is understandable. Many rooms are small and rather poky and corridors are not spacious. Busy SENCo and others give in-class support but parents give mixed reports. One parent felt that her dyspraxic son's problems were picked up very late and that the support he was subsequently offered was barely adequate. Similar reports from others. School, however, tells us that such comments are 'vastly outweighed by parents delighted with our SEN arrangements'. School unashamed of its high octane essence. 'Here we have traditional, hothouse academic teaching. It can be a bit of a shock for those who come in from outside.' G&T pupils offered Greek – where else in the state system is this a growth area?

Games, options, the arts: Despite having to travel for 30 minutes on a bus (to Twickenham) for rugby and football, these sports are not only popular but also strong. Vaughan teams are not to be messed with and are widely respected by their competitors in West London. The first XI recently won the cup in the QPR league, the second XI, no slouches either, won the shield. Athletics and cricket in the summer. Fixtures on Saturday mornings, though if you get a detention you are in danger of being dropped from the team – no leeway there. There is also a gymnasium on site in the 1990s extension known as the Pellegrini building, painted in bright blues and turquoises; the well-known 'boys at games' fragrance welcomed us as we observed a volleyball game. Rock climbing, basketball, table tennis also on offer. Girls in the sixth form can play netball, and some do rock climbing.

Several parents referred to a divide in the school between the 'sporty' and the 'musical' side. Music is certainly as keenly practised, respected and given an equal, if not even greater status as sport, and we were very impressed both with the sumptuous musical facilities and the array of opportunities for performance. When we visited

there was great excitement as the head of music rushed in to show Mr Stubbings an article in the Financial Times about a carol composed by one of their 15 year olds and performed on Radio 3. Large practice rooms and smart rooms for performance. There are several grand pianos for simple practice, you understand, and a plethora of choirs from the elite Schola Cantorum – replete with claret-coloured cassocks and leather-bound hymn sheets, providing music for the school's liturgies – to the sixth form choir and the school choir. As well as a full orchestra, chamber orchestra and various trios, there is the hugely busy Big Band that performs in concerts and events all over London.

Various venues are used for concerts including the Albert Hall, Cadogan Hall, St John Smith Square and Westminster Cathedral. The Schola goes on regular tours outside the UK, including Italy – all the grandest places in Rome – plus Spain, Greece, Holland, Germany, the USA and France. The Schola now has its own Songschool – just like in a regular cathedral choir school – in which the choir rehearses; a real boon. Those with a talent for singing also get the opportunity to sing in operas at the Royal Opera House as well as the ENO; recent productions have included La Bohème, Die Zauberflote, and Carmen. More light hearted musical productions take place in the summer – Guys and Dolls, Sweeney Todd, The Pyjama Game, to name a few. Other than the annual musical there is little drama to speak of – never a strength here and not an academic subject. School's original main building began life as a theatre and we wondered why so little use is made of it in this way – the stage and gallery are intact, if a little dog-eared. Good art: we liked what we saw of the ceramics, sculpture, mobiles, printing et al – lively creative stuff – and equally good DT: wood, metal and plastic work. Three workshops and lots of benches means there is plenty of room to work and create. Engineering and graphics popular at GCSE – this is where lots of that work takes place. Plenty of imaginative and rewarding extracurricular trips and visits – especially for the musicians; parents glow.

Background and atmosphere: The Vaughan is located in posh Holland Park – wide, quiet streets lined by well-appointed Victorian villas and mansion blocks. Shepherd's Bush, on the other side of the monster roundabout round the corner, is a world away, whereas Kensington High Street – about 15 minutes walk the other way – seems a natural neighbour. Founded in 1914, the school is a memorial to the third Archbishop of Westminster, Herbert, Cardinal Vaughan. It began life as an independent school with 29 pupils but became a grammar school in 1944 and a comprehensive in 1977. Girls were first admitted to the sixth form in 1980 and their presence is firmly established. They are not just a token presence, either – the ratio is 60 boys to 40 girls, which is significantly higher than their cousin school in the neighbouring borough. No chance of going co-ed throughout – simply no room. The original building – Addison Hall, which Mr Stubbings affectionately refers to as 'Hogwarts' – was a musical theatre, but its exterior – possibly what attracted its purchasers – is more reminiscent of a Rinascimento palazzo in pink stone. It now boasts an entrance with highly-wrought grillwork in which the school's motto, Amare et Servire, and crest are displayed. The Old Building, as it is known, houses years 11-13. The New Building was built in the 1960s and much added to since then. It has an attractive exterior with a pretty little garden and an impressive reception area, which abuts the main hall – full of pupils on supervised private study when we visited – no 'free' periods here. DT and IT are housed in the Pellegrini Building, named after a former head. Some roomy places inside but the overall impression is of a rather cramped school with little space – especially outside – and many rather bleak areas.

Situated in these leafy, pricey avenues, you'd expect an upmarket local school population. But it isn't so. School takes from all over, some travel from as far as the northern reaches of Barnet, Harrow and Hillingdon, others from the furthest reaches of Southwark, Merton and Kingston. The only common denominator is a commitment to the Roman Catholic faith. Previous head was wearily, but pugnaciously, defensive of the charge of being socially or academically elitist. He wrote, 'people ask why

Vaughan pupils address seriously 'the Dawkins delusion', 'the problem of free will' and 'the just war theory'

our pupils' performance goes so far beyond national averages. After all, our top results at A level and at GCSE, over the last five years, have improved six times more than national results. Is it because, as some would like to believe, we "cherry pick" pupils from privileged backgrounds? I don't think so.' Mr Stubbings, too, is often accused of running an elitist school, with only some 8 per cent of pupils on free school meals (against 21 per cent in the local authority as a whole). His retort? Selection is random.

The life of the school is imbued with its Roman Catholic inspiration. Everywhere are photographs of pontiffs, cathedrals and the school's own choir singing in various glorious cathedrals. Year groups go on retreats at Tyburn Convent and at Farm Street and the school day and week are punctuated by regular mass, confession, Benedictus, Angelus and so on – all lessons begin and end with the Sign of the Cross and some teachers have prayers in each of their lessons – to a degree rare even in RC schools. But there is also a spirit of enquiry. Vaughan pupils address seriously 'the Dawkins delusion', 'the problem of free will' and 'the just war theory'. Philosophy pupils attend Heythrop College for talks on philosophy of religion, epistemology and ethics, and theology pupils explore the history of Israel. The ethos is embraced and warmly defended by pupils when appropriate. They are aware of the privilege of being here and of the secular – and other – pressures that might have it otherwise. While most parents express great satisfaction with the school in general, we heard a few murmurs from those who are less than ecstatic. 'It's fine as long as all goes well'.. 'they're not brilliant at dealing with problems'.. 'they're not great at getting back to you' – (school says, 'we pride ourselves on excellent communications with parents and prompt responses to their queries') – and 'it's best for the really bright'. School warmly disputes this too. And most are truly grateful for what they receive.

Pastoral care and discipline: Discipline couldn't be much tighter. The boundaries are clear and few transgress. Immediate expulsion for 'supply' of drugs – sharing them with a friend; fixed term exclusion for possession. 'We don't have a drug problem in this school because they know the score,' asserts Mr Stubbings. The senior sixth former who was our guide was so concerned with punctuality that he didn't allow us to admire the work in the art room.

The atmosphere is orderly and you could hear a pin drop walking through the corridors during lesson time, despite the open doors into the class rooms. Occasional bullying is 'firmly and speedily dealt with'. The occasional idiot caught smoking in the streets – sixth form pupils are allowed out of school in breaks – is punished. 'If they're in my uniform it'll be exclusion,' says Mr Stubbings. We saw lots of Vaughan pupils out and about and they definitely do not frighten the horses. 'Old-fashioned good manners' expected and, in general, displayed. Catholic ethos underpins everything and is palpable. Sex ed taught 'by the RS dept for the moral side and the science dept for the biological details'. Four houses – Campion, Fisher, Mayne and More.

Pupils and parents: Pupils come from a wide area covering most of London, some from as far away as Hertfordshire and Surrey. Around half are from ethnic minority groups. Some 30 per cent speak English as an additional language. Here the offspring of a few of the well-heeled 'old' RC families from Kensington learn alongside those of their Filipino, Portuguese or Spanish live-in domestic staff and the children of Irish immigrants from Wembley, in a context hard to find elsewhere. Parents very appreciative of parents' evenings when teachers come to find them rather than the usual ghastly queuing for a two minute slot with a glazed-eyed teacher. Notable former pupils include actors Richard Greene – Robin Hood in earlier days – and Roger Delgado, footballers Bernard Joy of Arsenal and Fulham and the last amateur to represent the England national football team, Paul Parker, Kevin Gallen of QPR and Eddie Newton, novelist Helen Oyeyemi and comedian Dominic Holland. Also WWII flying aces Donald Garland VC and Paddy Finucane DSO and recent Olympic rowing gold medallists Martin Cross and Gary Herbert. Many seem, however, to have careers in the City.

Entrance: Pupils come from over 50 schools. Around 830 apply for the 120 places at 11+. At sixth form, around four apply for every place. Most of the sixth form entrants will be girls – lots from Sacred Heart – and the entrance requirements at that stage are primarily academic, although they do have to have been baptised and a priest has to attest to mass attendance – As and Bs in the subjects they will study in the sixth. School has long been (in)famous for the rigour of its admissions' criteria and stories abound of devoted little church-goers being rejected on account of imperfect catechism or knowledge of parables. 'Nonsense!' bellows school. Early baptism (within six months of birth), weekly attendance at mass, Holy Communion – all are taken for granted in applicants; no mention now of the 'family involvement' that was so contentious. Applicants split into three ability bands, 12 music

places. School uses 'random allocator' for the 70 or so places that remain after priority places have been taken (Catholic children in care, siblings etc).

Exit: A regular mighty handful to Oxbridge (12 in 2015), all doing solid subjects at real colleges. Most of the rest to heavyweight universities to do heavyweight subjects – law at King's, maths at Imperial etc – and a sensible fistful to eg sports psychology at Bournemouth. A notable number to architecture and engineering. Some 10 per cent leave after GCSEs – most to join other schools, a few to employment, another few to other RC colleges.

Money matters: Voluntary aided. School asks for a voluntary contribution of £300 pa for the Governors' Fund and the vast majority stumps up – some more, some less, but no-one comes after you if you don't. A few instrumental bursaries for sixth form entrants who must have reached at least grade 6 on an orchestral instrument.

Remarks: Some see the Vaughan as a 'quasi grammar school' and its cousin in Fulham as a 'quasi public school'. Whatever label you attach to it, our view is that it is the kind of school many parents in London are crying out out for but few, very few, ever find. A unique opportunity if you are lucky enough to qualify, however it won't suit all boys. Be sure your son is someone who responds to rigorous discipline and doesn't flake (or rebel) under stern authority.

Chepstow House School

108a Lancaster Road, London W11 1QS

Tel: 020 7243 0243

24

Independent · Pupils: 280 (including 30 in nursery) · Ages: 2–13 · Fees: £17,415 pa

Email: info@chepstowhouseschool.co.uk
Website: www.chepstowhouseschool.co.uk

Headteacher: Since 2010, Mrs Angela Barr BA Ed (40s). Has been head since school started. Previously head of the lower school at Pembridge Hall, another Alpha Plus school. Studied geography and education at Christchurch College, Kent University and then taught in a state school in Essex before taking off and travelling around Africa for a year, where she met her husband, Simon. 'I loved school and always wanted to be a teacher,' she says with passion.

Blonde, youthful, warm and attractive, head is a spirited, independent character who lives for the moment and is all about the 'doing now.' Asked where she sees herself in five years time she looks dismayed and then, grinning, says: 'on a beach with a gin and tonic.' She is very hands on and personally supports youngest pupils with their reading. 'I am a big believer in getting children reading,' she says. Also works hard to make sure her staff are teaching with all the different learning styles in mind – 'essential in a co-educational school.' Plenty of internal training – for assistants as well as for teachers. She says her biggest challenge is maintaining a sense of community among her 17 staff. When we visited a strong team spirit was evident. Head is very much a 'primus inter pares,' in the old style of monarchy.

Entrance: Non-selective, so it's a case of registration at or as soon as possible after birth (current cost £150 – non-refundable if you don't get a place). School allots five definite places a month, and tries to stagger them among children born at the beginning, middle and end of the month, so no advantage in booking your Caesarean for the first of September. Attempts are made to keep an even number of boys and girls and those who drop out are replaced like with like, as far as possible from the waiting list. That way they don't get a surfeit of, say, boys born in August. Priority given to siblings. Has just opened a nursery class, additional reception class and a year 3 class and moved to new premises; is expanding gradually to year 6 and possibly year 8.

Exit: Pupils can now stay on until 13. Before this, large number of boys, as you would expect, to Wetherby, and girls to Pembridge Hall (via a test, but most have got a place). Bute House a popular

choice for girls but not many jump through that hoop. A small number get to Colet Court and Westminster. Latymer Prep a popular choice as more and more parents opt for co-ed. The odd one to Thomas's, St Philip's or outside London.

Remarks: Born into the now well-established stable of Alpha Plus Group schools, the young colt that is Chepstow House barely wobbled on its hind legs before it was up and running. No doubt thanks in part to the huge demand there is for good schools in this leafy, sophisticated area of Notting Hill. However, the school has risen to meet that demand with style as well as results. Children look enchanting in their quaint red berets and jackets, girls in tartan pinafores, boys in red tank tops and grey shorts (some parents worry about their sons getting cold knees in the winter).

Classes named after birds – the further up the school, the bigger and more fierce the bird. Two classes of 20 in reception and year 1. Pupils start in Robins and Sparrows and then move into Woodpeckers and Kingfishers. For year 2, with exams looming in January, they divide into three groups of 12, with classes named after three types of owl – Barn, Snowy and Tawny.

Fencing and martial arts clubs in the morning. Swimming up the road at Porchester Baths, otherwise all sport happens on site. The children get fresh air and exercise

With a teacher and teaching assistant in each class the children get lots of support and attention. French and music start from reception. Three sets for maths in year 2 and lots of differentiation in the lower years. Each child has the use of an iPad – technology skills are learned on the job rather than in a separate lesson devoted to IT. We saw 5-year-olds using their iPads in a geography lesson, as well as other imaginative methods of teaching, including reception children learning how to tell the time in the playground through movement and action. Good-sized playground is frequently used for learning, both academic and physical.

Any learning difficulties are identified quickly, says head. High standards are set for reading and writing and development and progress are tracked in-house with a reading test as well as SEN assessment. Guided reading from reception helps with comprehension. Head told us: 'If a child has not taken off in reception we know that they will need support in year 1 and someone will work with that child every day – either me, or one of my assistant heads.'

The sense of purpose is palpable. When we visited children were working on 'big write,' a weekly activity for years 1 and 2 where pupils learn to develop their vocabulary and style of writing.

Music is vibrant. The only male teacher here is the music teacher and he introduces pupils to a number of different genres – Portuguese singer/songwriter Caetano Veloso when we visited. A number of pupils have violin, guitar and piano lessons taught by peripatetic teachers. Colourful and expressive art adorns the walls. Evidence of physical activity everywhere; much-loved Little Foxes franchise gets them learning ball skills. Fencing and martial arts clubs in the morning. Swimming up the road at Porchester Baths, otherwise all sport happens on site. The children get fresh air and exercise come rain or shine. Delicious food cooked on site and there is a remarkably civilised atmosphere as the children enjoy their lunch.

Ofsted (who visited just two terms after the school launched) concluded it was good across the board. All credit to the way the head and her team hit the ground running. We suspect the esteemed government inspectors will be even more impressed when they return.

Parents from all over the globe – plenty of Americans, Australians and Canadians, a fair few from Scandinavia, Eastern Europe and Russia, as well as French and Italians. Attracts the less traditional English who prefer co-ed at this stage. Parents are in media, finance, law as well as in the arts. Head makes good use of the parents' experience. One parent arranged for someone from Sky News to give a talk in assembly while another hosted expeditions to private art galleries hosted by another parent. Plenty of trips, including the favourite Bushcraft as well as to churches and Science Museum.

Lots of smiling faces, both parents and children, when they arrive first thing. Head welcomes everyone and is proud of school's open door policy. 'We are not hiding anything,' she says. Nor does she have to. These children are very lucky indeed to have such a focused and privileged start to their education.

Parents are generally very supportive and enthusiastic. 'It's a tight ship – with high energy,' we were told. All good, but there was some regret from a few quarters that the pressure of the 7+ perhaps took the joy out of learning for the child who finds it hard to sit still and concentrate on reading and writing. All this has now changed, with the whole school move to considerably larger premises in Lancaster Road (bang opposite rivals Notting Hill Prep). This not only makes for a larger school at the bottom, with a new nursery class, but has also enabled expansion to the age of 13. There is no longer the pressure to enter and pass an exam at the age of 6 and there should be scope for much more drama and a structured sport department, two things the school has lacked so far.

Definitely one to watch if you live in or near this very oversubscribed area of London.

Christly Church C of E Primary School Chelsea

1 Robinson Street, London SW3 4AA

State · Pupils: 210 · Ages: 4–11 · C of E

Tel: 020 7352 5708

25

Email: info@chchchelsea.rbkc.sch.uk
Website: www.chchchelsea.rbkc.sch.uk

Head: Since 2009, Mrs Avis Hawkins, BSc NPQH (40s). Read psychology at Royal Holloway with a view to becoming an educational psychologist, but got the teaching bug while training at the Institute of Education. Started her career in a state primary in Lewisham, then opted for a school in special measures (now 'inadequate' rating) for the challenge; 'That made me the teacher I am'. Appointed deputy at Christ Church in 2000 and was the natural choice to step into the role when previous head retired.

Attractive, energetic and disarmingly open, she has both children and parents on her side; 'So personable and friendly,' said one. Another added, 'Not the kind of head who just sits in their office', though with the white and grey Danish-look furniture, complete with functional teaching table – no leather sofas here – she might be tempted. 'Open door' policy taken literally; pupils appeared in her study and opened up cupboards and drawers in her desk during our chat. Her wide smile only wanes when lamenting the tight budget. In response, she has recently created an enrichment assistant, who makes the most of useful local contacts, whom she invites to talk to hand-picked groups of children. Recent visitors include a fashion designer, artists from the nearby Saatchi Gallery, and volunteers from the Chelsea Physic Garden. 'I am taking experience-based learning and applying it to the curriculum', she explains. Married with three children, two at the school, her hobbies range from food to DJ-ing. There is no doubt she leads by example. DJ Hawkins is one to watch on the education scene.

Entrance: Vastly oversubscribed C of E voluntary aided school, with perennial waiting list. Priority given to siblings and families attending St Luke's or Christ Church, Chelsea; remaining places for other C of E families and locals. Takes from RBKC and Wandsworth, with a few from as far afield as Hammersmith and Lambeth. Single class in-take at reception, with occasional places further up the school. One parent told how 'wealthy families used to take them out at 7', but it appears the wealthy have now got wise too, and none leave unless forced by relocation.

Exit: Increasing numbers, 30-50 per cent to independents, including Godolphin, Alleyn's, Dulwich, Westminster; lots bag bursaries and scholarships. Many to top London state schools: Lady Margaret,

The Grey Coat Hospital and Chelsea Academy, plus newly established Fulham Boys School. One parent felt, given increasing numbers opting for independent secondary schools, more help could be given to parents with bursary and scholarship applications.

The head also has a knack of finding restless retirees and enlisting them into some extracurricular activity: a retired headmaster takes gardening

Remarks: Located in the hushed affluence of a terraced square, in an area of celebrated artists, writers and politicians, this charming Victorian school has an exterior that harks back to a bygone age, when Chelsea was no more than a collection of small parishes, and church, schoolroom and public house all clustered together on one corner. 'A village school in the heart of London' was how one parent described it and the charm lingers on, with lollipop cherry trees and a butcher's boy bike poised to deliver lunches to a nearby nursery. However, step inside and you have a Narnia experience: the interior has been redesigned to a spacious and functional plan, with chic grey walls, birch wood trimming and rows of navy pillars. Purpose-built in 2005, the main building on the north of Christchurch Street opens out to accommodate an internal playground for reception, with multi-coloured apparatus, as well as an open central stairwell and roomy classrooms for years 1-3. Behind doors we found a cookery room, art studio and ICT suite, as well as cosy beanbags in the reading room (emphatically 'not a library') and a multi-use hall with gym and dining tables. As one parent put it, 'Every nook and cranny has to be made useful'. Outside and across a wide pavement (or 'The Piazza') the older years occupy what was the infant school, opened in 1850 by the patron, Earl Cadogan, we are reminded on a stone plaque. Three classrooms housing the older years have a more studious feel, with individual desks facing whiteboards, but each has its own corner with plump cushions for bookworm breaks. Opposite stands Christ Church, a Victorian gothic parent building, visited on feast days and Fridays by the school, while at the fourth corner of this tiny crossroads is the playground, discreetly hidden behind a tall wall of ivy, masking the children's shouts from the genteel residents. The large play area has been landscaped to accommodate a sports pitch, gardening plots, a pergola and free play areas. 'I would like a bit more playtime,' sighed one child, and we were not surprised. Several parents commented how well maintained the buildings were, and one ventured, 'environment helps behaviour'. The charming neighbourhood is reminiscent of a scene from Mary Poppins; all it lacks is a dancing chimney sweep.

This is a school that claims to take a holistic approach to education, nonetheless, it manages to hit the spot academically. Class sizes are 30, with a 22:1 student to staff ratio, but with lots of small groups or half-class sessions at specialist subjects. The head assures us, 'if you're looking for a school at the top of the league tables, we're not the school for you', but it is hard not to be impressed by these children's achievements on paper. When we asked the children what the school could do better, they suggested more time in the library. Numeracy and literacy is managed by the leadership team as a through-school experience, not split into key stages. Verbal reasoning and non-verbal reasoning are taken in year 6, 'We pay lip service to the 11+ exams,' says the head. 'Aspiration is important'. The national curriculum is supplemented by half-termly 'curriculum weeks' when the whole school shares a topic. Recent themes include healthy living; fashion; local studies. We witnessed a Friday afternoon English class hard at metaphor and meter – no slouches here. Inclusion is a watchword too, with several SEN children supported within each year group. A range of difficulties, from dyslexia to ASD, are managed by a dedicated department and visiting OT, SLT, nutritionist and school nurse. The head welcomes the differences: 'it makes everyone aware of social behaviours'.

Not surprisingly, the staff profile is 'very static'; several boast 10+ years of loyal service, so the head continually makes waves with professional training

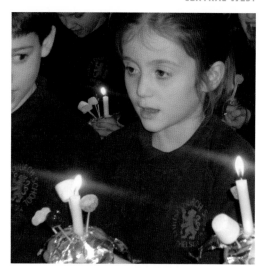

programmes. The school forms an alliance with four other local primaries, mutually inspecting and monitoring each other and offering suggestions. The head also has a knack of finding restless retirees and enlisting them into some extracurricular activity: a retired headmaster takes gardening, as a curriculum topic, directing the wheelbarrows, tending the chickens and watering the kale beds. Another ex-teacher runs cricket sessions in morning break, and several volunteers have become student teachers, and later join the staff. As one mum put it: 'They are very good at growing their own'.

We agreed with the mum who said: 'I knew it was good, but I was surprised how good it was'. A diminutive state primary school, which rivals the local independents

There's a daring zing to the curriculum, or, as the head puts it, 'I am trying to make the curriculum wide enough and rich enough so children can find their talents beyond the three Rs'. This is evident in music, where a specialist teacher with his own band inspires over 50 per cent of the school to take up an instrument. Youngsters can pick up a ukulele, trumpet or drums, as well as the more usual options, funded for a term by the school. Any child showing musical promise, can go on to one-to-one lessons, at their own expense. As an Artsmark school, there's an artist in residence in each year group, who encourages messy creativity in an upstairs studio. Year 1 recently completed a metal-bashing project, while the corridor was arrayed with giant paper planets – another group's work. A recent leaver went on to star in the West End production of Matilda, a talent no doubt fostered in the ambitious Christmas and Easter shows; productions have included King Lear and Richard III (abridged!). A specialist sports teacher co-ordinates trips over the bridge for team games in Battersea Park or to the beautiful Royal Hospital pitches nearby. There's room for football and netball on the hard court in the playground, dance for boys and girls in the hall, and swimming from year 2 at nearby Chelsea Sports Centre. Lately, they introduced teams to borough tournaments, and the girls' netball team ran off with the cup. A mass of after-school clubs include Mandarin, chess, judo, and knitting as well as a kayaking experience up river to Putney. One parent had to pinch herself when faced with the list of clubs, for fear she had confused it with the exclusive school up the road.

Christian values appear modestly within the school, as a poster on the doorway or mosaics of Biblical scenes on the walls. There is daily assembly, led by the head, or a celebratory one each Friday, known by the visiting vicars as 'The Oscars'. Here the children applaud each other's achievements and two Students of the Week are named from each year. Other incentives to good behaviour include an afternoon's golden time, sparingly reduced for poor behaviour. Anything more serious involves meeting the behaviour specialist, but we had difficulty finding anyone who had ever witnessed this: one parent

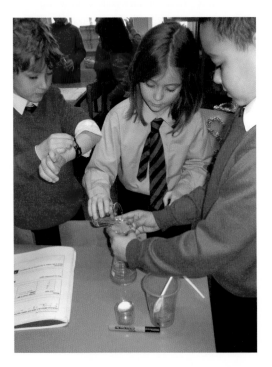

A recent leaver starred in the West End production of Matilda, a talent no doubt fostered in ambitious Christmas shows

said, 'They are all incredibly well behaved and respectful', and 'the last thing they would do is exclude a pupil'. The youngest children have a designated 'shepherd' from year 6 to sit with them at lunch. The system looks after the lambs but also instils a sense of responsibility in the older pupils. One mum worried that responsibility was not always shared evenly between the children: 'They could mix up responsible roles, like reading in church'.

Unlike many London prep schools, the pick up was not dominated by hooting 4x4s; instead, parents chatted outside in groups. The school's community spirit was evident; 'phenomenal at bringing everyone together. Very welcoming', thrilled one mum. Many meet up crossing the bridges from Battersea. One dad stressed the 'connectivity between teaching staff and parents'. There are parent workshops in maths and English, with crèche, to coach parents in helping with homework. Day to day queries are dealt with by phone or teacher meeting. More than one mum reported how they got an overnight response from the head and an invitation to meet the next day. Children are a more mixed bunch than at some local schools, or as the head put it, 'a mix of privilege and none', though all looked equally smart when dressed in the navy and cherry uniforms and stripy ties. Perhaps on World Book Day when the children walk up the King's Road to Waterstones in their PJs, they appear more individual. Their eyes lit up in anticipation of the trip, and again when discussing the lunches. Parents and offspring raved about the improved catering. The kitchen is literally a home-grown affair, using eggs and produce from the school's garden, cooked up into healthy meals by two mums, who have a background in catering, with a sprinkling of advice from the community nutritionist. One of the cooks even delivers carry-outs by bike to a nearby nursery. The result is an education in healthy eating and sustainability. According to the kids, it tastes good too, especially the pizza and apple crumble.

We agreed with the mum who said: 'I knew it was good, but I was surprised how good it was'. A diminutive state primary school, which rivals the local independents in the brainy stuff but which displays ingenuity and imagination in its broad curriculum. The resourceful head syncs her band of dedicated staff and parents to strike up a winning tune and lively, inquisitive children take up the chorus. Well, Chelsea is famous for its smart set.

Collingham Independent GCSE and Sixth Form College

23 Collingham Gardens, London SW5 0HL

Independent • Pupils: 220 • Ages: 14–20 • Sixth form pupils: 190 • Fees: up to £18,750 pa

Tel: 020 7244 7414

Email: london@collingham.co.uk
Website: www.collingham.co.uk

Principal: Since 2012, Dr Sally Powell BA MA PGCE (40s), a London and Oxford English specialist, lively, welcoming, delightful. Has notched up a not inconsiderable 10 years here (in fact many staff are of long standing and committed to the place).

Mr James Allder BA, a geographer (40s), is deputy principal and director of studies; an enthusiastic skier and snowboarder. Ms Emma Clay MSc oversees the GCSE department in Queen's Gate.

Academic matters: You go to Collingham for two things – the academics and the sense of being independent while, in reality, being nurtured and carefully monitored. The place, though, stands or falls on its teaching. 'We integrate modern methods with traditional teaching – the emphasis is always on the teaching; the rest is back-up.' So don't come here if you want wall-to-wall technology – not that it isn't where it's needed: interactive whiteboards in, eg, geography rooms and students port their laptops hither and yon. Facilities for both digital and trad photography indicate an imaginative approach and a small IT room right at the top of the school for the actual teaching of it. 29 GCSE subjects and an extraordinary 36 A level subjects

offered. In 2015, 23 per cent A*/A and 55 per cent A*-B grades at A level; 33 per cent of I/GCSE grades were A*/A.

In the black and white tiled hallway are little tables with students playing chess – no, they weren't put there to impress us: it is student-inspired and a student-pursued activity

All A level subjects taught in designated subject rooms, which are functional, not over-crowded with displays or other distractions and well-maintained. At GCSE, the average class size is five and never more than nine; at A level much the same, though, depending on what subjects you choose, you can be taught one-to-one – great for the students, and the teachers like it, too, of course. GCSE students usually in college 9.15am – 6.00pm; AS students get 20 hours of teaching weekly, A level students get 18. 'GCSEs are brilliantly taught,' one recent alumnus told us. 'I was rescued.' A few more popular classes – no room is huge – are rather cramped, but no-one minds much.

Learning support tutor sees those with SEN difficulties (charged extra) and subject teachers also do one-to-one as needed. Probably not for those with more than mild dyslexia or similar. Up to eight hours' weekly EAL support.

'We hope to be a village school in the middle of Kensington.' It doesn't feel quite like that

Games, options, the arts: Art produces an impressive range of work in many media, given the fact that college has only one small studio, with intense and dedicated ('fantastic' and 'amazing', students told us) practising artist, whose domain it is. 'I'm interested in teaching them to be artists – to express themselves in art,' he imparted, and students love it here. Corridors and stairwell round about display varied work in many disciplines – we liked especially the horse mobile made from cleverly coloured twisted paper. Twelve GCSE and 20 A level art students at the time of our visit – testament to the small is beautiful as successful ethos.

Sport is limited. GCSE students have a supervised two hours sports slot on Friday, where activities range for football and tennis to swimming. A level students can take part in weekly football training and are in a small inter-college league playing at the Westway sports centre. Clubs run if someone wants to run one, so debates happen one year and not the next. Drama is enthusiastic and curricular – classes take place in the Study Room, a small studio theatre is borrowed for exams and exam prep. Theatre studies trips to London shows. Citizenship course involves a good range of mind-broadening trips. Skiing and walking trips plus an annual concert. But you won't come here if the extracurricular life is what feeds your roots – this is a plus for most here: 'There's nothing to distract you from work'.

Background and atmosphere: Modest and understated six-storey house in Collingham Gardens – an equidistant five minutes' walk from Gloucester Road and Earl's Court tube stations in an unshowy bit of west Kensington; has been a school of a sort for much of its 130 years, having previously accommodated Gibbs' Prep School until the mid-1970s. So it is quite remarkable that the building retains many attractive features and is maintained in such a way as to preserve that sense of its being a house, not an institution – friezes, cornices, attractive mirrors and chandeliers about the place and a minimum

of ghastly fluorescent tubes, sludge-coloured paintwork and other municipally-inspired excrescences. In the black and white tiled hallway are little tables with students playing chess – no, they weren't put there to impress us: it is student-inspired and a student-pursued activity. The splendid first floor drawing room – now the Study Room – is library/exam/private study area, where, when not in use for exams, students go between taught periods to do homework etc. The individual subject rooms have small specialised book collections.

No outside space to speak of – a small patio at the back – but students are encouraged to use Kensington Gardens or Holland Park in the summer, not more than 15 minutes' walk away. Earl's Court is not devoid of bars and cafes and students know where they are. Tiny cafeteria in the basement, rather like the art room, produces range and quality of food in inverse proportion to its size: aroma of frying mushrooms nearly did for us – until we opened the door to the chemistry lab further down the basement corridor (very labby labs here).

The GCSE building in Queen's Gate Place – all white Regency elegance – accommodates most of the needs of the smallish contingent of students at this level. Supervision and monitoring very important here for students as young as these; the school secretary has an important pastoral role – this is a significant commitment to the other site and its, on occasions, perhaps more vulnerable denizens. Several full-time academic staff – the place succeeds largely on account of the inevitably close and trusting staff:pupil relationship which develops: 'We combine a homely, personal feeling with cutting edge teaching'. Interestingly, the families of the two founders still own the college – this contrasts, perhaps significantly in terms of ethos, with the much larger concerns which own most other tutorial colleges in central London.

Most students live locally, though some from further off stay with family – 'We love grandmothers'; a few overseas students board with host families. 'If we get it right, we can restore the spark they may have lost at their big schools' – many come having failed to thrive at their public schools, through sickness, bullying, perhaps some gentle eccentricity or simply just not being happy. 'Some who may have loved prep school boarding can just outgrow it. We hope to be a village school in the middle of Kensington.' It doesn't feel quite like that – too much general sophistication in the air – but in terms of the smallness and closeness of the community, it is spot on. Seen by many as providing a dry run for university without the sense of being cast adrift that some experience there.

Pastoral care and discipline: Punctuality is important – you are signed in for each class, not at the start of the day, and parents are called within 15 minutes in the case of no-shows. But you don't need to come in early if you don't have a class – think what that means to a 16 year old! A few smoking Collinghamers lurk on the pavement and college is pragmatic – 'We don't allow it on site and we don't like it, but we'd rather they do it where we can see them. Everywhere they are, we are'. Clear sanctions for those who don't work and occasional expulsions if they just won't. Not an option for druggies or bullies from elsewhere, 'We're too small to be a second chance saloon'. But, 'We are very happy to take anyone who's been ill or in a muddle, sensitive souls who need individual attention, perhaps if they've had an eating disorder – we will look after them'. Expulsion for drinking or drugging or bullying here virtually unheard of.

Parents have open access to their child's tutor – easy communication. 'They rescued my son,' one mother told us. 'I can't speak highly enough of their care.' 'The teachers are incredibly friendly,' an A level student told us. 'I was welcomed with open arms.'

Pupils and parents: You have to be able to raise the cash – and some pull out all the stops to do so – but it's cheaper than boarding. So everyone from global bankers to school secretaries, and the students mix, seemingly seamlessly. No scope for ostracising oddballs here – everyone accepts and is accepting. Considerable range of ability too. Very few join from the state sector. Roughly 55:45 boy:girl split. Notable leavers include Minnie Driver and Georgia May Jagger.

Entrance: Interviews, references from current/previous school and, if necessary, an exam – 'They've got to want to work with us'. Can take people at any time, so great for relocaters and those who've just gotta get out – flexible.

Exit: About a quarter to university in 2015: three to Oxbridge; around half to Russell Group.

Money matters: Given the small classes and the individual care and attention, it's not as much as you might think. Additional one-to-one tuition is charged extra by the hour, exams and materials for practical subjects likewise extra, so do check what you sign up for. Some bursaries in case of need.

Remarks: 'I am so happy here,' one bright A level spark told us. 'I'm with a lot of clever people; we're brilliantly taught. Everyone is perfectly normal – they just didn't like the regimentation of school life.' A fabulous opportunity to regroup and get on track if things have gone awry – and a good place for friendships too. Some come back years after to see staff. A gem.

Eaton House The Vale

Linked schools: Eaton House Belgravia, 88. For Eaton House the Manor Girls' School, Eaton House the Manor Preparatory and Pre-Preparatory School, see *The Good Schools Guide: London South*

2 Elvaston Place, London SW7 5QH

Tel: 020 7584 9515

Independent • Pupils: 85 • Ages: Girls 3-8; boys 3-11 • Fees: up to £14,670 pa

Email: admin@eatonhouseschools.com
Website: www.eatonhouseschools.com

27

Headmaster: Since 2008, Mr Robin Greenwood FTCL ARCM, BSc (40s) a scientist and musician. He was educated in South Africa, then London University, where he studied biological sciences. An accomplished pianist, he also studied music at Trinity College, London. Mr Greenwood taught at the

Eaton House Schools before becoming headmaster of Wetherby Prep and then returned to the fold to become headmaster of The Vale. Parents say the school is like one big family and Mr Greenwood is always on hand to discuss their child's progress.

Entrance: At 4+ non-selective entry on a first-come first-served basis. Children attending the nursery enter in the term leading up to the third birthday.

Exit: At 8+ boys to Colet Court, Eaton House The Manor Prep, Fulham Prep, Westminster Under or Westminster Cathedral Choir School; occasional one to boarding school. Girls at 8+ to eg Bassett House, Norland Place, Knightsbridge School; at 11+ eg Francis Holland, Godolphin & Latymer, St Mary's Calne, Downe House, Tudor Hall.

Remarks: The Vale is currently a co-ed nursery and prep school catering for boys from 3-8 and girls from 3-11. Traditional 3Rs curriculum with a focus on developing every child's abilities, both academic and non-academic. No streaming and class sizes are kept small to ensure lots of individual attention.

The school occupies a large six-storey Georgian house just off Gloucester Road, complete with kitchens and a dining area. Facilities are excellent for a small school, although slightly tight. Well-stocked library, ICT room, multi-purpose hall and own science lab. No outdoor space – pupils go for short walk during morning break and midday playtimes are held in Kensington Gardens. Two afternoons a week children go to Battersea Park with the games master for PE lessons. Pupils are introduced to around 10 different sports, including tennis, cricket and athletics, with matches, competitions and summer sports days being popular events. Exciting whole class drama and music; with around a third of the children learning an instrument, everyone performs in the regular plays and musicals.

Parents say the school is like one big family and Mr Greenwood is always on hand

For those with SEN, a part-time adviser organises additional support as needed by pupils. The school welcomes visiting specialists including speech and occupational therapists to support pupils with individual needs. Home/school communication is considered paramount – reading and message books are exchanged every day and five simple rules for everyone to follow to encourage thoughtfulness and sensible behaviour.

The children also benefit from being taken out to visit a variety of London sites and museums. After-school clubs include French, cookery, chess, healthy kids and lifestyles. Mr Greenwood has an open door policy for parents which helps create the nurturing and friendly atmosphere and, most importantly, yummy lunches, say the young ones.

École Française Jacques Prévert

59 Brook Green, London W6 7BE

Tel: 020 7602 6871

Independent • Pupils: 260 • Ages: 3–11 • Fees: up to £6,133 pa

Email: info@ecoleprevert.org.uk
Website: www.ecoleprevert.org.uk

Director: Since 2011, Patrice Possenti BA History (University of Lyon), Diplome Professeur des Écoles (French national certification), (40s), previously director of a primary school near Lyon for six years, and simultaneously at University of Lyon training new teachers and specialising in IT training for teachers. Special interests are languages and how children develop as multilinguists. He is also keen on the use of IT to improve learning. At Jacques Prevert he is always considering means of expanding the premises, but this is an on-going challenge in urban London.

The school is under the auspices of the AEFE (French Agency for the French Education Abroad, run by the French Ministry of Foreign Affairs), which oversees a network of French curriculum schools around the world, and appoints the directors of all its schools. The northern European ones meet regularly, and they are are generally rotated every five years.

Parents speak highly of Mr Possenti and the respect and affection with which he is held is tangible when walking through the school: youngsters of all ages call out to greet him and clamour for his attention to share news or show him their work. Acknowledging them by name, he makes each one feel important, even whilst escorting us through the school. He comes across as completely dedicated to his work, though he admits to a passion for figure-skating, which he now teaches as a school activity.

Entrance: Most children start in September, although as the community is an international one there is occasional movement during the school year. The cut-off date for birthdays is December, so those accustomed to September birthday deadlines may be surprised to find there are some younger peers in the class.

The admissions criteria are aligned with those of all AEFE schools. Priority is given to siblings, pupils coming from other AEFE schools abroad or in the UK (typically La Petite École Française in Notting Hill and L'École du Hérisson Hammersmith); academic ability isn't a factor. Siblings get preference. The school is normally over-subscribed with one or two forms in a year. Twenty-eight pupils admitted at age 4 and 16 new pupils at age 6. Parents recommend getting on the waiting list at the earliest possible opportunity and hanging on even if you don't get an offer for the first year, as vacancies can arise in later years. They also advise that if you aren't on the waiting list, and are not transferring in from a French school, 'you can forget it'.

Exit: Most pupils have gone to the London French Lycée Charles de Gaulle, where the director is able to track his pupils' progress, as the Lycée regularly sends progress reports back to Jacques Prevert. However, families also have the option of the College Français Bilingue de Londres in Kentish Town and the new Lycée Winston Churchill in Wembley. Some parents (Anglophones) opt to move their children into the English system at the end of the primary years. The school does not advise parents on specific schools, but the parents' association organises information sessions about the English system and the French Lycée organises a meeting in March about the French secondary system.

Remarks: French curriculum, with the addition of English classes taught by native speakers. Main language of instruction is French, in keeping with school's mission to promote bilingual education, which begins in kindergarten. As the children get older (8 upwards), some the subjects such as history, geography and eventually science are partially taught by English teachers working in parallel with their French colleagues.

Parents are pleased with the early childhood programme that integrates arts, crafts, singing and pre-reading skills such as learning letters. They move to the primary section at age 6, and are usually reading by the end of the first term. The school is exempt from following the EYFS.

Those in the primary section follow the prescribed French curriculum, which includes seven 'pillars': mastery of the French language, speaking a modern foreign language (English), acquiring basic knowledge in mathematics and science, developing a humanist culture, mastering common ICT, acquiring social and civic skills, and developing autonomy and initiative.

The first two-year cycle (roughly equivalent to British KS1) includes PE and sport, visual art, music and a modern foreign language (in this case, English, taught by native speakers). This is followed by a three-year 'consolidation cycle' (ages 8-11) roughly equivalent to English KS2. This is where the French imperative to teach grammar shines and the rigorous French history syllabus covers pre-history to the Middle Ages, the Enlightenment to the French Revolution, the 20th Century and the European Union. Geography is similarly Franco-centric.

Teachers are encouraged to integrate IT into the curriculum from 4-year-olds upwards. A cheerful library holds an impressive French collection; the English classroom holds the English language materials. There are no national exams for French primary school students; progress is internally assessed and there are detailed termly online reports.

Parents speak highly of Mr Possenti and the respect and affection with which he is held is tangible when walking through the school: youngsters of all ages call out to greet him

Because pupils are not necessarily fluent English speakers, juggling the English language levels is a continuous challenge; English classes are streamed by ability groups from 7 years, and the school provides some support to help new arrivals in the English-medium classes. The curriculum includes English grammar and comprehension.

Though the school is crowded, it is orderly. Some special classes give teachers the opportunity to work with smaller groups. On our visit we saw lots of variety in teaching approaches and learning activity, including PE, music and artists at work, all the students looking engaged and happy. The Maternelle Grande children were making elaborate models of castles in anticipation of a visit to the Tower of London.

Typical of many French schools, there is no specialist SEN support, but teachers use their free lessons to provide one-to-one teaching to pupils who are lagging behind. More flexible than most UK schools, it is not unheard of for a particularly strong or bright child to move up a year, or a struggling pupil to stay down.

PE includes ice skating, rock climbing, acrosport and badminton. Music is taught by a specialist, art mostly by class teachers. Parents point out that while extracurricular activities are not a big feature of traditional French schools, here a super-involved parent body organises clubs for eg tennis, judo, karate, chess, arts and crafts and singing at nominal extra cost. Morning club from 8am.

Founded in 1974 as a smaller, more family-friendly French primary school alternative to the larger Lycée Charles de Gaulle in South Kensington, the school is in a large converted house. There is a small outdoor playground, and children sometimes have free time on spacious Brook Green.

Discipline is quite strict. Pupils have the same teacher for most subjects so they know each other well. Lunches (included in the school fees) are well balanced and freshly prepared. On Wednesdays, which are half days, those staying on for afternoon activities bring a packed lunch.

The community is an international one with many dual-national bilingual families: more than half are French or French/British, about 15 per cent are British and the remainder come from a variety of countries, with speakers of Spanish, German, Arabic, Chinese all represented. It's not unusual for students to speak three or four languages. However, parents tell us that the lingua franca is English.

Most families are local, but there is a school bus service organised by parents. Active parents' association, kept up to date by a snazzy online newsletter with video links. In this small community everyone knows everyone else

Most families are local, but there is a school bus service organised by parents. Active parents' association, kept up to date by a snazzy online newsletter with video links. In this small community where everyone knows everyone else, parents feel obliged to play their part in committees, fund raising or generally helping out.

Subsidies from the French Government keep the fees down. French nationals are eligible to apply for scholarships.

For London families who want their children to have the advantage of developing or keeping up French language fluency in a small and friendly school environment, parents advise: 'Get on the waiting list'.

Falkner House

19 Brechin Place, London SW7 4QB

Independent · Pupils: 190 girls, 10 boys
· Ages: 4–11; nursery 3–4 · Fees: up to £16,680 pa

Tel: 020 7373 4501

Email: office@falknerhouse.co.uk
Website: www.falknerhouse.co.uk

28

Headteacher: Since 1999, Mrs Anita Griggs BA PGCE (60s). Educated at Queen's College, Harley Street, then studied history and economics at York University. Spent her early career at the Bank of England, before heading the economics department at St Paul's Girls' School.

Her mother, Flavia Nunes, was Falkner House's founding head and her father ran a successful boys' prep so she has the central London education system embedded in her DNA. Today she unites the best of British tradition with the decisively innovative. 'As soon as someone has a good idea, I would like it to happen,' she says. 'I'm an impatient person.'

Very much a hands-on head, she's at the gates every morning, constantly available to parents (her home number is on the school's website), pupils ('I don't teach, but I know the children from the back of their heads') and teachers. Forthright, purposeful

and positive ('never think you can't do something'), she's also bracingly down to earth. 'While I want girls to be happy and successful at 11, I also want them to be happy and successful at 31 and 41.'

She has no immediate intention of passing the baton to one of her four adult daughters (two of whom work in the school). 'There are other things I could do with my life. I do it because I love it.' Parents definitely appreciate this. 'She's immensely charming,' said one, 'and really fights for the girls.' 'She's given my children the most wonderful education,' said another.

Married to a city lawyer, she lives across the road from the school and in her off-duty hours is an 'obsessive reader' and enthusiastic traveller.

Entrance: Register as soon as possible after birth. Some enter at nursery (including boys), but a

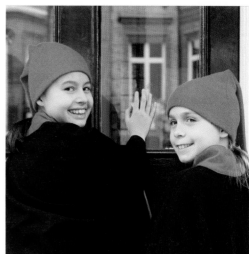

nursery spot does not guarantee passage to the main school. In the January before entry, about 130 girls compete for 22 reception places in an assessment that looks for 'focus, working memory and enthusiasm,' as well as more elusive qualities such as 'grit' and good manners.

'A child cannot be prepared and we don't assess whether or not they can read,' says the head. Many will inevitably be disappointed, but parents are let down as gently as possible. 'No selection system is perfect. We don't get false positives, but we sometimes get false negatives.' Occasional places (an average of one a year) are again filled by assessment. 'I'd rather leave a space than have the wrong fit,' adds the head.

Exit: The 'next step' is considered thoughtfully, with parents invited in for a planning meeting in year 5. 'We take endless care to ensure girls not only get into the best schools but the schools that are best for them.' The majority, now as always, to London's academic girls' schools (Francis Holland SW1, Queen's Gate, St Paul's, Godolphin & Latymer, Putney High, City) but co-ed Latymer Upper is also attracting increasing attention. Reasonable numbers to board, with Wycombe Abbey and St Mary's Ascot featuring strongly. Girls frequently leave garnered with scholarships, academic, music and sporting.

Remarks: Flavia Nunes set up Falkner House in 1954 with the intention of providing girls with the same standard of academic excellence enjoyed by their brothers – by no means a given in those days – and the school continues to provide a broad and challenging education taught by a dedicated, energetic and innovative staff. 'They're the real stars,' says the head.

Reading is central to the offering. All younger girls are expected to read nightly at home and a love of words and books is encouraged by regular attendance at two libraries, well-considered reading lists, a weekly library lesson from year 3 and freedom to bring in Kindles from year 4. Poetry is learned by heart and recited in class and competitions; recently launched own poetry anthology of verses 'every Falkner House child should know'. Girls become articulate and confident, both on the page and in conversation.

Art room buzzing and history of art taught from reception, with regular outings to museums and galleries. Dance and drama included in the core curriculum

Beyond the three Rs, a rainbow of opportunity. French throughout (with a fortnightly French assembly), classics from year 3, Latin from year 5. Debating now part of the curriculum. The arts, too, taken seriously. Music strong (four music scholarships in 2015) and varied with plenty in the way of performance (wind band, string group, choir, chamber music ensemble). Art room buzzing and history of art taught from reception, with regular outings to museums and galleries. Dance and drama included in the core curriculum, year 4 produced a class film rather than a class play, and a popular after-school ballet club allows those who wish to take external exams.

Technology here is not just for display on the timetable, but blazing a trail – a hardworking teacher has reinvented the year 5 and 6 curriculum to be delivered on iPads. In 2014 Apple named Falkner House one of six groundbreaking schools worldwide for its innovative approach.

Homework and exams introduced early (the former in reception, the latter twice yearly from year 3). 'It's important for girls to learn to take both the test and the results in their stride; to learn their best is good enough,' says the head.

This is a selective school and few have serious special educational needs. Mild difficulties, however, are addressed successfully by experienced staff and high fliers given regular extension work.

Despite a handkerchief playground, sport played competitively to a high level. Coaches ferry girls to Battersea, Kensington Gardens, Latchmere Leisure Centre and Chelsea and from year 3 the school fields A, B, and often C squads in netball, athletics, swimming, rounders and cross-country. 'It's a culture of "play the game within the spirit of the game",' says the head. 'We do not kill to win.' Win they do, however, producing recent champions at the London Schools Swimming Association and the British Schools Team Fencing Championship. Numerous extracurricular activities include clubs, trips (abroad and to the head's house in West Sussex) and treats (on Founder's Day an English National Ballet soloist came in to teach choreography).

Fresh food cooked daily – and described as 'amazing' by our guides, with staff monitoring manners and a balanced diet. 'We've taken out all mention of

healthy eating,' says the head. 'All children here eat healthy food, so why create more anxiety?'

The school is still located in the two spacious, multi-storeyed Victorian houses where it was founded and retains the echo of a post-war family home, with carpeted corridors and the head's office elegantly kitted out with antiques. Tradition, too, maintained with daily 'prayers' (Christian hymns and the Lord's Prayer) held in the delightful, parqueted assembly hall. All faiths welcome. Remembrance Day, carol service and the Queen's Jubilee accorded due dignity. 'The girls should understand the culture. That's not deprivation; it's enrichment.'

Other traditional strands include both a house and prefect system. Head girl, deputy and prefects appointed for half term stints, so most get a go, while other routes to glory include sports person or artist of the week, eco monitor and badge girl (responsible for helping the teacher).

Head's mission is to endow pupils with self confidence, independence of mind, kindness and good manners, and girls clearly enjoy the process. 'It's fun,' said one. Though the inevitable friendship groups form, all seem to get on. 'No one is not friends,' said another. Top year girls are paired with those coming into reception, and this union of 'grandes' and 'petites' means new arrivals are never left stranded. 'We play with them and introduce our petite to our friends' petites.' Precocity definitely discouraged (no nail varnish, no jewellery and only 'sensible' shoes).

Parents kept at well-informed arms' length. 'I'd prefer them not to come in and hang up the children's coats – children come to school to learn independence,' says the head, who is also firmly anti-PTA. 'I'm very proud of that. I don't want some alpha mummy in charge. I'd prefer her to come in and give me her bright ideas.'

The home-school link, however, is strong, with parental involvement expected with homework and music practice. Parents regularly invited to attend events, from ballet recitals to Father's Day breakfasts. The school website, updated weekly, keeps all in the loop, while the flexible early birds and late birds system allows drop off and pick up from early morning till late afternoon. 'If you're stuck in traffic you can just telephone,' said one parent. 'It's fantastic for working mothers.'

Families mainly within walking distance, then spreading out to Hammersmith, Chiswick, Fulham and Battersea. Predominantly British, highly qualified, working in financial services, but also numerous global citizens. Unsurprisingly, some can be a tad competitive, something the head keeps firmly in check. 'If someone rings up to demand why their daughter's not in the netball team, you just have to say, "I'm sorry you're cross, but let's try and be reasonable. There are other people better at netball".'

Given the location, families tend to be affluent. The website includes requests for housekeepers and year 6 parents are politely asked to plan family holidays 'to avoid jet lag'. No formal bursaries or scholarships, but the school has always helped out existing pupils in financial difficulties.

Fox Primary School

Kensington Place, London W8 7PP

State • Pupils: 330 • Ages: 4–11

Tel: 020 7727 7637

Email: info@fox.rbkc.sch.uk
Website: www.fox.rbkc.sch.uk

Headteacher: Since 2006, Paul Cotter BA PGCE (40s). Previously deputy head at Avondale Primary in North Kensington, bringing much of what he learnt there with him, including his young, extremely bright and capable deputy, Emma Madden – they make a formidable team. Swiftly injected energy and fresh blood into this ever-popular local school. Savvy – knows how to access funding and use it to the max.

Entrance: Heavily oversubscribed – over 200 applicants for 45 places. Priority (rather than catchment) area is mainly to the south towards Kensington rather than the north to Notting Hill, where greater density of state school provision. Lots of mobility, however, so places do crop up, and further up the school they have admitted children beyond this area. First priority to looked after children, those with particular medical or social needs, or an SEN statement/ECH plan, then siblings. Entrance procedure is administered by the borough and the head can exercise no preference. Children come from over 40 different nurseries, but parents we spoke to mentioned Strawberry Fields, Rolfes, St Peters and Kids Unlimited.

Exit: About half each year to Holland Park, a handful to the new-ish Chelsea Academy. More than a third to independent schools – a wide range including Latymer Upper, Godolphin and Latymer, City of London Boys' and Girls', St Paul's Boys' and Girls', some board at, eg, Christ's Hospital and Cheltenham Ladies' College, some win scholarships to, eg, Charterhouse. 'They can go wherever they want,' said one parent. Mr Cotter meets all secondary heads – 'they generally like Fox children,' he says proudly. Parents notice that he sees this as an integral part of his job – makes no judgement about the choice other than finding what's best for each individual.

Remarks: A buzzing local primary with a liberal, funky feel to it. A sea of colour greets you as you enter the well secured gates – brightly clad children (no uniform) playing noisily (as you would hope) in the imaginatively and tastefully decorated playground. As well as the main area for football and netball, a quieter arbour with wooden tables, canopies and lavender, the gentle rushing of water running around the perimeter. A popular place to trade Match Attacks and Go Gos on a Friday and for parents to discuss their next fundraising project after drop off. A giant chess board and climbing wall in the far corner while, behind the school, in the younger years' playground, allotments (where the children tend radishes and chillis as well as lychees) and a woodland trail. Dedicated play area with sand and water for reception children and beautiful mosaics on the walls.

We saw the house (named after four different species of fox) spellathon conducted like a prime time quiz show. Everyone had fun

The school is housed in a large 1930s building and has all the hallmarks of being purpose built, with wide corridors and staircases. Large windows into bright, spacious, airy classrooms. Every inch of space is used to benefit learning – the deputy head's office also has an interactive white board and desks. Music rooms, dedicated learning rooms for smaller groups, an IT room with 30 flat screen computers, a large hall with a huge white screen. IT is used to liven things up at every occasion, particularly the assemblies (which happen at 3pm, when 'everyone has had enough rather than first thing, which is prime learning time,' says head sensibly). We saw the house (named after four different species of fox) spellathon conducted like a prime time quiz show. Everyone had fun and everyone learnt something. This is clearly key to the ethos here.

A strong, dynamic teaching staff, average age less than 30. Larger number of women than men.

They bring fun and lots of motivation to the daily curriculum. Parents enthuse about the cohesive staff – by all accounts Mr Cotter has built a team of excellent teachers. Energy saving schemes (they are aiming for green flag system and have an 'eco team' of pupils to help them do it) and clever organisation have resulted in his being able to employ more staff and ensure the school is extremely well equipped. One of his cleverest achievements has to be the class sizes – reduced at every opportunity. Currently only 22 in two classes in reception, year 1, and years 4 to 6, with an ingenious scheme to allow for differentiation according to age and stage in years 2 and 3. Rightly proud of this innovation – 'Standards have shot up as a result,' he observes – Fox now rates as one of the top primary schools in the country.

Everyone achieves here – the bright ones as well as those with special needs. High ratio of staff to children in each class, and the SENCo teaches smaller groups of up to 10 who have learning difficulties (PTA funded laptops for this). About 15 per cent of children are currently on the SEN register, some with statements. One or two reports that it took a bit of prodding before school diagnosed, eg, dyslexia (school denies this, 'We have rigorous monitoring systems,' they say) but by all accounts, once any problems are discovered, school gives tremendous support. English is the second language for about one third of children – they catch up quickly. School accepts child as s/he is and works enthusiastically with what they've got, say parents – they don't try to iron out the problems and pretend they're not there.

Music and dance are central to the school day. Years 2 and 3 all learn the recorder in key stage 1, with over half the school going on to learn an instrument in key stage 2. An orchestra with regular concerts, jazz and dance throughout the year. Science week happens in the autumn term, arts week in the winter term and sports week (where they canoe and climb, do archery and judo as well as the sports you might normally expect) in the summer. Some 40 clubs are offered either before or after school – children can choose almost anything from Chinese to table tennis, sculpture to archery.

Delicious lunches cooked by their own chef (no imported catering service here) allow for every penny to be put back into the menu. Staff eat with pupils in the school hall. They don't need persuading to eat fresh Greek salad – after all, 'they are as fussy as the children,' acknowledges head.

Very supportive and active PTA raises significant sums of money each year, helping to fund, eg, the stunning areas of the playground. One parent described the parent body as having 'a can do attitude that you find in some private schools'. A number of parents were at Fox themselves – always a positive indicator. High number of professionals – barristers, journalists, diplomats, authors as well as artists and musicians, and 17 per cent of pupils are on free school meals. One parent spoke of the relief she felt that her daughter wouldn't grow up thinking everyone had a second home in Barbados.

A school with a strong, very positive identity (witness the 'mighty Fox' anthem, sung by the whole school at every successful achievement). One parent described it as mini UN – can be up to 15 nationalities in one class. School thrives on multiculturalism and diverse influences but 'doesn't see that as an excuse for poor performance,' emphasises one parent. School quick to point out that bilingual pupils outperform their monolingual peers. Bright eyed, confident, articulate and above all happy children who enjoy coming to school. A rare and precious jewel showing real life at its best – not to be overlooked in this super-affluent patch of London.

Fulham Prep and Pre-prep School

200 Greyhound Road, London W14 9SD

Tel: 020 7386 2444

Independent • Pupils: 625 • Ages: 4–13 • Fees: up to £16,695 pa

Email: prepadmin@fulhamprep.co.uk
Website: www.fulhamprep.co.uk

Principal: Mrs Jane Emmett is back in charge after the short-lived tenure (less than a year) of Richie Howells. She founded the school in 1996 along with other members of her family (it is a family company with some external shareholders).

Head of the pre-prep is Ms Di Steven BEd, educated at Glasgow University with PGCE from Dundee and an NPQH. She has been with the school for a decade, has one son in the pre-prep, a second son in a nearby nursery. Clearly in touch with the concerns of the modern parent, juggling work pressure with teaching her son to ride a bicycle. She is thorough and thoughtful with a pleasant manner and high standards. Her IT expertise ensures that the pre-prep is very well equipped.

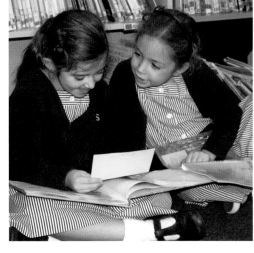

Entrance: The pre-prep is non-selective in reception, with 90 places offered on a first come first served basis. Priority and a discount given to siblings. Entry after reception involves spending a morning at the school. Automatic transfer to the prep. The prep holds examinations and interviews at 7+ 8+ and 11+.

Exit: Majority of pre-prep pupils move on to the prep. Has a reputation for getting each prep school child into the right senior school, often with scholarships. School is keen to encourage more girls to stay until 13 but this very much depends on the choice of destination as many girls' schools want them at 11+. Girls move on to boarding schools including Benenden, Downe House, Headington, St Mary's Ascot and St Mary's Calne, or to day schools such as Francis Holland, Godolphin & Latymer, Putney High, Wimbledon High, Lady Margaret, More House. Boys leave at 13 except those destined for Latymer or Westminster Under at 11. Their destinations include: King's College School, Dulwich, Eton, Harrow, Marlborough, St Paul's, Wellington, Westminster and King Edward's Oxford.

Remarks: The school is on two sites: there are transport arrangements between prep (on Greyhound Road) and pre-prep (on Fulham High Street) to assist busy parents, and January exam candidates are given the opportunity to visit in November for a treasure hunt so that they feel more at home when they come in for the dreaded tests.

The curriculum is not straitjacketed, and parents appreciate its variety and breadth. Although one class is given an accelerated pace (selected according to pupils' school destinations) this would 'not be fair on the others who do not need it,' remarks the principal. That said, there is an expectation that every child will be able to keep up with a dynamic academic programme. All are being prepared for competitive entrance examinations, and although some allowance is made for pupils from abroad, there is limited EAL support in school. Experienced and extremely caring SENCo supports those with mild learning difficulties. Parents confirm that if serious difficulties were to develop, a school move would be suggested. Pre-prep has its own SENCo, a 'godsend,' remarks Ms Steven and we noted some very good examples of provision for different abilities.

Music is a strength of the school with four choirs including school choir apprentices and chamber choir, a boys' choir, plus a parents' choir

Until year 4 pupils are classroom based, then they move round specialist facilities. Latin from year 5 and philosophy for years 4 to 6. Greek available in years 7 and 8. 'The teachers make lessons interesting, often involving games in them', pupils remarked to us. They also appreciate the way staff 'offer advice and support'. We saw a number of young, enthusiastic staff, with more males in evidence than is often the case. The principal is keen to stress the role models provided by the female head of science (who is also a great skier), and the male head of art. Class sizes between 14 and 20.

A listed Victorian school building accommodates the pre-prep reception classes, library, activity room and ICT suite. Adjoining is a modern three-storey block for years 1 and 2 as well as the spacious gym/hall, dark music room and light art studio. Large, well-equipped play areas including fabulous Astroturf and garden with shallow pond. We saw plenty of imaginative play equipment that can be re-arranged with different themes.

Do not expect soft furnishings, carpets and tasteful flower arrangements, or a palatial office for the principal. The prep school was originally a Victorian board school and the building still shows this, although it is light with high ceilings, classrooms leading off the wide corridors on several floors, and an impressive meeting room with raked seating. Welcoming library with enthusiastic librarian. Classrooms contain attractive displays and are well equipped with the usual interactive boards. Some access to laptops, but though good use is made of the intranet to support learning (a recent development), we felt that the ICT in the prep is not cutting edge (schools says, 'we have been very proactive in implementing a great deal of computer science, coding and digital literacy within our current programme.').

More boys than girls in the school, especially noticeable in years 7 and 8 when many of the girls have left for London day schools. Those girls that do remain can be assured of being given responsibility and participating in many sports. Pupils look happy and move about purposefully; they are polite and responsive but not precocious, though it takes a certain robustness to flourish here. Parents like the fact that 'there are all walks of life' and the school is not 'glitzy'.

Heaps for all to do here. 'There are lots of opportunities for children to try new activities, with loads of clubs from jewellery to street dancing,' commented a parent. 'There's also plenty of music, from award winning chamber choir to African drumming, orchestra and jazz group.' Music is a strength of the school with four choirs including school choir apprentices and chamber choir, a boys' choir, plus a parents' choir which sings at the carol service. All classes have two music lessons with three-quarters of the pupils taking individual instrumental or singing lessons in spacious accommodation. Pre-prep pupils learn the recorder and percussion.

The school has its own Astroturf, netball court and cricket nets, and there is one afternoon a week at Barn Elms. In years 3 and 4 every child is given the chance to play in a team. The second half of Friday afternoon is for sport, as are some Saturdays (though both of these may be avoided). The deputy head is especially pleased with the up-and-coming rugby players, and cricket is very popular. Girls play netball. The pre-prep makes frequent use of Hurlingham Park for games, swimming takes place at Fulham Pools and there's summer tennis coaching for years 1 and 2 in Bishops' Park.

'Pupils show tremendous loyalty to the four houses,' remarks Mr Howells. The house names fit the locality: Bishops, Crabtree, Hurlingham and Peterborough. Older pupils take their responsibilities seriously and look out for younger pupils. Even in the pre-prep pupils start to take responsibilities eg as house captains. All the houses raise funds for charities, and the school supports, for example, a local state primary for severely disabled children. Discipline system understood by all and parents believe any bullying is quickly acted upon. Pupils we spoke to were clear that the head sees anyone who seriously misbehaves, and cited swearing as a major offence. Matters are dealt with promptly. Strong communication between home and school, including an open door policy and regular daily contact, means potential problems are nipped in the bud.

Sibling discount; some bursaries for families in difficulties. Scholarships available for years 7 and 8.

Very much a local school, as evidenced by the numbers of bikes and scooters parked inside the gates. The pupils are polite and express themselves confidently; one parent commented that some parents choose Fulham Prep because they have been impressed by the behaviour of the children outside school and asked where they were educated. A 'really vibrant, caring school where pupils are nurtured and understood' is the parental consensus. No wonder it has grown so fast.

Garden House School

Turks Row, London SW3 4TW

Tel: 020 7730 1652

Independent · Pupils: 495 · Ages: 3–11 · Fees: up to £21,300 pa

Email: info@gardenhouseschool.co.uk
Website: www.gardenhouseschool.co.uk

30

Principal: Since 1973, Mrs Jill Oddy BA. She also runs three pre-prep schools in New York. As a long-serving member of the administrative department

– who appreciated the school's move in recent years to Turks Row just behind Sloane Square – proudly remarks: 'She has tremendous vision.'

Head of girls' school since September 2014, Mrs Charlotte Crofton BA (modern history, Newcastle) and PGCE (London), who has been a year 5 teacher here for eight years. She works alongside the head of the girls' lower school – Mrs Julia Adlard, who was previously head of kindergarten.

Head of the boys' school since 2006, Mr Christian Warland, with BA from Exeter, (40s), left his work in the City as a lawyer and seems here to stay. He has found the change very satisfying: 'We spent considerable time analysing what went wrong in the City whereas here we are constantly forward-looking and this is very positive.' An old Garden House boy himself (and son of the principal), his three sons have been, or are being, educated at Garden House.

All three heads value taking time to get to know the children, from shaking hands with them and making eye contact first thing in the morning to teaching. Head of boys teaches ICT to year 2 and current affairs to the rest.

Entrance: As part of the school's desire to involve parents from the start, the family is seen as a unit. Usually girls are interviewed by head of lower school in January for the following September and boys by headmaster in October/November. Regular tours are organised for prospective parents, Tuesdays for the boys' school and Wednesdays for the girls', and there is no entrance examination, thankfully, so it really is important to secure a place on the lengthy waiting list with £120 as soon as possible. The school states that GH children live in Kensington, Chelsea, Fulham, Battersea and Westminster and that English is spoken at home by

Specialist teachers for music, drama, games, French, IT, ballet, Latin, fencing, art from year 2 upwards and RE in the upper school

at least one parent, so very much a day school serving its local, smart area. Once a place is offered, a registration fee of £2,000 is payable. There is a 10 per cent discount for all siblings. Around 50 boys and 45 girls join reception. Entrants at 8+ (by exam and interview) are nearly all boys, to replace the 30 – 40 who leave at this stage; scholarships and generous bursaries available at this stage. There is a small amount of coming and going as families relocate so it is definitely worth checking.

Exit: Boys leave at 8+ (30-40) and 11+ (12-15) for top London day schools, including Colet Court, Sussex House, Westminster Under, Northcote Lodge, Wetherby Prep; one or two boarding prep schools such as Summer Fields, Ludgrove and Cothill House. Nearly all girls leave at 11; just under half go on to boarding schools including St Mary's Ascot, Downe House, Wycombe Abbey, with a consistent number to Francis Holland SW1, Queen's Gate, Godolphin and Latymer, St Paul's Girls' etc. Some go on with academic, art or sporting scholarships and awards.

Remarks: The exterior of the school, originally a British army barracks, is well maintained, but what awaits inside is quite magical. We were struck by the attention to detail and aesthetics; the entrance hall is beautifully arranged with rocking-horse, pupils' models and high quality art works by professionals, including an appealing watercolour of the school by a parent, Martin Millard, whose wife helps in the library. Classical music plays and flower arrangements and lighting produce a calming, civilising effect after the noise and bustle outside. Every corridor and every room shows a care for the surroundings, whether it be the recital room, art room, well-equipped ICT suite or classrooms with vibrant displays, and this contributes to the attention paid to individual pupils. As a current parent remarked: 'This is above all a nurturing school, where boys and girls receive a wonderful education. It is so nurturing both for parents and children.'

Heads are proud of broad curriculum and use of cross-curriculum planning. Every class has a teacher and classroom assistant, with specialist teachers for music, drama, games, French, IT, ballet, Latin, fencing, art from year 2 upwards and RE in the upper school. Boys and girls are taught separately after kindergarten but come together for playtime and musical and drama performances, as well as some trips. Average class size is 15 for girls and 14 for boys, with mixed ability teaching for all and some streaming only in mathematics. There is a learning zone on the website and plenty of interactive boards and laptops for research. There is a well-qualified learning support team with a range of expertise, including speech therapy, so pupils can be assessed in-house; some classroom assistants are trained in dyslexia. Alongside the learning support, there is also a gifted and talented coordinator, and year 6 get help with creative writing and mathematics ready for 11+ exams. The boys and girls share the

same broad curriculum, but many boys sit 8+ exams, so there is a different emphasis at this stage even for those staying till 11. Practice papers and internal assessments throughout the year help pupils to cope with different styles of questioning. Plenty of advice and guidance available to parents but tutoring is discouraged as unnecessary pressure.

The attractively-equipped kindergarten accommodates tiny tots in a separate building attached to Holy Trinity Church. There are morning sessions for 24 children and afternoon sessions for 12, and they share a play area with the C of E primary school over the road.

The behaviour policy, using traffic lights, is well thought out. A parent commented on how seriously the children take it and said that the red light is very rarely used – 'it is brilliant, a clear not emotional system.' The head was also reassuringly definite that she would have no hesitation in using the red light and contacting a parent if the need arose: if, for example, a child were bullied.

All three heads are keen for school to be fun and stimulating, as the enormous array of activities and events demonstrate. During our visit boys were producing leaves in IT and art enthusiastically for FebFest, and the older girls spoke of the delights of preparing music and performing at Cadogan Hall in the spring term to a packed audience. The FebFest programme, involving the whole school from year 2 upwards, is linked to a fictional character travelling the world and hearing music from many cultures and heritages. The school is handy for galleries, exhibitions, museums and concerts. Music is popular with pupils as the teacher makes 'music enjoyable using actions' and 'is not too serious but friendly.' We heard the boys singing with gusto, and the percussion teacher clearly had year 1 boys enthralled. Every year the chamber choir goes on tour to Normandy and sings in the chapel of Emmanuel College, Cambridge. The musical calendar is packed. Four productions a year at the Royal Court and the Christmas concert is held in the Holy Trinity Church. Numerous events and competitions include Varsity Challenge, House Shout and Garden House has Talent.

Sport is taken seriously with football, rugby, cricket, rounders, hockey, lacrosse, tennis, netball at nearby Burton Court and Ranelagh Gardens as well as swimming at the Queen Mother's Pool. As a parent remarked, 'It all happens seamlessly despite the school not having its own extensive grounds, as so much is in easy walking distance.' Pupils were keen to explain how inclusive the school is, with team places and encouragement even for the less talented.

Active and supportive PTA with a predominantly Anglo-American parent body. The pupils feel they are respected by the teachers; as one parent remarked, 'There is always a seasoned staff member who has expertise and experience alongside another with energy, who comes across as positive and not world-weary. The school is amazing'.

Fridays are half days, though older children can do supervised homework until 2.30pm. Popular with parents who feel younger children are ready for the shorter day by Friday, and with those who want to leave early for the country.

Not a cheap school, although the Harrods uniform is also available secondhand and there is a complimentary bus service at 4.00pm to Fulham.

Sparky teachers, male and female, give a sense of energy in a school community in which care, respect and kindness for all is very much the ethos.

Glendower Prep School

87 Queen's Gate, London SW7 5JX

Tel: 020 7370 1927

31

Independent • Pupils: 220 • Ages: 4–11 • Fees: £16,995 pa

Email: office@glendower.kensington.sch.uk
Website: www.glendowerprep.org

Headmistress: Since September 2012, Mrs Sarah Knollys (rhymes with tolls) BA PGCE (40s), educated at Wycombe Abbey and St Paul's Girls', Exeter (a degree in French and Italian) and Roehampton Universities. Started teaching career as SEN assistant at Finton House School, London; rose from form teacher to maths co-ordinator, SCITT mentor, key stage 2 manager, senior management team and school governor at Allfarthing School, London, a busy state school in Wandsworth, (1993-2000); founding head, Maple Walk School, London (2005-2012). Married to Christopher; they have two teenage sons.

Bright and bubbly, Mrs Knollys exudes warmth and is highly accessible. She is the kind of person

who rolls up her sleeves and gets on with it, whether it be teaching netball, transforming school lunches or wearing her slipper socks round the school on Red Nose day and dressing up in something crazy on Fun Friday. She is a woman who gets things done – as can be seen from her previous job at Maple Walk, the pioneer New Model school which started 'out of a trunk' as she puts it, with two pupils, and increased exponentially to 150 pupils by the time she left.

This is her first experience of a single sex school. 'I thought I'd miss the boys,' she remarks, 'but I don't miss the scraps in the playground – and our girls are very feisty.' She loves the girls, she says, because of their enthusiasm for everything, their lack of shame about excelling in science and maths and the more stable class dynamic – which can often be distorted by a predominance of one gender, she explains. She makes herself available to the parents, emails are responded to promptly, and she is there every morning to greet families. She is particularly on top of the 11 plus process, which starts with private meetings with her as early as year 4.

She is a good listener and we were told by one girl that 'she took on board our suggestions so we have much better lunches now, we no longer have to serve the younger children their lunch, and the loos and sinks are much nicer.' Her visible presence around the school includes teaching year 6 Latin, supporting maths in year 5 and English comprehension in year 4. That way she can properly understand each child and write detailed reports for the senior schools as well as giving fully informed advice to parents. She has one-to-one meetings with everyone from the kitchen staff through to the teaching staff and the parents. No one gets special treatment but everyone gets proper attention. This is a woman who throws herself into every aspect of the job and has been seen wiping her tears away during a music assembly. 'These are my girls,' she says unapologetically.

Entrance: Selective at 4 years. Far too many applicants for the 36 places. The girls are assessed on an informal basis – essentially to see if they interact well and can do the basics competently. Any parent who thinks coaching at this age is a good idea – forget it now. Sensible sibling policy means that often there are a fewer than 36 places open to newcomers. The tinies are assessed for 40 minutes in small groups. Older children applying for an occasional place will be assessed for longer – a

Natty purple berets, charming purple checked and striped uniform, purple website, purple chairs and folders in the class rooms

morning or perhaps a full day, careful note being taken on whether they can cope and how they interact with their peers. No particular feeder nurseries. Occasional places occur but school unlikely to fill them after year 5 – the cohesion of the year being seen as paramount. It's worth a call, though. Some bursaries available for needy local girls or those already in the school who fall on hard times. Unsuccessful applicants for 4+ entry and later applicants to the school will be placed on a waiting list for consideration should an occasional place arise.

Exit: Recently, quite a number to top boarding schools – among them, Benenden, Downe House, St Mary's Calne, Wycombe Abbey. A wide range of offers from London day schools – including the odd co-ed one – but girls tend to go to St Paul's, Godolphin & Latymer, Francis Holland SW1, St James's and even as far afield as South Hampstead, North London Collegiate and Putney High. Always a handful of scholarships each year – art and music as well as academic.

Remarks: Think purple. Think elegant. Think Glendower. Natty purple berets, charming purple checked and striped uniform, purple website, purple chairs and folders in the class rooms, purple benches and tables in the playground as well as the purple scooters that the girls arrive on. Plush carpets and sweeping staircase in a building that feels much more like a comfortable home than a school. The 1830s white building – Thomas Cundy III? – on Queen's Gate occupies a large corner plot facing Stanhope Gardens. Part of the adjacent building integrated with the school through a major development and refurbishment programme. The resulting six storey building is remarkably spacious. An airy, panelled and white-painted entrance hall, complete with wonderful large Quentin Blake originals, greets the visitor and is also used, with the doors opened to the adjacent library, as an assembly space. Library attractive and well-stocked. Excellent displays of work everywhere, lots of up-to-the-minute equipment in all rooms, which are remarkably orderly with inviting and interesting-looking work and resources.

From the moment you enter Mrs Knollys' study with its oak panelled walls, large Victorian partners' desks and oil portraits on the walls, you know this is a school with history. Founded by two spinsters in 1895, one of whose eyes (Edith Lloyd's) follow you around the room from above the fireplace, Glendower is a charitable trust, and has always been run as a not-for-profit organisation. A nostalgic relief as spanking new profit-making companies pop up throughout the city, establishing expensive schools to meet demand.

Girls get lots of attention here. One teacher/assistant to 11 girls, class sizes of between 16 and 18. Not a school for those with serious SENs but school will pick up and support those with mild difficulties and make individual learning plans for those who need them. Between five and 10 per cent of girls are on the SEN register, more being monitored. No stigma, just lots of support. There's a handwriting club during lunch break, some who have been diagnosed dyscalculic get support from outside – Emerson House for example; a learning support assistant will go into the classroom to give support with organisational/processing skills etc. No extra charge for this. Some five per cent come needing a little extra help with English and EFL is given in small groups or one-to-one as needed. Parents a real mix, US, Chinese, European – lots of bilingual, trilingual, English as a fourth language – but they are here for the duration – not much to-ing and fro-ing. Specialist teaching right from the start – French, music, drama and PE, and by year 4 almost all teaching is specialist. The academic programme includes DT and ICT, and Mrs Knollys is no Luddite – plans afoot to introduce

tablets in the classrooms. Science is well-equipped and busy. The girls enthused about identifying cells under a microscope using iodine.

The post 11 plus programme is excellent and includes touch typing, Latin and lots of public speaking – balloon debating competitions against other schools is a popular one. Poetry competitions all through the school, poems recited by heart, girls vote for the winners and finals judged by eg famous actresses and poets. Lots of music – and the twice weekly music assemblies can feature anything from Bollywood dancing to a harp recital. Most girls play at least one instrument and many take musical theatre exams. 'Music is as natural as breathing here,' glows Mrs Knollys. 'No-one is concerned about performing and there are no divas.' This school is no slouch when it comes to sport either, despite having no grounds to speak of. They are fiendish at netball and compete at national level as well as against other local schools and among themselves in inter-house matches. We saw several girls snatch some precious moments during break to practise their shooting skills. Theatrical productions and swimming take place at Imperial College, athletics in Chiswick. The girls also play tennis and rounders. Lunch: 'we are no longer vegetarian!' – another change introduced by the attentive Mrs Knollys. Fish on Fridays. Only vegetarian options on Mondays but the rest of the week meat galore. Food cooked fresh on the premises and they eat in their own dining room – no packed lunches here – hurrah!

Godolphin & Latymer

Iffley Road, London W6 0PG

Independent · Pupils: 780 · Ages: 11–18 · Sixth form
pupils: 215 · Fees: £18,180 pa

Tel: 020 8741 1936

4

Email: registrar@godolphinandlatymer.com
Website: www.godolphinandlatymer.com

Head Mistress: Since January 2009, Mrs Ruth Mercer BA (50s). A grammar school girl from Preston, she read history at Bedford College, trained as a teacher at Oxford, and began her teaching career at a state school in Liverpool. Arrived at Godolphin & Latymer as deputy head in 1998, took up a headship at Northwood College where she stayed for seven years, then back to Godolphin, this time in the top job. Married to the deputy head of an Ealing comprehensive, with a grown up son and daughter.

Brisk, forthright, no nonsense, but wholly committed to the girls in her care and to single sex education generally. 'The best schools are those that can focus on the needs of the children they have, and boys and girls have different needs as

they go through adolescence.' Gets to know all the new year 7s by rotating teaching history for half a term to each class. Parents praise her as grounded and hands on. 'She cheers the girls on at sports fixtures and helps set up the tables at parents' evenings'; 'The girls respond to her with respect and affection'; 'One of the best headmistresses I have ever met'; 'Very approachable, practical, common sense, progressive, genuine, deals with problems quickly and efficiently'.

Academic matters: Extremely impressive. In 2015, 94 per cent A*/A at GCSE, 64 per cent A*/A at A level, and a stellar points average of 40 for the IB, with one student achieving the maximum possible of

45. Even more impressively, this is achieved without (too much) pressure. All the parents we contacted were adamant that the school successfully balanced high academic standard with a rounded and friendly environment. 'Our daughter achieved straight A*s at GCSE whilst playing netball for the school, performing in school productions, and having a great time with her friends,' wrote one father. The school doesn't have a prize-giving because, they say, it isn't part of the G&L culture to single girls out for academic achievement: 'It's celebrated and praised, but we want the girls to take responsibility for their own successes.' The girls agree. 'We're worked hard here, but in a good way,' reported one. A parent confirmed, 'There is a competitive atmosphere in the school, and the expectations of the girls themselves are very high, but I think much of this is driven by the girls themselves, and I have not seen any undue pressure from the staff.' 'The amount of homework set is very manageable and appears to be less than other comparable schools,' added one mother.

Humanities continue popular, with a high take-up of subjects like English, history and philosophy. Interesting language curriculum: compulsory Mandarin in year 7, plus Latin, plus optional French, German or Spanish. The following year girls can drop the Mandarin, but only if they take up another language. From year 10 they can study Russian, Italian and Greek. Maths and science are strong and at least a third of the sixth form chooses to continue with them. 'The beauty of a girls' school is that the girls want to do everything,' says head, who is adamant that she would never consider bringing boys in at this stage.

Around 30 per cent of sixth formers opt to do the IB, which is now in its 10th year here, and Mrs Mercer admits to being a fan: 'I think it's a great programme, a philosophy of education rather than individual syllabuses tacked together.'

The amount of homework set is very manageable and appears to be less than other comparable schools

School says that it's 'very happy to receive applications from students with individual learning needs' – the term SEN isn't used here – and there are two members of staff employed to support them. That said, we have to add that not a single current parent of the many we contacted mentioned any such issues, suggesting that few girls here need this kind of help; and given the school's very selective intake, this many not be the place for pupils with more than mild difficulties. Parents of a recent leaver, however, were extremely positive that their daughter – who went on to one of the top universities – had received 'marvellous' support for her dyslexia from G&L staff, and were the more grateful that no charge for this help had ever been made.

All girls here treated as gifted and talented, and the emphasis is firmly on stretching and challenging everyone as far as they can go. It evidently works. As one parent wrote, 'The staff are dedicated to ensuring everyone achieves their potential and willingly give up their time to offer in-school clinics, extra lessons and other help when needed.'

Another wrote, 'The amazing results speak for themselves.'

Games, options, the arts: Sport at Godolphin used to have a bit of an exclusivity tag, with parents complaining that their daughters got sidelined if they weren't good enough for the A team. Not any more: the school has worked hard to extend the provision, and the word that both parents and pupils now use to describe it is 'inclusive'. In fact, every parent who contacted us praised the sporting provision and described the sports teachers as 'incredibly dedicated.' Hockey, netball, basketball, tennis, rounders, cricket, gymnastics and athletics are all flourishing, and the number of teams has dramatically increased to around 12 per year group. The school already boasts a full size Astroturf hockey pitch, three netball courts and 12 tennis courts, but there's more to come. A new £6m sports centre offers badminton courts, volleyball, trampolining, a climbing wall, fitness room and a dance studio. Lots of extracurricular options on offer too, such as rowing, pilates, squash, fencing, karate, kickboxing and yoga, plus dance options including zumba, hip-hop and street. No pool in the new centre – to include one would have put completion back by another five years – but the girls we spoke said they were fine with it. 'If I want to swim, I go swimming!' was the prevailing view, and there's certainly enough else to do.

Hockey, netball, basketball, tennis, rounders, cricket, gymnastics and athletics are all flourishing, and the number of teams has dramatically increased

Music and drama have always been strong at Godolphin, and continue to be so, although oddly enough none of the parents we spoke to said much about them, choosing to concentrate on the sport instead. The Rudland Music School, with its contemporary glass frontage, is home to state-of-the-art facilities. Lots of choirs, bands and ensembles for girls to join, and opportunities to learn all the usual range of instruments. Several drama productions a year, some of them student-led, and everyone has a chance to get involved. These are staged in the Bishop Centre (named after a former headmistress), formerly St John's Church and now a marvellous multi-purpose performance space, with flexible staging and seating expertly deployed by the school's own dedicated theatre technicians. Speech and drama exams are a popular extracurricular choice.

Art, housed in a pleasingly scruffy corridor with paint-splattered walls, is clearly flourishing, with some wonderful work on display, and lots of girls choosing to take the subject for GCSE and A level. Loads of clubs on offer, covering everything serious and non-serious – we thought the Inaccurate Classical Film Society looked great fun – and the school arranges a remarkable 150 trips a year to every conceivable destination. Plenty of opportunities for community work, and all year 11s get involved with Model United Nations. School is non-denominational, but has a strong Christian society.

Background and atmosphere: Built as a boarding school for boys in 1861 and called simply the Godolphin School, it became an independent day school for girls in 1905, hooked up with the Latymer Foundation and was re-named Godolphin & Latymer. A few decades of state-aided existence followed, until it was threatened with going comprehensive in 1977, and, rather than lose its academically selective ethos, it reverted to being fully independent again.

The walk from bustling Hammersmith is short, but the streets become abruptly quieter and leafier, and stepping into the school grounds is like entering a time-warp: red-brick Victorian tranquility was our first impression, quickly succeeded by admiration at the school's ultra-modern thumbing-in system. These contrasts abound throughout the site and create much of Godolphin's undeniable charm. The school hall – far too small for whole school assemblies these days – is delightfully old-fashioned, and adorned with traditional honours boards celebrating scholastic achievement; the library is a miracle of modern planning in a limited space, offering different rooms for silent, quiet or collaborative study. Sixth form common room and study areas on the top floor are light, airy, well-equipped, and obviously used by the girls with relish and affection. Facilities everywhere have been tastefully incorporated alongside the original buildings, and the effect is an enticing blend of monastic calm and youthful buzz. A lovely garden, complete with pond, is used by the girls for quiet reading.

An average of 23 pupils per class, slightly high for an independent school, but no sense of pupils being packed in. Everyone praised the friendly, supportive and lively atmosphere. Dolphins, as they're known here, are an eager and zesty bunch, joining in and seizing the opportunities here with both hands. One mother summed it up: 'A lively group of competitive girls, all with different talents, but sharing a great enthusiasm for life.'

Pastoral care and discipline: Previously not rated that highly by parents, but as with the sports, the

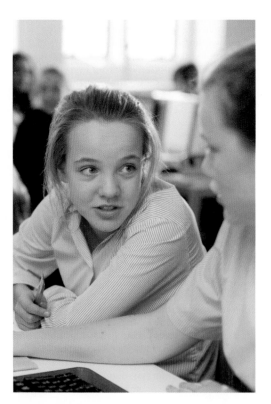

school has worked hard to raise its game in this area. There are two tutors per form group and the emphasis is on celebrating every kind of achievement. The result? 'Fair to outstanding, depending on the staff involved,' was one parent's verdict, but they all said how happy their daughters were and how much they loved their school. 'My daughter feels empowered and respected by the school. She feels the school belongs to her, not that she is a minion that belongs to it'; 'Pastoral care is diagnostic, not just a knee jerk reaction,' were typical comments. Communication with parents, once a source of complaints, is now almost universally rated as excellent.

Behaviour is relaxed, 'but there's no mucking about,' according to the students. No uniform for sixth formers, who are able to wear jeans provided they look 'appropriate'. For the rest of the school the uniform is modern, smart and smartly worn.

The variety and quality of the food came in for particular praise, with all parents and students seeing this as a vital part of caring properly for busy girls, and we can confirm that the smoked salmon and cream cheese bagels were wonderful.

Pupils and parents: As you would expect in this part of London, parents are hardworking, professional, mostly affluent, and ambitious for their daughters. Considerable cultural diversity, with numbers of students speaking more than one language, but inevitably less social mix than there used to be before the abolition of assisted places. Girls are confident, articulate, cheerful, and full of self-belief without being arrogant.

Entrance: Competitive, and becoming more so each year. At 11+, 820 applicants for 110 places, but school aims to keep the admissions process as fair as possible. School is part of the North London Consortium so uses their English and maths papers for the entrance tests, and every applicant is given two interviews. School looks for 'curiosity and a willingness to think for yourself: girls who are going to enjoy the learning experience here.' Emphasis also placed on primary school report. No guarantee of sibling places – girls have to be able to cope with the pace of lessons here – but, says head, 'I will always look very carefully at siblings, and for occasional places siblings are given priority.' About 25 per cent of girls come from the state sector.

At 16+ around 12-15 places available, all of them keenly competed for.

Exit: A small number – around 10 per cent – leave after GCSE to board, or to co-ed sixth forms at schools such as Westminster. At 18, almost everyone to university: 12 to Oxbridge in 2015, 12 to the USA/Canada, and pretty much all the rest to Russell Group institutions, including Imperial College.

Money matters: Music scholarships available at 11+ and 16+, art scholarships at 16+ only, worth anything up to 50 per cent of the fees. Around 10 per cent of girls on means-tested bursaries. Owing to its history as a state grammar, the school has no endowment, and the bursary fund exists solely through fundraising.

Remarks: To have your daughter offered a place here is a real gift. As one parent expressed it, 'I am a huge fan of Godolphin & Latymer. I have two daughters there, both very different girls, and both have really thrived.'

The Hampshire School, Chelsea

15 Manresa Road, London SW3 6NB

Independent • Pupils: 255 • Ages: 3–13 • Fees: up to £16,440 pa

Tel: 020 7352 7077

Email: info@ghs.gemsedu.co.uk
Website: www.ths.westminster.sch.uk

32

Headmaster: Since January 2014, Donal Brennan BEd (50s). Soft-spoken, bearded, kindly. A Kerry man, one of seven, who went to a tiny village school with two teachers and no electricity or running water: 'It was a fantastic place – education was everything there.' Always wanted to be a teacher. Read education, theology and art at Trinity College Dublin, then trained at the Froebel College as a primary school teacher. Taught at Hill House International for 25 years, where he ended up as under master, but wanted to head up his own school and was attracted by The Hampshire School's small class sizes and caring ethos. Not afraid to give parents his mobile number, and greets all the children personally every day – 'We celebrate the achievement of getting to school, and how you welcome children is hugely important.' Popular with parents:

'Approachable and genuinely caring,' was a typical comment.

Still teaches – his study doubles as a year 6 tutorial room – and a passionate believer in learning by doing: 'Climb the tree; afterwards you can write about it.' A music lover, for whom singing is an essential part of life; also still does the occasional Irish dance in his spare time. Firmly committed to the school's inclusive intake: 'Mixed ability is a reflection of real life. I don't believe it's healthy at a young age to be in a community that's already selective.'

Married to Rosie, a former science teacher, with two young sons.

Entrance: Entry points at age 3 into the nursery, age 5 into year 1 and age 8 into year 4 – informal interview and assessment, designed to put children and their families at ease. Small entry point into year 7, 'but we're quite selective at that age, because of needing to guide them to the right schools.' Occasional places in other year groups do sometimes come up – always worth enquiring.

Exit: To a wide range of destinations, mostly London day schools. Girls move on to places such as Francis Holland, More House, Queen's Gate, Emanuel, Latymer Upper, with occasional St Paul's Girls' and CLSG successes. Most leave at 11, but no pressure to do so, and some opt to stay on until 13 because they like it here. (The school has forged sporting links to other schools with 'small clusters of girls' at this age, which we thought eminently sensible.) Boys leave mostly at 13, to the likes of Latymer Upper, City of London, Emanuel, Dulwich, sometimes St Paul's and Westminster. Head is proud of the school's track record: 'No child here leaves without the school that's right for them.'

Remarks: Founded in Surrey as a dance school in 1928 by June Hampshire, mother of actress Susan, and originally known as Hampshire School. On moving to London in the 1930s the school became mainstream and for many years was seen as a very traditional prep. Since becoming part of the GEMS group in 2007, however, it has modernised considerably and now has a reputation for delivering sound up-to-date academics in an atmosphere of kindness and friendliness. Years 1 to 8 are accommodated in the main premises on Manresa Road, a wonderfully spacious Grade II listed building; it used to be the Chelsea library and still has the same air of calm tranquility.

Sheltering beneath the architectural grandeur is some pretty impressive modern technology: a

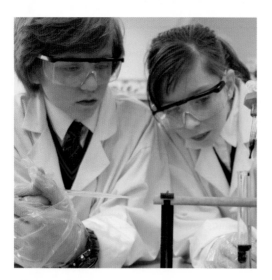

Extracurricular provision includes judo, table tennis, fencing, archery, football, rugby, cooking, chess, cards, computing, debating, art ...

splendid science laboratory, one of the best we've seen in a central London prep; height-adjustable interactive whiteboards; individual computer desks in the classrooms; and an excellent ICT suite where we saw children hard at work designing a restaurant. None of this has come at the expense of tradition, however, and bookworms would adore the fabulous school library: cavernous, marble-columned, galleried, and home to thousands of books. We thought it looked a tad underused, but the forthcoming appointment of a librarian is set to change that, whereat this will surely become one of the great strengths of the school's provision.

The school hall was in the news recently when a piece of the ceiling fell down, but school is anxious to point out that it was a very small piece; all has now been repaired, and it remains a great space for PE, concerts, plays, assemblies and dance – the Chelsea Ballet School visits every week. Lovely spacious classrooms, and a well-sized and equipped garden for the children to let off steam. Team games such as rugby are played off-site in Battersea Park, and the children go swimming at Chelsea and Fulham swimming baths. Lifts throughout the building mean that children with physical disabilities can be accommodated.

Broad extracurricular provision includes judo, table tennis, fencing, archery, football, rugby, cooking, chess, cards, computing, debating, art, drumming, ukulele – 'We're constantly seeking to add to our clubs,' affirmed head, adding that they hope to lay on activities at weekends in future. Music provision is good and there are plans to get it better. Children can learn piano, cello, violin, etc., and take part in choir, and there are regular concerts plus the annual Summer Arts Festival. No orchestra yet, and drama is currently confined to class rather than whole school productions, although the imminent arrival of a second drama teacher will bring more opportunities in this area. Lots of trips, including annual week-long jolly for the older children to places at home and abroad. Parent body is dedicated and 'very pro-active, very influential in supporting the family feeling of the school,' according to staff. Recent events organised by the PA include a Fathers' Day breakfast and a United Nations day where parents drew on their own variety of backgrounds to run stalls showcasing food from countries around the world.

We liked the pupil work that we saw on display, particularly the French, and this struck us as a school where children are free to flourish at their own pace. Teacher pupil ratio is 1:9, ensuring all students get the attention they need, and there's particularly strong SEN provision, both for those with diagnosed difficulties such as dyslexia and those assessed as gifted and talented. Full time SENCo is called head of enrichment, and is integral to the school. Speech and language therapist comes to the school to help on site. EFL is well catered for in-house: much demand for this, since this is a school with an international intake, reflecting the locality. Both parents and children very contented with their choice: 'The school gives an excellent balance between holding the kids accountable for high academic standards and a well rounded extra-curricular activity programme,' was one parent's verdict, and a pupil told us, 'I like everything I do here!'

Early years are housed a few streets away in Wetherby Place, in premises which felt rather small when contrasted with the main school. However, there's been a lot of refurbishment, and it's clearly becoming known as a smart choice for local parents: there is a waiting list for reception places, and the school recently opened a third class to accommodate the increasing numbers. Teaching rooms are bright and airy, and classes are small: 13 max for nursery, 14 max for reception. We saw child-friendly, child-centred learning and positive reinforcement everywhere, and the standard of work on the walls was high. The little ones go over to the main school for lessons such as art and PE and to use the library and play areas, thus ensuring that they remain part of the wider school, and a shuttle bus means that parents can drop their children off to either site.

In both locations, we were impressed by the peaceful, happy atmosphere. The bottle green and grey uniform is smartly worn, and children move about with a sense of calm purpose. Kindness really does seem to be the way here, and everyone we spoke to agreed. 'The teachers never, ever shout,' was one comment, 'they're really sensitive to the needs of the children.' As a charming and articulate young leaver put it, 'I've loved this school. I would have stayed here until I was 18 if I could.' 'My daughter's been made really welcome here, and we couldn't be happier,' confirmed a father.

Perhaps not the go-to choice for those seeking non-stop high-octane buzz from dawn till dusk, but a successful and busy school for all that, offering a supportive and relaxed environment in which children can be themselves and achieve their potential without having to compromise their nicer nature.

Hawkesdown House

27 Edge Street, London W8 7PN

Tel: 020 7727 9090

Independent · Pupils: 145 · Ages: 3–8 · Fees: up to £16,725 pa

Email: admin@hawkesdown.co.uk
Website: www.hawkesdown.co.uk

Head: Since 2010, Mrs Claire Renton-Bourne MA (known to the parents as Mrs Bourne), a Cambridge classicist and Nottingham theologian (50s). She spent three years at Perrott Hill School in Somerset, tutoring scholars and heading the classics and RS departments. This led to her fascination with theology and a Nottingham RE diploma, which she completed whilst deputy head at Knighton House in Dorset in 2001. Head there from 2004, continuing to teach classics. Her two children attended nearby Bryanston; one is now in PR and the other is training as a mechanical engineer. She is married to a civil servant; they have a bolt hole in Dorset to which they escape at weekends and she can enjoy gardening, playing the piano, which she finds relaxing, and attend local church.

A self-possessed, thoughtful, articulate individual, 'More modest than many, quiet, sensible, not brash, calm and steady,' comment current parents. Other comments: 'Amazing Mrs Bourne has the boys' best interests at heart 24/7. Parents are kept in the picture, communication is excellent and her door is open if there is a concern.' When questioned about the future, she replied, 'I love this school and am very happy. The longer I am here the more I can see the importance of my role in supporting the parents. I strongly believe in the importance of single sex education to 13.'

Parents feel she is doing a great job and appreciate her advice and the links she has made with the next schools so that each individual is considered. As one American remarked, 'The head is diplomatic. She explained the English system, the general landscape and was particularly helpful regarding the next school.'

Entrance: There are two main entry points. The first is the nursery (16 places) and the second is reception, which is made up of two classes of 20.There are no open days; instead Mrs Bourne gives individual tours with prospective parents lasting about an hour with a follow-up chat in her office. This is key, as she sees if the aims and ethos of parents are aligned with the school. The boys are asked for an introductory session in the autumn when they are due. This is purely to see if the boy would be happy in the school and whether it would be the best place for him. Mrs Bourne and the head of early years provide a variety of activities for a half hour session in the nursery adjacent to the courtyard, with opportunities for outside play. Those hoping to join in year 1 upwards spend a morning in the relevant class and are assessed in literacy and numeracy before being offered a place. The pupils come from a wide spread of local nurseries. There are no bursaries, scholarships or sibling discounts on offer.

Exit: Most to established London prep schools including: Colet Court, Westminster Under, Sussex House, Wetherby Prep, St Philip's, Latymer Prep. Others choose to board at a range including Caldicott, The Dragon, Summer Fields and Papplewick.

Remarks: The school was founded in 2000 by Mr and Mrs Loveridge and is part of a family group. This includes Devonshire House School and Lyndhurst House, both also in London. It is named after Hawkesdown Hill, in Devon, familiar to the Loveridge family, and where an ancient, gigantic, defence earthwork fortress was built. A colourful painting of Hawkesdown is on view in the entrance hall, a reminder of the qualities the school promotes – tradition, charm, community endeavour – and a source of inspiration.

The school provides a traditional curriculum with emphasis on the basics with literacy and numeracy sessions most mornings. 'This is necessary as the demands of the next selective preps are still very traditional, including English written composition and comprehension at a sophisticated level.' Topics and daily routine are deliberately time-tabled to cater for boys' interests and enjoyment. We saw evidence of solar system models, astronauts, aeroplanes, castles, and, in year 1, an imaginative life cycle display with very neat handwriting and illustrations, under the friendly eye of one of the few male teachers. Undoubtedly, once the wireless network is installed and running, the boys will also be able to enjoy more ICT opportunities across the curriculum than existed at the time of a recent inspection – development of ICT a current focus.

Navy blue and red uniform including blazers and caps is popular, and several parents commented, 'the boys look so cute'

One mother commented that having initially intended sending her son to a co-educational school, she now believes he would have suffered seated next to a girl with beautiful penmanship as boys have a definite rhythm of learning. 'They are,' as another parent acknowledged, 'wriggly'. That is catered for and understood completely by the staff at HH. French is taught from reception. No dedicated science laboratory, art or design technology rooms. The boys are prepared for serious entrance exams and given plenty of practice. 'The boys are not pushed too much

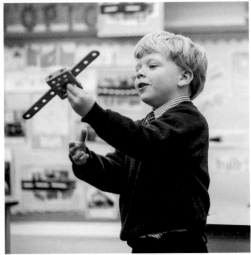

and they have a good balance of work and play.' In year 1, for example, judo is added to the timetable with chess in year 2 and fencing by year 3. Violin, piano and singing lessons are available from year 1, as well as Mandarin, with plenty of after-school clubs.

Parents tell us that pupils with SEN are well catered for because 'the school is small and there is plenty of support'. We saw happy boys with hearing aids and the sparky, young SEN coordinator supports form teachers, ensuring that individual plans are monitored carefully and reviewed. Setting in maths and English is realistic and understood: 'Kids quickly know where they stand'. A speech and language therapist comes in weekly and boys are offered High 5s sessions before beginning lessons as well as booster groups. TAs work with boys who need extra help. This is not the school for someone with disruptive behavioural problems or physical difficulties because of the school's layout, but emerging problems are dealt with in a caring way.

Young teachers and teaching assistants, some from abroad, are lively and enthusiastic and support the boys with different languages, an important feature as this school caters for international families, and there has been a recent focus on EAL. Pupil teacher ratio is approximately 8:1 with average class sizes of 17. Nobody has been on the staff for more than 10 years, but this is hardly surprising as it is a relatively new school.

One drawback, commented on by some parents, is the lack of space for a playgound. During indoor lunch break in their classrooms, the top year boys we saw looked extremely happy in K'nex heaven, constructing imaginative vehicles and missiles with great enthusiasm. Nevertheless, 'by the time the boys are in their final year they are big and notice the lack of space,' remarked one parent. They make use of Holland Park for PE in good weather, with football once a week, team games and formal matches arranged, and run around in Kensington Gardens enjoying plenty of controlled rough and tumble. Still, some boys, especially the older sporty ones, might find this frustrating. Judo is extremely popular, as are football, cricket and PE (no swimming). All boys play in fixtures against other schools at some point.

The house system with its homage to royalty, Plantagenet, Windsor and Tudor, has been revitalised to excellent effect. Parents are encouraged to be involved and are welcomed, once a fortnight, to attend Friday assemblies in the packed main hall. Boys are awarded pen licences, house points and many awards for tying of shoe laces and ties, good manners at lunch time and community spirit among others. The skills encouraged are spot on for this age and there's always a loud cheer for the winning house. The boys are taught to be courteous and polite and they respect the staff who know them so well. The positions of house captain, vice captain

and prefects merit special house ties, rather than the normal school tartan ties (which do look a little odd against the blue and white check shirts). The navy blue and red uniform including blazers and caps is popular, and several parents commented, 'the boys look so cute'.

An important duty for the house prefects is to ring the large bell outside the dining hall for lunch, serve food and clear up. One parent remarked just how great it was that the boys sat in houses for lunch. 'The younger ones look up to the older boys. My son told me he had learnt all about Lord of the Rings from another boy at lunch.' This social mixing may account for the ease with which the boys spoke during our visit. One recent newcomer was highly appreciative of the way he had been made to feel welcome and, a sensitive soul, had clearly benefited from another boy's support. Lunch is extremely popular, even more so since the arrival of a new chef who has a great following. Special themed meals, such as for Wimbledon (with strawberries and cream) and Independence Day, are a real hit with even the fussiest boys.

A thorough mix of English and international families with a number of bilingual pupils. Most parents live within walking distance of the school and many work in the financial sector. HH is reassuring to the many new to the English examination system; right from the start, it provides advice, support and the necessary preparation to give parents and pupils a very happy start in a caring, environment without undue pressure.

Hill House International School

17 Hans Place, London SW1X 0EP

Tel: 020 7584 1331

Independent • Pupils: 930 • Ages: 4–13 • Fees: up to £14,100 pa

Email: info@hillhouseschool.co.uk
Website: www.hillhouseschool.co.uk

Principal: Since October 2015, and for a two year tenure, Nicholas Allen, most recently head of Newton Prep and before that Arnold House. Edmund Townend, briefly principal, and the second son of previous principals Richard and Janet Townend, returns to deputy head, believing 'that it will be in the best interests of the school to have the benefit of more experienced leadership, in times when all schools are subject to increasing scrutiny and regulation' – no doubt referring to damning Ofsted report (see below). The Townends will undoubtedly stay in close contact. Each part of the school has its own head, known as heads of house..

Like Prince Charles, an old boy of the school, who is still waiting, Richard Townend had a long wait before getting his hands on the job that was always going to be his. The school was founded by his late father, the legendary Lt Col H Stuart Townend, whose image, influence and inspiration persist. The Colonel, as he was known to everyone, was 93 when he died in 2002 and ran the school as a tight ship right to the end. We got the impression that Richard's heart was really in his music – wonderful instruments all over the place, a harpsichord and clavichord in his flat, a splendid 456 pipe wooden organ in the main school and fabulous pianos and harps scattered throughout. 'I couldn't get up in the morning if I didn't play each day,' he said.

The Townends have always regarded their job as being to inspire the children – Richard's disdainful intolerance of petty inspectors who worry more about the site of sick bays and the use of Tippex in the register than the teaching and the evident happiness of the children was unashamed. However, this supercilious attitude bit the school on the head with publication of a highly damning Ofsted report in early 2015 (which the school is challenging). The school was found to be 'inadequate' in all five categories, including the quality of the teaching, the progress and achievement of the pupils and their safety.

Entrance: First come, first served at 4, but the school, famously, will fit people in if they possibly can and if they like them. At 6 a test in maths and English. Prospective parents are invited to turn up for a tour of the school on any morning without appointments. A pool of children are regularly on hand to show visitors round. When we visited, the front hall was filled with eager children waiting to escort equally eager, though slightly overwhelmed, prospective parents. Places occur at all stages. This is an international school – a lot of movement.

Exit: A wide and diverse spread – school has no truck with parents who don't carefully assess the right school for the child and will not spare them forceful advice. Most to leading London day schools, including Westminster, St. Paul's, Dulwich, City of London and King's College Wimbledon for boys and St. Paul's Girls', JAGS, Godolphin and Latymer, the two Francis Hollands, Queen's Gate and Queen's College for the girls.

A quarter of the boys and a few girls to boarding. No special boarding favourites, but spread of top schools which includes Eton, Harrow, Charterhouse, Winchester and Worth. Most pupils get their first choice of school and always a cluster of scholarships each year. No preparation for any boys to leave at 7 or 8 – this is not expected or supported.

Remarks: A tour of Hill House is unlike a tour of almost any other school and you get a real sense of what the hordes of children do each day. Rather like a line from Annie, little children everywhere, scampering around the rabbit warren of buildings. Each of the five sites is cramped and used to the max. The famously conspicuous brown knickerbockers and mustard cable knit woollies were designed as a uniform so the children didn't need to change for sport – no room for that kind of luxury. On our visit we spent much of the morning stomping around Chelsea and jumping on and off a Hill House minibus (the school owns a fleet). The two girls who showed us round were whipped off mid tour to rehearse their end of term play. Richard Townend scooped us up and we then interrupted a class music lesson in the organ room, while he gave an impromptu in-depth tour of each organ pipe.

This is a huge school – just shy of 1,000 children, spread over several sites in London, all of which are small town houses and short on space: no wonder little children marching in crocodile in their brown and mustard uniform through the streets of Chelsea are as much a part of the scenery of this chic and expensive area as the Venus statue in Sloane Square. They spread into the space that's available.

As soon as you enter the main hall at the senior school in Hans Place you are transported to a 19th century boarding prep school. A smell of faded grandeur – oak panels, Latin mottos, a plethora of gold leaf memorial boards, listing among other things past head choristers, various awards and scholarships, as well as contributors to the life of the school. A sweeping staircase, piles of silverware and even an Olympic flag (the Colonel was also an outstanding athlete who competed in the 1930 Empire – now Commonwealth – Games and was in charge of housing for the 1948 London Olympics).

Hill House was founded by the Colonel in 1951 and his aim from the first was to create a genuinely international school which nurtured each individual child's talents. Glion House in Switzerland, the Hill House chalet, used to be a major feature of the education here and though less so now, it is still used for anything ranging from geography field trips, ski and hiking trips to trumpet tours. The signature oak panels in all the London sites are intended as a reflection of their Swiss residence. Photos plastered all over the walls – lots of smiling children as well as fabulous Swiss landscapes, some dating from the 1970s, vaguely reminiscent of a teenage bedroom.

> *Glion House in Switzerland, the Hill House chalet, used to be a major feature of the education here and though less so now, it is still used*

The classes are unusually small, averaging 12 – just as well, as most rooms are too small for many more. At the top end of the school they get results – several scholarships, eg the King's scholarship to Eton and the top scholarship to Wellington, and almost all getting into their first choice school, partly, no doubt, as a result of school's shrewd guidance as to which school is right for the child. Boys and girls taught separately from year 5 (though they continue to do music and sport together); Latin from years 6 to 8. French from the beginning – teachers are all French ('Preferably not Parisian – they have the wrong attitude,' commented Richard Townend). Girls can do Mandarin in year 6. Lots of antipodean teachers – 'they are so good,' remarked Richard Townend, though not all parents agree.

Small classes also allow for individual help when needed (we are assured) and specialist SEN support in years 3-8. Several parents enthused about the proactivity of the school when it comes to spotting a problem and providing support from early on. 'The individual attention that having small class sizes allows makes this possible.' Nothing more than mild dyslexia catered for here, however: you would be advised to look elsewhere if this is going to be a problem. Rave reports from some parents, on the other hand, about how the gifted and talented fare here. 'My child has been set alight – his previous school just didn't recognise his talents,' commented one parent. The school motto is: 'A child is not a vessel to be filled but a fire to be kindled'.

This ethos permeates the music, a central feature of the curriculum, as you would expect from Richard Townend's influence. No grades allowed – 'that's just for the mothers to boast about with each other in the playground' – instead the school owns more than 300 instruments, from tubas to harps, on loan for individual use: 'If a parent knew what a bassoon costs, they might not let their child play it.' Thirty-two choral scholarships available to existing school choristers which enable them to attend residential music courses, often abroad. Parents enthuse about the whole school assemblies, which burst with music, that take place on Wednesday mornings in St Columba's, the Scottish Church in Pont Street – the only place suitable and big enough to fit the whole school.

Proper freshly cooked food at each site served in a civilised way, all children eating at long tables which magically appear at lunch time in some of the more cramped premises. No catering companies and no contract cleaners – staff, from the brilliant head of music to the chefs (winners of the Tatler award for best school food in 2011), recruited by keeping ears to the ground and poaching the good ones. 1950s style menus – no choice or puddings, but well prepared, and very fresh produce bought from New Covent Garden Market each day.

Lots of exercise had by all – an hour of sport each day; Duke of York Square is their local playing field and where Field Day happens at the end of each summer term, when the four houses compete vigorously. Hyde and Battersea Parks are also used,

Lots of exercise had by all – an hour of sport each day; Duke of York Square is their local playing field and where Field Day happens at the end of each summer term

as well as various local pools, halls and gyms, providing for a good range of physical activity – 24 sports, we're told.

The art teacher is a current parent and canny about entering the children into various art competitions – outside as well as within school. Lots of prizes are won and during our tour we were asked to choose our favourite painting of a flower from a wall where about 40 different flowers were displayed – not an easy task. Finally plumping for one, we were told, 'That child will win the prize this week'.

When we visited, the school had recently achieved an extraordinary coup in securing the purchase of the former Welsh Church in Radnor Walk. One of the advantages of not having governors nor any red tape – they could pounce quickly. These graceful premises, known as Founders Hall, are now used as a theatre, gym, art gallery and ICT centre. Music performances are held here and some teaching too. A beautiful lofty space and to Richard Townend's delight, it also came with the church organ thrown in.

Parents at Hill House come from all over the world and all walks of life – a few Chelsea football stars send their children, as well as a large number of embassy families. Many more first time buyers than a lot of London preps, primarily because the fees are relatively low (an advantage of having such a large school). Alumni equally diverse, from Prince Charles to Lily Allen. If a family needs help with fees, arrangements can be made but, as with so much here, no formal structures in place. Once you sign up, the deal is that you leave the education and the running of the school entirely to the school. No PTA (Richard Townend was as scornful of the motives for joining one of these as he was about the motives for doing music grades). Quite the contrary – parents are positively discouraged from becoming involved with the everyday life of the school, 'which I find a huge relief,' said one working mum.

The Ofsted report might easily have left chaos in its wake – with the wholesale departure of parents and/or staff. However, the remarkable result has instead been overwhelming support for the school. Immediately after the report a petition was circulated asserting: 'As a parent, guardian or carer of a child currently attending Hill House

International School, I strongly believe the school to be a good one, and that it has been badly misrepresented by the most recent Ofsted report.'

At the time of writing the petition has gathered over 800 signatures. We were inundated with parents keen to talk to us about how highly they rated their school. There has hardly been any staff turnover (apart from the retirements and maternity leave that you would expect) and only a tiny number of families have voted with their feet and decided to send their children elsewhere. The focus of supporters was on the individual attention given to the children – made possible partly by the small class sizes, the joy their children experience in school, increase in confidence experienced by the shy, the stimulation and enthusiasm experienced by the more outgoing.

The school was quick to react to Ofsted and employed a high profile company, Capita, to address the health and safety issues ('many of which', says Mr Edmund, 'were already in place'). The changes in management structure are partly a result of Ofsted but were due to happen anyway, and similarly they had already started to look at the curriculum. The criticism of teaching was 'what hurt most,' says Mr Edmund, who values the dedication and commitment of his teachers; on the comments made by Ofsted that several teachers had answered questionnaires to the effect that they received little support from the management in terms of their professional development, Mr Edmund says this is another facet they are 'actively addressing'. He made it clear to us that they are taking the report seriously and are not just saying 'it's all bunkum', but at the same time they are not prepared to change the ethos of the school.

For all the apparent chaos, it is clear that a huge amount of work is put into the children by a dedicated and loyal team of teachers, games staff, music teachers (all real musicians, pointed out Richard Townend, many of whom are old friends of his), caterers and cleaners, all of whom embrace the eccentric ethos of this family run school. It is a long day so everything can be packed in. The oldest boys stay until 6pm Monday to Thursday and 1pm on a Friday (a range of after-school activities are offered on Friday afternoons).

An overwhelming buzz of creativity and energy here, but if you are looking for calm, controlled order, with 'yes sir, no sir' boys and girls, this is definitely not the place for you.

Holland Park School

Airlie Gardens, Campden Hill Road, London W8 7AF

Tel: 020 7908 1000

State • Pupils: 1,335 • Ages: 11–18 • Sixth form pupils: 150

Email: admissions@hollandparkschool.co.uk
Website: www.hollandparkschool.co.uk

Head: Since 2001, Mr Colin Hall BA PGCE (mid 50s). Born and brought up in Durham, he was educated at Durham Wearside grammar school. He graduated with a history degree from Sheffield and went on to to do a PCGE at Cambridge. His career has been meteoric. Each employer recognised his hunger and determination, as well as fierce loyalty (a number of references are reproduced in the staff planner for the benefit of his aspiring teachers). He arrived here from Longford Community School

in Hounslow, his first headship; prior to that he had senior positions at Cheney School in Oxford and King Edward VI Morpeth in Northumberland. He still manages to find the time to teach English, which is the subject he has chosen to teach since his first job at Thurston Community School (now College) in Suffolk (his greatest joy, he says is reading and he read Sons and Lovers when he was 10). There is a more than a touch of Napoleon about him. A dynamo of man, we have rarely met someone who combines a seemingly unlimited supply of tenacity, fastidious attention to detail, boundless energy, aspiration for both pupils and staff alike and a total and passionate commitment to his vocation.

We were invited (unusually) to attend a staff meeting in the morning. Teachers here are (mostly) younger than 35 and Mr Hall invests as much nurturing and guidance in them as he does the pupils. Marking is assiduously scrutinised, lessons observed, goals and targets set. A canny head, he is also excellent at working the money and the room. The great and the good make up the body known as 'the friends of Holland Park'. Prizes such as the 'pupil premium award' are swept up, Alan Bennett attends whole school events, HRH the Duchess of Kent (known here as Katharine Kent) has her own set of keys to the building.

Deeply aspirational; 'no child is outside of our grasp,' he insists, 'no child is without ambition'. It does not surprise us at all that Michael Gove, the former education secretary, asked to come and 'observe Colin Hall' (although Mr Hall, with a disarming humility, says it did surprise him). Nor does it surprise us that when you Google him, Colin Hall appears among an elite band of 'super heads'. What is more surprising is that despite his Napoleonic appearance, parents describe him as having a big heart, a sensitive and empathetic approach. He also has a reliance on and affection for his trusted loyal advisers, the senior leadership team, but most notably his right hand man, David Chappell, associate head ('everyone is some sort of head,' remarked one parent. There are five deputy heads and five assistant head teachers as well as an associate head).

'They lit a spark in my son,' remarked one parent, 'with a combination of inspirational teaching and incentivising notes of encouragement from the head'

Academic matters: This is, unquestionably, a good fit for a bright, motivated pupil who has a particular flair for the humanities and English. A rigorous banding is applied across all subjects from the start. Band 1 pupils are considered by staff at pupils to be the crème de la crème. These are the ones taken on day trips to universities, for example and are the participants at the glamorous 'Perfect Tense' event in the summer term when star pupils, selected by staff for 'outstanding achievement', are celebrated at a black tie awards ceremony in Holland Park – attended by the 'friends' of the school as well as by parents and staff. One pupil we spoke to remarked that 'even those in the top of Band 2 rarely get to go to Perfect Tense.' While this isn't necessarily true, school admits to the disparity in numbers – approximately 65 per cent of band 1 pupils compared with five per cent of band 4 pupils are likely to be celebrated at Perfect Tense. Pupils (and parents) are keen to move up a band if they can swing it.

All this contributes to personal drive and aspiration and the results speak for themselves. In 2015, 74 per cent of pupils got 5+ A*-C at GCSE including English and maths and 43 per cent of GCSE grades were A*/A. A huge improvement on 12 years ago when the pass rate for GCSEs was 45 per cent. At A level in 2015, 72 per cent A*/A, 25 per cent A*/A. Not a wide range of A levels offered, but all 'proper subjects'. English and biology currently most popular at A levels. Fewer than 10 take Spanish and/or French. A tiny few do design or music.

Teachers here are thoroughly committed. They have to be or they wouldn't last. Parents talk of a high turnover of staff, particularly in the maths department, but Mr Hall holds on fast when he strikes gold, with a talented teacher. Lots of opportunity for career development and promotion. English, humanities and art are all strong here and the staff, in those subjects, long serving. Class rooms could be mistaken for museums – ordered, uncluttered, tastefully decorated and minimal. Mr Hall's attention to detail spares no corner. Lesson plans are scrutinised, progress reports monitored and the delivery of lessons constantly observed and remarked upon. We were given copies of the lesson plans of every lesson we saw, as well as examples of marking. All extremely thorough and impressive. The lower bands have the advantage of the some of the best teaching. No one is allowed to coast here. Parents particularly enthusiastic about geography, history and English teaching. 'They lit a spark in my son,' remarked one parent, 'with a combination of inspirational teaching and incentivising notes of encouragement from the head'. However, another parent deplored a 'boot camp approach' – evidenced by an inflexibility and greater concern for the results and statistics than what might be best for the individual.

Fresh flowers, designer furniture (Ercol tables and chairs even in the classrooms as well as the front hall and communal areas), no mess, no clutter

A measure of staff commitment is the practice of opening the school on Saturday mornings as well as for one week during the holidays – for what are called 'interventions'. About 200 children will come in on a Saturday to benefit from extra support and teaching. There may well be sports fixtures and practices on Saturdays too. As many as 600 students have lessons over the the Easter Holidays. Teachers aren't paid extra for this. Their professionalism demands it of them. Parents are impressed by the thoroughness with which progress is tracked. 'If my son gets a lower result than expected, the teacher will ring me to discuss why this might have happened.'

Many pupils take GCSEs early (a practice that is unlikely to be able to continue under the present regime). By year 10 some have already taken four or five subjects including French, Latin, English literature, history and RS. A few parents regret this suggesting, that their children weren't allowed enough time to enjoy the subject and study in depth, cramming in a short time instead. Others feel disappointed that their child might have been able to achieve an A* in a subject if they had taken it at the normal time. Pupils we spoke to bemoaned 'the exam culture', the constant pressure and the stress this can cause.

Not the school for a child with special educational needs, whether mild or severe, and by Mr Hall's own admission 'you have to be very sure you can meet them.' The school does have lifts, so can accommodate physical disabilities, and perhaps even a case of mild autism. There are a number of students here with 'emotional and behavioural difficulties', we were told. Full time SENco but one parent remarked on the high turnover of people in this role. In class support provided wherever possible; occasionally a student may be withdrawn from class to be given extra support.

Games, options, the arts: Excellent sporting facilities – lots of outside space, Astro and tarmac for netball, tennis, football and cricket on the doorstep, as well as a spanking, shiny, well-equipped gym with basketball courts etc in the basement, not to mention the 25m competition swimming pool. One of our year 11 guides enthused about netball. Girls in the team are keen and committed and will turn up for practice at 6.30am on a freezing winter's morning. There are house matches every term and a house sports week. As well as rugby, football, cricket and netball, plenty of minor sports also offered, including lacrosse, badminton, table tennis, athletics and rowing, and there are netball and football tours as well as a ski trip.

However, parents agree that the uptake and quality of boys' sport is patchy. Football is popular and the school competes impressively against the local competition which includes Cardinal Vaughan, Burlington Danes, Chelsea Academy and Latymer Upper. Matches and practice sessions are timetabled on Saturdays. Rugby and cricket, on the other hand, have some way to go. Although two hours a week is allocated, most do little above and beyond this; 'My son is getting overweight and has no way of letting off steam,' complained one parent. Perhaps the work pressure is such that students are afraid of committing too much time to doing anything outside the classroom? Either that or, as one parent put it, 'the boys aren't being enticed to do more sport'. However, the school will support pupils' enterprising initiatives – setting up an American football club, for example. A cricket tour to Ampleforth College in Yorkshire caused a great

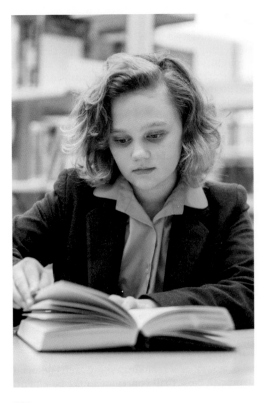

flurry of excitement, but 'the standard is low and enthusiasm quick to wane,' observed one parent.

The major drama production of the year is performed not by pupils, but by staff. The leadership team puts on an annual Shakespeare play each Lent term, well attended by the whole school community; it is clearly a strong bonding experience. Photographs of performances adorn the walls, and particularly amusing characters (who can't act for bacon, confesses one of the leadership team wryly) are discussed for months afterwards. With the exception of an annual 'drama evening' in March where a wide range of age groups perform a selection of pieces – perhaps from the A level or GCSE syllabus – it would seem that there is little drama for the students, apart from what takes place in the classroom during a drama lesson, or when studying a play during English. Apart from the school hall, used primarily for assembly, there is nowhere to put on productions on site, and no mention of any attempt to borrow or lease any local theatres.

A small but impressive choir is growing in quality and stature, and is led by one of the talented deputy heads. We were impressed when we saw a number of double basses and guitars in a music practice room, owned by the school but available for pupils' use. Some pupils receive financial support from the school to play their chosen instrument. Lots of prizes for music. There is clearly very positive encouragement coming from the top (and it helps that Katharine Kent is a strong supporter of the arts, especially music). An orchestra gets cobbled together from pupils who play an instrument 'outside school', but there is little continuity. When we asked one pupil why there are not more musical groups, she replied tartly, 'probably because they can't make us do an exam in it.' School is part of the tri-borough music service (which includes Westminster, Kensington and Hammersmith); however, one parent talked of the music as taking place 'in fits and starts'. Peripatetic music teachers are not accommodated as there is huge resistance to any pupil missing an academic lesson to fit in an instrumental lesson.

One of the assistant head teachers runs the dance department, which is burgeoning. Two dance studios in the school, and several teachers; dance is a popular mainstream subject as well as after school activity. We saw boys and girls, gawky and graceful, making shapes and loving it. When asked about drama productions, most parents we spoke to talked of dance performances.

The art department is exceptional – and pupils heavily rewarded with prizes and praise for creativity. Mr Chappell, the exceptional associate head, is currently steering a very talented group of students from year 10 through to the sixth form through A level art in the bohemian environment of Thorpe Lodge. A run-down and enchanting building, once inhabited by the governor of the Bank of England and with its own magical gardens, Thorpe Lodge is situated within the school gates and a stone's throw from the main building. Here, the art students are given free rein to express themselves, and so they do. Huge self-portraits in oil, spectacular installations and a plethora of other work was currently in progress when we visited. DT is well equipped with several laser printers as well as 3 D printer. With the art scholarship students and a passionate teaching team, the school well deserves its reputation as an excellent choice for those with a creative bent.

Background and atmosphere: What you see now when you enter the shimmering glass building, replete with tasteful furniture, aesthetically pleasing fixtures and fittings, not to mention the delicate fragrance of Jo Malone candles, bears almost no resemblance to the 60s monolith that was Holland Park Comprehensive several years ago. Mr Hall and his leadership team (referred to by one parent, wryly, as the 'men in black': though there are two women on the team, the preponderence of young white men – who when we visited were wearing black gowns – give some weight to the analogy) have wrought a remarkable change. It neither looks, nor, more importantly, smells like a school. Fresh flowers, designer furniture (Ercol tables and chairs even in the classrooms as well as the front hall and communal areas), no mess, no clutter, and above all no damage. Everything is immaculate. The staff room is tastefully adorned with simple two seater pale blue sofas and blue Smeg fridges, banks of daffodils decorated the assembly hall on our visit, thoughtfully framed posters, paintings, poems and catechisms adorn the freshly painted walls.

The building itself is all glass and (sun) shine. Every one of the 1,335 pupils is housed here. With the exception of A level art in Thorpe Lodge, all lessons and activities take place in this one building. Everything is open plan, from the library to the unisex WCs. It's not possible either to smoke in the lavatories, or curl up in a discreet corner with a book – the building is easy to police and its corridors regularly patrolled. There is nowhere to hide. We were standing on the 'bridge' during break and it was like observing an installation – a river of smartly dressed, well-behaved young men and women moving seamlessly and smoothly up and down stairs and along the wide spacious passageways.

Pastoral care and discipline: Hall and his henchman is a phrase that slips easily off the tongue – even if it is said with some irony. There is little scope for miscreants. The leadership team members are ever present and enforce good behaviour – from attire to skullduggery. The open design of the building ensures that no misdemeanour goes unnoticed. If you're sent out of the classroom for poor behaviour – it's like being sent into a gold-fish bowl. Uniform, attendance and behaviour all strictly observed. How else would the delicate Ercol chairs and tables that adorn all the classrooms contain not one scratch or speck of flicked ink or graffiti? These young adults are taught to take care of their surroundings, of themselves and of others.

In conversation, Mr Hall defies this appearance of zero tolerance. 'The development of individual relationships is so much more important than casting things in black and white,' he insists. He proudly states that no-one has been permanently excluded for five years, while accepting that sometimes the last resort is the only option. Parents are involved as soon as their child is excluded from lessons. Punishments include doing serious work over a period of two to three days – no break or lunch with friends. Restorative justice is a firmly held belief here – and constructive discipline.

Located in one of the most fashionable and expensive corners of London, its demographic is very different from many schools of its kind across the capital. But only because standards are high

Students are rigorously monitored. If they are disorganised, late or disruptive, are they getting enough support from home? Tutor system is key in pastoral care structure. If there is a lack of motivation in the class room, are individual teachers doing enough to support and guide – are work books being marked quickly enough, for example?

Pupils and parents: The school has had a glamorous history since its founding in 1958. It was the school of choice for the liberal left in the sixties (Tony Benn and Roy Jenkins both chose to move their sons from Westminster and Winchester respectively to Holland Park), and with Angelica Huston among the alumni, the school had a decidedly cool reputation. Colin Hall has restored much of this glamour during his 15 (plus) years. Although one parent referred to a 'champagne socialist' element among the parent body, it's no longer the choice of just the trendy left. A number of high profile members of right wing political parties are attracted to the school's rigour and aspirational ethos, but the creative, media element is still strong.

Located in one of the most fashionable and expensive corners of London, its demographic is very different from many schools of its kind across the capital. But only because standards are high. Parents who once might have saved and scrimped to go private are celebrating the fact that their children can be educated to such a high standard, funded by their taxes alone. You will still find here the odd Etonian or Wykehamist who has chosen to return to London in the sixth form. The catchment is narrow (currently a half mile radius) but it's not impossible to get a place if you live further afield if you can get in on the art scholarship ticket. Pupils here are smart, focused and polite. Ofsted rated behaviour outstanding and we agree. They know how much devotion comes from the top down into their education and they respond to it.

Entrance: The catchment area is getting smaller by the year. Now you have to live within about half a mile of the school to have a chance of getting in. About 1,600 applicants for 240 places. Can be as many as 50 appeals, with only a tiny few successful ones. Banding tests take place in the autumn of year 6. Siblings get priority; 24 places (10 per cent) are reserved for the specialist 'art aptitude test', with distance no object – 'you could live in Glasgow and get a place'. Normally about 380 apply for these 24 places. Applicants aren't interviewed, nor do they need to provide a portfolio, just two drawings under exam conditions. There's an art aptitude waiting list as well as a main waiting list – possible to sit on both. Large numbers from local primaries but particularly Fox up the road. Growing numbers from the independent junior schools.

Entrance into the sixth form is tough. 'This is a very academic sixth form' we were told – the high standard of the sixth form regarded as a role model to fuel the aspirations of students lower down the school. At least seven GCSEs graded A* to B including English and maths. Minimum of an A in the subject you want to study. Priority will be given to pupils from Holland Park, otherwise proximity to school will be the decider between two equally competing candidates.

Exit: After GCSE very few NEETs – almost all who leave join colleges, apprenticeships or other sixth forms. One or two to the independent sector but mostly to Holland Park sixth form (about 50) or to other state sixth forms (about 56) After A levels, 87 per cent to university. Around two-thirds to Russell Group Universities, including a few to Oxbridge (three in 2015). Quite a high number choose to take a gap year. Most popular are the London University colleges – particularly UCL and King's. Students choose to read a variety of courses from veterinary medicine, medicine, engineering and law, to English, classics, architecture and theology. A few go off to art college.

Money matters: Now an academy, but retaining its very close links with the Royal Borough of Kensington and Chelsea, it remains the area's flagship comprehensive school. Always well funded by the Royal Borough, this is now matched by funding from the Education Funding Agency. It has all the appearance of an exceptionally well-funded school, so we suspect Mr Hall is very clever at tapping any available and potential resources.

Remarks: Ofsted rates the school outstanding under every category – indeed 'beyond outstanding' in several, and the inspectors are superlative in their praise for the school. It would take a harsh critic to disagree. This is a sparkling environment and your child will emerge polished and bright if s/he is academically ambitious, prepared to toe the line and thrives under pressure. Comprehensive it may be, but it won't suit every child.

John Betts Primary School

Paddenswick Road, London W6 0UA

State • Pupils: 240 • Ages: Ages 4–11

Tel: 020 8748 2465

Email: admin@johnbetts.lbhf.sch.uk
Website: www.johnbetts.lbhf.sch.uk

5

Headteacher: Since April 2015, Miss Jessica Mair BA QTS NPQH, previously deputy and acting head at Queen's Manor Primary School, where she was also in charge of the special needs unit. Educated at Roehampton University and the Institute of Education. Has also taught at Sir John Cass Foundation School and at Ashburnham Community School, with responsibility for G&T and PE, and was deputy head at St Andrew's Scots School in Buenos Aires. Likes skiing, cooking and tennis.

Entrance: Over-subscribed. Priority given to children in care, those with statements of special educational needs, siblings and proximity to school (cut-off point is about a third of a mile from school as the crow flies). Occasional places become available further up school but are quickly filled. Waiting list in operation. Some 15 per cent speak English as an additional language.

Exit: Approximately half to independent schools. Popular private schools include Latymer Upper, St Paul's Girls', Godolphin & Latymer, Notting Hill and Ealing and Emanuel. State favourites are West London Free School and Holland Park.

Remarks: Housed in a dark, Victorian, listed building in Hammersmith: forbidding from exterior but classrooms are surprisingly light and welcoming. Stunning new block recently added comprising reception classroom, library and ICT room, each with huge French windows opening onto playground. Playground is big enough to play a game of netball, though no fixed play equipment and a bit grey. Redevelopment of playground is next on the agenda. Voluntary-aided school. One class per year of 30, with one 'bulge year' of 60.

English, maths and science taught to a high standard and foreign language teaching taken seriously. French taught from year 2 and Italian from year 3. Excellent reports about how nurturing the school is for pupils with special educational needs. All children are screened for dyslexia in year 2 or at point of entry thereafter. PTA partially funds four hours a week of specialist learning support. School employs a whole raft of support programmes. When we visited, numerous small groups of children were dotted around school being given individual or small group support. Currently 32 pupils are identified with some form of additional educational need; five pupils have statements. Gifted and talented pupils well catered for through extension work and master classes at local secondary schools. Masses of tutoring from year 5 onwards for those heading for independent sector. Parental peer pressure palpable as 11+ approaches.

Drama and music are strengths of the school. Annual performances, led by top year, are of an exceptionally high standard and are eagerly anticipated. Every child in school is involved. Recent performances include Oliver!, Beauty and the Beast and Lion King. In addition, year 5 performs an annual play in French and year 1 performs songs in French with local French nursery. School choir is thriving with over 50 members. Children are encouraged to join the borough choir and Saturday music school. Instrumental music lessons given out of school, run by borough. Band and orchestra currently not running, which one parent believes is 'an issue.' High standard of artwork throughout school. School takes part in a variety of inter-school sports events and uses nearby Ravenscourt Park for training. Extra sports coaches recently taken on. Cricket, football, skittle ball and netball all on offer. Pupils swim for three terms in total. Although some parents critical of lack of sports provision – 'not well organised,' commented one, and described as 'an afterthought,' by another – school does provide more than the national curriculum requires.

Residential school trips for year 6 to Isle of Wight and year 3 to Buckinghamshire with a focus on team-building. School subsidises pupils who cannot afford to go. Varied selection of clubs available before, during and after school. Science, gardening, drama, chess, athletics, football and art are currently popular. No limit on the number of clubs a child can do.

On-site kitchen with delicious hot meals on offer. Compulsory school lunch for all pupils to make it financially viable. General consensus that food is 'amazing.' One child claims that the best thing about school trips is the sandwiches which the school makes.

A small, traditional establishment with old fashioned values. Feels like a village school, in the heart of Hammersmith

Parents are very involved, through hearing reading, accompanying day outings, giving linguistic expertise in International Week, attending celebrations and fundraising. PTA described as 'brilliant': huge amounts raised each year which go towards subsidising workshops and other projects on head's wish list. Fairly affluent families with only 15 per cent of pupils entitled to free school meals. Parents have high expectations and are not afraid to voice their opinions. Prize-giving has been contentious in recent years with some parents feeling that the school gives out too many cups, leaving a minority without. No wraparound care available on site but a walking bus at the end of the day to an after-care service based at nearby school is a godsend for families where both parents work.

A small, traditional establishment with old fashioned values. Feels like a village school, in the heart of Hammersmith. One current parent feels it is a great school for hard working children, though possibly not as good for those who are less academic and in need of plenty of physical activity. Others disagree and feel it is the best primary school in the area where 'children feel safe because expectations are made clear. You know your child is going to get a thorough grounding at John Betts.'

Kensington Prep School

596 Fulham Road, London SW6 5PA

Tel: 020 7731 9300

Independent • Pupils: 295 • Ages: 4–11 • Fees: £15,213 pa

Email: enquiries@kenprep.gdst.net
Website: www.kensingtonprep.gdst.net

Head: Since 2003, Mrs Prudence Lynch MA PGCE (50s). Hails from Guernsey, studied psychology at St Andrews before going to Goldsmiths to do her PGCE. She has two grown up sons and is a proud and committed grandmother. A zany, thoroughly modern head, from her boldly stylish dress sense to her dropped vowels and upward inflection at the end of her sentences. She also brings a wealth of experience to the job – previously head of juniors at Notting Hill and Ealing, a sister GDST establishment, via Colet Court, where she initiated the SEN department, taught study skills, maths and 'thinking', a passion of hers. Here she teaches philosophy for children, which is 'too wonderful for words', where they discuss things like 'Is it helpful to have an unrealistic ambition?' or 'Is it ever right to kill someone?' She relishes encouraging them to think and listen to each other. 'Girls need to be as good as men at thinking up fresh ideas and taking risks. Spoon-feeding is not going to solve a credit crunch no one has ever experienced before,' she says.

Keen to inject an element of risk to the very safe school she inherited. While she accepts that not every child can achieve anything they want, she firmly believes that it's better to go for the thing you can nearly do rather than the thing you know you can do. Otherwise what have you learnt? 'I, too, am a risk taker,' she says.

A touch scatty – efficient administration is not one of her strengths, something remarked on by parents – and she freely admits that she forgets things all the time, while hastening to add that there are enough efficient administrators around her to make sure the school doesn't drop any balls. She is a head with something much more to offer, however – vision, a big heart and a huge sense of fun. 'I love playing,' she says, as she shows us her latest acquisition – a black rag doll that sits, rather incongruously, among the array of toys and clutter on her desk. Determined to counter the intense pressure felt by parents here and elsewhere in the 'ruthless' London day school system and trying to ensure that the girls still have 'dream time' and still enjoy their childhood. How refreshing.

Entrance: At 4+ more than 200 applicants for 44 places. Put your daughter's name down any time up to December prior to entry the following September.

Assessments in January. Girls are seen in groups of five or six and assessed during play. 'With a heavily oversubscribed school like this one there isn't an ideal fair way of doing it'. Also an official entrance point at 7+ – register any time up to September the year ahead, but the number of places varies and may be only as few as two. Occasional places do crop up – keep trying. Expects most siblings to join the school, but reserves the right to say no if it is felt to be in the child's interest.

Exit: Almost all to what parents here consider to be 'the top' London girls' day schools – St Paul's, Godolphin & Latymer, Putney High, Francis Holland and Queen's Gate. Most popular boarding school Wycombe Abbey plus one or two to Cheltenham Ladies', Downe House, Heathfield and St Swithuns. Lots of scholarships – music as well as academic.

Remarks: Housed in a former Marist convent on the corner of a busy junction of the Parsons Green neck of the Fulham Road, the school occupies a wonderful space. Wide corridors, large windows, spacious high-ceilinged classrooms, broad staircases – institutional but brightened with loud colourful murals of, eg, clowns and kites. A wonderful library in the former chapel, with stained glass windows, high beamed ceiling, some sturdy oak tables softened by comfortable sofas and beanbags – a soulful place to work and read.

Parents largely local – the Caffè Nero opposite is bursting at 8am with yummy Fulham mummies sipping lattes

The playground stretches into the distance complete with tennis courts, slides, colourful springy tarmac and a snazzy bandstand where they hold popular summer concerts. When the whole school is out here it doesn't look crowded, just a sea of bright colours (head swiftly replaced the drab grey tunics with the cheerful electric blues and reds – 'I wanted it to be fun for them to get dressed in the morning,' she says). At the ring of the bell all girls freeze in silence before filing obediently into their correct line ups – that's what they're like here, law-abiding and conscious of the school values. They couldn't fail to be – they are prominently displayed throughout the school, the positive balanced with the negative, 'Do listen, don't interrupt'. (They sometimes trip up on this one – our guides, a case in point, who were bubbling over in their desire to please and enthuse about their school.)

A GDST with a difference. It stands alone, so doesn't benefit from the resources that come with having a senior school attached. No bursaries at all and fees are a bit higher than at other GDSTs. But the no-nonsense high academic standards you would expect, combined with affluent and demanding parents, make this one of London's most competitive girls' schools. 'We are good at fast-paced education,' says head. Parents here feel hugely lucky if their daughter makes it through the assessments at 3, but we heard reports of a number of children getting tutoring further down the line because they want to ensure results. Our view is that this pressure doesn't necessarily come from the inside. A number of parents here want a seamless transition to schools they regard as being the best and are not always prepared to accept it if they are told their daughter may not be up to it.

Head does her best, and the curriculum is broad – lots of open homework and off piste whole school activities to stimulate thinking skills and collaborative team work through the year groups. 'The big freeze' had the whole school interpreting and creating. The result: swathes of tin foil around the school as well as a smashed mobile phone. Lots of interdisciplinary projects using art, DT and photography. Thursday morning is 'thinking time': 'What would it be like to have legs like jelly?' A whole afternoon dedicated to music and drama, another to music and art. We saw innovative teaching – the younger children on all fours marching round the room barking numbers one to 50. Computers everywhere and laptops widely used in every classroom. Year 6 create TV programmes as well as cook canapés, in addition to doing all the marketing and costing associated with the project.

Resident SENCo manages learning support, which is part of the package until key stage 2, from when it's organised on the same model as visiting music staff. Children can dip in and out or have more structured support over a period of several years, maybe just to boost their understanding of maths or to tackle a more serious problem like dyspraxia. However only mild to moderate learning difficulties can realistically be accommodated here. Mrs Lynch abhors the label 'gifted and talented' – 'they're far too young. It implies there's something rigid about who you are'. She infinitely prefers everyone to be stretched through lots of differentiation in class and the open-ended activities they do so well here.

French from year 1. 'Not mega,' says Mrs Lynch, 'but you get your "êtres" and "avoirs" and more formal stuff at the top to help those who go on to do CE elsewhere'. A relaxed taster of Latin in the final year. Class sizes of about 20, maximum 23. Young, (almost entirely) female staff who tend to stay for a long time. Only two or three men, including the recently appointed and much praised head of music, who has introduced a junior orchestra and won't stand for any waiting lists for girls who want to learn an instrument. 'We'll just get more teachers'.

Parents largely local – the Caffè Nero opposite is bursting at 8am with yummy Fulham mummies sipping lattes and testing their pretty daughters on their times tables. Dads very present in the school, too, helping with reading and on the parents' committee, 'We like to encourage that,' says Mrs Lynch. Lots of clubs – football run by a Chelsea FC player currently very popular, also bridge, Mandarin, Spanish cookery, craft, lots of music, as well as a host of others. School likes to keep a close eye to make sure girls don't do too much. 'Food amazing,' gushed our guides. Mango and orange red smoothie caused great excitement as we were shown the bright yellow and green dining room in the bowels of the building. Lots of trips, including a choir tour to Belgium, trips to France, Cornwall and the Isle of Wight.

A vibrant place in every respect. Girls here are earnest and keen, immensely privileged with impeccable manners. A quirky eccentric, whether she is fiercely bright or not, could get lost here (school refutes this – 'we are absolutely about inspiring quirky girls as much as the more conformist') but a wonderful start for your robust all-rounder.

Knightsbridge School

67 Pont Street, London SW1X 0BD

Independent · Pupils: 385 · Ages: 3–13 · Fees: up to £18,990 pa

Tel: 020 7590 9000

Email: registrar@knightsbridgeschool.com
Website: www.knightsbridgeschool.com

36

Principal: Since September 2015, Shona Colaço, MA, PGCE MSB CBiol, previously deputy head. Has taught EFL and worked in environmental management before teacher training at Oxford. A scientist, she also has a masters in education leadership. Loves to walk (dogs in tow), cycle, grow vegetables, bake and make preserves.

Entrance: Registration is followed by an informal interview with parents and child, who also spends a day at the school in the relevant class. Beware – your child will only be accepted once you have discussed the day together and all given it the thumbs up. School only wants enthusiastic, interested children. Nursery class for siblings only. Still some spaces at senior levels, but reception lists closed for several years to come.

Exit: A few leave at 7+ or 8+ for eg Westminster Under or Colet Court. Most popular 11+ destinations include Francis Holland SW1, Latymer Upper, City Girls, Queen's Gate, Queen's College, St James Girls and More House. Recent 13+ leavers

to Charterhouse, King Edward's Witney, Harrow, King's Wimbledon, City Boys, Portland Place, Emanuel, Latymer Upper, St Paul's, Marlborough.

Remarks: A school with great potential. Feels well-established and an exciting place to be. Children and staff alike are eager and enthusiastic and, judging by results, seem to be getting it right. Could fly pretty high.

Originally the Hellenic College until it closed down in 2006, the ideal situation for a new school. Did not require an enormous amount of reconstruction. On five floors including basement, where lunch is served by smiling domestic staff. 'Pretty good food – sometimes pizza; Thursday's pudding day, otherwise it's yogurt and fruit'. Lovely bright art rooms at the top. It's a bit of a ramble up and down different staircases, but children say it really doesn't take long to know your way around. Wonderful photographs and creative works displayed all over.

Formality is definitely not the name of the game. Teachers are called by their first names with an added Mr or Miss in the junior school; they do acquire surnames for the seniors. Classrooms contain happy, interested children listening to their teachers, not necessarily sitting quietly but totally absorbed. In the science room, when we visited, eager be-smocked children clustered together excitedly as a sheep's head was passed round – 'here, you have the eye now!' Parents say children really love it and will excel because they 'want to go to school, want to learn, want to do their homework'.

Formality is definitely not the name of the game. Teachers are called by their first names

A team of young, motivated teachers, average age about 30, ensure that all lessons are fun, interesting and stimulate a desire to learn. Class sizes no bigger than 18, average is more like 15. Location tends to mean varied nationalities, so different languages abound. All learn French from nursery, a second language from reception and the top seniors learn Latin. A variety of others taught and all cultures explored but no doubt about basic Englishness. Parents love this and say 'best blend of British school system with international flair' and 'play hard, work hard for juniors; work hard, play hard for seniors.'

All children informally screened for learning difficulties in reception, formally in year 1, and any necessary help given from then on. Parents say communication lines always open, never any problem making contact – teachers and head always

accessible. Also school stands behind every policy document – 'what you see is what you get'. Extra English support available for those who need it, but good understanding is essential to get a place at the school.

Good facilities and all mod cons – two computer suites, interactive white boards everywhere, laptops galore. Lovely, light, well-stocked library. Excellent music facilities, with rooms for individual lessons. Orchestras, choirs, theatrical facilities with a great stage where all perform. Fully-equipped gym and big school hall for daily assemblies. It's all there.

No outdoor play space, but uses St Columba's Church Hall across the road for break time and Burton's Court (Royal Hospital) for sports. Two buses take the under 5s to sports grounds and centres. The rest walk – not unusual in London. Some parents feel perhaps this is the one drawback, but the variety available is enormous and children are encouraged to try everything. The majority of the sports they will find at their public schools are here to be tasted – if they don't like one, they can try another. Good familiarisation and confidence builder for when they move on. Some parents love this, others wish they would concentrate on the competitive side a bit more. All know it is something they are working on and have total confidence that a perfectly balanced programme will evolve. Fencing and swimming given particular mention as outstanding. Matches in the usual sports played against other London day schools, and at weekends once a month matches against prep schools for the seniors. These will grow as the school expands.

Exceptionally strong parents' association which, hopefully, will continue to help the school in a meaningful way without interfering with the management – that belongs to the principal and his expert team of advisers. An entrepreneurial school which is continually thinking up new ideas to stretch its pupils, expand their horizons and involve the whole family. Seven means-tested bursaries for children in years 7 and 8. As the school suggests, most children skip in every day and walk slowly out of it. It is one of the happiest schools we have seen. Parents say: 'Good rounded education, strong academics, high quality teachers, not intimidating and not exclusive.'

Lady Margaret School

Parson's Green, London SW6 4UN

Tel: 020 7736 7138

State • Pupils: 720 • Ages: 11–18 • Sixth form pupils: 195 • C of E

Email: admin@ladymargaret.lbhf.sch.uk
Website: www.ladymargaret.lbhf.sch.uk

Headteacher: Since September 2015, Elisabeth Stevenson, previously deputy head and head of sixth form at Grey Coat Hospital. Degree in mediaeval history from St Andrews, PGCE from Durham; has also done part time degree in early modern European history at Birkbeck College whilst working. Taught history at Rickmansworth School before moving to Grey Coat Hospital in 2000 as head of history. A practising Anglican, she enjoys concerts and opera, plus playing the piano, reading and walking.

Academic matters: Pupils take eight GCSEs on average, including religious studies and a modern foreign language. In 2015, 72 per cent achieved five or more A*-C GCSEs, including maths and English; 37 per cent of grades were A*/A. At A level, 37 per cent A*/A grades; 69 per cent A*/B. English literature, biology and history all popular subjects. One girl we spoke to believed the art department was 'incredibly strong and popular.' School going for quality over quantity in terms of subjects it offers. 'We've made the decision to take on only academic subjects at A level. We're not big enough to take on everything. Despite pressure to introduce other subjects, we are committed to offering only core subjects. We just haven't got the facilities to offer drama or photography at A level.' Girls do have a pretty diverse choice though, with 24 different subjects offered, including psychology, sociology and music technology. School convinced that being all girls is a great advantage and accounts for more 'masculine' subjects such as physics being very popular.

For the first couple of years, class size is 30, down to 18 in the sixth form. Girls are placed in academic ability sets for maths and English from the second year, though sets are fluid and there's plenty of coming and going from one division to another. As one mother commented, 'I'm delighted that they put them in sets as there is a huge range of ability and application at Lady Margaret'. One parent we spoke to complained that 'the most able still aren't challenged enough until the final two years.' Another disagreed, saying she felt that the top sets moved at a pretty slick pace and, for the truly academic, 'the sky's the limit here'. Gifted and talented cohort encouraged to undertake independent research including EPQ. Though this is open to all, girls tend to self-select as it can be too much for some to juggle. Their presentations are apparently phenomenal and the standard is undergraduate level.

School convinced that being all girls is a great advantage and accounts for more 'masculine' subjects being very popular

Only three per cent of pupils have SEN. Sixteen currently have statements and these girls are given one-to-one help. School is able to support girls with a range of mild learning and behavioural difficulties, including dyslexia, dyspraxia and dyscalculia, as well as those on the autistic spectrum, hearing impaired and with global learning difficulties. We hear good reports about the provision on offer. School comments, 'We try to adapt to an individual's needs but we don't have a specialist team as we're a small school. We can't support those with extreme difficulties.'

Girls feel well-mentored by staff when considering subject choices and university applications. Healthy ratio of male and female teachers, both long-servers and newly qualified. School worries that it is going to become increasingly hard to recruit high calibre staff in the years ahead and has noticed that, for some subjects, the number of applicants has decreased significantly.

Some parents have felt that not enough homework has been set for the younger girls. This has been stepped up recently and one 11 year old we spoke to said she was given up to three subjects a night. School admits getting the homework issue right can be a challenge. 'Some parents want more, some want less. If some parents think we give too much and some think we give too little then we've probably got it about right!'

Games, options, the arts: Decent amount of sport on offer, including badminton, hockey, dance, basketball and football. School is successful in sporting competitions against other schools, state and independent, within the borough. Sport tends to played in local parks in Battersea, Fulham and Barnes. Netball features highly and is taken seriously. Girls have competed in national netball competitions and taken part in netball tours abroad. zumba and yoga also offered for those less keen on team sports. Pupils compete annually in the Lady Tavener's tournament at Lord's and PE department is heavily involved with London Youth Games. Some pupils enter the global Rock Challenge dance competition and they are moving on up the ranks. School also has links with local rowing club. About half the pupils in year 10 take Duke of Edinburgh bronze award.

School is renowned for its strong art department. Unusually for a comprehensive, history of art offered at A level. Music also strong: symphony orchestra, jazz band, pop group, ensembles, choirs (including chamber and gospel) and around half the school takes individual music lessons. One-to-one music lessons are subsidised for those who cannot afford the cost. Large inter-house music

festival involves half the girls in the school, and recitals and concerts occur regularly throughout the year. In the past, parents have complained that there was not enough drama on offer but there are now plenty of opportunities for budding thespians, including house productions, sixth form plays and biennial musicals. Older girls given the chance to direct. Many pupils involved in drama groups after school and at weekends, as a supplement to what

---

Sixth formers set up and run clubs for younger girls. They range from Dr Who club to a Manga club. Debating is particularly strong here

---

the school can offer.

In the penultimate week of the summer term, girls in years 7, 8 and 9 take part in residential trips in order to build leadership skills and resilience. Activity weeks abroad have been as far-flung as Spain, France and Germany, as well as water sports expeditions to Cornwall and day trips within London for those who are less keen on venturing too far afield. Parents pay for these excursions but financial support is on offer for those who cannot afford it. School tries to make sure that each girl gets one trip abroad during her time here.

Sixth formers set up and run clubs for younger girls. They range from Dr Who club to a Manga club. Debating is particularly strong here. School day can be extended for those girls who prefer to work at school rather than home. Library open from 7.30am until 5pm, staffed by a full-time librarian.

Background and atmosphere: In 1917, Whitelands College School (founded in 1842) was threatened with closure. A significant number of pupils and teachers were 'rescued' by Miss Moberly Bell (the second mistress) and Lady Margaret was formed. She remained head for the next 30 years and her portrait hangs in pride of place by the staircase. The school is named after Lady Margaret Beaufort, mother of Henry VII, and she is remembered in the school's red rose emblem. She also founded St John's and Christ's Colleges, Cambridge.

This school has had various guises over the years: a grammar school, then a voluntary aided school, next a comprehensive school, now an academy. Flourishes as a specialist maths and computing college with a second specialism in music.

Located right in the centre of prosperous and leafy Parsons Green, with an abundance of expensive shops, cafés and estate agents nearby. Comprises three Georgian listed buildings, as well as further buildings to the rear. Huge £6 million renovation programme is now complete, providing the school with seven further classrooms, improved accessibility, better dining amenities and some smaller areas for group teaching. The modern Olivier Centre is the sixth form girls' building comprising a recording room, a café, music rooms, quiet study areas as well as classrooms. Girls appear delighted with their own sixth form block.

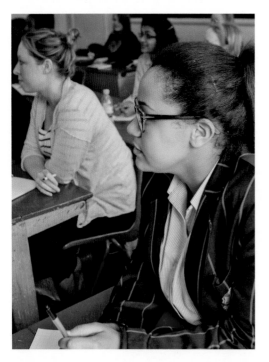

The modern Olivier Centre is the sixth form girls' building comprising a recording room, a café, music rooms, quiet study areas as well as classrooms

Pastoral care and discipline: School motto is 'I have a goodly heritage.' Strong Christian culture here. Has its own small chapel though 'we're not all Christians here,' said one girl. Pupils are expected to participate in Christian worship, even if they have no faith or a different faith. 'If a girl has a problem with the Christian ethos of the school, then this probably isn't the school for her.' Services held at church across the Green throughout the year, often well attended by alumnae.

Pastoral care very strong. Form tutors help with difficulties ranging from academic matters to social problems. School nurse, chaplain and counsellor available to help with worries. Counsellor tends to deal mainly with external problems and girls can self-refer or be referred by the school if they wish to see him. The girls we spoke to felt bullying was not a problem at the school. The odd case of anorexia is dealt with as and when it arises though the girls we spoke to felt that peers usually stepped in quickly if they felt one of their friends was not eating enough. Girls look out for each other here. Discipline not a major problem as girls here are a fairly biddable, motivated lot – very rare to have permanent exclusions for bad behaviour. None in the last two years. One neighbour commented that, in the past, a few sixth form girls have spent most of break time smoking behind parked cars in adjoining roads, though there was no evidence of this on the day we visited. Other neighbours feel the girls are generally polite out on the streets and full school uniform is worn until year 11. The pupils who showed us around were articulate, engaging and confident, with impeccable manners.

Excellent staff/pupil relationships. School proud that hard-working, committed staff willingly give time up to help the girls.

Older girls nurture and support younger pupils. House system helps all year groups to interact through regular inter-house competitions including a bake-off, sports day and University Challenge. Sixth formers help younger girls with creative writing.

Pupils and parents: Majority of pupils from white, British, middle-class families but a wide social mix from 'incredibly posh to the very loud'. Girls come from a spread of cultures but the school encourages all to embrace the shared values of good manners and respect. Many girls come from families with high aspirations where both parents work. Good home-school links, with weekly bulletins, and one mother we spoke to felt the school communicated well with parents. 'We're kept in the loop'. Only 14 per cent do not have English as their first language – a low number for Inner London – and no provision on offer to support ESL pupils. Just over 10 per cent of pupils are eligible for free school meals, though one pupil we spoke to said, 'there's no stigma at all attached to having free lunches. Lots of my friends do'.

Many parents actively support the school and run the Christmas and summer fairs. Money raised by parents has recently gone towards buying a new piano and an audio-visual system. School comments that 'most parents are on side' but concedes that expectations and pressure on the teachers increase year on year. The Rose Fund has been set up to encourage parents to make a financial contribution to the enrichment opportunities on offer here.

Old Girls include Janet Street-Porter, Martha Fiennes (film director), the rape law reformer Jill Saward and author Jessie Burton. One pupil said she felt inspired when she learnt what Old Girls have achieved from here and successful former pupils are celebrated.

The school birthday celebrations sum up the work hard, play hard attitude

Entrance: A four-form entry in year 7. Heavily oversubscribed, with 600+ applicants for 120 places. Sixty-seven foundation places reserved for girls who attend Church of England services regularly; 53 for other applicants of any or no religion. English and maths tests divide applicants into three ability bands. Looked-after children and those with special educational need given preference, as are siblings. Thereafter priority given to those who live closest to the school, as the crow flies, which means that those without a SW6 postcode probably won't make it. Accepting a broader intake than before. One recent applicant tells us that the entrance test morning was 'a scrum. I didn't even have time to say good-bye to my mother as we were all whisked off at top speed!'

School doubles in size in sixth form. 'We take on about 60 girls at this stage. They come from all over London, from independent schools as well as from other state schools which can't offer the traditional academic approach that we can.' The minimum requirement for entry into sixth form is six GCSEs at grade C, including English language and maths, as well as a B grade in the chosen A level subject; maths, languages and science need A grades. For economics, a grade B in maths in a prerequisite.

Exit: Some leave after GCSEs, opting for schools which offer a wider range of A levels or more practical courses (such as BTec diplomas). Nearly half stays on in the sixth form. Nearly all go on to higher education. The more able girls are encouraged to attend Oxbridge open days; four Oxbridge places in 2015. Practice interviews are given internally and externally but no extra Oxbridge preparation classes per se. Favoured courses currently include art foundation, biology, English literature and history. Girls tend to head for prestigious universities – London, Bristol, Newcastle, Leeds, Manchester and Oxford Brookes popular. Parents organise and run careers evenings.

Remarks: An undeniably successful state academy in the beautiful surroundings of Parsons Green, recently rated outstanding by Ofsted. 'The best comprehensive school in south-west London,' according to one satisfied parent. A very welcoming and warm place, with a traditional feel. Takes academic achievement seriously but the girls are allowed to have fun too. The school birthday celebrations sum up the work hard, play hard attitude of the school, according to head: on this day, a formal, respectful church service is followed by relaxed house plays where pupils are given a free rein and teachers are gently mocked. A punchy combination. No wonder the queue of girls hoping to join just keeps getting longer.

Latymer Prep School

Linked school: Latymer Upper School, 294

36 Upper Mall, London W6 9TA

Independent • Pupils: 160 • Ages: 7–11 • Fees: £16,125 pa

Tel: 0845 638 5700

Email: registrar@latymerprep.org
Website: www.latymerprep.org

Head: Since 2001, Mr Stuart Dorrian BA, former long-serving head of English and of lower school in the senior school who was persuaded to take over the prep, with the chief aim of upping the academics (for which he ticked the box long ago). You'll be hard pushed to find anyone (pupils included) who doesn't instantly warm to his gentle, warm nature, his excellent listening skills and his clear enthusiasm for his domain. His office, a homely room overlooking the river setting, has an open door policy, in which pupils think nothing of popping in to tell him something they're worried about or to just pick up a sports ball. Meanwhile, his regular use of the term 'my school' is said with pride and passion, never conceit. He still teaches, some sixth form English and drama to his year 3. Parents describe him as being 'emotionally alert to children's needs', with 'a huge emphasis on pastoral care', but he is also regarded as a serious educationalist.

Entrance: Highly selective, with around 220 competing at 7+ for the 38-40 places. They take an exam, with half invited back for some science-related activities and team-building exercises and observation. The gender split is 50/50, with each year split into two classes of 20 (occasionally 21). Families are mainly local, within 30 minutes' travel time, although the reach of the school has expanded in recent years to stretch as far as Kensington and Notting Hill.

Exit: Almost all move into the senior school, although transfer is not automatic, with all pupils required to sit the entrance exam.

Remarks: Rivercourt House, an attractive 1800s villa overlooking the Thames, is the main building. Full of light, with an elegant staircase and plenty of original features and creaky floorboards, it has the feel of a well-to-do, kindly, aunt's home and is an enviable environment for youngsters to learn in. Next door, Latymer House accommodates more classrooms, food tech, cookery, IT and art – all very well equipped, with plenty of space. Both utilise walls and corridors

The curriculum is future-orientated, with all pupils learning Mandarin and Spanish, and technology is genuinely embedded

to the max to display children's work. Even a window had lovely artwork draped across when we visited.

Opposite the rather limited outside space is an odd 1930s building, whose outside spiral staircase leads to the Seahorse Drama Studio, with a truly professional feel. In addition, pupils also regularly parade down the underpass under the A4 to Latymer Upper to make use of facilities such as the dining hall, sports and music facilities and drama hall (with recent productions including My Fair Lady, Toad of Toad Hall and Peter Pan). Other links with the upper school include shared teacher training on inset days and teachers doing regular observations of year 7 teaching to get a feel for standards. All this, agree parents and pupils, makes the transfer into the upper school pretty seamless. 'They don't get scared because they're already familiar with it,' explained one parent.

Expect specialist teaching from day one, so whilst each class has its own form room, pupils go to subject-dedicated rooms to learn. Of particular note is the large, fantastically well-equipped art room at the top of the school, where pupils were busy painting clay pots they'd made, and a delightful, well-stocked library. Delicious baking aromas drifted out of the food tech room when we visited, whilst in the science lab, pupils could hardly have looked more animated.

The curriculum is future-orientated, with all pupils learning Mandarin and Spanish, and technology is genuinely embedded throughout all subjects, with regular use of iPads in class, including art. This is not at the expense of more traditional learning, however. 'We want them to read and write before they can swipe,' says the head.

Music is strong, with every child playing a musical instrument and half of them playing two, for which one-to-one tuition is timetabled into the curriculum. Big on brass, with lots of children learning the French horn or trombone, whilst the cello also remains popular. Two main choirs – enthusiast singers (no audition necessary) and the chamber choir – accommodate 90 children in total. Music tech also a focal point. 'I was certain my kids had no talent with music and I've been truly shocked what they've brought out in them,' said one parent.

The focus on sport that the upper school is noted for is seen as equally important here, with specialist sports coaches teaching both girls and boys rugby, football, netball, cricket, dance,

rounders and – the particular strength of the school – swimming. New £14m new sports facility behind the 1930s building has revolutionised facilities. Sport is inclusive. 'Our aim is that every pupil leaves with one sport they like doing,' says the head. 'That might not sound very ambitious, but actually girls often fall away from sport because they're not given the opportunity to find something they love. Not here.'

Over 20 school clubs, including zumba, film studies, The Latymerian (school magazine), chess, bridge, drama, coding, Warhammer and karate. Most are free, although a few bought-in ones, such as zumba, do charge. No after-school care, but the prep room remains open until 4.30pm. Plenty of day trips to places including V&A and Kensington Gardens, whilst residential trips include Norfolk (year 5) and Italy (year 6).

This isn't a school that believes in lots of rules. 'There's just a general expectation of respect and being nice,' said one pupil. And with the exception of some year 6s who have passed their 11+ swanking around a bit, it's all pretty low-key, with a genuine feeling of innocence. About the worst behaviour you'll see, say teachers, is children running to the next class, when they should walk.

As for bullying, it's hard to imagine here. 'Of course children sometimes fall out, and there are situations in which children lack empathy or fail to see the implications of what they've done. But there's very little deliberate unkindness,' confirms the head. 'I think that's down to modelling by

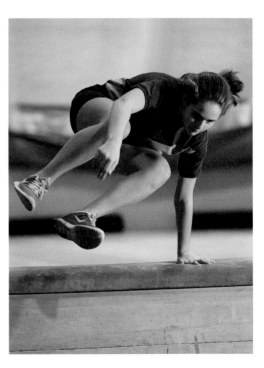

myself and my staff and the fact that, for the children, the absolute worst thing for them is feeling they've disappointed us. They can't bear it.'

'You learn through trying,' is an unofficial mantra of the school, with the staff encouraging intellectual risk-taking. 'We are constantly reminding the children that the point when you're not quite sure is the point when you learn,' explains the head. 'Getting to the top therefore isn't the be-all-and-end-all and we encourage them to see that and value the moment when they're not quite sure.'

There are pupils with SEN, including dyslexia and Asperger's, and they've also had students who are registered blind or deaf. 'We delight in being open,' says the head, explaining that anyone with any kind of learning challenge is encouraged to make full use of the upper school's learning support department (now known as the 'academic mentoring department' to remove stigma), which is run by three specialist and extremely well-liked women. 'They offer unbelievable support,' said one parent.

There's a lively PA, which does all the usual fundraising and organising of school fêtes and social events, along with each class having a 'rep' and 'dep,' who the head closely communicates with. 'If there's ever an issue or misunderstanding, the rep and dep won't encourage parents to write to me saying, "We all think this or that". It's much more a case of them coming to me informally and early to nip it in the bud.' Parents agree this works, and several praise the way they are encouraged to come into the school in the morning and afternoon, never hurried on as in some schools. They can also come in to help with reading.

We saw relaxed, engaged, happy and confident (but not precocious) children, who are clearly at home and keen to learn. 'You're encouraged to ask questions,' one pupil told us. 'In fact, if we are really interested in a particular area, that can drive the

We saw relaxed, engaged, happy and confident (but not precocious) children, who are clearly at home and keen to learn. 'You're encouraged to ask questions,' one pupil told us

class in a new direction.' 'Teachers always tell us, it's our enthusiasm they want to build on,' explained another. For this reason, comment a couple of parents, it's probably not the best school for shrinking violets. 'I think a really quiet and withdrawn child might feel a bit lost here,' said one.

Unlike in the upper school, there is a house system, all named after birds. 'It gives a sense of healthy competition and gets them out of their year groups,' said one parent. There's also a school council, although it's not particularly active.

This is a charming prep that children genuinely adore. 'My child is often up at 7am fully dressed and asking when it's time to go,' said one parent, whilst another said, 'The children might not come out looking as neat as they went in, but you know they've had a really lovely time.' Despite the expectation on high academic achievement (which some parents say can be tiring), there's a big emphasis on a rounded education, and above all it's lots of fun, with warm relationships between staff and pupils. This throws some children who come from more formal pre-preps or primaries, with parents also sometimes starting off feeling slightly hesitant about how relaxed and open the atmosphere is. But they soon feel liberated and by half term in year 3, children seem to have fully subscribed to the ethos of the school. As one pupil summed up, 'this school is like one, big warm hug.'

Latymer Upper School

Linked school: Latymer Prep School, 292

237 King Street, London W6 9LR

Tel: 020 8629 2024

Independent · Pupils: 1,180 · Ages: 11–18 · Sixth form pupils: 360 · Fees: £17,715 pa

Email: registrar@latymer-upper.org
Website: www.latymer-upper.org

9

Head: Since September 2012, Mr David Goodhew (MA Oxon), originally a local boy who has now moved 'back home', living 10 minutes down the road with his French wife, Céline, and their young son. Read classics at Oxford and previously deputy

head of Durham School. Spends at least one hour every day walking round the school – visits lessons for a few minutes, which both pupils and parents say sums up his 'hands-on approach' and 'openness to ideas for change'. Not stereotypical headmasterly, parents and pupils describe him as 'very approachable.'

Academic matters: Grades have been steadily improving over recent years and although research from the University of Durham found pupils are achieving either in line with – or better than – their abilities, results remain a notch short of stunning. A levels in 2015 saw 72 per cent A*/A grades, with 91 per cent at A*-B. GCSEs were 92 per cent A*/A.

Key aspects of the innovative curriculum include the introduction of the UCAS-accredited World Perspectives, which has replaced the 11th GCSE in the middle school. Exploring global political issues, pupils love it and parents delight in their children 'watching more news' and 'talking about bigger issues at the dinner table.'

All year 7s learn Mandarin (carried on from the prep school, if they went) and all pupils expected to do a modern language at GCSE. IT has been ditched in favour or computing and coding and technology is genuinely embedded into all learning, with all pupils from year 10 upwards given an iPad. 'I do all my essays on it, plus I can do things like surveys,' says one pupil, while one upper sixth pupil has even designed a rowing app that is now used by the GB Rowing Team.

In 2010, the school decided to go linear with the A level syllabus, with all exams taken at the end of upper sixth. There are two benefits, claims the head – better results and six extra weeks back in the lower sixth, allowing teachers to go deeper into subjects.

Majority of teachers hugely admired, with several references to them going the extra mile and being 'very imaginative in their teaching methods'.

'Staff really care, not just academically but in a pastoral way,' sums up one parent. 'I could frankly hug all of them,' says another. 'The teachers try and inspire you – there's no fobbing off of pupils' questions, ever,' remarks a pupil.

Careers and university advice is outstanding, thanks to a knowledgeable and dedicated team, including a careers specialist and international university admissions specialist. The latter post was brought in due to the recent surge in applications to American universities – a staggering 30 in 2014, including three to Princeton. 'Because of our rounded approach to education, it means our students are often drawn to the American university model of taking seriously areas like sport, music and drama, and the fact that you can delay specialisation,' explains the head.

Parents and pupils rave about the learning support department, which is now known as the 'academic mentoring department' (to remove stigma). Run by three specialist women who nobody seems to be able to praise more if they tried, pupils can visit for one-to-one sessions any time, whether they have severe dyslexia or just a piece of challenging homework, at no extra cost. The department's peer mentoring scheme is popular, whereby older pupils help younger ones, with benefits to both sides. 'If anything, the department could be bigger, though, as it's always full,' says one pupil, who adds that on results day, this is where you'll find students running to give staff a hug. School reckons on around 10 per cent needing some kind of support, with just two statemented.

Games, options, the arts: Mixed reports on sports. On one hand, it's famed throughout the western (London) world, particularly for rowing and football, these remain the school's strengths and are pursued with much enthusiasm and success. There's also notable accomplishment in swimming, netball and rugby, all of which are taught by professional coaches. Sport is also known for being inclusive, plenty of C, D and E teams, with enjoyment of sport valued as much as sporting prowess. One parent also points out how 'my son has been encouraged to try out sports he wouldn't normally opt for, which has been great for him.' Meanwhile, there are some strong examples of girls' sporting accomplishments, not least the fact that the senior girls' quad won Henley Royal Regatta (breaking three course records).

On the other hand, a number of parents complain that girls' sport is taken less seriously than boys and some told us they feel children could be pushed more. The chief whinge has been that facilities are tired and limited, with pupils doing main school games 15 minutes away in Wood Lane. Not so since September 2015, however, with the impressive £14m new sports centre leading to greater opportunities for teaching more sports simultaneously, as well as enabling classes in fencing, climbing, yoga and pilates.

All pupils take DT, art, music and drama to the end of year 9 and then choose, although we wonder how they decide. Art is outstanding, with talented and impressively free and imaginative artwork in just about every media, displayed everywhere from the head's office to the four good-sized studios. Similarly, DT is fantastically equipped, with an emphasis on creativity. 'The people who maintain the school use this room, so it's built to industrial standard,' raves one excited pupil who passionately talks me through some of the machines. 'I once asked to build a stomp rocket powered table tennis

ball dispenser for a project. I was allowed and it worked!' he adds.

Performing arts also taken seriously, with a commendable theatre (plus other studios) and plenty of year group plays, plus an annual all-school one. Meanwhile, each week 800 individual instrumental lessons are taught by 40 visiting music teachers in air-conditioned, sound-proofed, purpose-built rooms. Group music lessons focus on getting children enthused with practical work, not simply focusing on theory. Singing takes place across several choirs through to grungy bands, and everything in between. Students even have their own record label, 32 Bit Recordings, with profits from releases going into the school bursary fund. 'The arts aren't considered an alternative to academia here,' says one pupil. 'There's room for people to excel in both.'

'Staff really care, not just academically but in a pastoral way,' sums up one parent. 'I could frankly hug all of them,' says another. 'The teachers try and inspire you'

Astounding range of extracurriculars on offer, with over 100 clubs, as well as a good range of outside speaker. Trips, it seems, are organised to pretty much every corner of the earth, with the Horizon fund ensuring that no pupil is excluded for financial reasons. The annual 'activities week' causes much excitement, where students do anything from cycling coast-to-coast to building a shelter for teenage mums in Uganda. 'It all comes back to our rounded view of education,' says the head. 'Skills learned in leadership, resilience and teamwork matter every bit as much as academia.'

Background and atmosphere: Located on the banks of the Thames in West London, the grounds occupy a rectangular plot between King Street (where the main entrance is) and the busy A4 into London, under which runs a cunning underpass, through which children parade to the prep school, sports hall, pool and Latymer boat house.

But if you didn't know better, you could be forgiven for thinking the school is a church, since your eye is immediately drawn to the huge stained glass windows of the gothic, red-brick main hall, which is nestled behind a long, low gothic arched wall.

Dating from 1890, the hall now has several smart newer buildings surrounding it, most recently the striking glass-fronted library and science block, while the old car park has been transformed into a charming 'piazza,' complete with giant outdoor chess set, which students describe as the hub of the school during nice weather and exam time.

Back in the main hall, expect portraits of old heads and war memorial tablets, along with brown glazed tiles on the walls and blue carpets on the floor, which very much set the mood throughout the old building, with its seemingly endless supply of nooks and crannies, hidden staircases and innovative linkages between buildings. 'Pupils can be here five years and still discover new areas,' says one pupil. Wooden lockers, which are dotted around the school, had just been replaced with metal ones when we visited ('so much nicer,' says a pupil), while the mezzanine areas of many classrooms give a nice warmth to many of the teaching areas.

In contrast, lots of light wood and huge windows feature in the newer buildings, the most exceptional of which is the science and library block. The ground-floor library is exemplary and one that many towns would be proud of – well-stocked, not just with books and DVDs but computers, with genuinely studious looking pupils. Meanwhile, the corridors of the three floors of science boast interactive periodical table, television with live newsflashes and even live lizards and fish (not together) behind glass, among other innovative features. 'We're just about to do a class on how much vitamin C exists in fruit drinks,' says one excitable teacher as we walk past one of the well-equipped labs. On top is a roof garden, weather station and observatory.

Other areas of note through the school include the huge dining room and the well-used sixth form common room, with plentiful and colourful booths and sofas. Outside, expect inevitable queuing and log jams at changeover times, as a result of 1,400 students in limited space, but nobody seems to really mind.

Originally a boys' school, girls started coming in sixth form in the late 1990s, after which it became fully co-ed in 2004. Now 50/50 across every year group, with the head genuinely astounded that anyone could think single sex is preferable. Certainly, nobody could argue that uptake for maths and science among girls isn't strong here.

Active school council, which recently put together an initiative for more recycling bins and voted against bringing in a house system.

Pastoral care and discipline: There was a perception in the 1980s (and some argue, later) that the school was 'a bit rough,' admits the head. 'Not now. The behaviour is excellent.' Parents and pupils concur, putting it down to warm, mutually respectful rapport with staff, as well as pupils knowing exactly what's expected of them.

Head acknowledges that any school would be foolish to believe bullying is non-existent. What matters, he says, is what you do about it on the

rare occasions it occurs. 'There's a big focus on encouraging pupils or parents to report it immediately, after which it's dealt with it quickly and sensibly,' concurs one parent. Despite the unfortunate headline from the Daily Mail in 2010, which read 'Sixth-formers at top private school expelled after being found with cocaine at 'drunken' end of year prom,' the head says the zero tolerance to drink, smoking and drugs means it's not a problem now (and wasn't a big one then), which parents and pupils agree with.

The ground-floor library is exemplary and one that many towns would be proud of – well-stocked, not just with books and DVDs but computers

Teachers genuinely interested in pupils' well-being, and although there's not huge interaction between the different year groups, pupils seem at ease with different ages.

Pupils and parents: Around 90 per cent from within a three-mile radius, who arrive by tube, bike or on foot. Diverse population for an independent school, which the school is clearly proud of. 'We attract a real mix from hedge fund managers, media types and academics living in leafy streets through to families on the White City estate, which is surely better than just those from a privileged bubble mixing with each other. What life lessons that does that teach you?' explains the head. Parents agree, describing the school as 'grounded'. 'Privileged, yes, but posh, no,' says another. Communication with parents – both via the school and the Parents' Guild – is considered good.

Incredible list of alumni, including Hugh Grant, Alan Rickman, Christopher Guard, Imogen Poots, Mel Smith, Gus Prew. Also Walter Legge and Raphael Wallfisch, and Pete Townsend's dad, who was expelled. Then there's Kulveer Ranger, Keith Vaz, George Walden, Joshua Rozenberg, Andrew Slaughter, Heston Blumenthal, Dr Hilary Jones and Lily Cole. 'If you're lucky, you get to meet one of them at a prize giving,' says one pupil. 'My sister actually got to shake hands with Alan Rickman.'

Entrance: Of the 160 places available at 11+, 40 come from the school's own on-site prep. Of the remaining 120, 50 per cent come from local state primaries, with the other half coming from other preps. Some 1,100 candidates altogether. But while the English, maths, reasoning and interview required to get in used to make the local area a tutor's dream, the head has dropped the reasoning in an effort to create a more level playing field. He's also dropped the 13+ entry as there was only ever a handful of places, which around 80 (inevitably privately educated) would apply for. 'That's just mean,' he says. At 16+, over 200 candidates for 30 places.

Although attracting a high calibre at this age, entry for sixth form doesn't set a ridiculously high bar, with the school expecting minimum eight or nine GCSEs including maths and English, with A or A* grades in the subjects they wish to study (or related subject).

Exit: Careers and university advice considered second to none. Oxbridge (22 places in 2015), Manchester, Bristol and London are top choices. Growing numbers to US (16 places) and other top international unis. Also increasing numbers to professional colleges for music, art and drama, including RADA.

Money matters: Founder Edward Latymer, a wealthy puritan, pledged funds on his deathbed in 1624 to educate and feed 'eight poore boies'. So when the previous head came into post in 2002 and there were just seven free places (even less than Latymer's pledge) he took action.

The school has since raised £11m specifically for the bursary programme, with 115 pupils now on means-tested bursaries (including 77 free places). That amounts to 12 per cent of pupils with some form of means-tested financial assistance.

Remarks: Oodles of pupil pride about pretty much every aspect of the school, with only minor niggles from pupils and parents. 'If you're not academic, you'll struggle. But it's not just about the academia as there's this constant focus on being well-rounded,' says one pupil. If you're after a school that encourages academic curiosity and a real passion for life, this is it.

The London Oratory School Junior House

Linked school: The London Oratory School, 299

Seagrave Road, London SW6 1RX	Tel: 020 7385 0102
State • Pupils: 80 • Ages: 7–11 • RC	Email: admin@los.ac Website: www.london-oratory.org

Headmaster: Since 2007, Mr David McFadden, head of The London Oratory School in its entirety.

Entrance: Admits up to 20 boys at 7 into year 3, up to 10 of whom are choristers. All applicants tested for general academic ability and for music aptitude; potential choristers also tested for choral aptitude and suitability. Priority to practising Catholics who attend mass frequently, baptism before 6 months, helping in church etc.

Exit: All move up to senior school.

Remarks: Not a separate school but a separate wing: the junior house, with four classrooms, a choir room and several practice rooms – as music is everything here – all recently refurbished. The junior house, rather appropriately, is situated in the heart of the music school. Old-fashioned classrooms, old-fashioned desks that lift up to contain a motley jumble of books and stationary. Music practice rooms adjoin and creakings of strings, blasting of brass form the background noise. Officially it is part of the senior school, but it is the part which takes junior-age boys (7-11). It operates rather like a choir school, or an old fashioned prep school – only without the boarding. It is one of very few state choir schools.

It really is tiny, with only 80 boys in the entire school (20 in each of years 3-6) and can't really be regarded in a school in its own right. Parents talk of the shock arriving here after a state primary – 'This is not like a primary school. You entrust your children to the teachers here. You're not sure what goes on from the time you drop them at the gate,' said one parent. Ms McKay, who is junior house master – ie she runs the junior house on a day to day basis – is ex-RAF and feared by the parents, though loved by the boys. 'She obviously adores the boys,' said one parent, 'but I am a bit worried about approaching her.' Her attitude appears to be that the job of educating the boys is the school's, the less interference from parents the better.

Boys here are committed and robust. The day starts early with an hour's choir practice from 8am, if you are in the Schola. All boys play two instruments – one orchestral, normally supported by the piano. For potential applicants, who must be of at least average academic ability, musical promise is the only criterion which counts here, once you have demonstrated your Catholic credentials – all the boys have musical potential. Not all boys are in the Schola – some just follow an instrumental course. The Schola sings every Saturday evening in the Brompton Oratory. Junior house boys play every instrument you can name, under the care of innumerable peripatetic teachers of high quality, and use all the senior school facilities. They tour, record and give stunning concerts They work hard and play hard.

Not just music, sport too. Tag rugby is organised against other schools. They swim once a week in the school pool, and water polo is a popular after-school club. Plenty of other after-school clubs too – including Lego, programming and chess, but many boys are just too tired at the end of the school day. Art is vibrant and boys get to use the facilities of the senior school. They learn about eg Da Vinci in lessons then put their learning into practical effect in the art room. Not a lot of drama, but plenty of musical productions – again, use of the senior school facilities greatly enhances the experience. This is true, too, of science. Science is taught in the senior school labs, and they get the benefit of having specialist teachers from an early age – not just the form teacher.

Boys are tested at the end of each term and reports are sent to parents, which detail their results, progress and targets. Otherwise, you get to meet your son's teachers only once a year. Some complain about poor communication lines between school and home, but say that on the whole they put up with this because they trust the school. 'You might not get to hear about a concert until two nights before,' remarked one parent. The school is totally integrated into the senior school – junior house boys even have lunch, as the senior boys do, in class rooms that become 'house rooms' at lunch time. However, there is little interaction with senior boys. Play times are organised so as not to coincide with the traffic of burly teenagers, and the whole of junior house has lunch at a different time from the senior boys.

A lot of boys in junior house have brothers in the senior school, and 'being such a small school, the parents tend to bond quite closely and stick together,' said one parent. The pace is fast and it's 'hard core,' said another. 'While there is a sense of exclusivity – the bar is so high to get in and you feel so lucky – these are very normal boys, not precious and geeky'. A wonderful start in life for your musical, resilient, self-motivated, Catholic little boy.

The London Oratory School

Linked school: The London Oratory School Junior House, 298

Seagrave Road, London SW6 1RX

State • Pupils: 1,380 • Ages: 11–18 • Sixth form pupils: 360 (80 girls) • RC

Tel: 020 7385 0102

Email: registrar@los.ac
Website: www.london–oratory.org

11

Headmaster: Since 2007, Mr David McFadden BSc MA (a youthful late 50s). Read zoology at King's College London and taught biology in his early years at schools in and around London. Part of a large Catholic family – one of six siblings – he grew up in Hammersmith. His sisters went to Sacred Heart, he and his brothers came here. He was head at two independent schools in Australia, Aquinas College and the Christian Brothers' College in Fremantle, before being approached to succeed the long-serving

(29 years) John McIntosh CBE, who was his headmaster when he was a boy here in the early 70s. 'He stands,' in his own words, spoken with a humility, typical of him, 'on the shoulders of giants.'

Immediately warm and engaging, Mr McFadden is a head who listens and empathises. He comes across as a man who has weathered many storms, and with three grown up daughters of his own, one senses he doesn't judge, just understands. He takes his gorgeous dog, Teddy (an ever-present character around the school) on walks with troubled pupils to help them talk as they walk. A sensitive man, he has a deep interest and understanding of the journey that young, and old, are making in this life. While his predecessor may have focused primarily on discipline and standards, Mr McFadden, while working to preserve the excellence, is shifting the focus slightly to the personal and spiritual development of his pupils. He regards this development as involving two journeys, 'the surface journey' which incorporates the pragmatics – passing exams, gaining qualifications – and the 'internal journey', which involves reflecting on themselves, the universe and God. He has initiated what is known as the 'formation programme', which embraces a number of aspects from retreats to service programmes in the local primary schools and old people's homes, as well as mentoring within the school.

Some pupils remark that he is rarely seen around the school, but he avers that he knows all the pupils and their stories, fitting this around a punishing schedule of negotiating with builders (the stunning new development which has transformed the working life of the school has reached completion), defending court actions (the

Good results can partly be attributed to good and committed teaching, but must largely stem from an excellent work ethic that is drilled in from the start

Humanist society is tireless in its challenges of the admissions criteria), and appeals hearings. He shows a remarkable tolerance when discussing the judicial review and adjudicator proceedings that seem to be constantly under way. 'It is a small price to pay for living in a democracy,' he remarks.

Academic matters: Results impressive, a bit of a dip when compared to its notable local competitor, but not to be sniffed at. What we like particularly is the range of subjects boys are choosing to take at both GCSE and at A level. Large numbers do maths and sciences – and a healthy helping of A* in these subjects – but the humanities and languages are not neglected. History particularly popular, and double figures do art and DT each year. Heartening in an (almost entirely) boys' school to see this range, and we were particularly encouraged by a thriving German department. A level results in 2015 were 65 per cent A*-B and 38 per cent A*/A grades. At GCSE, 88 per cent of pupils got 5+ A*-C grades including maths and English; 51 per cent A*/A grades. School will endeavour to facilitate any language if there is a demand, however low the numbers – Russian, Arabic, Chinese, Portuguese and Polish all offered and a good solid classics department encourages a number of people to take Latin and Greek GCSE. A few go on to A level.

Good results can partly be attributed to good and committed teaching, but must largely stem from an excellent work ethic that is drilled in from the start. Homework is rigorously monitored and it's a detention for repeated failure to produce it. Setting from year 9 and a number of GCSEs are taken in year 10. Sixth formers have to work together in a large room during study periods. No lounging around on comfy sofas here. A member of staff is ever present to monitor behaviour and we were conscious of our noisy footfall when we peeked in.

The less academically able are offered a sixth form course in advanced business – a hybrid of two A levels and an AS, leading to qualifications in business and computing, a practical alternative to a sixth form college course for those who can't bear to leave. Plans afoot to introduce the Extended Project Qualification. Classes felt by some to be too big – can be as many as 30 at GCSE; sixth form numbers are higher than elsewhere too. However, with 10 or so a year gaining places at Oxbridge, the Sutton Trust continues to rank it among the highest performing state schools in the country. Standards here are high and pupils strive to maintain those standards.

SENs catered for – attracts standard numbers of the usual spread of needs. Currently Mr McFadden estimates there are approximately 40 with Statements/EHC plans – a range of those on the autistic spectrum as well as some with emotional issues, social and/or communication issues. School can accommodate pupils with cerebral palsy. By all accounts the SENCo is 'magnificent' and there is an army of teaching assistants as well as learning support staff. In-class help along with withdrawal where appropriate. Murmurings of discontent in certain quarters – particularly parents who have sons with no identifiable special need, but may simply be dreamy or disorganised. 'Faulty communication lines and support is not swiftly forthcoming' are the central complaints. Wheelchair-friendly and SENs seen, in general, as just part of life.

Games, options, the arts: This is a big rugby school and rowing is also 'massive', as our proud and enthusiastic sixth form guides told us. If your son is a keen football player he will struggle to find much here apart from the house soccer competition. Rugby fixtures against a huge number of schools including the top public schools, many on a Saturday. Six teams in the first form alone, and more than 20 in total, so plenty of opportunities for everyone to have a go. Boys are bussed to Barn Elms in Barnes for training – a round trip of not much less than an hour.

Water polo also popular, with fixtures against other schools; hockey, skating and basketball are other main activities at present; also a good, well-used, on-site 17m pool and gym where you can see many rowers in training. World Challenge has more participants than any other school in the country – state and independent – and sends boys on exciting, self-financed trips of a lifetime. Also popular is D of E. CCF perhaps the biggest in any state school, both army and RAF – tours, camps and expeditions of all kinds. Lots of sixth involved in community work – helping at local schools and care homes, soup kitchens on Saturdays, the offices of a local charity etc.

He regales us with his plans for a dance studio, which is in the pipeline

Mr McFadden has a delightfully refreshing and modern attitude to educating boys. 'Arts are very important in a boys' school,' he says, and regales us with his plans for a dance studio, which is in the pipeline. 'The boys will respond really well to dance classes,' he enthuses. He is right, agrees one parent, who remembers how much her son enjoyed knitting and crocheting while in the Junior House. Boys here will throw themselves into anything. The key thing is to make it fun.

Music is excellent, fuelled by those who come up from the Junior House, all of whom have exceptional aptitude. Some 600+ pupils learn at least one instrument. Bands, including the popular Seagrave Stompers, choirs and orchestras thrive and are well-housed in the arts centre. The chamber choir recently went on a tour to Prague, and recorded their first CD with music sung on the tour. The Schola Cantorum is a choir of professional standard and considerable significance in the world of RC – and secular – music: three visits to Rome in as many months, including representing the Vatican in Al Gore's Live Earth initiative. They record for films and TV, were one of the main choirs at the mass for the beatification of Cardinal Newman on the Papal visit to Britain and are regarded with deserved respect. They sing at the weekly vigil mass at the Brompton Oratory. A recent performance of St John Passion was by all accounts breath-taking – but this is the norm here. Concerts take place at St John's Smith Square as well as the school theatre, and there are plenty of other choirs – these boys (and girls) want to sing. A recent highlight was the girls' choir performance at the Vigil mass in Westminster Cathedral.

School's on-site arts centre is an impressive asset and includes stunning 300-seat galleried theatre in which full scale shows are mounted –a minimum of four performances each year, including one musical. When we visited, Sophocles' Antigone was in rehearsal – the sixth form play. Recent productions include Guys and Dolls, The Government Inspector and Henry V, as well as Joseph and his Technicolour Dreamcoat – performed by the junior boys. Good display spaces – a stimulating photo show by member of staff was good to see, along with a vast Paolozzi brutalist sculpture. Pupils go on to study art/art history and architecture at prestigious institutions. No photography or textiles on offer, though both are available in extracurricular clubs.

Lots of overseas trips in the holidays – foreign exchanges, cultural and historical visits. Rugby tours to far-flung places and singers and instrumental players performing far and wide.

Services here are intimate and spiritual – only room for one of the houses each day and for the young boys in Junior House; part of the Schola sing, eg, Fauré Requiem

Background and atmosphere: Founded in 1863 by the Oratorian Fathers, the school has recently celebrated its 150th anniversary. It moved to its present site and buildings – in the lee of Chelsea FC's massive stadium – in the 1970s and has worn surprisingly well. Splendid extension and refurbishment of main teaching area recently completed. A bright glass central atrium with pods of different sizes round the edge – for smaller groups and lessons away from the main central area, which is the school library. This is where sixth formers come during their free periods. There is calm peacefulness, no doubt enhanced by the Seven Virtues of Man, which are encapsulated in images and text in panels that climb to the glass roof at the top. Around the outer edges the Beatitudes are depicted. On ground level in the centre is a stunning modern statue of Mary with an adolescent Jesus, complete with apron and the tools of his carpentry trade. A welcome change from the Madonna and child, and so fitting in a school where mothers and sons are working out this next phase in their relationship.

This stunning new development is a modern and dynamic contrast to the old-fashioned class rooms for years 7 and 8, complete with the old style wooden desks, storage inside and inkwell on top. Everyone eats by house in their 'house rooms' (aka classrooms outside feeding times) with six separate serveries. An unusual system, but it seems to work. Some rooms and corridors, notably in the sixth form areas, are scruffy and lacking in soul, but with plans for landscape gardening afoot for the sixth form garden, as well as the creation of a quiet room for reflection and contemplation, it is apparent that there is always attention on improvement and change. We liked the brick courtyard, Chapel Courtyard, with its lead flashing. No football in break and at lunch time here. Health and safety has stopped that. The infrastructure has undergone a profound makeover since we last visited and the boys and staff reinforce an air of engagement and pride, a sense of collaborative energy and achievement.

The chapel, opened in 1992 by Basil Hume and dedicated to St Philip Neri and St Edward the Confessor, is simple in design and has a warm and gentle feel. Services here are intimate and spiritual – only room for one of the houses each day and for the young boys in Junior House; part of the

Schola sing, eg, Faure Requiem. Beautiful. Major ceremonies held in the famous, huge, Italianate Oratory Church in South Kensington. The Catholic ethos underlies all aspects of the school but not obtrusively or obsessively – it is simply a given and central also to Mr McFadden's plans to develop the community involvement of the school. While a practising Catholic himself, Mr McFadden has a much lighter touch than many heads in similar kinds of school. He maintains a sense of wry irony, which many see as a much-needed balance to the rigorous demands of a Catholic education. Long-standing commitment to local primary schools and charities – such as SURF and the SVP soup kitchen – with sixth formers carrying out voluntary work and the music department involved in outreach programmes.

Pastoral care and discipline: Discipline is acknowledged to be tight – rules are strict and enforced strictly. Any mobile phones spotted on the premises will be confiscated and have to be collected by parents. Eight boys were expelled or left in Mr McFadden's first year after two cannabis smoking incidents. 'You need a clear-cut policy, but you have to have a listening ear and heart.' The approach is 'compassionate', but zero tolerance for physical violence – automatic suspension for anyone who tries to sort a problem by 'raising a hand against someone else'.

House system – there are six houses with 200 pupils in each house – encourages friendships between the year groups and boys in the sixth can mentor those younger who need support over a subject or a problem. Parents mostly praise the staff for their pastoral care – especially the deputy heads – of whom one has been in the school for 20+ years since the start of her career and the other who is a past pupil of the school. However – as with the academics – a complaint we keep hearing is about communication channels and the prompt resolution of problems. Whereas under the old regime parents would balk at going straight to the top, the current head is much more approachable and is available. There is a culture of deference among parents here, however, so it still takes some boldness to take a proactive step. The sixth form girls talk of close relationships across the two year groups – a benefit of having only 80 girls in total.

Mr McFadden has brought with him a definite shift in emphasis – which is taking time to seep through decades of rigorous and sometimes steely discipline. He would like to see less 'reaction' and more proactivity, and his vision is that through charitable service programmes, and the self-reflection programme that goes with that, the young adults under his supervision will acquire a taste for 'goodness' and doing and being good. The sixth formers go on 'twilight retreats' at Heythrop College, where they attend talks and discuss issues of life over dinner. Part of this vision has been the establishment of the charitable foundation that is linked with the school, an achievement he is particularly proud of.

Pupils and parents: From a vast geographical area, most London boroughs, inner and outer – some leave home before dawn breaks to come here. Over 50 languages spoken at home; serious Roman Catholicism the only – but unifying – common denominator. A higher number of professional families than in most inner London comprehensives, and the school still has a traditional public school air about it. Parents are warming to head's drive to involve them in all ways – social, educational and practical. Parents' groups for sports, music and food, and more to follow.

Reports are now termly and home-school contact far more a normal thing, though complaints persist of parents not being kept in touch. Children appreciate the knock-ons of greater parental involvement and find it supportive and helpful. The boys themselves are relaxed, friendly, ambitious and hard-working. Classes are head down and concentrating. We heard no raised voices, saw few inattentive faces. Pupils have a sense of pride in themselves and in the school which one would wish to see replicated everywhere. The only boy who wouldn't like it here, we were told, was someone who didn't want to involve himself.

The sixth formers go on 'twilight retreats' at Heythrop College, where they attend talks and discuss issues of life over dinner

Sixth form girls are no mere modern import designed to boost results. They date back to a link with a girls' school in the 19th century and were incorporated into the sixth in the 1950s after a merger. Their numbers are small but, says head, 'they add so much to the school'. It was good to see girls and boys out and about in the lunch hour clearly in relaxed friendship and at ease – no cattle market or points system here. Popular among politicians – Tony Blair and Nick Clegg both sent their sons here. Notable former pupils include Simon Callow, rugby union star Michael Swift and Hayley Atwell. Oh – and David McFadden.

Entrance: Simpler than hitherto, but heart-sinking for anyone other than an assiduously practising Roman Catholic family. In fact, don't bother to apply unless you are a pillar of your local church and known to your priest, who will have to vouch for your bona fides – both pupil's and family's; early baptism essential. Admission process involves completing the school's Religious Inquiry Form and a local authority Common Application Form. Eight hundred plus apply for the 160 places. Junior House boys transfer automatically and parents praise the seamless transition. Sixth form also over-subscribed. Requirement is B grades in six GCSEs and at least a C in maths and English. This is the stated requirement, but parents we spoke to said the standard was in fact much higher. Beware the postman if your son looks like he won't make the standard expected at A level. A letter is likely to arrive during year 11 to warn that you need to find a place elsewhere. Forty places for girls attract 200 applicants and, again, the RC credentials are what counts, plus 'expected performance at GCSE and suitability for an A level course which will be sought from each pupil's current school'. Likely applicants are invited to a 'course suitability meeting'. Girls join from Sacred Heart – virtually the whole year applies – Gumley, the Ursuline Convent and a few from Lady Margaret's.

School was subject to another damning report from the Office of the Schools Adjudicator, which found it to have broken over 100 aspects of the schools admissions code over the last two years, using its entry system to cherry pick a disproportionately privileged and white pupil population. This, the latest of several reports with similar findings, requires the school to change its admissions policies 'as quickly as possible'. The school has amended the 2015 admissions criteria – now boils down to early baptism and child and parent having attended mass at the London Oratory church every Sunday for at least three years – but is already in the process of changing it back.

Exit: Most (around 75 per cent) stay on after GCSE; almost 400 in sixth form. Regularly win Oxbridge places (10 in 2015), covering the range of disciplines. There are always a few who do music, but a good and fairly equal spread of arts, sciences and practical subjects. Otherwise to good universities everywhere to read everything. Refreshingly few silly subjects pursued – these pupils have been properly taught and sensibly advised.

Remarks: Much that is excellent and not just the obvious – the music, the academics, but also the attention given to spiritual and emotional development. An ideal choice for a son (or sixth form daughter) who tows the line. Approach with caution if you have a scatty child who balks at authority.

Lycee Français Charles de Gaulle

35 Cromwell Road, London SW7 2DG

Tel: 020 7584 6322

Independent · Pupils: 2,370 · Ages: 3–18 · Sixth form pupils: 530 · Fees: up to £10,890 pa

Email: inscription@lyceefrancais.org.uk
Website: www.lyceefrancais.org.uk

37

Proviseur: Since 2012, Mr Olivier Rauch. Degrees in history and geography from University of Lyon as well as Agregation (French civil servant educational leadership qualification). Previously head of lycée in Rabat and a lycée in Toulouse (which included a preparatory programme for the prestigious Grandes Ecoles). Started career as a history and geography teacher. Married, with three grown up children who live abroad.

Urbane and distinguished, he is confident in his preparation, knowledge and previous experience of running large French lycées, yet a touch of humility makes for easy conversation. He's also head of the three satellite primary feeder schools.

One of his major concerns is the launch of a new school in Wembley in 2015. He and his leadership team are working on the bigger problem of how to redistribute London's French school-age children into satellite French schools, and how to use the space this would free up at Charles de Gaulle – more student lounges, common areas and specialist classrooms. However he knows families worry how the inevitable change in location for some might affect them.

Another goal is to assess the anomalies between the French baccalaureate and A levels that seem to impede his leavers' entry into some British university courses (medicine for example). And if that weren't enough, he's also got the school's centenary in 2015.

Parents comment that discipline has improved since head's arrival – he thinks this may be a result of his close communication with students via the student council.

Academic matters: Lycée Charles de Gaulle is the premier French school in Britain and one of the largest in the world. The raison d'être is to provide French education leading to the French baccalaureate, regarded by many as one of the most robust school-leaving qualifications there is. With many dual national French-English families enrolled, the Lycée also offers GCSE and A levels.

Most parents seem to feel that overall the kids are well taught, learning lots, enjoying the challenge and loving the school's international community

The French model has the following divisions: maternelle (reception and year 1), primaire (years 2-6), college (years 7-10) and lycée (years 11-13). In primaire and college, the school offers the French curriculum in French. From the final year of college (year 10) students either move over to the British section to do GCSEs and IGCSEs followed by A levels or continue through to the French baccalaureate. Parent perspectives on the Lycée vary significantly depending on their own cultural expectations of what constitutes a school education, but most parents seem to feel that overall the kids are well taught, learning lots, enjoying the challenge and loving the school's international community.

Primary class teachers do everything (including art and PE) while specialists support IT and music. The quality of the art is down to the creativity of the teacher but we've heard of some great stuff with cross-curricular projects and older classes partnering with younger ones. Parents say there's 'frequent assessment and evaluation' so a struggling child is quickly identified. A primary parent with British school experience describes the French system as 'less flexible, but of high standard.' Class sizes are about 28, with an assistant in each class. Classroom arrangements are fairly traditional, with desks in rows, though we saw some more varied arrangements.

College is another story. Some students entering college come from schools where the entire enrolment is less than the year group they are joining. Students move around for different lessons in what one parent described as an 'anonymous teacher environment.' Students have advisers whom they see for maybe 30 minutes per week and there's no expectation of pastoral care on the adviser's part. They monitor pupils' progress through frequent assessment and parents are kept informed. The problem is that it's public knowledge, so if you are bottom of the heap everyone knows, which can take its toll

on the self-esteem of less confident adolescents. The survivors – and there are plenty who thrive on the mounting pressure – develop strong independent skills and learn to manage their time and work successfully, attributes French parents expect to see.

The French curriculum is followed in the French section for the oldest students (confusingly called the 'lycée'). In year 12 there are three French baccalaureate pathways: economics and social science, literature and science, where the subjects studied vary as do the number of hours devoted to each. The word is that there is pressure from both school and parents to go down the prestigious science route. Because so many students are fluent in English, many do a GSCE in English within the French bacc stream.

The international version of the French baccalaureate (which follows the French bacc curriculum but has more courses in English and leads to the same official French bacc exams) has recently been introduced, so it's too soon to evaluate. (Not to be confused with the IB diploma). Students join this programme in year 10; transfer from this programme into the British section is only available in year 12 and depends on availability of space. No 'bacc-light' – this programme reputedly demands an even heavier time commitment than the regular bacc.

The British section offers the GCSE/A level pathway. Students must be fluent enough in English to manage. Discipline is also an issue – nobody with a rap sheet gets in. Occasionally this route is apparently recommended for students who may not succeed with the French bacc.

Year 10 pupils do a wide range of about 10 courses, including French of course, but also a third language (pupils are spoilt for choice – Italian, Spanish, German, Arabic, Russian, Greek and Latin on offer). French IGCSE exams are compulsory, which pleases parents, though there seem to be some questions about timing with kids sitting exams too early.

Places in the British section are competitive; with the Lycée full to capacity, expansion of this programme seems unlikely

In year 11 students generally drop one or two subjects as they get into their AS level and A level subjects. Parents rave about the maths, chemistry and physics, but suggest that those interested in the arts tend to look elsewhere (French education is not noted for intellectual autonomy or commitment to creativity, which are fairly fundamental for art). French and PE are compulsory until year 13; since 2015, A level French is taken in year 13.

Deciding which route to choose – French bacc or British A levels – can be daunting. Those opting for the British tend to be dual nationals, non-French who joined the Lycée because their kids were in a French system and Anglophile French families setting down permanent roots in the UK.

The appeal of the French bacc is its strong global reputation, with its slavish commitment to developing intellectual rigour. But it's hard work, rigid, requires lots of memorisation and absorbing of new information. 'The French system crams knowledge into your brain – and we know the brain is a muscle that can be stretched,' says one French parent.

But some French students aiming for a UK university question the need to do the full-blown bacc when they can focus on more specialised A levels. Plus it's no secret that class sizes in the British section are smaller (about 12 compared to 28 to 30 for the French section) and the teaching style is more conducive to project work, class discussions and debates.

The appeal of the French bacc is its strong global reputation, with its slavish commitment to developing intellectual rigour. But it's hard work

The French bacc classes, 'no wishy-washy child-centred approach,' are more traditional, 'cruelly elite' in a 'sink or swim' learning environment. 'Teachers instruct with minimal empathy. You listen and absorb the learning, which can be a challenge for students with strong personalities inclined to engage in debate and, God forbid, challenge the teacher.' Then there is the matter of 'loyalty to French heritage.' If they move to the British section some families lament the move away from the French educational tradition, even though it may be the right decision educationally. British section kids have more time for extracurricular activities. Places in the British section are competitive; with the Lycée full to capacity, expansion of this programme seems unlikely. But more French students are considering the advantages of the A level university pathway, so there are more applicants than spaces.

Ongoing discussion amongst parents about A level results. The small size of the A level cohort means there are limited courses offered and time-tabling clashes can prevent kids from taking the courses they want, leading some frustrated families to change schools after GCSEs. It has also been suggested that some French parents whose children are in the British section have a hard time overcoming the 'pedagogical cultural divide' between the French and British systems; they simply don't understand the flexibility that British teachers have in delivering the curriculum.

The governance and management structure of the Lycée is naturally focused on the French curriculum. For a British deputy head, finding a way to sit within that institutional culture is undoubtedly a challenge. Although the policy of rotating the head makes sense for Lycées worldwide, it probably has an impact on attention to GCSEs, A levels etc in the British section. Each new head has to get up to speed with the whole (and for them, anomalous) British programme, along with all the other challenges of running such a large institution. It's a steep learning curve for even a top educationalist.

French bacc results are excellent, above the French national average. In 2015, 72 per cent of students got 'mention bien' or 'mention très bien' grades.

A levels are by comparison less impressive, with 46 per cent A*/A grades in 2015. French A level results could be more impressive, given the context, although the school points out that students only have three hours a week for French and take the exam a year earlier than other schools. I/GCSE results show roughly 57 per cent A*/A grades in 2015. Parents think this differential in results between the French bacc and A level has been taken on board by the head.

Although French nationality, language and heritage is the common denominator here, some kids are not completely fluent in French. It's full immersion, so if a child isn't capable of fully functioning in French by the age of 5, parents say they'll struggle when reading and writing begins. Others move their children out as they get older because parents lack sufficient French language to fully support them – unless they have a French-speaking nanny at home to sustain the French speaking day and supervise homework. English as a second language is taught from primary, with some setting for levels in consideration of the native speakers. In college, students are streamed for English. Other languages are available but no mother tongue instruction other than French and English.

For students with special needs, the educational psychologist and speech and language adviser recommends what sort of specialist might help manage the student's learning (dyslexia is not uncommon) but the school itself does not provide much support in-house. School has disabled access in all but one building but the logistics of the daily timetables and student movements mean that students with mobility challenges would struggle here.

Many teachers (average age early 40s) are civil servants, with professionalism and benefits for which French teachers are renowned. Forty-five per cent have been at the Lycée for more than 10 years.

Games, options, the arts: On Wednesdays, primary classes end early but extra activities like cooking, crafts, IT, sports and games are offered. Human Rights Club, Justice in the Heart and House of Students are student-led activities the British and French section students do together, but French section students have less time to devote to these.

Curriculum-related residential trips abroad include India, Berlin (history), Paris (Comédie Française), Greece (classics), Venice (Italian), New York (art), Moscow (Russian). Compulsory work experience programmes in years 10 or 11 are organised by parents.

Lycée has spread and now occupies a city block across from the Natural History Museum. If approaching the area during pick-up you'll think you've alighted at the wrong end of the Eurostar

A few hundred students do sports, many on Saturdays at the sports facility in Raynes Park, competing against London schools and schools abroad. There's a school sports day but parents warn: 'Don't expect to get a ribbon unless you place first, second, or third.' Music is popular, with ensembles, orchestra or choir to choose from.

Background and atmosphere: School was founded to serve London's French population, but also to further France's 'mission civilisatrice' – making French culture and education available to the Brits. During the Second World War it became the home of the Free French and the head sits in the office once occupied by General de Gaulle, so the school's name has meaning. British section was created 60 years ago to offer the French programme in English, but the differences in the French bacc and A levels meant that a marriage was not practical, so the British section sits within the organisation as a 'stand alone'. Over the years the Lycée has spread and now occupies a city block across from the Natural History Museum. If approaching the area during pick-up you'll think you've alighted at the wrong end of the Eurostar.

Part of the AEFE (Agency for Teaching of French Education Abroad), the Lycée is one of more than 100 overseas schools directed by the Ministry of Education and is governed by a committee including the French ambassador and other diplomats. Heads are rotated, with posts lasting up to five years. British section is managed by Kelvin Zane, dapper ex-deputy-head of a London comprehensive, whose fluid command of French has enabled him

to adapt to this large French organisation. His UK experience is invaluable when it comes to matters such as child protection and Ofsted.

Facilities have been renovated to absorb increasing student numbers – a combination of inter-connected new build and Victoriana and using lots of cheerful colours. Buildings open out at the back to play area shared by all ages. Parents say 'it looks confusing, but the kids figure it out in a day or two.' Primary is in a building shared by upper classes on the top floor. There's a large hall for dramatic and musical performances, music and art rooms; PE is outside in the central yard, at local sports facilities or own grounds in Raynes Park. The yard has large canopies with seating areas to provide all-weather cover; no indoor play area.

A large library mushrooms over several floors, separated into college and lycée sections. Classrooms have desks in traditional rows. Computers in the libraries, study rooms and computer lab, but not much evidence of technology inside the classrooms.

Lunch is served in a bright, clean cafeteria. Youngest have their own lunch room; lunch is compulsory unless there are extraordinary dietary needs. Varied three course menu looks just short of Cordon Bleu by usual school standards. Considering that the chef turns out more than 2,500 meals a day, the food looked and smelled very appealing; fish always on offer for those with Kosher or Halal preferences.

School also boasts an impressive medical centre, staffed with sympathetic nurses and a full-time doctor. Parents are happy with home-school communication, and it's easy to have a quick chat with the primary teacher at dismissal. The formal communication cycle is 'front loaded' with year-group parent events at the beginning of the year; after that it's up to parents to seek out the teachers – but they'll be in touch if there's a problem.

Pastoral care and discipline: With such an enormous student body, parents' reports are mixed. Some parents insist the kids 'don't get lost, are well looked after,' while others say that once in college 'students are a number and their teachers hardly know them.' For students joining college, the school tries to put them in classes with three designated friends to ease the culture shock of coping with the sheer scale of the Lycée. This is less a concern for rising Lycée primary students already familiar with the environment.

Playground attendants are a prominent French feature – supervisors keeping an eye on everyone. College students may leave campus provided they have parents' permission (most don't); in the top years most go out for lunch. A nifty school diary is issued to track home-school communication; the back cover has every student's photo, identification and timetable so anyone trying to slip out can be identified and sent back to class.

The children are cheerful and polite; primary teachers remind them about the importance of greeting people respectfully. No lockers – backpacks are stored here and there. No reports of any significant behaviour issues; everyone knows what is expected. If students fall short, they may be given more homework or required to attend school on Saturday. School psychologist offers counselling for students. Secondary school year group leaders have offices in their own sections of the school, with a secretary to manage the 300 or so kids in each level.

Parents warn that drop off and pick up can be stressful. By staggering start and finish times the school manages the flow of traffic pretty well under the circumstances. But parents need to be prepared for the possibly overwhelming feeling of chaos and confusion at the start.

Pupils and parents: The French connection is the common denominator. Vast majority are French nationals with at least one French parent, some dual nationals (British/French), a few British. Other nationalities include Canadian, American, Italian, Spanish, Lebanese, Moroccan and Russian. Many parents are in London on short-term assignments – diplomatic, financial services, media, industry. The generously subsidised fees (not available in the British section) widen the socio-economic net, attracting families who may not normally aspire to private education. Parents prefer this more realistic reflection of society to the rarefied atmosphere of economic privilege that they associate with many London independent schools.

Students come from all over – some with long commutes on public transport – but they feel it's worth it. In some cases the main wage-earner commutes to France or travels internationally but the family has chosen to stay in London in order to keep the kids at the Lycée.

The APL (parents' association) organises after-school activities, raises funds, supports the athletics programme and serves as a sounding board for issues of community interest. Some non-French speakers say it's difficult to become involved. Eclectic list of 'vieux garçons et filles' includes Jacqueline Bisset, the late Natasha Richardson, Gyles Brandreth, Lady Olga Maitland, Roland Joffé.

Entrance: Registration process begins around April of the entry year, with decisions sent in early May. Highly over-subscribed, entry is described as 'a nightmare, haphazard and chaotic.' Families normally apply to other schools as well; some start off elsewhere to await an offer. There's a priority list of criteria: children of French diplomats, siblings (in primary only), children from another official French school (locally or abroad), including

Varied three course menu looks just short of Cordon Bleu by usual school standards. Considering that the chef turns out more than 2,500 meals a day, the food looked and smelled very appealing

students following the CNED (the French distance learning programme), then any miscellany of Francophones fortunate enough to get in.

Siblings trump everything else in primary so families bank on getting one tiny first foot in the door, knowing the others are pretty much a shoe-in. One French national tells us she put her children on the waiting list from the earliest time allowed. Her eldest was unsuccessful but a few days after the term began the younger one was offered a place, posing a dilemma for managing two-school runs simultaneously. When she explained this to the school, they somehow magicked up a space for the second child.

Best tip for locals is to transfer from one of the official AEFE Ecole Homologuée nursery schools such as Ecole le Hérisson, L'Ecole des Petits (Fulham) or La Petite Ecole. Feeders for primaire entry include the annexe schools – Wix (Clapham), South Kensington, Ealing and Fulham. Year 7 feeders include Ecole Jacques Prévert, L'Ecole Bilingue, L'Ecole des Petits and L'Ecole de Battersea. For year 10 (British section) and year 11 (French section) it's the Bilingual College in Kentish Town (CFBL). Beware though – not all schools with emphasis on French language are official AEFE schools, so check the Lycée's website if you're banking on this as your golden ticket. Families do move on so vacancies arise mid-year, but school always refers to the waiting list. According to one successful mother, 'this is the only hope for a local family wanting their child to go to the Lycée' and requires strategic planning of Napoleonic proportions.

No admissions testing and once a child is in, parents have no worries about future entrance exams such as 11+ or CE.

Exit: The Lycée prides itself on its careers department, with advisers specialising in UK, US and French universities. Careers counselling begins in year 11; a major careers forum involves experts and university reps from three continents. Some parents feel more coordination is required to rationalise the Lycée exams and Oxbridge and Russell Group entrance criteria, and more focus needed on writing UCAS personal statements.

Roughly one quarter go to French universities, with 10 per cent of bacc graduates gaining entry into the Grandes Ecoles. British destinations include Oxbridge, Manchester, Bristol, Essex, King's College London, Southampton and Surrey; American destinations include Rhodes Island School of Design, Virginia, McGill, Santa Clara and NYU. A few do gap years.

Money matters: A 50 per cent AEFE subsidy (except for those in the British section) makes for bargain tuition by London standards. Some welfare grants and bursaries – and APL has been known to rally when a family falls on hard times.

Remarks: This is a huge institution yet parents say children are happy, well taught and love the cultural diversity. The waiting lists are testimony to the school's overall success. With the French and Francophile population growing daily, it seems that the entente cordiale is alive and well in this petit coin of London.

Mander Portman Woodward (MPW)

90–92 Queen's Gate, London SW7 5AB

Independent • Pupils: 600 • Ages: 14–19 • Sixth form pupils: 550 • Fees: up to £26,784 pa

Tel: 020 7835 1355

Email: london@mpw.co.uk
Website: www.mpw.co.uk

38

Principal: Since 1997, Steven Boyes BA MSc PGCE (40s). Originally from Leeds, he won a scholarship to read geography and English at Lancaster University, before taking a PGCE and MSc in management sciences at Durham. Since then, his entire career has been spent in sixth form colleges – starting out with teaching A level and Oxbridge candidates before rising rapidly to headship of MPW at the age of 31. As a director of the MPW group, he took time out a few years ago to work on various development projects, but took up the baton again in 2010. Formerly a senior examiner and reviser for A level geography for Edexcel, chair of CIFE (the professional association of English independent sixth form colleges), and prep school governor, he sits on the ISA Inspections and Academic Affairs Committees. He lives near Brighton, with his wife, a lawyer, and two teenage children, filling spare moments with sport, crime fiction and crosswords. Parents praise him for his (undoubted) professionalism, but what he feels proudest of is MPW's ability to 'raise students' aspirations and give them the confidence to believe they can achieve their goals.'

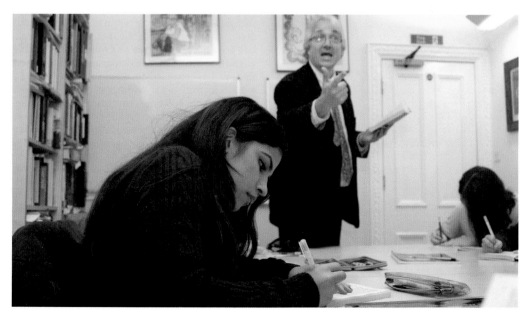

Academic matters: Once primarily a 'crammer' helping students with short-term goals, such as exam retakes or Oxbridge entrance, today MPW is a thriving sixth form college, with over 70 per cent taking two-year A level courses. What marks it out is the range and flexibility of options on offer, with 44 subjects provided in virtually any combination. A long day (9am-6pm) and 36 classrooms allow a timetable that suits almost all ('It doesn't always look pretty, but that's the price you pay for flexibility.'). The college also provides a stand-alone one-year A level programme, handy for aspiring medics moving from arts to science or those with weak results wanting to try their hand at something new. Results overall are strong (34 per cent A*/A, 67 per cent A*-B in 2015), particularly in light of the wide-ranging intake, and a hefty dollop of star performers deliver top grades.

Without doubt, an exam-oriented place, with a persistent spotlight on the syllabus and exam technique honed by regular timed tests and ample supplies of homework, but students confirm it's far more than an exam factory. 'The teachers' knowledge is so broad, they make subjects more interesting because you're able to explore in more depth.' All pupils get plenty of close attention in classes never larger than eight. 'We always deliver on that, never let it creep up to nine,' says the head – which means there's no place to hide. 'At my old

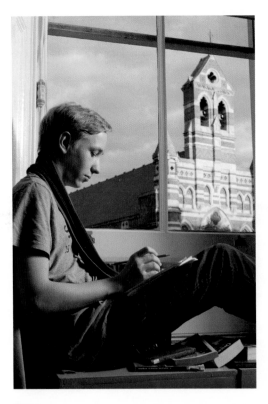

school,' said one pupil. 'I used to sit at the back and not pay attention. You can't do that here.' Well-qualified staff, many of whom are public examiners or have published text books, receive extravagant praise ('brilliant', 'second-to none', 'amazing') not only for their expert subject knowledge but for their willingness to go above and beyond. ('Even when I was away from college in the middle of exams I would email them and they would reply within 15 minutes,' said one former pupil). Teaching style is egalitarian and conversational with technology firmly embedded in the delivery. 'Virtual learning is an efficient and engaging way of getting information across,' says the head. 'There's now such a wealth of information available on line that students need to develop the skills to pare it down.'

About 50 a year take GCSEs (or IGCSEs) either as a two-year course for those joining in year 10, or as one year from year 11 (excellent for those recovering from ill health or recently arrived in the UK). Results good, with 43 per cent A*/A grades in 2015.

About a fifth of students here have some form of special educational need, and the school copes well with mild difficulties, with an SEN specialist, general learning and study skills and individual education plans. ('We're clear what we can do, and if we can't do something we will tell parents there are places much better equipped to help.') MPW continues to provide its traditional refuge for those taking re-sits, with a remarkably flexible range of options to allow for gap year plans. For overseas applicants looking to UK universities without the requisite qualifications, MPW has also recently introduced the University of London International Foundation Programme, developed and assessed by LSE.

Games, options, the arts: Art is a particular strength, with dedicated studios for ceramics, textiles, graphic design and photography. Music taught as an A level, but no school orchestras or groups, so 'not a big school for music.' Extracurricular, once very much an also ran, has become mainstream as MPW has developed its identity as a sixth form college. Today, you'll find the usual add-ons – student council, Duke of Edinburgh (bronze taken by all year 10s) and Bank of England Interest Rate Challenge. Sport has 'improved massively' (though, as one parent commented, 'It's still nothing like at school.'). Compulsory once a week for GCSE students, optional thereafter. Big menu of activities on Wednesday afternoons, with a fleet of coaches delivering to a host of venues. Well-qualified coaching staff in rugby, football and tennis, supplemented by experts in activities like golf. Rugby popular and successful, with matches against leading independents like Dulwich College and Epsom. Football, too, has an enthusiastic following. Those allergic to team sports can enjoy tennis, dance and yoga, and all students have free access to a local gym. Plenty going on outside the classroom: debating,

Staff, many of whom are public examiners or have published text books, receive extravagant praise ('brilliant', 'second-to none', 'amazing') not only for their expert subject knowledge but for their willingness to go above and beyond

poetry competition (this year's theme, Remember, advertised on whiteboards through the college), college magazine, widely attended lecture series. Students also make full use of local museums and theatres with regular trips. Diminutive basement canteen provides healthy-eating options, but local eateries a big draw.

Background and atmosphere: Founded in 1973 by three Cambridge graduates who hoped to apply the best bits of the Cambridge tutorial system to a school, providing more choice and less tradition. Now part of the MPW group, with branches in Cambridge and Birmingham, the London HQ is housed in a series of high-ceilinged, stucco-fronted Victorian buildings in South Kensington. Indoors, all very 21st century, with computers everywhere (including folding into desks). Excellent facilities, too, for the myriad of subjects on offer, including fully-equipped media suites, computing and film rooms, separate art studios for photography and ceramics, new drama studio, and five specially-designed science laboratories. Co-ed throughout (slightly more boys than girls), the atmosphere is grown up, academically disciplined, but socially relaxed. Pupils have a strong sense of community. 'We had an absolute blast, while getting the A level grades we needed to get on the courses we wanted,' said a recent leaver. The size undoubtedly helps. 'My year group feels like a family and I can approach anyone to talk to.'

Pastoral care and discipline: Pastoral care is central to the MPW approach. Each student is assigned a director of studies, who acts as the pivot of their personal and academic life (as well as the main point of contact for parents). 'It's very personalised learning,' says the head. 'We feel if they're nurtured, they'll prosper.' Directors of studies gain a detailed overview of the student's strengths and weaknesses, help manage the workload and deal with other aspects of daily life. 'As well as reading 10 drafts of my personal statement,' said one overseas student, 'my director of studies advised me on practical matters like getting a GP and organising the paperwork needed for a school trip to Italy.'

A level students only required to be in college when they have lessons. GCSE pupils kept under close supervision between classes and given timetabled library sessions to complete homework. Parents are kept in the loop, with plenty of feedback, positive as well as negative. 'They shouldn't feel that every time they receive a call from the college it will be bad news.' Classrooms and libraries orderly and focused, corridors silent. 'The amount of time spent on behavioural management here is miniscule,' says the head. This serenity, however, is achieved by clearly defined boundaries. 'We're very consistent on enforcing the rules. You have to attend, have to behave and have to be on time.' Two or three generally expelled annually. 'The most common reason is a lack of work ethic, which is a corrosive influence on others.' Immediate expulsion for drugs, too, whether on the premises or off, and random drug testing. Fresher's week type activities help integrate newcomers. 'Over 50 per cent of the college is new in any one academic year, but these are well-rounded young people and make friends quickly.'

Pupils and parents: Significant number of refugees from leading independent schools, day and boarding, plus the usual international clientele (about 25 per cent). At A level, incomers are those looking for greater freedom and informality, or for A level combinations or subjects not offered at their current school. Pupils tend to be articulate, friendly and mature.

Entrance: More or less non-selective academically, but the average applicant will have good middling grades (three As, three Bs, a couple of Cs.) 'We have a strong top end, but we'll take someone with six Cs.' What they won't take is someone who doesn't fit the mould. All students are interviewed by the head or senior member of staff to establish whether they have a strong work ethic and understand that 'the price of freedom is behaving like an adult'. 'We're looking for the curious and motivated,' says the head. School references assiduously pursued. 'We want to be sure they're not involved in bullying or other misdemeanours.' International students given admissions tests and interviews. Majority of GCSE students stay on for A level, even if they arrive with other plans. 'Once they've seen it, they find they like the atmosphere.' Some join in the second year of A levels after a hiccup elsewhere.

Exit: Over 70 per to leading Russell Group universities (particularly in London – Imperial, UCL, and LSE all popular). Three to Oxbridge in 2015. About 28 per cent annually to professional degrees (medicine, dentistry, veterinary medicine, science and law) and high numbers, too, to leading art colleges. Specialist preparation for Oxbridge, medics etc.

Money matters: Tutorial colleges will never be the cheapest A level or GCSE option, but most consider MPW good value for money. For the 'talented', there are a limited range of scholarships and bursaries and, for those planning 'worthwhile' travel in a gap years or holiday, there are also travel scholarships worth up to a £1,000.

Remarks: A positive, professional place, with strong teaching and outstanding pastoral care.

Miles Coverdale Primary School

Coverdale Road, Shepherds Bush, London W12 8JJ

State • Pupils: 250 • Ages: Ages 3–11

Tel: 020 8743 5847

Email: admin@milescoverdale.lbhf.sch.uk
Website: www.milescoverdaleprimary.co.uk

Headteacher: Since 2008, Mrs Taranum Baig BEd with French, NPQH. Has studied at the Sorbonne. Previously acting head and deputy head of Dairy Meadow Primary, Ealing and acting deputy head at Stanhope Primary, Greenford. About to become an Ofsted inspector. Born in India and moved to London as a child. Conscientious and hard-working, though encourages staff not to stay too late at school, so they can get a healthy work/life balance. Gentle sense of humour. Likes travelling and heads abroad as often as possible. Enjoys tennis in her spare time. Married. No children. Head says her vision for the school is best summed up by a quotation of Martin Luther King, 'Intelligence plus character – that is the goal of true education.' Head adds, 'irrespective of background.'

Entrance: At 3 into the nursery. Admissions to the nursery are managed by the school office, but from reception to year 6 they are handled by LA, Hammersmith and Fulham. A place at nursery does not guarantee a place in reception. Heavily oversubscribed. Roughly 130 applicants apply for 25 places in nursery; 130 applicants for 30 places in reception. Intake drawn according to local authority's admissions procedure. One form entry.

Exit: Pupils go on to Fulham Cross, Phoenix High School (one in 2015) and Hammersmith Academy (12 in 2015). Some move to schools out of the borough. None to independent sector.

Remarks: School is named after Myles Coverdale, who in the 16th century produced the first complete printed translation of the bible into English. Today, the school accepts all faiths. About to celebrate its centenary. School has gone from strength to strength on current head's watch. She puts this down to high expectations of pupils and staff 'knowing the data' (school keeps a close eye on anyone falling behind), quality of teaching and an excellent team of governors. 'A combination of delivery and accountability,' explains head.

Housed in a vast, Victorian building in the busy heart of Shepherd's Bush. School population reflects the area's multi-cultural mix. Largest contingent is West African, followed by white British/other. Sixty-six per cent do not have English as a first language. Languages spoken at home include Somali, Arabic and a variety of Eastern European tongues. Thirty-one per cent of pupils eligible for free school meals. Head acknowledges that a number of pupils come from unsettled backgrounds, so 'we can give them the stability they sometimes lack at home.' A very inclusive school.

Rated outstanding by Ofsted and placed in the top 100 schools nationally over last three years. Academically, each year group performs well above national average. Head confident that pupils can begin with low attainment levels but will have excellent results under their belts by the time they leave. 'We maximise potential.' Children fully engaged in their lessons and teachers full of energy on the day we visited. School works hard to narrow the gap between higher and lower attainers. Booster classes given to year 6 before Sats to make sure everyone performs well. A handful achieves a remarkable level 6 in maths and in grammar, spelling and punctuation before leaving. School has been awarded a gold club award by Boris Johnson for 'succeeding against the odds in improving pupils' aspirations and achievements.' Head is delighted that she has been made a National Leader of Education and the school has been designated a National Support School, in recognition of the continued school improvement work with other schools at local, national and international levels. A real feather in her cap.

Currently nearly 30 children with statements of special educational need. Early targeted support is the order of the day here, with maths and reading intervention groups for those falling behind. Specialist unit offers speech and language classes for children with language impairment (the only one of its kind in the borough). Pupils here are seen as being very much part of the mainstream school. These classes provide support for 20 pupils, between the ages of 3 and 7, in two classes of 10. Wide variety of difficulties catered for, from those who are unable to produce speech sounds to others who find it challenging to recall words. Most pupils then transfer to their local mainstream school at 7 or, if still in need of on-going help, stay at Miles Coverdale where they receive additional support.

Full-time speech and language therapist. Children must have a statement before being accepted. A counsellor visits twice weekly to help with children with social and behavioural problems.

Strikingly attractive, bright and colourful school. Most classrooms are huge, often two rooms knocked into one. Food technology room where all pupils are given the opportunity to cook; large ICT suite; welcoming library, complete with dinosaur statue made by a member of staff. New library is wonderful: comfy sofas, bright murals of book characters and inventive furniture, all of which underline the emphasis on reading within the school. Even the most reluctant readers must be enchanted. Lots of small rooms dotted around the place for one-to-one support or small group sessions. Two playgrounds, one for each key stage, with plenty of equipment and a quiet area 'which doesn't get used very often!' Separate outside play area for reception pupils, complete with sand pits and water tables.

Staff consists of a mix of long servers of more than 20 years and more newly qualified. Low teacher turnover. Head keen on constant training of staff. 'We see ourselves as a learning community. We all need to keep learning. Every member of staff needs to keep developing to have an impact.' High pupil/teacher ratio, with two or more assistants per class of 30. High morale among the dedicated staff. One parent felt 'the teachers are close to the parents. They're welcoming and friendly. If you have an issue, they are happy to discuss it. They don't tell you to arrange a meeting and come back another time. They are very willing to talk to parents.' A teacher we spoke to happily gives up his free time to take pupils to events at weekends, such as chess tournaments.

Music is a strength of the school. Music co-ordinator encourages the children to join musical events going on out of school. 'I keep my eyes open for those with that something extra, then I push them on. I even go to the auditions with the parents'. Dynamic department which uses IT to great effect. Choirs put on performances for elderly in local nursing homes. Drama is also strong. Plays include an annual Black History performance as well as Christmas and year 6 productions. Poetry recitals, debates and presentations also encouraged. According to one mother, the performances are highly anticipated and 'parents always love the plays they put on.' Numerous outings and trips for all age groups including to Royal Opera House, Lyric Theatre as well as frequent workshops including with English National Ballet and maths magicians. Children are exposed to a variety of enriching experiences from Shakespeare to street dance. Head says, 'The reason for us arranging these activities is that the core of the children here doesn't have access to this sort of experience otherwise. I want them to be introduced to the multi-cultural aspects of Britishness, to British values.' Residential activity trip for year 6 leavers. A hugely busy extracurricular timetable on offer here.

The school participates in inter-school sport tournaments and events but a lack of silverware reflects the dearth of recent victories. Coaches come in from nearby QPR football club. Fencing and football popular and cricket also offered in the summer.

Extended school day available to help working parents with a breakfast club and a nearby after-school play centre, meaning children can do a 10 hour day. Pupils able to attend up to three clubs a week and all are free; current clubs include karate, basketball and dance. Homework club for pupils who need help. A popular five-week summer school is led by teachers and support staff and includes maths and literacy lessons as well as plenty of fun 'for those children who don't get away on holiday

all summer.' Head very aware that many families struggle to cope and the school does all it can to give the pupils a chance to enjoy life as well as excel academically.

High parental satisfaction. Those we spoke to were very supportive of the school and felt there were plenty of chances to get involved. A number of the parents work here as support staff. One mother said she was happy to 'let the school get on with it' as she felt 'it takes good care of the boys and girls.' School reaches out to parents and adult classes are held within the school buildings during the day, including English, computer-literacy, sewing and bike-riding. Workshops also on offer which show parents how they can best support their children with maths. Coffee mornings held regularly at the school for parents. A feeling among the parents that they are very lucky to have found this high-achieving school. One mother we spoke to had experienced seven other schools before coming here and she believed that this one was head and shoulders above the rest.

Outward looking school which is very involved in local community. Teachers work with numerous outside agencies and school provides placements for work experience, teacher training and volunteering. Now has much higher profile within the community and is seen in a positive light by neighbours. Christmas and summer fêtes sponsored by local businesses. School takes fundraising seriously and raises a substantial amount for charity each year.

Head says, 'We are what we are. We're successful. The results speak for themselves'. Year 1's mission statement sums up the ethos of the school: to 'respect each other, sing out loud, smile often and work hard.' Head has certainly transformed this school from one which had 'a poor attitude and negative feel' to one that is firing on all cylinders. Seriously impressive on every level.

More House School (London)

22–24 Pont Street, London SW1X 0AA

Tel: 020 7235 2855

39

Independent · Pupils: 220 · Ages: 11–18 · Sixth form pupils: 40 · RC · Fees: £17,160 pa

Email: office@morehousemail.org.uk
Website: www.morehouse.org.uk

Headmistress: Since April 2014, Amanda Leach, previously deputy head here for eight years. BSc in sports science from Liverpool and PGCE from Exeter. Has taught at Cranbrook School, Kent, and Uffculme School in Devon. Spent a year teaching EFL in Rome. Joined More House in 1998 as a science

teacher, and has also taught ICT and PE here. 'Why would I want to leave here? I love it so much,' she enthuses. Married with two daughters; husband is director of sport at Bedales. 'I love being outdoors with my family. My kids are into gymnastics. We are not allowed to sit still for very long at home!'

Described by one parent as being 'approachable and down to earth, though we don't see much of her.' Another said, 'I love Mrs Leach. She is breathing new life into the place. She has lots of energy and is a total delight.' Enthusiastic, effervescent and warm. Can be seen cycling to school from Putney every morning and girls wave to her along the Kings Road as she races past. A breath of fresh air.

Academic matters: Wide range of academic ability. As one parent put it, 'There are less intellectually confident girls here who are nurtured, but there are also some very clever girls, whose parents have chosen the school because it is Catholic.' Core subjects taken in year 7 alongside Latin, history of art, dance, music and drama. All girls take two modern foreign languages and those that are bilingual can take that GCSE early. Maths, science and modern languages taught in ability sets. Religious studies compulsory for GCSE and many choose to continue with it at A level. Head favours the philosophy and ethics course as it 'encourages girl to question their spirituality.' Pupils take eight to 11 GCSEs. Thirty-five per cent A*/A in 2015 and nearly 60 per cent A*-B.

French currently popular at A level, though subjects wax and wane, depending upon the cohort. School happy to have only one or two pupils taking a subject at A level. Polish, Russian and Arabic all fell into this category recently. Timetable built around what girls want to do and school tries to be flexible in terms of what it offers. Twenty-six different subjects currently taught at A level. In 2015, 45 per cent A*/B and 21 per cent A*/A grades. Extended Project Qualification taken by lower sixth. No plans for Pre-U or IB due to school's size.

Head has tightened up on academic rigour, making some significant changes since her appointment. Templates now printed in exercise books to ensure that feedback from teachers is detailed and effective and that there is constant dialogue between staff and pupils. School is also getting better at monitoring girls, with assessment points five times a year to ensure those not making enough progress are quickly identified. Colour-coded boards in staff room help teachers to see when a pupil is falling behind in subjects other than their own and gives a more holistic view of each girl's overall progress. Staff appraisals take place more regularly and twilight sessions help ensure staff members are on board with changes being implemented.

Excellent provision for girls with specific learn-

All musical tastes and talents catered for, from chamber choirs to karaoke and geek club, which involves hand–bell ringing for the Christmas concert. 'The music is exceptional'

ing difficulties. The department comprises a full-time SENCo, speech and language therapist and a part-time ESOL teacher. EAL girls have extra English support until it is up to scratch. School can support girls with dyslexia, dyscalculia and dyspraxia; currently one or two per year group have quite severe difficulties. Currently two girls with Asperger's. About 25-30 girls currently receiving one-to-one support, with others having help with maths and English in small booster groups. Some girls stop support lessons around year 9 and then come back to having support nearer to GCSEs. 'It is flexible. Girls can dip in and out, depending upon their need.' All subjects offer weekly intervention classes for year 11 and above, from October through to start of exams. One parent feels that 'girls have to flag up their need for support themselves, but once the school is aware of it, provision is made pretty quickly'.

Gifted and talented programme for the brightest pupils. 'The top end is identified within three or four weeks of being here. A learning mentor then sits down with them and asks them whether they are being challenged in each subject. We listen to them'. Extension work might include Italian classes for able linguists. School explains, 'It's not just a case of giving them an extra worksheet. It's more undercover than that, but we know who has a special talent or ability. We take notice, but they don't feel pressurized.' Scholars and gifted pupils are invited to join More's Household, which offers lunchtime talks, given by internal and external speakers. Girls here regularly enter and win external prizes, such as national poetry and storytelling competitions. One girl recently made the finals of The Big Bang UK Young Scientists Fair.

Games, options, the arts: Creative and performing arts at the heart of the school. Deserves its artistic reputation and currently boasts a textiles specialist, a painter and a mixed-media artist. Head believes that the art department is good at seeing where a girl's artistic talents lie and then giving her the opportunity to develop her interests whether in clay, textiles or fine art. Weekly, after-school life-drawing classes put on for sixth formers. Numerous visits arranged to London galleries.

Three-quarters of girls have individual music lessons. All year 7 girls play an instrument (brass, string or woodwind), bought through PTA fundraising. Strong choral tradition. All year 7 and 8 girls are in a choir. Optional thereafter. In the last choral concert, 130 girls sang alongside staff, parents and alumnae. Annual international music tour. On a recent choir tour of Rome, girls performed with papal choir in St Peter's in front of Pope and 75,000 spectators. All musical tastes and talents catered for, from chamber choirs to karaoke and geek club, which involves hand-bell ringing for the Christmas concert. 'The music is exceptional. All-inclusive. You don't have to be talented in order to be allowed to perform,' according to one parent.

Drama is another strength of the school. Sold-out drama productions of As You Like It and Grimm's Fairy Tales. Biannual play and musical which run on a carousel system. Musical is staged in a professional theatre. If a smaller production is put on one year then a junior production is also staged so that as many girls as possible can perform. 'Everyone is given a chance,' and certainly no shortage of opportunities for those who want to be in the spotlight.

'PE is being taken much more seriously than in the past,' according to one delighted parent, and sports department is well led. New PE kit has made a world of difference and hoodies without pockets mean that girls are more likely to catch the rounders ball! Practice takes place all over London, including the climbing wall at Imperial College, athletics in Battersea Park, swimming at St Mary's, Paddington and tennis in Cadogan Gardens. For the first three years, all girls participate in netball, rounders, hockey, athletics and dance as well as a healthy active lifestyle programme. Years 10-11 may also do circuit training, fitness classes, spinning and climbing and sixth form takes part in boot camp. Two girls recently selected to represent borough in London Youth Games netball team. Annual sportswomen's dinner in summer term celebrates athletic achievement. Teachers run the London marathon and raise significant amounts for charity in the process. 'The great thing about sport at More House is that everyone participates,' commented one parent. As head explains, 'We are competing against bigger schools. Sometimes we win, sometimes we lose, but all girls get the chance to play in a team.'

Plenty of early morning and lunch time clubs, such as a thriving debating club, as well as play-doh modelling and knitting for those who prefer something more sedate. 'We want the girls to keep their childhood as long as possible. We also offer flower pressing. We don't want girls to bypass that lovely age,' says head. Touch-typing compulsory for all in year 7. Confirmation preparation also offered. Most clubs are run by sixth formers and year 11 girls; some are run by professionals. Enviable overseas trips to Europe as well as ski-ing in America. Year 8 trip to France is a particular highlight, involving canoeing and camping overnight. Those that cannot afford the trips are subsidised, and alternative trips are also organised in London. 'Always lots going on here. That's why I am such a fan of the school,' said one satisfied parent.

Background and atmosphere: Founded in 1953 by canonesses of St Augustine at the request of a group of parents who wanted to send their daughters to a Catholic London day school. Since 1971, the school has been under lay management. Named after Sir Thomas More, the Tudor theologian.

In the heart of Knightsbridge, though not as glamorous as its location might suggest. Described by one parent as being 'essentially two houses in Pont Street with minimal outside space. Pretty scruffy and quite dark.' Much of the school (apart from the head's office and communal areas) was looking distinctly tired, but all has been transformed this summer: classrooms ripped out, new furniture installed and redecorating throughout. One delighted mother told us, 'Mrs Leach has 'been busy tidying up the place, decorating where it was needed and making it more aesthetically pleasing.'

Head is determined that the school should 'not be a pressure cooker. We're not waiting for that top to blow off.' This is a very nurturing environment in which girls are constantly encouraged. One mother commented, 'At parents' evening, the teachers always highlight the girls' strengths and are keen to build on these, rather than just dwelling on what they can't do. It boosts the girls' confidence.' Very small classes which do not change from year 7 to GCSEs. 'That's my one gripe about the school. It would be good for everybody if the classes were mixed up regularly,' said one mother. Almost all classes have no more than 16 girls up till GCSE. Sixth form classes range from one pupil to 10. Family feel to school and all age groups mix well together, partly due to flourishing house system.

Pastoral care and discipline: Catholic heritage and ethos strong, with many crucifixes on display around the school. Currently 40 per cent Catholic, though there are girls of all faiths and none. School has its own chapel and the chaplain takes mass once a week. 'Catholicism is quite a big deal here,' said one parent. 'We get the balance right between Catholic and non-Catholic,' believes head. 'It's part of our foundation, to respect each other and to be kind. I'm not a Catholic, though I went to a convent school and then on to a missionary school, so faith is very much part of me.' Spiritual growth fostered here. Girls also raise decent sums for charity and this is seen an important part of their education.

Excellent relationships between staff and pupils. Girls see their teachers as approachable. As one parent put it, 'The teachers know the girls so well'

Parents cite the pastoral care as being a main strength of the school, and those we spoke to felt that issues were dealt with efficiently and effectively. Head is keen that girls should develop a sense of perspective, and frequently reminds them that 'It's not failure you should worry about. It's how you pick yourselves up. I don't paint a perfect image of myself. We all have ups and downs. It's my duty to help the girls through their difficulties.' Head stands at the door each morning as the girls file past. She can usually spot when something is amiss with a pupil. Girls know they can, and do, knock on her door any time. Layers of support in place, including tutors, and all 'minis' (year 7s) have a 'big sister' in sixth form. Because it is such a small school, eating disorders and emotional difficulties are spotted quickly. Hard for pupils to hide under the radar here.

Excellent relationships between staff and pupils. Girls see their teachers as approachable. As one parent put it, 'The teachers know the girls so well, that's the beauty of a small school.' Occasional short-term suspensions for rudeness to a member of staff but head is not overly quick to punish girls. 'If a girl has messed up, she's going to get an earful from her parents. I tend to ask them what they'd do differently next time.' Saturday detentions recently introduced for persistent offenders.

Pupils and parents: Roughly 70 per cent British. International contingent from all over, including Spain, France, China, Russia, America and Middle East. 'A mixed bag. Some with lots of money, who are driven in and out by chauffeurs, and others who are struggling. Quite diverse, with a good percentage of different cultures,' according to one mother. Girls travel from all over London.

Parents mostly professional. 'I don't think I have the most demanding parents in London. That's a reflection of the girls who are here. These parents want the best for their daughters. They are not idealistic in terms of what their daughters are capable of. They are realistic and know we're going to do the best job we can for them', explains head. Parents feel the communication is good: 'We are kept fully informed, both with the good and bad. We are kept in the loop.'

Entrance: One open day only but private tours given by head throughout year. Part of North London Consortium with exams in English and maths. Prospective pupils spend a half day at More House in the autumn of year 6, which involves an interview with head and sample lessons. Interview is pivotal in many ways. Head always tells girls that they will be able to answer all the questions as they are about themselves, so no need to be nervous. Increasing numbers of applicants every year but lists are closed once 150 have registered. Normally 32 places available (two forms of 16) though some bulge years of 48 (three forms). Girls are either offered a definite place or put on the wait-list. Very few turned down completely and when they are it is 'because they are not More House material as they are off the scale at either end. I can't support the very lowest ability or very highest ability, given the cohort I've got. I don't want one girl on her own at the top. If a girl can't be challenged intellectually by peers here, she's better off elsewhere. It would be great for my results to take them on, but I won't do it,' explains head. Occasional vacancies further up the school are filled quickly. Three or four join in sixth form. Head says she is looking for potential as much as performance at each stage. 'I want to find the golden nugget that's hidden somewhere in a girl. I want to watch them blossom.'

Exit: About 80 per cent stay on for sixth form. 'The ones who leave are those who are too cool for school. I'd rather have the ones who want to be here,' explains head. Some depart for co-ed establishments or go to local sixth form colleges.

Post A level, many go to art college. Others head to universities all over, from Essex to Cardiff. One parent felt the school 'isn't striving to get everyone into university. That's not what they are about. They try to support the girl in finding out what is best for them.' Even if a girl is deemed to be Oxbridge material, there is no pressure on her to apply if it's not the right course for her. Usually one girl to Oxbridge every couple of years. School is now focusing on more careers advice for girls and is aware that it should tap into the expertise of its alumnae more.

Money matters: School offers a number of academic scholarships and exhibitions as well as creative and performing arts scholarships to year 7 and lower sixth. Entry bursaries for those starting the school in year 7, as well as special governors' bursaries offered in response to a particular set of circumstances, and come with provisions attached. Normally only awarded to girls who are already at the school and in examination years. Five per cent off school fees for eldest daughter when there are three or more sisters attending school at same time.

Remarks: If your daughter needs a large, competitive school with plenty of space, this is probably not the place for her. But, as one satisfied customer put it, 'If you're after an all girls Catholic school in central London, this is a great choice. It's not for everyone, but if your daughter wants a small, happy and supportive school, this couldn't be better. If I had my time over, I'd send my daughter here again like a shot'. Head is aware that many parents do not know about More House yet, but that 'word is getting out as we're getting better and better.' The way things are moving, this school is not going to remain a secret for much longer.

Norland Place School

162–166 Holland Park Avenue, London W11 4UH

Tel: 020 7603 9103

Independent • Pupils: 245 • Ages: Girls 4–11; boys 4–8 • Fees: up to £16,389 pa

Email: office@norlandplace.com
Website: www.norlandplace.com

40

Headmaster: Since 2002, Mr Patrick Mattar LRAM MA (40s), a Brummie (though you wouldn't know it), educated at Solihull, one of four siblings all of whom are talented musicians and went to various prestigious music colleges. Came here in 1989 as director of music straight from the Royal Academy of Music. He says if he had gone to an academic establishment he would have been more of an arts/language person than a scientist. A six-year interlude at Wetherby from 1996, where he ended up being deputy head, before returning to Norland to run the school when he was only 36. Married with two young sons. His wife teaches at Sussex House, where several boys move on to from here each year.

Works very closely with his bursar and with proprietor Sylvia Garnsey, who ran the school for 40 years. 'She gives me a loose rein but needs to know what's going on'. Since his arrival a huge number of building and structural systems put in place

With his background one would expect the school to be heavily weighted in favour of music (he confessed to being secretly delighted when asked by parents to do a recital to a packed Steinway Hall in Marylebone to raise money for an auction) but he stresses that equal weight is given to art and sports. 'I've never been one of those heads who thinks "I'm musical and therefore want the school to be musical,"' he says.

Very popular with parents, who comment on his approachable, natural manner and understanding of the children. He teaches years 3 through to year 6 – current affairs, reasoning and some Latin in year 6. He has a good feel for senior schools and which would suit each child, but says he will be as involved as parents want him to be when deciding where their children should go. His quiet confidence brims with integrity. You would think ambition might be making him restless but he clearly loves the job – 'There's never a dull moment – and my favourite part is the children: they're the easiest,' he grins.

Entrance: At 4-years-old. Not selective, so you need to get your child's name down as soon after birth as is feasibly possible – preferably on the day. Parents are given forms so they can apply before birth and deliver it on the way back from the hospital! If you don't get it in until your child is a week old, you will end up on the waiting list. Mr Mattar will make sure he sees all parents who have places, so they understand the ethos here and know what they're signing up to. Children come from a number of local nurseries including The Acorn,

Miss Delaney's, Ladbroke Square, Strawberry Fields, Rolfes and Mynors – no particular feeder. Siblings won't automatically get places – they still have to be registered and will be given priority on the waiting list, but be warned: siblings of a daughter who has left early to go to, eg, Bute, are unlikely to be given priority. 'There's no point coming here unless you want Norland and want it all the way,' head warns.

Exit: Pupils progress to vast range of schools. Boys at 8+ to, eg, Westminster Under, Colet Court, Sussex House, Westminster Cathedral Choir School, Wetherby Prep, St Philips, St Anthony's, Fulham Prep and the odd one to board at, eg, Caldicott.

'There's never a dull moment – and my favourite part is the children: they're the easiest,' he grins

Girls at 11+ to St Paul's, Godolphin and Latymer (head points out that recently nearly half the year got in here – impressive for a non-selective school), Francis Holland (NW1 & SW3), Wycombe Abbey, St Swithun's, Downe House, City of London, Harrodian, Latymer Upper, More House, Notting Hill & Ealing, Oundle, Portland Place, Putney High, Queen's College, Queen's Gate, South Hampstead High and St Mary's Calne.

Remarks: Founded in 1876, situated on bustling Holland Park Avenue in three town houses connected by a maze of corridors and staircases, giving it a very up and down feel, but with two smallish playgrounds and a plethora of outdoor toys. Unashamedly traditional – boys are in shorts, girls neat in blue and white checks, berets are worn in winter, boaters in summer.

A definite flavour of 'old money'. Parents here are terribly discreet and reluctant to be drawn into talking about the school or each other. Increasingly families come from Shepherds Bush and Hammersmith rather than round the corner, as Notting Hill becomes more flashy. To the casual observer it appears very English – though school anxious to point out that it does not select on any criteria at all. Families here seem grounded, wanting what's best for their children without being drawn into the competitive London day school fever which is more susceptible to brand rather than ethos. Lots of children here had parents and grandparents at the school. George Osborne and Hilary Benn are among the alumni. We witnessed excellent rapport between staff and pupils, which was confirmed by parents. Senior girls are natural, mature and responsible but humorous and not fawning.

A wide range of ability. Children assessed for SEN from reception, when any concerns are flagged up and watched. Mild to moderate SEN can be catered for, but children have to be able to make the benchmark each year. EAL is dealt with in class, help often given before school. From early in the morning teachers are on hand to support and stretch those who need stretching, but a charge is made for timetabled learning support lessons.

For the more able ('I try to avoid labelling them as gifted and talented,' says head) lots of opportunity to differentiate and split lessons for English and maths in years 4, 5 and 6, but not setting or streaming. The ethos here is that children support each other – 'everyone has different talents'. Specialist teaching for English, maths and science from year 4.

Two forms per year until year 3, when boys and girls divide. Boys then get their heads down to prepare for the 8+ and one form for girls from years 4

We saw an assembly littered with bunting, every child waving a flag (including the odd German one), a number of them wearing hard hats and 40s style headscarves

to 6. French is taught from the start, with a smattering of Latin from Mr Mattar at the end. 'We're very good at not pressurising the children,' says Mr Mattar, 'while still getting the results.' Humanities has had an injection of energy with the appointment of the dynamic and greatly loved Mrs Hart, who brings history vividly to the present with dramatic interpretrations of, eg, VE day. We saw an assembly littered with bunting, every child waving a flag (including the odd German one), a number of them wearing hard hats and 40s style headscarves and the whole school doing the Lambeth walk.

Nothing is done on a grand scale but we met with great enthusiasm for what is on offer – only one afternoon of sport a week: football and cricket for the boys, a bus ride away; netball and rounders for the girls. Two PE lessons a week happen in the playground and hall. Swimming from year 2 at Kensington leisure centre. DT is incorporated into art – we were shown bird boxes that the year 5s were making for their gardens while others bubbled about growing chickens in incubators. The atmosphere of grounded traditionalism is epitomised by the traditional desks in the classrooms which, when opened, not only reveal neat piles of books but also colourful personal displays – photos, glitter, magazine cut outs – decorated by each child.

A good traditional London day school that prepares each child for the next stage beautifully and punches well above its weight.

Notting Hill Preparatory School

95 Lancaster Road, London W11 1QQ

Tel: 020 7221 0727

Independent • Pupils: 305 • Ages: 4–13 • Fees: £17,460 pa

Email: admin@nottinghillprep.com
Website: www.nottinghillprep.com

41

Headmistress: Since September 2003, Mrs Jane Cameron BEd (50s). Married with three grown-up children. She had run the Acorn Nursery in Lansdowne Crescent for 25 years, and parents there encouraged her to translate its ethos of teacher/parent partnership into a prep school.

Approachable, dynamic, greatly respected by parents and pupils, 'terribly hands-on and involved,' said a parent. 'Problems get sorted out very quickly because she'll invite you straight in to see her.' Another said: 'She is the backbone of the school. She brings a committed energy and a genuine passion in the joy of learning. She is an inspiration to us all.'

Entrance: Has two reception classes; younger children are offered a gentler introduction with some shorter school days. Automatic places for siblings; the rest are allocated by ballot – separate ballots for boys and girls and for September to February birthdays and March to August birthdays. Ballot is drawn in May, 16 months before date of entry. Highest waiting list places allocated to those who signed up soonest after birth. Those successful in the ballot are asked to pay a £1,000 deposit 18 months before entry. Places higher up by assessment. Some, mostly boys, join in year 7, and there are one or two bursaries a year available for children from state primaries. 'It was lovely to hear from a boy from one of the local high-rise estates [who had moved on to a top boarding school] that rowing was now his favourite sport.' Can cater for some specific learning difficulties and EAL.

Exit: About half the girls and a handful of boys leave at 11, moving on to eg Latymer Upper, Godolphin & Latymer, South Hampstead, Harrodian, Francis Holland; or to board at eg Cheltenham Ladies', Wycombe Abbey, Benenden, St Swithun's. Boys mostly stay on till 13, then head for eg St Paul's, Westminster, City of London, UCS; or board at eg Eton, Harrow, Charterhouse, Winchester. Boys and a few girls leave at 13 for co-ed boarding schools eg Marlborough, Wellington, Rugby, Bedales, St Edward's. Music awards from Latymer Upper, City of London Girls, Winchester and Wells Cathedral School.

Remarks: On the borders of achingly trendy Notting Hill (Hugh Grant expected to stroll idly by at any minute) and grittier Ladbroke Grove, with tubes on the Hammersmith and City line and cars on the elevated Westway forming the northern horizon, and Portobello market just down the road. The school opened in 2003 with 57 pupils in a 1900s school building (currently owned by Campden Charities) which still has the painted brick classroom walls and high windows of a classic Victorian school. Some Acorn parents found out that the property was available, gathered shareholders, and moved fast to secure the lease, and the fledgling school was set up within a whirlwind nine months. 'We got a band of great teachers together, some of whom still work here.'

'There is a real onus on independent thinking and this seems to give the children an enormous self-confidence'

There's a large hall with stage for assemblies, plays and concerts; art room adorned with clay models, papier mâché shields and a cardboard violin; small library with comfy sofa. A painted timeline starts in the entrance hall with dinosaurs and continues up the stairs and through the ages.

The upper school building across the road, purpose-built and opened in 2008, is shoehorned into an intricate space where a Belgo restaurant once stood. Wood-clad, with whitewashed walls, rooflights and curved ceilings, it includes a basement dining/assembly/dance and drama room as well

321

as classrooms, science lab, music and computer rooms for years 4 to 8. It looks out one way onto Ladbroke Grove tube station and Chicken Village fast food restaurant, the other onto wooded slopes that border the tube line.

'I feel passionately that I'd like our children to be educated in the true sense of the word, but we also have to manage preparation for very narrow tests at the end of the road. We do aim to light the fire rather than just filling the bucket.' Children from reception upwards encouraged to express opinions, with plenty of small group discussions. Philosophy4Children and de Bono Thinking Hats systems used to encourage enquiring, reasoning approaches to learning. 'There is a real onus on independent thinking and this seems to give the children an enormous self-confidence and sense of self,' said a parent. Practical, fun teaching; year 2 was investigating friction and gravity using toy cars and ramps of books during our visit. Kung Fu Maths, a NHP invention, sees children awarded 'belts' in assembly for learning tables, knowing number bonds, solving problems of increasing complexity. 'The teaching staff at all levels are extraordinary,' said a parent. 'Their talent, enthusiasm and dedication are an inspiration to the pupils'.

As children move into year 4 and the upper school building, the pace of learning changes too. 'The early years are particularly gentle and nurturing,' said a parent. 'When they cross over the road they graduate to a much more serious work ethic. It's a very successful symbol.' Another commented: 'You see a real mix between academic rigour and the fostering of imagination.'

'I feel passionately that I'd like our children to be educated in the true sense of the word, but we also have to manage preparation for very narrow tests at the end'

Non-selective system means particular needs do crop up. 'If a teacher raises concerns, the SENCo will observe the child in class and suggest strategies. For the first two years, we will give extra support and keep watching. If it becomes evident we can't meet the child's needs we'll discuss it with the parents.' The SENCo can give one-to-one help at extra cost; speech and language and OT experts available to visit.

Music is a particular strength. The school has twice performed pieces written by the 'amazing, hugely enthusiastic and charismatic' music master at the Schools Proms at the Albert Hall – most recently The Eagle, based on a Tennyson poem.

Some two-thirds of pupils play an instrument and many join the choir, orchestra or ensemble groups. Plenty of opportunities to perform, in assemblies, concerts, poetry recitals, school plays – Hansel and Gretel was under rehearsal during our visit. Art imaginative and inspiring.

Much parental involvement, whether helping in the library or giving a talk on the nature of consciousness

Sport was the only area picked out as a weaker link in last ISI report; Jane Cameron acknowledges the challenges a new-ish school (and particularly a co-ed one) faces in setting up a fixture list. Football (boys' and girls'), rugby, netball, cricket and rounders matches played with varying degrees of success; the swimming squad is apparently 'second to none'. Compact playground, so sport involves travelling: most matches, and many sports lessons, at the Linford Christie stadium; they also use the Westway Sports Centre and Kensington Leisure Centre.

Clubs range from Greek to chess to netball to lateral thinking; they make good use of London, with trips down the Thames, to a Hindu temple, to City Hall and the Olympic site; they go off to Normandy, skiing, on outdoor pursuits courses and field trips.

Much parental involvement, whether helping in the library, giving a talk on the nature of consciousness or on Leonardo da Vinci, giving a violin recital or running a crafts workshop. 'There is a constant stream of authors, musicians, journalists, actors and artists, not only dropping off and collecting their children, but generously volunteering their time and talent by speaking at assemblies and judging various competitions, such as poetry and public speaking,' commented a parent.

Great parental praise for the 'pervasive caring ethos' of the school. 'The NHP community is one in which the children show an enormous and unusual amount of empathy.' 'Every child feels valued, and different talents are truly celebrated. Children take great pride in the achievements of their peers, not only academically but in music, art and extracurricular areas.' 'Altruistic behaviour happens all the time. It is the way things work at NHP and what we treasure most.' 'We feel indebted to NHP for giving our children a love of learning, a sense of belonging and pride.'

Our Lady of Victories RC Primary School

Clareville Street, London SW7 5AQ

State • Pupils: 240 • Ages: 3–11 • RC

Tel: 020 7373 4491

Email: sarah.mcbennett@olov.rbkc.sch.uk
Website: www.olov.rbkc.sch.uk/

42

Headteacher: Since 2007, Mrs Sarah McBennett BEd (40s). After university in Belfast, started her career in education and has taught children across the primary age range from reception to year 6. These days she is mainly managerial and tends only to teach to cover staff absences. Formerly head of primary section of an international community school in Jordan, then deputy at a large Catholic primary in Kent. Something of a whizz with the budget, parents tell us, she works extremely hard for the school and puts in many extra hours. Committed and kindly personality, with an open door policy, always happy to spend time talking to parents, pupils and staff. Supported by a long-serving deputy head, school secretary and lively PTA.

Entrance: Pupils come from the parishes of Our Lady of Victories, Our Lady of Mount Carmel and St Simon Stock. Priority goes to baptised, practising Catholics; all applications must be supported by letter from the parish priest. Where possible siblings get priority followed by those living closest to the school. Children attending the nursery are not automatically guaranteed a place in the reception class, which is always oversubscribed. Contact the school for occasional places in older age groups.

Exit: To state schools and independents in many different directions. Co-eds St Thomas More, Holland Park, Emanuel, St Benedict's, Latymer Upper. Boys, London Oratory, Cardinal Vaughan, independents Westminster, St Paul's, Dulwich College and City of London Boys. Girls, Sacred Heart, Hammersmith, Gumley House, independents More House, Queensgate, Francis Holland, Godolphin and Latymer. A few to Catholic boarding schools eg St Mary's Ascot, Worth and Ampleforth.

Remarks: Very high standards across the curriculum continue to make this a successful and sought-after primary. All teaching is graded outstanding. Lots of attention to detail, personal successes, the pupils are encouraged to take pride in everything they do. Continuous assessment and monitoring ensure everybody reaches their potential, and those who need additional support are identified. Parents tell us enthusiastic staff always want to make sure the children really enjoy themselves and develop socially as well as academically. School aims to pick up SEN early; pupils are supported by differentiated teaching, specialist teachers and therapists in small groups or one-to-one. International clientele so lots of EAL tuition for those who need.

Tall Victorian buildings with lots of stairs, however, good-sized classrooms, beautifully decorated; the school has gold Artsmark. Displays show that even the tiny children have beautiful handwriting. Nursery and reception classes have been redesigned so 3 to 5-year-olds are taught in a large, open plan space with its own playground. French starts at key stage 2, other languages via clubs, year 6 have French penfriends and make an annual trip to Cannes. Sadly, Latin has disappeared from the curriculum. After-school verbal reasoning club in the run-up to 11+ exams. Inner city location means outdoor spaces are tight, but they are well-maintained and decorated with mosaics made by the children. Younger horticulturalists grow many colourful flowers and shrubs through the gardening club which they organise themselves.

The school has a Sportsmark; multi-purpose hall is large enough for short tennis, gymnastics and ballet lessons. Outdoor sports take place at Battersea Park; professional coaches, including ex-Middlesex cricketer, teach good range of team games. Specialist teachers for both art and music, pupils can have individual instrumental tuition on a range of five different instruments, and often join the young musicians' performances at the Albert Hall. Enticing range of extracurricular activities, clubs, trips and special visitors; year 5s can complete their cycling proficiency certificates at school.

Professional coaches, including ex-Middlesex cricketer, teach good range of team games. Specialist teachers for both art and music, pupils can have individual instrumental tuition

Parents say pastoral care is very good and inclusive, the weekly newsletter keeps everybody up-to-date with events and pupils are given a voice through the school council which meets regularly with the deputy head. Food is often on the agenda, as the school has Food for Life Award, everything is cooked on site and where possible locally sourced. Encouraged to be involved in the school community, parents run cookery classes, listen to readers and raise large amounts of money which go towards paying for improvements and equipment for the school as well as for outside charities. Catholic beliefs remain at the heart of the warm, family atmosphere of the school. First rate and first choice school for Catholic families in Kensington.

Parsons Green Prep School

Eridge House, 1 Fulham Park Road, Fulham, London SW6 4LJ

Independent • Pupils: 200 • Ages: 4–11 • Fees: up to £16,185 pa

Tel: 020 7371 9009

Email: admissions@parsonsgreenprep.co.uk
Website: www.parsonsgreenprep.co.uk

13

Headteacher: Since 2014, Miss Helen Stavert BEd. Year 6 class teacher and numeracy co-ordinator at the school since 2011 and deputy head for two years prior to her appointment as head. Previously head of year 6 at The International School in Marbella and prior to that taught at a state school in Gloucestershire. Originally from the Cotswolds (did her degree at University of Gloucestershire in Cheltenham), she lives in Putney and unwinds on long walks with her dog and by practising yoga.

Now in her 30s, but easily passing for younger, she took over the headship following the departure of her predecessor after a year – liked by parents but she didn't feel she was the right fit. Some natural angst at the change amongst some parents, but those who have experienced Miss Stavert as

a class teacher are spreading the word, saying to us, 'I believe she will thrive' and 'she is respected, committed to the school, approachable and caring about the children as individuals.' She continues to teach year 6 in the mornings.

Mrs Lucinda Waring (40s) is the founding principal (since 2001) and majority shareholder. Originally trained at St Nicholas' Montessori College in Knightsbridge, she founded her first nurseries at the age of 26. Naturally inspiring some envy amongst her high-flying parent body, she aims to remain firmly 'back office' but has stepped up recently to aid the transition of the new head. The school is very much her vision – to create a school where children could thrive without undue pressure; she is on top of every detail and the children know and greet her throughout the school. She is married with one child.

Entrance: Parents can register from birth (£100 registration fee). Once on the waiting list, entrance into reception via pre-entry checks, including a full academic report from current educational setting. Easy-going families preferred. Sibling policy: 10 per cent off for second and third child, 20 per cent off for a fourth.

The maximum number entering reception is 44, with almost twice this number on the current waiting list. Pupils enter from Fulham nurseries in the main. Occasional places in year 1 upwards (with references and assessment). A deposit of £1,500 to secure the place.

Exit: Preparations for exit at 11 plus are thorough and commence from year 4. Perhaps there is little the school can do to alleviate the inevitable pressure parents and children feel, but one parent says, 'Children need to be confident enough to be able to think: yes, I can do it! That's what this school gives them'. Both the principal and head insist they will speak up in the face of ambitious parents to try and ensure that children will move on to schools where they will above all be happy. Recent destinations include St Paul's Girls' School, Godolphin & Latymer, City of London Boys', Dulwich College, King's College Wimbledon, Francis Holland, Putney High and Ibstock Place.

Remarks: The school has undergone a name change, becoming Parsons Green Prep at Eridge House (previously Eridge House). Despite the marketing-friendly name change, and ambitious air of the principal, there are no plans to expand the school: 200 pupils would be the absolute maximum.

The school was founded in 2001 in a formerly derelict Victorian villa in an enviable location and with that rare thing, some outside space behind a high garden wall, offering privacy and enough room to run around. The original building was restored and modern additions blended, offering new classrooms and the large assembly hall used for everything from staging productions to PE. The end result is a smart blend of light, modern-seeming classrooms large and small, wide enough corridors with spick and span displays and lots of stairs. Come August and with class sizes finalised, the staff may be busily swapping rooms so that each class is accommodated in the best possible space.

The playground is Astroturfed throughout, with just enough room for football and netball, and a good in and out space for the early years, with wooden play equipment. Very physical older children may need more space, not that it will be easy to find in central London. The stockpile of micro-scooters racked on the playground walls points to pupils mostly living nearby.

Class sizes range from 22 each in the two reception classes to one class of 18 and 12 currently in years 5 and 6.

The school sets out to provide a creative curriculum, but is well ahead of the curve at primary level in putting STEM subjects at the heart of the maths curriculum, following three years of careful training and planning.

Parents say: 'Reading in the early years is extremely well taught'. Maths and English are taught in small ability groups. One of the numeracy tools has been effectively adopted from Montessori methods. The Mac suite has been upgraded and there is improved wireless technology around the school. Years 5 and 6 have their own individual android tablets with keyboards.

We were impressed by the individual targets on each child's work in every lesson. Teaching aims to take pupils from their learning comfort zone, where they might be engaged but not excited, to their learning challenge zone where they are encouraged to take risks. The school is currently increasing its expertise in stretching the able, gifted and talented. We found children eager to talk to us in every classroom we visited, either explaining clearly what they were working on, or coming unprompted to share their work.

Playground is Astroturfed throughout, with just enough room for football and netball, and a good in and out space for the early years

Parents praise cross-curricular topic work, saying 'subjects are really brought to life', such as the year 6 challenge to design a theme park, using mathematical knowledge to design the rides and calculate their profits, whilst utilising art and creative writing to design the posters. Humanities teaching seems fun, too: we observed Horrible Histories style hygiene tips for the Tudors, whilst philosophy for children inspires pupils to interrogate the world around them. Science day saw staff joined by a team from the science museum – children made gigantic bubbles, launched rockets and made goop.

French is taught weekly throughout the school with a specialist French programme, which continues after school, for those children who are already fluent French speakers. The occasional pupil exits to the Lycée.

Two assemblies per week. Christmas concert not a carol service. When we visited in October, they were looking forward to going crazy on Christmas decorations.

A third of the 36 staff has been at the school for more than 10 years. We have rarely heard so much praise for teaching assistants: in the main extremely youthful, so they have sufficient energy to keep up with their charges. 'Right people in the right places,' says principal and 'no staff who get stale'. Parents say: 'often young and enthusiastic about teaching'; 'lovely teachers allow children to be children'; 'willing to try a multitude of different ways to captivate children'. Teachers feel looked after by the school and are part of a very thorough programme of ongoing training. They describe themselves as 'creative, motivated and committed.'

Teachers are addressed (by everyone – parents, other staff) as Miss or Mr plus first name, so Miss Lucinda or Miss Helen, which we found a bit Beatrix Potter-ish, but the principal says, correctly, 'it's friendlier for the children'.

Most parents are content with 'sensible homework', none during school holidays until key stage 2, and there is a dedicated homework session at school. Children are deliberately not over-loaded. Trips could be to the local community supermarket or fire station, but also make the most of London from Fulham football club on the doorstep to Pudding Lane. From year 3 residential trips begin with camping and a French day trip.

Seven per cent of pupils have EAL needs. The school seems to have fewer than average number of children with learning differences, but a SENCo in place to ensure their needs are met.

Parents universally describe children who love going to school and 'can't wait to get in at the gate'. We can report beaming smiles and diligent application in every class we visited, and parents agree, describing the school as 'a happy place to learn'; 'intimate, caring, quietly competitive' and 'children do not feel any pressure at all and yet are making good progress'.

Some gripes about sport persist: 'No way near enough sport,' said one parent and another added, 'Not enough boys in year 3 to field a football team'. However, year 2 upwards play football, tag rugby, cricket, netball, rounders and have weekly swimming lessons. The school has recently joined the Independent Schools Association, which means more sporting competitions. The usual summer sports day and swimming gala. The upper school makes use of Hurlingham Park. Keen sports players had better be early risers as squad practice takes place before school most days.

Children are taught guitar, piano, violin and now drum lessons – singing and guitar most popular. There's an orchestra and a choir.

'The summer performance is always excellent,' said a parent. Most recently A Midsummer Night's Dream and The Wind in the Willows. 'Would like more drama opportunities,' said another. A few entries for the LAMDA drama exams with several distinctions.

Chess is huge here, deliberately encouraged to develop logical thinking. Greatly improved clubs, say parents. Those now on offer pre- and post-school or at lunchtime encompass the fun and fashionable, including photography, fencing, orchestra, Mandarin, soccer, chess, baking, sewing, ukulele, running and study skills. Hot lunches and after-school clubs cost extra.

The school is very clear about the standards expected of the children, and parents see pastoral care as a real strength of the school: 'My child had been unhappy at a different school, but has thrived here'; 'I really like the atmosphere: it is very caring but with high standards of behaviour'; 'bullying isn't tolerated and the staff has been quick to act' and 'not much gets by the staff'. The new buddy benches in the playground have been a big hit, too.

Frequent mentions by parents of this school being well suited to a child who might be quite shy initially: 'a sensitive soul ' or 'young in year or late developers'. But parents with more than more child here, the majority, report it suiting all sorts of temperaments and abilities: 'outgoing children can shine'. A teacher believes it works well for 'bright children who are not afraid to take risks and who want to learn'.

Parents are without doubt a smart, city crowd: 'Friendly, international and professional with lots of dual-working parents,' said one. Many agree on a friendly welcome from other parents. Every other parent describes the school community as 'international' but the principal says this is more perception than actuality. Parent volunteers do everything and anything from weekend hospitality for the science lab chicks, to designing the logos for the houses, to being part of the eco committee growing and harvesting crops in the school garden.

Any parents with low-flying or tiger-ish tendencies, this may well not be the school for you. Those who are searching for somewhere to nurture and inspire happy, confident children – look no further.

Pembridge Hall School

18 Pembridge Square, London W2 4EH

Independent • Pupils: 410 • Ages: 4–11 • Fees: £19,620 pa

Tel: 020 7229 0121

Email: contact@pembridgehall.co.uk
Website: www.pembridgehall.co.uk

Headmaster: Since September 2012, Mr Henry Keighley-Elstub BA PGCE (40s), previously deputy head at Wetherby Prep. Educated at Eton and Leeds University, where he read classical civilization. He has taught history at Ludgrove, Cothill and Chesham Prep, where he was head of department and also senior master. As well as this being his first headship, it is also his first experience of an all girls' school, and one that finishes at 11 years rather than 13. 'I was worried about that at first,' he admits, 'but now I barely notice, and communicating with an 11-year-old girl is equivalent to talking to a 13-year-old boy.' Married to Sarah who works at IBM ('I have no idea what she does', he confides. 'Perhaps she's a spy.') They have a young daughter.

Mr Keighley-Elstub, slight of build, has an immediately warm, engaging and enthusiastic personality that makes even the stiffest person unfurl. His conversation is littered with verbs and adjectives like 'skip along' and 'groovy'. His upbeat, chipper approach is directed at everyone. As well as the girls, the parents and the teachers it embraces the peripatetic music staff, games staff and the odd visitor. Despite being an Old Etonian with an unusually complicated name both to spell and pronounce (think 'Keithly'), Mr Keighley-Elstub is remarkably down to earth. He attributes this to his Northern pedigree (his father was a Yorkshireman but practised as a GP in Wimbledon where Mr Keighley-Elstub grew up). His family used to turn up at Eton in a clapped out old VW, but 'that wasn't remotely embarrassing,' he avers. 'Eton's not smart at all. The greatest compliment anyone could pay me,' he continues, 'is to turn up to meet me in jeans.' If he weren't so refreshingly open you wouldn't guess it – he looks immaculate in his well-cut suit and playfully shrieks when he discovers the odd crisp on the floor in a classroom.

He loves music – his wife is a violinist and he has recently formed a staff choir. He is also an enthusiastic sportsman (running is his thing) and he is determined that the girls here start winning some matches for a change. He champions all departments – art, music, sport and drama – equally and works to get them all to enjoy working together rather than being at loggerheads, as happens so often. He is relishing the challenges of his first headship and is not unaware of the benefits

> *Lovely wide corridors and staircases that seem to go up and up for ever. Lush red carpet (to match the uniform?) in the lower school*

of running a school that is part of the Alpha Plus group. He talks of the wealth of resources available to him, from legal to financial as well as the supportive but 'hands off' nature of the governing body. Although ambitious with lots of energy, he is clearly here to stay for some time – 'I couldn't leave while there is still so much to do,' he says. 'I want to transform a good school into an outstanding one'.

Entrance: Names down at birth – 'but realistically that means within two weeks of birth,' says head. He is keen to dispel the myth that you need to plan a Caesarean and father needs to put the form through the letter box as the baby arrives. It absolutely makes no difference at all on what day of the month your child is born. They divide the months into thirds and take an equal number from each third. Non-refundable registration fee (currently £150) does not guarantee you a tour of the school. Personal tours with the head offered as soon as you are off the waiting list and offered a place (something Mr Keighley-Elstub has recently introduced – prior to his arrival tours with a member of staff offered at deposit decision time – close to starting). The competitive market (for children more than the schools) and wealthy catchment of West London means that parents don't blink at paying these sort of sums without even being given the chance to see the school before making a decision. The alternative to long waiting lists is a selection process at 3, and that would mean 'we may miss the wild wacky ones that add colour to the place,' says Mr Keighley-Elstub. Nevertheless, close liaison with feeder nurseries (he mentioned The Acorn, Rolfe's, Strawberry Fields, Minors and Ladbroke Square) to make sure girls will manage.

Exit: Plenty of scholarships, academic, sporting as well as musical and artistic, each year and fine boards in the upper school hall to commemorate them (11 in 2015).

Most popular day destinations in 2015 were Francis Holland (Clarence Gate), Godolphin & Latymer, Latymer Upper, More House, Queen's College and St Paul's. Most popular boarding destinations were Downe House, St Mary's Ascot and Wycombe Abbey.

Remarks: Situated in a particularly leafy, white stucco square in Notting Hill Gate, the lower school is in a tall building a minutes' walk from an identical building containing the upper school. In between is Wetherby pre-prep – the boys' equivalent – and also owned by the Alpha Plus group. In the basement of number 10 (the Upper School) is Minors Nursery – another Alpha Plus establishment: no wonder such direct communication about the character and ability of the girls can be made.

Round the corner in St Petersburg Place is the splendid St Matthew's Church where whole school assemblies take place each week. We joined a river of red blazered and straw boatered girls as they walked immaculately to the church. An overwhelmingly white collection of girls for such a multicultural part of London; they are international – American, Russian, European as well – but only about 10 out of 400 girls receive EAL help. Mr Keighley-Elstub described the ethos as 'lightly Anglican' but a very English education, which seemed to be requirement of even the most foreign of families.

Girls here are well spoken, eager to please and confident. Lots of awards and prizes and opportunities to speak publicly and take responsibility to build that confidence. We were particularly impressed with an astonishing game designed by a 10-year-old girl out of a cardboard box, which intricately displayed the planets and included chance and question cards which she had devised herself. She then explained through a microphone how to play the game to an audience of about 450 people in the church, including parents as well as teachers and children.

Classrooms spacious, bright and airy with wonderful high ceilings and tall windows. Lovely wide corridors and staircases that seem to go up and up for ever. Lush red carpet (to match the uniform?) in the lower school, upper school mirrors the lower school but in blue. We saw some very impressive still life work in the very studio-like space at the top of the school, which had brilliant ceiling windows, creating an excellent space to be creative. Well-equipped science labs in the basement with a good old-fashioned full-sized skeleton in the corner. Super space in the basement for drama and productions with a wealth of colourful and imaginative costumes and hats. All years get a chance to perform: year 5s do a Shakespearean medley, year 6s do their annual play in the local Tabernacle Theatre. Both buildings have large halls which double as dining rooms at lunch time. Wide choice of healthy cooked lunches and imaginative fruit (watermelon and pineapple – not just your regular apples and bananas). How refreshing not to see children eating packed lunches at their desks.

Healthy number of male teachers and the arrival of Mr Keighley-Elstub has seen barely any staff turnover at all. He feels proud of having injected renewed energy and purpose into the place and acknowledges that when he arrived there was

a lot of reassurance to be done. Parents were rattled and there was a lack of direction. Those we spoke to referred to a terrible lack of communication. Many considered moving their daughters but remarkably few did, explaining that the pastoral care remained excellent throughout and they didn't want to uproot a happy child. Emphasis is now on communication – particularly with parents; improvement and consolidation of the academics; and improvement of sport.

Tennis a club rather than a school sport, and rounders possibly on its way out. 'I don't see the point of it,' says Mr Keighley Elstub. 'It's rather a poor man's cricket'

Girls are starting to win netball matches now – and we were proudly told of how they beat Glendower recently. Netball and hockey played in nearby Avondale Park and Holland Park, athletics at the Linford Christie stadium in Wood Lane and swimming at the Porchester Baths. Plenty of inter-house matches so that everyone can have a go. Tennis as a club rather than a school sport, and rounders possibly on its way out. 'I don't see the point of it,' says Mr Keighley Elstub. 'It's rather a poor man's cricket'. He is very open to the idea of introducing football and cricket for the girls but so far there doesn't seem to be the demand. Several outside spaces in both buildings for fresh air between lessons and 'unless there's the threat of a tornado out they go,' says head, who can't understand why the girls have been treated with such velvet gloves in the past, with the mere threat of rain resulting in their reading inside.

Three classes of 20 in each year. Setting only in maths from year 3. Serious preparation for the 11 plus starts in year 5 but the groundwork is now being laid much earlier. Mr Keighley–Elstub teaches years 5 and 6 so he can give well informed advice about schools. He is not afraid to tell a parent if they are being overly ambitious academically but will look at the whole child and advise which is the most appropriate school on that basis. Vast majority of parents here are in finance – though the odd one is glamorously famous, you wouldn't describe this as a trendy school. Mr Keighley-Elstub famously put a stop to the cashmere scarves as part of the school uniform and supplied by a parent: this isn't the image he wants to nurture.

Large, busy, and traditional with a dynamic head, Pembridge Hall can only get better and better and could be an excellent choice for your enthusiastic daughter.

Queen's Gate Junior School

Linked school: Queen's Gate School, 331

125–126 Queen's Gate, London SW7 5LE

Independent • Pupils: 150 • Ages: 4–11 • Fees: £15,750 pa

Tel: 020 7761 0303

Email: registrar@queensgate.org.uk
Website: www.queensgate.org.uk

44

Headmistress: Since January 2015, Mrs Ceri Thomson, BEd MEd EYPP. Read music and education at Cardiff University, and returned to do a masters there later.

Previously a deputy head in Oxford and also a head of music. Married with two children. Enjoys music, playing squash and walking the dog.

Entrance: Around 100 applicants for each of the 23 places at reception. One 7+ competitive academic scholarship worth a third of the annual fees. Assessment morning with groups of 8-10 children given tasks and observed by the headmistress and other staff.

Exit: Around three-quarters to the senior school. Rest to a range of good London schools and a few to boarding.

Remarks: A few doors down from the senior school and an equally discreet entrance belies the warmth, fun and productive activity that goes on

here. Up to 23 tots in the first two years – each in a good sized room with teacher and two teaching assistants. Happy, absorbed children are relaxed and busy in rooms that are stimulating without being frantic. Some older classes quite noisy with a buzz of activity but everywhere, even the art room, is orderly and purposeful. Quiet, sustained work for the oldest girls, who would change nothing about the school save its lack of outdoors, and really like their friends. Rooms light and recently refurbished – and at a sensible temperature. Good sized hall – like the senior school, the old salon in grand architectural style. Good-sized library, well-used with a real, 'very hard-working' librarian shared with big sister school. Lots of multi-purpose spaces and facilities. Good IT suite.

Lots of music – choirs and an orchestra. Very lively art; we encountered Dragolina, an immense dragon being constructed for the coming Chinese New Year – and were glad to see good old-fashioned crayon work. Tastes of French, Spanish, German, Italian and Latin as the girls progress through the school. Fun, but some parents query the purpose, 'they really don't know any French at all when they go into the senior school'. Teaching of eg science done by senior school staff. By bus to sports facilities all over the place – ensures plenty of indoor and outdoor sports. Lots of lovely after-school clubs three days of the week – 'So hard to choose, Mummy!'

Parents happy. 'It's traditional, though the new head is livening things up. It really suits my daughter.' Staff now mostly young and pretty international. We warmed to the sight of children spontaneously hugging their teachers (probably illegal!) A safe, cosy and well-structured start for your precious daughter. And once she's there, you could really forget about her education for the next 14 years and trust them to give her all she needs.

Queen's Gate School

Linked school: Queen's Gate Junior School, 330

133 Queen's Gate, London SW7 5LE

Tel: 020 7589 3587

Independent • Pupils: 530 • Ages: 11–18 • Sixth form pupils: 60 • Fees: up to £18,300 pa

Email: registrar@queensgate.org.uk
Website: www.queensgate.org.uk

45

Principal: Since 2006, Mrs Rosalynd Kamaryc BA MSc PGCE (50s). Petite, chic and with a lovely soft Irish voice, Mrs Kamaryc immediately comes across as the warm, calm and practical person to whom you'd want to entrust your precious daughter. A mathematician who still teaches – in her case, the bottom GCSE set. 'I just love teaching,' she says and 'counts it a privilege to walk the school' once a day.

Mrs Kamaryc has an impressive pedigree, this being her second headship. She began teaching in Scotland and spent 10 years as head of Wykeham House School, Fareham – via Forest School and Woodbridge School. Parents enthuse: 'She gives terrific support to the girls,' we were told. 'She's extremely capable, a very safe pair of hands with a very clear vision for the school.' 'Very approachable though can seem a little shy.' Her catwalk walk at a school fashion show wowed everyone. 'She commands respect but she can kick up her heels too. She's fun.'

Academic matters: 'It punches above its weight academically,' one parent told us and the results bear this out. French, English, maths, art and geography shine brightly. Tiny sets at A level – often ones and twos – a rare privilege and at half the cost of the top tutorial companies. They will run an A level course with one pupil and don't ditch the subject – or its teacher – if it has no takers in a given year. Art, French and maths have biggest numbers. If a subject has more than seven takers they split the group. Some depts seen as better than others. 'English and history are very strong; art is amazing,' we heard repeatedly and 'though the teachers are all lovely, their actual teaching isn't always great – a little dull and uncreative sometimes.' But A level results are remarkable these days, 50 per cent A*/A in 2015 with a just a few at grade C or lower.

Good range of GCSE subjects for so small a school. Ancient history and classical civilisation, Latin and Greek and lots of modern languages available – and not just for native speakers. Good results in English, geography, French, drama, art – but no weaklings here (70 per cent A*/A in 2015). 'We chose it,' said a parent, echoed by more,

> *You walk past this school and back again without knowing it's there, so discreet is its little brass nameplate*

'because it is not obsessed by exam results.' 'It's not a hoop-jumping school.'

School has 1.5 staff on learning support team – much praised. 'Incredible support for my daughter's mild dyslexia. Possibly not for much else,' thought a parent, and this is borne out by the head.

Games, options, the arts: Parents glow and when you make it to the loftily-situated art dept you understand why. The main studio entrance is festooned with trompe l'oeil blue velvet curtains and abutted by a display of white paper insects; inside is a huge range of work, all demonstrating boldness, creativity and imagination. 'We do some gruesome stuff,' chortled the dynamic and experimental head of art as we gaped at the 'urban zombies', the girl under a blanket of fresh minced steak and various startling depictions of blood and vomit. It was reassuring to turn to the multi-coloured shoes on every step of the staircase, the cardboard relief masks, the fun, wit, skill of it all. DT even more surprising; facilities include a laser cutter, 3D printer and vacuum former. Products we saw included acrylic pencil and iPad holders and electronic dice. We warmed to a girl (flatteringly, given our age) mistaking us for a potential parent, who insisted on telling us: 'If someone wanted to do product design, they really mustn't go anywhere else.' Art and DT results from here are outstanding.

'Our drama teacher is so dedicated and lovely.' We interrupted a rehearsal of Darkwood Manor – a bit of gothic horror written by the girls, gory in their white and cicatriced faces, blood and masks. No theatre, though a small semi-studio – 'we don't need a 100 seater theatre,' claimed a proud parent. Good music room with lovely Broadwood grand and reassuring number of real instruments plus modern keyboards with headphones. Many learn instruments and school music is lively and popular.

Sports regarded as much improved during Mrs Kamaryc's tenure, though almost all involves bussing hither and yon. 'We don't mind, it's not an issue,' parents feel, though some pupils we spoke to yearned for playing fields and pitches. It probably isn't ideal for your jumping bean, though on offer now are rowing, squash, fencing among others and girls love it all. 'We have 95 clubs,' we were told and a buzz of jolly fun activities and try-outs pervades the place. Some little sorrow that not everyone joins in with all this opportunity as fully they might.

Background and atmosphere: Queen's Gate is a smart, elegant road in anyone's book. You walk past this school and back again without knowing it's there, so discreet is its little brass nameplate. 'It's a fantastic location,' gush Kensington mummies, 'just like a house.' And so it is – three houses, in fact, knocked together and inside – apart from the fabulous cornices, ceiling roses etc, it's yer actual rabbit warren. 'Yes,' nods a wise mummy, 'but good teaching can take place in a tent.' We lost count of the number of floors and semi-floors above the basement (ICT, lab, lockers and gym and still somehow redolent of the butler's clipped footfalls and scurrying maids). Some upper floor corridors are so narrow that we fear future generations of Tubby Tillies may get stuck. Not that we saw any such here, of course.

Main entrance hall embellished with wall-mounted bell, a set of gongs, a digital clock, fire extinguisher, staff pigeon-holes, a vintage radiator, a vitrine bulging with silver trophies and a venerable wooden post box we couldn't open. All this somehow seemed to sum up the whole. Wonderful main hall confected from the two adjoining salons from the houses' glory days – newish wooden floor and matching brass chandeliers. No playground, just a couple of tiny roof gardens for the younger years. Otherwise, breaks are taken in classrooms – and these, on, admittedly, a dark January day, were some of the most overheated we have encountered. Pupils and staff were busily fanning themselves as the rude bell shattered the silence and doors opened. 'It does get very hot,' a youngster confided, 'and sometimes it gets very cold.' Black (for pupils and staff) and white (for pupils) dining rooms, wonderfully elegant and decidedly different. Food reckoned to be good – around half bring in their own. Some come for breakfasts which sounded more than worth sliding out of bed and down the road for.

Main library is a beautiful room with splendid polished oak tables and equally venerable stock in many cases (nothing wrong with that) and a lovely place to work. Sixth form has surprisingly spacious common rooms with sofas. Also a kitchen and a work room, but work decidedly not happening when we peeked in.

No uniform, most dressed perfectly sensibly though this feature of the school clearly stresses a few. 'Some girls bring in ridiculous designer bags,' one mum kvetched, but no-one looked especially coutured to us – though perhaps we are not the best judges. Certainly a divisive issue for some – though not exactly on an 'in/out of the EU?' scale.

Pastoral care and discipline: Everyone praises the pastoral care. 'They are very good at sorting out individuals,' one father told us. 'My daughter is very happy there.' Another praised the good relations between the girls, fostered by the staff and the care taken to build inter-year relationships. A third described the amount of extra time and effort put in by the teaching staff. A fourth said: 'My daughter feels there is always a teacher to chat to if she has a problem' – and so on. Each term has a 'pastoral day' and a trip to France in year 7 is 'brilliant for bonding us'. Very little sense of serious disciplinary problems being on anyone's radar.

Pupils and parents: Head stresses: 'We're a very English school with an international community. Many of our parents came here from overseas as students – and stayed. We are a Christian foundation but we celebrate all faiths and cultures.' Evidence was the great excitement – and splendid dragon – we witnessed in preparation for the Chinese new year. Largest number of overseas nationals probably Italian, followed by French, Spanish, US, Aussies, Qataris and a few Russians. Much-loved by its Old Girls, many of whom are current parents; good supportive parents' group. Only, but repeated, gripe is that 'communications are not great' – a surprise to the school but something they are addressing.

Notable OGs include HRH the Duchess of Cornwall, various Redgraves, Sieffs, Guinnesses, Amanda de Souza, Jane Martineau, Nigella Lawson, Lucinda Lambton, Tracey Boyd, Aurelia Cecil, Trinny Woodall and Imogen Poots. Former head of MI5 Eliza Manningham Buller used to be on the staff.

Entrance: Most of the school's own junior school join the senior school. Around six applicants per

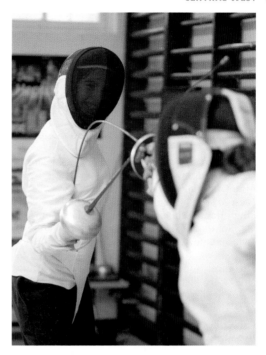

place at 11+. Waiting list for all years, but occasional places occur so worth a phone call. A few in at year 12 but 'we are very selective' and A*/As at GCSE are a requirement. Head meets all prospective parents before anyone is tested on anything.

Exit: Almost all stay to A level. Of the 20 per cent or so who try pastures co-ed, boarding or state, some scuttle back tout de suite. Head says that she encourages them to 'be brave and look elsewhere' at this stage. You'd be brave – or rash – to move from so small and nurturing a community to a place where no-one knows a thing about you. Year 13 leavers go to a wonderfully eclectic bunch of good universities around the globe. Oxbridge is not uncommon, solid Russell group for most but around a quarter much further afield. Art, art history and classics more common than science

Money matters: All 11+ entrants are automatic scholarship candidates and 25 per cent fee remission offered to high flyers. Art, drama, music and sports scholarships also available – apply on registering. Similar 25 per cent remission available to sixth applicants. Means-tested bursaries too, but no point in applying until a place is offered.

Remarks: A lovely school for lovely girls in a classy and sophisticated milieu. Tiny classes, delightful teachers, charming friends with a faint St Trinian's spicy edge. Not for you if you want gritty urban reality – except, perhaps, in the art room.

Ravenscourt Park Preparatory School

16 Ravenscourt Avenue, London W6 0SL

Independent • Pupils: 415 • Ages: 4–11 • Fees: £15,606 pa

Tel: 020 8846 9153

Email: secretary@rpps.co.uk
Website: www.rpps.co.uk

14

Head: Since September 2015, Carl Howes, previously deputy head at Colet Court. Natural sciences degree from Cambridge and PGCE from St Luke's, Exeter; has also been head of maths and second master at King's House School in Richmond. Married to Mel, a teacher at St Stephen's Primary School, Twickenham, and has two teenage children.

Entrance: Non-selective, the September after a child's 4th birthday. It is vital to register a child on his/her first birthday. Can't be registered before. After that it is a lottery. Siblings get priority, then names are drawn randomly and places allotted strictly to obtain an equal number of boys and girls.

Exit: Traditionally, to London day schools, but with changing local demographics, some parents now looking to send their children to top boarding schools. Therefore some boys are leaving early, although, as one parent said, 'this is not a light decision'. So, occasionally boys at end of year 5 to country prep schools or London day schools that go through to year 8 (Fulham Prep, King's House).

Girls headed to a wide variety of schools, including Godolphin & Latymer, Francis Holland, Clarence Gate, Notting Hill and Ealing High School, Putney High, Lady Eleanor Holles and St Paul's Girls'. Boys' choices included Hampton, Westminster Under, Colet Court, City of London Boys' and University College School. Some to co-eds like new sister school Kew House and Latymer Upper.

Remarks: Parents said before we visited: 'Not a hothouse', 'kind and nurturing', 'safe environment', and 'excellent communication'. We found no reason to argue with these comments. Teachers and children buzzed with enthusiasm, the atmosphere felt relaxed although each time we walked into a classroom work stopped, the children leapt to their feet, chimed 'good morning' and stood there until we left. This apparently always happens and, we felt, emphasises the edge of formality at the school. However, everywhere we went we were made to feel more than welcome. Parents also feel 'there really is an open door policy'.

Founded in 1991 by Maria and Ted Gardener, former teachers, this school has grown and gone from strength to strength. Its most recent building, opened in September 2011, has enabled it to move from two-form entry to three, gradually adding 20 more children to each year. No problem filling the spaces. There is some feeling that it would, perhaps, have been better to have added two more years, thus solving the problem of boys leaving early.

(They say this is not a problem.) Some parents feel perhaps too much emphasis on the business side, 'definitely an eye for profit above all'. For instance: 'Why do we have to pay extra for lunch, when it is compulsory and our children are not allowed to bring a packed version?'

Fantastic facilities. The new building has enabled the top three years to move into nine bright new classrooms, colour coded per floor. 'We chose our own colours,' said our two of our guides proudly. And, 'look we've even got a lift but we can't use it without permission!' Splendid new science lab with all the latest equipment; a light, bright art room displaying a friendship bench, 'to sit on when you feel lonely', being painted by the art club and, very exciting, including a kiln; a music room where children were reading notes displayed on an interactive white board – of course these abound; an ICT lab with a laptop per child, 'we're making our own websites'. Perhaps best of all, as far as our guides were concerned, was the new school hall/theatre: 'The choir sings from the balcony', 'we can learn to operate the light and sound'. All very impressive.

A tad more cosy, the rest of the school is housed in two buildings, with a separate good-sized dining block. All food cooked on site and children served at their tables by catering staff. Most meals are hot, always healthy and compulsory unless a child has a dietary problem. As we walked across the large, mainly tarmacked playground, our guides pointed out equipment for active play (including balls galore) and soft area for the younger ones to climb, slide and play safely. We were later informed that there is an imminently scheduled building project to update the whole playground. Our younger guides proudly showed their fully equipped classrooms, interactive whiteboards and all. Children's work, art and otherwise, on display all over. All pupils appeared happy and relaxed, quick to say hello and answer questions. Unmissable code of conduct pinned up all over. Our guides were quick to explain the provenance of the many badges they were wearing. As one

parent said: 'Lots of smiley teachers, lots of smiley children, such a happy school!'

A reasonably varied curriculum, at least for the first five years. The importance of 11+ kicks in during the summer term in year 5 and children are given lots of homework for the holidays. From then on English and mathematics dominate until all entrance exams are over; afterwards lessons become theme based, more adventurous and relaxed; children take part in a whole range of different activities, home and away. Recently, year 6s wrote traditional stories which they then read to the reception classes. The change of pace must work well because the majority of pupils get into their first choice of secondary school, parents having been well advised by the head, of course.

All pupils in years 1 and 3 screened for literacy and specific areas of difficulty. Parents informed of any problems and help given where necessary. Small group lessons focusing on literacy and motor skills, if needed, once or twice a week for half an hour. One-to-one help also provided occasionally, if absolutely necessary. 'No extra ever charged for special needs support'. Say they wouldn't normally decline a place to a child with pre-identified minor learning difficulties. A special needs room in each building. Teachers always available to talk to parents.

Extracurricular regarded as important and many different after-school clubs, sporty, arty, intellectual, musical. The range changes from term to term. Several orchestras and choirs, individual lessons offered on a wide variety of instruments. Recently a year 3 boy scored one of the highest marks in the country for his piano exam. A full programme of outings, cultural and academic, plus some residential trips for older children. All the usual charity fundraisers – luckily some parents take these very seriously and are happy to organise. They have already built one school in Burma and currently a major project is to raise sufficient funds to build another.

Redcliffe School

47 Redcliffe Gardens, London SW10 9JH

Independent • Pupils: 170 • Ages: 3–11 girls; 3–8 boys • Fees: up to £14,610 pa

Tel: 020 7352 9247

Email: admissions@redcliffeschool.com
Website: www.redcliffeschool.com

Headmistress: Since 2006, Mrs Susan Bourne BSc (50s). Read chemistry at Manchester University. Previously deputy head of the Old Vicarage School in Richmond and taught chemistry in both the

state and independent sector. 'I still love teaching and teach the year 6 science lessons.' The sort of sensible woman you could rely on in an emergency, her calm demeanour permeates the whole school.

Married to a management consultant ('he's my anchor') with three grown up daughters, she took time out while based in Geneva and Paris with a young family so knows what it's like to be a parent both at home and in an international setting. 'She really understands,' said one mother. Now lives in Richmond but escapes most weekends down the M3 to cottage in the New Forest where she and her husband sail their boat ('but only in calm weather!')

Entrance: Entrance to the nursery is first come first served but it is advisable to put names down within 6 months of birth. Places are sometimes available at the last minute due to parents in this area applying to lots of different schools, so it's worth staying on the waiting list. Entrance to the main school is by assessment and an interview with the head. 'When we assess children for entry to the main school, we are looking for more than just academic ability,' said Mrs Bourne. 'We are looking for sociable children who are going to be happy here. For example, I choose children who are comfortable when separated from their carer.' Most children go through to the main school from the nursery. Two mixed forms from reception to year 3, then one form of girls in each year.

Exit: Boys go at 8+ to schools such as Colet Court, Northcote Lodge, Wetherby Prep, Westminster Cathedral Choir School and Sussex House. Girls leave at 11+ to a mixture of boarding and day schools with Benenden, Putney High, Queen's College, Godolphin & Latymer and City of London being popular recent choices. Regular music, academic and art scholarships.

Remarks: This well-established prep school is situated on two sites on Redcliffe Gardens – a busy thoroughfare taking traffic from north to south London. Although it has expanded over the last few years and now has 170 pupils from nursery age up to 11, it still feels small and intimate.

The upper school is housed in the original main building, which when you enter looks more like a rather scruffy family home than a school. The cosy atmosphere is continued in the head's office, where visitors sit on a comfy but rather shabby sofa. However, when you enter the classrooms it's an entirely different matter. The recently refurbished hall in the basement (which is also used as a dining room) is splendid, and when we visited during morning assembly, a Mendelssohn concerto was being played through a brand new music system. (A different composer is studied each week.) Children filed in and sat with their eyes closed so that they could appreciate the music. When the deputy head asked them what they were going to do that day, one girl replied, 'have fun,' which summed up the attitude around the school. (The answer she was actually looking for was 'work hard!')

A new extension at the back of the school is light and airy, while the other classrooms upstairs, although a little cramped, have high ceilings and natural light. The top floor houses the music room where piano, violin, flute, trumpet, guitar and voice are taught by peripatetic teachers. Music is one of the school's strengths, with some children gaining music scholarships to their next schools. The school orchestra plays at school events such as the carol service and prize-giving and there are concerts for parents and friends at least twice a year.

The lower school, at St Luke's church a quarter of a mile down the road, comprises five bright and well-lit classrooms in the basement of the church (one for nursery and two classes each of reception and year 1). A large hall is used for indoor sports and lunch (which is trolleyed down from the upper school kitchen), and is also the venue for whole school assemblies on Thursdays and Fridays which parents are encouraged to attend. 'Sometimes it's standing room only as these have become such popular events,' explained the head proudly. Children use a specially designed play area outside, with climbing frames built on an artificial grass covering with toys and scooters available. 'We like to spend as much time outside as possible.'

Children use a specially designed play area outside, with climbing frames built on an artificial grass covering with toys, and scooters available

The teacher to student ratio is high, with a maximum of 16 in each class. There are specialist teachers for music, sport, French and drama. Recent productions include Minibeast Madness by the lower school and A Midsummer Night's Dream by the upper school. Extra EAL lessons support children who require help (particularly when they first join the school) and a learning support teacher sees a number of children (around 10) twice a week on a one-to-one basis to help with specific learning difficulties such as mild dyslexia (but this costs extra). Most of the staff are women (three have been there for over 10 years), with one male teaching assistant and a male PE teacher, and this does give the school (especially since boys leave at 8) a rather female atmosphere. 'We would like to recruit more good male staff,' said the head.

Food is cooked on the upper school site and there are themed lunches for events such as Halloween and Bonfire Night. 'Children who have left the school write back to say how much they miss the food.' Parents are regularly invited in to have lunch with the staff and the children. 'We always feel very welcome at the school,' said one mother.

Children are bussed to nearby parks once a week for sports – football and netball in the autumn term, hockey and tag rugby in the spring and rounders, cricket and athletics in the summer. Weekly swimming lessons all year round at Fulham Pools. They compete against other schools and also have their own swimming galas and sports days. On Friday afternoons school finishes early and children can take part in a wide variety of sporting activities from yoga to fencing. 'We used to finish early on Fridays to enable our families with country properties to leave London before the rush hour but more and more are staying on to take advantage of the sports clubs,' said the head.

Families are drawn from the local area – half the children have either one or two international parents. 'Most of the schools round here have a high number of international families,' says one American mother, 'but this school seems very British still.' Another mother commented: 'It's very down to earth for a prep school in this area and you don't need to worry if you turn up at the school gate in the morning with no make up on. No one will judge you.'

Former pupils include Daniel Radcliffe. 'He was a rather quiet boy,' said the deputy head. 'We never expected him to become famous.' But Redcliffe is nothing like Hogwarts, and all in all this is a warm and cosy school with a nurturing environment. The atmosphere feels somewhat cloistered and it probably wouldn't suit a boisterous child who likes to run around a lot. But this could be just the place for gentler, less confident children to flourish.

Sacred Heart High School (Hammersmith)

212 Hammersmith Road, London W6 7DG

State • Pupils: 925 • Ages: 11–18 • Sixth form pupils: 80 • RC

Tel: 020 8748 7600

15

Email: info@sacredh.lbhf.sch.uk
Website: www.sacredhearthighschoolhammersmith. org.uk

Headteacher: Since 2014, Mrs Marian Doyle MA NPQH (50s). Previously deputy head since 1997. Before that, she taught English and RE at Haggerston School, Hackney, Phoenix High School, Hammersmith and latterly Holland Park School, Notting Hill Gate. A world away from the previous head (a deeply traditional woman who reigned for 23 years with what girls describe as a combination of awe and fear), Doyle is softer around the edges and fresher in her outlook. Not only does she look more modern (she wore fabulous killer heels when we met her), but the school itself feels more alive, with walls now adorned with colourful canvases of the girls at work and many inspirational quotes. School systems (from admin through to bullying policies) have also had an overhaul, thanks to the head's key vision of the school being run seamlessly. A parent herself, she is big on boundaries and 'tough love', but is also approachable and smiley, and is regularly seen around the school, popping into lessons and talking to the girls at break times. 'She is very keen to make sure that we like it here,' said one girl.

Academic matters: Impressive results, by anyone's standards. In 2015, 85 per cent achieved five or more A*-C passes at GCSE including maths and English, 48 per cent A*/A grades. New sixth form opened in 2013, with first A level results 58 per cent A*-B.

Maths the strongest subject, followed by English. RE, history and geography also stand out. In terms of languages, Spanish and French are on offer, and a group of around 15 girls are put forward for Latin GCSE, which they study at St Paul's. Science highly promoted, with 60 per cent doing science and maths post-16.

Each year group has five form groups, with setting across all subjects from year 7 into five or six groups, depending on the subject, with plenty of flexibility to move about as necessary. Class sizes vary, with many as large as 35.

Expectation under new headship for all pupils to do at least two after-school clubs (which they call enrichment), which has been accommodated by changes to the school day (which now comprises five 60 minute lessons and finishes at 3.05pm) and an expectation that staff stay longer to run these clubs on Tuesdays and Wednesdays. Outside facilitators brought in too. Subjects include all the usual suspects such as choir, sport, maths challenge, sci-

---

Subjects include all the usual suspects such as choir, sport, maths challenge, science clubs, drama etc as well as more unusual offerings

---

ence clubs, drama etc as well as more unusual offerings including yoga and gardening.

One full-time staff member (qualified teacher, as well as a dyslexic specialist; has the national SENCo leadership award) is responsible for SEN, although no special unit. She puts in place three tiered levels of support – firstly, qualified teachers' support in mainstream, with the aim that specialist subject teachers can support in their areas of expertise; second (if necessary) additional support before and after school; finally (again if necessary) involvement of school counsellor or outside services, such as speech and language and occupational therapy. Difficulties catered for include dyslexia and other needs that are physical, such as hearing loss or severe long-term conditions, communication and language difficulties, ADD, ADHD. School also claims there are some serious mental health concerns. School reckoned there were 65 in total with SEN when we visited, five of whom are statemented. Very rarely, if a child's needs cannot be fully met, the school works closely with parents and the local authority to find alternatives. Help for gifted and talented through a range of enrichment and additional opportunities.

'The help my daughter has received for her dyslexia has been second to none, including trying out a range of different techniques, and the communication with us has been excellent too,' said one parent. 'Her self-confidence has rocketed and she's doing really well in exams.'

School is designated as a national teaching school, leading the West London Teaching School Alliance, which means working closely with 28 other primary and secondary schools in west London to improve standards of teaching and share best practice on issues including initial teacher training, professional development, research and development, succession planning and mentoring. Head says it's her vision for the school to become known for its drive for excellence. 'I put the same level of effort into training and development for the staff as I do teaching the girls, because I believe the two are inextricably linked,' she says.

Although the teaching staff we saw were a pretty glum-looking lot (particularly unwelcoming when we went near their classrooms), girls are clearly impressed with their level of commitment. 'Lessons are really engaging,' said one. 'They make sure nobody gets missed,' added another. Indeed, girls are regularly reminded of a quote from one of the founders: 'For the sake of one child, I would have founded the society,' after which they're told, 'You are the one child.'

Games, options, the arts: For a small inner-city site, they certainly pack in the sports facilities, all of which are utilised to the max, with the girls doing at least two hours of PE per week and with the option of PE as both a GCSE and A level subject. In addition to the two tennis/netball courts (which double up as rounders pitches), there's a gym and activity studio for the likes of dance, pilates and yoga. The new £8m sports and science block – imminent when we visited – is home to a massive sports hall that can facilitate three teaching groups simultaneously. 'It's four times the size of our current gym,' enthused one girl. Also new in autumn 2015 is a running track and outdoor gym of the ilk you see in parks, all of which means the long-standing link with Hammersmith and Fulham Health and Fitness Centre will start to diminish. Rowing, softball, basketball and volleyball on offer, along with all the usual suspects, and after-school clubs include street dance, yoga, cheerleading, fencing, trampolining and football, among others. Plenty of inter-house sports competitions, the highlight of which is the annual sports day held at St Paul's fields (originally owned by Sacred Heart but sadly they sold it off years ago), and the school has increasing success in the borough in hockey, rounders, netball and athletics.

No shortage of peripatetic teachers for musical instruments including piano, flute, trombone, drums etc. There are junior and senior choirs, various ensembles, and the girls talk highly of the general music classes, as well as about the annual Battle of the Bands. 'Music is really good fun here,' one girl told us. We particularly like the random pianos in the corridors, all of which girls say get played regularly for practice, making for a lovely ambience when walking through the corridors.

Links to various theatres, including the Donmar, and the drama school LAMDA, give a flavour of how seriously drama is taken here, with annual all-school productions such as Hairspray and Annie. Art and DT studios are spacious, with state-of-the-art equipment and some extremely talented artwork produced by the girls. No cookery on offer when we visited, but this is being re-examined.

Background and atmosphere: The school, or 'convent of the Sacred Heart,' is built on a site steeped in Catholic history dating back to the early 17th century. During its 330 year history, four different orders of nuns have taught here. Today's Tudor-style, red-brick buildings were built in the late 19th century and there's no shortage of religious reminders inside, notably the huge, austere-looking religious murals all the way along the wide, spacious corridors of the cloisters, as well as the chapel, which doubles up as the main school hall. 'We have daily morning prayers,' said one girl, 'but apart from that, the presence of Catholicism in our everyday life is through the school's ethos and values.' 'The school provides a good moral compass, but there's no hard-line religion,' agreed a parent, who added that there's a sensible and modern approach to sex education too, within the context of the Catholic Church teaching.

In 1948 the convent school was reorganised as a secondary grammar school, continuing as a grammar school until 1976, when it received its first comprehensive intake. The school then took on academy status in 2012.

Most pupils use the entrance on Bute Gardens, whilst sixth form and visitors use the main entrance on Hammersmith Road, where you'll be greeted by a single receptionist behind an oak veneer desk and a couple of rows of cream leather chairs. The hum of traffic is loud, but it doesn't take many more steps into the school to feel as if you're in an oasis of calm – not at all what you'd expect from an inner-city comp. Even during class switch-over times, when the extra-wide corridors are packed with animated girls, it somehow manages to avoid the feeling of chaos that many other schools have (probably helped by the very strictly policed one-way walking system).

A steep stone staircase leads down to the converted basement, which forms the buzzy social space and café for sixth formers. The rest of the girls eat in the dining room which, head admits, 'could be more funky' and where the 'food is 'ok.' Those who have packed lunch eat at temporary tables that are laid out daily in the wide corridors.

Asked what they'd improve, girls told us they could do with more quiet study space, especially in sixth form. 'We are allowed to use the library,'

said one, 'but it's not ideal.' Indeed, when we visited, the library was being used by an entire class and was by no means quiet, although in fairness it is two-story, with doors shutting out such sound on the top level. Well-stocked and imaginatively designed, the library is also very light and inviting. Classrooms are bog-standard, with stand-out facilities for drama and music. Great excitement about the new science block, which will transform this current provision beyond recognition.

Impressive amounts of charitable work overall, including £10,500 raised for a sister school in Kenya for disabled children via activities including sponging teachers

Girls encouraged to be proactive, rather than spoon fed, with lots of emphasis on them doing things, rather than talking about things. When we visited, a group of girls had gone to Mexico to rebuild houses for those in poverty. A further group of six girls went to Lourdes with the Handicapped Children Pilgrimage Trust. Impressive amounts of charitable work overall, including £10,500 raised for a sister school in Kenya for disabled children via activities including sponging teachers, making teachers eat chilli, sponsored walks and rowing the distance of the Channel in the gym. School is also part of a worldwide network of schools in 45 countries which creates opportunities such as a head girls' meet up to discuss leadership ideas and pupil exchanges across different countries.

Plenty of school trips to universities, BBC, Houses of Parliament, businesses including JP Morgan and all the usual museums and art galleries. Residential trips largely music-related, including to places such as Austria and Paris, whilst whole school European ski trips take place each year.

Strong student voice, with elected student members having requested that the science garden become more appealing, as well as having offered responses to the school's Equality Plan.

Pastoral care and discipline: Although current head is considered 'less scary and strict' than her predecessor, she is equally dedicated to high standards, pointing out that your daughter will be in detention if she arrives even five seconds after the bell goes. 'The point is that in professional life, if you had a meeting at 10am, you wouldn't arrive just after 10am,' she explains. 'We also want a calm start to the day.' It clearly works – there are few detentions in reality, with the girls we talked to never having been late in their entire six years. Other zero-tolerance aspects of school life include school uniform (especially length of skirts) and good behaviour, although pastoral care is highly praised here, with all the parents we talked to calling it 'very nurturing and caring.' Pupils are frequently reminded they can talk to form teachers, non-teaching pastoral support managers, the chaplain or two full-time school counsellors. In addition, there are strong links with Child and Adolescent Mental Health Services (CAMHS) and the charity Mind. 'One of my daughters went off the rails and had some counselling, which promptly nipped it in the bud,' said one parent. Head is by no means resting on her laurels, though. 'Like most schools,' she says, 'we have seen an increase in mental health issues and are very aware we need to talk about it in a more real and open way.' Peer mentoring scheme between year 7s and year 11s encourages cross-year relationships and older girls to take a leadership role.

Pupils and parents: This is top of the state school list for many families, not only in west London, but as far as Islington (with Tony Blair's daughter being the obvious example). Although it's non-selective and fully comprehensive, the majority of families are middle-class and with English as a first language. That said, there is genuine poverty among some of the girls, with head reporting that this is increasingly the case. 'We have 14 per cent identified as having free school meals and many others with an income only just above the threshold where parents struggle to make ends meet,' she says.

Strong PA and links between parents generally. 'It's unusually sociable among parents for an inner-city comprehensive, with lots of mums' nights out, quiz nights and family-focused activities,' said one parent. Good communications between school and parents, although some parents think the annual parents' evening, which falls in the summer term, is far too late in the academic year.

Entrance: Parents keep an extremely beady eye on the admissions policy of this heavily oversubscribed school, and many are unswerving in their commitment to find some way for their daughter to become one of the approximately 198 pupils to enter year 7. But you'll need to start early, as all girls need to have been baptised before they were 6 months old (although we did to talk to one parent who did it slightly later due to illness in the family) and to have attended one of 11 feeder schools, all named on the website. If you meet all the criteria, you won't need to sweat so much about how close you are to the school. Be warned that siblings don't automatically gain entry and are sometimes turned away. Separate admissions procedures for girls with a Statement of special educational needs or the new Education, Health and Care Plan. Parents praise the transition from primary school. Up to 40 external applicants to sixth form, for which you'll need eight A*-Cs, including subject-specific requirements.

Exit: Clear expectation to remain at the school to do A levels, with 80 out of 164 staying on in the first year of sixth form and 145 internal applicants for 2016 in the second year. Others commonly go onto Cardinal Vaughan or The London Oratory, with a handful going into the independent sector, including UCS, St Benedict's and Latymer Upper. One Oxbridge place amongst the first year 13 students - engineering at Oxford - with plenty of places at other top universities to study eg English, history and medicine.

Remarks: An exceptional and relatively small inner-city state school that provides girls who are prepared to behave impeccably with a traditional education and sense of community that will set them up for life.

St Charles Catholic Sixth Form College

74 St Charles Square, London W10 6EY

State • Pupils: 1,200 • Ages: 16–19 • RC

Tel: 020 8968 7755

Email: admissions@stcharles.ac.uk
Website: www.stcharles.ac.uk

47

Principal: Since September 2015, Mrs Elaine Taylor, previously vice principal. She joined the college in 2009 from St Francis Xavier College, where she had been assistant principal.

Academic matters: Whilst around three-quarters of the students follow traditional A level courses, St Charles also offers BTecs, certificates and diplomas, vocational courses and foundation skills in English and mathematics. The college also offers GCSE retakes for those wanting to improve their grades. More able students can take the Extended Project Qualification. Students are all taught to plan and develop their work alongside how best to manage their time. Being a rounded, thinking individual is part of the college's mission: everyone follows the compulsory general RE programme, which involves much critical discussion around the purpose and meaning of life through theology and philosophy. Students who are successful in completing the course gain the nationally recognised Certificate in Religious Investigation and Moral Reasoning. The school is well-known for added value, with six per cent of A level grades A*/A in 2015 and 29 per cent A*-B; this is no mean achievement for a mixed ability college. Spread across two floors, the library provides quiet areas for working and a good range of books, multimedia, newspapers and periodicals. Active and well-resourced learning support department provides assistance to students with a range of specific needs. The building is now fully wheelchair accessible. Intensive courses for students with English as an additional language are organised for small groups to ensure much personal attention.

Games, options, the arts: Impressive and modern sports facilities; sports block also incorporates new IT suites. Huge sports hall, four new indoor courts and fitness suite; students can also use the Birkbeck College sports ground for football and rugby. Basketball team has won the London Pioneers for three out of the last four years. Very strong art and design department puts on well-attended exhibitions, and a number of students go on to foundation courses at top London art schools. Drama and music are also popular and the school produces plays and musicals, with auditions open to all students. Film and media students are involved with projects run

by the British Film Institute, enabling them to show and discuss their creative work with film and television professionals. Very enthusiastic and successful

---

The full-time chaplain looks after the small but beautiful chapel, where morning prayers are said daily

young enterprise team recently won Best Overall Company for North Central London. The college links up with other organisations to provide community out-reach opportunities, be it helping older people gain ICT skills or mentoring other young people. Students can also become involved in the CitySafe initiative run by London Citizens, an organisation committed to improving young people's lives and skills and combating street violence.

Background and atmosphere: As you walk into the entrance hall, a peaceful and positive atmosphere is immediately apparent, the most inspiring design taken from Milan Cathedral. Everywhere is spotlessly clean, and well cared for corridors positively shine. The college is named after St Charles Borromeo, a 16th century Italian archbishop who believed strongly in the redeeming powers of education. Founded by Basil Hume in 1990, it continues to go from strength to strength. Quite overwhelming feedback from staff that St Charles is a breath of fresh air, organised, and with a positive attitude across all disciplines. The college is conveniently located in St Charles's Square, often referred to as 'The Little Vatican', due to the neighbouring Catholic primary and secondary schools, St Pius Church and a Carmelite monastery. Much about the college is designed around hope and inspiration, and a large amount of wall space is dedicated to portraits of students with accompanying testimonials and histories of their educational and career development. Interestingly, quite a few ex-students return to work at the college in both academic and non-academic posts.

Pastoral care and discipline: St Charles's continues to work very hard to ensure the best possible pastoral care and that every student feels part of the community. Everyone has a tutor group under one of the pastoral managers which looks after their progress and well-being. There is a referral system for students with academic and/or personal problems. An outside agency provides both male and female counsellors who visit the school on a weekly basis. The full-time chaplain looks after the small but beautiful chapel, where morning prayers are said daily and a mass takes place every Friday lunchtime. The chaplain is available to students on a drop-in basis. Whilst supporting students, he also organises voluntary work experience and charity work. Students are provided with a code of conduct, so everyone knows exactly what is expected of them in all aspects of college life and behaviour. Zero tolerance towards smoking, alcohol and drugs, all banned from the site.

Pupils and parents: Very diverse 21st-century London group of students, from all over the world, Portuguese, Filipino, Hispanic, Afro-Caribbean and Eastern European. About 80 per cent from ethnic minorities, many of whom are the first members of their family to have the opportunity to attend an A level college and go on to university.

Entrance: First priority goes to those with specific needs, then to students applying from four partner Catholic secondary schools, which makes up about 20 per cent of the intake. Other than that, fairly open access; students come from around 150 feeder schools. Everyone applying on time will be offered an interview to discuss their application and suitable course.

Exit: Approximately 75 per cent go on to university, others to art colleges or FE colleges to follow vocational training courses or apprenticeships.

Money matters: College raises some funds by hiring out the excellent facilities including the large hall, indoor and outdoor sports areas and equipment, and spacious restaurant and catering area. The student bursary scheme provides grants for those in financial hardship while studying full time.

Remarks: Some remarkable achievements happen here. Great place for motivated and hard-working young people from all walks of life who want to move on, regardless of previous achievements or background.

St James Junior School

Linked school: St James Senior Girls' School, 347

Earsby Street, London W14 8SH

Independent • Pupils: 250 • Ages: 4–11 • Fees: up to £15,960 pa

Tel: 020 7348 1793

Email: admissions@stjamesjunior.org
Website: www.stjamesjuniors.co.uk

16

Headmistress: Since 2009, Mrs Catherine Thomlinson, BA in English and history from Roehampton (40s). A St James' disciple to her fingers' ends, having spent almost all of her teaching career here after being educated at sister school, St Vedast (brief spell in South Africa before coming back to the fold). Two children, a son and a daughter, both of whom attended St James from age 4 right through senior school. A thoroughly lovely lady who radiates kindness, humanity and good humour, and this despite having a shocking cold when we met. The study oft proclaims the head, we've found, and Mrs Thomlinson's was sparely but beautifully furnished,

bright and calm. Amidst some exquisite pictures of quiet seas, a joyous tract reads, 'Let your light shine!' – and hers most assuredly does.

Despite her lifelong loyalty to the St James traditions, Mrs Thomlinson has not been afraid to modernise. She has pushed through substantial curriculum development, including DT, French and dance; and both boys and girls now do cookery, woodwork and sewing. Introduced interactive whiteboards for upper junior classrooms ('a fantastic tool'), and is looking to bring these in throughout the school. Major development of EYFS provision, following criticism in recent inspection report. Parents report improved communication. Continues to uphold strong emphasis on speech, drama and music, 'because they really touch the emotional intelligence'.

Entrance: 'We don't take children on an academic basis,' says head, and accordingly there's no entrance exam at age 4; instead, the school holds informal assessments that involve meeting both child and parents, plus a report from child's nursery where applicable. Children of alumni and siblings have priority, as do those whose parents registered them early for a place. School looks for 'a certain confidence, and for children and families who value what we value'. Places higher up the school occasionally become available, and children who apply aged 7+ take assessments in reading, writing and mathematics to establish whether they're able to manage within the standard of the established class.

Exit: Junior girls stay until the end of year 5, when virtually all of them progress to St James Senior Girls, which begins at year 6 and is situated on the same site. Overwhelming majority of parents are happy with this. 'I'm very grateful that neither they nor I will have to face the 11 plus,' one mother of two daughters commented. This is just as well, since for girls to change schools at this point would be extremely difficult. Very occasionally, however, a girl may opt to do her final junior year elsewhere, and Bute House has been one such destination.

St James Senior Boys is out at Ashford (a very comprehensive coach service is provided by St James Schools), so boys stay on at St James Junior

All the children, even the little ones, learn Sanskrit, in accordance with the school's belief that the Eastern philosophies have much to teach us

for their year 6 and can be prepped for common entrance to other senior schools at parents' request, 'but more and more boys are staying and going through to Ashford,' currently 66 per cent. Once again, it seems, parents appreciate the automatic entry. Where boys do go elsewhere, routes include Fulham Prep, Latymer Upper, Wetherby Prep, Hampton and Colet Court.

Remarks: A frieze of the goddess Athene gazes down benevolently from one of the foyer walls, and this may explain the air of gentle wisdom that really does pervade this unusual and admirable little school. It nestles quietly within residential streets, the outside resembling a monastery, with its high walls and expanse of sheer red brick, but the tableau through the security gate wasn't in the least forbidding. Children played cheerfully in a pretty, cloistered courtyard under the eye of a watchful but serene-looking teacher, and the whole was framed by light and airy corridors – a preponderance of new glass giving a modern, clean balance to the Victorian charm of the original building. The atmosphere, as far as we could judge, was one of kindness and peaceful activity. Parents all confirmed this: 'It's a very happy place.' 'It's an extremely happy school.'

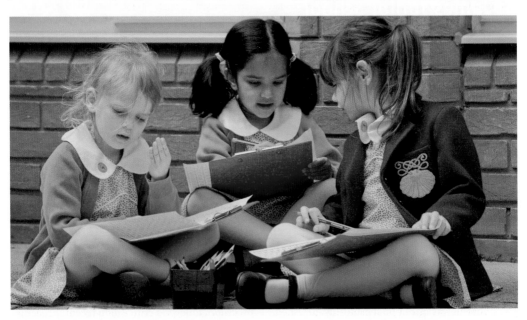

'A warm and nurturing environment.' 'My child has loved being there from the very beginning.'

The school's ethos places an unusually high emphasis on generosity, mutual respect and 'being the best human beings we can be,' and achieves this through a number of distinctive practices. Every lesson begins and ends with a 'moment of stillness'. Such moments 'give you that sense of ease and reflection,' says head. These pauses, as they're known, are popular with parents and children: 'It gives you a chance to be still,' said a year 6 child, whose demeanour was courteous and mature beyond his years. Parents agree. 'One of the main benefits of St James is the peacefulness,' was one comment, and 'One of the reasons we send our children to the school is to learn early on to take a pause, allow the noise to stop,' was another.

All the children, even the little ones, learn Sanskrit, in accordance with the school's belief that the Eastern philosophies have much to teach us; and both children and parents insisted to us that this was one of the things they 'really loved' about the school. St James describes itself as 'multi-religious', and philosophy itself is a very important part of the curriculum. The school teaches a Socratic method of dialogue and questioning, and the children are taught to develop open-ended questions and to debate as a class ('No putting-down of others' opinions is allowed,' says head firmly). The school motto – 'Speak the truth, be generous and kind, be your best' – seems to mean more here than such saws do in other schools. St James's policy of teaching boys and girls separately, then bringing them together for social activities (break-times, lunch, productions, trips, etc) may also be a key factor in establishing such good relationships between the children. 'You can see the boys, but you don't always have to be with them,' said a grateful year 5 girl, with which one of the boys countered, 'The girls think they're best, and we just get on with being even better.' We suspect this is amiable posturing: a number of parents confirmed to us that their child's closest schoolfriends included those of the opposite gender.

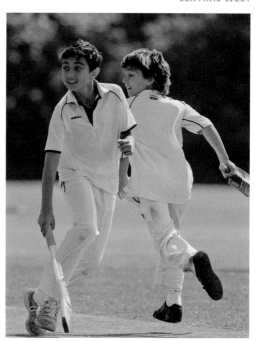

A frieze of the goddess Athene gazes down benevolently from one of the foyer walls, and this may explain the air of gentle wisdom that pervades this little school

Academic performance is strong, with the standard of written work exceptionally high, both in content and accuracy – all the more impressive, given that the school's intake is not academically selective. 'I'm a great advocate for academic rigour,' confirms the head, adding, 'but I'm just as passionate about children finding out what they love.' All classes have weekly sessions in the well-stocked library, run by a dedicated librarian, and there are regular visits by children's authors. ('My son very quickly developed a love of reading,' reported a satisfied parent.) SEN provision is good, with about 30 EAL children cared for within the classroom set-up. We applaud the emphasis on using Shakespeare as a teaching resource at all levels, more so than in any other school we've visited. We saw verses from The Winter's Tale charmingly illustrated by the reception children, and read some excellent commentaries on Polonius's advice to his son ('To thine own self be true') by the year 3 boys. 'We love Shakespeare,' the head acknowledged. 'We did A Midsummer Night's Dream and The Tempest last year. And Mozart's The Magic Flute. We have a great cultural reservoir to draw on – why not give them the best material?' Why not indeed!

And in fact the drama on offer is very impressive, with all the children involved in at least one performance every year. 'We like big productions!' beamed a member of staff, before hurrying off to oversee preparations for Fiddler On The Roof, for which the school hired the Britten Theatre at the Royal College of Music because 'we like to be ambitious'. Previous big productions include My Fair Lady, The Railway Children and The Sound of Music. For in-house performances, the school's hall has been recently refurbished and hosts frequent verse-speaking, plus dance for both girls and boys as well as drama productions. Music is strong, with 70 children taking instrumental lessons at school on 'pretty much anything they want', and regular concerts, often featuring the school's orchestra. The children sing every day in assembly – repertoire by Mozart, Purcell and Vivaldi is popular – and have music lessons every week. Artwork of an astonishingly high standard adorns the walls, produced in the attractive art room under the gaze of the stuffed menagerie up on the shelf: a goose, a grouse, a heron and a weasel.

'We like big productions!' beamed a member of staff, before hurrying off to oversee preparations for Fiddler On The Roof

All children have a period of games or sport every day, be it gym, dance, swimming or ball skills, and the upper juniors (years 3-6) go off-site once a week to Barn Elms to hone their skills at netball, rugby, cricket, athletics, cross-country and the like. There are lots of inter-school competitions, and the children told us proudly about recent triumphs over Wetherby and Fulham Prep. Swimming is held in nearby Fulham Pools, and ISA golds and silvers have been a feature of recent years. St James Junior is a member of Forest Schools UK, with two of its staff trained as Forest Leaders, and there are many trips to Minstead Study Centre in the New Forest. 'I've been seven times!' enthused one upper junior boy, 'and I enjoyed it SO MUCH!' A varied programme of outings closer to home has encompassed museums, art galleries, theatres, and the usual London fare. Excellent range of lunchtime and after-school

clubs includes guitar, yoga, cookery, gymnastics, model-making, archery, fencing, lacrosse and the perennially popular Mad Science Club. The head actively encourages all her staff to take up hobbies themselves, and the staff music band, we're told, is going from strength to strength. Use of ICT across the school has increased, although actual ICT lessons are still for year 6 only, so the boys get them in their final junior year, and the girls in their first year at the senior school. Children are 'encouraged to use ICT at home,' which may or may not be enough preparation for the increasingly ICT-based curriculum they'll face at senior school. But the junior school's stated priority is to develop clear cursive handwriting in its pupils, and from what we saw, they definitely succeed.

Food here is vegetarian, so that all the children can eat together, and is included in the fees. We were impressed by what we saw: a delicious-smelling vegetable curry, fresh bread being baked, home-made leek and potato soup, and lots of genuinely appetizing fresh fruit. The number of clean plates testified to its popularity with the young clientèle, and one solemn little girl was particularly enthusiastic about it to us as she lowered her elbow into her coleslaw. No problem, though – the lower juniors (years R-2) wear smocks down to lunch, which we thought eminently sensible.

All aspects of the pastoral care were rated excellent in the latest inspection report, which commented on the 'family atmosphere of mutual respect,' adding that 'the pupils thrive in the positive, caring environment' and are 'very well cared for.' The pupils concur. 'It's fun here,' 'The teachers are very kind,' 'Everyone is really nice,' 'You don't feel you have to be afraid of anything,' 'You can be yourself,' 'You can be proud of yourself,' 'The teachers are proud of us and they trust us,' were some of the many tributes we heard. This is all the more inspiring, given that the School of Economic Science, which founded the St James schools, attracted some very different comments from its embittered pupils a few decades back (see our online entry on the St James Independent Boys' School).

But all that is history. St James Junior impressed us as such a kind and enlightened medium in which to culture young minds, that we occasionally had to remind ourselves that this was a school we'd stepped into and not a Botticelli painting. It was almost a relief to see one small boy aim a punch at another, to hear an indignant cry of 'I was first!' and to meet a teacher who was unmistakeably knackered after her morning's work. But these tiny wrinkles only served to throw into greater focus the sweetness and calm of this remarkable community. Not a school for budding Piers Morgans, we suspect. But who cares?

St James Senior Girls' School

Linked school: St James Junior School, 343

Earsby Street, London W14 8SH

Independent · Pupils: 320 · Ages: 10–18 · Sixth form
pupils: 65 · Fees: £17,310 pa

Tel: 020 7348 1777

Email: admissions@sjsg.org.uk
Website: www.stjamesgirls.co.uk

17

Headmistress: Since September 2014, Mrs Sarah Labram BA (40s), formerly deputy head (academic) here. A classicist with a degree from King's College London, she is totally imbued with the St James ethos: a former pupil and head girl, whose two daughters were both educated at the junior and senior schools. She joined St James in 1996 as a classics teacher and has risen through the ranks to become head of department and then deputy head.

Academic matters: Girls take the IGCSE in maths and all three sciences – for greater rigour. At GCSE, 76 A*/A grades in 2015. Stunning success in physics, history and English and at least respectable everywhere else. At A level the 20 subject options now include theatre studies, Spanish and art history. Results creditable in most subjects – few grades below B – and English and maths impressive. In 2015, 75 per cent of A level entries were graded A*-B (63 per cent A*/A). School also offers EPQ to give students the opportunity to get deeply involved in a subject that interests them, to pull together learning from other subjects and to develop extended research and writing skills – all of which are hugely valuable preparations for university study.

But this is not a school to think of solely in these terms. The school's culture largely determines the extended curriculum. Sanskrit is continued for those who join from the junior school (introductory course offered to those joining in year 7) and available as an option at GCSE. Singing and philosophy are taken by all and everything is taught from the philosophical perspective which underpins the St James schools' ethos. This approach extends to the SEN provision which is managed on the basis of an individual's needs, although the hope is that most pupils can work independently by the end of year 8. Thereafter, the SENCo sees girls individually or in small groups according to need – no withdrawal from academic lessons. The staff monitor progress with care. Strong gifted and talented provision.

Games, options, the arts: This is a compact city site so anything involving running takes place at the Chiswick playing grounds, a bus ride away. On site, they cram in netball, aerobics, gymnastics, health-related fitness and dance etc and off site lacrosse, netball, athletics, rounders and tennis are the main sports. They have their own adventure club – the St James Challengers – and D of E. Two good art rooms in which, largely, the trad skills are taught by much-admired staff. Visiting instructors add to the core curriculum and the school now has a kiln but no dark room. And no DT. One of the best schools we know at actually displaying its own pupils' art – everywhere and with style. Music is big here (again under charismatic leadership); everyone sings – we heard it everywhere. Lots of individual lessons and good collaboration on concerts and productions with the boys' school – despite the distance. Drama popular and lively; new drama studio. The 'art of hospitality' is taught to years 6 and 7 – cookery, but not as you might have known it elsewhere: the thrust here is on sharing food and using it as a way of nurturing relationships. The sixth form cook for each other, have formal dinners with high profile guests etc. In year 10, all go on a residential week which focuses on 'becoming an adult' – life skills, presenting oneself at interview and being a responsible citizen etc. Much emphasis on community service.

Background and atmosphere: Founded, along with its sibling junior school and senior boys' school, in 1975 by the School of Economic Science (see our online review of the senior boys' school for background and history), the girls' school and junior

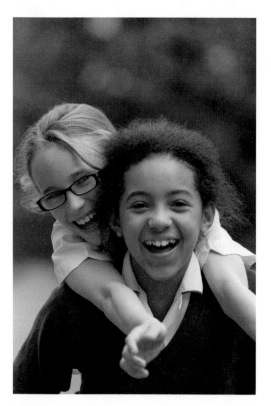

school moved to their impressive modern accommodation in 2001. The outside is daunting. The main gate, within sight of Olympia down a quiet side road, is encased in uniquely secure architecture – grilles, grids, gratings and entry phone. If you happen to be a billionaire or high profile political refugee, you will deposit your daughter here in the mornings, confident that the bad world will be kept firmly outside.

The junior and senior schools co-exist happily and it is rather nice – if surprising – to come across classrooms full of 6-year-olds as you cruise around the corridors. Nonetheless, the schools are finding, as was inevitable, that both need more elbow room. School has planning permission to build a new sixth form centre in a nearby park, which will free up space for a larger library, another science lab and expanded classrooms. The place is in good nick – lots of white-painted corridors, blue carpets, good wall displays and useful noticeboards. The sixth form have privileges – eating in the staff dining room, for one – and responsibilities which are taken seriously.

Classrooms, while not quite providing the 'beautiful environment' aimed at, are orderly and well-kept and all now have whiteboards and projectors. The library is clearly too small and a new library is part of the building plan. Outside space is limited though care has been taken to provide little trellised alcoves for quiet chat around the tarmac playground. A sense of cheery collaborativeness abounds – girls look relaxed and happy and appreciate their unusual school. Staff, according to parents, 'always smile and are friendly'. 'Silence, stillness and meditation' are important – everyone has a few moments for these at the start and finish of each lesson. The food is vegetarian and the tables are laid invitingly – hot home-cooked food plus fresh fruit, salad, bread and cheese.

The boys' school move to Ashford has provided much-needed expansion space in a very attractive position. But while the arrangement presents opportunities for the St James schools, there may well be difficulties now that the family of schools is spread over a wider geographic area. How families wanting the St James brand of education for their boys, girls, juniors and seniors will adapt remains to be seen. Nevertheless, we hear that so far the majority of the junior boys are still transferring to the senior boys' school. Senior boys and girls also enjoy a good number of extracurricular activities together.

Pastoral care and discipline: Highly praised. Pupils like the mentoring system and the 'strong bond' they feel to many teachers. Younger pupils are assigned sixth form prefects as mentors, sixth formers have form tutors. 'Your tutor is your friend – you go to her with any problems – not just academic ones.' School relies on the 'very strong programme of education' to guard against the usual teenage problems. 'We emphasise strengthening a girl's

'Silence, stillness and meditation' are important – everyone has a few moments for these at the start and finish of each lesson

social conscience and confidence.. if you present with difficulties we will help you so long as you are not harming the rest of the community.' On bullying, 'we keep working at it.. stressing the importance of unity and not harming each other.'

The school's strong spiritual ethos underpins the disciplinary side but girls don't feel it's thrust down their throats. A parent expressed the general view – 'we like the way they approach education – they believe strongly in the spiritual side of it – it doesn't invade life but they look at the whole development of the girl and believe that the academics will follow.' Who wouldn't fit in? 'Someone who is only out for themselves wouldn't find themselves in their natural environment..our girls are gentle on the outside but inwardly strong and independent – they are women of some integrity.'

Pupils and parents: Mixed as befits its west London location. Unsurprisingly, given the influence of 'the wisdom traditions of east and west', the school has an appeal to families with Asian backgrounds who make up around a fifth. A few of the staff are members of the School of Economic Science, some are ex-pupils, but a large majority of the pupils are now from families who have no direct connection with the SES. Some pupils come from great distances – at least for the first five years – though most are relatively local. Former pupils include actresses Emily Watson and Sasha Behar and novelist Laura Wilson.

Entrance: St James Junior girls move seamlessly through – NB at year 6. Main prep feeders are Pembridge Hall, Orchard House, Chiswick and Bedford Park, Glendower, Ravenscourt Park Prep, St Nicholas Prep, The Falcons School, Bute House, Garden House, Kew Green Prep, Thomas' Battersea and Thomas' Kensington. Some also from St Mary Abbots, Barnes, Belmont and Fox primary schools. A few join at year 6 but main intake into year 7 when around 200 apply for around 25 places. School is part of the North London Consortium so tests in maths and English. School's own reasoning test day also includes activities in baking, art, drama, dance and chemistry. A few come in at year 12.

Exit: Currently around 25 per cent leave after GCSEs; some to co-eds, often to colleges, occasionally to board or to nearer home. A pity as the sixth form classes are small – one-to-one in some cases – the teaching is good and nothing beats the continuity of staying where you are known. Some gap years. Thereafter to a range from UCL and SOAS to the Prince's Drawing School. An increasing number are pursuing science degrees and over the last three years a third have left to study science of some kind. Many pursue careers in which they contribute to the community. One to Oxford in 2015.

Money matters: The school operates a means-tested bursary scheme. All current and future parents may apply. Future parents need to be registered with the school. This is not a rich school so don't look for masses of help.

Remarks: If the high moral tone appeals and you enjoy the repetition of words such as 'fine', 'wise' and 'beautiful' you have achieved nirvana here. A tiny, peaceful school offering what many parents dream of.

St Paul's Girls' School

Brook Green, London W6 7BS

Tel: 020 7603 2288

18

Independent • Pupils: 741 • Ages: 11–18 • Sixth form pupils (known as VII and VIII forms): 215 • Fees: up to £23,562 pa

Email: admissions@spgs.org
Website: www.spgs.org

High Mistress: Since 2006, Ms Clarissa Farr MA PGCE (50s), who previously spent 14 years at Queenswood, the last 10 as head. She has also taught English in Hong Kong, in a Bristol comprehensive and in a sixth form college in Farnborough. She is married to a sports journalist and has two teenage children.

As the established incumbent of one of the most exposed headships in the land, she exudes an elegant, intellectual confidence that could intimidate nervous potential parents and pupils. 'She seemed aloof initially,' said a mother, 'but she's much warmer when you get to meet her.' As a parent commented, 'You could easily get the wrong impression of her – she seems like a cut-glass ladies' college type – but my daughter really likes her.' 'Mine is really scared of her,' admitted another, 'but I noticed that the head girl and her team are all very relaxed with her, and they all clearly value each other's opinions.' Another added, 'She's always around, she knows them all by name. And my daughter says she'll sometimes give her particular look that makes you feel very important – as if you're the one person who matters.' By all accounts always present at school events, 'even the little drama club productions'.

Academic matters: Pretty close to unbeatable. School can afford a lofty disdain for league tables as it is always at or near number one (44 per cent A*s and 86 per cent A*/A grades at A level in 2015; 89 per cent A*s, 98 per cent A*/A at GCSE). The common claim to prioritise a broad education is undoubtedly justified here: many parents chose the school amidst a plethora of offers from other London powerhouses for this very reason. 'It really does feed a broader intellectual curiosity,' said one. Another commented: 'The teaching is second to none – exciting and stimulating. The teachers really get the children and make the most of them.'

Those few with special educational needs often have coping strategies in place before they arrive, but the school is well set up to help. 'They've been astonishingly good at responding to my daughter's needs, and put in plenty of support for her,' said a parent, 'so it hasn't been too much of an issue. But they have made it clear that she is expected to meet the standards of the school.'

Tight group of almost entirely academic subjects at GCSE and A level, which includes Italian, Chinese and Russian in the wide range of languages, though with relatively few takers at A level, and the recently added government and politics and theatre studies A level. Maths is by far the most popular A level subject, as one would expect, with a fairly even spread between the runners up biology, chemistry, English and history.

'Art here is very special.' The top floor art rooms include a terrace with a panorama of the London skyline where girls learn about architecture

The school considered offering the IB but decided against it. 'We decided that A levels are a more flexible instrument – you have time to do things outside the curriculum that are not measured, and you can be a specialist or a generalist. It also gives more time for the bespoke Paulina unique co-curricular opportunities.' These include the Senior Scholarship project, which sees girls between years 12 and 13 carrying out projects with titles ranging from 'Is There Beauty in Chaos?' to 'Visualising Polytopes in 4 Dimensions'; and the Friday lectures from luminaries such as Shami Chakrabarti from Liberty and documentary maker Michael Cockerell on his latest work, The Life of Boris Johnston.

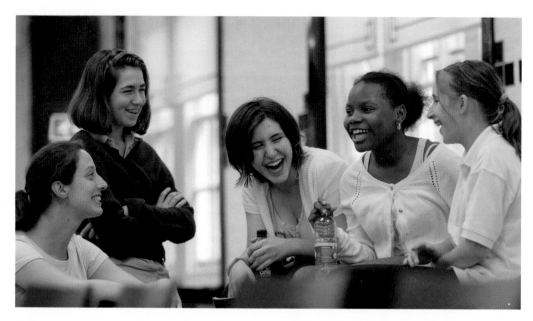

Games, options, the arts: With a legacy of Gustav Holst as first director of music and in-house composer, music has always been exceptional. Indeed, the recently renovated music department and singing hall – 'where Holst and Miss Gray [the then high mistress] listened to girls singing' – are an important nerve centre of the school. There are orchestras, music ensembles and choirs open to all, but the symphony orchestra and senior choirs are by audition only and perform at astonishingly high levels.

Art, too, is high profile. When we visited, the impressive coursework for the school-directed art GCSE course was on display in the hall. 'Art here is very special,' commented a student. The top floor art rooms include a terrace with a panorama of the London skyline where girls learn about architecture. There are spaces for digital art, animation, ceramics, sculpture and print-making as well as painting and drawing. DT is a GCSE option only as part of art and design (a school-designed course), but an example of the talent was an impressive pupil-designed bus shelter that adorned the entrance drive when we visited.

Drama has perhaps been a poorer relation in the past. 'Music and art have always been great strengths,' says Ms Farr, 'but theatre studies is my second subject, and it struck me that drama had not developed to the same level, so we have evolved a separate drama department.' It is a successful GCSE and A level option (though a mother commented that she was unusual in encouraging her daughter to take two arts subjects at GCSE: 'Lots of parents only want their daughters to do academic subjects'.) The purpose-built Celia Johnson Theatre hosts several annual school plays, with smaller scale productions in the drama studio. Students devise and direct their own plays, including the year 12 Colet Play, which has been performed at the Edinburgh Fringe on several occasions. Girls also join in St Paul's Boys' School productions.

Lacrosse is the main sport, with 7.30am practices for team players ('they all love it, so it's fine', commented a less devoted pupil), international tours and players often making county and area squads. The school also competes successfully at sports including netball, basketball, rowing, cross county, fencing and swimming. However, there are opportunities for the less talented too, with teams down to D and E in the lower years. 'My younger daughter is in a team even though she's rubbish,' said a parent honestly.

One parent commented: 'It's very inclusive. There's choirs and orchestras anyone can be in, and the same for drama and sport.' Amidst so many very talented girls, however, some of the younger ones in particular can take time to gain confidence and find their niche. 'My daughter plays an instrument but hasn't been asked to take part in anything so

far. She and her friends like singing, but they found the choir too highbrow. And they were very disheartened when none of them got through to the second round of auditions for the school musical.' Another parent said, 'There are huge opportunities, but it's up to them to make the most of it.'

Huge numbers of clubs, seminars and trips: writing courses, physics and maths competitions, conferences in Paris, museum visits in St Petersburg, dance shows and debating competitions. 'The girls get caught up in the energy of the place,' says Ms Farr, and a parent commented, 'My daughter always comes home having done amazing things.'

Background and atmosphere: Some 400 years after John Colet founded St Paul's School 'for the children [not girls, naturally] of all nations and countries', the Mercers' livery company, guardians of his estate, decided girls were also worthy of an education and set up SPGS. Its red-brick main house, designed by Gerald Horsley, with marble-floored corridors, and panelled and galleried great hall, has a gracious, traditional and peaceful feel. 'But if you go in at break time it's very buzzy,' said a parent. 'They're all running round the hall, there's music blaring out.' Lack of uniform gives an informal air, with most girls dressed in ubiquitous jeans or shorts and tee shirts.

Ms Farr recognises that the school has an underserved reputation for being 'very formal, starchy, cold, highly competitive, ruthless and unforgiving'.

But once families join, she says, 'they find it's much friendlier than expected, and more informal. We like to do things in a friendly, collegiate way.' Parents agree: 'It's a much more normal place than you'd think from its image. It's much nicer from the inside than from the outside.' 'They really care about the individual.'

Impressive admin: 'It's really well run, which means a lot to us,' said a mother. 'Induction week in particular is brilliantly organised. They told the girls what would happen, and it did. They're very accommodating and very professional.' Another said, 'Unlike at my son's school, I don't feel I have to stress about homework and deadlines. I leave it to them.'

Pressure to achieve tends to come from highly-ambitious girls and their families rather than from the school. However, some feel that the school could do more to mitigate anxieties. 'Success is taken so seriously that it sends out a message of pressure,' said a parent. 'Lots of girls really worry about how they are going to do in school exams. You can feel very unsuccessful if you aren't brilliant.' Some parents of younger girls feel the homework can be overwhelming. 'It tends to take much longer than intended because they're perfectionists,' said a year 7 parent. 'She and her friends take all evening doing homework.' 'I don't know how they cope if they miss anything, because lessons move at such a fast pace,' said another.

'We had the preconception that you had to be pretty, funny and clever to fit in here,' said a mother. 'But my retiring daughter has come home

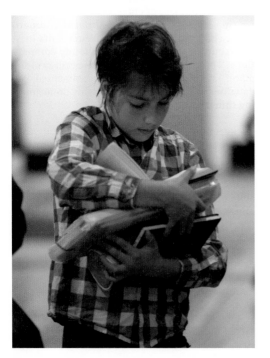

beaming from day one.' Another said that her daughter has found it tough: 'It took her a while to make friends. Coming from a state primary was particularly hard from a social point of view. But she's already gaining in confidence. They make the girls feel really proud of being there.'

'There is a view that you must be super-confident to succeed here,' says Ms Farr, 'but girls vary here as much as anywhere'

Girls are encouraged to take the initiative. 'If you come up with an idea, the school will back you up and support you all the way,' said a sixth former, citing the in-house second-hand clothes shop, housed in a restored Victorian coal cellar that previously acted as a junk room, set up and run by students to raise money for local charities.

Pastoral care and discipline: 'I like to think it is a kinder school than it was,' says Ms Farr, who has increased the emphasis on the pastoral side. 'We have clear boundaries but lots of room for independent expression. We treat the girls like adults as soon as possible.' 'There's a marked lack of rules,' agreed a parent. 'There's a respect and a feeling of equality between teachers and girls.'

Some of these highly-ambitious girls do succumb to eating disorders or other expressions of teenage angst, but the school is very conscious of the problem and encourages a relaxed approach to eating. The dining room has recently been refurbished and the food, said a pupil, is 'amazing. I feel as if I am eating in a restaurant every day. Food is important to Paulinas.'

Small tutor groups of 12 girls keep the same tutor for two years in the lower school and three in the middle school. The sixth form has a vertical system to enable those in different forms to share experiences. The sister scheme sees girls from the middle and upper schools help new girls settle in, and two year 13 girls are attached to each lower year group, available for mentoring and encouragement. 'The sixth form isn't hived off in its own area but is very much part of the school. The girls are role models and figures to look up to for the younger ones.' 'Very approachable' school nurse.

Pupils and parents: Intellectual, ambitious, often multi-national families. 'I sometimes feel that my daughter's in a minority having two English parents. Lots of girls speak a second language fluently.' From a range of backgrounds – journalists and artists, academics and scientists, with a large proportion of bankers and lawyers ('You can spot those with bursaries,' said a parent wryly, 'because their dads aren't bankers.') Largest single cohort from Bute House, which regularly sends up to 20 or so girls here; the rest from a wide range of preps and primaries across London and beyond.

'There is a view that you must be super-confident to succeed here,' says Ms Farr, 'but girls vary here as much as anywhere. We do have a place for sensitive, quieter girls, and we enjoy the challenge of bringing them out. However, some parents still don't feel that their daughter is tough enough.' Parents agree that eccentricities are well tolerated. 'Of course the top dogs are the cool girls,' said one, 'but you can be a total geek and it's not a problem.'

Old Paulinas include (amongst many) Harriet Harman, Shirley Williams, Carol Thatcher, Stephanie Flanders, Rosalind Franklin, Rachel Weisz, Imogen Stubbs, Marghanita Lanski, Dodie Smith and Rachel Johnson.

Entrance: A computer-based test in November, aimed to be tutor proof and to identify 'girls with intellectual potential', deselects around 20 per cent of applicants. 'There's a vast industry preparing girls for St Paul's, and we don't want to miss bright sparks who haven't been tutored.' The rest take maths, English and comprehension exams in January, with those short-listed invited back for interviews. 'Our admissions process is a very careful, solemn business. We try to make it humane as well as thoughtful, and we discuss every candidate in detail.' The school optimistically asks parents to state if their daughter has been tutored, 'though we know they will answer what they think we want to hear'. They are trying to increase the proportion of successful state school applicants (currently around 15-25 per cent), and run a series of enrichment days for gifted and talented year 4 and 5 girls from local state primaries. Parents are given information about bursaries and encouraged to attend an open evening. 'We don't positively

discriminate, but we do try to see through disadvantage.' The school is clear that it is looking for a particular type of girl. 'Our girls devour intellectual material very quickly. Those who want to work at a slower pace will be happier elsewhere.'

Exit: No-one is asked to leave because of poor academic performance (though they might reconsider someone who showed a lack of interest in learning). 'We make an undertaking to see them through, and every year we take through one or two girls whose GCSE performance is less than starry.' Minimal numbers leave after GCSE (a few are tempted off to co-ed sixth forms, particularly Westminster). Vast majority stays the course and moves on to do mostly solidly academic subjects at a very narrow range of top universities. Around half get Oxbridge offers (44 in 2015); 12 off to study; liberal arts at Yale, Harvard and other Ivy League universities; virtually all the rest to Durham, Edinburgh, Bristol and the London universities. The school is investigating European destinations, but no-one has been tempted across the Channel as yet.

Money matters: Four music (£100 a year and free music tuition) and four academic (£250 a year) scholarships at 11+; various art, music and academic scholarships at 16+, all worth £250 a year. The school aims to fund 20 per cent of girls through its means-tested bursary programme – 'we would like to feel that any girl from any setting could plot her way here' – and staff visit likely families at home to ensure they are not running a fleet of Ferraris from a multi-million pound mansion. Those on 100 per cent bursaries also receive a grant towards music or PE lessons, school trips, textbooks and travel.

Remarks: Unmatched environment for girls who thrive on hard work and have an appetite for intellectual experiences. 'What is on offer is exceptional. They have so many wonderful opportunities.'

St Philip's School

6 Wetherby Place, London SW7 4NE

Tel: 020 7373 3944

Independent • Pupils: 110 • Ages: 7–13 • RC
• Fees: £14,100 pa

Email: info@stphilipschool.co.uk
Website: www.stphilipschool.co.uk

48

Headmaster: From January 2016, Alexander Wulffen Thomas (30s), who is currently deputy head at Westminster Cathedral Choir School. He was educated at Stonyhurst College and Durham University, where he read Russian. He worked for

a specialist risk consultancy before joining WCCS in 2010.

Head since 1990, Mr Harry Biggs-Davison MA (50s). Educated at St Philip's, Downside and Fitzwilliam College, Cambridge, where he read geography. Immediately returned to St Philip's to teach games in 1978 and has stayed ever since. Married with two grown up sons, his wife, Anna, is an invaluable part of the teaching team as the SENCo and with her own year 4 class. Head speaks of the school (his school) with enthusiasm and pragmatism, and of the boys and his staff with insight, pride and affection – and a healthy dose of good humour.

Retiring in December 2015.

Entrance: Boys come from local pre-prep and primary schools and most live within three miles of the school. Entry is into year 3 (10 boys) and year 4 (10 boys). School over-subscribed at both points but so far the temptation to select purely on the basis of ability has been resisted. Priority is given to brothers of current pupils and to Roman Catholics. After that, references from schools and observations made during an activity afternoon form the basis of any decision to offer a place. The head is well aware that for some parents St Philip's may represent a fall-back option; understandably he prefers to offer places to boys and parents for whom it is a firm favourite. It's hardly a gamble; there are plenty of parents who simply like what they see so the school does not need to change its modus operandi.

Exit: At 13+ roughly half to London day schools and half to boarding schools, including St Paul's, Westminster, Harrow, Wellington, Downside, Ampleforth, Radley, The Oratory (Reading), The London Oratory, Charterhouse, Eton, Worth.

Remarks: A school with few pretensions and a big heart, St Philip's feels like a large, slightly unconventional family. It reflects the best of Roman Catholicism; the religious ethos that underpins the day-to-day life of the school produces genuine humanity and flexibility in the education of the young boys for whom it caters. The boys themselves are confident, polite and enthusiastic and willingly engage with any interested adult.

About 80 per cent of pupils have British passports but many have dual nationality, with numbers from Europe and South America. However, this does not mean that the pupil body is a transitory one and most stay from beginning to end.

Mr BD says happily that there is 'room for eccentrics here', and we saw evidence to support this, although 'quirky' might be a fairer description. Staff are a good mix – many are young, several have been there for years, even decades. Stable staffing has not led to stagnation; teaching we observed was dynamic, technology is used to good effect across the curriculum but without sacrificing the rigour of more traditional methods. The balance seems just about right. In a year 8 Latin lesson boys were highlighting words they had problems remembering, followed by a session based around

a series of pictures to assist those who were visual learners. The image of a shouting clam (clamo – to call, shout) or a vampire sinking its teeth into its victim's jugular (neco – to kill, slay) certainly seemed to do the trick.

Outdoor space into which boys spill enthusiastically at break and lunchtime is something of a gem: a garden rather than a playground

Music has a high profile; more than half learn at least one instrument. The young director of music is one of the country's top organists: he has played the organ for the Pope and is credited by Mr BD for the number of music scholarships and exhibitions won recently by St Philip's pupils to eg Ampleforth and Winchester.

Differentiation in the earlier years and streaming in year 8 enables effective teaching across the ability range and impressive results at 13. Learning support is offered both inside and outside the classroom for the relatively few boys with mild learning difficulties. School accepts that life is not always easy for some children, often through no fault of their own, and sensitive, expert counselling is also available for those perceived to be in need. Head says parental expectations are managed through trust and 'not being too dogmatic'. He admits they are 'having to raise the bar', but some parents we spoke to expressed concern that the academic push does not come early enough for the pre-tests and opportunities are missed.

School housed in a red-brick Victorian building cleverly arranged to best accommodate pupils (and staff). Science and ICT are situated on the top floor, 'the only purpose-built part of the school'. Sport takes place off site at Barn Elms playing fields (which are currently being redeveloped in what Mr BD claims is 'an exciting fashion') and at Fulham Pools. The parents' association is very active and, allegedly, organises 'the best match teas in London'.

The outdoor space into which boys spill enthusiastically at break and lunchtime is something of a gem: a garden rather than a playground. It is an oasis of green with fruit trees, climbing roses, shrubs, flowers, vegetables and herbs. The boys play games around and within the vegetation as well as in the slightly more open areas where table tennis tables and badminton nets are erected. There are quiet corners for the quieter boys and plenty of staff on duty or simply outside because it's a great place to be. Mr Biggs-Davison admits that 'by year 8 the boys are outgrowing the space', but, of course, that is exactly as it should be.

Servite RC Primary School

252 Fulham Road, London SW10 9NA

State • Pupils: 240 • Ages: 3–11 • RC

Tel: 020 7352 2588

Email: info@servite.rbkc.sch.uk
Website: www.serviteprimaryschool.co.uk

Executive Head Teacher: Since 2002, Mrs Kathleen Williams BEd NPQH (40s). Has spent all her teaching career in borough of Kensington and Chelsea. Previously deputy head of St Mary's Primary, Ladbroke Grove. Married with a young child, who (she hopes) will soon be a pupil here. 'I couldn't think of my son going anywhere else. I want him to have the grounded education which Servite provides,' she says. Loves theatre, opera and all things musical. Friendly, capable and calm; an experienced pair of hands. Servite works in partnership with less serene local schools, in order to help raise standards and strengthen leadership. Head is ably supported by associate head teacher, Claude Gauci, who takes over the reins when she is out nurturing other schools. They make a robust team. Head admits that teaching is a demanding profession, but 'we're lucky. It's a privilege to be part of this happy school.'

Entrance: At 3 to nursery but a separate application is required for entry into reception. If they don't meet the strict criteria, then nursery children don't make it through to reception. Over-subscribed:

approximately 60-80 apply for 30 places in nursery and 170-200 vie for 30 places in reception. Ever-decreasing catchment area (currently about half a mile). Pupils come predominantly from World's End estate and Earls Court. Priority given to baptised, practising Catholics who worship next door at Our Lady of Dolours. Occasional places further up school, though pretty rare due to low pupil mobility. V few non-Catholics. School currently at full capacity with 30 pupils per class.

Exit: Not a feeder for one particular school. Vast majority go to local Catholic state schools, including Cardinal Vaughan, Sacred Heart, St Thomas More and London Oratory, as well as a handful each year to Chelsea Academy. One or two go down the independent path, usually to Queen's Gate on bursaries. No special preparation given for 11+ and school seems to have escaped fanatical tutoring which goes on elsewhere in final years. A breath of fresh air.

Remarks: This successful school is tucked away behind an unprepossessing façade on the Fulham Road, opposite Chelsea and Westminster Hospital.

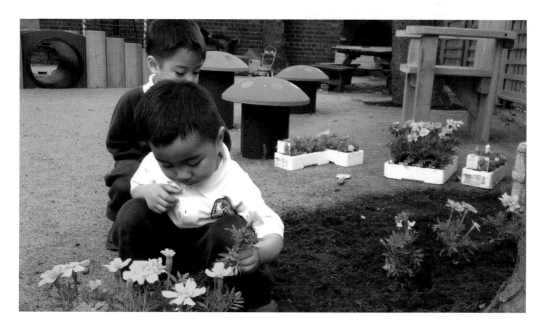

Surprisingly spacious once inside with large, light classrooms and three playgrounds for different year groups (the one for the smallest children particularly colourful and welcoming). Impressively large hall which transforms into a dining room, gym and theatre and boasts sophisticated lighting and sound equipment.

Head believes Servite offers a broad education, which encourages self-confidence and independence. Children are well prepared for life at secondary school by the time they leave. 'Servite gave my daughter the firm foundations on which to build,' said one grateful parent. Parents value the close association with the church which backs onto the playground. Pupils visit on holy days and every week one class celebrates mass there. Only three school rules –follow instructions; use kind and helpful words; keep hands, feet and objects to yourself. Pupils seemed to be adhering to these when we visited, though last rule appeared hardest to uphold.

Significant proportion of male teachers now. Staff consists of dedicated long-servers whose average age is 40. Appear devoted to the school and appreciate its family feel. 'They go the extra mile,' says head, 'and attend events at weekends such as school family mass with parents. No matter where the teachers live, they come to these events and the parents really appreciate it.' New teachers aren't

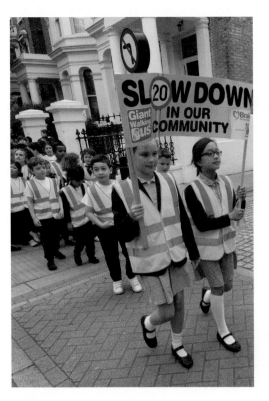

taken on if they won't make a strong commitment to the school, beyond the classroom basics. Palpably strong relationships between teachers, parents and pupils. 'We have an open door policy,' says head, 'but within a structure. Not mayhem! Boundaries are set in a respectful way and issues are dealt with quickly.' One parent said, 'The school is professional but understanding'. Problems tend not to fester for too long.

Netball, football, athletics and swimming taught either on site, in Battersea Park or Chelsea baths

Academic standard has been raised and school now boasts impressive results. Able children are extended through creative writing groups and extra maths support. Some bright sparks achieve level 6 in maths. Links fostered with Imperial College and Royal Institution to extend knowledge and develop understanding of science. Spanish, music, dance and art taught by specialist teachers. Homework every night from the beginning. Project work given to older children to encourage effective time management and independent learning. School has pupils with a range of special needs, including autism, cerebral palsy and moderate specific learning difficulties. Behaviour support, learning support and pupil referral units offer considerable help to those in need. Currently five children with statements.

School reflects the international, mixed community in which it finds itself. Head comments that many pupils come from, 'poor, working families, where parents are often in domestic service.' Many families struggling but tend not to be on benefits. One in five pupils is entitled to free school meals. Roughly 60 per cent has English as a second language. Many pupils hail from Philippines, South America, East Africa and Western Europe. Main languages spoken at home are Spanish and Tagalog. Extra language support catered for through small targeted group work and some one-to-one support on offer. Parents happy with speedy progress made by those with limited English on arrival. 'Now you wouldn't know which ones were behind with English when they started,' commented one.

Fantastic, flexible wrap-around care on offer but school admits it's hard to sustain at a competitive price. Includes breakfast at start of day as well as tea, activities and opportunities to do homework at the end of the day. Children can be looked after from 8am-6pm. Parents aware they are lucky and are the envy of other schools nearby which don't have extended care on-site.

Impressive range of sport on offer and given as taster sessions. Netball, football, athletics and swimming taught either on site, in Battersea Park or Chelsea baths. Dance and gym compulsory. A wide assortment of clubs including taekwondo, yoga, zumba and street dance. Football, drama and cooking currently very popular. Parents pay for these. Good use made of the local community and has strong links with neighbouring Chelsea Football Club. School participates in 'Educate through Sport' initiative and an English reading programme offered by the club. Paul Canoville, first black player for Chelsea, regularly visits the school as part of its programme to promote positive attitudes towards racial diversity.

Excellent use made of its central London location. 'You name it, we've been there!' says associate head. From designing apparatus for Cirque du Soleil acrobats to jump over in the Albert Hall to PGL visits to Weymouth, the pupils have fun here. Parents pay for school trips, but school helps those who are genuinely struggling to meet the cost. School payment plan in operation and parents encouraged to save for trips on a weekly basis.

Impressive art, drama and music. Annual art show to which parents are invited. Fantastic, carved Viking longboats on display and amusing portraits done by pupils of the staff line the stairs. Christmas nativity put on by youngest children and year 5 performs The Passion at Easter. Two nights in July are devoted to a musical production, generally led by year 6 leavers, and about which parents rave. Years 1-6 learn a class instrument, including ocarina, violin and ukulele. Currently 75 taking one-to-one lessons in piano, violin or guitar.

Effective communication between school and parents via weekly newsletter. Parent council is parent-led and discusses initiatives such as school meals and uniform. Money raised by PTA tends to be spent on travel expenses for school trips, restocking library and equipment for playground.

School lives by its motto: 'Learning to love and loving to learn.' Family feel to the place. Children skip in each morning and enjoy their time here. On the day we visited, ambulance sirens blared incessantly on the road outside while the children danced around merrily in the playground, totally oblivious to the noise and fumes that engulfed them.

Above all, a welcoming school. No wonder head won't be considering anywhere else for her son.

Sussex House School

68 Cadogan Square, London SW1X 0EA

Independent • Pupils: 184 • Ages: 8–13 • C of E
• Fees: £17,490 pa

Tel: 020 7584 1741

50

Email: registrar@sussexhouseschool.co.uk
Website: www.sussexhouseschool.co.uk

Headmaster: Since 1994, the engaging, cultured Mr Nicholas Kaye MA ACP, Cambridge English graduate followed by music research (60s). Whilst deputy head here, following a brief spell at Asra Hawariat School in Addis Ababa, of which he is a trustee and fundraiser, the opportunity arose to acquire the school from the Vernon Trust, which he seized with typical energy, creating an independent charitable trust. Sussex House has never looked back, going from strength to strength, achieving the recent accolade of Best Prep School award. Parents admire this 'erudite man' and the boys sum him up as 'diverse, really talented, passionate about music, poetry, architecture, and a playwright'. His study/Victorian parlour is crammed with book shelves containing leather-bound volumes and novels by past Old Cadogans, an ornamental pianoforte ('The best pianoforte is the concert Steinway in the ballroom,' remarks the head) along with a cornucopia of porcelain, potted plants, objets d'art, furniture,

rugs and oriental carpets illuminated by wooden lamp stands with large lampshades.

As one might expect in this very traditional institution, there are school photographs, house shields and embroidered banners made for the Jubilee and carried in procession on special occasions such as the annual All Souls' Day Requiem at St Mary Magdalene, Little Venice, which we attended. Conducted by Mr Kaye, this was an uplifting service in which the Sussex House choristers sang exquisitely. Mr Kaye enthusiastically teaches 10 periods to the top years with a focus on creative writing and literature. All the parents we spoke to agreed 'he has an excellent rapport with the boys'. One parent remarked, 'The headmaster has a key role in setting the tone of the school. Even more amazing is the fact that he sees the best in every child and gets the best out of every child.' Another commented, 'He teaches the VIth English in his study and they appreciate their elevated status. The sessions are challenging, quite adult, like an Oxford tutorial'. He is very ably supported by his PA/registrar who firmly declares, when questioned on the future, 'We are certainly not ready to hang up our boots yet!' And fortunately they show no signs of it.

Entrance: At 8+ and only later if there happens to be a place available. Thirty-six pupils are selected on the basis of a rigorous, competitive entrance examination in English, maths, reasoning and interview. Strong English is a key requirement and there are no boys in the school with EAL requirements; however, it does cater for up to 23 boys on the SEN register who are given support without additional charges. Parents suggest, 'Not a school of mixed ability, although mild learning difficulties such as dyspraxia are dealt with'. Prospective parents are all given a personal tour by the registrar, meet the headmaster and are invited to a special evening led by members of the VIth form. The majority of boys live within a few miles of Cadogan Square. Regular feeders are Garden House, Eaton House, and other central London pre-preps. There are no sibling discounts on offer but bursaries and scholarships are available according to need and are up to the full remission of fees in cases of genuine need.

Exit: Majority to Eton and Winchester, some to Harrow, just under a third going to London day schools such as St Paul's and Westminster, with some major academic, art and music scholarships in recent years.

Remarks: Mr Kaye chose the aspirational school motto 'Lead me to the rock that is higher than

Up the ornate mahogany staircase is the ballroom, which provides a venue for daily assemblies, lessons around polished tables and tea time concerts

I', and, as he explains, 'This implies a journey which, unlike climbing Everest, is never complete'. Unusually for a day school, there is an Anglican school chaplain who leads important services in the local church which acts as the school chapel.

This is a distinctive, remarkable school which is unashamedly academic. After being greeted by gowned school marshal, Sergeant Khim Sherchan, formerly of the Gurkhas, you are ushered into a grand Norman Shaw arts and crafts town house with William Morris wallpaper, stunning fresh flower arrangements, a realisation of Morris' tenet 'Have nothing in your house that you do not know to be useful or believe to be beautiful'. Parents who would prefer something more modern and spacious, where boys can let off steam at break times kicking a ball, should look elsewhere. Up the wide, ornate mahogany staircase is the ballroom, which provides a venue for daily assemblies, lessons around polished tables and tea time concerts. These concerts are an example of how every effort is made to encourage budding musicians at all levels. The music is stunning and every year concerts with a professional orchestra take place at the Cadogan Hall along with an annual musical at the

Fortune Theatre. We heard a talented 9 year old play the violin with incredible skill and learnt he is also a valued member of the football team. One parent we spoke to remarked, 'The school is small enough so that each boy finds a niche.' Creativity abounds and is an intrinsic part of life at Sussex House along with its nurturing approach, and why many parents choose it over other top prep schools. As a parent commented, 'The wonderful drama is performed in the West End, giving unparalleled opportunities for this age'.

During our visit we saw some excellent architectural models in the making, in readiness for the annual exhibition with the theme of Iconic Chelsea. The clubs and art lessons include opportunities to do pottery and oil painting as well as making use of laptops for presentations about artists. The subject specialist staff are long-serving and popular with their pupils. All the boys we met commented on how the staff are prepared to give up their own time to help individuals.The boys themselves are a superb advertisement for the school: intelligent, polite, lively, responsive and articulate. 'They are confident without being arrogant,' commented a parent, adding candidly, 'That is not to say that they are not sometimes boisterous, and need careful handling in this confined space by their form teacher and/or the deputy head.' They are given Stars for rewards and Stripes for punish-

---

The music is stunning and every year concerts with a professional orchestra take place at the Cadogan Hall along with an annual musical at the Forture Theatre. We heard a talented 9 year old play the violin with incredible skill

ments. The sixth formers are prefects and wear gowns unless they fall from grace and are no longer allowed to wear a gown: a great incentive. They have opportunities to exercise at Battersea Park at least twice a week, and A, B, C and D teams regularly play fixtures against other schools. The school day includes regular walks to Nicholls Hall for gym, fencing and music. Fencing is excellent here and the school magazine The Cadogan records many sporting achievements and activities, as well as superb poetry. The classrooms for younger boys still house old-fashioned lacquered desks, which are confining, and it is important to be aware that break times are spent inside the school, which would not suit all boys.

Average size of classes 18, with 12 in the top year when a scholarship group is formed. The curriculum is carefully tailored to suit the needs of individuals who will sit various school examinations. Mr Kaye would love to have a six day week, 'but that is not possible', so much is packed in: orchestra practice and Greek before school, for example. As there is no dining room or kitchen, boys must bring packed lunches; 'not ideal,' state parents, but lunch time is a social occasion with the form teacher followed by numerous, popular clubs including architecture and discussion group. One ex-parent remarked on how 'well-rounded SH boys are', and that out of 250 boys at Eton in her son's year, three of the 12 chosen for the Eton debating competition were SH boys. The boys we chatted to would love to play rugby, but revel in football alongside options such as fencing, tennis, cricket, golf and swimming. They appreciate the spacious new science laboratory and find the art they do inspiring.

For those parents seeking a Summer Fields in central London, Sussex House fits the bill. Parents agree, 'It really does prepare boys for boarding at 13+ and gives them a wonderful, well-rounded platform'. It is not surprising that so many Old Cadogans hold the school with great affection. They include novelists Edward St Aubyn, Jason Goodwin and Richard Mason, along with actors Daniel Radcliffe, Jasper Britton, and Christopher and Jay Villiers, composer Michael Csanyi Wills, and many more recorded in the annual, very impressive magazine.

Thomas Jones Primary School

St Mark's Road, London W11 1RQ

State • Pupils: 235 • Ages: 3–11

Tel: 020 7727 1423

Email: info@tj.rbkc.sch.uk
Website: www.thomasjonesschool.org

51

Head: Since 2001, Mr David Sellens, BA English, Goldsmiths (40s). Cut his teeth in teaching at New End Primary school in Hampstead, where he worked for five years as the youngest member of staff; 'I had a lot of energy, and the head at the time afforded me the luxury of opportunity.' His energy and enthusiasm swiftly saw him on the leadership team, at a time when the national curriculum was being implemented. However, feeling slightly constrained and wanting to do things his way, he started looking for a post where, he says, 'I could make a difference.' The role of deputy head came up at Ashburnham school and the young, enterprising Sellens, bursting with ideas, hotfooted it straight from artistic and aspirational Hampstead to a school south of the river in dire straits; 'I was suddenly thrust into an environment where results and aspirations were very low.' He and the new head, working closely together for sometimes up to 80 hour weeks, turned the school around over the next four years into Ofsted outstanding and awarded beacon status. Shortly afterwards, he was alerted to the fact that nearby Thomas Jones Primary School was on the verge of closure and, keen to become a head teacher, he applied for the post and promptly set about changing the fortunes

of the school. Fourteen years on, he has exceeded the expectations of even the most optimistic.

In his second decade of tenure, Mr Sellens still appears like an enthusiastic and irrepressible newbie to the post. He is a hard man to pin down and his boundless energy sees him flit from one room to another, starting with the 8.45am meet and greet of all pupils and parents at the school gates; 'You'll like this' he assures us; 'apologies if it gets a bit loud with the bell.' He describes his approach as radical rather than traditional. He teaches year 6 pupils English and says he doesn't pay 'too much attention' to the national curriculum. When asked if he sees himself as a bit of a maverick (after all, this is a head who walks into assembly eating a bowl of porridge and banana extolling the virtues of having a healthy breakfast, a head who ditches the traditional end of year musical, opting instead for Under Milk Wood), he says that although this comment has been levelled at him many times, he sees himself more as an individual who occasionally likes to 'buck the trend.'

Mr Sellens admits that he is 'incredibly fussy' about a lot of things. 'I'm fussy about [the state of] buildings, pupils' attire, their demeanour.' He also insists that pupils make eye contact with people and greet visitors with a handshake: 'He has meticulous attention to detail', one parent told us. This head is also big on homework – year 6 pupils can do up to two hours a night. Even with this 'bossy' approach, he says that he doesn't face much protest from pupils or parents, as there is a sense that 'it is being done for all the right reasons and the outcome is extremely strong.' One pupil said he was 'controlling – but in a good way.'

In his second decade of tenure, Mr Sellens still appears like an enthusiastic and irrepressible newbie

Brought up on the south coast, Mr Sellens says he was the typical story of an 'industrious' child from a humble background who won a place at grammar school and worked hard to better his situation. He always carried with him a strong sense of social justice which is what motivates him daily; 'I want to give every pupil the opportunity to shine, to look back and think they don't have regrets and it doesn't matter what they do, as long as they enjoy doing it.' When asked if he has any children of his own, he replies 'no', then pauses, has a think and says 'yes, 235 of them!'

Entrance: The catchment is so small for this one form primary school that you virtually have to live in the grounds to get in (we kid you not – one pupil who lives two doors away last year didn't qualify. Such was the outcry, she eventually managed to secure a place). The head says he is sometimes overwhelmed by the number of prospective parents, 'some with children who have yet to be born.' Distance from the school is now measured from the centre of the school outwards. (Mostly therefore to those in the nearby housing estate and their siblings).

Exit: Mainly to the local comprehensives – Holland Park or new Kensington Aldridge Academy; some try to gain bursaries or scholarships to independent schools. Last year, three children secured bursaries and scholarships to nearby Notting Hill Prep and further afield Christ's Hospital, West Sussex and King Edward's, Surrey.

Remarks: There are primary schools, and then there's Thomas Jones Primary school. Former secretary of state for education Michael Gove has waxed lyrical about this school on many occasions, claiming in one speech that it offers a better education than nearby £19,620 pa prep school which taught the heirs to the throne. He said: 'There are state primary schools every bit as ambitious, as supportive, as

exciting, as the smartest of private prep schools – like for example, Thomas Jones Primary in West London.'

Named after Thomas Jones of North Carolina – a passionate crusader against the evils of slavery in the early part of the 19th century – this state primary in the borough of Kensington and Chelsea (a short walk from bustling Ladbroke Grove) – is as true to its ideological namesake as it is to his inspirational work. By any stretch of the imagination it is a major achievement for a primary school serving a deprived inner city area to secure a rolling five year average 99.4 per cent of children achieving level 4 and above in maths and English – about three-quarters achieving grade 5+ and a quarter per cent achieving level 6 in maths (often top in the borough for both subjects). What makes Thomas Jones's achievement even more remarkable is that barely any pupils who sit the tests come from an indigenous English-speaking background, with one in three speaking Arabic as their first language. Moreover, 30 per cent of last year's cohort were on the SEN register.

Nowhere is London's diversity of culture or chasm of social inequality better highlighted than at this school. One side of the school (Lancaster Road) is flanked by grand period properties where a three bedroom maisonette can set you back a mere £2m. The other side (St Mark's Road entrance) is a stone's throw away from a large, austere housing estate, 'not fit for purpose' we are told, which accounts for roughly 70 per cent of the school's intake. More than half of the pupils live in difficult circumstances and are entitled to free school meals; some of them, we are told, 'don't own a desk and do their homework on an upturned tray or in the local library.' One parent we spoke to told us that the strength of the school is its diversity, 'and that it caters for all.'

There is nothing ordinary about this school – certainly not if one compares it to other inner city state primaries. The interior is so immaculate and shiny we could see our own reflection in the wooden parquet flooring and the walls looked as if they had been freshly painted; 'we keep them white so it's easy to match and cover any dirt marks.' When asked how they manage to keep a primary school of 230 children so unbelievably pristine, Mr Sellens tells us that the pupils demonstrate real pride in the school and often ask to be on the 'cleaning rota.' For a bog standard (architecturally speaking) 1970s prefab, as this school is from the outside, the inside came as quite a revelation. Light and bright 'to create an illusion of space', the open plan and organic design is quite remarkable both in terms of its functionality and aesthetics.

The artwork which adorned the walls had been carefully selected and beautifully displayed, and we were particularly struck by some stunningly creative models of castles made from toilet rolls and other household objects, displayed outside the year 3 classroom. We also liked a large, colourful mosaic of Elmer the elephant with a large caption reading 'It's good to be different.'

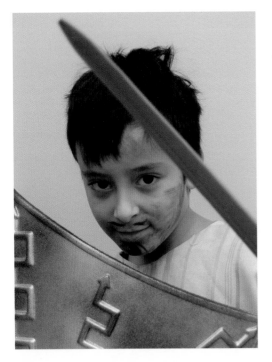

Scented candles, wafting scents of vanilla or lavender, flickered on teachers' desks in all classrooms bar the ones with the youngest pupils

And then there are the candles! This most certainly was a first for us and we wondered whether this was part school and part holistic retreat. Large (glass-encased) scented candles, wafting scents of vanilla or lavender, flickered on teachers' desks in all classrooms bar the ones with the youngest pupils. The result was a calm, almost hypnotic ambience, 'the antithesis of what some students get at home,' the head told us. We even heard classical music (from Schindler's List) emanate from the year 6 classroom as they were in deep discussion about their current literature book. As Ofsted remarked, 'Immersion in the plays of Shakespeare and high quality literature, such as Lord of the Flies, has instilled in pupils a love of literature and has enabled them to reflect with confidence.'

No doubt the school's recruitment policy has played some part in its outstanding achievement. Many teachers are recruited straight from university and stay for a few years before moving on, possibly to jobs outside London where they can more easily afford a home. 'Some of them are very talented, they are enthusiastic and idealistic..they want to teach in this type of environment – even if sometimes they don't stop for very long.' Sellens attributes the quality of what is afforded to pupils to his skilled and deft team and especially the deputy Lindsay Johnson, who exudes gravitas and energy. She has worked at the school for 20 years and is, in Sellens' words, 'the lynchpin of the school's success.'

We were taken on a tour of the school by six well-mannered, extremely articulate and very lovely pupils of varying ages, who each in turn solemnly shook our hands, looked us directly in the eye and said 'welcome to Thomas Jones primary school.' This editor couldn't have felt more revered if she were the Duchess of Cambridge. Pupils were as pristinely turned out as the school they inhabited. Hairclips and bobbles matched their uniform and we were hard pushed to find a strand of anything out of place. The head told us it is extremely important to him that all students look exactly the same and 'exquisite in their uniform, so there is no way of telling their background.' Those from deprived backgrounds can get help with the cost of the uniform.

Future plans for the school include a beehive, which the school says is its modest way of contributing to the eco-system and 'teaching the pupils to care for something.' This will add to the existing mini outdoor nature reserve set amongst pretty, manicured gardens and (slightly sparse) play areas. Indeed, dare we say it, our one criticism of the school would be the lack of outdoor facilities (although we appreciate this is an inner city school) or much time given over to sports, which seems to be a criticism echoed by a couple of parents we spoke to. One told us: 'There's not much in the way of drama or sports at this school which is probably indicative of most state schools nowadays. Sadly, when schools are monitored so closely, something has to give.' However, netball, football and athletics teams, training after school, sometimes with professional coaches, have enjoyed significant successes in borough leagues in recent years.

Ofsted has praised the school for high aspirations: 'Year 6 pupils don white coats for science lessons and eagerly respond to the school's expectation that they are preparing for university.' We also noticed that pupils called their smart navy blue school bags their 'briefcases' and year 6 pupils are expected to pick up a daily newspaper, because as one former student told us, 'pupils need to experience language they don't normally use.' It is not unusual, according to Mr Sellens, to hear the children talking about going to university or becoming barristers or doctors when they leave school.

Everything about this school is aspirational. You won't find a 'home corner' filled with dolls, cookers or microwaves in the gorgeous and colourful nursery. Instead there is a medical corner filled with realistic medical apparatus and costumes. Similarly, we loved the weekly interchangeable corner in reception which encouraged playing various professional roles such as doctor or teacher. Year 4 children were recently treated to a trip to a Jamie Oliver restaurant and have been learning how to make sushi wraps using healthy ingredients – and fish fingers and baked beans are banned from the school menu because 'we want to afford them food they wouldn't get at home.'

Thomas's Fulham

Linked schools: Thomas's Kensington, 365; Thomas's Clapham, Thomas's Battersea, see *The Good Schools Guide: London South*

Hugon Road, London SW6 3ES

Independent • Pupils: 399 • Ages: 4 – 11 • Fees: up to £17,580 pa

Tel: 020 7751 8200

Email: fulham@thomas-s.co.uk
Website: www.thomas-s.co.uk

19

Headmistress: Since school opened in 2005, Miss Annette Dobson BEd. Trained at Homerton College, Cambridge and has SpLD postgraduate certificate. Taught at North Bridge House before joining Thomas's Clapham, where she worked for 10 years, latterly as head of the lower school. Highly regarded by parents, who feel she has guided the school well through its growing years. Approachable and relaxed, children and parents alike find her easy to talk to. Has succeeded in creating a happy school with a relaxed atmosphere despite the solid drive behind everything that is going on.

Entrance: Selective at 4. Assessment in January before September entry. Sociable, confident children preferred. Must be able to cope and take what the school has to offer. Head personally sees all possible pupils. Sibling policy. Best to get children on waiting list as early as possible. Occasional places further up the school when children will spend half a day with peer group to see if they can cope. From year 3 assessment of academic potential and letter from previous school essential.

Exit: No preparation for 7+ or 8+ so majority move at 11. About a third transfer to Thomas's Clapham and Battersea for their last two years, some boys having done the pre-assessment test for eg Eton, King's Wimbledon and St Paul's Boys. At 11+ Ibstock Place, Francis Holland, Godolphin & Latymer, Emmanuel, Downe House, Kew House, St Paul's Girls, Putney High, Wimbledon High, Whitgift etc. Numerous academic and other scholarships (twelve awarded in 2015).

Remarks: A busy, buzzy school that packs a huge amount into each day. A place where parents say their children are exceptionally happy and never say they'd rather be at home! Possibly not for the very timid but somewhere that does seem to build a child's confidence. We looked for the flaws but couldn't find them and Ofsted agreed – declaring the school 'outstanding' in 2014.

The newest of the four Thomas's preparatory schools in South West London, it has, perhaps, the youngest team of teachers we've met. Average age early 30s, passionate and imaginative, a good mix of male and female, they help create a generally happy atmosphere and a school full of enthusiastic children. Our guides, two of the most self confident 10-year-olds ever, led us round excitedly pointing out the things they really like and introducing us to their school. Different coloured staircases, painted in house colours, took us up and down, around and about, in and out of classrooms, laboratories, music rooms, art rooms, everything a child needs to stimulate interest and a hunger for education.

Parents say, 'they work them very hard', 'they are really driven', but these are parents who want their children to succeed. Work hard, play hard seems to be the ethos. For the top year, the Michaelmas Term is heavy on homework. Two 11+ practice papers at weekends together with other revision. But they take this in their stride, it's only for one term. They are being taught about competitiveness. This work ethic builds up slowly as they move through the school. Lots of play and fun at the bottom, lots of work and fun at the top. Streamed in maths from year 3 and taught in different groupings in year 6, depending on whether they are doing 11+ or not.

Teachers find different and innovative ways of getting them to learn. For instance, as you move from one classroom to another, you could come across a subject-based quiz challenge on a board. Find the answers to the questions, put them in a coloured envelope and gain points for your house. Our guides were thrilled by this. 'My son never felt pressured,' says a parent, 'but they still managed to stretch him gently and bring out the best in him'. Another parent said, 'my child finds learning to read a bit of a struggle but it never worries her. Teachers boost her confidence and she thinks she's the best in the class!'

The theatre, as in all Joanna Thomas's schools, is very much a focal point. Loads of drama on the curriculum with a major production a year for each age group, as well as several clubs extending the experience for those who want it. To see the photographs of the becostumed children is to gasp in admiration. Ballet is compulsory for all children in reception and for girls in years 1 and 2. We didn't discover what the boys do while the girls pirouette.

Lots of matches, inter-house, inter-Thomas's and against similar London schools. Several clubs to learn non-run-of-the-mill sports as well. The huge variety of clubs is extraordinary

Maybe they are out kicking balls around?

Music also strong (parents say 'fantastic'), four choirs and various orchestral ensembles. A wide variety of individual instruments played, some to grade 5; lessons timetabled on a rotational basis but practising has to be done at home. 'Their performances are wonderful,' we were told, 'not just run of the mill; there was a lovely group of five boys drumming at a recent concert'.

Originally late Victorian school for 1000+ children; later, part of Chelsea College of Art and Design; the airy rooms and tall windows result in bright classrooms throughout. Light pervades. Largish school hall, doubling up as gymnasium, where assemblies are held twice a week either by year or for the whole school, when, we gather, it becomes quite a squash. Dining area canteen style. Pupils come in year by year, gobbling down food as fast as possible to let the next lot in. Some overflow into the school hall. They all say food is delicious and they like the choice. A parent said, 'the chef is a genius'.

Good playground space (recently redeveloped) divided into two sections for older and younger pupils. Lots of ride-on equipment for the little ones alongside good soft landing area with slides, climbing equipment and some very popular toadstools. Outdoor play in most weathers is regarded as essential at least twice a day.

Parents say sport top notch. Mostly in South Park opposite and round the corner in Hurlingham Park. Some busing in the top years. Lots of matches, inter-house, inter-Thomas's and against similar London schools. Several clubs to learn non-run-of-the-mill sports as well. The huge variety of clubs is extraordinary, covering indoor activities as well as sports (Hip Hop and Mandarin recent additions) and there is one for homework, phew. Green initiative against being driven to school means large piles of scooters and bicycles by the back gate – must be fun sorting through them at going home time.

Mild cognitive problems dealt with and extra help brought in if necessary. One-to-one tuition available at an extra charge. Systems seem to be in place for identifying potential problems though one parent felt they could possibly have spotted her child's earlier. 'All our pupils speak English', they say, even if some need a little extra help. Eighteen different languages are spoken in their homes, though. Also extra for the gifted and talented with occasional higher level classes. Parents kept informed of progress, via email.

Systems in place to prevent any suggestion of unkindness to others. Parents say children 'really do care and want to be kind'. Worry boxes in each classroom. Older children have sessions working with the younger ones, keeping barriers down. New 'values-based education' includes silver unicorns for live school values alongside golden unicorns for work and effort.

Generally good communication all over. Parents say open door policy and can talk to teachers any time. New all singing and dancing parent portal, just launched, tells everything that is going on and answers all queries. So no excuses for forgetting violins or games kit now.

Thomas's Kensington

Linked schools: Thomas's Fulham, 363; Thomas's Battersea and Thomas's Clapham in *The Good Schools Guide London South*

17–19 Cottesmore Gardens, London W8 5PR

Tel: 020 7361 6500

52

Independent · Pupils: 362 · Ages: 4–11 · C of E · Fees: up to £19,140 pa

Email: kensington@thomas-s.co.uk
Website: www.thomas-s.co.uk

Headmistress: Since 2012, Miss Joanna Ebner BEd MA PG Dip Couns Cert FT NPQH (40s), previously head of The Royal School, Hampstead (now absorbed by North Bridge House). A north Londoner by background, educated at North London Collegiate, Homerton College, Cambridge, and the Institute of Education, started teaching at Primrose Hill Primary School in Camden. She then went on to take a postgraduate diploma at the Training Institute of Family Therapy and City University and combined her teaching with a role as a school counsellor at South Hampstead High School. Once her children were of school age, she had to choose between teaching or counselling and teaching won. She returned to teaching at the North West London Jewish Day School, a primary school in Willesden, followed by a successful stint as deputy head of the junior school at The Hall, Hampstead.

After completing the NPQH (National Professional Qualification for Headship), she was appointed head at The Royal School, Hampstead in 2006. The mother of three children (two girls and a boy), she has also managed to fit in co-authorship of Counselling in Schools and contributed to the Girls' Schools' Association's bestseller, Your Daughter, as well as their My Daughter website.

Entrance: School full of large families, mainly from Kensington and Chelsea, with a few from further afield, Brook Green and Notting Hill Gate figuring highly. Mostly within walking, or at any rate, cycling distance. School keen to discourage motoring. Very over-subscribed, so best to get on list as soon as possible after birth. Assessments in November before 4-year-old entry in September. Sibling priority but not guaranteed. 'We must feel child will be able to cope.' Occasional places further up the school, so always worth asking.

Exit: About a third, mainly boys, to Thomas's Battersea, many already with conditional places at top schools. Parents say, despite sameness, children find it quite hard to break into, and the move across is tough, but also say good step up and preparation for bigger school. Otherwise a few leave at 7 and 8, but not prepared for these entrance exams, and the rest at 11+. Mainly to senior London day schools – Francis Holland, Godolphin & Latymer, Harrodian and Latymer Upper amongst others.

Remarks: A busy, happy, international school where children learn to love learning and have fun at the same time. A cosmopolitan place, reflecting the changing face of London, where the 'be kind' ethos seems to work and children and teachers alike are exceptionally supportive of each other. Not for the shy, withdrawn type: the pace is fast and the endless opportunities need to be grabbed with both hands. But there is a world of education to be had in the grabbing.

A school on three sites with very little outdoor play area, so much use is made of local tennis courts and the park. Tall Kensington buildings, with several staircases meandering in and out of bright, smallish classrooms and learning areas, give a comfortable old-fashioned feel, but teaching and facilities bang up to date. Parents say 'wonderful, local, cosy school'.

Lower school housed in an entire unit of its own. Bright classrooms, own hall, dining facilities, library, IT, music and art rooms. Go round the corner to the preparatory school for pottery. Also have own outdoor play area; presumably, as has been a school for a long time, neighbours are used to it and don't mind a little noise. Space for planting and growing too. A teaching assistant in each class. A gentle, friendly place to start.

A cosmopolitan place, reflecting the changing face of London, where the 'be kind' ethos seems to work and children and teachers alike are exceptionally supportive

Pace speeds up on the move to the preparatory school and setting begins in maths. Specialist teachers, so classrooms become subject-based and much more moving around. Teachers enthusiastic and relaxed, average age mid-30s, a third have been at the school for more than 10 years. Good male representation. Particularly high quality reading and writing. In recent national competition to write to the Prime Minister, a year 4 boy was runner up. Small outdoor area, for quiet study only, so mid-morning break in classrooms with quick race around neighbouring tennis courts to expel surplus energy. Lunch takes place in converted Leith cookery school round the corner. Fantastic ultra-modern kitchen and cafeteria-style service. Dining area doubles up as gym with plenty of equipment. This building also contains exciting, purpose-built theatre for all those ambitious, glitzy productions. Seats 80. Also used for lectures, concerts and as extra play space, probably much needed on wet winter days. Two music rooms as well. Around 40 per cent learn an individual instrument, currently up to grade 4.

Sport perhaps less successful although does take up 20 per cent of the timetable. Lack of playground and size of school not helpful, and for boisterous children it is not perfect, although school has worked hard to raise the profile of sport, including PTA sports reps. School says, 'when we play schools of similar size, we have been very successful' and 'in running and swimming we are right up there with the very best'. Some parents feel this does not help with integration when they move across to Battersea at 11+. Lots of bussing to various different grounds and sports centres, as at their sister schools, and several sport-based after-school clubs. Having said that, the top classes can go for a 3k run in the park before school, and sports scholarships to senior schools are not unknown.

Assistant head also head of learning support. Sympathetic, trained and highly experienced.

Makes sure all staff are well informed and the youngest pupils are properly monitored so problems can be picked up early. 'Must know how to spot and observe.' Good relationships with local dyslexia centre and occupational therapists. One-to-one support and laptop training when necessary. Makes sure specialist sports staff also aware of problems. Feels that school culture helps: 'sympathetic and calm'. Approximately a third exposed to language other than English at home. Plenty of help with speech and writing.

Parents say communications excellent and 'teachers very approachable and seem to really care', 'children really supportive of each other'. As at all Thomas's schools, loads of expeditions and outings, but here anything not involving overnight stay is included in the fees. Huge variety of after-school clubs including athletics in the summer. Lots of charity projects too. These children are really encouraged to help others.

Westminster Tutors

86 Old Brompton Road, London SW7 3LQ

Tel: 020 7584 1288

Independent • Pupils: 40 • Ages: 14–99 • Fees: up to £25,000 pa

Email: info@westminstertutors.co.uk
Website: www.westminstertutors.co.uk

53

Head: Since 2007, Ms Virginia Maguire BA MLitt (40s). Was previously director of studies at David Game College, and lectured at a Thai university for five years, publishing articles on sociolinguistics and aspects of Thai culture. She read English at UCL and gained distinction in her MLitt in English Studies from Strathclyde University. Her own mother took her A levels at Westminster Tutors. As well as running the college, she acts as SENCo, teaches English and delivers the PSHE programme.

Academic matters: This is a tiny organisation with under 50 pupils, most of whom are taking or retaking A levels. The retakers – who may be there for a term or a year – are often high achievers who narrowly missed a place at a top university, and may be adding on another A level to improve their chances next time. Those who come for the full two year course tend to be attracted by the very individual attention. 'A lot of students who haven't coped well in a big school setting do well with us.' There is also a very small number – some five in all – taking or retaking GCSEs.

In spite of its size, the college offers a wide range of subjects, ranging from Greek to law to physics, by dint of having a large pool of freelance tutors it can call on, many of them Oxbridge graduates. These may be students working on PhDs, musicians, writers or experienced teachers moving towards retirement who want to keep their hand in. 'I will try to find someone to teach anything – I keep an eye out for what we are likely to need.' A large proportion of lessons are one-to-one, and each student has an individual timetable: drawing these up to suit teachers and students is a fiendishly complicated exercise.

Around a third of students have special needs of one sort or another, mostly dyslexia. The one-to-one system also copes admirably with, for example, the very bright girl with Asperger's who likes being immersed in two-hour-long lessons, and the boy with ADHD who works best in short bursts, including supervised homework sessions. 'It's like having one's own private tutor,' said the parent of a pupil who had floundered elsewhere, 'but in a friendly college setting.' 'My daughter's motivated at last,' said another. 'She's actually keen to go to school and to get on with her homework.' The school has links with an educational psychologist, and will adapt teaching according to her reports, but cannot cope with severe behavioural problems.

Exam results are highly creditable for such a mixed, totally non-selective intake. 2015 saw 74 per cent A*-B, 32 per cent A*/A at A level, 63 per cent A*/A at GCSE.

The college also offers private tuition for mature students who, for example, want to study medicine and need science A levels, helps with common entrance exams, and specialises in preparing outside students for Oxbridge, medical and law school applications. The head originally set up Uniprep as a separate company, but it is now merged with the college. She specialises in medicine and dentistry preparation plus LNAT, and her Oxbridge graduate tutors provide preparation for their respective degree courses. The college also runs half term and holiday revision courses. 'We work very well across the spectrum from special needs to very bright.'

Games, options, the arts: Art and photography are both A level options. Students visit the linked David Game College in Notting Hill to use its facilities, either joining an existing group there or forming their own. A 'wonderful art teacher' provides enrichment classes as well as taking history of art students for fortnightly gallery visits. The college is handy for the South Kensington museums and for theatre trips.

Sport is not a high priority, but the college does field a five-a-side football team, and weekly sports sessions are held at Chelsea Leisure Centre on the King's Road. One ping-pong table – being used as a desk when we visited. Because of lack of space and facilities, the college cannot offer drama, dance, PE or media studies courses.

Background and atmosphere: The college was founded in 1934 and is one of the oldest tutorial colleges in the country. It is now one of the David Game group of colleges, which includes some 25 institutions in the UK and overseas.

'It's like having one's own private tutor,' said the parent of a pupil who had floundered elsewhere, 'but in a friendly college setting.'

It is based in two adjoining townhouses near South Kensington tube, and most of the space is decidedly compact. Staff and students share a common room. 'We're really small so we all mix in together.' Library, IT room, physics room and biology practical room that decidedly resembles a small kitchen (chemistry students use the labs at David Game College in Notting Hill).

Pastoral care and discipline: All students have personal tutors – one of these 'is brilliant with wayward boys: we give him the younger ones who need to be constantly chivvied'. But the head is the personal tutor for the A2 students, supporting them through UCAS, as well as being the main point of contact for all parents. 'If parents have any concerns they always deal directly with me.'

Non-attendance at any lesson is swiftly followed by a phone call – first to the student then, if they don't reply, to a parent. But otherwise the atmosphere is informal: 'We're not oppressive about rules. It's easier to have a cooperative environment'. Students organise dinners or parties, with the head boy and girl in charge of younger pupils; only over-18s are allowed to drink alcohol. Bad behaviour unlikely to go further than a recent incident of older students placing bets for younger ones at a shop down the road. 'A warning is usually as bad as it gets. If I'm cross they know why.'

Pupils and parents: Eclectic mix of those with special needs and others who have not thrived in the rough-and-tumble of larger, more traditional establishments, combined with high achievers who come for the expert teaching.

Entrance: By interview with the head. 'We talk about what they are doing now, what they are hoping to do, their university goals. I look at their results so far and their school reports. But we're non-selective academically, and my main criteria are whether they are going to be happy, suit our way of teaching and fit into the college. We don't want to upset the harmonious atmosphere here.' She will not take students who have been expelled elsewhere for serious behavioural problems, drug or drinking offences, but will probably turn a blind eye to one-off misdemeanours, and rarely turns people down. 'But sometimes I can sense attitude problems, and I might not be so encouraging about them coming here.'

Exit: Over 95 per cent to higher education, ranging from anthropology at Durham to nuclear engineering at Birmingham and dentistry at King's College London. Advice is always geared towards finding a course appropriate for the student. 'Some students are not suited to university, but I would always try to direct them to some sort of higher education. I try very hard to find a course that's right for them, which may have a very practical bent for someone with severe dyslexia.'

Money matters: As one would imagine, the one-to-one staff:student ratio does not come cheap. However, fees are comparable with other tutorial colleges that have much larger classes. Up to four A level scholarship places. A few statemented pupils funded by LAs.

Remarks: Has developed a niche providing one-to-one teaching for gifted students with special needs, and also helps prepare potential medics and Oxbridge candidates. The rest come because they are attracted to the cosy, friendly, supportive atmosphere, 'and you can be sure they getting the best chance to achieve,' commented a parent.

Wetherby School

Linked school: Wetherby Preparatory School, 214

11 Pembridge Square, London W2 4ED

Tel: 020 7727 9581

Independent · Pupils: 321 · Ages: 2–8 · Fees: £19,620 pa

Email: learn@wetherbyschool.co.uk
Website: www.wetherbyschool.co.uk

54

Head: Since 2009, Mr Mark Snell BA PGCE (mid 40s). Educated at Eastbourne College, University of Westminster (a degree in business studies) and Brighton University, where he gained his teaching qualification. His first job was at Eaton House the Manor. Utterly down to earth, direct, no nonsense and unpretentious (although one parent observed that his 'oikishness verges on the pretentious given his background'). With his buzz cut hair style and his gruff manner, Mr Snell is so robust and hearty he could pass for the manager of a medium sized football club. He is also deeply committed and completely devoted to the boys and their needs. 'I enjoy life and don't give a stuff what anyone thinks of me,' he says. Most parents love him ('he still makes time to for me to discuss my son even though he's no longer at the school') though a few dissenters bemoan his encouragement of the alpha in these already uber alpha boys.

Deputy for two years before taking over as head, he is completely au fait with the ethos of the place and is hugely respected by his fellow Alpha Plus heads. ('Nick Baker is a great bloke,' he says. Nick Baker – head of Wetherby Prep – thinks the same of Mark Snell, though he put it slightly differently.) Previously head of maths at King's College

Wimbledon, and prior to that he taught at Westminster Under where, he says, he really cut his teeth and learnt a lot of what he knows now ('though I'm thick as two short planks,' he repeatedly assured us). Despite his 'street' manner, he was born into prep school aristocracy and teaching is very much in the blood. He was brought up in a south coast prep school with his three siblings. His father inherited and ran Mowden School near Brighton (now the prep school to Lancing College), and the wider family are involved with Ludgrove Prep School (in Berkshire). His wife also teaches ('though she is much cleverer than me'). They have a son and a daughter, both school age.

His subject is maths, and though he kept telling us how dim he is, he had us stumped on more than one occasion as so many of his explanations were put in arithmetic form and he relishes statistics. Teaches maths to years 3 and 2, and loves it, he says. An added advantage is that he really knows each individual and can give informed advice on where next. 'If parents choose not to listen, that's fine,' he says; 'that's their prerogative, but I know the schools, understand the assessment data, and I know the boys.' Very accessible – to the boys especially, but to parents too. Many spoke of their complete confidence in him, his judgment, and his recruitment of teachers ('you feel confident that he will never employ a duff,' enthused one parent). A loyal Seagulls fan, his faux wood panelled study (a present from parents, along with most of the colourful decorations) has several Brighton and Hove flags and memorabilia and is brimming with evidence of his personality and the affection families past and present have for him.

Entrance: Non-selective. Register the month your baby is born, and ideally the day he is born. If you try to register any later than when your baby is 3 months old, you're too late. School gets approximately 35 applications a month – or about 360 a year for 88 places. Staggered entry by the month to avoid a preponderance of December (say) babies. You only get to see round the school if you are going to be offered a definite place. If you are on the waiting list there is still hope, but not a lot. Parents feel they have a golden ticket if their son gets a place here and are unlikely to turn it down for anything other than 'act of God'. Lots of international families and a number of children speak more than

Register the month your baby is born, and ideally the day he is born. If you try to register any later than when your baby is 3 months old, you're too late

one language at home, but not much EAL support needed, as most arrive here fluent in English. No longer as local as it once was, parents prepared to travel far for the first class education they feel their son will get here.

Exit: High numbers to the most academic prep schools. In recent years as many as 40 per cent to Westminster Under or Colet Court. Increasing numbers, currently 40 per cent, to Wetherby Prep, where entrance is automatic and the standards are rising, so why go through the stress of exams? The other 20 per cent elsewhere – including Sussex House, Westminster Cathedral School and St Philip's, or to board at Ludgrove, Summerfields, Caldicott or Cothill.

Remarks: The Wetherby brand is currently putting even Balenciaga in the shade. It is hard to find anyone, past, present or potential parent, who doesn't positively glow about the school. They single out the quality of the teaching – not only does Mr Snell recruit excellent teachers but he motivates them and makes them go the extra mile. Homework is 'innovative and thorough'. Communication with parents is 'exceptional', plus the 'school really understand boys and how to educate them.'

Lots of competitions and games inside the classroom as well as out. Learning here is fun, whether it's a project on the Romans or a fabulous end of year party, which incorporates an ice cream van and a bouncy castle. School is lucky enough to be able use the square opposite and the boys get lots of fresh air and exercise during breaks throughout the day. Reception and nursery children have their own outside playground, complete with springy tarmac and climbing wall, which is in constant use. On top of this they have several gym and swimming lessons (at Kensington Leisure Centre), as well as sport (in Hyde Park and Westway) in the afternoons. Lots of football and tag rugby in the winter, cricket in the summer. Plenty of fixtures against other schools, in swimming as well as field sports, and an annual sports day at the Wetherby sports grounds – at the Park Club in Acton. Dads' and boys' Saturday morning football is hugely popular, as are chess club, martial arts club, arts and crafts and drama. The choice of clubs is huge, from meditation and cookery to Lego and French.

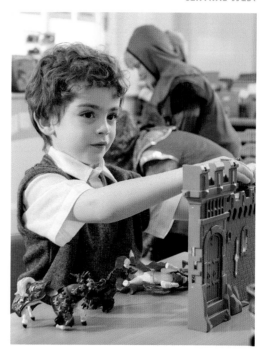

Lots of football and tag rugby in the winter, cricket in the summer. Plenty of fixtures against other schools, in swimming as well as field sports, and an annual sports day

Plenty of music too – a choir in each of years 1, 2 and 3 as well as the wonderful Wetherby singers, created for those who couldn't make it into the choir but still love to sing. 'They make a terrible noise,' growled Mr Snell, 'but parents love it.' More than half the school learns an instrument – peripatetic teachers for guitar, violin and piano. There are instrumental concerts at the end of each term in St Matthew's church up the road as well as impromptu recitals in the hall. Drama part of the timetable as well as offered as a club. There is a performance at the end of each term, and the year 3s perform a major production (in recent years Peter Pan and The Jungle Book) at the Tabernacle Theatre.

Despite being non-selective the pace is fast here. Boys are expected to work hard right from the word go. We saw boys as young as 3 and 4 reading and writing (beautifully). Standards are high and everyone is aspirational – teachers, head and parents alike. Children who need support are usually identified early – good systems in place for spotting and diagnosing any difficulties. What is done about it next depends on the level of support required. At the more severe end – boys with moderate learning difficulties – many parents choose to take them to Emerson House in Shepherds Bush to get that support. Others are taken out in groups for extra support – it could be the top, middle or bottom group in maths or English; others may have one-to-one support lessons. School employs one full-time and one other teacher who has half her timetable, dedicated to learning support.

Maximum class size 21. Boys get a lot of attention in the classroom. Ratio of pupils to teacher (or teaching assistant) is high – more than one teaching assistant in every class room as well a lot of floating teachers. Lots of differentiation – and boys taught according to academic capability not according to syllabus. 'We teach them when they're ready to learn'. Only in the final year, year 3, are they grouped according to ability, in maths, English and reasoning. Relatively high number of male teachers (14) unusual for this age group. 'We can attract a different kind of teacher – Alpha Plus pays very well, especially at this level, and we rarely lose anyone to another school,' says Snell. Although they couldn't fault the education in the classroom, some parents boldly suggested that more attention could be paid to the importance of moral values. The idea of being 'nice' to each other, so focused on in girls' schools, is missing here, they said. These are alpha boys with alpha parents and, parents observe, there is a limited public spiritedness where writing cheques replaces baking cakes.

School is currently expanding up to 362 pupils. The new building in Pembridge Villas, once the site of Chepstow House, is already being used for reception and Little Wetherby (the nursery). Despite an increase in the number of places, we doubt there will be less pressure on them. A busy, successful, well-run, well-resourced school, full of happy, spirited boys. For as long as this formula remains the same Wetherby is likely to remain the brand parents want.

West

Brent
Ealing
Harrow
Hillingdon
Hounslow
Richmond-Upon-Thames

M25

M1

23 Northwood

22
26

24
25

21

Pinner

HARROW

15
16 Edgware

Burnt Oak

Colindale
1 The Hyde
Brent Cross

Kenton

Harrow

14 13

BRENT

Ruislip

Ickenham

20 South
Ruislip

18

17 Wembley

Brent Park

2

Kilburn

Maida
Vale

St J
W

HILLINGDON

Uxbridge

19 Hillingdon

Northolt

EALING

Greenford

Harlesden

6

Hayes

7

9

10 5

4

Notting Hill

Kensingt

Southall

8 11

3

12

28 27

West
Drayton

Harlington

M4

Cranford

HOUNSLOW

Brentford

30

Chiswick

Fulham

Kew

29

Isleworth

Barnes

Hounslow

Richmond

RICHMOND
UPON
THAMES

Richmond
Park

Feltham

41

Ham

38

34 36

33

39

37

Wimbledon

35

Bushy Park

Kingston
upon Thames

Mit

40

31
32

New Malden

Morden

Surbiton

Worcester Park

Ca

1   2   3 Miles

WEST

An introduction to West London and its state schools

Brent

Gritty Brent with its huge ethnic mix is largely famous for Wembley Stadium. Even Brent Cross shopping centre is in neighbouring Barnet. The leafier northern part of the borough hosts JFS qv, the extremely popular secondary school that is the largest Jewish school in Europe – though downgraded in 2014 by Ofsted from outstanding to requires improvement, with inspectors voicing concerns about behaviour and safety. It moved from Camden to a purpose-built site in Kingsbury in 2002. Islamia Girls School, in Brondesbury, is rated as outstanding. Kingsbury High and Queen's Park Community schools are good local non-faith schools. Ark Academy in Wembley is a new all-through school. The new Lycée International de Londres, which opened in 2015 with years 1-11, is no doubt affecting the demographics of the area.

One of the best-rated primary schools is North West London Jewish Day School. St Joseph's and Our Lady of Grace are popular Catholic primary schools, whilst Malorees is an outstanding non-faith school, as is Oakington Manor School in Wembley, which has its own centre for children with speech and language difficulties.

Ealing

Ealing, a sprawling west London borough, comprises Acton and Ealing to the East, Greenford, Northolt and Perivale to the North and Hanwell and Southall to the West. It is the fourth most ethnically diverse borough with 55 per cent of residents coming from an ethnic minority. This is reflected in the make up of the schools. An influx of residents (there are large Polish communities, particularly in the north in Greenford, Perivale and Northolt, as well as Somali residents in Acton and Hanwell, and Indian communities in Southall) has resulted in most of the primary schools expanding from two form entry to three and in some cases four. The question many are asking is how the secondary schools are going to meet the greater demand for places.

One of the most popular secondary schools at the moment is Drayton Manor qv. Residents describe it as structured and old fashioned with good results but perhaps lacking a creative edge. The more arty child may be better suited to Brentside High, a modern site with shiny new facilities. Elthorne Park remains top of many parents' list – despite receiving a disappointing Ofsted report recently. The site is spectacular for an inner London comprehensive, with endless playing fields at the back, and excellent outside facilities. Results here are impressive too. Cardinal Wiseman (Greenford), Greenford High (Southall) and Twyford C of E High School qv (Acton) come out top on the results table but Elthorne is hot on their tails.

Twyford's reputation is phenonomenal. Parents are prepared to move mountains (by which we mean dedicate themselves and their weekends to the local church) in order to get their children in here. We agree, it is good, and probably worth the sweat, particularly shining in music and languages. One to watch is the new William Perkin C of E (also Church of England and linked to Twyford – they have the same executive head and board of trustees). Situated in a relatively deprived area of the borough, the main admissions criterion is proximity to school (rather than, like Twyford, years of church-going and brass-polishing). Will it ever be comparable to its sister school?

Practically all primary schools are good, some outstanding. Popular primary schools include Derwentwater, Berrymede and the Ark Priory in Acton, Fielding (which as its name suggests is lucky enough to have a lovely field rather than just usual bricked playground), North Ealing qv (known for good results) and Montpelier qv in Ealing, and Hobbayne, Mayfield and Brentside in Hanwell. Southall alone has 18 primaries, including one Sikh faith school. North Primary qv and Havelock are considered to be outstanding and the rest, with one or two exceptions, good. In contrast Perivale has only three primaries, one of which, St John Fisher, is Catholic and outstanding. In Northolt and Greenford (19 schools between them) ones to consider are Vicar's Green and Gifford.

Harrow

Harrow, with Hertfordshire to its northern border, is undoubtedly one of the leafier of the London boroughs, dotted with small detached and semi-detached houses and a good proportion of garden-for-money, though the affluent areas of Harrow-on-the-Hill (home of the eponymous Harrow School qv), Pinner and Stanmore contrast with more deprived areas such as Wealdstone. It is extremely diverse ethnically and religiously, with a large Indian population. Nower Hill High and Whitmore High are the top rated secondaries along with the girls' Sacred Heart Language College. St Dominic's Catholic Sixth Form College qv has an excellent record. Around half of its students are Catholic, nearly all the rest Hindu or Muslim.

It has several high-performing Catholic primary schools eg St Anselm's, St Bernadette's and St John Fisher. The Moriah Jewish Day School does well too. Popular non-faith schools include Newton Farm, Grimsdyke, Pinner Park, West Lodge and Whitchurch Junior.

Hillingdon

Hillingdon sits right on the western edge of London, a mix of green belt land and residential suburbia, with the Metropolitan line providing a quick link to the centre. Haydon School qv in Northwood is one of the most popular secondaries (specialises in languages and applied learning, with lots of BTec options), alongside Bishop Ramsay C of E in Ruislip, Douay Martyrs Catholic school and Vyners, both in Ickenham, and Queensmead in Ruislip.

Amongst the primary schools, Catholic St Swithun Wells, Sacred Heart and St Mary's all perform well. Other popular primaries are Whiteheath Junior, Hillingdon primary, Oak Farm Junior and Breakspear. Guru Nanak Sikh Primary Academy, half of whose pupils enter the school knowing little or no English, is vastly oversubscribed.

Hounslow

Hounslow, which abuts the Thames at Brentford and includes Osterley Park and Syon House, is a gateway to all roads west. Heathrow airport is a major employer (and the source of much flight noise), and the population is very diverse, with large numbers of families speaking English as an additional language.

Gumley House qv, in a Queen Anne house surrounded by lovely grounds, and St Mark's Catholic School, are popular faith-based schools. So is the Green School (girls, C of E) in Isleworth. Heathland School in Hounslow is a high-performing co-ed school. Cranford Community College takes large numbers of disadvantaged children, the vast majority from ethnic minorities, and is rated outstanding.

Belmont primary qv caters for an affluent area of Chiswick and gets some seven applicants for each place. Spring Grove, Grove Park, Blue C of E and Chatsworth are other popular primary schools, as are St Mary's RC schools in Chiswick and Isleworth.

Richmond

Straddling both sides of the Thames, Richmond's borough limits can confuse even locals (just as well they don't go in for drumming strangers out of town: they'd probably never leave).

But whether cosying up to Kingston (south bank) or Hounslow (north), schools suffer from the same overcrowding problem. The LA is tackling the problem, tacking on classrooms and building new schools from scratch. Meanwhile, living as close as you can to the desired school (dustbin in playground ideal if has own postcode) has never been a better idea.

Richmond comprehensives, with the notable exception of Waldegrave, were until recently been no better than they should be and, in many parents' eyes, rather worse, given excellence of primary school performance that should give pupils a substantial head start. As the only single sex senior school in the North of the borough, Waldegrave plunders the area's girls, boys currently accounting for approaching 60 per cent of pupil roll almost everywhere else. Another north-west of the river comprehensive, Orleans Park, with excellent extracurricular list (after-school Mandarin is on offer), is continuing to do well.

What won't now wash is the old excuse about under-investment. Teddington (rated 'good' in last inspection) was one of last schools to secure funding for a complete multi-million pound rebuild and is drop dead gorgeous (even if so big that you can spend the whole lunch hour trying to find your friends).

Though there's been similar makeover for Twickenham Academy - historically one to avoid with GCSE results and reputation lagging – there's still considerable way to go before it tops ambitious parents' wish lists. Ditto Hampton Academy which recently lost 40 per cent of its staff, including the principal), despite commitment from Swedish based sponsors who run both to effect Cinderella-style transformation. Richmond Park Academy (south of the river) currently no great shakes either.

New schools have been added, courting similar levels of controversy though for different reasons. St Richard Reynolds, an all-through Catholic school which opened in 2013 enraged locals when, as a voluntary aided rather than academy school, it was allowed to admit on a faith-only basis. Its recent glowing inspection won't have cooled tempers. Opened its doors for its first intake (mix of reception and year 7 pupils) in September 2013 and is, it says, 'passionate about improving the life skills and chances for children created in God's image.' (Doesn't say anything about chances for those who aren't).

Meanwhile, Turing House, also a secondary, has taken far longer to come to the boil than planned with problems over site (as well as allegations of political skullduggery; well, it was election year). Finally opened, amid relief, with 150 year 7 children in 2015 on a temporary site before moving to a permanent base in Twickenham.

The biggest impact is the addition of sixth forms to many schools - likely to impact on currently over-subscribed Richmond College, a popular post-16 state destination. First results, in summer 2016, will be eagerly awaited by indie sector parents wondering whether to take part in the post-16 state school shuffle or stay put.

Popular primaries north and west of the Thames are St Stephen's C of E, Archdeacon Cambridge's C of E and Hampton Junior, together with Collis, one of first to be surgically enhanced, now boasting indoor facilities so good that at least one envious visiting teacher had to be coaxed to leave for own less impressive establishment. Downsides headed by danger of low-flying helicopter parents (as well as flight path noise).

Following amalgamation of formerly separate infants and juniors departments, Stanley School, with head count of 800 plus, though worlds apart from quaint little village school, is academically very much on the up.

Borough-wide praise for staff, whose own enthusiasms translate into impressive extra curricular activity. St John the Baptist's head is a Shakespeare nut, busily abridging plays (three so far and counting) highlight a performance of Macbeth in nearby Hampton Court Palace. Hampton Hill, in contrast, excels at music – nine ensembles and four choirs including – wonder of wonders - one for boys only as well as audition-entry chamber group, while at Chase Bridge, also equipped with lovely new buildings, makes most of links both with army music centre Kneller Hall and Twickenham stadium (both nearby).

At primary level, too, it's been a mixed year for Richmond's budding free schools. Bellevue Educational Trust Sponsors plan to open Richmond Bridge School in 2016, location yet to be confirmed, but ideally close to school-starved East Twickenham. This is their second in the borough first is opening across the river to add to their 'family' of schools (they're busily at work elsewhere in London too) – posh looking blazers, crests, names (multiple references to 'parks' and 'houses', reassuring burgundies and navy blues on the corporate literature give it an up-market ambiance that's definitely part of their distinctive house style.

Also opened in 2015 is Twickenham Primary Academy, sponsored by educational group GEMS, a for profit international organisation with a strong charitable dimension, which offersty 60 reception places and an abundance of 'laughter and delight' (measurement criteria will be interesting), as well as a longer school day (let's hope the two are compatible).

The icing on the cake? Securing dream catchment area to allow seamless primary to secondary move. Good bet, for those with daughters and deep pockets, is Twickenham Green, pairing Trafalgar at primary level (spiffing buildings, horribly oversubscribed, par for the course) with one of UK's top small comprehensives, Waldegrave Girls.

ACS Hillingdon International School

Hillingdon Court, 108 Vine Lane, Hillingdon, Middlesex UB10 0BE

Independent • Pupils: 595 • Ages: 4–18 • Sixth form pupils: 110 • Fees: up to £22,550 pa

Tel: 01895 259771

Email: hillingdonadmissions@acs-schools.com
Website: www.acs-schools.com

Head of School: Since 2012, Linda LaPine; from the USA; BA (urban studies) State University of New York; MPS (master professional studies, special educational needs), Manhattanville College, New York; teaching and principal certification. She was a special needs teacher in New York, also in private practice, before going abroad to International School of Tanganyika, American School in Singapore, Anglo-American in Moscow as deputy head, most recently International School of Panama as director. Now as head of a school that is part of a larger group of four, she devotes most of her time to running Hillingdon, while collaborating with the other ACS heads and board developing programmes and policies for the ACS schools group.

In her words, she came into a good school with no major issues to resolve. After significant developments at ACS Qatar, Egham and Cobham, Hillingdon likely to be the next candidate within the ACS schools group for capital investment, so Ms LaPine is working with colleagues to determine what that might be: strengthening of curriculum, technology, internationalism and/or use of the outdoor environment. 'I am not aspiring for ACS Hillingdon to be a "magnet school",

I just want to provide an overall inclusive educational programme that is based on a strong school community. Academics are priority, but it's also about the overall family experience, the kids being comfortable and happy, and every child feeling important.' Two daughters attend the school.

Academic matters: Take a deep breath before you try to penetrate ACS's patchwork quilt curricula. Start with American-style pre-K – grade 4 with international add-ons including some IPC (International Primary Curriculum) units, language and cultural studies to grade 2, then Spanish plus PTSA (Parent Teacher Student Association) led multicultural weeks (grades 3-5); IB Middle Years Programme with Spanish or French, followed by the last two years of high school with the IB diploma, a fair range of AP courses (11 on offer), high school honours (which is really just 'regular' level, meaning not IB or AP), or a combination thereof. The early childhood programme is a nice blend of learning-through-play and structure, supplemented by specialist teachers for music, art and PE, and cultural classes. Language and cultural studies expose the youngest ones to languages represented in the school community. A different language and culture is featured each month, and children learn basic phrases, explore traditions and sample food.

So it combines American school roots with academic programmes, legacies of previous ACS International Schools leadership and the experiences of the sister campuses – sewn together, with some added layers of internationalism appliquéd on top to embellish the whole work of art. Parents seem happy with what's on offer, and kids are moving forward successfully in their various academic paths. IB average in 2015 was 34 points.

Parents like the fact that the primary principal is very much around in the classrooms, engaged with the kids and monitoring progress. One of the few complaints is that some feel that homework is somewhat inconsistent, with more in the lower school than in the middle school. (The school says it has a coherent homework policy published in its handbooks).

There are two full-time counsellors in the high school at Hillingdon alongside an IB co-ordinator. School provides counselling on course selection and university and career planning – beginning in 9th grade. Students who are less likely to be successful with the full IB are given some early guidance, leaving it up to the student and family to decide whether to go for full diploma or certificates. About 60 per cent of students go the IB diploma route.

Plenty of up-to-date technology is apparent throughout busy tech labs, with ample use of interactive whiteboards and smart TVs. An Apple school, students from grade 1-12 have iPads issued by the school. The IT team includes three 'integrationists' who work with teachers to integrate technology into the classroom. The IT team is available for students and even parents who need minor repairs or tech support.

The NLE (Native Language Enrichment programme – an ACS schools feature) provides mother tongue instruction. With a minimum of three students of similar ages and levels, languages are supported by classes funded by the school (if fewer than three, the school helps find a tutor but classes are paid by parents), scheduled after school for one hour each week. The idea is to maintain reading, writing and oral proficiency; typically on offer are up to 10 languages including Spanish, French, Dutch, German, Arabic and Japanese taught by native speakers. Parents appreciate this but say they'd like to see more, and it can be difficult to enthuse children about taking the mother tongue when their chums are doing 'fun' after-school activities, so they may revert to Saturday schools. At IB level, the provision ramps up to mother tongue language A courses (Japanese and Dutch currently offered).

Lots of monitoring and MAP (Measures of Academic Progress – a data-led approach originated in the US) tests to track progress.

There's been a proposal from kids for a sleepover in the mansion to see if there's any truth to the rumour that it is haunted

EAL specialists support pupils in regular classes to help each student acquire basic vocabulary and vocabulary relevant to classroom topics. Beginner non-English speakers are accepted up to grade 7; after that some proficiency in English is required. The youngest ones have full-immersion English, with specialists either working alongside them in the mainstream classroom, or withdrawing them for one-to-one or small group support. For middle school EAL is scheduled during French and Spanish classes.

Faculty made up of some 17 nationalities, roughly one third each British and US, the remaining from Canada, Australia, New Zealand plus other countries. Average staff age is 40s, and some have been there for quite a long time; average tenure is 7-10 years.

Games, options, the arts: After-school clubs (and some activities offered during lunch) for all ages range from crafts to Model United Nations, Duke of Edinburgh, International Schools Theatre Association, National Honour Society and scouts to sports; there are even middle school magic and Lego robotics clubs. A popular Saturday sports programme for grades K-8 features basketball, tennis, football and baseball. There's been a proposal from the kids for a sleepover in the mansion to see if there's any truth to the rumour that Hillingdon Court is haunted. All suggestions obviously considered!

Quite aside from one parent's comment that sports may not be this school's strong suit, ACS Hillingdon has the highest uptake of the three UK ACS schools: 70 per cent of the students do extracurricular sports. Staff say it's not so much about winning and victory as it is about getting involved, having fun and being well-rounded. But despite all that fun and well-roundedness, the riot of banners and plaques prominently displayed in the gym are testimony to plenty of winning over the years. Recent notable achievements include boys' rugby, basketball and tennis, and girls' basketball and softball. Kids participate in the usual international school sports fixtures, travelling to other countries for tournaments. Sports fields are out in Iver Heath, about a 12-minute bus ride away; an impressive double gymnasium and tennis courts are on site.

Student art work is exhibited everywhere including revolving exhibitions in the head's office (a proud primary student was in the office taking a photo of this to send to his grandmother), and the centrally-located Bridge Gallery. Most music activities (including lots of music tech and a recording studio) are based in Harmony House. Primary music takes place in the main mansion, in a stunning room with high ceilings, sculpted crown mouldings, cornices, coving and massive windows overlooking the gardens – surely one of the most elegant international primary school music rooms on the planet. Many kids (grades 4-12) take private music lessons during the school day, and various musical ensembles are available for middle and high school students. Hillingdon's Got Talent is hugely popular for the whole school community. In fact, parents described the overall arts programme as 'phenomenal'.

When compared to other local international schools, community service at ACS Hillingdon seems a bit more focused on fundraising for good causes rather than hands-on action. That said, IB students do projects at an orphanage in Bulgaria (running for several years now), help in a local nursing home, and also do volunteer activities within the school.

Internationalism is celebrated with lots of support from the PTSA Multicultural Committee and events such as International Spirit Week. Lots of trips locally (starting with a grade 4 camping trip) and abroad as part of the curriculum; middle school trips to Spain or France take place on alternate years linked to the language programmes.

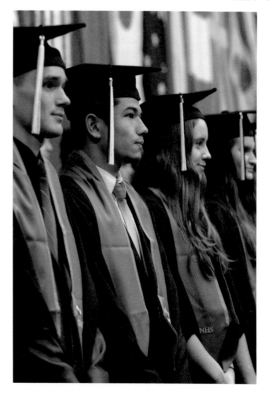

Background and atmosphere: Located in a residential pocket of Hillingdon, a west London suburb on the former estate of Lord Hillingdon, the original Victorian mansion was used during the war as a nursing home. Modern buildings added onto the lovingly maintained 19th century house are a bit at odds with the beautiful proportions of the house, but do accommodate the school's many classes and activities.

A proud primary student was in the office taking a photo to send to his grandmother

Entrance through the manned security gates leads to a morning room conservatory, the reception area, a splendid ground floor entry room used for various meetings and events, the admissions office in a beautiful wood-panelled study, and the music room and high school library – several of which overlook the manicured gardens. The aim has been to give the kids access to these beautiful reception rooms, and not to restrict them to the modern parts where most of their classes now take place. The fact that the head's office is not in the auspicious rooms of the original house, but more centrally located at the heart of the school, says something about the school's values.

Lots of nice bright classrooms, generous space for art rooms, numerous science labs, music rooms. Two areas for drama (the auditorium and a smaller mirrored dance or drama rehearsal studio); two libraries, one each for primary and middle/high school, both located in the mansion.

Each section of the school is in a more or less self-contained area, which parents like. Pre-K and K have their own self-contained pavilion (a calm oasis on the day of our visit) with a small library and colourful outdoor play area behind the main house overlooking the gardens. Beyond the gardens are some outdoor sports grounds and tennis courts, and somewhere out there two vegetable gardens tended by students.

Though the school has won awards for its healthy catering, kids say the lunch room food is 'okay'; but parents love the touch fingerprint payment system as well as the school's flexibility, so kids can buy there or bring their own lunch without the need to handle money.

Hillingdon is one of four ACS International Schools (three in UK, one new one in Qatar), governed by a board of independent, non-executive directors (who typically have international and UK experience across a range of areas including education, finance and law). According to the school's website, the board 'supports the development and the day-to-day operations of the schools'. We interpret this to mean that they support the ACS leadership team that meets regularly and consists of the managing director, the heads of finance, marketing, HR, and Ms LaPine and the three other ACS heads.

Pastoral care and discipline: Positive feedback from everyone, including parents, about the strong sense of community. The counsellors are reportedly excellent at helping students integrate into the school and families to cope with the transition to a new country and school, particularly at the primary school level, in addition to supporting the usual issues such as relationships, self-esteem and behaviour. They've also developed with teachers a cyber-safety programme for kids and parents, starting with the youngest children. No mention of serious behaviour issues; good home-school communication; teachers are responsive to emails.

Pupils and parents: About 40 nationalities: 34 per cent US, 14 per cent British, and, among many others, a recent increase in families from the Middle East. Parents are made up of a good many

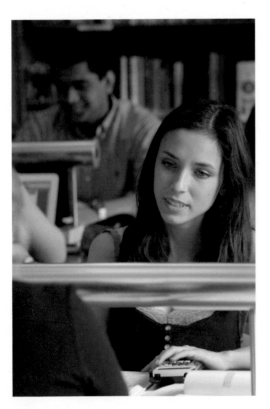

Despite all that fun and well-roundedness, the riot of banners and plaques displayed in the gym are testimony to plenty of winning over the years

corporate expats (particularly finance and pharmaceuticals, many based at Stockley Park), US embassy and other diplomats, and private entrepreneurs, and the international diversity is part of the attraction, according to many parents we spoke to. Some of the British students are repatriating from abroad and prefer to stay in the international school environment with its more relaxed and varied teaching approach. As is true in other London international schools, total annual turnover is lower than one might expect: about 17-20 per cent. Families (including staff kids) are staying longer.

A super-active PTSA organises events for parents to socialise and get acclimated with London, and also works with the school to make sure all new families are contacted. Buses are available and cover a wide net: from Maidenhead and High Wycombe to the west, Watford and Amersham to the north, central London to the east, and Heathrow and Windsor to the south. It's a combination of door-to-door or pick up point, and a very good late and late, late bus service is appreciated by families whose children get involved in after-school activities. (Pre K and K students are not allowed to take the late buses.) Forty per cent of the school's kids are bussed from central London. Parents love the availability of this service, but suggest parents consider realistically the likely travel time.

Entrance: Non-selective; will admit students they feel they can serve and who will benefit from the programme. Admission based on previous school records and testing scores; family statements and references from previous school are preferred, though the admissions director understands that for last-minute summer transfers these are sometimes difficult to obtain. Additional assessment or writing samples may be requested. Academic English required for non-native speakers to enter grades 8-12, assessed through a test that can be sent abroad to the current school to administer. Decisions to admit students (grades 5-12) with diagnosed special educational needs are made in consultation with the specialists. It is sometimes possible – and recommended – that prospective students spend a day in the school.

Exit: Students generally leave because of family moves. Very few leave to attend other local schools:

most juniors continue on to ACS Hillingdon's middle school and then the high school.

About 40 per cent of students go to North American universities (eg Boston College, Brigham Young, NYU, Notre Dame, San Diego State, Emory, American in the US, McGill, Uni of British Columbia in Canada); about 40 per cent go to UK (UCL, Royal Holloway, LSE, Warwick, Bath, Lancaster, Edinburgh, King's). A handful go to countries such as Japan (eg Waseda, Keio), Australia, Germany and Denmark (eg Technical University). Most of the UK applicants are IB students, though some AP candidates as well.

Money matters: ACS Hillingdon is privately owned by a for-profit corporation, fee-supported with no endowment. The school relies on income from fees, with surpluses reinvested in the schools to maintain high standards; it is evident that there has been continued investment in the school facilities.

Limited need-based financial aid is available from the ACS Foundation. No big development and advancement programmes; the PTSA does fundraising activities to support school programmes and events.

Remarks: This is a happy, internationally diverse school that is ticking along nicely. The head with her strong international school pedigree and a special interest in curriculum is bound to bring some changes to the programme once she's had the opportunity to do the prerequisite observation, research and consultation. She'll no doubt want to preserve the positive features of the school. Some holistic soul-searching about this American international educational institution may well lead to some interesting developments in the years to come.

The Arts Educational School (London)

Cone Ripman House, 14 Bath Road, London W4 1LY

Tel: 020 8987 6600

Independent • Pupils: 205 • Ages: 11–18 • Sixth form pupils: 70 • Fees: up to £15,250 pa

Email: pupils@artsed.co.uk
Website: www.artsed.co.uk

27

Headmaster: Since 2012, Mr Adrian Blake (40s) BEd MAPgDip NPQH. Formerly the director of teaching and learning at Arts Educational Schools since 2009. Started his career as lecturer in performing arts at NESCOT followed by director of thinking and learning and advanced skills teacher at Greenshaw High School, before becoming assistant principal at Lambeth Academy. He is also education consultant for Kestrel Visual Learning and for BEST Education on a range of educational topics.

Academic matters: 'Arts Educational School is not a stage school. The academic emphasis in the school is equal to the vocational importance and the aim is to produce well-rounded, interesting and interested young people who have the confidence to perform both on stage and in the classroom.' This might come as a surprise to visitors who are surrounded by leotards and leggings, girls' hair scraped into buns, choruses and piano rehearsals booming out of each room. But the complex timetable is firmly balanced.

At GCSE, everyone takes biology and chemistry, along with two Englishes, maths (setted from the off), French and three options from a number of blocks – art, dance, drama, geography, history, music, science and media studies. The head of modern langs speaks seven languages himself and would find teachers for any language a pupil wanted to take. In 2015, 86 per cent of pupils got 5+ A*-C grades at GCSE including English and maths; 41 per cent of grades were A*/A. The academic corridors look much as anywhere, and good displays on historical topics make a reassuring change from the glitzy pictures of past productions elsewhere.

School now runs two parallel courses in the sixth form: a trad A level course along with classes in dance/drama/music, or two ASs and two As plus a foundation course in musical theatre, which is now an accredited BTec. More pupils are choosing to stay on and a number of new students come in at that stage. Ten AS/A level subjects offered – including

This might come as a surprise to visitors who are surrounded by leotards and leggings, choruses and piano rehearsals booming out of each room

philosophy, history, photography, maths, history of art and media studies, plus the musical theatre course. Creditable results – 34 per cent A*/A grades and 70 per cent A*-B grades at A level in 2015.

Games, options, the arts: On admission in year 7 pupils choose to major in either dance or drama – but both groups have classes in both subjects. Sport is offered three or four times a week at the nearby sports centre but, as one parent said, 'the school is so full of energy and they do so much physical activity, neither of our children feel locked in or worried about the lack of outside space' – which is just as well as there isn't any and you'd be wise to go elsewhere if you need to get seriously muddy twice a week. Everyone dances their socks off, and yoga, stage combat and dances like hip hop also use up surplus energies. Vocational courses include spoken voice, audition technique, text in performance, choreography, dance of all kinds and music.

Music is impressive – loads of individual lessons, good resources – now with excellent facilities for music tech. Everyone has music twice a week. Four choirs, various instrumental groups including a jazz group. Everyone performs all the time and it is most refreshing to go into a studio and see 13-year-olds of both sexes improvising without self-consciousness – no blushful hanging back here. Three major productions a year – aided by professional wardrobe, stage management and set-building staff – and every corridor has racks of costumes just waiting to be donned. Pupils help on the backstage side and learn about the technical aspects of production, as well as acting for camera. Production values are professional and exacting. Unlike at stage schools, however, pupils are not encouraged to have agents and to take off long periods for professional work – school life and work come first. However, film producers do drop round to choose children for roles – some in major productions, some in ads.

The art rooms are a quiet relief and art is a popular GCSE and A level here. Work is varied, colourful and clever. Sixth form now has eight new laptops for photographic work – very popular. Plenty of trips to concerts and galleries.

Background and atmosphere: It's a long, three-storey, plain red brick building, unimpressively occupying about 100 yards of prime Bedford Park along the Bath Road in pricey west London and surrounded by leafy roads housing TV executives in semis which go for £2m++ apiece. Inside it's a different world – once you are past the new turnstile and security system – and security now stops you at each corridor, for which you need an ID card. Plain corridors, plain rehearsal rooms – dozens of them, which all look much the same to visitors, apart from some being black and curtained and others bright and light, but clearly have very different feels to the students, eg 'that's where I do tap; I couldn't think of acting in there,' etc.

A proscenium arch theatre, lots of storage space for costumes and sets, a good-sized, adaptable studio which mimics 'fringe' conditions – everything is geared to preparation for the outside reality. Students look bright-eyed and busy – you cannot tread water here and drown quickly if you try. Parents rave about 'the positive energy of the place'. Little recreation space – the sixth form has space which acts as a common room but that's it and no outside. Little time for traditional teenage bickering here – 'it's very friendly and you have to work together,' says sage 12-year-old student.

A good canteen and good food, though not cheap. Most pupils eat a hot meal at lunchtime – lots of pasta, always a vegetarian option and all prepared on site by unusually friendly staff. Good salad bar. Breakfast daily from 7.45am – a good idea, considering that some pupils commute from as far as Kent or Reading. It's a long day, especially for dance students – 8.30am-5.30pm.

The school shares a building and facilities with the schools of acting and musical theatre. So the foyer and common areas are full of creatively dressed and coiffed students who mingle indistinguishably from the sixth formers. Lots of hugging and kissing and a real sense of cooperation and mutual support. Lots of development going on: new studios and classrooms, IT suite, smartboards throughout, ramps and lifts. It has opened the Andrew Lloyd Webber Foundation Theatre plus a brand new film and TV studio.

Awarded the Independent Schools Association Excellence Award in 2015, in recognition of 'excellent academic standards, alongside specialist performing arts provision and record numbers of pupils achieving places at universities and conservatoires'.

Pastoral care and discipline: Ambiance is energetic and purposeful and the emphasis is on self-discipline. Few, having got here, would want to jeopardise their place, and few drop out though some, obviously, realise after a while that the life of a performing pro is not for them. Carefully structured tutorial system. Students are remarkably focused and learn quickly that success isn't easily

won. Drugs, cigarettes and alcohol are seldom a problem at the school because the students are too busy and committed to their chosen courses to have time for such things. Clear policies on all these sins.

Pupils appear to love their teachers – 'they aren't "showbiz" – they're here to help us with technique'; 'my daughter's science teacher is a hero to her – even though she's not at all into science'; 'the teachers are all so friendly – I mean, not too friendly but just, well, lovely and they are brilliantly supportive'; 'my second daughter isn't into performing but her sister is so happy there, it seemed unfair not to send her too and the academics – more her thing – have been excellent.'

Pupils and parents: From a huge radius round London and very mixed in all ways: the common denominators are talent, a willingness to work, enthusiasm – and parents who can afford the fees. Some sixth formers from far afield are put up in local digs. Very beautiful and talented young people who may have stars in their eyes but definitely feet on the ground.

Students look bright–eyed and busy – you cannot tread water here and drown quickly if you try . Parents rave about 'the positive energy'

Many parents are in the business and appreciate the school's values – 'the performances are always professional.. an excellent training for young aspiring actors and it is most emphatically NOT a stage school and all that implies,' we were told. 'I wish I'd gone there,' mused one noted actor. Former pupils include Julie Andrews, Sarah Brightman, Darcey Bussell, Martin Clunes, Joan Collins, Leslie Crowther, Janie Dee, Nigel Havers, Cherie Lunghi, Will Young, Glynis Johns and loads and loads of others. Lots of high calibre thesps among current parents – all clearly loving the school.

Entrance: By vocational workshops and audition. Pieces prepared for audition depend on which course you are applying for, eg dance solos, drama monologues, sung or instrumental pieces. Then participation in unprepared workshops and classes. Tests in English and maths. Don't come along seeing yourself as the next soap star or Billy Elliot: 'We're looking for team-workers'.

Exit: Some 40 per cent leave post-GCSE to study at institutions that offer the science subjects at A level or to larger, non-fee paying schools. Majority of sixth form leavers go on to study at drama schools and dance schools in the UK and overseas, including LAMDA, RADA, Drama Centre, Rambert, The Central School of Speech and Drama, Bristol Old Vic Theatre School, Mountview Theatre School, Trinity Laban Conservatoire of Music and Dance, London Studios, The Urdang Academy, New York Film Academy. A few stay on and join the degree courses in the same building. Some to other degree courses at eg Royal Holloway, Birmingham University.

Money matters: No government or local authority help. The school has a bursary fund to help existing pupils and is currently looking at ways of increasing it. Various charitable trusts might help an existing pupil in case of collapsed finances but the bottom line is, you'll have to find the fees – which are very reasonable given what is provided.

Remarks: For those who are serious about the work involved in performing arts – with the accent on the work. It's huge fun, but you need energy, commitment and camaraderie. Now with excellent academic teaching too. If you can cut the mustard at audition, you'll have a ball.

Belmont Primary School

Belmont Road, London W4 5UL

State • Pupils: 470 • Ages: 3–11

Tel: 020 8994 7677

28

Email: office@belmont.hounslow.sch.uk
Website: www.belmontprimaryschool.org.uk

Head: Since 2010, Ms Verity Coates MA PGCE (40s). She has been in various roles at Belmont since 1996, including deputy head from 2005. She graduated with a degree in mathematics from Newnham College, Cambridge in 1987 and after a PGCE at York and a brief spell at a London primary school she worked abroad in Africa. On returning to England in the mid 90s, she started as a class teacher and SEN coordinator at Belmont and is fiercely loyal to the school.

Keen to press her commitment to state education, she appeared anxious about Belmont being perceived as the middle class answer to independent schooling. Tight-lipped when challenged on the question of Sats results and the high numbers of pupils who have private tutoring – she is determined that her staff too get some credit. Quite right too.

Entrance: Preference given to siblings. Next in the pecking order are those who live within the Primary Admissions Area – 'catchment' to you and me. In recent years, even living in the catchment has not guaranteed a place at the school. Children in public care and those with medical/ social needs come high up in the pecking order. After that – don't even try. Very over-subscribed. Parents are known to rent property within the area just to qualify, and then..? More hope from year 2, however, as a steady trickle leaves to go to prep school/move out of London. Places are snapped up, though, and school tends to be full all the way through to year 6.

Exit: About half to Chiswick School, although the numbers are decreasing with the advent of competition in the area. A clutch to West London Free School and Hammersmith Academy as well as the usual numbers to Twyford, Lady Margaret, Gunnersbury and the Green school. The rest (about 20 per cent) to local independents, including Godolphin & Latymer, Notting Hill and Ealing High, Latymer Upper, Hampton, Ibstock Place. The occasional one to Colet Court at 8 as well as at 11.

An abundance of facilities – from musical instruments, playground play equipment, books and materials to the brand new stage for dramatic perfomances

Ms Coates asks for a financial contribution for the school reports required for entry into such schools. Lots of outside coaching during years 5 and 6 to prepare for independent school entrance exams.

Remarks: The reluctance of the head and her staff to welcome us to look round this super, over-subscribed, well-funded state primary (or indeed respond to our messages) bemused us – especially considering that Belmont is one of the most successful and popular state primaries in West London, with seven applications for each place.

The sunny, enthusiastic (and overwhelmingly white for this inner London area) pupils bubbled with enthusiasm and love for their school as they showed us round. An abundance of facilities – from musical instruments, playground play equipment, books and materials to the brand new stage for dramatic performances. Results are excellent, showing much higher than expected progress between key stages 1 and 2 and a quarter of pupils in their final year sitting the optional level 6 in reading and maths.

The school caters for an affluent corner of Chiswick and the catchment area is becoming ever tighter. Families from sumptuous houses in the Bedford Park area can no longer expect to get a place. Were it not for the council accommodation on the school's doorstep, you might not get the social mix one would expect in an inner London state primary school at all. Head keen to give precise statistics: 52 per cent of pupils from minority ethnic groups. In any event, a first impression of faces in the playground is that there is an unusually high proportion of white middle class kids. Those who would not come under the umbrella of middle class or British tend to come from Eastern Europe, a few affluent UK residents from say, Canada or Sweden. This ain't your typical London primary.

This big bustling school is housed in a large, three-storey brick building that benefits from the high ceilings, large windows, well-proportioned rooms and wide corridors typical of Victorian buildings of its kind. A generous refurbishment programme has resulted in shiny polished floors and child-friendly primaries and pastels (plenty of aqua and primrose) painted on the walls – helping the building to fall firmly on the side of happy, cheerful school rather than gloomy Victorian mental institution.

Far from being the rabbit warren of most independent schools in the area, Belmont is beautifully mapped out, with two classes at either end of each spacious floor, each one charmingly named after fruit – apples, pears, cherries. The main hall in the middle space between classrooms is used for play (reception and year 1 – lots of dressing up and imaginary play goes on here), assemblies (years 2 and 3 on the middle floor) and drama and gym (years 5 and 6 on the top floor). As well as the classrooms, on the fringes of the hall there are yet more rooms – housing musical instruments galore (drum kits, pianos, flutes, various percussion), two well-stocked libraries, two ICT suites (the juniors have the luxury of one computer each, one between two for the infants) and dedicated SEN provision. Teaching up to the end of year 2 is mixed ability. Setting in maths and English arrives in year 3. Two sets – the higher being slightly the larger and having, therefore, up to 32 children to the lower set's 28-ish. The upper set has just one teacher, no classroom assistant being needed with these children because, of course, they are motivated and keen to learn. We couldn't see much problem with the lower sets either.

Two classes at either end of each spacious floor, each one charmingly named after fruit – apples, pears, cherries

About 20 per cent of children identified as having special educational needs but a very small proportion of these have statements (nine pupils). One of these on the autistic spectrum, no one currently in the school with Down's. School has coped in the past with more severe special needs, but children must be able to climb stairs.

About a quarter of pupils don't have English as a first language (about 43 different first languages other than English recorded) but no marked difference in the performance of these children – credit to the school. Dedicated part time EAL teacher as well as SEN coordinator with a team of teaching assistants give support in the class room. Sats results in all subjects are at least 10 per cent above local and national averages and are far higher by year 6. Those with EAL needs are seen individually or in small groups for as long as necessary, until they are up to the general standard. Teaching assistants support individuals, pairs or groups under the supervision of the SENCo. A reading recovery teacher sees individuals who, by year 1, are falling behind – with 'fantastic' results. When we visited, there had been a relatively high turnover of staff (head assures us that this is a result of career progression, maternity – no reflection on the school). Five male teachers – always a bonus. Years 3 to 6 have 40 minutes of French weekly. Everyone has two hours of physical activity weekly.

All classes have class music lessons and learn singing with a specialist teacher. In addition to class music, many learn individually – often more than one instrument. Recorder is offered to the whole of year 3 and there is a choir. Swanky staging facilitates an annual production from year 6. Other year groups, sometimes working together, also put on shows each year. Photographs on display suggest a high level of dramatic productions, much supported by parents, many of whom are 'in the arts'.

Good sports provision. A school sports partnership linked to Chiswick School and an outsourced sports programme (football, netball and athletics) in addition to members of staff teaching sport. On Friday afternoons here there is 'enrichment time', when for 30 minutes children can choose from a wide variety of activities, from Glee Club to comic making. Strong after-school club provision. These include, as well as the sport and music, Big Bang Science and Doughlightful – a clay modelling activity.

The locality is certainly urban – school is on a crossroads with Sainsbury's and Starbucks opposite, lots of residential streets and light industry all around, near the tube and on a bus route. But once inside, the enormous playground creates a safe, comfortable and peaceful environment. The Belmont Home School Association – PTA to you and me – raises between £20,000 and £30,000 each year. This has helped make the playground ever more luxuriant, with designated spaces for quiet reflection, a wilderness garden, covered areas for performances with costume boxes, lots of bike sheds, a super climbing wall painted by parents and plenty of gardening boxes replete with flowers, herbs and plants. At playtime out come the toys (from hula hoops to skipping ropes, racquets and balls) and the place is filled with the sound of happy laughter.

The early years spill out beautifully into carefully designed outdoor play areas, secure from the rest of the large playground. The nursery is particularly roomy and attractive – 52 places with sessions of a maximum of 39 children, an à la carte choice of mornings or afternoons or a combination of whole days and half time sessions. Three large rooms, own toilet facilities and a large kitchen area ('mummy sometimes comes in to help us cook', said an

excited 3 year old) as well as access to the hall and library. Few chic little independent nurseries provide as much as this. Everyone eats in the school canteen and the number of pupils having cooked lunches delivered by the borough increases all the time. The rest bring their own.

Ofsted hasn't done a full report since 2007, when school was judged 'outstanding' (confirmed by an interim assessment in 2011). Head is greatly aided by a posse of 'liberal middle class' parents only too eager to help in all areas of school life, including arranging fundraising events to enable disadvantaged pupils who might not otherwise be able to afford to take part in trips etc. She is aided, too, by an excellent governing body, as well as by a good relationship with her local authority. A very small number of exclusions in previous years, but none for some time. A proper and well-understood system of sanctions. Also an established homework system with extension work on the school website for those who want to push their offspring further – this school is working on all fronts.

Many parents commented that they were sometimes frustrated by the blank wall that meets their follow up questions on their child's progress and results. 'Teachers can be cagey', remarked one parent, 'which makes me nervous. I might be surprised'. If you can cope with this and a certain complacency ('we don't need publicity', remarked the head at one point), then this is a no brainer – an excellent state school with most of the advantages of an independent school without the fees.

Drayton Manor High School

Drayton Bridge Road, London W7 1EU

State • Pupils: 1560 • Ages: 11–19 • Sixth form pupils: 360

Tel: 020 8357 1900

Email: adminoffice@draytonmanorhighschool.co.uk

Website: www.draytonmanorhighschool.co.uk

3

Head: Since 1994, Sir Pritpal Singh BSc MA FRSA, educated at Highgate School and London University, where he read chemistry (50s). Previously deputy head at Cranford Community School, prior to which he was head of chemistry, head of science and head of year in various other comprehensive schools, mainly in London. His own schooling (DMHS has academic links with Highgate) and, perhaps, his current school's early history as a grammar, underlie his approach, and grammar school virtues seem subtly to strengthen this non-selective comprehensive. Premier league football clubs could learn from Sir Pritpal's career.

Put a good man in a moderately-achieving school and let him get on with it for long enough to find a vision, amass the means and expertise to realise it and then build on it. The high-flying Drayton Manor High of today is the result and Sir Pritpal – along with numerous other honours and awards – was knighted for services to education. Supported by many long-serving staff, notably the senior deputy head – here since 1983 – he is relaxed, candid, softly-spoken, smiley, winning in manner, and, though wholly on top of 'initiatives' and the latest government plans, is refreshingly free of edu-speak.

His tenure has not been without controversy. In 2008, he went head to head with Ealing Council over admissions. Accused of trying to select middle class children, the school was vindicated and the result is an admissions policy which allows children to come to Drayton Manor if it is the nearest school to their home. See below for explanation of what seems obvious. In 2011, the school was granted academy status. The attempt to seek parental opinion was only a partial success – very few replies. 'I like to think it was that they trusted us,' remarks Sir Pritpal, somewhat beadily and probably correctly. Those parents who do involve themselves are appreciative – 'he runs a tight ship... his staff are happy and, mostly, they stay... he is always there at parents' evenings and events'. This last is significant as some 'superheads' more or less disappear from the day-to-day life of their schools. Staff likewise pay tribute – 'he has added to the culture of the place and made it what it is today; it was hard work, especially on standards and behaviour. He took us back to the fundamentals and it has worked'. Drayton Manor struggled for decades but now, under professional management and sound educational principles, it is giving the local independents real competition.

Academic matters: Now outperforms other Ealing state schools and some of the local independents at A level – this reflecting, but only to some extent, the height of the academic bar to A level courses. Thirty A level subjects on offer plus extensive Wednesday afternoon enrichment programme which includes EPQ and citizenship courses worth half an A2.

Latin survives at GCSE with excellent results, though struggles at A level; German also battles on; best language results in French at GCSE and A level. Separate sciences at GCSE with exemplary results – much parental praise for staff, also in history and English. Starry A level results in government and politics, history, English, media and further maths. Overall, results impress – 63 per cent A*-B grades at A level, with 30 per cent A*/A, in 2015. A few non-A level sixth form courses available for those who don't make the grade at GCSE - site and facilities don't allow for more. At GCSE in 2015, 65 per cent of pupils got five plus A*-C including English and maths, with 28 per cent of grades A*/A.

'I've got a lot of time for the teachers – they require grammar school standards'

Setting in maths from year 7, in science and languages later on. Enlightened approach re setting – 'We don't have an ideology – we look each year at what will work best' – and parents praise the flexibility of pupils moving up and down as appropriate. Library not huge for the size of school – good stock of popular fiction plus smallish, though interesting, stock of subject books. Parents say, 'I've got a lot of time for all the teachers – they require grammar school standards: our children have achieved even more highly than we had hoped, due to them'; 'They like lively discussion to promote learning.'

Around 20 per cent have some type of SEN: support is rigorous, systematic and professional under head of inclusion. Good links with primaries, baseline assessment on arrival, SENCo involvement with subject and class teachers and constant target setting and monitoring make for unusual progress. Thirty-four statemented children, 290 on school action or school action plus; eight with an ASD, 157 with MLD or SLD and 61 with behavioural or social difficulties. EAL support offered on a withdrawal or in-class basis, mentoring, masterclasses, tracking. Inclusion centre takes children on a last warning and is staffed by 'our best teachers', who offer individualised teaching to 'develop positive behaviour for learning' – a narrow curriculum, taught in small groups in 'a nurturing environment'. Those identified as gifted and talented are monitored by the intervention department, who check they are sufficiently stretched and challenged.

Games, options, the arts: Great range of sports, much success. Sporting ambition fostered in teams and individuals. Lots of showings in the higher levels of Middlesex tournaments and beyond – boys' 1st XI won the Middlesex Cup; both girls' and boys' football teams reached English School national finals last year. Netball and dance also outstanding. On site provision of numerous hard courts and field supplemented by nearby pitches – the best for a state school in Ealing, we are told. New all-weather surface in the offing. Lively drama, culminating in the key stage 3 expressive arts festival (art, music and drama) every summer including the inter-house drama festival, the Shakespeare Schools Festival and the school production attended by many of the feeder primaries as part of the transition programme. A good idea. Art is produced by an enthusiastic minority but we were not wowed by what we saw; most work, however, to be done on music where the talent has yet to be harnessed and developed. 'We're determined for it to be of the highest standard – we are working very

Francis Moore Building named after much-loved deputy head. Venerable trees, well-tended shrubbery beds and a few hanging baskets greet the visitor, and the reception is more friendly smiles than forbidding security measures

hard behind the scenes,' says the head, acknowledging the problem. However, a flautist is part of the National Youth Orchestra and has performed nationwide. Food tech, DT and textiles all with specialist provision. New arts building – the Sir Montague Sharpe Building – opened in 2014. Lots of trips and visits – we are particularly pleased to see London theatres featuring prominently. Also, impressive range of speakers from the Big Outside.

Background and atmosphere: Began life as a grammar in 1930 and has the solid, handsome building you'd expect, though now supplemented by later blocks of varying quality around the central piazza – tastefully developed in recent years during multi-million pound developments, including large scale refurbishments to buildings and sports facilities and new science labs, with more in progress. Outstanding is the Frances Moore Building, named after much-loved deputy head. Impressively broad corridors. Venerable trees, well-tended shrubbery beds and a few hanging baskets greet the visitor, and the reception area is more friendly smiles than forbidding security measures. Pupils are well-turned out, the place is in good nick and we saw little litter. Classroom after classroom was engaged in orderly and seemingly quiet, collaborative work. Few eye-catching displays – though some good blow-ups of current pupils are an attractive feature – little to distract and a purposeful, no frills approach pervades the school. Lots of IT; trad school hall used for productions and gatherings. Good newish dining hall with new caterers and excellent and popular food – a particularly wide choice and reasonably priced – though we wondered about chocolate peanut butter cheesecake. All foods prepared on-site using fresh ingredients – healthy options predominate. Sixth formers have a common room for each year – spacious, well-used and appreciated. Pupils have a cleaning rota! Some sense that house system is underused and that pupils have little idea what those outside their immediate circle do. The head sees the truth in this and says, 'we're on to it.'

Pastoral care and discipline: 'We've had one smoking incident on site in the last 10 years,' says the head. One or two permanent exclusions or 'managed moves' annually for persistent disruptive behaviour. Very rare drugs incidents – 'they know that if they do that they jeopardise their own future'. Good structured pastoral care system, mentoring, buddying, quick pick-up on problems. We heard no reports of bullying not jumped on and dealt with. 'Care, courtesy, consideration and integrity come before anything else,' says the head. Staff call each other 'sir' and 'miss' as they pass in the corridors. Parents praise the inclusive atmosphere – 'everyone is included in awards, not just the high achievers but those who've made progress. The ethos encourages aspiration'. Also appreciation of the disciplined approach – 'they are hot on punctuality and attendance' – and the efficient staff-home communication. Uniform and sixth form dress code seemingly adhered to – though they don't look like automata either. Much in place to guide towards post-school life though some students felt it needed to start earlier and be more pro-active. Again, Sir Pritpal, wonderfully undefensive in the face of criticism, sees this as something he is happy to address – new careers coordinator now appointed.

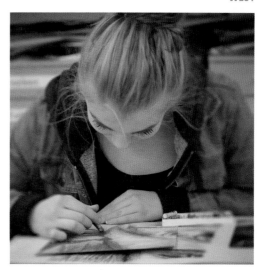

Excellent and popular food – a particularly wide choice and reasonably priced – though we wondered about chocolate peanut butter cheesecake

Pupils and parents: From a very narrow chunk of Ealing these days as the school's popularity and reputation have grown. With a catchment area that takes in everything from the neat Edwardian terraces opposite, the detached grandeur of the Victorian houses a few hundred yards to the east and the council estates of west Ealing and Hanwell, the mix could not be richer. A vast range of backgrounds – 57 different home languages spoken and 34 per cent have English as second language. Lots of after-school classes, notably in ESOL and English, offered to parents alongside other support classes. Pervasive culture of aspiration melds and blends and whatever background you came with, you leave with a sense of your own potential. Notable former pupils include Lord Justice Sir Michael Fox, Martin Rowlands, artist/producer Steve McQueen, Jay Kay, Rick Wakeman and 'if I hadn't been a footballer I'd have been a virgin', Peter Crouch.

Entrance: Vastly over-subscribed. Lots of siblings. Usual local authority criteria apply but the successful court case means that children will gain a place at Drayton Manor if it is the nearest school to their home. In practice this means that if you live a mile from the school but it remains the nearest school to home, then you will have priority over children who live half a mile away but have other schools from which they can choose. Some 50 per cent come from five local primaries – Drayton Green, Hathaway, Hobbayne, Montpelier and North Ealing. Odd disparity in local population and in other local schools means that all years have more boys than girls. Entry to the sixth form depends on five good GCSEs including English and maths as well as other stipulated grades depending on your choice of A level – most subjects requiring Bs at GCSE. These requirements apply to existing students and to applicants from outside.

Exit: Around a third leave after GCSEs – to employment or vocational courses elsewhere. Virtually all sixth form leavers to university – two to Oxbridge in 2015; several vets, medics, dentists and pharmacists; quite a few engineers; Brunel, Queen Mary's, Westminster and Sussex popular. A partnership with Sir Pritpal's alma mater, Highgate School, sees shared expertise on careers workshops and Oxbridge preparation.

Money matters: An annual £10 contribution is asked for.

Remarks: Get clear about the admissions policy and move house. This is about as good as it gets.

The Ellen Wilkinson School for Girls

Queen's Drive, London W3 0HW

Tel: 020 8752 1525

State · Pupils: 1,450 · Ages: 11–18 · Sixth form pupils: 350

Email: office@ellenwilkinson.ealing.sch.uk
Website: www.ellenwilkinson.ealing.sch.uk

Headteacher: Since March 2014, Ms Rachel Kruger, previously acting head. She joined the school in 2012 as deputy head. South African born, she is a maths and music graduate and a trained opera singer.

Academic matters: In 2015, 69 per cent of students got 5+ A*-C grades including English and maths (a third of exams with A*/A grades). English, sciences, languages (including Arabic and Latin) all strong. A specialist maths and science college – a healthy proportion take maths, biology and chemistry A level (increasing numbers opting for physics with plenty of A grades). Arabic, further maths, psychology and philosophy are recent additions to the A level choices. In 2015, 43 per cent A*-B grades at A level and 19 per cent A*/A grades. Several vocational options at level 2 and 3, including business studies, travel and tourism, health and social care and ICT. Runs maths and science taster sessions and masterclasses for feeder primary schools, with excited pupils trying out practical experiments in real science labs.

Some 50 per cent of students speak English as a second language – EAL support is excellent. 'Most speak English enough to be understood. The difficulties arise with subtleties of language – maths terminology, for example.' So both English and EAL lessons focus on the specifics of language, and learning foreign languages can help with sentence structure. Drama is particularly helpful for some girls who get little conversation practice outside school because their close female relatives do not speak English. Literacy catch-up programme in year 7 for those who need it, plus personalised online reading programme. Study support available instead of a second language in year 8, and optional support higher up supports learning throughout the curriculum. Good SEN help, in and out of the classroom. Extracurricular gifted and talented enrichment activities. Scores very well on value-added basis, and is probably the best-performing Ealing school that does not select on academic or religious grounds.

Games, options, the arts: PE facilities have been transformed by new sports and performing arts building. Plenty of outdoor space, with grass and all-weather hockey pitches and netball/tennis courts. Sport is popular and high on the agenda – 'Because we're an all-girls school it's cool to be sporty'. Successful basketball and netball teams, lots of clubs, eg dance, trampoline, badminton, ultimate frisbee, inter-form matches. 'We do competition here. We celebrate people taking part but we reward winners too. Students need to be resilient.'

Art studios ablaze with papier mâché, silk screen printing, life model drawings. The (smallish) canteen is decorated with exotic designs created during the year 7 arts and crafts day. Everyone does drama in years 7 and 8 and a fair number carry on to GCSE and A level. Plenty of performance opportunities: monthly concerts, Christmas musical extravaganza, school musicals, year 12 pantomime, orchestra, rock band, choirs and the wonderful Ukulele Ladies.

Sport is popular and high on the agenda. 'We do competition here. We celebrate people taking part but we reward winners too. Students need to be resilient'

Gardening is a popular club – paths are lined with daffodils and crocuses, flowers bloom in brightly painted pots, herb gardens and vegetable gardens. Other clubs include Amnesty, debating, chess, film. Students go on geography field trips, D of E, language exchanges; they take part in mock bar trials, science, technology and maths challenges, debating competitions, classes with visiting artists, musicians and actors.

Background and atmosphere: Named for Mancunian Ellen Wilkinson, who was a Labour MP during the '20s, '30s and '40s, one of the leaders of the Jarrow March in 1936, and became the first female Minister for Education in 1945. The school sits amidst comfortable, leafy, mock-Tudor suburbia, though few pupils live in the immediate vicinity. Brick buildings, mostly one or two storeys high, flanked by grass and flower beds planted by the gardening club, with a tube line running behind a high wall round the edge of the playing fields. New sixth form centre and study rooms, library and resource area.

The only all-girls state school in Ealing. 'This makes them unselfconscious: they're happy to sit and make daisy chains in the summer, they're keen on science and sport, they're very appreciative of each other. They don't grow up quite so quickly.'

Pastoral care and discipline: Well-ordered. Girls are put in one of four divisions – similar to houses – and stay in these throughout their time at the school. 'It's like having a smaller school within a bigger school, with a family feel.' For some girls from difficult backgrounds, school is the most stable aspect of their lives, and discipline is based round 'catching them being good'. Learners of the Month are celebrated, awards for perseverance and

commitment. Most are well-behaved girls, who give the school a good name. A member of the audience during a recent class trip to the National Theatre wrote to the school to praise the exemplary behaviour of its students.

Pupils and parents: Great ethnic mix, with around 20 per cent white, 20 per cent black, 20 per cent Asian and 20 per cent Arabic. The rest come from a variety of backgrounds, eg Polish, Chinese. Most of the well-heeled residents in the immediate vicinity patronise independent schools, though several Japanese girls from the local enclave have been choosing it recently in preference to their community's school. The catchment area tends to spread along the local tube lines and bus routes.

Entrance: Increasingly oversubscribed, with over 600 applicants for 216 places. Priority to siblings, looked-after children and those with specific medical or social needs. Then 10 per cent from linked Ealing primary schools. Other Ealing primaries get next preference, with the remaining places filled by those living nearest. In practice, this probably means less than two miles away.

About 40 girls from other schools join the sixth form each year, with a baseline of 5+ A*-C GCSE grades for A level courses, including Bs in their A level subjects. Those who don't make the grade can take level 2 courses.

Exit: The 30 per cent or so who leave after GCSEs tend to go to mixed sixth forms or colleges, or follow vocational courses elsewhere. A few high-fliers are lured by scholarships to local independent schools.

Paths are lined with daffodils and crocuses, herb and vegetable gardens

Sixth form leavers mostly go on to university, with a trickle to Oxbridge, but some potential students find it socially alien and the majority stays in London. Imperial is particularly popular; as are SOAS, Kings, Queen Mary, Royal Holloway and Brunel; recent others include Liverpool, Leeds, Lancaster, Sussex and Anglia Ruskin. Biomedical sciences, business and law figure highly, with English close behind.

Remarks: An increasingly successful and popular school. Huge social and ethnic mix, egalitarian traditions. Stable staff, nice girls, few discipline problems. For many pupils it is a haven and a springboard to academic success.

Glebe Primary School

Sussex Road, Ickenham, Uxbridge, Middlesex UB10 8PH

Tel: 01895 671951

State • Pupils: 440 (plus 60 in nursery) • Ages: 3–11

Email: glebe@hgfl.org.uk
Website: www.glebe.hillingdon.sch.uk

Headteacher: Since 2006, Mr Nick Alford BA PGCE NPQH (40s). Previously taught in Weston-super-Mare, then at schools in London for 10 years before moving to Glebe Primary.

Married to a teacher (who is deputy head at an independent school). 'We talk a lot about education and compare notes,' he says. Young son attends nearby state primary school. 'I did think about him coming here,' he told us, 'but if he ever got picked to be in a school play or for the school football team then parents would always think it was because he was the head's son.'

A cheerful, down-to-earth chap who admits to being a long-suffering supporter of Plymouth Argyle. His other passions are cricket and music (The Smiths and The Beatles).

Parents praise him for being very approachable. 'He's always in the playground in the morning and knows every child's name,' one mother told us. 'It means he can spot potential difficulties before they become a problem.'

Entrance: For nursery places apply direct to the nursery and for the school apply through the local authority. Usual criteria apply.

Exit: One or two go to the independent sector and a few to local grammars, but the majority head to Vyners School in Ickenham or Douay Martyrs.

Remarks: Set in the deepest London suburbs (Ickenham tube is near the end of the Piccadilly and Metropolitan lines) and built in the 1970s, the school caters for a mixed intake. Ten per cent of pupils come from military families stationed at the local RAF base and often only stay for a short time. Most pupils are drawn from the local area but the catchment area has shrunk in recent years as the school has grown more popular. 'When I first started as head I used to see some local children walking away from Glebe to a primary school further away which had a better reputation,' said the head. 'But now I'm proud to say that those children are now coming back to Glebe and even transferring from the other school.'

Sats results are above the national average but the most recent Ofsted report found that 'more able pupils have not always done as well as expected.' However the head told us that this point has been addressed 'through setting and focus groups for more able children over the last few years' and as a result, level 5 Sats results have risen to well above the national average. There is a joint project for gifted and talented pupils with a neighbouring school and Glebe recently won the Hillingdon Maths Challenge. School also has links with nearby Brunel University – for science and PE lessons.

The school's go-getting motto is 'We can and we will!' and first impressions reminded us more of a private school than a state primary. Photos on the wall of the head boy, head girl and house captains show the ambitious nature of the place and the head told us that he was keen 'to replicate some of the best aspects of independent schools, such as widening opportunities in sports, music and introducing a house system and prefects.'

A cheerful, down-to-earth chap who admits to being a long-suffering supporter of Plymouth Argyle

Much of the games teaching is delivered by a specialist sports coach. Sports include football, netball, cross-country, athletics, cricket and tag rugby (supported by an enthusiastic year 6 teacher). The school takes part in inter-school competitions and recently won the Uxbridge football competition.

All children get the chance to study a musical instrument. This starts in year 2 with recorders and free tuition on the keyboard from year 4. Parents can pay for tuition in violin, cello, clarinet or flute if they want their children to take music exams. Two guitar clubs after school and when we visited we saw a group of year 4 children strumming away confidently. School choir performs regularly in different concerts, including one at the 02 Arena. 'The music provision is wonderful,' said an appreciative parent. Former pupils include TV presenter Sue Cook and London 2012 athlete Julia Bleasdale.

The school is a regional centre for those with impaired hearing. The SRP – specialist resourced provision for hearing-impaired children – has two teaching areas and a speech therapy room. Each classroom has a Soundfield system, amplifying the sound of the teacher's voice. There are places for nine hearing impaired children and the school employs two specialist teachers of the deaf. All the children are on the roll of their mainstream class and school aims for them to be taught in class alongside their hearing peers, with support if necessary.

School has recently moved into a new two-storey building, to great parental relief, and can at last serve hot lunches.

Parents are very supportive and reckon the school has a strong nurturing ethos. 'It feels like a little village school and it has a very caring environment,' said one. 'All the children are aware of each other and support each other.' Another told us: 'I wouldn't hesitate to recommend it to anyone. I feel that I struck gold when I found Glebe.'

Gumley House School FCJ

St John's Road, Isleworth, Middlesex TW7 6XF

State • Pupils: 1,100 • Ages: 11–18 • Sixth form pupils: 200 (including a few boys) • RC

Tel: 020 8568 8692

Email: general@gumley.hounslow.sch.uk
Website: www.gumley.hounslow.sch.uk

29

Headteacher: Since 2012, Mrs Ewa Kolczynska, previously deputy head (50s). A no-nonsense character who had reams of experience at six other schools before joining Gumley House. Read English at London University and then did a PGCE at King's. Originally from Poland, moved to London at the age of 7, not speaking a word of English. Educated at St Augustine's, Ealing and still lives in Ealing. Husband is a teacher turned education consultant. One grown up son.

Hobbies include theatre, reading, opera (her father was an opera singer). She also loves dancing whenever she gets the chance. Parents find her very approachable. 'She's such a lovely person and is always there if the girls or parents need to talk,' enthused one parent. 'She has a great sense of humour,' said another.

Academic matters: For a non-selective state school, very good results. Compares extremely favourably with local and national averages. In 2015, 64 per cent A*-B and 30 per cent A*-A grades at A level. At GCSE, 82 per cent achieved 5+ A*-C grades including English and maths (40 per cent A*/A grades). Designated as a high performing specialist school and has a languages specialism. First school in the borough to teach Mandarin (taught all the way through from year 7 to 13).

Very committed to special needs provision. Three full qualified teachers and 11 learning support assistants. SEN catered for include physical difficulties, learning difficulties, ASD, dyslexia, Down's Syndrome. To make sure they miss nobody, school's policy is to screen for literacy at the start of year 7 and organise support as appropriate – literacy tuition, in-class support, reading clubs or monitoring as appropriate. Wheelchair access throughout the school seen as part of ethos. 'We encourage concern for the disabled, the marginalised and the needy,' says the school. Sixth formers involved in helping younger pupils.

Superbly equipped library in former chapel (just the place for inspired contemplation) and sensational octagonal assembly hall for whole school events

Important links with world of work. School's director of global learning and communication organises science and enterprise projects with Imperial College, where girls compete with other schools. 'We want to prepare our students fully for the commercial and globalised world,' she explains. The school's motto is Vive Ut Vivas (live that you may have life) and the school extols this to the full with partnerships with schools in Africa, India and Singapore.

Games, options, the arts: Netball, hockey and athletics very strong – school regularly wins all local tournaments. Eight tennis courts, all-weather surface hockey/football pitch set in spacious 10 acres. Dance and fitness studio (very popular) and two drama studios. Thriving orchestra (has performed at European venues) and plethora of private instrument lessons on offer. Annual art exhibitions, drama productions, poetry festivals – some of which are open to the public.

All extracurricular clubs (including science, debating, languages, geography, drama, art and sport) are free. The only extras parents have to pay for are LAMDA classes and private music lessons – 'but we do have money available for those on free school meals,' says the school.

Background and atmosphere: Founded in 1841 as a school and convent by the Faithful Companions of Jesus. The Queen Anne house, surrounded by lovely grounds, creates a peaceful oasis in west London. Superbly equipped library in former chapel (just the place for inspired contemplation) and sensational octagonal assembly hall for whole school

events. 'The school even has its own cemetery which is unique,' said one parent.

Pastoral care and discipline: School prides itself on discipline. Truancy is very rare and school/home links are strong. Distinctive uniform – 'the colour brown is so unflattering, though,' complained one mother, although the head commented: 'The uniform can be brightened up by the striped blazer.'

Strong emphasis on religious, spiritual and moral formation of pupils. Very supportive staff. Two part-time counsellors (who make up one full-time post) and two pastoral managers support the heads of year. 'We have a zero policy on bullying but if it occurs we have very clear procedures and it's dealt with justly,' explained the head. Special IT system to detect internet bullying. Peer mentors are trained to help younger students and look after the year 7 students particularly well.

School offers great support for students coping with exams. One mother told us that when her year 10 daughter was finding the workload difficult her head of year organised relaxation classes for any girls who were feeling stressed. 'It's not just about results,' she said. 'They really make sure that the whole person is happy.'

Pupils and parents: The catchment area covers a wide area of west London (from Southall to Twickenham) so a broad mix of intake and 63 feeder schools. Majority of girls from Hounslow and Ealing, with others coming from Richmond, Hammersmith and Fulham, Hillingdon and even Southwark. Sixty-four languages spoken – main one is Polish. Parents are asked to make a voluntary contribution to the school's development fund each month.

'My vision is of a Gumley family,' enthused the head, pointing out that many former pupils send their daughters to the school. Parents concurred. 'Even though there are over 1,000 girls at the school, it doesn't feel that big and you feel that your child is looked after,' one parent told us. 'I can't recommend it highly enough,' said another.

Entrance: Non-selective academically at the age of 11 – but girls and their parents must be practising Roman Catholics (baptism certificate and written proof required from parish priest) and must attend mass every Sunday. Other entrance criterion is distance from school. School is heavily oversubscribed but places sometimes come up for non-Catholics so it's worth getting on the waiting list. Open policy with no faith requirement for year 12 (including boys – there is currently a handful in the sixth form) but students need to have five A* -Cs at GCSE and Bs in the subjects they wish to study at A level (for maths A*/A recommended).

Exit: One to Oxford in 2015; others to a range including many top universities eg maths at St Andrew's, architecture at UCL, theology at Durham, mechanical engineering at Birmingham.

Some students go for gap years or apprenticeships.

Remarks: A very caring school in lovely surroundings that achieves good results. Well worth a visit.

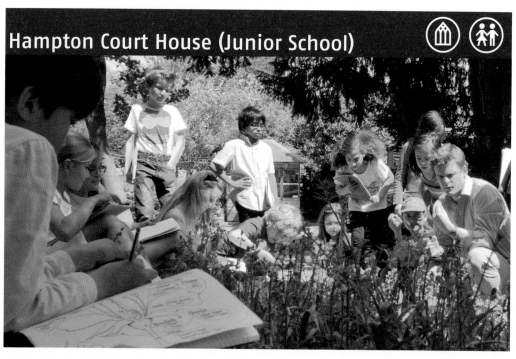

Hampton Court House (Junior School)

Linked school: Hampton Court House (Senior School), 402

The Green, Hampton Court Road, East Molesey, Surrey
KT8 9BS

Independent • Pupils: 130 • Ages: 3–11 • Fees: up to
£14,953 pa

Tel: 020 8943 0889

Email: sarah@hamptoncourthouse.co.uk
Website: www.hamptoncourthouse.co.uk

31

Headmaster: Since 2012, Guy Holloway MA (Cantab), who is also head of the senior school.

Entrance: At 3 into the nursery via informal interview with child and parents. Head looks for families who will be in sympathy with school's aims and ethos and will tell them if he feels they aren't. Into pre-prep via reading and interview. Likewise into the prep – looking for potential, a capacity to think and imagine rather than the crammed and tutored child. At 10, the children are tested more conventionally in English and maths.

Exit: As some come in, some go out. Oddly, you may think, still thinks of itself as a prep and some 11 and 13-year-olds sit for other schools at this stage

– although school says the vast majority now stay on, with a few going off to eg Kingston Grammar and Bryanston.

Remarks: It's a magic place and little children must be wowed to have the run of the stunning old house, its gardens, sizeable pond, outbuildings – and all in one's home clothes too. The educational principles warm the heart. The 3Rs predominate – hooray! – in the early years, but discrete subject teaching starts early too and everyone learns Latin from year 5 right through to CE. Language learning is a fundamental. French is taught through teaching other subjects (such as mathematics and humanities) in French – from day one and by native speakers 'with perfect accents.' All children who go through the prep emerge as at least competent, if not fluent, communicators in French. One hears it as one passes down corridors – spoken, chanted, sung, from room after room. Spanish also lively and enthusiastic and Mandarin taught from year 5.

Art, drama and music seen as central to education in its broadest and deepest senses and divinity is taught very much with an eye on the art it has inspired. Music seen as exceptional by everyone. IT now well provided for with a designated room full of Macs with big screens. We watched a class of happy 9-year-olds working on music animation programmes. Some on-site sport but swimming etc a ride away.

Garden a wonderful asset for outdoor play (tree climbing allowed in moderation) and early years have their own dedicated garden, also used as an outdoor classroom.

Continental teaching methods are important here – head impressed by, for example, maths as taught in Hungary and Poland and incorporates principles derived therefrom. The academic staff are multi-national – around half from abroad and many more with overseas experience. Internationalism flavours the wider curriculum and prep school children learn about major world figures, eg Leonardo da Vinci, Dante, Mozart and great European dynasties, eg the Hapsburgs and the Holy Roman Empire. Science takes a Socratic approach – discussion is as important as experimentation.

Little children must be wowed to have the run of the old house, its gardens, sizeable pond – and all in one's home clothes too

Unusually flexible about keeping children down a year or bumping them up one – in consultation with parents. This can work exceptionally well, especially in a case of mild bullying, exceptional aptitude or slowness, but can also have adverse consequences and be a problem if the child wants to move elsewhere.

SEN provision, previously reportedly 'well-meaning,' now tightened up and 'outstanding,' as far as Ofsted is concerned (they praised IEPs). Provision for more than mild dyses may need careful enquiry. Not that caring, dedication and attention to individuals are lacking – it's just that in this haven of the love of learning, one can, maybe uniquely, appreciate officialdom's insistence on policies, systems and strategies. Certainly some parents, seduced by the trumpeted ethos, flee after a while, scared off by the realities of the place. Not a school for the conservative, the conventional, nor those who snuggle down of an evening with health and safety reports as bedtime reading.

Hampton Court House (Senior School)

Linked school: Hampton Court House (Junior School), 401

The Green, Hampton Court Road, East Molesey, Surrey KT8 9BS

Independent · Pupils: 105 · Ages: 11–18 · Sixth form pupils: 15–20 · Fees: up to £17,340 pa

Tel: 020 8614 0857

Email: admissions@hchnet.co.uk
Website: www.hamptoncourthouse.co.uk

Headmaster: Since 2011, Guy Holloway MA. He studied at King's College School, Wimbledon, before reading English at Peterhouse, Cambridge. He is a passionate educationalist, fascinated by how children learn and the vastly different approaches to education across the world. For several years he was a volunteer with Save the Children UK, working with disadvantaged children aged 6 to 12. He spent many years in Paris, first at the international PR firm, Burson-Marsteller, and then at the École Active Bilingue, where he was head of English in the section Britannique, teaching A level and preparing his first students for Oxbridge, whilst simultaneously creating chaos in the section Française, teaching his beloved classe de seconde.

He was part of the 1993 founding team which opened the Harrodian School, where he was director of studies. He runs a weekly seminar – a comprehensive history of music course for all children in years 1 to 8 – and teaches cultural studies to years 10 and 11.

His interests include piano, record collecting (vinyl LPs of 1950s and 1960s), concert-going, foreign travel, languages, mathematics (statistics), chess, film directing, and theatre (has directed over 30 plays).

Academic matters: Languages, the arts, civilised values and culture reign here and it is a UNESCO associated school. If you want your child to be a linguist, to study academic subjects with values attached, to learn about art, music and to develop individual interests in a liberal, relaxed atmosphere, you'll probably love it, particularly if your offspring is bright, motivated and responsive to opportunities. At GCSE, an admirable range of options for so small a cohort includes five languages – old and new. We watched an attentive and large class of year 11, seemingly all girls, doing psychology.

Forty-four per cent of GCSE grades were A* or A in 2015. The emphasis is on self-motivation, if you don't want to work no one exerts much pressure – and this may also be true of some pupils' families.

Creating chaos in the section Française, teaching his beloved classe de seconde

School says, however, that things are changing here – 'more discipline and rigour', while keeping the 'ethos of happiness', and clearly the intellectual and cultural values will not be sacrificed to a galumph up league tables – and grace à Dieu for that. But Latin and the languages, art, music – all acknowledged to be superb – flourish and Mandarin has recently been introduced. IT now well-provided for with a designated room full of Macs with big screens, and the school is recognised as a lead school in computer science. Teachers – many from abroad – provide intellectual clout.

School very accepting and inclusive of SENs. SEN department consists of a SENCo plus two others, one trained and the other very experienced. They work in small groups or one-to-one, as best suits the child. Nineteen per cent of pupils on SEN register – mostly mild to moderate dyslexia but school will support ADHD and dyspraxia. Ofsted praised good use of IEPs. Invitingly crowded and well-stocked, smallish and recently refurbished library with views over the park.

Opened a sixth form in September 2015 – led by former Westminster head Tristram Jones-Parry and with lessons running from 1.30pm to 7pm.

Games, options, the arts: Arts are strong, strong, strong and part of the feel of the place. Art seen as anything but a discrete subject – rather very much part of the philosophy that underpins the educational approach. Delicious things like the band kit set up in the old ice house in the garden, music everywhere – around half the pupils take individual classes and everyone throws themselves into drama and art. Music department comprises professional, practising performers (an impressive list) and children here are clearly exposed to the best. Several of the ones we spoke to had performing ambitions and clearly no shyness about such things prevails here. This confidence also evident in the manner of the children as they move around the school and address each other and the staff.

School says a newly appointed head of sport is leading a focus on football, netball and athletics, with fixtures throughout the school. D of E is taken

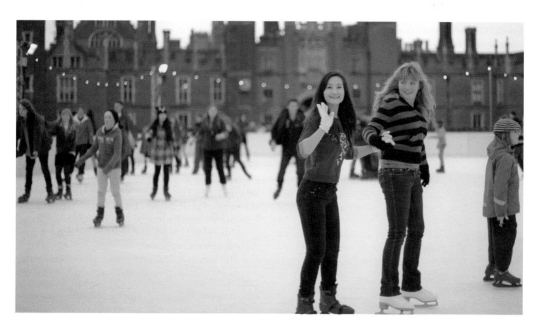

up by 90 per cent of year 10 cohort and year 10 and 11 pupils do Young Enterprise. Lunchtime sports clubs and after-school activities are available every day.

Background and atmosphere: Built in 1757 by the gloriously named George Montague Dunk, second Earl of Halifax, the house is stunning. Its entrance hall – as pictured on the prospectus – has to be seen, columns, gallery, ceiling fireplace 'n' all. To say nothing of the view over Bushy Park, the proximity to Hampton Court itself and the fabulous neighbouring houses on the little lane one drives down to reach the gate. The lake, grotto and ice house in the garden were added in 1771 and, when his lordship died, the house was left to his mistress, Mrs Donaldson, and, on her death, to their daughter. Nice work if you can get it. The house then passed through a succession of tenants and, in 1871, was sold to Marmaduke Blake Sampson, city correspondent of The Times and Argentine consul in London. He built the picture gallery, later a ballroom and subsequently concert room. Then a further century of lettings and sales – among them to the tea-planting Twinings – until, in the 1980s, it became a Save the Children home for refugee Vietnamese boat children. You couldn't make it up.

The school began in 2001 as a pre-prep and prep but, as the first pupils got to leaving age, it seemed natural to continue into the complex realms of senior education. Ofsted recognised the school as 'good, and increasingly outstanding' in 2013.

Children of all ages mix and mingle – lots of hugging in break time, which we liked. No uniform, though 'you have to look presentable' – and they do: rather more here than in many uniformed schools where the rules are stretched to the scruffy limits. The teachers too – some in suits, others very casual, but no-one pushing at the boundaries.

Clearly the intellectual and cultural values will be not sacrificed to a galumph up the league tables – and grace à Dieu for that

Happy parents love the 'warmth and liberality of the ethos – it's just what we wanted. Not perfect but so much better than a hothouse.'

Pastoral care and discipline: Discipline is expected to come from within rather than be imposed. School's philosophy is a belief that all – pupils and staff – should be treated equally and with respect. Politeness and good manners are insisted upon and bullying, we are told, is not countenanced, though some parental feeling that, on occasions when it occurs, the bully is accorded rather more TLC than the bullee. School aghast at this allegation, but reports of bullying not adequately dealt with reached us more than once. On the other hand, we learned of other such incidents which were swiftly and sensitively sorted.

Children who need space and air can breathe here and find they do want to learn. We witnessed a cheerful confrontation between a teacher and a genial but recalcitrant fifth former on our visit – amicable and polite, but clearly a conflict between equals rather than one in which authority was firmly exercised. Children with a more mature understanding of personal relationships will think they've come to heaven.

Pupils and parents: Popular with French families for its commitment to French. School does not claim to be bilingual from year 5 upwards – with the breadth and transience of the school population it could hardly be by senior stage. Pupils from a 30-mile radius – school bus collects and deposits. Attracts the unconventional, the liberal, the arty. Lively Friends of HCH have outings, balls and shopping events to support both school and a Sri Lankan orphanage.

Entrance: Via interview with candidate and parents, plus maths and English tests. Head must be satisfied that the pupil and family are in sympathy with the school's ethos and approach. From Cameron House, Hill House, Wetherby and local juniors. Entrants to the new sixth form need at least six B grades at GCSE, with As in subjects to be studied at A level.

Exit: As diverse as you could imagine. Leavers to Kingston Grammar, UCS, Hockerill Anglo-European, The Brit School, Hampton, DLD, Bryanston,

Halliford, Westminster, Hurtwood House, Latymer Upper, Richmond or Esher Colleges, Wellington, Eton, City of London. Can now stay on for new sixth form.

Money matters: Up to three scholarships – academic, music, arts – annually, worth 10 per cent of fees max – all 11+ candidates automatically entered.

Remarks: Ideal place to grow and learn for those who will thrive on the relaxed and civilised values of the place, now with new sixth form. Historically seen as a refuge for those who couldn't get on elsewhere – sometimes the obstructive or wayward – but now more selective, though the head will continue to take on those with something to offer that may not be conventionally academic. And so he should.

Hampton School

Hanworth Road, Hampton, Middlesex TW12 3HD

Independent • Pupils: 1,200 • Ages: 11–18 • Sixth form pupils: 360 • Fees: £17,550 pa

Tel: 020 8979 5526

Email: admissions@hamptonschool.org.uk
Website: www.hamptonschool.org.uk

33

Headmaster: Since September 2013, Mr Kevin Knibbs MA (40s), previously principal deputy head. Educated at King Edward VI Grammar School, Chelmsford and read history at Oxford (won two football blues). Was head of lower school and senior master at Bolton School Boys' Division before joining Hampton in 2007.

Has helped the Hampton U15 football team to national success and keenly promotes rugby at the school, including the building of the new all-weather pitch and strengthened links with the London Wasps.

Firmly believes that academic success flows from a balanced all-round education in a supportive, unpretentious environment and says

his ambition is to enable boys to grow into well-rounded, happy individuals who aim for personal success while supporting those around them.

Academic matters: A consistently tip-top performer locally with already good results moving onwards and upwards. At GCSE, number of A*/A grades has been rising markedly – 91 per cent in 2015 – putting the school amongst the top independent schools in the country. At A level in 2015, 93 per cent A*/Bs and 73 per cent A*/As keeps the school in the top 25 – without anyone being asked to leave after GCSE (and very few choose to), so no large intake of high-flyers into the sixth form. The in-house Hampton extended project qualification now forms an important part of the broad sixth form enrichment programme. Although the school is no slouch on the Oxbridge front, with 27 places in 2015, many parents see the absence of a hothouse atmosphere as a strength (and one of the reasons why they choose the school). Wide range of subjects on offer with plenty of take-up in languages and science subjects.

IGCSE science and maths are taught – no coursework and more testing. Some boys take one or two GCSEs early. Setting is organised to ensure that no boy is in the bottom set for all subjects – 'No Hamptonian should, nor does, see himself as a bottom set boy,' explains Mr Knibbs. Year 7 boys choose between French, German and Spanish. Latin is compulsory until year 8. The launch of Mandarin is a proven success.

Average class size on entry is 23/24, though the size of teaching groups is often much less, with nine or fewer for German GCSE not uncommon. Sixth form sets are in single figures to low teens. A modern extension houses English, technology and art, and the myriad of machinery and art equipment gives the impression of being very well used, as are the various IT suites. All boys can now access their computer-based work files from home. The Atrium houses 11 fully-equipped classrooms and an additional biology lab. All classrooms have Apple

The ideal school for a budding Beckham: unlike most private schools, football is a major sport here

TVs and digital projectors and most staff and many pupils have iPads.

The library is welcoming, open even in the holidays, and extremely well-stocked. Careers advice has a high priority and is impressive (although one parent bemoaned lack of advice for A level choices) with efforts being made to think more globally. Plenty of females on the staff. Average age of staff 37 and they are top drawer – plenty of Oxbridge graduates and PhDs. Several old boys also to be found in the staff room. Turnover never out of single figures.

Special needs are catered for free of charge through a head of learning support, but the school is cagey about how many boys or how much work this entails – delve deep if you want to send an SEN boy here. Provision for children with English as an additional language is negligible.

Games, options, the arts: Sport is very strong: 16 current boys have won international honours for England or GB at nine different sports. All the necessary facilities are on site, apart from the new boathouse shared with neighbouring girls' school, Lady Eleanor Holles (LEH), a mile or so away. Each boy chooses the sport he wants to play – a key success factor, according to the school: 'The boys taking part are there because they want to be and there are none who don't, which makes for higher quality sessions'. All sports spawn international players.

The ideal school for a budding Beckham: unlike most private schools, football is a major sport here with the U15 and first XI often winning the Independent Schools Football Association Cup. Have also twice won the inaugural ISFA Fair Play trophy in recognition of on field conduct and respect for officials. Rugby has taken off in similar leagues recently with the first XV having won the Esher President's Cup, the inaugural U18 Topflight International Schools' Shield, and having been named Rugby World Team of the Month. New all-weather pitch is apparently a 'unique facility' as accredited for football and rugby. Rowing is big, big news – one of the leading UK schools (check the provenance of the Oxbridge Blues next Boat Race day). Notably strong in cricket, the first XI winning the 50/40 league for several consecutive years. But not all brawn and no brain – chess thriving: up to four teams playing matches each week.

Music takes many forms and can be at a very high level. Has recently had its first BBC Young Musician of the Year finalist, now at the Royal College of Music on a full scholarship, and three organ scholars in residence at Oxbridge, as well as several choral scholars. Plenty of light-hearted groups and joint performances with LEH each term too. Drama productions sometimes shared with the girls but often all-male affairs. The recent 450 Hall (it actually seats 400 – built to celebrate the school's 450th anniversary) was designed as a centre of excellence for the performing arts and is an exceptional facility both for the school and for use by the outside community.

The list of co-curricular activities is so long that you wonder how they can all be fitted in, especially since most boys, reliant on the school coach service, go home promptly at 4pm. The answer is the extended lunch hour – where plentiful and reportedly high quality food is served over a long enough period to fit around all the clubs. In addition to all the extracurricular activities, a very popular lunchtime programme of eminent speakers – politicians, businesspeople, academics, media figures and famous old boys: Dr David Starkey is on the list of speakers as well as Jeremy Paxman, Zac Goldsmith, Iain Duncan-Smith and John le Carré, and don't forget Tara Palmer-Tomkinson. The boys who are busy at their sports clubs don't know what they're missing!

Similarly, so many trips and activities in the holidays you wonder if the boys ever see their families. Beware – all these jolly jaunts are not included in the fees. For those desirous of helping their fellow man plenty of opportunities for helping in the local community, as well as links with African communities in Uganda and Malawi. Jointly with LEH won first place in the Barnardo's People Recognition awards for their Saturday activity club for children with disabilities – all the result of a huge commitment from the staff to the wider curriculum.

Background and atmosphere: In the heart of suburbia surrounded by houses and other schools. Parents can breathe a small sigh of relief – girls may be nearby but not a shop or pub in sight. Superbly spacious grounds; buildings not an architectural gem though well-maintained and constantly being updated. Loads of outdoor space – quads, gardens and playing fields which many boarding schools would envy. Interiors are light and airy and remarkably tidy – even the corridor outside the rowing ergo rooms presents kitbags in a long, neatish row. The sixth formers are proud of their common room with its own café selling vital sustenance at break time and a flatscreen TV tuned to Sky Sports.

Claims to be the first school in the country to go 'climate neutral' through off-setting emissions caused by its daily running. Climate Care, the link

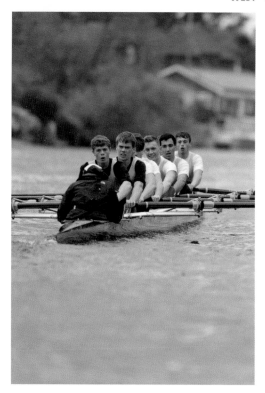

company, offsets through projects including renewable energy and energy efficiency schemes in Southern Africa and India and forest restoration in Uganda. Has its own borehole for irrigation of its playing fields, solar panels and a wind turbine. Continues to raise pupils' awareness of climate issues – the boys conduct regular audits of the school's energy consumption.

Even the corridor outside the rowing rooms presents kitbags in a neatish row

Formerly a state grammar school (went independent in 1975); about 50 per cent of the pupils come from state primary schools, and is fully committed to a large 13+ entry from prep schools. Many of the parents were not independently educated and definitely not a school for Hooray Henrys, although within school the boys look the part in blazers and ties (even in the sixth form). However the minute they leave the school gates the shirts become magically untucked and the ties unknotted – these guys know the meaning of 'grunge'. A marriage here of public school ethos and London lads.

Proximity to Lady Eleanor Holles is supposed to provide 'the best of both worlds' – single sex teaching means that monosyllabic 14 year olds are not intimidated by garrulous girls, but 'The boys certainly know what girls are,' says the head. The two schools have audited their joint activities with a view to expansion. Hampton has also established sixth form management courses with Surbiton High.

Pastoral care and discipline: New boys at 11 are given as much help as possible to settle in with their peers – an overnight team-building exercise is very popular, with boys returning 'raring to go'. Similar jaunt for 13+ entrants. Mentors from the upper school are allocated to newcomers. New boys are closely monitored and any who are found to be struggling with work or organisation given special support and help with study skills. Counselling is readily available; a parent whose son had an extended illness felt that staff went the extra mile to ensure an efficient return to school – 'He was even met at the door by the head of year'.

Assemblies celebrate a range of achievements – concentration on success is more important than telling the boys what they have done wrong and exceptional work is presented to the head. Stringent illegal substance policy – expulsion is a serious threat.

'Most people in the Hampton community both give and consequently receive a lot'

Pupils and parents: No obvious Hampton boy but, if you want your son to be kept busy, here is an environment to suit all sorts. 'Like most things in life, it's what you put in that counts,' said one parent, 'and most people in the Hampton community both give and consequently receive a lot – it might not be the right school for a boy if he's not the type to roll up his sleeves and join in.' Delightfully suburban – no smart cars, champers and party frocks here on prize-giving day but a nice mix of keen mums and dads from a wide range of backgrounds. All faiths represented and celebrated, according to the head. Huge west London and Surrey catchment area bolstered by the extensive school coach network shared with LEH. Socially, neither the boys (nor LEH girls!) complain about bussing, but parents take note – it's not cheap, and be prepared to spend hours in the car at weekends to pick up and deliver from far flung friends' houses. Once a Hampton boy, always a Hampton boy – contacts with ex-Hamptonians are strong.

Counselling is readily available; a parent whose son had an extended illness felt that staff went the extra mile – 'He was even met at the door by the head of year'

Entrance: Two-thirds come at 11 (mostly from state primaries) and one third at 13, from more than 200 schools. (Denmead School is part of the same foundation but is no more 'tied' than any other.) Majority of 13+ candidates are pre-selected at 11, then need 65 per cent at common entrance. Four applicants for every place at both 11+ and 13+ entry.

Advance place exam available for 10 year olds to avoid the scramble at 11, but boys who don't make it early are encouraged to re-sit with no prejudice. Both the 11+ and 13+ pre-tests consist of three papers: maths, words and reasoning, English response and composition. Locally, the tests are perceived as demanding – according to the school, 'The entrance exam is designed to identify innate ability rather than to test what has been taught or coached'. The local private tutors, who make a tidy sum coaching for this and other school exams, would no doubt disagree. Acceptance is based on school's own exam, interview and school report combined with an age allowance. What is clear: it is not enough just to be academic – the school also assesses 'a pupil's likely positive contribution through good behaviour to the aims, ethos and co-curricular life of the school'.

Acceptance at sixth form is based on at least six GCSEs at A or A*, interview, school report, personal statement and written assessment.

Exit: Hardly any leave after GCSEs. Almost all sixth formers to top universities or medical schools. In 2015, 27 Oxbridge places, though not all the brightest choose to apply – school is relaxed about this. UCL, Bath, Bristol, Nottingham, Durham and Exeter all particularly popular; increasing numbers to US, often on academic or sporting scholarships; also Dublin, Belfast, Sydney, RADA and Central St Martin's.

Money matters: Academic, all-rounder, art, music and choral scholarships. Means-tested bursaries.

Remarks: A super outward-looking school keen to preserve its strengths (not about to go co-ed), but ready to embrace change if it will further educational achievement. Ideal for high calibre all rounders, but don't think of sending toffs, tremblies or tearaways.

Harrow School

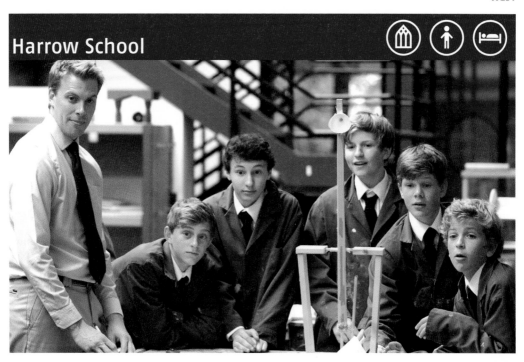

5 High Street, Harrow on the Hill, Middlesex HA1 3HP

Tel: 020 8872 8007

Independent • Pupils: 830 • Ages: 13–18 • Sixth form pupils: 350 • Fees: £34,590 pa

Email: admissions@harrowschool.org.uk
Website: www.harrowschool.org.uk

Head Master: Since 2011, Mr Jim Hawkins MA (40s). Educated at King Edward VI Camp Hill School for Boys in Birmingham and read maths at Brasenose College, Oxford (he was a year above David Cameron and knew the PM slightly). Did PGCE at Oxford before first teaching job at Radley – perfect combination of teaching maths and coaching rugby and rowing. Head of maths at Forest School in Walthamstow, then deputy head at Chigwell School. Prior to Harrow he was head of Norwich School for nine years – 'a fantastic school in a beautiful city.' Norwich went co-ed during during his headship but there are 'no plans' whatsoever to follow suit at Harrow. 'We are very happy as we are,' he says firmly.

Proud of the fact that Harrow enables boys to enjoy being boys. With a plethora of activities from dawn till dusk, he reckons the school suits 'the kind of boy who wants to take the opportunities we offer and throw himself into things.' He says education at Harrow goes 'way beyond the exam syllabus' and that there's 'no better place for the really bright boy with a strong attitude towards life and learning, the sort of boy who is going to contribute and soak everything up.' School sends loads of boys to Oxbridge but head is equally proud of those who 'work jolly hard to get their As and Bs. They are some of our great successes.' When we asked who the school wouldn't suit he was unequivocal. 'It wouldn't suit someone who wanted a sixth form college sort of experience. Harrow is a highly organised, very busy school and it's very clear what the demands are.'

Dynamic, focused and urbane, with dashing good looks. Still keeps his hand in at the chalk-face by teaching 'a bit of maths' to the youngest boys at the start of the academic year. 'It's really nice to have 40 minutes when you are focusing on something entirely educational,' he says. 'The key thing as a head is to find ways of interacting with the boys. Without that you lose touch with reality.' He makes a point of having lunch with boys and in the 'beaks' dining room' when he can. Very sporty – he rowed for Oxford's lightweight crew and was captain of Brasenose rowing. Ran the 10-mile Long Ducker, school's annual charity race from Hyde Park to Harrow, in 90 minutes, though laughingly admits that the director of studies did a faster time.

Loves his job, although he admits 'the highs are very high and the lows are quite challenging'. Says there are three main educational areas he wants to develop. First is the 'super curriculum' to encourage academic scholarship above and beyond the timetabled curriculum, research, independent thinking and university-style learning. Second is to look at preparing boys even better for university – he's already appointed a five-strong universities team with specific knowledge of Oxbridge, medicine and the US universities – and third is to concentrate on 'leadership and service'. School is already very active in local community (links with primary schools, tea parties for elderly, projects with Mothers Against Gangs charity etc) but head would like to do more. 'We want the boys to understand that leadership and service go hand in hand,' he says.

Wife Zoe is an artist and they have a young daughter. They live right in the heart of the school (along with their newly acquired cocker spaniel puppy) and regularly invite boys for breakfast – 'bacon butties and croissants.' Enjoys music, sport, reading and the theatre.

Academic matters: Teachers, parents and the boys themselves describe Harrow as an 'academic' school. Harrow's results don't appear in league tables – head says he's fed up with the 'one-dimensional snapshot' they deliver – but results are impressive. At A level in 2015, 67 per cent A*/A grades and 83 per cent A*/A at IGCSE. IGCSEs taken in English, French, German, Spanish, history, geography, maths, as well as biology, chemistry and physics. Drama and PE introduced at GCSE this year. Thirty-one subjects on offer at A level – all the usual, plus business studies, government and politics, history of art, music technology, photography and theatre studies, with a range of languages. Maths is the most popular subject at A level, with nearly two-thirds taking it. Half the boys do four subjects at A level rather than the usual three (one boy recently did nine). Sixth form electives are a recent innovation for sixth form pupils – a chance for boys to experience university-style teaching in specialist areas. Cerebral subjects on offer include programming, the history of western art, the greats of European philosophy, psychoanalysis and its impact on European culture, and financial mathematics.

Dazzling array of languages on offer – French, German, Spanish, Italian, Russian, Turkish, Polish, Japanese, Arabic and Chinese. All three sciences are compulsory at IGCSE. School has its own observatory with three telescopes and astronomy offered as a GCSE. At GCSE classes range between 14 and 20 pupils while at A level the average is 8.5 and none are greater than 12. School caters for mild dyspraxia and dyslexia. One-to-one help given off-timetable, at no additional cost. Dedicated band of teachers (or 'beaks' as they are known at Harrow) includes many writers of scholarly books. Women make up 19 per cent of staff.

Games, options, the arts: There's no doubt about it, Harrow is a very sporty school, with hordes of teams regularly trouncing their opponents. Sport played five afternoons a week, 32 sports on offer and director of sport encourages even the less enthusiastic to 'have a go' at something. Main sports are rugby, soccer, cricket and Harrow football. The latter is played with a pork-pie shaped ball which absorbs the wet and can be propelled by any part of the body. Even though it's played in the depths of winter and is a very muddy affair the boys love it and only wish more schools played it (Harrow is the only one). When we visited pupils were counting the days till their Harrow football match against an OH team. Last year lots of their fathers had played and there was even one grandfather in the side – 'but we were very careful with him.'

Vast expanse of playing fields, sports centre with indoor climbing wall, weights room, 25m pool and sports hall, courts for tennis, rackets and squash, nine-hole golf course and Olympic-sized running track. School boasts national champions in rackets, fencing, fives and judo, two boys playing rugby for England and number of cricketers playing at national and county level. The mother of a gifted sportsman was full of admiration for the way the school nurtured her son's sporting talent whilst keeping him focused on his academic studies and helping him achieve stellar grades. 'The school sees each boy as an individual and were very supportive and flexible,' she told us.

Beautiful Fourth Form room is also where Professor Flitwick's charm classes were shot in the first Harry Potter film (lots of tourists gazing admiringly when we visited)

Head of music admits that when he arrived eight years ago there was a perception among rival directors of music that Harrow was 'an old-fashioned school where little value was placed on music and the arts.' To his delight he found the reverse was true and there's a 'wealth of musical talent.' Half the boys learn musical instruments and 50 per cent of these achieve grade 8 or better by the time they leave. Practice sessions timetabled for younger boys. Loads of orchestras, choirs and strong tradition of singing. More than 100 concerts a year, with recent performances at the Royal Albert Hall and Royal Festival Hall. Steady stream of boys to top universities and conservatoires to read music too.

Excellent Ryan Theatre seats 400 and is used for school and professional productions but annual Shakespeare productions take place in the beautiful arts and crafts Speech Room. A huge, wood-panelled half-moon, it boasts authentic Globe-style staging and seats the entire school. Wonderful art and, befittingly for a school where photography pioneer William Fox Talbot was a pupil, photography. There's no lounging around with nothing to do at weekends either – scores of extra curricular activities to choose from, everything from the Alexander Society for boys interested in military history to the Turf Club for horse racing fans.

Background and atmosphere: Harrow is one of only three all-boys, full-boarding schools left in the UK (along with Eton and Radley). Boys have been educated here since the 13th century but the school was founded in 1572 under a royal charter granted to local farmer John Lyon by Elizabeth I (Lyon's, the newest boarding house, is named after him). The aim was for the school to provide free education for 30 local scholars, a number later increased to 40 by the governors. School sits in picturesque Harrow on the Hill, surrounded by 400 acres and with panoramic views across London – of it, yet remote from it, as we said last time. On a clear day you can see Canary Wharf from the head's study and it's just 25 minutes by tube to Green Park. Visitors to the undulating school site take note – flat shoes are a must.

School is steeped in tradition and history. The 17th century Old Schools contain the beautiful Fourth Form room, with names carved into every inch of panelling, from Byron to Robert Peel. It's also where Professor Flitwick's charm classes were shot in the first Harry Potter film (lots of tourists gazing admiringly when we visited). The stunning Vaughan Library, designed by architect Gilbert Scott (he also created London's St Pancras Station) has chess sets on tables and stays open late during exam periods. War Memorial Building commemorates the 633 OHs who died in the First World War. You can't help but be profoundly moved by the Alex Fitch Room, an Elizabethan wood panelled room with stained glass windows and a Cromwellian table, given by a grieving mother in honour of her 19-year-old son after he died in the First World War. She asked that it should be used for the purpose of boys meeting their mothers and that a light should always be left on over her son's portrait. Plaques and memorials commemorating quirky events are everywhere. Charles I rested here while preparing to surrender and little inclines have memorable names like Obadiah Slope, wittily named after Trollope's unctuous Barchester Towers character.

Harrow Songs are legendary. No Harrovian, either past or present, fails to mention the strength of feeling they engender and the lump in the throat they provoke. Songs have been an important part

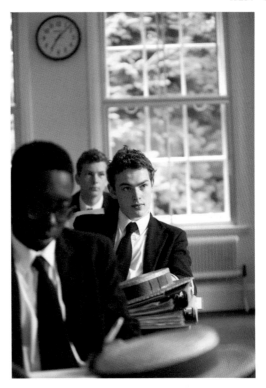

of the school since 1864, when the head of music wrote the first song, and they are considered to be 'a unifying force.' In November each year the whole school assembles in Speech Room in honour of its most famous alumni, Sir Winston Churchill, for the Churchill Songs. Like rival Eton, school has its own jargon. 'Skew' is a punishment, 'tosh' is a shower, 'tolley up' is permission to work late and so on.

Pastoral care and discipline: Pastoral care is meticulous, with highly structured system of resident housemasters, assistant housemasters and matrons. Harrow's 12 houses are integral to the school and boys are fiercely loyal to their own house. Some houses are regarded as stricter than others and parents we spoke to said it's important 'to pick and choose carefully.' One of the houses – West Acre – was recently the subject of an ITN documentary series, following the life of the school for a whole year. Housemasters in post for 12 years and as well as doing most of the admissions assessments each gives their house its character and reputation. They also work round the clock – 'at the beginning of every term I say to my wife "see you at the end of term",' one housemaster told us with a grin.

Harrow takes a pragmatic approach to technology and social media but the boys are so busy there isn't much time to sit around and play computer games. Pupils understand that bullying is 'completely unacceptable' and head says that it has plummeted, 'not down to zero, but pretty close.' School does a bullying survey every winter and housemasters, year group tutors, matrons, two school chaplains, health education tutors and school psychologist pick up on most things. Discipline is clear and firm but the place feels pretty relaxed, with boys knowing exactly where they stand. 'You are given freedom but if you abuse the freedom you would be punished,' one boy told us. Zero tolerance on drugs and use or supply in term-time or holidays means expulsion. Anyone found with spirits suspended and warned while smoking is handled through 'escalating sequence of sanctions imposed by housemasters.'

Smart uniform of dark blue jackets (bluers), grey flannels (greyers), white shirts and ties, plus, of course, Harrow's infamous boaters. Boys wear them or carry them and either love them or loathe them. They're allowed to write their names and draw pictures on the inner rim and spray them with varnish to protect them. Members of Philathletic Club (school's top sportsmen) get to wear bow ties. Sunday wear is black tailcoat and the whole kit and caboodle.

Pupils and parents: Pupils come from all over and school is proud of its 'broad and varied intake.' We said last time that it's the sort of place where a Yorkshire farmer's son will be sharing a room with

the offspring of a City banker – and it still holds true. Between 10 and 15 per cent are progeny of OHs, while 20 per cent are from overseas (some ex-pat, others from vast range of countries – 40 at last count). Twenty-five with EAL requirements. Most boys are C of E but there's a 'significant' RC community. Small numbers of all other main faiths or none.

Members of the Philathletic Club (school's top sportsmen) get to wear bow ties

The boys we met were engaging, appreciative of the fine education they get and very proud of their school. 'It doesn't give you a sense of entitlement, just a great responsibility to give something back,' one boy told us, while a sixth former who'd joined from a state school at 16 said that he'd been 'pushed and challenged' and that there was 'a lot more opportunity for debate' than at his previous school.

Parents reckon the school suits all-rounders who work hard and like sport. 'It's very disciplined and the boys are busy all the time so they have to be organised,' one mother said. 'There isn't any time to get up to any mischief and the boys are really tired by the end of term. There's a real camaraderie about the place and the boys make life-long friends. I can't fault it.' Another reckoned that even though it's 'strict,' any boy would thrive at Harrow, as long as they can cope with being in a large school where they won't necessarily be 'king pin.'

Long and distinguished list of former pupils – seven former prime ministers (including Sir Robert Peel, Lord Palmerston, Stanley Baldwin and Sir Winston Churchill), 19th century philanthropist Lord Shaftesbury ('a towering figure – we refer to him a lot,' says the head), Jawaharlal Nehru, King Hussein of Jordon, Lord Cardigan (who led the Charge of the Light Brigade), General Sir Peter de la Billière, plus countless other men of military renown (20 holders of the Victoria Cross and one George Cross holder). The arts and sciences are equally well represented, with a dazzling list of luminaries including Lord Byron, Richard Brinsley Sheridan, Anthony Trollope, Terence Rattigan, John Galsworthy, Cecil Beaton, Edward and William Fox, Richard Curtis, Benedict Cumberbatch and James Blunt, plus Crispin Odey (one of the UK's most successful hedge fund managers), Julian Metcalfe (founder of Pret à Manger), cricketer Nick Compton and Tim Bentinck (better known as David Archer).

Entrance: Very competitive. Around 600 apply for the 160 places on offer at 13. Prospective pupils are assessed at the start of year 7, through tests, interviews and school reference. Offers are made – subject to CE or scholarship exams 18 months later. Sixty per cent expected at CE. 'Some weight' given to sons of OHs and boys' siblings – 'but brothers don't automatically get in,' said a parent. Boys arrive from more than 100 regular feeder schools. All-boys' boarding preps like Caldicott and Cothill top the pack but others from a myriad of co-ed and day schools.

Total of 24 new pupils a year into the 340-strong sixth form. Candidates need at least seven or eight A*/A at GCSE but many will have straight A*s. Candidates write a CV, plus letter to the head explaining why they want to come to Harrow, and take tests in their proposed A level subjects. The best attend a day of interviews and assessments.

Exit: Ninety-nine per cent to university – 18 to Oxbridge in 2015 and most of the rest to Russell Group. Significant number opting for Ivy League universities in the US and other top international institutions.

Money matters: School has given franchises to Harrow Beijing, Harrow Bangkok and Harrow Hong Kong, with a fourth likely to follow in the next few years. These are all successful enterprises carefully monitored by Harrow and also fund generous bursary schemes at home.

Wide range of scholarships and bursaries at 13 or 16. School offers means-tested bursaries of up to 100 per cent of fees to pupils who win a scholarship of any sort. Up to 30 scholarships a year for academic excellence, music, art or talent in a particular area (normally worth five per cent of fees). There are also Peter Beckwith scholarships for gifted and talented boys whose parents can't afford to send them to Harrow. Two awarded each year to boys aged between 10 and 13 – these can cover fees at a private school from the age of 11 and Harrow fees from 13.

Remarks: Parents looking for a top notch, blue chip, full boarding, all boys' school will be hard-pressed to beat Harrow. This is a school on top of its game.

Haydon School

Wiltshire Lane, Eastcote, Pinner, Middlesex HA5 2LX

State • Pupils: 2,010 • Ages: 11–18 • Sixth form pupils: 500

Tel: 020 8429 0005

Email: info@haydonschool.org.uk
Website: www.haydonschool.com

21

Headteacher: Since 2006, Robert Jones (40s). Read economics at LSE and taught in Hong Kong for four years before returning to the UK. Moved to Haydon in 1999 and quickly moved up the ranks to become assistant head, then head. Married to drama teacher. Two sons – one grown up, one at primary school. Originally from Manchester, he's a huge Man United fan and looks rather like an ex-professional footballer himself. Still plays football and coaches Ascot United under 7s (his son plays for the team) and keeps fit by running a number of half marathons each year.

Academic matters: Seventy per cent of students achieved at least five A*-C grades including maths and English at GCSE in 2015 (28 per cent A*/A grades). Language provision is excellent, with students starting off with French and Italian or Spanish and German. Options for taking on further languages (such as Mandarin and Latin) higher up the school. 'Around 100 opted for Mandarin this year,' says the head proudly. Forty per cent take two foreign languages at GCSE.

More than 30 GCSE and BTec options. 'We want to offer as broad a curriculum as possible,' explains the head. Applied learning specialism allows the school to offer a wide array of courses, from Greek to construction. 'There is a broad range of subjects offered,' one parent told us.

All KS3 teaching (apart from maths and technology) is in mixed ability groups. 'We believe this gives all of our students the best possible chance of achieving their best,' explains the head. Parents like the fact that class sizes are around 25, but some would prefer more streaming. 'At present in year 7 there is streaming just for maths,' said one parent. 'I would like to see this extended to other key subjects such as English and science as is the practice in other local schools'.

At A level 51 per cent A*-B grades in 2015. Again, a wide choice of subjects available. Parents praise the quality of teaching and particularly the revision lessons offered around exam time. Students need six GCSEs at A*-C (including maths and English) to study four A levels. Those who do not have a minimum of a C in English or maths are able to retake these and can study three A levels.

SENCo and team support 22 statemented pupils pupils. There is also a special centre where students can be taught in small groups. When we visited we met a group of students learning to express their emotions through making Star Wars masks.

Games, options, the arts: School has scored successes in a host of sports – at both local and county level. Particular strengths are rugby, rounders and indoor athletics and there is even an ultimate frisbee team in the sixth form. New sports hall.

Haydon has benefited from new facilities in recent years, including £5 million art and design building and £2 million music and performing arts centre (three music rooms, drama studio and music mixing room. plus one-to-one teaching rooms). School has two orchestras, jazz band, samba band and wide variety of other music groups. Four big concerts a year as well as annual musical or play.

Thriving art department achieves excellent exam results. Students can study art, textiles and photography at A level. Lots of school trips too – to France, Germany, Italy, Peru and Swaziland.

Background and atmosphere: School is situated on the edge of the Northwood Hills in Pinner, with spacious playing fields. Rather nondescript 1950s buildings – originally two grammar schools that merged in 1977. Lots of building work going on when we visited.

Food in the sixth form café is so good that the staff choose to eat there. Food in the canteen for the rest of the school has less favourable reports but new caterers were about to be appointed when we visited so this will hopefully improve. Some of the

New positive reward system introduced. One of the top awards means pupils get a special lunch with the head (mums sadly aren't eligible to compete for this)

toilets need a little TLC but these are in the process of being refurbished. 'The boys' changing rooms are a real state,' one student told us, but we weren't shown these on our tour. We were very taken with the pool table and primary colours in the rather groovy sixth form common room though.

Pastoral care and discipline: A new positive reward system has recently been introduced. 'The reward system is a great motivator,' one parent told us. 'My child strives to get good news notes, commendations and other rewards.' Meanwhile a year 8 student said: 'I really look forward to the awards assembly. It's a way of showing how hard we are working.' One of the top awards means pupils get a special lunch with the head (mums sadly aren't eligible to compete for this award).

Students excluded for threatening behaviour or repeated disruption in lessons (four permanent exclusions last year). Parents are happy with school's approach to behaviour. 'I have always found that a high level of discipline is maintained from the minute the children arrive at the school,' said one. When we visited, students seemed well behaved and friendly.

Pupils and parents: 'Haydon has a really good reputation round here,' a student told us, 'and all my friends at other schools wish they were here.' The school offers both pupils and parents a chance to voice their opinions – parent voice group meets four times per year.

Entrance: Most students live locally (within a mile or so of the school). Admissions criteria are: children in public care, then siblings, then children living nearest to the school, then employees' children. An additional 60 students join in the sixth form.

Exit: A quarter of pupils leave after GCSEs – for college, other schools, apprenticeships or employment. Around three-quarters of sixth formers to university, and about a third of these to top universities eg Southampton and Nottingham, including sometimes one or two a year to Oxbridge.

Remarks: A friendly comprehensive that really does cater for all, with strong vocational courses as well as the more traditional A levels – all taught to a high standard. 'I would have no hesitation recommending Haydon,' said one parent. 'I feel my children are lucky to attend the school.'

International School of London

139 Gunnersbury Avenue, London W3 8LG

Independent • Pupils: 440 • Ages: 3–18 • Sixth form pupils: 70 • Fees: up to £24,600 pa

Tel: 020 8992 5823

Email: mail@ISLLondon.org
Website: www.ISLLondon.org

30

Head of School: Since 2009, Mr Huw Davies, Oxford University MA (PPE) PGCE. Has long experience at ISL: previously deputy head, IB diploma coordinator, higher education advisor, history and theory of knowledge teacher. Generous with his extensive IB knowledge and experience, is an IB consultant to prospective IB schools and often on authorising teams for IB schools worldwide. A man of few words, he comes across as an archetypal British ex-history master, yet he clearly has a foot firmly in the international education world. Parents did not have a lot to say about Mr Davies; he is possibly more engaged in the behind the scenes day-to-day school management and the big-picture strategic jobs (school refurbishments, increased capacity for growing demand, mother tongue programme etc); delegating more of the 'front of house' interactions to his teachers and principals.

Academic matters: The school offers the IB primary, middle years and diploma continuum. Some high school students opt out of the full diploma, earning instead an ISL High School Diploma. There's a good selection of IB courses, with more online through Pamoja Education.

Primary students have specialist teachers for music and PE; art is taught by class teachers. From middle school, specialists teach art, drama, music and PE (through grade 10). Strong level of support in primary classes with plenty of assistants for classes that can number up to 20.

The major draw for every single family we spoke to is the 'terrific' mother tongue programme. It may cost extra depending on numbers, but mother tongue classes are offered from primary through to high school with about 16 IB languages leading to the added advantage of a bilingual IB diploma. If a new child's language is not on the list, they will try to find a teacher. EAL support is also strong.

Some primary parents prefer the slight 'delay' in reading for younger children when compared to the local English schools. For families coming from countries where formal schooling begins at the age of 6 or 7, ISL's gentle introductory literacy approach at age 5 is more comfortable. However, others comment that while they're very happy at ISL, the range of English fluency may have an effect on the academic pace and rigour compared with other independent schools.

He comes across as an archetypal British ex-history master, yet he clearly has a foot firmly in the international education world

Laptops are lent to students and kept at school, so away from school students access their work online. Interactive whiteboards or smart TVs in many classrooms. We noticed there weren't as many students 'connected to devices' as in seen in other London international schools – for better or worse.

Engaged and cheerful children everywhere we went. A parade of primary students with yummy sandwiches headed to the dining hall, leaving behind open exercise books in their classroom, with individually written recipes for 'my favourite healthy sandwich' (part of their healthy living unit using hands-on IB primary years approach); youngest children eating and chatting while teaching assistants circulated attentively; middle school students debating the value of democracy and the advantages of a student council that can organise fun activities, in preparation for an upcoming assembly; CDT students sawing away at wood; art students busily tidying up their room to head to the assembly...everyone looked settled and at ease. Great esprit de corps apparent from fact that the entire secondary participates in assemblies.

IB results steadily rising in recent year though average point score in 2015 dipped to 31.

Parents generally happy with communication with the school. There's good overall consultation. Some say response to emails are occasionally inconsistent: while issues raised in an emails seem to be addressed by staff, parents aren't always kept informed of the follow up. The parent of a younger child was a surprised when parents were not invited to accompany children to see the classrooms on orientation day. Parents new to the IB curricula sometimes may struggle if they don't attend the parent education events provided by the school.

With families coming from so many different national education systems, everyone has his own idea about the 'right way' to do things. Managing these expectations and helping children adapt is part of the ISL challenge, and for the most part, parents report they do a great job.

Engaged and cheerful children. A parade of primary students with yummy sandwiches headed to the dining hall

Approximately 90 teachers, average age is early 40s, with several part-time language teachers. About 15 have been there for over 10 years.

Games, options, the arts: There's a mix of after-school clubs, though some primary parents would like to see more, and juggling after-school pick up can be tricky if a younger sibling has nothing to do. Usual international school sports such as volleyball, football, basketball and tennis, and triathlon offered too, with international tournaments. Primary PE and sports take place on site in the hall, small playground, or neighbouring park.

Secondary kids go to a nearby sports centres or the park. Weekly swimming for all up to grade 10 at Brentford Leisure Centre. One parent suggests ISL may not suit the 'uber-athlete'; 'it's fun and competitive to a point, but for serious athletes, families join local sports clubs.'

Private instrumental lessons scheduled during the school day, with ensembles practising after school. ISL takes advantage of London as a vast field trip opportunity; early in the year there's a week when nearly everyone from grade 4 vacates the school for three to five day trips. Some incorporate team-building to integrate newcomers; in the middle years they're language-related (Beijing just added). Only the youngest and the IB students (except those on a biology trip) stay behind. Primary parents tell us that the idea of sending their 9-year-olds off on a residential trip 'takes some getting used to'.

Many community service opportunities on offer by school and students also organise their own. One returned to her native India to volunteer in a school for the summer. ISL has work experience programme for all grade 9 students; the school helps organise, or parents and students find their own placement. Though they're a bit young to work, it can inspire their thinking about what IB courses they may select. For one student it also led to summer job opportunities and a gap year project after graduation.

Background and atmosphere: A secondary school founded in north London in 1972, ISL was one of the first authorised IB diploma schools in the country. The school merged in the late 80s with the International Community College, a primary school founded by the Makarem family, becoming a full 4-18 school and moving into a former Catholic school on the North Circular Road in west London. The school is still owned by the Makarems, who recently opened schools in Qatar and in Surrey (buying Shell's former Dutch school). The group is managed by Amin Makarem, the founder's son, who oversees the leadership team of the three schools. Parents say the ISL's quite independent of the other two; not much inter-school activity at student level apart from some sports competition with the Surrey school, but we hear more collaboration is planned.

The building would not win any architectural prizes, but it is undergoing a major refurbishment to modernise and make more it attractive. The primary is located in an annex rented from the next door church; the school reports that it has no plans to relinquish this space even when the refurbishment is completed. ISL is a rabbit warren of hallways and stairwells with every nook and cranny utilised – the staff room, practically in the rafters, is a hive of energetic teachers planning and conversing in umpteen languages – a very positive vibe.

Every nook and cranny utilised – the staff room, practically in the rafters, is a hive of energetic teachers planning and conversing in umpteen languages

The school definitely needs sprucing up; it's not easy to see any rationale to the arrangements of secondary school classrooms, corridors and public spaces. Possibly due to building works under way, the school can feel cramped and disorganised. The head and school leadership team are considering how to reconfigure the classroom arrangements once the refurbishment is complete.

The primary lunch room is uninspiring, and the play area out front is basically a hard surface to run around and play a few ball games on, though as a result of the construction the kids are going to the park more, which is a lovely treat and very handy.

There's a two-level art room and a photo lab, a great CDT classroom, functional science labs of a certain age, a useful multi-purpose hall, a library (which will be relocated after the refurb) and lots of multi-use classrooms of various sizes. Middle and high school students share classrooms and primary share some of the language and specialist classrooms; primary parents reassure us that it's a happy family atmosphere, and of course the teachers are always supervising youngsters as they move through the building.

But the likelihood is that if a family visits ISL for the first time after seeing other international schools in the area, the facilities and environment may not quite measure up. One parent said that when they first drove up to the school, 'we could have cried', but having got past that, it was their first choice school, and they are very happy there. Despite the tight spaces, the students are friendly, polite and seem to move through the building in a pretty organised fashion, and it bodes well for world peace if kids of 50+ nationalities can get along so well in these relatively cramped quarters. The strong message coming from parents is 'don't be put off by first impressions'.

The school is aware of its limitations, hence the renovation programme. It is also always on the lookout for suitable additional space, and if the appropriate solution were found, might relocate the IB diploma years to its own centre. Families considering ISL may bear this in mind, and that other schools in urban London face similar challenges when planning ahead.

Grades 11 and 12 may leave campus for lunch, early years eat in their classrooms, and everyone in between eats in the dining canteen. Parents we spoke to say their children prefer to take lunch from home over the optional lunch programme booked termly. Door-to-door bus service is available; with growing London traffic problems, they strongly recommend that families choose from neighbourhoods like Kew, Chiswick or Ealing.

Pastoral care and discipline: The strong sense of community provides a solid foundation for the behaviour and discipline in the school, which is of course guided by the IB Learner Profiles. The school handbook directs parents to home room tutors for everyday matters, or the divisional principals, with more serious or school-wide concerns then directed to the head. Some less IT-savvy parents seem to be having some teething problems with a new online communications system. But their main concern is the welfare of their children, and as one happy parent said, 'at ISL children are treated like royals.' No big discipline worries came to our attention.

Pupils and parents: Possibly the most international school in the city if not the country; ISL's students come from 55 countries – the largest single group representing only 13 per cent. It creates fertile conditions for developing open-mindedness and international understanding for students, as well as parents and faculty. With many dual-national families, some kids hold as many as three or four passports. Parents love this environment where 'if you speak several languages, you're not unusual'.

It creates fertile conditions for developing open-mindedness and international understanding for students

Parents are also drawn to ISL by its smaller size and the friendly and approachable staff, who they credit with helping children to settle in so easily and comfortably, knowing 'how to manage the adjustment for children coming from very different school systems'. Teachers are approachable and deal with new children individually (and also help parents with tips to manage the family transitions). At ISL, this is more than marketing hype.

We hear that families interact socially outside of school; ISL parents believe that having their children learn to understand peers from all backgrounds is a huge advantage. Parents of older students report that their children meet at weekends, and most are happy for them use public transport to arrange this; week nights are spent at home with their noses in the books.

Very active PTA; many families regard the school as the heart of the community. They plan outings and orientation activities for new parents. Parents arriving mid-year are welcomed with newcomers' events and even English language lessons. One parent told us of a group of families who regularly take weekend trips around the UK. Another said she sometimes feels there are more activities for parents than for the kids. PTA got praise from everyone we spoke to.

Most are expats on temporary assignment in the UK, many based at the nearby Brentford business park or growing hub of international companies in Hammersmith, or one of the many embassies. A number lives within easy distance of the school, which makes managing the social life a bit easier, and parents know one advantage in living away from the centre of London is that their money goes further – bigger houses, bigger gardens.

Entrance: Rolling admissions allows students to apply from all over the world, all year round, although there are waiting lists for some year groups. Apply before Easter to improve chances. Admission is determined by previous records, a teacher reference, student and family questionnaires. Interviews are always welcomed (required for IB diploma). No testing (English language is assessed after admission); students with special educational need to provide diagnostic assessments used to determine whether the school can properly serve the student. Non-English speakers with good academic reports are admitted up to grade 10. During interviews there's a lot of discussion about the mother tongue programme and the possible fees for this service.

Although the school does not comment on a sibling policy, parents say they make an effort to ensure all children in a family get a place. Admissions director gets high marks for his thoroughness, efficiency, responsiveness and care and he can tell you about every student in the school. Though on first impression he may appear somewhat diffident, with his many years' experience working with ISL families 'he knows his onions'.

Exit: About 70 per cent go to UK universities, although more now applying to American universities. Some return to their home countries and ISL has a long history of helping students find the right fit in a wide range of countries – an important consideration for families. Even students who earn the ISL High School Diploma gain entry into UK universities. Very occasionally, a student may leave ISL to pursue A levels. Edinburgh, Oxford, Warwick, UCL, King's, Imperial, St George's Medical School and Queen Mary popular; overseas destinations include Tokyo Science University, Kyoto University, Keio McGill, Technical University of Budapest, University of Chicago, University of Texas, Bocconi Milan, and École Supérieure du Commerce. An impressive list, but parents are advised to ask the school specifically about the more recent successes.

Money matters: No scholarships as such as most pupils have corporate support, but school will keep a child in extreme circumstances if a family financial problem arises.

Remarks: A school with a solid academic track record that has clearly won over the hearts and minds of its many international families. Many organisations, not to mention a few world leaders, could learn a lot about fostering global understanding from this school.

JFS

The Mall, Kenton, Harrow, Middlesex HA3 9TE

Tel: 020 8206 3100

State • Pupils: 2,070 • Ages: 11–18 • Sixth form pupils: 570 pupils • Jewish

Email: admin@jfs.brent.sch.uk
Website: www.jfs.brent.sch.uk

Headteacher: Since January 2008, Mr Jonathan Miller BSc MA NPQH (40s). Educated at Carmel College and Imperial College London, he has been at JFS for many years. A former head of chemistry and head of science, he was responsible for planning the school's timetable and IT strategy when it relocated to Kenton, also deputy head. Articulate and highly respected, considered even-handed, even-tempered and level-headed, well able to preserve the happy balance which exists between pupils of a wide range of religious observance within the school.

Academic matters: A very large comprehensive that compares favourably with many grammar schools in terms of results. In 2015, 48 per cent of A level grades A*/A and 77 per cent A*-B, while 75 per cent of students gained 5+ A*-C grades including English and maths at GCSE, and more than 48 per cent of grades were A*/A.

Has a strong family feel – often parents, grandparents and even great grandparents are former pupils – with an outstanding sense of continuity, community, warmth and commitment

New pupils are admitted into 10 accelerated or mixed ability tutor groups and all subjects are set by ability in year 8. Both upper and lower ends are given unusually strong support. The gifted and talented have accelerated classes from year 7, while the large special needs department – with over 80 statemented children – has its own suite, six special needs teachers and six permanent teaching assistants. Those struggling at the bottom of the middle band are perhaps the least well served. Ofsted commented that less able students make slower progress than others. French for all in year 7, Spanish for all from year 8. IT bang up to the minute, with interactive whiteboards in every classroom. Science, too, unusually well equipped with 15 laboratories.

First-rate, highly sought after, academic sixth form with around 550 pupils, housed in its own discrete space (though with some lessons taught in the main school). Large expansion of the curriculum at this point, with applied art (including photography and graphics), economics, business studies, psychology, sociology, childhood studies, theatre studies, media studies, politics and critical thinking added to the GCSE basics. Masterclasses, too, for the 25 or so Oxbridge candidates, including some pupils from neighbouring boroughs.

A core of long-serving staff provides some outstanding teaching in all subjects. 'A child who wants to work could not receive a better education anywhere in the country,' said one mother, whose son recently left for a top-flight university. Teaching is carefully monitored, with videoing of lessons – prides itself on its continuing professional development and places the training of teachers from a number of teacher training institutions high on its agenda: about a third of its trainees stay on as teachers, so few problems with recruitment.

Games, options, the arts: Outstanding range of facilities, which include 14 acres of playing fields, two sports halls, a dance studio and a multi-gym for students and staff. Games lessons focus on athletics, ball games, gymnastics and dance.

Strong music department – all students take music in years 7, 8 and 9 and about 15 per cent also take instrumental lessons with visiting staff. Ten practice rooms, keyboard laboratory, recording studio, two specialist classrooms, plus music masterclasses. Large auditorium which seats 900, plus a concert hall for 450. Amphitheatre for outdoor concerts and performances. Five interconnecting art rooms, plus a sculpture terrace. Media studio with professional standard film and television equipment and an editing suite. Well-equipped library.

Annual reading festival and poetry competition. Excellent range of school trips, including Poland (for sixth form Holocaust studies), Israel (year 9 residential scheme), Prague, Strasbourg, Flanders and Paris. Duke of Edinburgh, Young Enterprise. Kosher kitchen with a healthy and balanced diet – no other food can be brought into school.

Background and atmosphere: The largest Jewish comprehensive in Europe, with a particularly distinguished history and tradition. Founded originally in the East End in 1732, it had, by the 19th century, become the largest school in the world, with 4,000 students, mainly poor Jewish immigrants. Bombed in WW2, it was rebuilt in Camden Town in 1958, but by the time it transferred to Kenton in 2002 the accommodation had, in the words of its previous head, become a 'cesspit'. Now on a large and leafy site in north west London with light, modern buildings, wide curved corridors and impressive technology. Has a strong family feel – often parents, grandparents and even great-grandparents are former pupils – with an outstanding sense of continuity, community, warmth and commitment. The social side of school life is particularly prized by parents and most students enjoy coming to school and make life-long friends.

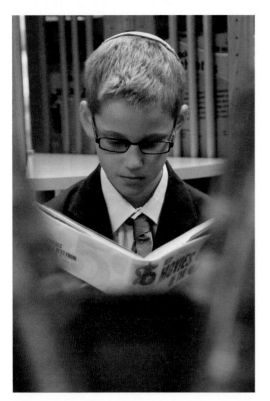

School was downgraded by Ofsted from outstanding to requires improvement in July 2014, following concerns raised about behaviour and safety for a minority of students. After the initial shock, school got down to sorting out the issues raised, and the following December, following a monitoring visit, Ofsted reported that it was back on the right track, commenting that the JFS leadership had 'acted professionally and resolutely to start tackling the areas for improvement.' This wasn't a reinspection, so the school wasn't regraded, and the 'requires improvement' status remains in place for the time being. Nonetheless, after visiting the school in July 2015, we concluded that JFS remains a pretty excellent place, with academic results that put it in the top one per cent of non-selective schools in the UK, and around 70 per cent of leavers going on to Russell group universities.

Pupils are sparky, articulate, motivated and – when we saw them, at least – impeccably behaved. Parents we approached generally reported themselves very happy. Typical comments were: 'I think very highly of the school. My children are different in every way and the school's been brilliant with both of them'; 'The support to my child has been fantastic – staff have bent over backwards to help him'; 'I would recommend the school 100 per cent'; 'Positive working atmosphere in the school – my daughter has been very happy at JFS'; 'The academic standards are excellent'; 'The school has found a way to reward each of my children for what they do well.' A few commented said that whilst the school dealt with problems very well once it had been made aware of them, they felt it could do more to spot them developing, a criticism that seemed to accord with some of the Ofsted findings. But even one very critical parent added, 'Our overall experiences of JFS have been very good, and my children have had an excellent education.' Students we spoke to concurred. 'Overall, my experience here has been fantastic,' remarked a cheerful year 12 boy, and another told us, 'The teaching is amazing, and the pastoral care is really good – any issues I have are taken up when I raise them.' A year 7 child said he'd found the school 'really good, really welcoming, and the teachers have really helped me to settle in.'

Pastoral care and discipline: Blue and white uniform, which meets the demands of the most Orthodox – so girls in skirts with arms covered, respectful necklines and 'no ironmongery', boys with heads covered with skull caps (albeit some only when they see the head approaching).

In such a large school, the organisation of the pastoral side is of vital significance. On entry, the intake of 300 is subdivided into 10 groups of 30. Each student joins a tutor group and is assigned a

Girls in skirts with arms covered, respectful necklines and 'no ironmongery', boys with heads covered with skull caps (albeit some only when head approaching)

tutor – who stays with them throughout – a year manager and director of studies, so three adults looking after every child. Also buddy and peer-mentoring systems. The ethos is strict, determined but kind. Discipline is certainly not a major issue, with quiet and orderly classrooms. Famous detention room – Room 17 – for any persistent offenders and a designated behaviour team to deal with transgressors. 'One or two per cent take up all the time, but I don't know of a single child we haven't turned around,' said the head.

Outlook and practice is Orthodox and one of the key aims is to further Jewish values. Very strong Jewish studies programme and all take GCSE in religious studies. Modern Hebrew and Israel studies are included as part of the Hebrew education programme. Accelerated GCSE in modern Hebrew. Daily services, led by students. Wonderful light, purpose-built synagogue with delicate stained glass windows, where volunteers teach additional Jewish education to the most Orthodox.

Pupils and parents: A very broad spectrum of religious belief, from 'those considering rabbinical studies to those who've never seen a candle lit on Friday night'. Nonetheless, you would probably not feel comfortable here if you didn't want your child to be involved with the Jewish experience. Indeed, for some non-practising parents, it offers a religious opportunity they feel they can't provide at home. 'We're not observant,' said one mother, 'and one of the nicest things about the school was that it enabled my son to have a bar mitzvah.'

Entrance: Some 700 applicants for 300 places. In 2009, following a much-publicised court case, the applications process altered and it was forced to abandon the principle of giving priority to those children who are Jewish according to the religious principles stated by the Chief Rabbi. Instead, in common with other Jewish schools, it now gives priority to those who meet a test of religious practice. Parents for year 7 places have to provide a certificate to testify to synagogue attendance, evidence of a formal Jewish education and/or of family activity in the Jewish community. Places awarded on a points system, which also applies to siblings and external applicants for the sixth form. Those applying for admissions should study the criteria carefully.

Exit: Around 10-15 per cent leave after GCSEs. Of those who stay on for sixth form, a sizeable majority go to top universities. In 2015, 10 to Oxbridge; Leeds, Bristol, Nottingham, Nottingham Trent, Birmingham and Manchester other popular destinations.

Remarks: An outstandingly well-run comprehensive, with a warm and well-ordered atmosphere, in bright and spacious modern buildings – and, despite recent Ofsted downgrading, with strong support from parents and pupils. Ideal for those looking for a strong education within a secure environment and Jewish cultural tradition.

The John Lyon School

Middle Road, Harrow, Middlesex HA2 0HN

Independent • Pupils: 600 • Ages: 11–18 • Sixth form pupils: 180 • Fees: up to £16,644 pa

Tel: 020 8515 9400

Email: enquiries@johnlyon.org
Website: www.johnlyon.org

14

Head: Since 2009, Miss Katherine Haynes BA MEd NPQH, a mathematician (40s). Miss Haynes was the first woman to be appointed head of an HMC, boys only, school – a notable milestone. Previously head of maths at Warwick School, prior to which she held the same post at Edgbaston High. This is a look-you-straight-in-the-eye-plus-firm-handshake head, one whose palpable intensity of purpose masks, you feel, warmth and a sense of fun. She is articulate, forthright, focused. 'What a school provides needs to match its location...I want teaching that is dynamic and energetic, that enables boys to learn in the way that is best for them.' She is realistic about the physical limits of the school site – 'It's a question of going with what we can do rather than "what if?"' Perhaps less visible about the school than her popular and relaxed predecessor, Miss Haynes initiated a crackdown on 'standards' and discipline from day one – clearly a bit of a bombshell for some but appreciated by most. All recognise that 'she is keen to do good things with the school'...'she is going to up its game'...'she's obviously keen to do her best'. Whatever uncertainty and scepticism might have rippled through the school on her appointment, it sure as anything isn't there now and parents, staff and boys look puzzled at the idea that a woman in the job is unusual. She took on an interesting school at an interesting time – boys' only day schools are thin on the ground these days. In her hands, John Lyon is a school of which north west London is going to sit up and take notice.

Academic matters: Mainstream trad curriculum. Maths much the most popular A level subject with majority getting A*/As. Chemistry, history, religious studies and economics also with good uptake and results mostly in the A/B band. Biology more of an A-C spread. Few modern linguists – nothing unusual there in a boys' school – though Spanish now an ab initio option with French which may strengthen both. School also offers psychology, drama and music tech at this level. In 2015, 41 per cent A*/A at A level, 64 per cent at GCSE. Maths IGCSE taken and results are impressive. All three sciences also very strong. The Englishes now IGCSE and get mostly A*/B. Latin and Roman civilisation taken by year 10 pupils with strong results. German now, sadly, dead. No obvious weak areas. Able to take advantage of big brother school up the hill, ie Harrow, for individual language specialisms among other perks. IT hitherto seen as integral to learning in general and not as 'a subject' but this is changing – all take it in the first two years – no shortage of computers about the place. No DT, though – simply not possible given the constraints of the site and, seemingly, no pupil or parental pressure to bring it into what otherwise might be

Girls from several chic local schools compete at auditions to play opposite the boys in big, well-appointed productions

seen as a natural home.

Learning support dept works in classroom and via withdrawal. Around 60 on the register at the time of our visit. Mainly assists dyslexics and dyspraxics – of a mild to moderate kind – and has boys on the ASD spectrum too. Site is a bit up and down but most is accessible and wheelchairs are 'not impossible'. We grilled many parents and boys and no subject is seen as weak – most staff, in fact, praised for the support they give. Library full of PCs and much fiction. Somewhat eclectic stock otherwise and what appeared to us an unusual cataloguing system.

Games, options, the arts: Drama clearly lively and popular – possibly not unrelated to the fact that girls from several chic local schools eg St Helen's, Northwood College and North London Collegiate compete at auditions to play opposite the boys in big, well-appointed productions. We witnessed some younger boys improvising with none of the coyness and self-consciousness common elsewhere at this age group. Provision is good – two studios and the big hall, though no performing arts centre here – no space. Parents enthuse about productions. Music also exceptional despite unglamorous accommodation – school musters all manner of ensembles and boys play a great range of instruments. Good to see, alongside the bands and R and B, a motet choir and string ensembles. Music tech growing. 'The standard of music and drama is amazing,' a parent told us. 'The last concert was so moving I came out in tears.' Art in a series of studios and some good displays of pupil work here and there in otherwise rather uninspiring corridors. Good to see art done by staff on display – and not just by art staff. Sports hall – though not of the cavernous size found elsewhere – and provision otherwise is good: impressive fitness centre, excellent pool, playing fields up and down the hill and much borrowing of Harrow's fields and pitches also enhances opportunities. Cricket an exceptional strength. Lots of popular expeditions, sporting, educational and charitable – classroom building in Uganda, India and Vietnam occasioned particularly zesty response along with mountaineering in the Alps.

All seemingly mix and coexist with the school needing to do very little to help it along. An overall ethos of work and collaboration does all that's needed

Background and atmosphere: It's tucked into a winding road on the Harrow hill, still reminiscent of the quiet leafy village this must have been. Harrow School dominates the hill and its fields and structures abut John Lyon's, but this is a happy, brotherly co-existence, and the cadet school benefits in many ways from the senior. School sits on the edge of two conservation areas, which concentrates creative thinking as far as development is concerned. The main school building is Victorian gothic. One small new-build – under the 'estate strategy' – enabled it to change its designation from housing economics and dining to become a new sixth form centre. It includes a dedicated sixth form work space with impressive IT facilities, as well as a space for relaxation. Pretty arts and crafts villa now the admin hub. Most corridors, painted white under fluorescent lighting and with municipal carpet, are pretty stark. Good-sized school hall, with picture windows and views on two sides. The site is not spacious and few buildings delight the eye but it doesn't feel crowded – partly because of the surrounding pitches and fields.

Limited space means that the population has to stay at more or less its present size – the relative smallness of the school seen by all as a great attraction. Parents are united – 'everyone knows everyone – they all mix, older and younger, especially on the school bus and all are very accepting of each other'...'sport and drama means they make good friends across the age groups'...'because it's small they get a lot of individual attention and that develops and strengthens their confidence'. Three-quarters eat school food which, reportedly, 'could be better' and assuredly needs a more comfortable home. Atmosphere is healthily but not aggressively male – good number of women teachers probably helps. Parents pay tribute – 'the school is very good at bringing on their confidence'...'it's academic but not pushy'...'it's an academic school but people aren't separated into geeks and jocks'.. 'not cliquey...everyone is treated equally'...'good at parent-teacher contact'.. 'my son is very happy there.'

Pastoral care and discipline: All lessons start and end with boys standing for the teacher – we approve. Year 13 boys are peer mentors for the younger boys – trained and monitored by professional school counsellor. Clear disciplinary structure – detentions and brief suspensions sort most problems and these are mostly related to late work or behaviour. Two exclusions since Miss Haynes's advent – both for unacceptable behaviour. Drugs/smoking/drink infringements seemingly unknown. Bullying managed by prevention so very little goes on. Self-discipline is the ethos and it seems to work. Pupils clearly proud to be here.

Pupils and parents: Huge ethnic and social mix reflecting the local area. Thirty-odd home languages. Around two-thirds a mix of Asians – mostly Indian. All seemingly mix and co-exist with the school needing to do very little to help it along. An overall ethos of work and collaboration does all that's needed. Most live within two miles of the school but they do come from further afield into eg Ealing, Hounslow, Watford and Bucks. Five bus routes. Noted Old Boys include actors Julian Rhind-Tutt and Timothy West, writers Geoff Atkinson and Liam Halligan.

Entrance: Main feeders at 11+ are Alpha Prep, Reddiford; at 13+ St Martin's, St John's, Quainton Hall, Clifton Lodge. At 11, c60 places and c40 at 13. Heavily over-subscribed at both levels. Selection via exam – an online test and an essay at 11. Then an interview with some mental maths. NB part of a group of independent co-ed/boys' schools that coordinate 11+ results, but forbid those who have accepted a place at one school from taking up a subsequent waiting list offer from another. At 13+

exams in maths, English, science and French plus interview. At 16 there are additional places and well worth applying. A grades needed in A level subjects and a minimum of six GCSE grades A-B* grades.

Exit: A range of subjects and universities – economics, IT, business, engineering, biomedical sciences and dentistry loom large. UCL, King's, Manchester, Durham, Nottingham, Birmingham and Bristol all popular. Lots, seemingly, reapply post A level results – better matching their results to their choice of course, perhaps, and school offers good support.

Money matters: Good number of bursaries – all means-tested. Scholarships worth up to £2,000 remission of the tuition fees in academics, sports, art & design, music, drama and all-rounder. If you have a gifted son and no money you could get a fabulous deal here.

Remarks: Solid, sound and sensible. Deserves to be far better known.

The Lady Eleanor Holles School, Junior Department

Linked school: The Lady Eleanor Holles School, 426

Burlington House, 177 Uxbridge Road, Hampton Hill, Middx TW12 1BD

Independent • Pupils: 190 • Ages: 7–11 • C of E • Fees: £15,105 pa

Tel: 020 8979 2173

Email: junior-office@lehs.org.uk
Website: www.lehs.org.uk

34

Head of Juniors: Since 2011, Mrs Ffion Robinson BA MA PGCE (30s). She came from King's House boys' prep, where she had been assistant head. Prior to this she taught at The Pointer School in Blackheath. Both her degree and PGCE were taken in her native Wales – she is a Welsh speaker – and like many prep school teachers, she can turn her hand to many things. She still teaches each class once a week – maths, history, RE, English and guided reading. 'I love the creative subjects,' she says, 'and it's great to keep my hand in the classroom'. Quietly enthusiastic and plainly delighted with her job, she is smiley and efficient. Parents, similarly, are quietly confident that this is a good appointment and thank heavens their daughters are pupils here.

Head of whole school is Mrs Heather Hanbury (see senior school entry).

Entrance: School's own entrance tests in English and maths at 7+, and top performers invited back for an activity session. About 48 places. Only about two girls trying for every place, but don't be fooled – the older they get, the faster the ride, so best for tots who seem exceptionally bright and eager to learn. Pupils come from lots of primaries and many from pre-preps like Athelstan House, Denmead and Jack and Jill.

Exit: Sensible system for moving from junior department to senior department. 'I was concerned that preparation for the 11+ entrance exam dominated the curriculum. We were creating all this inevitable anxiety and a division between the two parts of the school. Now the junior department girls are assessed on the basis of their classroom work and school exams and offered a guaranteed place in year 5. The very small number who are not offered

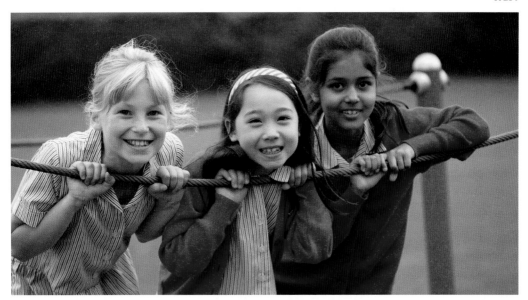

such a place are given lots of support and extra help to prepare for tests to other schools and they may still sit our exam if they wish'. Those who wish to try for a scholarship also sit the entrance exams, along with the outside applicants.

Around 80 per cent move to the senior department. Others go to eg Tiffin Girls, St Paul's Girls or Latymer Upper.

Remarks: Inside, you can still see relics of the attractive old house at the heart of the school. Outside, it is a somewhat forbidding three-storey block with a one-storey extension in unattractive brick and PVC windows. However, unlike preps elsewhere, it has lovely outside space – real space. A super garden area with excellent climbing frames and other apparatus, courts and pitches, much of it, of course, shared with the senior school. Then there are the adored 'hedge homes' – little dens in the hedges abutting the brook separating the school from the grounds. Apparently the girls use pebbles for money and run these little domestic havens just as they would their brick and drain-pipe equivalents.

Inside, everywhere is carpeted – it makes for quiet corridors and a civilised feel. Classrooms are airy and light, while classes are attentive and absorbed. Girls look a treat in their grey/red/blue tartan skirts and red sweatshirts. A sense of purpose and concentration pervades the school and we saw much to delight and impress. We especially liked the cross-curricular approach to much of the teaching – something that plainly inspires the girls. If they learn about the ancient Greeks they make Greek vases. If they learn about Rio de Janeiro and Brazil, they make carnival masks. Arts and

crafts throughout are unusual and clever. We particularly enjoyed the silhouette work and girls enthused about the animated films they make using their own clay and cut-out models.

Then there are the adored 'hedge homes' – little dens in the hedges abutting the brook separating the school from the grounds

The library, though inviting and piled high with books, is small and barely adequate for this number of girls. Trips to interesting places – including a local Gurdwara and the National Archives at Kew to look at Victorian prison records (after which they 'used metaphors to write poems as if we'd been in prison'). This is imaginative and lively teaching of the kind we don't see everywhere. Terrific sports (great preparation here for the legendary sporting culture of the senior department) and lucky girls use many of the older girls' facilities. Good traditional hall for productions, assemblies and younger girls' gym, and they use the wonderful senior school theatre.

The school food (eaten by most) is 'brilliant' and the place hums with happy learning. 'We let little girls be little girls,' says the head reassuringly. 'People are kind here,' one year 6 girl confided. 'If someone is being bullied they go to a friend or a buddy, but it doesn't happen much'. 'There's so much for them to do,' a parent enthused. 'My girls just love going to school'.

The Lady Eleanor Holles School

Linked school: The Lady Eleanor Holles School, Junior Department, 424

Hanworth Road, Hampton, Middlesex TW12 3HF

Tel: 020 8979 1601

Independent • Pupils: 700 • Ages: 11–18 • Sixth form
pupils: 175 • Fees: up to £18,234 pa

Email: office@lehs.org.uk
Website: www.lehs.org.uk

Headmistress: Since September 2014, Heather Hanbury (40s), previously head of Wimbledon High. MA Edinburgh, MSc Cambridge in geography then land economy. A breath of fresh air with experience in the 'real world' prior to teaching – spent nine years working in various management consultancy roles in the City, then as a corporate fundraiser. She was always told she should teach ('and resisted it because I don't like to do the expected'), eventually had a change of heart and took a PGCE with the express ambition of becoming a head. 'I always wanted to run things,' says Mrs Hanbury. 'I like making organisations efficient, effective and happy.' Began her teaching career at Blackheath High School in 1996, quickly rising through the ranks to head of sixth form, before moving on to Haberdashers' Aske's School for Girls, thence deputy head of Latymer Upper School. She hums with energy, is quick to smile and laugh and is intent on injecting some fun into school life.

Academic matters: Few do education better and it's done via thrilling, not drilling. Committed to A levels rather than the IB or Pre-U, the school ups its academic offering at the top end via the AQA Bacc and the Extended Project Qualification, plus an enrichment programme. Maths the most popular A level. Relatively few take modern languages despite exemplary results – German flourishes here as nowhere else we know. Good range of new sixth form subjects – eg classical civilization, psychology and economics (in which virtually all get A*/A). 2015 saw 79 per cent A*-A grades. GCSEs similarly outstanding – 95 per cent A*/A. Grown-up attitude to all subject areas exemplified by the regular Focus newsletters published by the school – excellence aimed for across the board. A culture of enquiry and exploration fostered throughout.

Few with more than mild learning difficulties here, though SEN support is embedded and SENCo is abetted by a specialist who's in school four days a week. One-to-one when needed and lots of support. Seriously good school to consider if you have mobility problems or are wheelchair-bound – flattish site, lifts and wide corridors, plus can-do approach.

Games, options, the arts: Legendary for sports and the facilities here are second to none for a girls' day school. Some parents choose the school on the strength of the sports – academics, what's that? Lacrosse the main winter game and played to win – which they do. We heard about the first lax team's match against the first rugby team from Hampton – sounds a hoot. Rowing also a speciality – a welcome rarity in a girls' school. Sports tours to eg Barbados and America. We visited at a time when the arts were surviving in annexes and temporary accommodation, pending the unveiling of a splendid new performing arts building with theatre and purpose-built or cleverly converted space for art, drama and music, which opened in 2013. This meant the rehoming of sixth form common rooms and other amenities and involved a considerable – though highly desirable – upgrading all round. Drama here is seen as 'brilliant', music is exceptional – The Holles Singers were BBC Youth Choir of the Year recently. We enjoyed the art we saw – particularly the ceramics – although we felt that far more of it could be displayed around the school. Also lively textiles, but only to GCSE. The extracurricular life of the school is exceptional – especially so for a day school. Parents enthuse – 'there are so many opportunities – a huge amount going on all the time'.

Background and atmosphere: The school was established in 1711 under the will of Lady Eleanor Holles, daughter of John Holles, 2nd Earl of Clare. This makes it one of the oldest girls' schools in the country. It began life in the Cripplegate Ward of the City of London, then moved to other premises in the City till 1878, thence to Mare Street in Hackney (that building now houses the London College of Fashion). The current school, purpose-built and designed in the shape of an E, opened in 1937. Such a long history is scarcely uncommon in many of our great public schools but rare in girls' schools. A palpable pride underpins the place. The staffroom has seen many distinguished names. They include Pauline Cox, former head of Tiffin Girls', Margaret Hustler, former head of Harrogate Ladies' College, Cynthia Hall, former head of Wycombe Abbey, and Frances King, former head of Roedean, who all taught here.

Very long, horizontal, featureless and functional, the two-storey main building doesn't delight the eye but then again, it doesn't offend it either. Inside, the corridors are wide, the rooms are light and everywhere is well-kept. The place is somewhat hospital-like with its lengthy corridors and polished wood floors. The pupils insist, though, that 'the thing that brings it alive is the girls' – which is fair enough. Excellent sixth form centre features small teaching rooms – ideal for a history seminar or session on poetic form. The sixth form library somehow exemplifies the whole. It's light, overlooks the pitches, is exceptionally well-stocked and has neat tables for study and rows of PCs. But while the stark white walls (one, admittedly, temporary at the time of our visit) allow for no distraction, it's pretty Spartan and cries out for more display. Big main library, again well-stocked, especially with classic and modern fiction.

Focused and purposeful atmosphere. Girls are

> *Girls take a typically pragmatic attitude: 'It's very helpful in debating – it makes a huge difference having to do it in front of boys as well,' they said*

well turned out in grey uniforms and the sixth formers look fresh and neat in casual dress. A sense of order pervades throughout, including the monitoring and assessment of pupils' progress. Parents praise the ethos of the place. 'It's cool to be clever and cool to be good at sport,' said one, while others told us: 'It's a real all-round school. You've got to be bright to get in. They don't mince their words and you've got to keep up. They expect a lot from the girls from an early stage – they have to take responsibility for themselves. If you don't turn up for a practice, you don't stay on the team'. Strong links with Hampton School – the boys' school just across the playing fields. They share a boathouse, coach service and drama. Girls take a typically pragmatic attitude: 'It's very helpful in debating – it makes a huge difference having to do it in front of boys as well,' they said.

Pastoral care and discipline: House system going great guns. 'It expands the range of extracurricular activities and the opportunities for leadership and taking responsibility'. The girls themselves enjoy getting to know older and younger pupils and the houses make for greater cohesion and community. This is continued through outreach work and the increasing involvement of alumnae. Much praise for the pastoral care system – a clear structure and everyone knows who to go to. All heads of year have their own offices. Good system of buddying, and a feeling that no transgressors would get away with it for long. No noteworthy sins of the drink/drugs/fags kind and minor bullying problems are dealt with swiftly. A culture of openness means that it's all right to tell someone if you're not happy. Academic monitoring also praised. 'They've always recognised that my daughter has potential – the teachers are patient, encouraging and they've helped her to reach the point of realising just how well she can do,' one parent told us. Everyone likes the food – a huge range of options.

Pupils and parents: From a wide area – Acton to Woking, and all points in between. Families are mostly professional and clever and increasingly ethnically diverse. Lots of parents have boys at Hampton – a good mix. The common denominator is a valuing of what this school offers.

Entrance: Around a third come up from junior department, the rest from schools like Newland House, Twickenham Prep, The Study, Bute House, Holy Cross Prep, Kew College. Girls come from as many as 40 different schools. Four to five applicants for each place. Tests in maths, English, non-verbal reasoning and a general paper. School also sets its own exams for sixth form applicants. No GCSE hurdle here. 'We trust our judgment,' say staff, who look at exams, interviews and reports from current schools. Grateful parents of girls who came through 11+ selection are impressed by the process. 'It was by far the most individual interview system,' one told us. 'It was slick and in 20 minutes they seemed to have learned everything about her'.

Exit: Relatively narrow range of universities, perhaps resulting from word of mouth and established traditions. Over recent years, on average, 80 per

> *'It was slick and in 20 minutes they seemed to have learned everything about her'*

cent to Russell Group universities. Destinations include Oxbridge (16 in 2015), Durham, Bristol and London. A couple to Trinity College Dublin and the USA. No limits to what they study – good courses in everything. Notable old girls include Lynn Barber, Charlotte Attenborough, Carola Hicks, Annie Nightingale, Saskia Reeves, Jay Hunt and Gail (University Challenge) Trimble.

Money matters: Drive under way to increase the number and value of bursaries. Means-tested and reviewed annually. Academic scholarships worth up to 10 per cent of fees at 11+ and sixth form level. Arts scholarships up to 10 per cent, plus free instrumental tuition.

Remarks: 'It's been just what we hoped for,' one mother told us, while an imminent leaver sighed happily, 'I've enjoyed every day'.

Little St Helen's and St Helen's Junior school

Linked school: St Helen's School, 473

Eastbury Road, Northwood, Middlesex HA6 3AS

Independent · Pupils: 470 · Ages: 3–11 · C of E · Fees: up to £12,129

Tel: 01923 843210

Email: admissions@sthelens.london
Website: www.sthelens.london

Headmistress: Since 20011, Dr Mary Short, overall head of St Helen's. Has taught undergraduates at Cambridge and pupils at independent schools including St Paul's Girls, City of London Boys and Haberdashers' Aske's Girls (deputy head).

Entrance: At 3 or 4 by observation and interview. At 7 by tests in English and maths and interview.

Exit: Usually a smooth transition from LSH to the juniors and from juniors to seniors, St Helen's. Very few to local state grammars, boarding or competition: 'I asked my daughter if she would like to look at other schools; she looked at me as if I was bonkers.'

Remarks: 'Makes learning exciting, with no pressure', to quote a parent of her 4-year-old – gets

crisper as they get older of course. The nursery, Little St Helen's, and the junior school are all housed in buildings around this beautiful site and share many of the facilities of the senior school. Some buildings have more inviting exteriors than others; however each has bright, airy classrooms, excellent, thoughtful displays and exhibited artwork, libraries, gyms, good-sized halls or studios and is well-resourced. Much given to heartening mottoes: 'Enter with an Open Mind', 'Reach Higher than Your Dreams' – an improvement on the school's Latin one, which is an odd combination of conquering, crosses and daisies.

Lots of ICT, good DT and everyone tries out three languages before they move up to the senior school. All do ballet, PE, music and speech and drama as part of the curriculum. Happy atmosphere, lovely bright uniform, civilised loos and teachers who say 'ladies, will you please take off your shoes now' to a crocodile of receptive 6-year-olds.

A teacher and teaching assistant to each class in Little Saints plus a newly-qualified TA, some teaching assistants in junior school. 'I think these girls are so lucky,' sighed the registrar wistfully as we strolled. 'We are the lucky ones,' replied a passing teacher.

The Mall School

185 Hampton Road, Twickenham, Middlesex TW2 5NQ

Tel: 020 8977 2523

36

Independent · Pupils: 320 · Ages: 4–13 · Fees: up to £13,530 pa

Email: admissions@themallschool.org.uk
Website: www.themallschool.org.uk

Headmaster: Since 2011, Mr David Price BSc (environmental science) MA (school and college management) PGCE (40s). Worked in a conservation unit for a few years before starting his career in a state primary school some 20 years ago. He has also been head of juniors and director of studies here. Previously he was head of English and deputy principal at Latymer Prep and before that taught at Melbourne Grammar School in Australia, where he lived with his family for three years.

Seems to be doing well in this, his first headship. Obviously knows the school inside out and so has been able to leap straight into action – no root and branch reformation, rather a gentle reorganisation in a few areas. Physically and procedurally, he's been tidying up the place and has improved the management structure, appointing a senior tutor for years 7/8 and a head of the 'middles'.

Tremendously affable, he has an open-door policy for staff and parents and consults widely before deciding anything, but he will always have the final word and is prepared to put his foot down where necessary. 'He's really personable, but don't cross him,' advises one parent. Parents generally seem to appreciate the fact that he's 'one of us' and 'a family man'. He lives locally with his Australian wife Lindy and two school-age children (a son at The Mall, and an older daughter), and 'he totally gets where we are coming from,' said a mother. 'He's got the same concerns as we do and I've got nothing but praise for him,' agreed another.

He's quite a stickler for the rules and likes things neat and organised – that includes the boys and their uniforms, and he's not above manning the school gates himself to check that all is shipshape. A precise person who believes that standards must be maintained in all areas and if you bother to have a policy you should follow it through. He's strict, but not feared – 'I would say the boys like him and have a lot of respect for him,' said one mother. 'He's easy to speak to,' confirmed our young tour guides. Not remote and office-bound, he still fits in some RS teaching, runs breakfast meetings with parent reps and attends all the concerts and sports matches. 'I think he's dynamic and wonderful,' said one fan. 'Nothing is too much trouble,' said another.

Out of school he enjoys walking, cycling and socialising, plus frequent trips to visit family in Australia.

Entrance: Non-selective at reception, it's first come, first served – register two years ahead. A DP innovation has been to invite boys joining in September to spend time at the school during the previous summer term. 'We obviously have a look at them and see reports from nursery, but it's not an entrance test,' he says. These infants join one of two mixed ability classes. Joiners thereafter will be assessed in English and maths, and anyone joining after year 4 will be additionally assessed in French and science. Almost self-selects because of its reputation as an academic school, although DP is keen to move away from possibly harsh connotations associated with that reputation. But even so, the bottom 25 per cent of pupils at The Mall end up in the top half of the national average. No dedicated feeder; The Mall takes from over 20 local pre-schools and nurseries including Jack and Jill, Sunflower, Windsor, Pavilion, Maria Grey and De

'I am here to get the less able boys through too and I like to see a wide range of abilities.' To this end school has a series of strategies to help and support

Lacey. Scholarships available for outstanding candidates joining at 7+ or 8+.

Exit: No links to any one school, but does have a close relationship with neighbouring senior school, Hampton, whose head is on Mall board of governors. Typically two-thirds of leavers go to Hampton, King's College Wimbledon, Westminster and St Paul's. 'It varies according to parental mood and which senior school is flavour of the month.' Others to St George's in Weybridge and Reeds in Cobham and a handful to board. Boys are expected to stay to 13+ so are not really prepared for 11+ exams, though a few do leave then, usually for a grammar school place.

Remarks: A well-established prep which knows exactly what it has to do and achieves more.

Things start gently, with reception and year 1 pupils based in a separate building, five minutes from the main school, on a fairly busy, semi-residential road; you can't drop off on site or outside, need to park up and walk. Parents like the fact that their little ones are physically separated from the older, bigger boys; 'I think it makes it easier for them as they start,' said a mother.

The infants' building is a converted Victorian vicarage, with two reception classes downstairs and two year 1 classes upstairs – maximum 22 in each class, generally around 18. Not masses of space for 80+ little boys, but neither are they jammed in. Bright classrooms enlivened with colourful displays. Lessons we saw were very settled and children seemed happy and focused. There is lots of topic-based work eg on space, where we saw some inventive designs for 'a planet unlike Earth'. Each class teacher has a full-time classroom assistant and there are specialist teachers for music and swimming – both strengths of this place, of which more later. Homework twice a week, spellings once a week and reading every night. Boys needing extra help with work will be peeled off for extra tuition with SENCo – no stigma, no extra cost at this level, but you will be charged higher up the school. Also a charge for help with EFL, but school says boys generally catch up quickly, typically within a term or so.

There's one large room, not grand enough to be called a hall, but where the whole infant school can gather for assemblies. Year 1 eat their packed lunches here too – no hot meals for infants – and reception pupils eat their lunch at their desk. Sounds messy, but school says it works.

Some nice touches outside – a bird box/camera and raised beds where the boys can plant – go some way to compensate for limited outdoor space including a sadly under-used grassy area ('little boys and grass don't mix,' said school).

Generally the atmosphere is relaxed, but not sloppy. All staff expect and receive respect – for example, the boys will be asked to re-enter a room if they have not entered it properly. 'I like the place and the pace here,' said one mother. 'It's perfect for little boys, with quite a lot of play-based learning in the early years as they improve their fine motor skills, then things hot up as they move through the school.'

From year 2 the boys move to the purpose-built main site, with 7+ entrants joining in year 3. Everyone automatically transfers to the senior section from year 4 (ages 8 to 13) to take up the common entrance curriculum. Years ago boys would be asked to leave if they did not make the grade – all that changed under the previous headmaster and Mr Price shares this same philosophy. 'I am here to get the less able boys through too and I like to see a wide range of abilities.' To this end school has a series of strategies to help and support the less able and is very keen on early intervention, 'the earlier the better'. Then in senior school there is a director of personalised learning, who develops individual plans. DP is also setting up a programme for non-academic scholarships and Mall pupils have already had some success in winning music, art

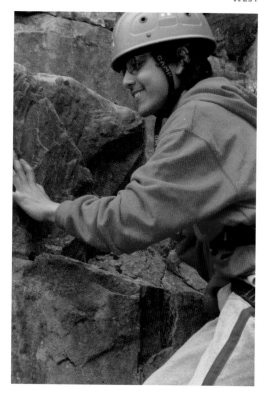

and all-rounder places. Lots of mocks and target-setting, overseen by newly introduced 'academic tutors', aim to ensure early detection of anyone not working up to their capability. Currently 26 boys with SEN, mostly mild dyslexia and dyspraxia. 'From year 4 parents can pay for additional support if they choose', says school.

That said, academics is the focus here – no bones about it; that's why most parents choose The Mall in the first place. It's heads down every day as soon as the boys arrive, with assembly timetabled for just before lunch, so the work is done when the boys are at their freshest. Streaming and setting at the top of the school – in year 7 an accelerated class is introduced, from which come the scholarship boys, while the other class goes at 'ordinary pace'.

'It's a very good all-round school, but its USP is the learning environment – they have got it just right,' said a father. 'The all-round atmosphere is extremely conducive to learning,' agreed a mother. 'As we looked around it felt like we had come home. It's all brilliant from the get-go and I like the drive in this place. They let boys be boys, but also push them to do their absolute best.'

Parents seem to share an unerring confidence in this school and trust it to do right by their sons. There is an orderly, comfortable atmosphere and the boys are well-prepared for their CE. The ongoing tests and plenty of exam practice mean that the boys are so au fait with the whole procedure that it's no biggie when the important ones come around. 'They are totally familiar with what's expected and almost relaxed about it,' said a mother.

There is a fair amount of homework, including holiday homework – building up so that by year 7 there's about an hour a night, 1.5 hours by year 8. Teaching is strong across the board so it is invidious to pick stand-out subjects – 'Really it's all good,' chant parents – but suffice to say French ('extremely well-taught' by native speakers) history and music all mentioned time and again. All year 2 boys play recorder to get them ready and interested and 140+ boys go on to play instruments – we saw boys having great fun drumming and composing. There is also an 80-strong choir – 'It's one of the nice things about a single-sex school,' says one parent. 'Boys are simple creatures and follow what others are doing, so they don't see singing as "girly".' Plenty of chances to perform via regular productions – DP plans for the standard of school concerts to be even better. 'I think he just wants the boys to practise more,' said one mother. 'To make the shows a bit more polished'.

Facilities generally on a par with similar London day schools, with some outstanding features. There's a splendid theatre, a sublime swimming pool and a new sports hall. There are two full games

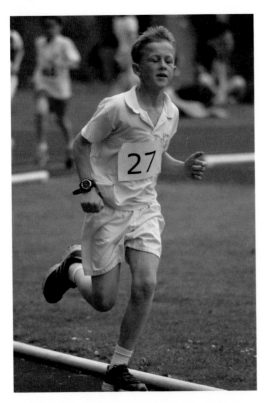

Mothers' day breakfast designed to tug at the heart strings: each boy paints a picture of his mother which he presents to her along with a red rose – most mums cry

afternoons each week and although school is lacking in lush grounds, it is but a short skip and a jump to the bosky expanses of nearby Bushy Park for football, rugby and cricket. There's not so much athletics or tennis and some parents feel sport is not taken as seriously as at some other schools in the area – with the exception of swimming, where the U10 team are IAPS national champions. But most agree that it does 'well enough' for their sons and praise 'smashing' sports staff. 'I wouldn't say it's for a very sporty child,' said one. 'It doesn't have the focus that it does in other schools, which irritates some of us'.

Not masses of extracurricular activities on offer, though there's all the usual art, DT, chess and of course a swimming club – it would be criminal not to make the most of their gorgeous pool. Offering of clubs has been beefed up to include computing, karate, judo and science. Some of the clubs are at lunchtime as it's already quite a long day (8.25am-4pm) but school has to balance this against the fact that many Mall parents are both working and would appreciate their sons being able to enjoy a longer school day.

Apparently there's no such thing as a typical Mallian: 'We prefer them to remain individuals,' says DP. But he will concede uniformity in that they are confident ('not arrogant,' he stresses), well-mannered and well-rounded young men. 'I think they are all quite different really,' agreed one mother. 'And I like the way they are encouraged to develop their own interests and skills'.

Staff have good relationships with the boys – good humour abounds, house points (plus or minus) moderate behaviour and are delivered with some theatrical flourish by school deputy. Head says there is something in The Mall's DNA that promotes good staff/pupil relationships here, bringing out the best in everyone. 'I'm continually impressed by the conversations we can have with them at a very early stage,' he says. Boys are encouraged and taught how to speak confidently in public and to vent their opinions through lots of debating activities. Pupil council and prefects' programme are all part of promoting leadership qualities in the boys. But they are equally encouraged to embrace sentimentality on occasion, such as the mothers' day breakfast (DP imported the idea from Australia) designed to tug at the heart strings: each boy paints a picture of his mother which he presents to her along with a red rose after reading her a poem – most mums cry.

There's a fairly cosmopolitan mix of families here with a wider diversity of cultural backgrounds than seen in other preps in this area of south west London – Asian, Chinese and European boys in the mix. 'I think it's fantastic that The Mall has such a varied population – it's not the rarefied exclusively white intake typical of schools around here,' said one mother. School minibuses run in the morning from Kew, Osterley and Kingston, other pupils from Hounslow, Isleworth, St Margaret's, Richmond, Twickenham, Teddington and Hampton.

Friendly bunch of parents – busy PTA does lots of fundraising but has recently changed its focus to include more social events to get people together. Class reps effective and take the role seriously.

Parents say they feel welcome in school and well informed. Lots of good advice about 'where next?' and DP has introduced a 'future schools information evening' to boost this area. The place is very upfront, it's easy to get to see staff and DP has introduced the Clarion call text communication system which parents have been crying out for. 'They've always been great if I've had a problem,' said a parent. 'There's always a nice atmosphere and I feel very comfortable talking to them,' said another.

School runs a good and thriving thrift shop for uniform. Overall parents feel extras are relatively small, not many super-expensive ones, but neither is much available for free. Because The Mall is a small school there are not a lot of big expeditions and sometimes not enough takers to make an expensive jaunt viable. But that's not to say the boys don't get about; there's a year 3 residential trip to PGL Marchants Hill, older pupils to York and France, plus the occasional sports tour.

In all a happy, high-achieving academic school displaying a kinder attitude than of old – trying to be more inclusive. A settled, focused, organised place, which does exactly what it says on the tin.

Maple Walk School

62a Crownhill Road, London NW10 4EB

Tel: 020 8963 3890

Independent • Pupils: 200 • Ages: 4–11 • Fees: £8,538 pa

Email: admissions@maplewalkschool.co.uk
Website: www.maplewalkschool.co.uk

2

Headmistress: Since 2012, Mrs Sarah Gillam, previously head of the now defunct White House Prep School in Wokingham. Her 30-year career includes two middle school headships and one head of junior science. She has a BEd from Homerton College Cambridge and is married with three university-age daughters.

Entrance: Non-selective intake of 40 at reception stage. Siblings get preference, then in order of registration – waiting lists for several years ahead. For spaces higher up the school, the head meets the parents and the child has a trial day in the relevant class, 'to check that they will fit in socially and academically'.

Exit: To a wide variety of schools, including Francis Holland, Aldenham, Notting Hill and Ealing, Channing, John Lyon, Queen's College, Portland Place and North Bridge House in the private sector, and St Marylebone, Hampstead School and West London Free School in the state sector. Younger children have also gained places at, amongst others, Wetherby Prep, Notting Hill Prep, Bute House and Sunningdale Prep.

Remarks: The New Model School Company (NMS) was set up by Civitas (but is now an independent entity) when research identified a gap in the market for a low-cost chain of not-for-profit independent primary schools. Maple Walk was the first NMS school, starting in a rented room in a sports centre off Ladbroke Grove in 2004 with one teacher, two pupils and school materials stored in a trunk. A year later the fledgling school of a dozen pupils moved to the upper floor of a church hall off Kensal Road. In September 2009 the school – by now with classes up to year 4 – moved to its own purpose-built premises in Harlesden, which have impeccable ecological credentials: a sedum roof, solar panels, a ground source heat pump and a rainwater harvesting system, plus a no-car travel plan. It has added a form each year and now has a full complement of 200 children.

The education is traditional, with reading taught by phonics, French throughout, history taught chronologically. A strong emphasis on politeness and courtesy, with every child shaking their teacher's hand at the beginning and end of the day. The first Ofsted report, written in 2008 when the school was still in temporary accommodation, is surprisingly lukewarm, but the previous head was sanguine about it: 'The weaknesses were mostly to do with paperwork and correct materials. We were able to address the areas they highlighted immediately.' Recent Independent Schools Inspectorate report praises the 'good' teaching standards, 'excellent' personal development and 'outstanding' relationships between parents and school.

Certainly parents are happy. 'They seem to be getting a very good grounding,' said one. 'They have really nice teachers who know the children well.' 'They're doing incredible work,' said another. 'I think it's outstanding.' The head's after-school secondary transfer club introduces exam techniques to older children, and the year 6 class teacher 'is very experienced at secondary transfers'. 'They do their absolute best to make sure they are well prepared,' said a parent.

The school can cope with mild SEN – 'we don't assess children coming into reception, but we do ask parents to be honest and transparent and we may talk to their nursery if we have any concerns'. One-to-one literacy and numeracy assistance at extra cost; some children get speech and language support outside school.

An emphasis on children becoming confident public performers: the annual Craigmyle poetry competition (named for the charitable trust that paid for the new site and building works) involves everyone from reception upwards reciting a poem by heart, and there are public speaking competitions, music concerts and drama performances. 'The children are very confident,' said a parent. 'They have nice manners, they can talk to adults, they look you in the eye.'

The school's outdoor space includes playgrounds for infants and for juniors – with a climbing frame purchased by parents from Ebay – and a football/netball court with climbing wall (also funded by the PTA, Friends of Maple Walk). The gardening club grows vegetables in tiered beds and a butterfly/bee-friendly area is in concept. The children learn to swim at a local pool and try out a different sport each half term. A dance group – 'the youngest by a long stretch' – came third in the Dance Challenge UK national finals at the Cadogan Hall.

'There's a nice, cosy, community feel,' said one. 'I liked the fact that it is small, pioneering and affordable,' said another. 'It's a really vibrant, eclectic community'

This is a low-cost, no-frills school, which depends on plenty of parental involvement. The PTA has raised funds for part-time specialist dance and sports teachers, and parents have donated computers, including a suite of Netbooks that travel round different classrooms. Parents run clubs and help organise book weeks, art extravaganzas – 'delicious organised chaos' – and cultural celebrations. The school is a Christian one, with weekly religious assemblies and nativity plays, but all faiths are welcome and Jewish and Muslim parents come in to talk about their religions.

Despite the low fees, it is still very much a white, middle class demographic – albeit mostly journalists, artists and musicians rather than bankers and lawyers. However the school is building links with the local state primary school just down the road, with shared activities, teacher training, netball and football matches. Now the school has its own settled base in a very diverse area, it hopes to attract a wider social and ethnic mix of families.

Parents cite the 'village school' atmosphere as one of their main reasons for choosing Maple Walk. 'There's a nice, cosy, community feel,' said one. 'I liked the fact that it is small, pioneering and affordable,' said another. 'It's a really vibrant, eclectic community.' Parents emphasise how happy their children are – 'mine will look back and feel they've been part of something really special and exciting'.

Merchant Taylors' School

Sandy Lodge, Northwood, Middlesex HA6 2HT

Independent • Pupils: 890 • Ages: 11–18 • Sixth form pupils: 285 • C of E • Fees: £18,770 pa

Tel: 01923 845514

Email: admissions@mtsn.org.uk
Website: www.mtsn.org.uk

Head Master: Since 2013, Mr Simon Everson MA PGCE, born in Hertfordshire then educated at Solihull School and Cambridge (English) before completing a masters in philosophy at Nottingham. Has taught both in state maintained and independent schools as well as in Japan and was latterly head at Skinners' School in Tunbridge Wells, where he also took over a local failing school, guiding its transformation to academy status. Was adamant that very few schools would tempt him away but couldn't resist the lure back to Herts and MTS, where he took over 'a school with wonderful tradition, but one that's vibrant and relevant now.' Still 'loves the classroom' and 'borrows classes' when time allows. Moved immediately upon appointment to reintroduce significant financial benefits

to scholars, with scholarships for the brightest and most able across the board now worth at least 10 per cent of fees: 'We are determined to seek out excellence and reward it.' Enjoys walking, bird watching, Scotland and is a recently qualified apiarist (beekeeper). An electric guitar sits tucked in the corner of his office – 'I wanted to put myself in the boys' shoes and remember how it feels to struggle to learn something new,' he says. Business-like and sincere. Married to Ginny, a psychotherapist.

Academic matters: A school populated by an intellectually curious and highly motivated cohort. Academic rigour – and ultimately success – is par for the course here but head is clear that they do not want to create a monoculture: 'We reject the philosophy of moulding children into specific types.' Boys inspired by staff who, in head's words, are 'fiercely intelligent – no school is better than the quality of its staff', and are striking to visitors either for their youth, energy and enthusiasm or wit, wisdom and worldliness. Humour and empathy pervade the classrooms, evident as much in the way staff speak to the boys as the quirky touches around the buildings – we've never seen fairy lights or a Ferrari flag in a biology lab in any other school. Dead Poets Society springs to mind more than once on our tour.

Traditional curriculum, not known for any single specialism – boys as likely to read medicine at university as English – and, although one parent said that academically 'it's not for the faint hearted,' school adamant that it's 'not merely a conveyor belt to top results'. 'Exam results are a given,' says school; 'it's about what else they leave with.' Boys take IGCSEs in majority of subjects with consistently outstanding results: 71 per cent of A levels graded A*/A and 92 per cent A*-B in 2015. At GCSE, 86 per cent either A* or A. Flexible setting in maths from year 9 and science from year 10, with some 'banding' in English literature from that point too. 'We tend to separate out the boys who read; the ones who can handle Chaucer and Shakespeare with no problem'. Top half takes maths IGCSE in year 10, with one third also taking French a year early. It's French and Latin in the languages department in years 7 and 8 with the addition of German, Spanish or Greek in year 9, all available at A level. Around 60 per cent take the EPQ. Maths, economics and the sciences top choices at A level with around half the number opting for humanities and English but with no less stellar results. Small numbers for languages – although school still timetables minority subjects such as Greek even for lone students.

School really shows its mettle in university application process and careers advice

Excellent standard of art and DT, which has 'outstanding' teaching, according to parents – MTS has a produced higher number of Arkwright Scholars than any other school since the scheme began in the 1990s. This strength likely to snowball with the 2015 opening of school's cutting edge new DT building. Atmosphere surprisingly relaxed and no sign of the macho testosterone culture that's endemic in so many boys' schools. 'We achieve results by inspiring boys,' says head. Enrichment programme for most able scholars 'turns seamlessly' in Oxbridge preparation.

An electric guitar sits tucked in the corner of his office – 'I wanted to put myself in the boys' shoes and remember how it feels'

Learning support (mild dyslexia, dyscalculia some ASD) viewed in the same way as educating the most able children: 'they just need a slightly different educational experience to everyone else,' although school also quick to point out that even those with individual needs 'must be able to keep up with the pace here.' New SENCo 'with a wealth of experience' recently appointed to monitor and work with specific learning difficulties – but strictly no withdrawal from class. ESL students must be instantly able to access curriculum as are fully immersed from day one. Can accommodate pupils with mobility problems, including wheelchairs.

School really shows its mettle in university application process and careers advice, an area which head says has reached 'Rolls Royce quality.' Parents describe the UCAS application process as 'incredibly well organised', with each sixth former assigned to the head of department of their chosen subject who acts as advisor and referee. Personal references from tutors are the cherry on top of the holistic application process. Boys encouraged to begin thinking about future careers early with a 'World of Work' Day in year 11, plus a joint careers conference with the girls of nearby St Helen's School. OMTs highly visible as mentors to current pupils, who are encouraged to use active database of over 600 old boys willing to offer work experience, and allowed time out of school to pursue such opportunities. A unique 'entrepreneur in residence' runs a start-up business from the DT building to give boys an insight into a world beyond the corporate giants who will doubtless be clamouring for their affections come milk round time.

Games, options, the arts: Sport seen as a hugely important part of the universal education at the heart of the MTS ethos, with sportsmanship and camaraderie as high on the agenda as winning. Part of the strong community feel comes from the whole school, including 80 per cent of the teaching staff, heading out to the (spectacular) sports fields together twice a week. Rugby, hockey and cricket are major sports and although there are varying degrees of success in the former (there was almost a hint of pride in the boy who self-effacingly told us he was in the 'least successful rugby A team on school record'), hockey and cricket are flying increasingly high with victories aplenty, and the fixture list growing annually to encompass more top schools. School boasts over 60 county and five national sportsmen and the U15 cricket team is county champion. This in no small part due to dedicated directors for each major sport (hockey coach is ex-England international), as well as regular visiting coaches; recently the Australian cricket team, who requested that their pre-Ashes tour training take place at MTS. Sport for all – every boy competes for the school as often as is feasible with as much celebration when the 'Super E' rugby team (unbeaten) brings home a victory as the more elite squads.

With over 20 minor sports from riding to kayaking, sailing and golf boys have no excuse not to find something they love. One of our guides was not overly keen on main team sports but was on the first team for fives. Two others were keener on playing electric guitar in their band – but that was seen as valuable too. One or two grumbles about lack of footie until sixth form, but that doesn't stop boys having a good kick around the quad at break times, and school provides goalposts for the purpose. World class facilities include all the usual suspects plus all weather hockey pitches ('better than the Olympic ones,' one keen player assured us), heated indoor pool, athletics track, lakes for sailing and kayaking, squash and fives courts, an assault course and fencing salle.

Endless opportunities to get stuck in outside of the classroom and sports field at lunch times and after school. Every sport imaginable, from sub aqua to cycling, has a society and there's chess, bridge or stamp club for those more inclined towards brain sports. Boys can flex their journalistic muscles by contributing to one of six school magazines or try their hand at societies ranging from the possibly unique dissection society to debating, most of these included in fees. Music and drama 'amazingly active,' says head, with ensembles and choirs galore, including Dixieland, Merchants of Groove and swing band in addition to a host of more traditional offerings. Two major theatrical productions take place each year in the Great Hall, in addition to smaller endeavours and a fiercely fought house drama competition. Parents rave about quality of productions, with recent extravaganzas including Grease. Active CCF (one of the largest in the UK) in conjunction with St Helen's, and D of E schemes offer super opportunities to follow outdoor pursuits and take part in trips to eg Morocco, Canada or Nepal. Huge sense of collective pride in relation to outstanding work with Phab, with funds raised throughout the year and an annual residential care week staffed by senior pupils, who consider it a great honour to be selected to take part.

Copious amount of trips. Rugby and hockey tours to South Africa and Australia and cricket to Barbados. Years 7 and 8 classics trip to Naples,

geography to Iceland and history to Istanbul. Eleven language trips each year and six language exchange programmes across year groups.

Background and atmosphere: Founded in the City of London in 1561 by the Worshipful Company of Merchants, then the largest school in the country. Relocated in 1933 to its current location – a 250 acre site comprising a core of listed art deco buildings plus a host of sympathetically incorporated modern additions set before endless playing fields leading down to a lake that homes countless wildlife species. Visitors greeted by exquisite formal gardens and a handsome fascia. School lacks dreaming spires and turrets but gives an immediate sense of purposefulness and solid endeavour. Some areas (entrance hall, library, politics and economics centre, sixth form common room) more pristine than others but a sense of calm and mutual respect prevails.

'Civilised' a word that comes up again and again, along with a sense of a truly cohesive community spirit. Older boys mentor the younger, the whole school eats together (no exceptions, no packed lunches) and assembles together – 'invaluable', says head. 'We are a corporate body not a disparate group'. There's also a great sense of the traditional juxtaposed with gleaming new facilities – a feeling that a boy who has walked the corridors of MTS would not be remotely overwhelmed walking into an Oxford or Cambridge college for the first time.

Pastoral care and discipline: Discipline 'almost always low profile due to our hugely positive culture,' says school. Boys are not 'spiky' or 'entitled', transgressions rare and bullying almost non-existent ('I couldn't believe how much friendlier it was than my prep school', said one happy boy). Vertical tutor system praised almost unanimously by parents and boys with only a few grumbles relating to tutors moving on to pastures new mentally checking out in advance. For the most part, parents described them as 'almost part of the family', and many keep in contact with former tutees way beyond the A level years. Thriving house system facilitates yet more cross-fertilisation for friendships and opportunities for boys to shine in competitions, with pupils praising weekly house assemblies covering topics from 'the art of small talk' and 'how to tie a bow tie' to rocket building in teams. Plenty of chances for responsibility at the top of the school. Head boy voted in by 50 per cent student vote, supported by 10 elected monitors and a JCR of a further 30 boys. School run on Christian ethos, with services held in chapel and all faiths welcome, but there's also a Muslim prayer room and societies for all main faiths.

Pupils and parents: 'What makes a Merchant Taylors' boy?' we asked. 'Well, we don't really do posh,' came the smiling reply. Our opinion: smart, charming, self-effacing and diverse. Not a hooray Henry in sight or any trace of plums in mouths, but a group of boys wearing their school tie with humility and an awareness of privilege rather than entitlement. Fun to sit with (yes, even year 10s) in the dining room and totally at ease with adult company. Minds of staff and pupils alike on higher things than the tedious minutiae of shiny shoes

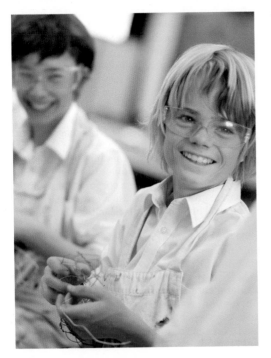

Endless playing fields leading down to a lake that homes countless wildlife species. Visitors greeted by exquisite formal gardens and a handsome fascia

and tidy haircuts obsessed over at so many schools. Head says school is 'always hanging on the coat tails of the pupils' enthusiasm', and keenly supports pupil-led initiatives, most recently a drone club, instigated by one young scientist. Perhaps because around a quarter of boys receive some level of financial assistance, social awareness is a key factor in their all-round pleasantness – 'It just wouldn't be the done thing to crow about wealth or status,' said one parent. 'Many families make huge sacrifices to send their sons here.' School concurs: 'Those from affluent backgrounds wear their wealth lightly'.

A school where three worlds don't so much collide as mesh. A hybrid London/country school with appeal to local, north and west London and Herts/Bucks families. The London crowd loves the spacious campus, laid back feel and multitude of sporting options on offer, especially in comparison to nearby competitors, and those from the shires enjoy the slightly edgier, more worldly feel than they find in schools closer to home. Reflective of local area, around 40 per cent British-Asian, a large Jewish contingent and all other main faiths represented. Wonderfully inclusive – 'there's zero tolerance of racism or homophobia,' boys told us – and although firm friendships are formed on the tube trains and coaches that transport boys in from eg Highgate, St John's Wood and Ealing, plus suburbs from St Albans and Harpenden to Beaconsfield and Gerrards Cross, all reported that new friends are constantly made through tutor groups, form groups which are mixed up each year, subject choices (from year 12 forms are grouped according to A level choices) and activities.

Unlike many secondaries, parents maintain close contact with school, attending events and committees in droves. Head reported around 200 attendees at one of his recent termly parent forums. In turn, school has unique relationship with many OMTs well beyond the A level years, with tutors speaking with deep fondness of past tutees' achievements. Actor and alumnus Riz Ahmed chose MT as the backdrop for one his first movies and Grammy Award winning OMT band Nero (the lead singer read philosophy at Oxford, incidentally) recently returned as the surprise act at leavers' ball. Other famous alumni include Nobel prize-winning medic Sir John Sulston, Lord Coggan (former Archbishop of Canterbury), Sir Alan Duncan and Boris Karloff, as well as a host of others from the worlds of politics, business, sport, the military and the arts.

Entrance: Selective with two main intakes at 11+ and 13+. At 11+ around 380 boys (roughly two-thirds from state primaries) apply for 60 places. At this point, applicants tested in maths, English and verbal reasoning with those delivering the goods on paper invited back for a one-to-one interview ('not as intimidating as it sounds – they always leave with a smile on their face,' says school). Worth remembering that many will be applying for several schools, so not as competitive as it first appears. A further 100 places available at 13+ with fewer applicants (about two to one) for each place but larger hurdles to clear: boys are interviewed first in May/June of year 7 on strength of prep head's report with high fliers offered 'unconditional' places at that point in the expectation that the exam will present no problems. Those offered a 'conditional' place after interview will need to pass every paper in the CE-style exam in January. School clear that parents tutoring boys heavily for the exam 'are not doing them any favours – we're looking for intellectual curiosity, a passion for something, reasoning skills and ways in which boys can make a wider contribution to the school.'

Up to 40 or 50 feeders at 11+, with preps including Radlett Prep, Manor Lodge, Buckingham College, Reddiford and Gayhurst. At 13+ large numbers from St John's, Northwood Prep, Durston House and St Martin's, plus a few each from The Beacon, Davenies, Orley Farm, York House and St Anthony's, amongst others.

Exit: Very little fall out after GCSE. Sixteen to Oxbridge in 2015 with vast majority of remainder to Russell Group universities. London colleges feature highly (particularly Imperial, LSE and UCL) as do Birmingham, Bristol, Durham, Nottingham and Warwick. Very strong numbers to read medicine, economics and engineering but diversity across the board from sports science to English, humanities, law and the occasional one choosing film or drama school over university offers, or heading to university overseas.

Money matters: The old school tie doesn't come into the selection process and school prides itself on staying true to the ethos on which it was founded – to offer an excellent all-round education to boys from all walks of life and offer financial aid to those who would most benefit – these days, around 200 boys at any one time. Academic scholarships awarded to boys who perform particularly well in the entrance papers, with scholars benefiting from an enrichment programme. Up to five major academic scholarships at both 11+ and 13+ worth at least 10 per cent of fees. Also sport, art, drama, DT, music and all-rounder scholarships.

Remarks: A rare breed – a London school with a country feel, offering the best of both worlds to boys from the city and the shires. Sitting coolly around the top of the league tables, seemingly without trying too hard, a testament to teachers who inspire without applying undue pressure. Wonderful breadth of sporting opportunities for both the elite and the enthusiastic. Not the most obvious choice for macho rugby types, or for the parent hoping for their son to leave school with a public school swagger, but for those looking for an environment that actively encourages boys to 'lean in to difficult questions', get involved in enriching activities outside of the classroom, and that values the quirky and erudite, look no further.

Montpelier Primary School

Montpelier Road, Ealing, London W5 2QT

Tel: 020 8997 5855

State • Pupils: 670 • Ages: 4–11

Email: admin@montpelier.ealing.sch.uk
Website: www.montpelierschool.net

Headteacher: Since 2003, Mr Am Rai (40s). BA in sociology, Birmingham Poly, MA in educational management and administration at University of London, Institute of Education. Married, two children. Very experienced head who had already worked in seven London state primaries prior to his arrival at Montpelier. He had been twice seconded to rescue failing schools. And you can see why. He is a man of very clear vision and sound, liberal educational principles. He is highly articulate, straightforward and frank in conversation. In two hours' conversation, we were wearied by no jargon, no pseudo-academic parroting, no political posturing – so refreshing. There is no disguising Mr Rai's confidence and his ambition – both personal and, more overtly, for his pupils. The results are there for all to see. Montpelier's most recent (2012) Ofsted – with only two days' notice – achieved a full house of grade 1s. The children are stimulated, creative, challenged, smiley and rewarded. A very good head.

Entrance: Oversubscribed but high turnover among local international community means occasional places are not uncommon. All managed by Ealing LA and, if you have no special circumstances, you need to live up close and purposeful if you are to get in. And families increasingly swap their large homes in less well provided for bits of the borough for flats round the corner from this school.

Exit: Some leave for local preps at end of year 4. Of the remainder, around 30 per cent go to the local hotshot comprehensive – Drayton Manor HS. Around 15 per cent to Ellen Wilkinson HS – the local girls' comprehensive. The rest either to local RC or CE high schools or to the local independents – Notting Hill and Ealing, St Benedict's, St Augustine's. Increasingly, some to the Tiffins, to Bucks, Berks or Middlesex grammars, to St Paul's Boys' or Girls', Latymer Upper or John Lyon, and some parents even move house after their bright buttons gain places there or at eg Henrietta Barnett. No disaster schools in the area – another good reason for coming here.

Remarks: Sited on a corner of two quiet, tree-lined roads and adjoining a pretty park. The surrounding streets are similarly well-appointed, orderly and solidly middle class – this is suburban bliss,

Super project on Medusa, and another class displayed illustrations of the Lady of Shalott with sensitive use of quotes

though the North Circular grinds along only a couple of hundred yards away. The nearest schools are all independent and, not surprisingly, they are the chosen destinations for a sizeable minority of Montpelier leavers.

Three connected school buildings, and only one – due for renovation – makes the heart sink. The latest is a clever extension housing reception and admin. Infants and reception on ground floor – makes sense. Four playgrounds with good play equipment though not over-provided with soft flooring. Reception classes have integral loos, so no tots trailing down corridors. No overheated classrooms here – though we visited on a dull January morning – and no class feels over full, despite 30 in each and staff. Windows have replaced doors wherever possible – school has a light and open feel. Reception in large classroom with a teacher, a nursery nurse, a student teacher and a teaching assistant. Corner with fresh fruit and drinks available all day for whoever feels inclined. Some 40 per cent bring food from home but the school lunch menu – outside caterers – looked varied and appetising.

Infants' classes full of quiet, concentrated activity – seven or eight things going on in each room – water, measuring, building, weighing, word work, writing etc. Every class has a whiteboard and IT used imaginatively round the school – connecting people and activities and joining things up. Learning legacy boards provide testimony to what has been learned during the term. Monitoring and appraisal embedded into everything – each child has her own targets for the core skills and a list of 'I Can' statements to keep parents abreast of what has been mastered and what still needs to be done. This complemented by the clever use of iPads by teachers who photograph work and load it onto a parents' portal so that latest work can be admired at home.

Lots of imaginative cross-curricular learning: displays everywhere are evidence of lively thinking and teaching. Year 2 work on portraits looked at what portraits can teach us rather than being merely an excuse to draw ourselves. Super project on Medusa – each child had made a 'Wanted' poster with clever text – and another class displayed illustrations of The Lady of Shalott with sensitive use of quotes. Oxford Reading Tree used throughout with built-in encouragement for parental participation and each child has weekly guided reading session to build comprehension skills rather than just skimming speed. A good hall/gym, a nice little library – properly used for lending and reading – two IT suites, art room, and every class has an art week in which they can drop everything else and experience sustained and concentrated work on a project of their own. Unusually strong music – 150+ learn an instrument in or after school – and school provides child care for siblings until 5.00pm to facilitate music activities. Everyone has an afternoon of sport weekly. Not much but better than many.

Remarkable amount of support given to those who need extra help with eg language, writing task or maths. We saw one-to-one sessions and numerous small groups in all available spaces. Also, for those with an SEN to whom – until recent changes in government SEN provision, at least – school

has given exemplary support. And organised time made to equip those who arrive with no English with key words and skills. As socially diverse as any school in the capital. Around 55 per cent speak a language other than English at home – huge range of languages and cultures – among which highest proportions from the Middle East and Japan, then India and various bits of Europe. Families include a lot of 'corporate nomads' ie those with three or five year contracts who may be relocated anywhere on the globe. After-school language (French, Spanish, Arabic, Mandarin) and many other clubs.

The first thing that strikes you on an ordinary school day is how quiet it is and how class after class of 30 diverse children work absorbedly and happily together. In this large, highly organised school – and it is a large primary by any standards – children look relaxed and secure and, even amongst the smallest, there is a sense that school is about learning. Few behavioural problems – jumped on smartly when they occur. Head 'will exclude if a child is spoiling the lives of other children', but no-one excluded for bullying in eight years prior to our visit.

Parental talk of 'the warm community feeling', express gratitude that 'the children are looked after well and are happy,' and pay tribute to the truly multi-cultural ethos – 'all faiths and beliefs are celebrated'. Very active PTA and lots of community activities eg annual international food fair and remarkably effective fundraising summer fête.

Most staff – many are young – highly praised. Head is seen as dynamic and approachable by some and by others as remote and over-protective of his staff. No-one, however, wishes they had sent their children elsewhere, and none would dispute that he has made a stunning success of a school which, before, had been content to be good enough. 'We judge things by the happiness of our children,' asserts head wisely.

Newland House School

32– 34 Waldegrave Park, Twickenham, Middlesex TW1 4TQ

Tel: 020 8865 1305

Independent • Pupils: 410 • Ages: 4–13 • Fees: up to £11,790 pa

Email: admissions@newlandhouse.net
Website: www.newlandhouse.net

37

Headmaster: Since 2010, Mr David Alexander BMus Dip NCOS (50s). Previously head of Norland Place School and Haddon Dene School. Warm, welcoming and with a good sense of humour. Very kind and doesn't have a bad word to say about anybody.

Justifiably proud of his charges. 'Our 13-year-old boys are a delight, as are our 11-year-old girls. I'm very proud to know any of them. I like what the school has done for them.' Parents say, 'What you see is what you get. Pupils and parents respect him but he knows how to laugh too.' Believes one of his main jobs is to steer parents towards the right school for their child: he wants his pupils to be at the top of their game at their senior schools. The children adore him because he's such fun: he is currently keen for the school to buy a boat which can act as a floating classroom on the Thames. Holds a commercial flying licence and commands a reserve RAF squadron at weekends. Mr Alexander selects the head boy and head girl by deciding which pupils he would most like to have lunch with.

Entrance: Over-subscribed – best register your child as soon as possible after birth. Two main points of entry: 4+ and 7+. At 4+ entry is on a first-come, first-served basis, with siblings given priority. Forty places available at this stage (increasing to 60 from 2016) and a waiting list in operation. Once at the pre-prep, a place is guaranteed at the prep school. At 7+ pupils are tested in English and maths. Twenty more places available at this stage, but 7+ entries will be phased out from 2018 in favour of three-form reception entry and school will become non-selective school from this point (mid-year joiners will still have entry assessments).

Academic and music bursaries available – up to 50 per cent of fees, negotiated on a yearly basis. Ten per cent discount for third sibling when all are in school together.

Exit: Predominantly private day schools, including Hampton, St Paul's, KCS Wimbledon, St George's College, Reeds, Surbiton High, Wimbledon High and Lady Eleanor Holles. A couple each year head for boarding schools such as Marlborough and Wellington. Girls leave at 11 and boys at 13. Girls can stay on to 13, but don't. 'It would be a leap of faith' says head. Consistently high number of

Head gives out CE results to boys as they sit around a camp fire in Wales. 'A lovely touch and the boys never forget it'

academic, sports, music and all-rounder scholarships. Head puts this down to outstanding teaching and the fact that the children are in a happy environment and so want to learn.

Remarks: Pre-prep is run by the approachable and calm Tracey Chong. All-female staff ('by coincidence') give it a homely air. Building very tired-looking but a brand new pre-prep is being built on the site, bang next door to the main school, and will open in September 2016. Pupils venture across the road to main school for ICT and games. 'At the moment we're very much one school despite being on two sites, but we look forward to the shared benefits that joining the two schools will bring when we open the doors to our new pre-prep next door to the main school', says head. 'The teachers at Number 11 (the pre-prep) are lovely and smiley and it rubs off on the children,' says one parent.

Classes at the prep are mixed ability, maximum 20 children. Lessons are lively and fast-paced with specialist teachers for PE, art, music and ICT from the start. Separate sciences taught from year 4. Children set for English, French and maths from year 5. Days are long, especially for those who start with the full cooked breakfast on offer at 7.30am.

Once the girls leave at the end of year 6, the boys are placed in two mixed ability classes and one small scholarship set; vacancies left by girls are not filled.

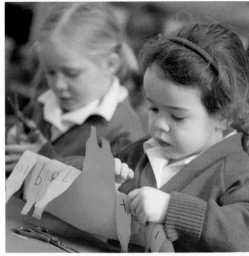

Greek on offer to potential scholars. Parents love the fact that children get so much individual attention at the top of the school. 'A real strength,' said one. Children are well prepared for 11+, 13+ and scholarships. As the head puts it: 'We are a preparatory school. It's our job to prepare them for the exams for entry to their next schools.' Parents report that a massive amount of coaching goes on in the final years, of which the head is critical. 'It's not necessary. We are all fighting a coaching culture but people get sucked into it.' Head gives out CE results to boys as they sit around a camp fire on the year 8 trip to Wales. 'A lovely touch, and the boys never forget it. It's a gesture typical of the school,' says one parent.

Classrooms are spacious and light, with traditional wooden desks arranged in neat rows. Impressive ICT suite, tablets about to be introduced but head keen this shouldn't be a gimmick. The school enters a huge number of national and international competitions with frequent success. Recently won three World Maths Day trophies, out of a total of five awarded to UK schools. DT department is the envy of other schools and recently assembled a car for the Shell Eco-Marathon that achieved a mileage of 1,000 miles per gallon. Currently a group of senior boys is investigating the effect of tyre pressure on the environment and presentations have been made to MPs.

Plenty of choirs for each year group, new pop choir for year 7/8 boys is thriving. Several hundred individual instrumental and singing lessons take place every week. Lots of bands, ensembles and orchestras. Children have recently taken part in performances at the Kingston Music Festival and concerts at the Barbican with the London Symphony Orchestra.

Has retained old fashioned values (pupils call the head 'Sir' and scramble to their feet)

Art clubs include weekend activities where parents can become involved. Local artists exhibit and sell their work in the reception area and include a couple of inexpensive pieces so that children can buy a picture if it catches their eye.

Sport is a real strength of the school. Boys play rugby, football and cricket; girls play netball, rounders and hockey. Swimming, cross-country and athletics also on offer and even more sport possible through numerous after-school clubs, including golf at neighbouring club. Main playing fields are five minutes away by mini-bus; two multi-purpose, all-weather courts and four cricket nets on site. Lots of tournaments and matches mean everyone gets the chance to compete.

Full-time head of SEN. Head believes 'a good learning support culture enhances what you do'. Provision for mild dyslexia, dyspraxia and dyscalculia, though not the place to send a child with severe difficulties.

Many long-serving staff. Head did away with 'teaching' and 'non-teaching' labels when he arrived. 'We're all teaching the children in different ways,' he says. One satisfied parent commented that staff were 'prepared to go the extra mile for the children.' Teachers are lively, good humoured and passionate about their subjects. Two gap year students help with sport and a French assistant teaches conversational French.

Parents are typically hard-working professionals. 'The school reflects the local community and lots of the children arrive at school on foot or by scooter,' says head of pre-prep. Active PTA raises substantial funds, half money raised goes to charity, the other half to the school – recently paid for a climbing wall. Activity-based wraparound club from 7.30am to 6pm.

A competitive, purposeful and demanding school which has retained old fashioned values (the pupils call the head 'Sir' and scramble to their feet when an adult enters the room). Pupils are challenged on all fronts and, as one parent put it, 'By the time the children reach year 5, they are under pressure to perform. It's not a soft school but, for the right child, there simply isn't anywhere better in the area.' One mother felt that 'it's not for the retiring child. I think they'd get trampled underfoot.' The head disagrees and feels the school caters for all personalities and abilities as there is so much on offer and so many chances to shine.

North Ealing Primary School

Pitshanger Lane, Ealing, London W5 1RP

State · Pupils: 695 · Ages: 3–11

Tel: 020 8997 2653

Email: admin@northealing.ealing.sch.uk
Website: www.northealingprimary.co.uk

Head: Since September 2014, Sally Flowers, previously deputy head. She joined the school as assistant head in 2011.

Entrance: Wider catchment area now due to three form entry but pupils still need to live within a mile of the school to get a place.

Exit: Majority go to Brentside High, a few others to Drayton Manor, Ellen Wilkinson, Twyford and Cardinal Wiseman. A handful each year to grammar schools. One third go private – St Augustine's, Latymer, St Benedict's, Notting Hill and Ealing and John Lyon.

Remarks: Hidden away behind the main road, the sunflowers and flower tubs welcomed us in as we walked across the playground to the school entrance. The school is divided into three main areas. Reception and nursery classes are housed in a bright and airy modern building at the back of the site where outdoor classrooms are covered for use in all weathers, allowing free flow back and forth. 'The children are so lucky to have a new building and they love being able to explore inside and outside,' enthused one parent.

Years 1 and 2 are in equally bright classrooms and at the end of their corridor is a dedicated music room. There is also a hall where we observed new reception children doing a movement class. 'Bend knees!'

Children are also separated at play time: nursery, reception and year 1 all have their own separate playgrounds. Years 2, 3 and 4 have the back playground and years 5 and 6 are at the front. The school even has its own garden which backs on to Pitshanger park.

Years 5 and 6 are housed in the old part of the school (100 year old Victorian building). Classes here a bit cramped but bright wall displays, eg a display about the local Brentham estate in Victorian times, make them feel welcoming and warm.

Key stage 2 children are set for maths and we observed an able and talented maths group being taught in the library, preparing for the Primary Maths Challenge. Around a third of year 6 students achieve level 6 in their maths Sats and results in reading and writing are among the best in the borough. 'We saw a great improvement in our reading levels after we introduced guided reading in 2011,' explained the deputy head.

Music and drama are particularly strong, with the school choir taking part in local music festivals. Children can learn the recorder in key stage 2 and there is also the opportunity to study the violin, cello or guitar. Each year the head directs the year 6 production; last year it was Bugsy Malone. 'The standard of the drama is really high, thanks to the head's passion for theatre,' explained one parent.

Sports are also very high profile, with a glass cabinet bulging with cups in the school reception. Netball, football and all the usual sports teams win prizes each year. There are numerous sports clubs before and after school most days.

Very active PTA organises regular quiz nights etc. 'As well as raising money, these events are a great way to meet other parents.'

A competition each week where the school cleaners choose the tidiest class and their prize is to go first at lunch

Hot dinners are cooked on the premises – half the children have school dinners and half bring packed lunches. The school has a healthy eating policy – no sweets or chocolates are allowed in children's lunch boxes. 'We don't check the staff room, though,' quipped the deputy head. Senior staff are on duty at lunch time and there's a staggered system so that no one has to wait too long.

There is also a tidy classroom competition each week where the school cleaners choose the tidiest class and their prize is to go first at lunch.

All the usual EAL, SEN and inclusion provision. Anti-bullying guidelines are adhered to and there is a buddy system where older pupils support younger pupils. Former pupils include Peter Crouch and Honor Blackman.

A very friendly and welcoming local school that achieves excellent results.

North London Collegiate School Junior School

Linked school: North London Collegiate School, 447

Canons, Canons Drive, Edgware, Middlesex HA8 7RJ

Independent • Pupils: 305 • Ages: 4–11 • Fees: £15,642 pa

Tel: 020 8952 1276

Email: office@nlcs.org.uk
Website: www.nlcs.org.uk

15

Head of Junior School: Since 2003, Mrs Jo Newman BEd (50s). An old girl of North London, Mrs Newman read geography and education at Homerton College, Cambridge. After leaving, she dabbled briefly with the idea of retail – 'I love people and I think I would have been equally happy in a number of jobs' – before starting her teaching career at Haberdashers' Aske's Boys' Prep. Deputy head of the NLCS First School, then moved briefly to Spain for her husband's work. On her return, spent three years as head of Channing Junior School. Warm, can-do sort of person, excellent at team building (her last three director of studies have moved on to headships elsewhere) and involving others. Cares passionately about education (part of a recent sabbatical was spent visiting schools in New York) and those in her charge. 'She knows every girl well,' said one mother, 'and really fights for their happiness.' Married to an accountant, with two adult daughters (both of whom attended the school), she spends off-duty moments cooking, visiting the theatre and walking.

Entrance: Some 250 try for 40 places at 4. A first edit establishes whether children have good basic 'pre-school' skills (such as holding a pencil and being able to use it) and takes numbers down to 90. A second evaluates 'learning, listening and following'. 'They look at pictures, play games, engage in conversation.' Reading and writing definitely not required. 'They will not be asked,' says the head firmly. Children assessed carefully in relation to those of the same age. ('There's rarely a month's difference in their assessment groups.') Much time spent, too, working with nurseries to encourage applications. An early refusal does not mean don't ask again. 'We try to get across to parents that, if a child is not ready at 4, please bring them back at 7.' At that point, a further 8-10 places, with about 127 applicants, again assessed in two rounds. 'We want to know what they can do, not what they can't; we'd rather they spelt "enormous" wrong than "big" right.' Also assessments for occasional places for those already registered.

Exit: Virtually all to the senior school. ('We're aiming to provide an all-through education and the expectation is that girls will move up to the senior school.') All sit the entrance test, however: 'Our research shows that it gives them confidence they're as good as those coming from outside.' For one or two this might not be the right route, and parents are advised well in advance. 'The art is to make the right decision for each girl.' Some girls leave to board, a trickle to leading state schools, such as Henrietta Barnett and Watford Grammar School for Girls, but no cramming for entrance tests. 'We prepare them for secondary education not for 11+,' says the head. 'Our aim is to instil a love of learning and a breadth of opportunity.'

Remarks: North London is, as it always has been, an unashamedly academic school, whose aim is 'to enable girls to recognise academic excellence and realise that it's attainable'. This is achieved through outstanding teaching and a holistic approach to learning, not by hot competition. Here the goal is always 'personal best' rather than 'beat your neighbour'.

National curriculum followed throughout, but work often goes well beyond and around it. (In years 2 and 3, for example, girls learn to play chess.) Classes throughout primarily taught by a form teacher, with specialist subject teaching introduced early on. Senior school staff ease final year girls into their prospective home, though the junior school also has its own subject specialists. A medley of foreign languages on offer (Spanish in year 3, German in year 4, Mandarin in year 5, French in year 6) as an introduction to the senior school range.

'Learning habits' (flexibility of mind, empathy, collaboration, resilience, reflectiveness, good judgement, self-assurance, curiosity, focus, risk-taking, persistence, initiative, originality) introduced early and made explicit. Year 6 guides on our trip were fully genned up on the terminology, pointing out their 6-year-old peers in full creative flow ('We're making pop-up sea creatures,' said one year 1. 'It's very creative and very fun,' glossed an older girl).

Homework from the off, with reading and spelling in reception and year 1. Older girls get about 40 minutes. 'It's not all work, work, work,'

Their achievements: an adventure playground, a bird feeder, a poetry competition (with a cup) and a raffle (with the prize of shadowing the head for a day)

said one. 'You don't feel scared or embarrassed if you can't finish.'

Two school libraries, clearly much-loved habitats. Golden Book Oscars awarded for best author, etc, with teachers striding the literary red carpet dressed as Voldemort and other fictional stars. Prominently displayed list of 50 Books to Read Before You Leave Junior School ('I've read 47,' confided one year 6), with 'more mature' literature for the eldest.

Special needs carefully monitored. 'We look out for obvious signs in assessment,' says the head. 'We're very attuned to early identification.' Strong in-school support, led by a SENCo, for those with dyspraxia, etc. 'Every case has a conference.' The site itself works well for those facing physical challenges, and the school has, when required, incorporated additional aids, such as a hearing loop.

Extracurricular – 'the hidden curriculum' – very much the bedrock of a North London education, whatever your age or stage, and girls here are active and energetic participants, whether in the latest theatrical production or music competition. A multitude of after-school clubs (with late transport on offer) ranges from cookery to bridge, and many take a range of three or four activities each week.

Drama important, with an annual play for each year group and a major year 6 extravaganza. 'It feels like a professional play,' said one, 'with costumes and make up.' Over 90 per cent learn one or more musical instruments, with plenty of performance opportunities. (Two all-comers' choirs, plus an auditioned year 5/6/7 choir competing on the international stage.) Games three time a week, plus swimming lessons, plus after-school sports club, plus school teams. 'Squads are very exciting,' said one girl (and perform well against other schools).

Like its senior counterpart, the junior school was founded by the formidable Frances Mary Buss, one of the Victorian era's most dynamic crusaders for women's education. The school originated in Camden Town, but, in 1929, purchased Canons, the former home of the Duke of Chandos. The First School (reception to year 2) opened in 1993. Today, the junior school is housed in its own building, in two separate parts, one for the First School (with its own hall, library, adventure playground and playhouse); the other for years 3-6 (with a science lab, ICT suite and art studio). Girls also make use of the large, leafy grounds, senior school's excellent sports facilities (including pool) and dining hall.

Older girls poised, purposeful and articulate. An encounter with representatives of the junior school council demonstrated school democracy in action. Their aim: 'to improve the school'; their achievements: the introduction of an adventure playground, a bird feeder, a poetry competition (with a cup) and a raffle (with the prize of shadowing the head for a day). Sadly, a motion to supply sushi at lunch fell by the wayside.

Classroom teachers take responsibility for pastoral care, with a not-many-rules policy that stems from the founder. Discipline not really a significant issue. 'No one gets in trouble,' said one girl. 'If we do something wrong, we apologise.' Occasionally, there might be 'a warning' (for 'saying a rude word'), even more rarely parents are notified and the miscreant misses break.

More problematic issues dealt with sensitively, aided by a school counsellor and good communication with parents. 'We don't want little problems to become big problems,' says the head. She herself is very involved, with an 'open-door' policy. Parents kept well informed, with a regular curriculum newsletter, home-school diary ('Today x lost a tooth,' read one, the tooth itself carefully enclosed) and plenty of information evenings. 'Parents can be anxious, and we want to make them feel comfortable.' Parents themselves very proactive: 'All you have to do is mention an exhibition and they trot off to the museum.'

The school runs an extensive coach service importing girls from a large swathe of north and west London and Hertfordshire. Families – from all over the world – often have both parents working (so supervised breakfast and after-school care a godsend.)

A stimulating education, provided in an idyllic setting, producing articulate, confident, enthusiastic girls.

North London Collegiate School

Linked school: North London Collegiate School Junior School, 445

Canons, Canons Drive, Edgware, Middlesex HA8 7RJ

Tel: 020 8952 0912

Independent • Pupils: 770 • Ages: 11–18 • Sixth form pupils: 245 • Fees: £18,507 pa

Email: office@nlcs.org.uk
Website: www.nlcs.org.uk

Headmistress: Since 1997, Bernice McCabe BA MBA FRSA (50s). Mrs McCabe grew up in Bristol, where she was educated at Clifton High School ('What I loved about my school was that it showed me the possibility I could do anything; it was very much modelled on North London') and Bristol University, where she studied English. Taught at a number of co-ed comprehensives in Bristol and London, including The Heathland School in Hounslow, before becoming head of high-flying girls' grammar Chelmsford County High. While here, she took an MBA because she found 'the broader aspects of education leadership' appealing. Her priority, however, now as always, is the quality of teaching. 'The children here are passionate about their subjects because the teachers are also passionate.' She herself continues to take all year 7 for English ('It gives you a fighting chance of knowing everyone') and invites a shifting kaleidoscope of girls weekly to cakes and conversation in her comfortable study. Younger girls are slightly in awe; sixth formers completely at their ease.

Went into teaching because she wanted 'to make a difference', and outside North London has been an energetic participant in the national and international education landscape. A member of the National Curriculum Review Advisory Committee since 2010, in 2013 she was appointed an Expert Advisor for the London Schools Excellence Fund. She also co-directs The Prince's Teaching Institute. Despite this demanding co-curricular schedule, she tries to limit her time on committees. 'The school is my number one priority; it's the most amazing, affirming place to be head of.'

Undoubtedly one of the UK's most glamorous heads, as noted for her fashionable dress sense as her shifting shades of nail varnish, Mrs McCabe may be softly spoken and stylish, but her priorities are clear sighted and she leads a school with the highest aspirations for both girls and staff. Down time (how does she find any?) is spent at the gym, the cinema, painting and gardening.

Academic matters: North London provides an unashamedly ambitious, academic education, consistently sitting in the top five schools nationally in terms of its exams results. In the sixth form, it is one of the rare London schools to offer both the IB and a mixture of A levels and Pre-Us. Virtually all pupils do outstandingly well in all exams. (In 2015, 83 per cent of A levels were graded A* or A, 46 per cent A*; average IB score, 41. Similarly superhuman outcome at GCSE, with 95 per cent A* or A.) The head puts this down primarily to the quality of the teaching: 'We don't teach to the test, we work well beyond it.' Parents agree teaching is 'inspirational'. 'The staff remain stable but are never allowed to get stale.' Girls are expected to (and do) work very hard, with plenty of homework from the off. 'You work as hard as you need to or want to,' said one recent arrival. Research skills are carefully nurtured and girls learn how to address their workload in a disciplined and organised manner.

Post-GCSE, English, history, physics and maths are notably popular. ('No gender bias! Hurrah!' commented one parent.) Modern languages (six on offer including Mandarin, Russian and Italian) and classics are unusually strong, with Latin for all in years 7-9. Traditionally, many took five AS levels, with many keeping a balance of arts and science, but the new A level regime will reduce this to four, with any slack addressed by 'an independent research essay'. Parents praise the school's flexibility in meeting individual interests, particularly in the sixth form. 'There's no pick-one-from-column-A procedure,' said one father. 'They don't mind if only one girl opts for a subject. They're willing to give one-to-one teaching if necessary.' Girls are free to choose what really interests them. 'They'll only query something if they feel a girl is being pushed by her parents or considering a subject which would put her out of contention for certain degrees.' Equally, however, they won't micro-manage any downside once choices have been made. 'No one told us our daughter wasn't very good at history and much better at English, which she was doing as a fifth AS level. We had to fight for her to be allowed to change.'

Eager proto-journalists produced enough journals and publications to stock a newsagent, on topics as diverse as economics to Ebola – not to forget cutting edge 'Wintour'

About 40 pupils have some kind of learning support. All receive an 'individual education plan', with students seen by a SENCo without losing lesson time. Despite its extensive and complex site, the school is also happy to cope with physical disabilities – 'as long as the pupil can communicate and access the curriculum' – working with parents to ensure the right support is in place.

Games, options, the arts: You could never be bored here, though you might end up exhausted. Every possible interest is catered for, from philosophy to animal welfare. Last year, pupils had a choice of 40 clubs and societies, 30 overseas trips and 30 concerts and productions. Actors to the Edinburgh Fringe, musical groups to Tuscany, and eager proto-journalists produced enough journals and publications (50 this year) to stock a newsagent, on topics as diverse as economics to Ebola – not to forget the cutting edge 'Wintour', named after celebrated old girl Anna Wintour, editor of American Vogue. 'We feel it's the extracurricular involvement which helps produce the academic success,' says the head. 'There's something for everyone, something to capture the imagination.' Activities for senior girls take place after school, those for younger ones in the lunch hour. Finding time can still prove a problem. 'Sometimes it's hard to fit it all in,' said a year 8 girl. 'You have to decide.' No doubt, all part of the learning process.

Lacrosse is the dominant sport, though plenty of choice, too, for those not unduly captivated by fresh air and outdoor competition, with a fitness suite, trampolining and dance in a smart new dance 'space'. Well-used and buzzing art department, packed with enthusiasts and a range of high-quality work.

Extensive range of enrichment activities (Duke of Edinburgh's, Model United Nations, debating, Young Enterprise) help develop public-speaking skills and an appreciation of the world elsewhere. The school has a strong international perspective and offers exchange programmes with schools in the USA, Australia and Germany. In 2011, North London opened an overseas campus in South Korea, NLCS Jeju, and students have the opportunity to visit the campus and do internships here. Charity also firmly emphasised, including raising money for and teaching at a school in Zambia and visiting a local school for severely disabled children.

Background and atmosphere: Founded in Camden Town in 1850 by the formidable Frances Mary Buss, a highly effective crusader in the cause of education for women. (She also established Camden School for Girls, with whom North London continues to share a Founder's Day). The school bought its current spacious, 30-acre semi-rural site in 1929 to use as a sports ground, and relocated here fully in 1940. The estate formerly belonged to the 1st Duke of Chandos and, during his time, Handel was composer in residence. The central core of the building is a country house of 1760, now joined by a multitude of varied later additions. Pupils appreciate their attractive surroundings. 'It's so beautiful,' said one. 'When I first came here, I was blown away by the grounds.'

The atmosphere is calm, orderly, and purposeful, and most find it an enjoyable place to be. A recent arrival from the junior school, when asked if she'd thought about alternatives, said, 'I stayed here, because I couldn't see a fault with the school.' Some parents, however, find it quite protective (a good thing or bad, depending on your perspective).

Though the school is academic and fast-paced, it's not pushy. There are no academic rankings or prizes below the sixth form, for example. That said, a girl who doesn't tick along at the same speed could be less content. 'The academic stuff is just baseline,' said one parent. 'They're expected to get involved in clubs, societies, music, sport and community service.' Some also feel that a girl who needs plenty of validation or isn't super confident may occasionally feel swamped. 'I do know people who have pulled their daughter out, though it's usually more about the parents wanting their girls to be top in everything, which is just not going to happen at NLCS.'

Long list of illustrious old girls includes: Judith Weir, Stella Gibbons, Susie Orbach, Marie Stopes, Stevie Smith, Myfanwy Piper, Dame Helen Gardner, Gillian Tett.

Pastoral care and discipline: Girls here are generally industrious and motivated and heavyweight disciplinary issues are rare. 'I can count on the fingers of one hand the number of girls I've had to see about a serious matter in my study,' says the head. Her general approach can be summarized as: 'give girls plenty of freedom, make them engaged and feel valued'; purpose and focus will then follow. It undoubtedly seems to work, and even the youngest here appear remarkably poised and mature.

This is very much an education preparing girls for life as well as exams. The head feels that single-sex education gives them the freedom and security to experiment and develop confidence. Career aspirations are set high and reinforced with photographs of high-flying former pupils ornamenting the corridor walls. 'Our old girls often work in environments of domineering boys from public schools and hold their own,' says the head. 'The school helps give them the courage to do that.' An active alumnae office furthers access to a valuable network. Student voice here is important and heard, with a school council and elected prefects – 'the Big 6' – who play a significant role.

Brown and blue uniform for younger girls, sixth formers can do their own things (big shawls this year's 'look'). Most appear stylish and smart, with few fashion extremes.

Pupils and parents: Mainly cosmopolitan, ambitious, middle-class professionals, many of whom run their own business or work in financial services. Girls come from every conceivable ethnic background (over 50 languages spoken at home), but an increasing number of Europeans (French, Dutch, Russian) and Americans, as well as the traditional high percentage of Asian and Jewish families. An extensive coach service, with long arms stretching out north, south, east and west, makes this a

'We want flair and interests, a decent vocabulary and logical ability'

far from 'local' school. 'The girls reflect the demographic of London,' said one mother.

Entrance: At 11, 65 places for external applicants (joining 40 or so coming up from the junior school). Apply between June and November of the year before entry, with exams in English and maths in January of the year of entry. About 600 apply, with about 200 interviewed. 'We're looking for teachability and girls who will thrive and flourish with the pace of life here,' says the head. 'We want flair and interests, a decent vocabulary and logical ability.' Excellent at establishing whether these qualities exist. 'The interview process is very good,' said one parent. 'It's rare for someone to slip in who isn't suited.' About 20 extra places available at sixth form. Apply between July and November of the year before entry, with tests in four subjects. Occasional places awarded throughout to fill any vacancies, when those already registered will sit appropriate exams.

Exit: Once girls are in, the expectation is that 'we see them all the way through'. A handful move on after GCSE to co-ed or state schools (but a few find the grass greener elsewhere). No-one asked to leave on the basis of exam results. 'They do not cull,' said one mother. 'Even if a girl is struggling, they'll do everything they can to keep her if she is happy.' Almost all get into their first-choice university; with 35 to Oxbridge in 2015 and six to the USA.

Money matters: North London has always prided itself on being affordable and accessible and offers plenty in the way of scholarships and bursaries. Academic scholarships (of up to 50 per cent of the fees) are awarded on the basis of performance in the entrance exams at 11 and 16. Music scholarships at 11 (girls must pass the entrance exam as well as the audition in which grade 5 is generally the expected minimum). Means-tested bursaries (reviewed annually) range from 10-100 per cent of fees and can be awarded in conjunction with scholarships. Bursary funding is partially underwritten by the South Korean franchise, and the school is looking for other projects to further extend these opportunities.

Remarks: An outstanding school for the girl who is quick and hard working and enjoys being busy and involved. Probably not the ideal place for those who might feel the pressure to be 'top' in an environment where everyone is.

North Primary School

Meadow Road, Southall, Middlesex UB1 2JE

State • Pupils: 420 • Ages: 4–11

Tel: 020 8571 7749

Email: admin@north.ealing.sch.uk
Website: www.northprimary.co.uk

Headteacher: Since September 2015, Ms Nicola Forster, previously head of Ryefield Primary in Uxbridge. BA in education and geography and a PGDip in primary education; has extensive teaching experience in various schools across London. She loves to sail small dinghies and regularly goes running to keep fit.

Entrance: Admissions handled by the London borough of Ealing – the usual criteria apply. Main feeder is Grove House Nursery. No one except looked-after children will get into the early years from out of catchment; a waiting list for all years. Key stage 2 applicants may have more luck – entrants (often new arrivals from abroad) in the later years.

Exit: Most go on to Villiers HS, some to Greenford HS, a few to Guru Nanak or Cardinal Wiseman. A handful each year try for the Berkshire grammars or Tiffin schools – around seven or eight get in.

Remarks: We went as sceptics but came away converts – and in love. Twenty-two languages are spoken at home by these children – mostly Punjabi or Gujerati, though significant numbers of Singhalese children and Somalis too. According to social deprivation statistics, school's population is in the top 80 per cent. Also has significant numbers on School Action or School Action Plus, though not huge numbers with many SENs other than EAL. Ninety-eight per cent of pupils speak English as a second language, but English unifies the school and everyone is open and friendly. We were struck by the clear and helpful delivery of the teachers – they mean children to understand, back up their words with helpful body language when needed and everyone learns. We were impressed with every class we went into – and we went into them all.

Sats results are astonishing – especially given this intake and the fact that children come at all stages with little or no English. Everyone except a few SEN pupils reaches level 4 or higher in English – this is extraordinary and is achieved, in part, by determined individual catch up sessions with those who fall behind or arrive with little English. In both science and maths, 90+ per cent get level 4. Large percentages at level 5. This puts it way ahead of comparable schools, both locally and nationally.

Not that it teaches to the test – teaching has to be good from reception onwards, not just year 6. This is a lead school for good practice in EAL provision and the induction process for each new child is meticulous. Has translators and resources in all its main languages and works hard at involving parents. We were touched by the care taken to instruct each new child in, for example, how to ask in English for the loo.

So – a modern, purpose-built jewel in Ealing's crown? Hardly. The core is an 1851 schoolroom, still in remarkable nick and surmounted by the original bell tower, complete with pullable bell chain – still used on special occasions. Later add-ons are solid and functional and make for a well-structured, two-storey building overall. We have yet to see a tidier, cleaner school – everywhere is freshly painted in bright but not garish colours, and we spotted not one piece of litter in our entire visit. Children are proud of their school and it shows. Outside is just tarmac and apparatus, but well marked out for the younger children and reasonably spacious, with railings separating the older children from the tots. Older children have a tarmac football pitch. The school is in a quiet residential nook at the east end of Southall close to an old village green and with some splendid older buildings round about, reminding one of the village this once was.

The little garden is eagerly worked on by the children, who grow vegetables from seed – and then eat the results in the school canteen. Home cooked food a good mix

In every classroom the children were attentive, engaged and absorbed. Every inch of wall space has excellent displays – pupil and teacher-made – all helping to structure and illustrate the work in hand. Everyone can see at a glance what the term's syllabus and aims are in all curriculum areas. Corridor displays on everything from black history to symmetry, musical notation, bridges and forces. Boards for improvement, achievement and attendance encourage everyone. Community project volunteers have provided imaginative murals here and there – we especially liked the Aztec drinking fountains. Excellent new ICT suite is an exciting addition and each class has a whiteboard. Resources are carefully used. The key stage 2 library is better-stocked than those in many senior schools we know and as inviting and orderly as everywhere else in this welcoming, safe-feeling school.

All classes are orderly and inviting. Although a few looked rather crowded and were decidedly too warm. What goes on in them is consistently impressive. Reception and year 1 children work purposefully in small groups but all together in a big sectioned room with teachers and support staff. We enjoyed a year 2 French class taught by a native speaker with a mouth-watering unison recitation of the constituents of une salade. A year 5 class was working on rhetorical questions and a year 6 class writing 'recounts' of events and being given demanding literary objectives – which they seemed to relish. Both key stages have good-sized, airy halls and we warmed to the way children really spoke out in rehearsal of their Easter assembly.

G and T children are well-catered for by a designated teacher, who provides 'challenge boxes' for each class, brings in graduate volunteers and runs a chess club and newspaper club exclusively for these children. Lots of other clubs for everyone.

Most children with SpLD are supported in class. Part-time SENCo and TA will take children individually – some have a differentiated curriculum. An Alexander Technique teacher comes in on occasions. We saw a lesson taken by a supply teacher with an entirely attentive class. Each child is assessed every half term for progress in reading, writing and maths.

Music is big here: won the local Rotary's best ensemble award several years running – their ensemble containing instruments from every bit of the globe is a major investment but at the heart of its ethos. Good ceramics and a collection of musical instruments made from recycled materials which included a beautiful harp. The little garden is eagerly worked on by the children, who grow vegetables from seed – and then eat the results in the school's canteen. The home-cooked food is a good mix of the trad and the healthy – we drooled at fisherman's pie, Asian pasta and chunks of fresh oranges. Parents are helped to continue the healthy eating approach at home and encouraged to involve themselves in all activities. Many do. The school's annual fête – the mela – along with its concerts and shows are huge events, and several parents help in class. Children look good in white shirts, grey trousers and scarlet cardigans.

A model for primaries everywhere.

Northwood College for Girls Junior School (GDST)

Linked school: Northwood College for Girls (GDST), 453

Maxwell Road, Northwood, Middlesex HA6 2YE

Independent · Pupils: 360 · Ages: 3–11 · Fees: up to £12,924 pa

Tel: 01923 825446

Email: admissions@nwc.gdst.net
Website: www.northwoodcollege.co.uk

24

Head of the Junior School: Since 2012, Mrs Hina Thaker, who had previously taught at the school for 10 years. Lives in Stanmore with her husband and teenage son; likes to relax by painting and practising yoga.

Entrance: At 3+ into the nursery via observation and little tasks, ditto at 4+ into reception. Forty-eight places at this stage. At 7, via maths, English, reasoning and interview – up to 10 new places at this stage.

Exit: Nearly all to senior school.

Remarks: Junior school in three buildings on same site as senior school. The early years centre, home to 80 nursery and reception children, is a super building, sensitively conceived and completed. Sensory garden, excellent playground, and lots of lovely touches and thoughtful additions – wellies for rainy days, masses of well-integrated IT, colourful toys, space, cookery, a beautiful library. We loved the collage on the life cycle of a hen and the display about the Philosophy Bear who 'likes to look at things carefully and ask questions'. Years 1 and 2 in Vincent House, 3 and 4 in junior school – both attractive, small scale houses. All safe, well-maintained, full of impeccable and attractive displays. Parents are thrilled – 'My daughter was so shy – they've really brought her out. They're so caring and nurturing'; 'They take the child and encourage her to be the best she can, but according to their own character – they don't have to fit a mould'.

School is pioneering 'thinking skills' and approaches this seriously from nursery onwards via 'cognitive development programme', plus f/t director to coordinate it. We were seriously impressed – junior school pupils feel empowered and the

results are tangible. School held a recent Dragons' Den event – with high profile 'dragons' – and even juniors' projects were taken seriously.

Girls – many from British Asian families, with a moveable contingent from local NATO base – venture out into college grounds for science experiments and maths trials; they tap dance, play chess, learn k-kwon-do or do speech and drama. Food exceptional – home-made soups and yogurts, lots of fresh everything; everyone above nursery eats school lunch, which is included in the fee.

Northwood College for Girls (GDST)

Linked school: Northwood College for Girls Junior School (GDST), 452

Maxwell Road, Northwood, Middlesex HA6 2YE

Tel: 01923 825446

25

Independent · Pupils: 565 · Ages: 11–18 · Sixth form pupils: 155 · Fees: up to £15,636 pa

Email: admissions@nwc.gdst.net
Website: www.northwoodcollege.co.uk

Head Mistress: Since January 2009, Miss Jacqualyn Pain MA MA MBA PGCE NPQH (50s), a theology and philosophy graduate and a most experienced head. Two previous headships, both impressive – Henrietta Barnett and St Albans High – prior to which she'd been deputy head at Northwood. She'd had no intention of leaving St Albans until Mrs Ruth Mercer, her predecessor at Northwood College,

was appointed to the headship of Godolphin & Latymer. Miss Pain, who believed 'so strongly in the ethos of the school – that it does so well by every kind of girl' – couldn't resist coming back and is a round peg in a spherical hole, if ever we saw one. 'The school has changed, of course,' she admits cheerfully, 'because schools must move on, but the underlying principles are the same and I passionately believe in them.'

Highly competent, understated, relaxed, elegant and popular, she is quietly but enthusiastically building on the energetic modernisation initiated by Mrs Mercer. She likes cats and chocolate. Northwood College for Girls, too long the unsung school in this well provided for part of the world, is lucky to have her.

Academic matters: Takes a spread of ability – but well above the national average. Value-added very strong here so you should achieve your potential, whatever it is, and not feel pressured while you do it. Your 10 A*s pupil happily coexists with your artsy, mathematical struggler and both feel good about themselves. This is very much the Northwood ethos and the one Miss Pain was keen to come back to and strengthen.

At GCSE, all take two Englishes, maths, a language, three sciences; options include art, classical civilisation, drama, Latin and Greek, home economics, RE and textiles. RE is the star subject – taken by most with exemplary results; maths (IGCSE) and English pretty good too. 2015 results saw 68 per cent of subjects taken achieve A*/A. At A level, maths, economics and RE impress. Maths, the sciences and psychology are popular. Tiny numbers for history and English (though good results), reflecting the science orientation and aspirations of the school's current core constituency. The same is true for languages, but scope for new-ish HoD (a French and Mandarin specialist) to boost numbers and broaden curriculum. Much to be done here, especially in increasing the uptake at A level of a broader range of subjects – parents as well as girls will need to be convinced – and the school, in fact, offers an admirable range. In 2015, 77 per cent A*/B grades and 44 per cent A*/A.

Most mild SENs managed in lessons with occasional extra temporary support and withdrawals. Can cope with mild ADHD and Asperger's along with dyses. Older parts of site not really set up to accommodate serious motor difficulties, though will adapt where possible.

Boys long since gone, but touching tribute paid to their presence – especially to those who went on to fight and fall in the two wars

School is pioneering 'thinking skills' and they approach this seriously from nursery to sixth form via 'cognitive development programme', plus f/t director to coordinate it. We were seriously impressed – junior school pupils feel empowered and the results are tangible. School held a recent Dragons' Den event – with high profile 'dragons' – and even juniors' projects were taken seriously, to the extent of possible commissions from the commercial world outside. Clever stuff, integral to the overall ethos of the place and a real selling point.

Games, options, the arts: It's got the lot – in miniature, in some cases. Yer actual sports hall, of course, plus 25m pool –and everyone swims all year. Pitches and courts abut the main campus and most girls are keen. Some parental feeling that more effort is needed and girls should be pushed harder. Performing arts centre cleverly shoehorned in, and now providing good drama studio, range of music teaching/practice rooms and much-used recital room. No room here for grand theatre or concert hall, but assembly hall does as well and, though hardly glitzy, has all a good school needs. Art is enthusiastic – painting, modelling, textiles, principally. Music likewise, enthusiastic – 50-strong orchestra, jazz bands and lots of fun had in staging productions – more Oliver! than Othello. Forty-nine page booklet details all the extracurricular activities from the physical (trampolining, badminton etc) to the cerebral (think club, puzzle club, chess) to the fun (book club, bridge, life drawing etc etc) – good stuff. 'Fabulous' trips – 'we went to Brazil for a month on World Challenge' – and closer to home, eg Regent's Park theatre, and good in-school events, eg African drumming evening.

Background and atmosphere: Founded in 1878 in Endsleigh Gardens, Bloomsbury, with around 25 boarders and a few day girls. Headmistress, Miss Buchan-Smith, who had modern ideas about the importance of the extracurricular as well as the curricular, and was concerned about the unsavoury influence of the Euston area on her girls, moved the school to Northwood in 1893. Interestingly, this area – now leafy, prosperous and safe as £1m+ houses can be – was, in 1871, described as 'a destitute district near Moor Park'. But the coming of the tube, a few years later, changed all that and made Northwood a jolly useful commutable suburb, which it remains. In 1893, the present, late arts 'n' crafts red-brick with leaded lights building was opened for 20 boarders and two day girls; the next door Briary accommodated little boys. Boys long since gone, but touching tribute paid to their presence – especially to those who went on to fight and fall in the two wars: school still lays an annual wreath at Ypres.

More land has been acquired, more buildings built and the school is now a nest of attractive, disparate edifices, centred on a couple of tennis courts, which make a kind of quad. To the side of the school are the pitches and playing fields – the overall feeling is one of a slightly crowded campus made up of pleasant, purpose-built or acquired blocks forming a cosy community. Despite the somewhat cramped feeling, it is a surprise, in a quiet residential street, to find it there at all. The latest additions – the early years centre and the performing arts block – are notable assets, in terms both of their additional provision and imaginative design, which cannot, here as elsewhere, be said for the few, lesser, 1960s architectural indiscretions.

Cosy, civilised library in old, converted, vaulted gym. Excellent string of sixth form studies – each shared by five/six girls – for private work in free periods (boarding ended in 1990). Exemplary displays everywhere. Good dining room, cafeteria system, food exceptional – home-made soups and yoghurts, lots of fresh everything; everyone above nursery eats school lunch, which is included in the fee. A formal partnership with the nearby John Lyon boys' school enables collaboration on curricular and extracurricular matters, to the considerable benefit of both communities – a sensible and enlightened move begun by Mrs Mercer and Kevin Riley, former head of John Lyon, and continued by its current head, Katherine Haynes.

Part of the Girls' Day School Trust (GDST) since November 2013 and combined with Heathfield School for Girls in September 2014. A most unusual move – it is rare for schools to join the GDST family, although Heathfield was acquired by the Trust in 1987. The school is continuing with the same head on the same site and all Heathfield girls were promised places – requiring ingenuity and creativity as the Northwood College for Girls site is not generously endowed with space. But we are promised exciting and imaginative developments and will watch with interest.

Pastoral care and discipline: Year heads and form tutors handle most pastoral matters. Tutor changes annually. Discipline seldom a problem here – one minor recent drugs incident. Girls feel involved in decisions – 'Miss Pain really wants to hear from us – our ideas about what can be improved,' we heard. 'The girls do as well as they do here because of the way we nurture them,' says Miss Pain, and parents concur. Overall sense of a relaxed, orderly community in which little disturbs and everything encourages.

Pupils and parents: As you'd expect in this cosmopolitan, well-heeled suburb: majority are British Asians – mostly Hindus – and Christians and sprinklings of everyone else. Little need for EAL. Contingent from local NATO base makes for movement in and out and enriches the mix. Five extensive coach routes bring in girls from Ealing, Edgware, Kenton, Gerrards Cross and Radlett. Proximity to the Metropolitan line makes tubing it easy. Sense of community, and devoted parents from all backgrounds pitching in to support. Former notable pupils include judge Dame Margaret Booth and actress Sue Holderness.

Entrance: At 11, via the exams set by the North London Consortium, to which the school belongs, plus online test and group interview – 30 places. One out of three girls who apply usually gains a place, many off the waiting list.

At 16, conditional on GCSE results, plus online test and interview – 20 places. Occasional places do occur in other years – particularly on account of NATO personnel coming and going, so always worth a call. 'We're looking for girls who will fit into the school,' says Miss Pain. 'We're academically selective but not narrowly exclusive – we want people who will benefit from an all-round, holistic education.'

Exit: Nearly all stay on to sixth form. Majority go to a range of Russell Group and newer universities; one to Oxford in 2015. School produces an extraordinary number of pharmacists and a good number of dentists; otherwise anything from art to retail, English to – well, pharmacy.

Money matters: A few means-tested bursaries – up to full fees. Also scholarships for academics, art, music and sport.

Remarks: The parents have it: 'My daughter has been given opportunities and she's flourishing'; 'Northwood has given my daughters so many opportunities'; 'It was the best decision we ever made'.

Notting Hill and Ealing High School Junior School

Linked school: Notting Hill and Ealing High School, 458

26 St Stephen's Road, London W13 8HH

Independent • Pupils: 312 • Ages: 4–11 • Fees: £12,849 pa

Tel: 020 8799 8484

Email: enquiries@nhehs.gdst.net
Website: www.nhehs.gdst.net

8

Headmistress: Since September 2013, Mrs Silvana Silva BEd (40s). Previously deputy head for 11 years. Married with one son (reading chemistry at Warwick). Has been at NHEHS since arriving in 1989 as a young teacher, has 'absolutely loved every minute' and worked her way up the ranks. She covered the previous head's maternity leave confidently and with complete success. Well known to pupils and parents and completely committed to the school and to each girl's individual success and happiness. The school's open door policy, approachability and sympathetic ear to concerns seem in safe hands here.

Comfortable with the GDST ethos. Clear educational vision – 'our job is to spark an interest in learning,' she says. Wholly committed to single sex education. 'Girls tend to have low self-esteem and aren't risk takers,' she says, determined to inspire them with confidence and encourage them to learn interactively and independently. A great rôle model for budding young girls.

Entrance: Heavily oversubscribed and fiercely competitive – about 100 applicants for 40 places. Assessed just before fourth birthday – three staff will work with four children for an hour and half. 'We want to see how they play and how they interact. We're looking for inner confidence and self assurance,' says the head. 'It's not about knowing your ABC or how to count to 2,000 – we can teach them that.' Very flexible before assessment – will reschedule for illness; takes into account what a child's previous experience has been. But no budging after assessment and no sibling policy – it was the talk of Ealing when a child with four older sisters who had been through the school was refused a place. At year 3 (age 7) eight places and usually 30+ applicants. They sit papers in English, maths and verbal reasoning, plus interview for those who have done well enough. Other than these two entrance points it's very rare for an occasional place to come up, but it does happen.

Exit: Almost all to senior school – informed in year 5 if eligible, then do exam in January of year 6, primarily for the purpose of setting in senior school and to award academic and music scholarships (usually a handful of these). Help is given to the (very) few who are not up to it (these will normally have left at 7 anyway) – they are placed at, eg, Heathfield and Northwood College. Tiny few to St Paul's or Latymer Upper – tends to be for a specific reason – eg proximity to home or availability of scholarships.

Remarks: All the hallmarks of a GDST – excellent delivery of the curriculum, thorough assessment of children, down to earth professional parents. Bright spacious classrooms – lots of windows and impressive displays in corridors as well as in classrooms, some of the best (and most genuine) we've

---

'We want to see how they play and interact. We're looking for inner confidence and self assurance. It's not about knowing your ABC or how to count to 2,000'

seen. Large playground with imaginative places to sit and to play – gazebo with benches, round tables and chairs, assault course, springy colourful tarmac and netball hoops. Separate playground for reception where the little ones can spill out to play with sand, Wendy house and puppet theatre. Funky lavatories decorated in bright girly colours – lots of pinks and purples reminiscent of a Vue cinema. The senior school is 100 yards to the rear, younger girls share their swimming pool, netball courts and dining room and perform the odd concert in the

grand West Wing auditorium, but otherwise it's a separate entity.

Always near the top in the league tables. Wouldn't suit a child that isn't up to it academically: if she can't keep up she may find herself excluded – even in the playground, reports one parent. (School surprised at these reports and keen to deny them.) Year 1 class teacher doubles up as SENCo – a few on the dys–strata and some with mild Asperger's. They can have extra help at a cost – not the school to send your daughter if she has serious learning difficulties. As for the gifted and talented, 'all girls here would be given that label,' says the head – and she clearly knows. The particularly brilliant (about four in each class) are catered for with differentiation and extension exercises – 'it helps that they can bounce off each other'. Mandarin, formerly an extracurricular option, is now a timetabled subject from year 3 and there are plans to introduce it for years 1 and 2.

Good discipline and pastoral care. Girls are taught right from the beginning to wait their turn and to respect others, but do have fun and are encouraged to participate. Our guide proudly related the teaching behind the catch words, THINK ('Is it truthful, is it helpful, is it inspiring, is it necessary, is it kind? If not, don't say it') and TAG (tell person how you're feeling, ask them to stop, get help from an adult). It clearly sticks.

You can do almost anything from chess to yoga and gardening in spare time but the music is particularly strong. Ninety per cent of girls learn a musical instrument, one third of the school is in the main orchestra. Impressive carol concerts in St Barnabas. Larks and tone deaf given equal attention – the hugely committed head of music holds 8am sessions in the week for the enthusiasts, of which many.

Most parents working professionals – ladies who lunch thin on the ground. Children of BBC types, lawyers and doctors come mainly from the local area, but a fair number prepared to travel the distance from Shepherd's Bush and Ruislip – determined to get their daughter an excellent education from 4 to 18.

If your daughter wants to work hard and play hard, this is an excellent choice.

Notting Hill and Ealing High School

Linked school: Notting Hill and Ealing High School Junior School, 456

---

2 Cleveland Road, London W13 8AX

Independent • Pupils: 595 • Ages: 11–18 • Sixth form pupils: 150 • Fees: £16,521 pa

Tel: 020 8799 8400

Email: enquiries@nhehs.gdst.net
Website: www.nhehs.gdst.net

Head: Since 2008, Ms Lucinda Hunt BSc ARCS PGCE (Oxon) (40s). Formerly deputy head at St Paul's Girls, read physics at Imperial. Striking, clear-sighted and determined, enjoying a meteoric career in education with a year's secondment at Goldman Sachs to boot. Working in a bank reinforced her appetite for teaching – 'when profit is the motivator the bottom line is that it's dull'. In the early years of her career she taught science, maths and geology in Australia and France. Well versed in the ethos of GDST (and very happy with it) – a period at Putney High and eight years at Wimbledon High, where she rose to head of sixth form.

'I'm not afraid to rock the boat if it needs rocking,' declares Ms Hunt, but adds that she is no Hazel Blears and will only make changes that are needed. Quick as a flash, she has fearlessly cut swathes

through the existing management structure. At the same time she is well tuned to the relatively gentle spirit of the place – 'that indefinable quality that makes a school different from the others, despite the fact that we all say the same sort of things,' she explains. One of her aims is to open up the windows and doors – 'at the moment not enough people know what we're about'. Parents agree and some comment on poor communication about the day to day. She starts with her own door which, unlike that of her predecessor, is always open to staff and pupils alike. The best thing about the job is the 'wry, intelligent' girls, she says, despite the fact that she doesn't teach any. The energy that she brings to the place is tangible. Here's someone whose influence is restoring the school to its former status as one of the best girls' schools in west London.

Academic matters: At GCSE in 2015, 90 per cent of results were A*/A while at A level 64 per cent were A*/A and 87 per cent A*/B. This is a very high level of achievement indeed. Subjects taught are wide ranging, including philosophy of religion and ethics, and psychology. Maths and geography strong. Chemistry and biology also popular as well as drama, history and English. Year 12s choose a general studies option, which can range from jewellery making or music technology to Russian, Mandarin or Ancient Greek. Mandarin compulsory in year 7, which they learn alongside a European language, and also available up to A level. Class sizes large for an independent school – maximum 30 in years 7-9, average 22 in years 10-11. A lot of young teaching blood – Ms Hunt asserts the usual turnover you would expect in every London school. Twenty per cent have been at the school for more than 10 years, one third men. Pupils speak of the commitment of the staff and generally feel well supported.

Enjoying a meteoric career in education. Working in a bank reinforced her appetite for teaching – 'when profit is the motivator the bottom line is that it's dull'

Ms Hunt reluctant to be drawn into specific learning difficulties – wary of labeling, she explains – but five to 10 per cent of children are eligible to have extra time in exams and school is becoming more adept at identifying who should be screened. The SEN teacher will go into lessons to work with individuals. No extra charge for any extra support. School proud of its success with one girl with serious visual impairment who went on to read English at Durham University. 'The term "gifted and talented" could describe almost every girl in the school,' says Ms Hunt. These are catered for with the various activities that take place during the school week including whole school assemblies. Parents praise an inclusive approach to academics – girls in lower sets are not ignored as 'dunces'.

Games, options, the arts: As with most suburban schools, space has always been at a premium, and this school now has little outside space. In September 2013, however, it unveiled a massive and beautiful new building at its heart which includes a huge, subterranean sports hall, big hall for assemblies and concerts, good-sized studio theatre and large dance studio. Four Astroturf pitches, swimming pool and tennis and netball courts also on site.

For hockey, rounders and athletics girls can run or be bussed to nearby sports grounds. Not known, hitherto, for its sporting achievements – 'but girls get plenty of physical activity,' one parent told us and the new build looks set to transform opportunities. Mutterings among some that if their daughter is not in the tennis team they are left to play among themselves. Ms Hunt keen to introduce some less conventional individual sports for which you 'don't have to get undressed (so many girls just prefer not to)' – fencing currently riding a wave of enthusiasm; other innovations may follow.

Drama jolly good fun. Music well provided for – orchestras, choirs and ensemble groups, with about half the school playing a musical instrument; school will accommodate the few who want to do it at A level. The choir has performed in Tuscany, Venice and New York. Plenty of trips abroad for the non-musical too – recent trips have included a classics expedition to Rome, an art history trip to the museums and galleries of New York, geographers to Barcelona and Iceland, history trips to Russia, Germany and the battlefields of northern France, physicists to Cern and a sixth form trip to China led by the economics department. French students go to Paris and Spanish ones to Andalucia. Lots of enthusiasm for debating – whether it be competing against other schools in debating competitions or Model United Nations events. Duke of Edinburgh awards – most girls take bronze, over a third take silver and a thriving gold award group in the sixth.

Background and atmosphere: Founded in 1873 – the oldest of the Girls' Day School Trust schools. Moved from Notting Hill to its present site in a large house (grand entrance with columns) in a broad Ealing residential avenue in 1931 and a number of features of the original building moved with it.

People we spoke to commented, rather blandly, on the warmth and friendliness of the school: Ms Hunt attributes this partly to the intimacy created by the leafy central quadrangle that connects the old with the new – lots of meeting and greeting as girls pass each other on stairs. Refurbished and much extended dining room with a bright, airy feel and plenty of space.

Newish sixth form centre in a separate building on the south west corner of the main site – a listed modernist building that had been a children's home, lying empty since 2006. It was gutted and converted into a bright, modern, airy building with seminar rooms, common room (with the obligatory leather sofas), multigym, café and outside terrace.

Strong community sense around this school – current pupils often the daughters or grand-daughters of Old Girls and their annual OG bash always a sell-out.

Pastoral care and discipline: Girls are noticeably well behaved around the school – some of the quietest entrances in and out of assembly that we have seen anywhere. Head acknowledges instances of bullying (a good sign – it's the ones who deny any at all that one has to look out for). New area of concern, not just here, is the opportunity for students to use cyber space to make each others' lives difficult. Ms Hunt well aware of this and ready to take on the challenge. With her modern, forward-thinking approach, if anyone born in the early '60s can meet that challenge, she is your woman. A few worrying reports from parents about having nobody to go to talk to about pastoral issues ('Don't want to be nuisance and worry the head – she's got enough on her plate'), but encouraging signs that school is on to this and attempts are being made to plug the gap.

Not so pressured as their contemporaries in more central schools – they can work hard without being cowed by expectation and league tables

Pupils and parents: Families more modest than you would find at most London independent schools – typical GDST parents: professional, ambitious, looking for value for money but not prepared to compromise on their daughters' education. It's a local school – but some come from as far as Richmond, Perivale, Harrow and Greenford to the west and Notting Hill to the east. Cosmopolitan (particularly Asian), community – reflective of the local area. Lots of doctors and dentists, chartered surveyors, but creative types too – record producers, fashion journalists, business consultants. A wide range, ethnically, culturally and economically.

We saw lots of initiative – girls writing scores for musicals, scripts for witty renditions of the Theseus myth and amusing dance routines for mythical monsters

Girls here are focused but enjoying life. Not so pressured as their contemporaries in more central schools – they can work hard without being cowed by expectation and league tables. We saw lots of initiative – girls writing scores for musicals, scripts for witty renditions of the Theseus and Ariadne myth and choreographing amusing Michael Jackson dance routines for mythical monsters. They emerge articulate and confident, full of west London sophistication, but without the trendy, street-wise demeanour characteristic of their peers in more high profile schools in west London. OGs include Angela Rumbold, writer and TV presenter Bettany Hughes, BBC children's presenter Angellica Bell and Blue Peter's Konnie Huq.

Entrance: Competitive consortium examination in maths and English plus interview. About half come up from the junior school, the rest from west London state and independent schools. Most go on to the sixth form. External sixth form applicants have interviews in their potential A level subjects and sit a general paper; They are expected to have obtained A*/A grades in their chosen A Level subjects, with A or above in the majority of their other GCSEs. For the occasional place in the senior school girls are tested according to their age and stage.

Exit: Now losing far fewer after GCSE. Why go elsewhere with these results and facilities? A lot read sciences – and not just medicine. History, politics and English are also popular. Birmingham, Bristol, Durham and Edinburgh favourites at the moment; none to Oxbridge in 2015.

Remarks: A well run, efficient GDST school that does exactly what it says on the tin. Your daughter will get a very good, balanced education here. Oversubscribed, and no longer in the shade of other schools of its kind. The dynamic Ms Hunt has been busily making the school her own – without altering the relatively relaxed, down to earth friendliness of the place.

Orley Farm School

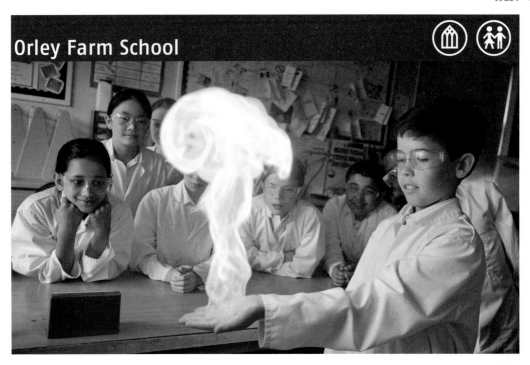

South Hill Avenue, Harrow, Middlesex HA1 3NU

Tel: 020 8869 7600

Independent • Pupils: 490 • Ages: 4–13 • Fees: up to £14,811 pa

Email: office@orleyfarm.harrow.sch.uk
Website: www.orleyfarm.harrow.sch.uk

Headmaster: Since February 2013, Mr Tim Calvey, previously an art teacher and propelled from the deputy headship at a moment's notice after the abrupt and bizarre resignation of Mr Mark Dunning, who had been an unexceptionable head for seven years. Mr Dunning left after what the school described as an 'error of judgement'. Evidently, after some years' attrition with a departing member of staff, Mr Dunning expressed his feelings, weakly disguised in an acrostic-style sentence, in a newsletter to parents. Nothing has got Harrow and Sudbury buzzing quite so loud since the young Lord Byron led a revolt against the headmaster at the place up the hill.

Entrance: Virtually all enter at 4 though occasional other places crop up – more since the recession. From 40+ nurseries and none. Some 165 applicants for 60 places. Good-sized entry again at 11+ when the girls and some boys leave – around 30 applicants for 13 or so places. School keeps waiting lists at all stages. Assessment via observed activities and games – all age-appropriate. School confident that the process picks out those for whom Orley will work; later tests (parents say there are lots) attest to this – 'we know what is expected of an Orley Farm

pupil and we want the children to be happy. We'd be doing them a great disservice if we took them and they couldn't cope with, enjoy and flourish in the life we have here'. Pupils concur. 'You do need to have a natural drive and everyone is really trying to push themselves,' one young man told us. 'We all want to succeed.'

Exit: Breadth again – to a creditable range of schools and many scholarships. Boys to Aldenham, Berkhampsted, Charterhouse, City of London, Eton, Haberdashers' Aske's, Haileybury, Hampton, Harrow, John Lyon, Merchant Taylors', Mill Hill, Radley, Radnor House, Rugby, St Benedict's, St Paul's, UCS, Westminster. Girls to Aldenham, Belmont, Francis Holland, Godolphin and Latymer, Haberdashers' Aske's, Haileybury, Henrietta Barnet, Notting Hill and Ealing, Kew House, Lady Eleanor Holles, North London Collegiate, Northwood College, Royal Masonic, South Hampstead High, St Augustine's, St Margaret's Bushey, St Helen's, St Mary's Calne, St Paul's Girls', Tiffin.

Remarks: You won't find a parent or a pupil who doesn't think the options and opportunities here are outstanding. The teachers, likewise, are warmly praised – 'our teachers are interactive,' an earnest year 8 boy told us. 'They don't act as "teachers" – superior: they're there to help you.' 'The school is very good at finding out what you're good at and helping you get better at it,' another affirmed.

Broad academic curriculum, all heading for 11+ for girls and 13+ for boys, though one or two girls are to be found in years 7 and 8 – either joiners or stayers. French and Latin for all and Greek comes in as a taster for the soon-to-be leavers. Twenty children per class and fewer in sets for maths and English. Specialist subject teachers in music, drama, ICT and PE from pre-prep up and for science, French and Latin later. Previous head doubled the number of classroom assistants, all of whom support English and maths. Some sense among parents of the less able that they have to really push themselves to keep up – witness one remark worth quoting from a year 6 boy: 'We were given an IGCSE maths paper – it was an insult to my intelligence'.

Full-time learning support teacher plus part-timers assist those who need it – mostly mild dyslexics. All support given in class or in small groups elsewhere. Eighty pupils on learning support register at time of our visit – 45 on school action plus. Not an easy school for those with mobility problems – very narrow corridors and up and down site. Outside tutoring is common – not because of deficiencies in the school's provision: more likely to support English when the home language is something else or because life is very full-on at Orley and the quieter ones may just need that bit of one-to-one to boost confidence. So parents feel, anyway.

All do DT and art – good studios for both. We were especially impressed by the range and quality – real imaginative breadth and care in execution

Expeditions week a big thing – from mid-Wales mountaineering to 'total immersion' in a château. Wildly popular

too. Lovely models of early airplanes, Masai shields, mosaic tiles and more. Displays changed termly and with respect for the work. Carousel system for these subjects and some pupil grouses that not enough time to complete DT projects before you have to move to your art term, but with so much on offer and different curriculum requirements it's easy to see why some things have to give. Drama – previously limp – now burgeoning under much-lauded new teacher and productions clearly zing. Music a jewel in Orley's crown – 90+ per cent learn at least one instrument, the concerts cause grown men to weep with joy and music scholarships abound.

Privileged sports – can any prep in a London borough claim such riches? Forty acres, gym and sports hall, pool and Astroturf and far more on offer than in most London preps. Sports praised by everyone – the only problem being that Orley is big enough to field C, D and E teams, but they'd have no-one to play against. It's hard cheese for the also-rans and some complaints that the less than starry don't have such a good time. Expeditions week is a big thing here – a regular annual programme which takes everyone from year 3s up out everywhere, from mid-Wales mountaineering to 'total immersion' in a château. Wildly popular – and included in the fees. Plus tours and trips of all kinds everywhere – the optional trips taken in the holidays can be very expensive if your child is keen but your pocket isn't.

Orley, again unusually, has a purpose-built home – an attractive, two/three storey long red-brick house nestling at the foot of Harrow-on-the-Hill, all quiet leafiness and shady detached residences. It began in 1850, in two houses, one of which was the model for Trollope's Orley Farm, so the school was named after that. The aim was to prepare boys for the big school up the hill. By the turn of the century the school had outgrown the old house so a new one was commissioned, and in 1901 the present building was proudly opened. Its first head was 47 years in post. Since then it has grown and four buildings now surround the central quad, providing excellent sports, arts and teaching provision. The main building – with its top floor all narrow corridors and very reminiscent still of the boarding that went, finally, in 1984 – is all good-sized rooms, well-supplied and organised. Three libraries – stocked mostly with fiction. Pre-prep rooms all have integral loos and cloakroom.

New dining room with very appetizing food – eaten by all. Breakfast club from 7.45am. Lots of pretty gardens and outside space with adventure playground and play equipment. It looks and feels like a well-appointed village school. £11m refurbishment programme ongoing.

Thriving house system – pupils like it as they get to know all year groups and school encourages this (older children escort younger ones hither and yon and help with reading etc). 'It's like a very, very, very, very big family,' said one girl. Any problems to the form teacher – 'The teachers are very good at helping you if you are new. You're assigned a partner to look after you, and they do.' Classrooms all quietly buzzing when we visited – not all silent, thankfully, but purposeful and a sense of self-control at work rather than teacher-control. We heard no teacher shout.

School hotting up on eco matters – car share system for parents, tree planting project, annual school clean-up etc. Good home-school communications in that all staff have voicemail and email accounts available to parents and children have diary to be signed by home and school, but 'not always working as efficiently as it should,' we were told. Family backgrounds as mixed as you'd expect in north west London – many languages spoken at home, all blend easily at school. Former pupils of note include Lord Butler (former Cabinet Secretary), Anthony Horowitz and the late Simon McCorkindale.

'My children are all so different but they've all been happy there,' a parent said, and others concurred. Previous head delighted us when he extolled the virtues of a schooling which is about far more than exams and results – 'the world is changing fast. There are opportunities out there that we can't even imagine. That's why giving them breadth is so important.' We agreed and we await developments.

Radnor House School

Pope's Villa, Cross Deep, Twickenham, Middlesex TW1 4QG

Independent • Pupils: 354 • Ages: 7–18 • Fees: up to £17,160 pa

Tel: 020 8891 6264

Email: info@radnorhouse.org
Website: www.radnorhouse.org

38

Headmaster: Founded by David Paton MA in 2010, when he was just 32 years old. Previously head of sixth form at Harrodian (four years) and deputy head of the senior school at Dulwich College (three years). BA from University of Edinburgh and masters at the Institute of Education. Still teaches economics to the lower sixth. Unapologetically entrepreneurial (both in terms of seeing the school as a fast-growing business and teaching the kids themselves to think entrepreneurially in preparation for the world of work), with more business jargon than some CEOs. Big on visionary statements, but easy going with it and the kind of person you'd be happy to placed next to at a dinner party, and who the children clearly like and respect. Initially lived locally, but when the third of his neighbours sent a child to his school, he felt it was time for some distance. Now lives eight miles down the road in Leatherhead with his wife, Jo, a lawyer, and their three young children.

Academic matters: Second intake of GCSE results in 2015 much improved on previous year, with 36 per cent A*/A grades (70 per cent A*-B). School says initial intake was a challenged year group, who were actually predicted much lower grades when they joined (in year 9), and parents across younger year groups certainly aren't put off, with many insisting that their children are stretched far more than at previous schools. 'It's important to remember the school wasn't really selective at that point,' says one parent. 'Back then it was about getting bums on seats. It's only since then that entrance has got much tougher.'

Not surprisingly, given the location, it's best known for rowing, with four squads

Most do 10 GCSEs (including the three sciences as separate subjects), with lower sixth pupils (sixth form opened in 2014) expected to take four or five AS level courses (plus the Extended Project Qualification and critical thinking). Those in the upper sixth take three or four A2 level courses.

Big push to ensure lessons are top-drawer – progressive, evidence-based, embedded with technology and student-driven where relevant. Teachers nearly all young and known for being inspirational. 'We get lots of applications from people with long careers in academic schools, but then find they have nothing to interest a 12-year-old with, so we're not interested either,' says the head. Parents point to a worryingly high staff turnover in the early years ('Not a week would go by without hearing of another one leaving at one point,' said one) but there's a consensus that the current lot look set to stay. 'The dedication of some teachers is almost scary,' said one pupil. 'They could not be more enthusiastic and helpful.' 'You get a couple that aren't so good, but the quality is amazing overall,' said a parent.

You get on the Aspire programme, which stretches children even more and is generally accepted as the road to Oxbridge

Pupils taught by form teachers, with some specialist teachers from year 3, and entirely specialist teachers from year 5. Broadly follows the national curriculum, but with some added extras and a clear bias towards computing, genuinely embedding technology across lessons from year 3 upwards and with digital literacy taught from year 7 upwards, including the likes of coding, programming, robotics and web design. Science is the most popular core subject, with a healthy female interest. Chemistry gets the best results across the school and a third of students take physics A level. Languages strong with Spanish and French from year 3, plus Latin in year 5. In year 9, pupils can drop one of the three.

Instead of Gifted and Talented, there's 'Excellent Pupil Programme' (EPP). 'Excellence is something every pupil can work at; being gifted isn't,' explains the head. Twice a year, children are nominated by subject specialist teachers for EPP either because they're worked their socks off or because they've shown particular talent, after which a whole bunch of doors open up to them, including special school trips and extra learning. If you get five EPP nominations across subjects, you get on the Aspire programme, which stretches pupils even more and is generally accepted as the road to Oxbridge. SEN is also dealt with innovatively. Once a learning need is identified, an entirely classroom-based package of support is set up. 'What's the point of a special department when all the research shows help needs to be in the classroom itself?' says the head. Only two statemented children in the school when we visited.

Games, options, the arts: No on-site sports facilities to speak of, although there is a tennis/netball court up a small road opposite and a small Astroturf area at the back of the school for break and lunch times. Instead, most of the sport takes place at the 40 acre sports site at St Mary's University just down the road, with a decent number of fixtures for a school so new. Not surprisingly, given the location, it's best known for rowing, with four squads of 20 rowers, run from Twickenham and Walbrook Rowing Clubs, and which all includes all pupils from year 7 upwards. Other key sports very gendered, with boys doing rugby, football and cricket, while the focus for girls is mainly netball, hockey and rounders. School claims it is trying to address the balance, and points out that it does have a girls' football team. One of the few schools with a qualified mountain leader on their staff (the head). 'Not a school for the super sporty,' said one parent, 'but that's not to say it's bad.'

Art lessons take a particular period in history as the starting point, which makes for some interesting projects. Main emphasis on fine arts, but we also saw evidence of sculpture, textiles, photography and computer-based art, with plenty of innovative displays around the school. Disappointing space for drama – even the main hall only has a tiny stage – but this is all set to change with the new blacked out drama studio.

Music part of the majority of children's experience, with lessons taking place in the chapel and IT suite, whilst peripatetic teachers deliver lessons including strings, woodwind, brass, drumming and guitar in the three practice rooms. Junior and senior choirs, both open to all, plus close harmony group for the more advanced. Bands include wind, rock and African drumming. Every six weeks, there's a soirée and there are twice yearly productions separately from juniors and seniors, plus whole school musical in February, with examples including Hairspray and Joseph. House music competitions every March, around which there tends to be a lot of excitement.

These are the kind of children you feel will leave motivated, and making the right decisions when parents aren't looking

Lots of days out, mostly to London museums and Hampton Court, whilst trips include skiing from year 7, as well as constantly changing destinations including Rome, Berlin, Iceland, Cambodia, New York and South Africa. 'The location depends on the interest of the teacher and the topic being studied, rather than a set agenda that year 4 goes

We particularly liked that there are no out-of-bounds areas, with many children chatting and laughing in the library or gathering round the Chesterfield

here and year 6 goes there,' explains the head. That said, there is a team building activity course in years 7 and 9 for new and old pupils to get to know each other at the start of the academic year. Plenty of extracurricular activities – all the usual, plus less likely ones such as foreign film club and Amnesty International.

Background and atmosphere: 'I was sitting in my office at Harrodian one day, thinking, "The guy who started this place has done well. Surely, I could do it too",' explains the head. 'A few months later, a Knight Frank brochure dropped on my desk showing this place, then St James Boys' School, which was moving on to bigger premises.' Blown away by the beautiful riverside building, where the celebrated poet Alexander Pope lived in the 18th century, he put together a business plan and raised £9m through city contacts. A year later, in September 2011, voilà – the school opened with 137 pupils, a figure that's now nearing 400 as the first students enter the upper sixth.

Parents mainly attracted to the head's vision of producing happy and confident children. 'If kids feel good about themselves, they are much more likely to reach their full potential, and although a lot of heads say that, in reality they tend to have a blinkered view of league tables,' he says. Certainly plenty of evidence during our visit of lively children genuinely enjoying their environment and at ease with themselves, each other and staff. We particularly liked that there are no out-of-bounds areas, with many children chatting and laughing in the library or gathering round the Chesterfield just off reception during breaks. But whilst you'd think the modern café – complete with a double story outdoor terrace overlooking the Thames – would be the place they'd most likely flock to, we found it strangely quiet during break time. 'In theory, we can go there,' explained one student. 'But the fact that teachers regularly meet each other or parents there puts us off a bit.' And to be fair to the outside area, it was raining when we visited.

As you'd expect from a building on the banks of the Thames, many of the classrooms overlook the river itself and all are light and airy, if a bit on the small side. Space, agree some (although not all) pupils and parents, is an issue, and is the reason the previous school moved on. Drama

facilities and sixth form common areas particularly cramped, although both are being expanded, and pupils agree it can be hard to find a quiet place to study. Innovative use of the space that is available, however, is clear with the history classroom, for example, brought alive with hanging flags when we visited, whilst occasional classes are even held in the 'grotto' – a truly magical cave area that runs underground the school and which pupils agree makes for 'some pretty atmospheric poetry studies'. Science labs are roomy enough, as is the colourful and inviting bistro, where food is widely praised. Meanwhile, outside, there's the terrace area, as well as the Astroturf, where younger ones tend to flock at break times.

Maximum of 20 children per class, with one class per year in juniors, three classes per year in middle and senior schools and about 50 pupils per year in sixth form. Significantly more boys in the older years, with only a handful of girls in year 10, but more equal gender divide in years 8 and below. 'When we opened, there was a shortage of boys' schools,' explains the head. Lots of mixing of year groups, including mentoring and reading schemes.

Big push on links with the community, helped by the annual Make a Difference Day, which involves every child going off-site for a day to work on good causes, with examples including food banks and environmental trust. These relationships tend to persist and, from what pupils say, echo the school's values. 'Some of those days changed my life,' said one pupil. Student council relatively new, but has already brought down prices in the café, more soap in the boys' toilets and changed the ruling about girls' hair needing to be tied up.

Pastoral care and discipline: This isn't the kind of school with lots of rules written down, but there's no shortage of unwritten expectations, mainly focusing around manners and respect, and the head very quickly proved he won't put up with anyone who repeatedly fails to toe the line, having kicked out six children all at once during the first year. 'You have to focus on what you stand for – no more so than when you are new,' he says. You can't help wonder what they did (no-one will say), given that pupils and parents agree the school is quick to kick pupils out, whatever help is needed. This is the kind of head that even brings up issues that others might shy away from, including cyberbullying and sexting.

There's a feeling here that teachers talk to pupils, rather than at them, as well as a sense that pupils, parents and staff are growing together. 'It's so refreshing that you don't get teachers saying, "We've been around 200 years and this is how we've always done things",' explained one parent. 'And I've seen for myself how that mutual respect leads to a lot less frustration in the teenage years.'

Pupils and parents: Mainly white British, with a sprinkling of other nationalities. Families rarely live more than five miles away, with most children walking, cycling or using public transport (those further afield tend to get the tube to Richmond and the bus from there). Wide mix of occupations amongst parents, many of whom work all hours afford to send their kids here, along with your usual hedge fund and city types. Communication between school and parents praised for being responsive and pleasantly informal, with parents invited to come in any time to meet staff in the café. Parents themselves – a non-competitive bunch who have huge confidence in the school – socialise and fundraise via the PA.

Entrance: Main intakes at ages 7+ (being phased out in favour of a 9+ entry from 2018), 11+ and 13+, with occasional spaces at other ages. Four separate entrance criteria (each of which carry equal measure) include an interview, reference from previous school's head, maths paper and English test. Children from a mix of private preps and state schools, almost all privately tutored. Indeed, the tests are now known for being pretty tough, something that one parent says 'would have been unthinkable just a few years ago'. Heavy expectation to stay on at sixth form, with around 20 places for newcomers. Entry on a case by case basis, but based on predicted GCSE grades.

Exit: Too early to tell, but the aim is for most to go on to Russell Group universities.

Money matters: Means-tested bursaries available for sixth form applications, although no set numbers.

Remarks: This is a school that's clearly trying to position itself as a more compassionate alternative to many of its more pushy academic competitors, which Radnor House believes have become out of touch with children of today. We certainly found it refreshing to see no hint of an old boys' network, nor the all-too-familiar obsession with academic results. We also liked the way it seems to really 'get' today's kids and the fact that its thoroughly modern take on teaching puts the personality back into learning. These are the kind of children you feel will leave thoroughly motivated, and making the right decisions when their parents aren't looking. There's a savviness about this school, too. So whilst some schools rave about the fact that the children refer to them as being like a big family, protecting them from the outside world, this is a school that embraces that outside world, and prepares youngsters for it. Initial results could be better, and we found it disappointing that whilst there's endless talk about it being an evolving school (and we could see how for ourselves how it has truly embraced change so far) nobody seemed to want to talk about what next, with rather scripted and guarded answers slipping out a little too easily. It would be such a shame for it to rest on its laurels already.

St Benedict's Junior School

Linked school: St Benedict's School, 467

5 Montpelier Avenue, London W5 2XP

Independent • Pupils: 275 • Ages: 3–11 • RC • Fees: up to £12,810 pa

Tel: 020 8862 2254

Email: enquiries@stbenedicts.org.uk
Website: www.stbenedicts.org.uk

10

Headmaster: Since 2005, Mr Rob Simmons BA, the second secular head. A historian, he spent time teaching in Dominica after graduating and, realising teaching was for him, returned to do a PGCE at Sussex. Has worked at St Benedict's for over 20 years, teaching mediaeval and modern history in the senior school and becoming a head of year before his appointment as junior school head.

Entrance: Non-selective at 3 or 4. Some flexibility now allowed on number of days per week in the

nursery; From 3 to 11 children of other faiths (not Catholic) are now accepted into the school.

Exit: Almost all to senior school on site; a few on occasion to Merchant Taylors', Cardinal Vaughan and London Oratory.

Remarks: Junior school housed in very large, very attractive Victorian red-brick building across the playground from senior school (playground shared but times staggered so tinies not swamped by six foot rugger types). Playground also encloses new small area for tots. Building recently and carefully extended to provide lovely, light new hall and classrooms. New rooms include excellent ICT suite with modern low tables and matching chairs and inviting, comfortable library overlooking the abbey and lawns. Interactive whiteboards in every classroom and well used. Leafy Ealing far more apparent here – super trees with space to grow and local family homes just across the way. Excellent displays everywhere – really interesting, too, on stone carving, perspective, shape and colour. A good orderly feel with happy, confident-looking pupils in a school recently commended in ISI report for excellent music and ADT. Pastoral care, too, clearly exceptional. A great start for your son or daughter and big school just across the playground. New nursery housed in super refurbished Victorian house just down the road. Last Ofsted inspection rated the early years foundation stage provision as outstanding.

St Benedict's School

Linked school: St Benedict's Junior School, 466

54 Eaton Rise, London W5 2ES

Independent • Pupils: 816 • Ages: 11–18 • Sixth form pupils: 225 • RC • Fees: £14,550 pa

Tel: 020 8862 2254

Email: enquiries@stbenedicts.org.uk
Website: www.stbenedicts.org.uk

11

Headmaster: Since 2002, Mr Christopher Cleugh (rhymes with rough) BSc MSc (50s). Read chemistry at Hull. Resonant Liverpool accent ('I prefer Everton,' he says), he grew up and taught on Merseyside until he came here. Educated at St Mary's Crosby, where he returned as a teacher for 17 years (by the time he left he was deputy head). Went on to become head of St Anselm's in Birkenhead for eight years, before moving south to run St Benedict's, which felt fated: 'I remember the day I saw the advert,' he says. Married with two sons and two daughters – his wife is head of a Catholic primary school in Acton, his first grandchild is a pupil in the junior school here. Utterly unpretentious and forthright, Mr Cleugh is a keen sports fan and loves his cricket and football. Warm and humorous, one nevertheless detects steel beneath the avuncular surface.

Only the second lay headmaster since the school was founded, Mr Cleugh is a practising Catholic and a firm believer in co-education – 'in the modern world it's the right way forward. It's a co-ed world out there and this is the natural preamble to it,' he says, adding that there's 'all sorts of nonsense about which environment produces the best academic performance, but at the end of the day it's nothing to do with single sex or co-education – it's the way they're taught and how you instil confidence and self discipline.'

You know where you are with this head, who is not afraid to risk unpopularity for the good of the community, and is a man of quiet but total conviction. Knows, and knows about, all his pupils, and has a sensitive understanding of their concerns.

Much loved by parents and pupils alike – 'he's always around'; 'easy to talk to'; 'makes time for everyone'; 'you can talk to him about anything – he never makes you feel uncomfortable' is the resounding message. Mr Cleugh unequivocal too about his favourite thing about the job – the children.

Retiring in July 2016. His successor will be Andrew Johnston, currently head of Stonyhurst. Educated at Bristol (French and Spanish) and Portsmouth (education management). Has also been deputy head at Birkdale and head of modern languages at Winchester. Married to Dawn, with two sons, currently studying for A levels.

Academic matters: Respectable results, especially bearing in mind the school is not highly selective academically. Sixty-seven per cent A*/B grades at A level in 2015, 37 per cent A*/A. However, a starry place in league tables is not what they're about, Mr Cleugh is keen to point out, and what he cares most about is that each child fulfils his or her potential. Among those who got A*s, As and Bs there would have been

a number who would have fallen by the wayside in a more pressured environment. A good range of GCSE subjects on offer with everyone taking RS. RS curriculum largely RC in content and other faiths learned about in PSHE. Excellent ICT facilities. The subject is well taught and IT skills used extensively in other areas including art and music. History, maths and chemistry most popular subjects at A level. In 2015, an encouraging 52 per cent A*/A grades at GCSE. Modern languages reasonably popular and take place in language labs in the £6.2 million development.

Rugby is huge (they don't play football, nor do they row, and it's not the place for your son if he's mad about ballet)

Wheelchair access throughout the school (lifts and ramps) means they have been able to accommodate a number of children with severe physical disabilities. 'As long as I feel they would be happy I will take them,' says head. Full time SENCo who occasionally withdraws pupils from lessons but prefers to provide in-class support as well as extra time pre- and post-school. Lots of support given to children with their organisational skills and the SEN room provides a useful base for children who need more help. Very positive noises from parents about the caring and supportive approach of the school to a whole range of special needs. At the other end of the spectrum, a Gifted and Talented Coordinator runs a programme through the curriculum, but also does a lot outside.

Games, options, the arts: Rugby is huge here. It's the main winter sport for boys (they don't play football, nor do they row, and it's not the place for your son if he's mad about ballet) and school recently ranked the top rugby school in the country (currently slipped to fourth but we suspect not for long). Tours to Dubai, Japan and New Zealand. Girls as keen to perform well as the boys. Netball tours to Sri Lanka and Barbados. Full size Astroturf pitch. Cricket, athletics, rounders and tennis in the summer. School uses 14 acres of playing fields in Perivale about a mile away and plays hard, winning more than losing. Games staff everywhere – proper professionals in their matching coaching kit.

On-site sports hall, sparkling multi-gym and fitness centre as well as fencing salle and dance studio. Fencing a major sports option with regular fixtures against other schools. Basketball, volleyball and yoga are also offered.

Less than world-class pupils appreciate the school's attitude to sports – 'everyone's given a chance,' said one in heartfelt tones, having experienced the 'if you're not in the first team you're nobody' syndrome elsewhere.

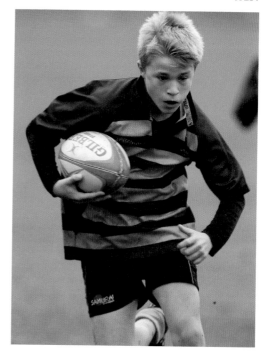

Music strong and there's a huge variety – a symphony orchestra, lots of singing – four choirs (strongly influenced by the Abbey choir), jazz band, big band, swing band, string ensembles and brass groups. (Almost) everyone gets involved at some stage and one parent remarked on how well talent is spotted and nurtured. Excellent facilities, three grand pianos and lots of uprights in tip top condition. An IT lab is dedicated to music, posters of Led Zeppelin and the Beatles decorate the walls, lots of computers equipped with piano keyboards.

Exciting art. Intensely imaginative, disciplined and creative sculptures are dotted around the school and spectacular oil paintings adorn the reception area. IT facilities dedicated to art in the attractive one-storey modern art/DT block. Before – and after – school study supervision in the library on offer, and over 80 clubs which include karate, history society, CCF, D of E, Saint Vincent de Paul charity fundraising, debating and current affairs. One boy keen to point out that if you want to do something new, school will make it happen.

Background and atmosphere: Founded in 1902 by the monks of Downside Abbey, St Benedict's is the only Benedictine day school in the country. Its sister schools are Worth, Downside and Ampleforth which, like St Benedict's, have all relatively recently started to take girls all the way through. (There have been girls in the sixth form here since the 1970s, from year 7 since 2008). The Roman Catholic faith is evident in every aspect of the atmosphere and the environment of the school, its publications, its ethos, yet almost half the pupils in the senior school are not Catholic. Eighty-five-ish per cent are Christian including those from other denominations, and you will find Muslims, Sikhs, Hindus, and Jews. The only condition is that they must respect the Catholic faith and take part in the regular masses that take place throughout the school year.

The buildings are a mix of un-gloomy Victorian red-brick and various 20th century extensions, additions and blocks – some of which are wearing better than others. The Cloisters, a stunning development costing £6.2 million, is the first thing you come to as you enter the school and has the same contemporary feel as some of the underground stations on the Jubilee line. Smooth concrete walls, aesthetic balconies, quadrangles and colonnades, an imaginative foil to the glorious abbey, which is situated across the playground and adjacent to the junior school. Whole school mass is said in the warm and totally unforbidding abbey, but smaller class mass is said in the intimate chapel in the modern Cloisters development – stunningly light and bright with a large window in the shape of a cross taking up most of the ceiling. New art block and sixth form centre under construction.

Trust in the Benedictine ethos of respect for each other, and an unquestioned local reputation for quite exceptional pastoral care, have been battered by a storm of revelations, the most recent relating to 2007. See the website for the report of an inquiry, commissioned by the school's trustees and conducted by Lord Carlile (who we rate as unquestionably independent). The school tells us that it has fully implemented his recommendations. It is now fully independent of the Abbey Trust; the governing body has a lay majority and a lay chair, whilst three members of the monastic community are governors and another three work at the school. It regularly reviews its safeguarding and child protection policies.

Against that background, parents and pupils pay tribute to the trouble taken over the smallest worry, and pupils feel supported and secure. Advent of girls throughout has also contributed to modernisation and a sense of opening up.

Pastoral care and discipline: Very strict – until the sixth form all children carry around a yellow card – reminiscent of the traditional satis cards (short for satisfecit – has he done enough?) in order that their behaviour – good and bad – can be constantly monitored. Parents are kept in the loop, they sign it each week and house points are affected. However, it's not inflexibly strict – 'first and foremost I'm a parent – I know children can get it wrong sometimes,' is Mr Cleugh's humane approach. Regular parent forums on, eg the dangers of ICT at home; 'I would ban Facebook if I had my way,' Mr Cleugh exclaims. He likes to keep the sixth form in at lunch time (though they can go out). There is so much to do here,' he says, 'plus there are a few too many muggings in Ealing'.

Pupils and parents: 'Pupils in state schools think we're posh but Latymer kids think we're common,' a sixth former told us. You don't get many posey trust fund kids here. Solidly middle class but a genuinely wide range of parents, a number of single

Intimate chapel in the modern Cloisters development – stunningly light and bright with a large window in the shape of a cross taking up most of the ceiling

mothers and families who have made huge sacrifices to get a good education for their children. A number of parents talked of how supportive the school was – not just of their child but of the family as a whole. One boy commented on how no-one is arrogant about money – the influence of the abbey means that everyone feels welcome. Mostly local. Some come from as far afield as Barnes or Holland Park. Just over 50 per cent are Catholic.

One girl we spoke to was keen to mention that girls are not treated as second class citizens, attributing it to the fact that there have been girls in the sixth form for over 30 years. There are good inter-year relationships. Mentoring schemes where the older ones help out with the juniors and whole school involvement in drama and music. Pupils here are extremely courteous and mature. Old Priorians (the official title for former St Benedict's pupils) include Julian Clary, Lord (Chris) Patten (who also sits as an advisor on the governing board), Peter Ackroyd, Declan Donnellan, Andy Serkis, Professor Denis MacShane MP and poet/songwriter Labi Siffre, as well as plenty of rugby players, including Hugo Ellis and Joe Simpson of Wasps.

Entrance: Very nearly all start at 11 – though school will still take the occasional few at 13. Ninety-six places, 40 of which go to the children coming up from the junior school (almost all transfer automatically). Entrance exams in maths, English and verbal reasoning. Most interviewed. Looking to discover what the child will give back to the school. NB part of a group of independent co-ed/boys' schools that coordinate 11+ results, but forbid those who have accepted a place at one school from taking up a subsequent waiting list offer from another. Sixth form requirements – a minimum of six GCSEs at B or above and Bs in A level subjects. A few join in the sixth form from local girls' schools.

It's no longer true that if you don't get in anywhere else you will get a place at St Benedict's. Although Mr Cleugh is keen not to be too selective, as numbers rise priority will have to be given to Catholics and siblings.

Exit: Virtually all sixth formers to good universities and to an impressive range of courses – no stereotypes here. Two to Oxbridge in 2014; others to eg Bristol, Nottingham, Durham, Exeter and Leeds for subjects ranging from aerospace engineering to theatre performance. Some 20 per cent leave after GCSE to go to eg Latymer Upper, Catholic state schools or sixth form colleges.

Money matters: School has increased provision for scholarships and bursaries. About half a dozen on 100 per cent bursaries, lots of others get help. Academic scholarships at 11+ and at sixth form – up to 50 per cent fees and can be augmented by bursaries. 'Once a child is in if a parent falls on hard times we will do our best to help them,' says Mr Cleugh.

Remarks: We said, 'A wholly unpretentious, good, solid school with sound values that is never going to squash your child into a box. Exactly the school for your brightish but quietish child who would sink in a larger, or tougher, environment. An honest, hard-working place with a gentle and loving approach', and we still think that that is a fair description. Although there are still occasional ripples from its troubled past, the school is now a very different place.

St Dominic's Sixth Form College

Mount Park Avenue, Harrow on the Hill, Middlesex HA1 3HX

State • Pupils: 1,199 • Ages: 16–19 • RC

Tel: 020 8422 8084

Email: admissions@stdoms.ac.uk
Website: www.stdoms.ac.uk

Principal: Since 2013, Andrew Parkin. Educated at St John's RC Comprehensive School and Queen Elizabeth Sixth Form College in Darlington. Studied music at Durham and Cambridge and started his professional career in London at The St Marylebone Girls' School. Went on to be deputy head teacher at Sion Manning Girls' School in Kensington and then St Augustine's High School in Westminster. He is a keen amateur musician and is chairman of the BBC Symphony Chorus.

Academic matters: Very wide range of courses – some 30 subjects available in more-or-less any combination. Maths much the most popular subject, with chemistry, biology and economics close behind. Impressive results: 67 per cent A*-B grades and 37 per cent A*/A grades in 2015. Option to change subjects in the first week or two if you really loath psychology or have just developed a passionate interest in Italian. A level 3 BTec in business studies is the only vocational course on offer, but those of a less academic bent can take a BTec in travel and tourism or engineering, or a lower level business studies BTec, at the Sacred Heart and Salvatorian sixth form centre down the road. Acts as a Pathfinder College for new core maths qualification.

Nearly everyone does an extended project. 'They have a free choice of subject, but it makes sense to relate it to a subject they may do at university, and gives something to talk about at interview.' Large numbers of aspiring medics, so the college runs a programme of BMAT preparation and mock interviews. Excellent university and careers advice. 'We're realistic and honest, and allow no poverty of aspiration.'

The Study Plus learning support centre is staffed by a manager and three assistants. Some drop in from time to time, whilst others, often identified at initial interviews, are assigned one-to-one help. 'Some resent it at first but soon don't want to be taken off the list.' Student mentors train to offer help with specific subjects eg chemistry and maths.

Games, options, the arts: Sports hall completed in 2010 includes a multigym and hall for badminton, table tennis and five-a-side football, with its use juggled between A level PE students and general recreation. Sport is not compulsory, but the new hall 'has increased motivation and attendance. We've been pleasantly surprised that participation rates have been very high.' On the morning of our visit the multigym was full of (mostly) young men working out – many of whom, we were told, would not normally have come to college so early. The only outdoor space is a five-a-side football/netball court, but the college fields football (girls' and boys'), rugby, netball and cricket teams. It also offers opportunities for cheerleading and street dance for those less competitively inclined.

Sits on a hill above a leafy, gated estate of substantial houses that could have strayed from the Chilterns

Small numbers do music A level, but many keep up their instrumental skills, and play in the termly concerts. Top floor studios show sophisticated artwork and fashion creations, and several each year go on to art and design courses. No college drama productions, but theatre studies students showcase their devised pieces.

Volunteering and fundraising are important parts of the ethos. 'Charity efforts spring up out of nowhere.' Students do sponsored walks and sleep outs, work in soup kitchens, volunteer on a Catholic farm, go off to work in a school in Uganda, join a pilgrimage to Lourdes. 'There's an ethos of respecting other people and helping the wider community,' said a teacher.

Background and atmosphere: Opened in 1979 in what had been St Dominic's Independent Grammar School for Girls, run by Dominican nuns. Sits on a hill above a leafy, gated estate of substantial houses with large gardens that could have strayed from the Chilterns, with views across the west London fringes to Ealing. By the entrance to the site is the chapel, a peaceful and atmospheric building with lovely stained glass, 'the heart of the college'. Assemblies and introductory talks take place here, as well as morning masses, and Muslim students use a side room for prayer.

Planning permission is not easy to come by here – it can take up to seven years – but the college has gradually developed most of its open space and is well off for indoor facilities (remodelled library, ICT suite, music and art rooms) if not outdoor. No common room, but students gather in the canteen, and can work in the library, which has a mezzanine floor with a row of computers. New all-day coffee kiosk augments the canteen offerings.

Faith is a major part of the deal here. mass is held every week, tutor groups take it in turns to choose readings, everyone studies RE. 'We want our students to develop on an academic, moral and spiritual level. We want them to critically examine their faith, to mix with people from other faiths and hear why it is important to them. It makes a tremendous difference to what we can offer and how they develop in later life.'

About 50 per cent of the staff is Catholic, but all teach RE and buy into the ethos. 'It's a very happy place to work,' said one. Prayers are said each morning and each tutor period. 'It is a moment for thinking outside oneself – a lovely sharing moment.' Very good relationships amongst staff and between staff and pupils. A student commented: 'The staff are so committed and positive.'

Pastoral care and discipline: The atmosphere may be relaxed, with staff and students on first name terms, but students are under tight control. Electronic registration for every lesson means that everyone is accounted for: the pastoral team phones parent and student if the student is not in by 10am. Effort and achievement grades given every six weeks. 'Our monitoring is much more frequent than they have time to do in schools. All our staff are focused on the sixth form – not on settling in year 7s or helping year 9s choose GCSE subjects – and we're very good at it.'

Zero tolerance for drugs or violence. No drugs problems for many years – 'why would they do it here?' The rare offenders usually withdraw, 'and we support them to move on elsewhere'.

To mitigate severe government funding cuts, college has increased student numbers, and lengthened the day – now 8.30am-4.25pm – to accommodate the extra students without increasing class sizes.

Pupils and parents: About 50 per cent Catholic, most of the rest Hindu or Muslim. Homogeneous in that all take their religious faith seriously and may talk about it at interview. Also tend to be serious about academic life, since the college offers virtually no vocational courses, and there is a high level of competition for places amongst non-Catholics in particular. Mostly from Harrow, but some from further afield from a wide range of schools.

Entrance: About 30 per cent from its two partner schools, Salvatorian College and Sacred Heart Language College – these students are guaranteed a place providing they get at least 5 A*-C GCSE grades including English language. All other applicants must get at least seven A*-Cs and meet the individual subject requirements. These range from a C in English for religious studies to an A in maths for further maths. Priority to Catholics, then other practising Christians, then other faiths and no faith. Applicants must provide a reference from their religious leader and fill in a form about their own religious commitment. Conditional offers, are made in April, and are based on academic references, including predicted grades. Any remaining places offered based on subjects with spaces and highest GCSE average score.

Exit: Around 90 per cent to higher education. University of Hertfordshire very popular, as are many of the London universities, Nottingham and Warwick. Law and medical/biomedical subjects tend to top the tables. Fewer Oxbridge applicants than one might expect given the calibre of students (five places in 2015), largely because so many are prospective medics – 19, plus five dentists in 2015.

Money matters: Free if you're under 19. Excellent and enlightened system of bursaries for students and staff to fund specific projects and trips.

Remarks: Greatly sought-after college in pleasant leafy location with high academic standards and a strong Catholic ethos of care for each other. 'A lovely place to work and study,' say staff and students.

St Helen's School

Linked school: Little St Helen's and St Helen's Junior school, 428

Eastbury Road, Northwood, Middlesex HA6 3AS

Tel: 01923 843210

Independent • Pupils: 650 • Ages: 11–18 • Sixth form pupils: 155 • Fees: up to £15,438 pa

Email: admissions@sthelens.london
Website: www.sthelens.london

Headmistress: Since 2011, Dr Mary Short BA PGCE PhD (50s) – did her PhD, in the politics of budget-setting in the 1920s, at Cambridge. Has taught undergraduates at Cambridge and pupils at independent schools including St Paul's Girls, City of London Boys and Haberdashers' Aske's Girls (deputy head). She has teaching in her blood and is married to a fellow teacher. Apart from history,

likes walking, bread-making and travel. Aims to up the academic performance, partly by 'reviewing the admissions process to more accurately identify academic potential', but more by curriculum reviews, consistency of aims, better monitoring of performance, peer review of teachers, that sort of thing. Good relationship with her top-notch governors.

A smile of measured mischief, and a fascination with bringing the best out of each pupil. Her eyes light up when describing how the school is going about sorting out one of her more troublesome charges. 'Is quietly powerful', says a parent, 'I really, really like her, and so do the girls.'

Academic matters: Not the top of the highly competitive North London academic tree, but no slouch. Lots of male teachers, lots of teachers who have had other professional lives before or even during teaching. Every pupil we talked to had at least one teacher they found truly inspiring. Pupils describe the atmosphere as 'competitive but collaborative': in maths, for instance, where randomly chosen pairs of girls help each other to tackle problems and be the best pair in the class.

In 2015, 62 per cent A*/A at A level and 84 per cent A*/A at GCSE. Good range of subjects in the sixth. The overwhelmingly popular subjects at this level are the sciences, maths, economics and history, with maths results particularly strong. Physics as ever with girls the slightly weaker relation, but school working hard to encourage and take-up is growing – the Heath Robinson Club is clearly popular and interest in engineering is strong. The cuttings that adorn the corridor walls in the science department are totally fascinating, and would repay an hour's dawdling. Sixth form curriculum enriched by EPQ, lecture series, university preparation courses.

Way ahead of the government on the EBacc: has been doing it for years, with a strong emphasis on having a second language. Tendency to do art and/or drama as the 'free' choices. Highly IT literate: great facilities and teachers who know how to use them. Students are able to: complement their A level programme with the 'St Helen's Portfolio', which comprises additional qualifications such as the European Computer Driving Licence; take up modules offered by the Open University; continue with languages they have studied to GCSE or acquire additional languages or study further mathematics; also recognises CCF, D of E, other clubs and societies

---

No sign of separation among the pupils. Watch them swirl around you at break time and wish that all the world could be like that

Thoroughly sympathetic to SEN, from the headmistress down. Everyone is screened at 7 and 11 for potential educational difficulties. 'We then discuss with parents how we can make it better.' Individual Needs Department created in 2013 with three staff providing support to pupils from age 7. School can and does support autistic spectrum difficulties, mild dyslexia and dyspraxia, mild speech difficulties and children with hearing impairments. Currently focusing on better provision for those who struggle with numbers – some children have extra help with maths. 'All take iGCSE maths – we have no intention of becoming a specialist centre for dyscalculics, but do want to become much more effective at picking up those who struggle with

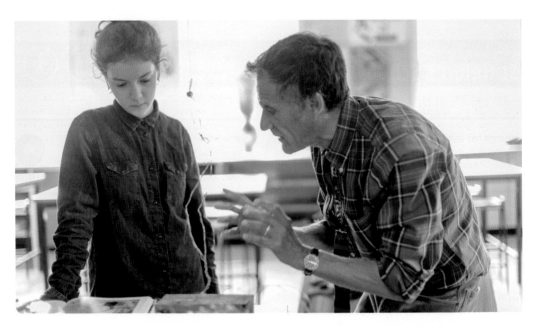

number work before they become paralysed by algebra!' Support, but not separate teaching, for those who have English as an additional language. Some 100+ children currently identified as Gifted and Talented and supported with 'differentiated work schemes and activities'.

Games, options, the arts: The huge surprise for anyone visiting St Helen's and who, perhaps, has only seen it behind its sedate hedges and modest perimeter walls, is the unbelievable amount of space it has. Acres of playing fields, courts and pitches extend in all directions and you begin to realise that most of this end of Northwood is St Helen's! A vast new sports complex and superb, seemingly endless pool, in a stunning new building, in enthusiastic use. Lacrosse, netball, rugby, tennis, athletics, badminton and rounders all popular and many other games and activities available including pilates, aerobics, fencing, climbing and trampolining. Lots of success – representation in lacrosse, swimming, cross-country, netball and badminton national teams and much success for school teams in all these sports plus athletics and rounders at impressive levels. Supports those who excel (and need time off for national teams) and has no beef with those who prefer music (but still have to do games).

Art, DT and drama housed in the June Leader building, named after school's outstanding, and aptly named, head of 20 years (1966-1986), the great builder of the school, both in physical terms and in terms of the quality of education and values promulgated here under her uniquely humane regime. First rate art – teachers are real artists, teaching combines strong basic skills such as life drawing with experimentation, breadth and understanding. DT bubbling and well taught if not as jazzily equipped as some (though there is CAD and a 3D printer). Dance and drama (some joint with Merchant Taylors') much enjoyed, especially in the context of the annual House Arts festival. It is good to see the arts so strong in a school whose spirit is essentially academic. The Centre is a new multipurpose space for the performing arts and sport (converted from the existing gym).

Music – with real musicians with flourishing musical careers as teachers – going from strength to strength with numerous orchestras, choirs and, bands. The jazz band has made a CD, the huge choir tours abroad annually, there are many and varied opportunities for performance in school and the wider community, including regular concerts at St John's, Smith Square, London. The majority of girls play at least one instrument.

Collaboration with Merchant Taylors' also in CCF. D of E and Young Enterprise also popular. Visits from profs, writers and theatre companies. Successes in debating, maths and

physics Olympiads, technology competitions. Lots of trips – Madrid, Kobe, Ypres, Berlin, CERN, Kew, Rome, House of Commons, Paris, British Museum, galleries.

Underlying ethos of opportunity, progression and support. Hundreds of things for pupils to try and, when they latch on to one, the school will find ways of allowing it to be taken further – as far, indeed, as the girl can go.

Background and atmosphere: Founded at the end of the 19th century with a vision of education for the whole child, which it still holds dear. A spacious school, trim and imaginative grounds, relaxed, not at all authoritarian. Dark green uniform up to 16; conservative freedom in the sixth.

Strong Indian, Tamil and Jewish (a strong JSoc and well-established links with the local synagogue) contingents, but absolutely no sign of segmentation or separation among the pupils, and parents report that it's like that with the ones they bring home too. Watch them swirl around you at break time and wish the world could be like that. Strong and growing relationship with Merchant Taylors', already noted, supplies all the male element the girls want, and no more.

Notable absence of the unhealthily thin. Eating is a social rite here – you stumble across snacking groups all the time. School encourages this with decent breaks, delicious cookies and time enough for lunch.

The junior school is an integral part of the whole (new junior school building opening in September 2016). Situated centrally, it is natural for girls here to stay the course – now from 3 to 18 – and continue to feel that it's all in the family. Longworthe, one of the former boarding houses, is now used for before and after school care in which pupils with busy parents can spend a long day – breakfast and tea included and quiet places for prep and recreation. Nicely decorated rooms for sixth form relaxation and study (much studiousness observed).

Pastoral care and discipline: Each individual teacher is expected to notice and to care how their charges are, and to react supportively and promptly to any sign of trouble. As a result, while teachers talk of all the usual friendship and family problems, the girls seem hardly aware of them, and prefects do not see dealing with social ills as a significant part of their remit. Relationships within houses, year groups and tutor groups all seem close, giving girls a variety of communities to turn to.

Staff/student relationships palpably cordial. 'A lot of our teachers are role models,' said one sixth former. 'They are so kind and helpful and it doesn't just stop in the classroom. They will keep helping you achieve what you want to achieve.' A younger pupil agreed, 'and', she added, 'you just have to be friendly here because everyone is. The teachers are so sweet – they really look after you – there's always someone to talk to and problems are sorted out really quickly.' 'Never a door closed, they always have time for you'. The same applies to the medical room, with its welcoming nurse, and the school counsellor (called a confidential listener).

Clear sanctions policy. System of warning and detention cards. MP3s/mobiles illegal in school time. No drugs incidents in living memory. The

Notable absence of the unhealthily thin. Eating is a social rite here – you stumble across snacking groups all the time. School encourages this with delicious cookies

occasional foolish misdemeanour is dealt with individually but 'sanely. It's never public, it's not about humiliation – ever.' You're allowed to slip here.

Pupils and parents: Resilient, personable, happy, chatty girls who 'know who we are and why we are here', and whose attitude to problems is to 'tackle not buckle'. Alongside, that is, a deep-rooted conservatism: wary of the poetry shelves in the library and reluctant to take gap years (although the pupil we talked to whose ambition was to be an inventor was thought eccentric, she was still very much one of the girls). The head 'hopes to encourage greater risk-taking'.

Northwood is prosperous, with lots of large detached houses. Girls come from wide area – good coach service covers Beaconsfield, Elstree, Barnet, Amersham, Ealing, Hemel Hempstead and points between.

Old Girls' network huge and devoted. St Helen's inspires great loyalty. Alumnae include Patricia Hodge, a great supporter, Vanessa Lawrence (director general Ordnance Survey), Lady Lowry, Luisa Baldini, Penny Marshall and Maria Djurkovic.

Entrance: School part of North London Consortium which shares tests at 11. First point of entry is at 3 into Little St Helen's. At 11, exams in English and maths; around 460 apply for approximately 100 places – not too terrifying as lots apply elsewhere but school is increasingly candidates' first choice. Junior school girls have to sit the exam too, and most make the transition. Around half of the senior school places are filled by St Helen's Junior School girls.

Interview and reference from current school as important as scores. 'Aim is to explore potential and to ensure that girls will be able to take full advantage of the curriculum and wider opportunities the school has to offer,' says the school. As ever true but never spelt out, parents should remember that they are on show too.

At sixth form, 'places are available for girls who the school considers will benefit from the educational programme offered and who will enjoy becoming members of the school community. We don't fix the number of places.' You need 7+ GCSEs at B+ including good grades in the subjects relevant to the A level choices.

Exit: About 15-20 per cent leave post-GCSE. All sixth formers to higher education. Handful to Oxbridge annually (eight places in 2015), otherwise a wide spread of universities and courses (London, Sheffield, Leeds, Warwick, Birmingham are popular). About a third science-related: strong bias to medical, biological and engineering courses, with a high proportion of dentistry and medical offers. Careers advice considered by the girls to be top notch, and in general they have a much clearer idea than usual of what courses they would like and what careers they might pursue afterwards.

Money matters: Range of scholarships and means-tested bursaries. Bursaries awarded annually and are either awarded to girls whose parents could not otherwise meet fees or to girls whose families are experiencing temporary difficulties.

Remarks: Thoroughly impressive. Not in hock to the league tables, but plenty of ambition for its pupils, academically and otherwise.

St James's Catholic Primary School

260 Stanley Road, Twickenham, Middlesex TW2 5NP

Tel: 020 8898 4670

State • Pupils: 680 (52 in nursery) • Ages: 3–11 • RC

Email: info@st-james.richmond.sch.uk
Website: www.st-james.richmond.sch.uk

39

Headteacher: Since January 2013, Mrs Clare Webber BA PGCE NPQH. Read history at university. Comes from a commercial background and spent time in recruitment, then became a full-time mother when her children were young. Has two sons, now both at university. Both her grandfather and father were heads – 'so teaching was in the blood'. Taught at the school for 12 years, followed by promotion to deputy and then acting head.

Charming, with a good sense of humour. Loves her job, takes her responsibilities very seriously and says the main challenge for her now is 'to continue to be an outstanding school'. One parent told us: 'We're very lucky to have her. She's fantastic'. Huge amounts of energy – keeps fit with boot camp before school and enjoys regular trips to the V&A. Very visible at school events and in the playground at break time. Not a head who hides herself away in her office.

Entrance: At 3 to nursery (52 places) and 4 to the main school (90 places). St. James's is a Roman Catholic school serving the four parishes of St James (Twickenham), St Francis de Sales (Hampton Hill), St Margaret (East Twickenham) and St Theodore (Hampton). Priority given to those baptised within a year of birth who are devout, practising Catholics. Siblings given priority. Heavily over-subscribed, with more than two applicants for every place. Occasional places become available in higher years, though there isn't huge pupil mobility. 'We don't lose many pupils further up the school, only if the families relocate', says the head. 'We certainly don't lose them to private schools'.

A place in the nursery does not automatically lead to a place in reception – 'though it is very rare for this not to happen'.

Exit: Between 20 to 50 per cent to independent schools. Hampton Boys' is popular and 'girls go everywhere', including Tiffin Girls' School, Gumley House and Waldegrave. One mother commented that many parents have chosen historically to go down the independent school route due to the dearth of good state secondary schools nearby – 'especially with the Oratory having reduced its catchment area'. That looks set to change with the new St Richard Reynolds Catholic High School in Twickenham starting to be an extremely popular destination.

Remarks: Head describes the school as having high academic standards, coupled with a strong Catholic ethos. 'Faith is central to what we do here', she told us. 'It is made explicit to parents. If you are a Catholic teacher, part of teaching is a mission as well as a job'.

School is large, spacious and well-run. Housed in fairly new accommodation in a leafy cul-de-sac. Light classrooms with generous windows and colourful displays abound. Two huge halls, well used for sport, dance, plays and assemblies. Glorious outdoor space where children can let off steam. Climbing frames, trees and quieter areas for those in need of tranquillity. Plenty of greenery surrounding the school. Rolling playing fields at the back and local golf club on the other side give the school a distinctly country feel.

School is at full capacity, with three parallel classes of 30 children from reception up to year 6. Children very engaged and focused when we visited and some impressive manners in evidence. Very strong academically. Rigorous analysis of progress and attainment of each pupil at each stage. Head aware of the importance of pupils becoming independent thinkers and thinking skills now embedded in the curriculum.

Small turnover of staff with a respectable number of long servers. Specialist teaching for art and some games. Masses of lesson observations going on – at all levels – to maintain high standards.

Head believes that sport is a vital part of the curriculum and it is taken seriously here, with the school competing at a high level. Recent borough athletic champions and 12 children competed at the national swimming championships in Sheffield – 'a great achievement', says the head, 'as they're normally dominated by private schools'. Football, netball, rugby, cricket and tennis on offer. Reciprocal sharing of swimming pool and games pitches with The Mall, prep school next door.

Music is strong. A symphony orchestra, three choirs (chamber choir is by invitation only), two rock bands and about half of key stage 2 pupils have private music lessons. Musical events arranged with local schools and there are opportunities to perform at the Barbican in the London Symphony Orchestra's Discovery Series.

Hordes of children in jolly yellow and grey uniforms race along the pavement on scooters

The art department definitely holds its own. Head is excited that, as part of the Take One Picture scheme, pupils have been selected to exhibit their work at the National Gallery. 'I can't wait to go', she says.

Number of children requiring learning support is quite small. Limited number with IEPs but one-to-one help is on offer for those in need. 'Our special needs children make exceptional progress and are very well provided for', says head. Full-time SENCo and part-time learning support staff. George Tancred Centre is based at the school and caters for 10 children with moderate autism. Regular opportunities for these pupils to be included in lessons at the main school but they can withdraw back to the centre when activities become too distracting. Their playground is separate from, but adjacent to, main school. The pupils with autism are 'very much part of our school', says head. Pupils from the

Huge amounts of energy – keeps fit with boot camp before school and enjoys regular trips to the V&A. Very visible at school events and in the playground

main school can choose to visit and play with the children from the centre at break times.

No wrap-around care on offer but plenty of before and after-school clubs, so the school day can be extended to help working parents. A variety of tastes catered for at clubs – football, cricket, basketball, French, Spanish, Italian, Jamming Together and ballet. Basketball is currently very popular. Plenty of school trips on offer. Year 6 get a week in Norfolk and year 5 head for Dorset as part of the history curriculum. Day outings include visits to art galleries and RHS gardens at Wisley.

Children at St James's are expected to work hard. Lots of homework from reception onwards, culminating in a couple of hours a night by year 6. Parents are generally supportive of this. Some tutoring goes on at the top of the school – head is relaxed, as long as it does not become excessive.

Significant number of bilingual children – mostly Spanish, French and Italian. Parents are welcomed into the school and appreciate the open-door policy in place. Head knows most of the families well and believes parental involvement in the school is invaluable, either on trips or within the classroom. 'We'd be mad not to include them', she says. Parents are a fairly affluent, middle class group, reflecting the local area. Minuscule percentage on free school meals. Very active PTFA raises £30,000 annually. Money recently spent on the early years garden and subsidising school trips.

School has an excellent reputation in the local neighbourhood and parents feel lucky to have secured their child a place. At the start of the day, hordes of children in jolly yellow and grey uniforms race along the pavements on scooters. Ongoing problems over road congestion outside, however, and local residents aren't always happy. As one parent put it, 'it's a big, busy primary school. In the morning, the traffic can be horrendous'. Head encourages less driving to school and has even gone so far as to employ numberplate recognition surveillance for repeat parking offenders.

This is an outward-looking school that offers an excellent academic education in a nurturing Catholic environment. Ably led by an inspiring head and with high expectations of pupils, staff and parents, it's impressive on many fronts.

Twickenham Preparatory School

Beveree, 43 High Street, Hampton, Middlesex TW12 2SA

Tel: 020 8979 6216

Independent • Pupils: 274 • Ages: 4–13 • Fees: up to £10,890 pa

Email: office@twickenhamprep.co.uk
Website: www.twickenhamprep.co.uk

Headmaster: Since 2005, Mr David Malam BA Southampton (history), PGCE King Alfred's College, Winchester (40s). Has been at the school for over 15 years, having joined as a history teacher, then deputy head. Before that taught in junior and first schools in Southampton (unusually including a year in a reception class) and at Logos International School in Cyprus, teaching ages 7-16.

He's very popular with pupils, gets to know them all well and is warm and funny around them. 'They are very fond of him, but also really respect him', said a mother. 'He has natural authority and never needs to shout; has a great gift with children', said another. 'He's better with the children than with parents', said a third. 'Personally I agree it's all about the kids, but lots of parents seem to want indulging and he's not good at that side of things'. However, those that know him best say he is 'an excellent headmaster'.

He's a great sports fan, especially football and squash, and he has also played chess at a high level. Lives locally, married, with five children who are, or have been, at the school. 'He treats them just the same as anybody else, they're not his favourites', said our year 6 tour guides confidently.

Entrance: Non-selective at reception, and while perhaps not necessary to register at birth, think about it by a first birthday. No religious requirement in the admission criteria; if you are happy with the ethos they are happy to have you. That's not to say school will say yes to everyone; you've got to fit in socially, behaviourally and academically. Largely a local intake. Other places are occasionally available subject to assessments in English, maths and reasoning. Bus service runs from Richmond and Twickenham.

Exit: All over, especially, at 11, girls to Lady Eleanor Holles, Surbiton High, Wimbledon High, Sir William Perkins, Kingston Grammar, St Catherine's. At 13+ boys to Hampton, Halliford, Reeds and St George's. A few to St Paul's and King's College Wimbledon. Usually a healthy number of scholarships.

Remarks: A popular co-ed prep which prides itself on its positive, family atmosphere and strong Christian ethos. Non-selective, so not packed with academic boffs, but it's no place for a slouch either – increasing numbers of scholars attest to the academic thrust here in recent times. Not as pressured a place as some Surrey schools, but still seriously ambitious for its children, who are indeed going on to win places at the county's top senior schools.

Carefully guided by Mr Malam, Twickenham Prep children will not sit many entrance exams – no more than two or three. 'The eight or nine some do is ridiculous,' he says. 'It's unnecessary; we know our children very well and therefore know which school will suit them best'.

Specialist subject teaching from the off in French, ICT, music and PE. By year 4 all teaching is subject-specific, with pupils moving from room to room for their lessons. No streaming, but setting for maths from year 4. Latin for most girls from year 5 and for boys when they move onto the common entrance programme. French for all, with a little bit of Greek and an introduction to Spanish for those up to it. Nice small classes, typically of 18. Homework is reasonably low key; 'I don't see it as a means of destroying family life,' says Mr Malam. Starts gently with some reading and spelling up to year 2, then one to two homeworks a night, reaching 40 minutes a night by year 6. Thrice-weekly homework clubs similarly take the pressure off family time.

Pupils seem well-engaged with their lessons, and the school's atmosphere is calm and purposeful. ISI inspectors judge teaching here to be always good, and sometimes outstanding, with provision for children with learning difficulties or disabilities said to be 'excellent'. However, it is not the place for a more serious special need, and none of the LDD children currently on roll are statemented.

Music is something of a strength here – there's a large choir and 80 per cent of pupils are swept up for music lessons and get plenty of opportunities to play and perform. Sport is often a bugbear in a small-ish set up like this one – on-site practice space is limited and it's hard to beat some of the larger schools in the area. But on the plus side, the school does have use of Hampton Football Club's facilities, which are directly behind it, and has notched up

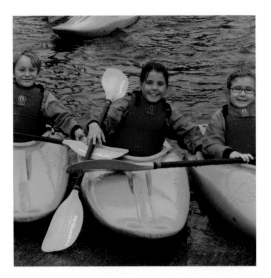

some major tournament wins of late. Parents appreciate the fact that the school's approach is inclusive, with all the children getting an opportunity to play competitively if they want to, with C teams fielded if necessary. Swimming from years 1 to 5 off site. Year 7 and year 8 boys pick up squash and badminton too.

'At first I though it was some sort of hideous team–building exercise beloved of large organisations, but in fact it does get children thinking in a different way'

Nice extracurricular clubs, including music and movement, historic adventures and sewing for pre-prep, and touch-typing, table tennis and knitting for prep pupils. Wrap-around pre- and after-school care. Mr Malam, and therefore his school, is a big fan of the Mind Lab (thinking abilities and life skills) programme which is time-tabled as a weekly lesson. Typically the children play strategy games and learn about lateral thinking. The idea is that this work makes pupils more adaptable and less easily fazed when encountering a new problem for the first time. Mr Malam seems to have converted parents, who praise the programme. 'At first I thought it was some sort of hideous team-building exercise beloved of large organisations, but in fact it does get the children thinking in a different way', said one. 'They think they are just playing games, but really they are learning. And with all the verbal and non-verbal reasoning involved in many entrance exams these days, it does seem to give them a great basis for working things out'.

More mind games come in the form of chess – another Malam passion – or 'obsession' as one mother wryly observed. The school has built up quite a reputation as IAPs champions, English Schools national finalists and borough champions. Grandmaster Daniel King works with the school, involving up to 50 of the children regularly, with up to 30 of them going on to play for school teams.

Parents view the school as very strong pastorally – again, ISI says its provision in this area is 'outstanding'. The school is a really nurturing place; welcoming and warm, a gentle and kind environment with no sharp edges. Watchwords for the pupils are 'calm, courteous, courageous and considerate'. 'And they don't just pay lip-service to those words, they really count for something here,' said a mother. Discipline not really an issue – teachers use positive reinforcement ('Praising a child who is doing well has quite an effect on a child who is not doing as well themselves', says Mr Malam). Losing or winning house points an equally effective device here.

And as you'd expect from a Christian school, bible-based religious education is taken seriously here and children say prayers together. There's no affiliation to any one church, but close links with nearby St Mary's which the children visit for Christmas and harvest services. Assemblies are Christian-based, with a bible story/theme and a moral message. School has its own hymn book, teaches the Lord's Prayer, hosts visits from local Christian community and other faiths.

But that's not to say that the families at this school are all regular worshippers or indeed even Christian – several we spoke to were in fact agnostic or atheist or practitioners of another religion entirely – but obviously these parents share a willingness for their children to be taught about Christian values. 'We don't believe in ignorance of other religions and so have people in to talk about other faiths and cultures too', says Mr Malam. 'Generally I find our parents want their children in a school where they at least understand the ethos, rather than put them into a more secular environment.'

Attracts professional and business-type families, mostly local from Teddington, Twickenham, Sunbury and St Margaret's. The name Twickenham

Prep is actually something of a misnomer, as the school is actually in Hampton – it was originally on Twickenham Green and chose to retain its by then well-established name when it relocated in 1992. Set in unexpectedly peaceful and leafy location behind a busy road, the main school building, Beveree, was once owned by John Blow, King's Musician to Charles II, and is grade 2 listed. Overall not masses of space, despite major extensions, but school makes the most of what there is and has sectioned off some space for a well-used amphitheatre and an adventure playground.

And, lest it all sound too unruffled and worthy, the children also have great fun along the way. A recent fundraising auction of promises saw one boy's family successfully bid for him to take over as headmaster for a day. He took a lesson, spoke to staff, was included in an interview and allowed to introduce some of his own for-one-day-only initiatives. These included arranging for an ice-cream van to visit at the close of school and awarding headmaster's commendation certificates to genuine supporters of Fulham football club.

Increasingly strong academically, it's offering its happy and settled pupils a good all-round education, generally allowing them their pick of all the best local day schools. Holding its own in an area packed with competitive offerings. Not pressured or pushy, rather kind, inspiring and creative.

Twyford Church of England High School

Twyford Crescent, London W3 9PP

State • Pupils: 1,484 • Ages: 11–18 • Sixth form pupils: 505 • C of E

Tel: 020 8752 0141

Email: admissions@twyford.ealing.sch.uk
Website: www.twyford.ealing.sch.uk

12

Executive Head Teacher: Since 2002, Ms Alice Hudson MA (Oxon) (40s), educated at Slough Girls' High and Leighton Park, then St Hilda's, Oxford, where she read English. Previously deputy head at Brentside HS, also in Ealing, and prior to that taught at Central Foundation Boys, Islington and Maria Fidelis, Euston. Joined Twyford in 2000, first as deputy, then acting head and appointed head in September 2002. Married to Michael Lyon. He works for the Bank of England ('more public servant than banker,' she says). He is Roman Catholic, she and their four children are Anglican. Her eldest daughter was given a place at Oxford to read modern languages having completed the sixth form here; her son also attends the school.

'The first five years were Herculean,' she says, 'cleaning out the stables'. (She comes from a family

of classicists and her conversation is littered with references to the ancient world.) There was the thorny issue of a divided community: the haves and have-nots. The crude observer would put it in plain black and white terms – the churchgoing but poorer and underachieving black community as opposed to the playing-by-the-book, aspirational and privileged white community. Ms Hudson takes a more sophisticated approach. 'The cultural capitalisers and disenfranchised,' she elegantly puts it, 'overlaid with typical inner London underachievement issues connected to socio-economic disadvantage, race and gender'. Whichever description you prefer, Ms Hudson was determined to 'harness the diversity of the student/parent body'. 'Exclusions were high,' she continues, 'and I didn't want to exclude, but to sustain a positive culture.'

She proudly announces that she has now achieved three of her original goals: fixed behaviour and attainment, fixed cohesion, fixed aspiration. An intelligent and sensitive woman, she explains she learnt from watching the children; 'you have to read your institution,' she says.

She has introduced a house system (there are seven houses named after cathedrals a process of electing head boy and girl, the new post of school chaplain (allowing her to employ high calibre teaching staff who are not necessarily practising Christians), Latin and geology. Ms Hudson is a team player and her team consists of all the staff, all the students and all the parents.

Refreshing to see the head of a challenging, big state comprehensive not just running a business but also a passionate educator, lover of youth, life and learning. Not always the case in this inspection and results driven age. Parents and pupils admire her quiet authority (you could hear a pin drop in the assembly she took when she stopped mid-flow to say, 'distressed to hear three people talking', looking directly at them across the packed school hall). This, combined with more than a superficial knowledge of all the pupils as well as their parents, her infectious enthusiasm, disarming modesty, and striking physical presence – 'Miss Hudson is everywhere,' said one admiring 15 year old – and her sensitive awareness of every nuance, all contribute to making her an outstanding head. Lucky school.

Twyford is now part of a Multi Academy Trust – Twyford Church of England Academies Trust, with a sister school in Greenford – William Perkin Church of England High School (a free school that opened in 2013). The only flicker of concern is whether Ms Hudson's eye will be taken off the ball as she combines her work here with executive head-teachership at William Perkin.

All pupils have to learn to speak the language, not just from text books, and there are numerous exchanges, to China as well as obvious European destinations

Operations at both schools are 'directed strategically from the centre'. Ofsted, reporting in May 2012 (unsurprisingly, rating the school 'outstanding' in all categories), also picked up on this concern among parents. Ms Hudson is channelling an enormous amount of energy into the project and has the team building skills to pull off her vision, she is your woman. Again, unsurprisingly, Ofsted agreed.

New associate head teacher since September 2013 is Karen Barrie, previously deputy head at the school for nine years. She is a mathematician with a degree from Manchester.

Academic matters: Results just get better and better in this academically, non-selective school. In 2015, 67 per cent A*-B and 38 per cent A*/A grades at A level. Top ability students complete extended project – mostly with A*s. Maths results exceptional. Choices include economics, music tech, photography (very successful), psychology, sociology. Biggest improvement is in sixth form – head's especial baby – 'it's a reliable place for your high-achieving child.. we chase them much more in the sixth form', but the less academic well supported too. In 2015 GCSE results saw 87 per cent of students achieve 5+ passes at C or above (including English and maths), with 40 per cent A*/A grades.

ICT (we saw loads of computers) a developing area though head refreshingly cheery when asked about the poor showing of interactive whiteboards; 'the most important interactive resource in the classroom is the teacher', she observes. Head sees wisdom in steering the less academic to the practical and creative which 'can be studied alongside A level', so double AVCE in ICT popular along with other more vocational subjects. Visual arts are a considerable strength of the school with significant numbers of students going on to art colleges.

Twelve per cent have SLD or SEN ('disproportionately high number of children with statements,' remarks Ms Hudson, 'skewed towards the severe end'). About five per cent of these include those with autism (across the spectrum) and Down's syndrome. All pupils are well supported, either by regular staff or from outside. 'They will be valued and survive here,' says head, 'and parents are also given support – we have very good home-school links.' Although 280 pupils have EAL – first languages in this very ethnically mixed area Gujurati, Punjabi, Arabic and Urdu – no one needs additional help in English.

Since she arrived there has been a tremendous push on languages and it became a specialisation (along with music) several years ago. 'We identify potential linguists in year 7, accelerate them in French and, in year 8, give them a choice of German and Spanish.' The person responsible for the language programme 'is a zealot' she says. All children have to learn to speak the language, not just from text books, and there are numerous exchanges, to China as well as to the obvious European destinations. Latin is taught once a fortnight and pupils can also choose to do it after school. It's not just a hobby, but also a GCSE option. One girl we met who moved here from the Middle East achieved an A* in GCSE Arabic at the end of year 9. If there is a demand or a talent, the school will make it possible to follow that talent and achieve the potential. Other GCSE options include food technology and electronics but DT has been temporarily paused. Setting in most subjects (including science, maths and languages from year 7, English and the humanities from year 9). From year 9 boys and girls are separated in the top two sets in English. There are at least eight sets straddling seven forms plus a tiny nurture group for the extreme special needs. Parents remark on the fluidity of movement between sets, 'you don't just get labelled as D set.' Pupils can sit the more rigorous IGCSEs in maths

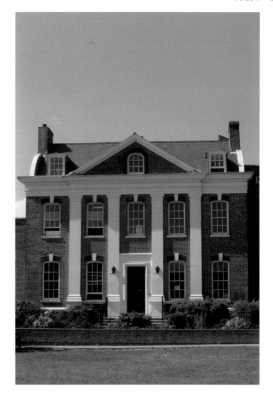

and science (Harrow school provides support with this). RE very much a feature of everyday school life and supported in the sixth form by two conferences each year, often with outside speakers on moral or spiritual topics. Curriculum taught on an alternating two-week cycle, which some find confusing at first, but they get used to it.

Everyone stays to watch the big matches. Another of Ms Hudson's community-knitting devices

We heard some mutterings about the SEN department not always picking up strugglers (without statements) as fast as it should nor providing the continuous support needed. We wonder whether the major advances at the upper end of the ability range are sufficiently matched by rigorous attention to those who are finding work hard. There is no doubt that the formidable Ms Hudson, with her passionate eye for detail, would not like to give less than her full attention to everything, but it's a question of priorities. Expectations are undoubtedly high. Referring to one boy, who happens to be of African/Caribbean descent, who recently achieved eight A*s in his mock GCSEs, Ms

Hudson says, 'unless he achieves 10 A*s when he sits the exams, we will have failed him.' When it comes to academic achievement, Ms Hudson comments, 'The big issue is that although we are doing well as a comprehensive state school, an independent school would be expecting those results. We need to push beyond.'

Games, options, the arts: Remarkable playing fields (albeit rented, not owned), well-concealed along this urban high street site. Netball especially strong here, but you can choose to play hockey, tennis, football, cricket and basketball too. Inter-form competitions are a major event. Everyone stays to watch the big matches. Another one of Ms Hudson's effective community-knitting devices. Dance and athletics popular. Rugby coached by pros from London Wasps. Consistent successes in many sporting areas and representation in borough and regional levels. Thriving art, and stunning music (some parents confessed they wished sport was given as much emphasis as music). The church influence from gospel to choral filters through at every level. A main orchestra plus smaller groups and ensembles present opportunities for lots of live performing. At every assembly there will be live music. When we visited we witnessed a potential Rumer, singing from the heart as she accompanied herself on the piano. Music and music tech

One parent commented on the enthusiasm and commitment of her usually shy and reluctant daughter while acting as one of the boys in Oliver!

facilities impressive and well-used (including the state-of-the-art audio-visual recording studio). Drama is popular and lively and as well as smaller studio performances throughout the year the main event is the massive whole school production that takes place in February. The King and I and Oliver! have recently been performed and one parent commented on the enthusiasm and commitment of her usually shy and reluctant daughter while acting as one of the boys in Oliver!

There is a good work placement programme, though we heard some talk of the aspiring white middle classes with lots of contacts in the world of media and law etc getting plum placements while the less advantaged among the black community ended up working in the charity shop in Shepherd's Bush. School keen to point out that there is support (large database with useful leads, past placements etc, plus an 'Aspirations' conference run annually which invites successful black professionals and entrepreneurs to speak about their work), but the students have to take initiative to tap into that support. The pushy ones are sorted by the end of Lent term, the more lackadaisical are scrabbling around for something a week before they have to start towards the end of the summer term. You can take a horse to water and all that. Pupils enthuse about the number and quality of trips and expeditions – everywhere from St Petersburg to the New Forest for every activity imaginable – photography to water skiing. Lots of charity work.

Background and atmosphere: School tucked behind rare bit of green along the Uxbridge Road. Main building, grade 2 listed The Elms, an elegant, early Georgian house, built 1735, well-preserved and sensibly painted in blues, houses the admin and offices side of things. A diverse mixture of less distinguished and pretty scruffy later blocks, A, B, then, unaccountably, D and M, house rest of school. Rather alarmingly nicknamed 'The Cage' is the large central piece of tarmac surrounded by fencing where 650 pupils line up in alphabetical order each morning. A logistical challenge in a disciplined corporate environment, at Twyford C of E High School it's like sliding a knife through butter. Some attractive modern buildings have emerged organically, including a wonderfully peaceful chapel, a contemporary and refreshingly un-institutional cafeteria (more Café Nero than trad school cafeteria), state-of-the-art performance centre, creative media suite with radio station and refurbished music areas.

Black uniform with white shirts creates somewhat sombre impression but most pupils look tidy (head strides around, not averse to pointing out, amicably, 'shirt!' to any wearer of stray shirt tails) and overall impression is of a good-humoured, confident mix of the boisterous and the purposeful. No uniform for the sixth. Huge ethnic diversity – 52 per cent from non-white British backgrounds, of whom the largest number from Afro-Caribbean families; Asians make up next biggest group. Christian principles in practice evident in staff's approach to all aspects of this richly diverse community. While Anglicanism predominates, all churches and faiths are celebrated and explored here and everyone feels part of the school. Two minutes' daily silent reflection before lessons – 'everyone is quiet', said a sixth former. 'Faith has a big profile here', says head. 'We place a high premium on formal acts of worship.' Everyone attends a termly communion service and there is a weekly voluntary one. Assemblies are inclusive but have an unashamed Christian bias. 'The key to inter-faith issues,' believes head, 'is to be clear about what one's standpoint is.' She talks of the validity of each individual's own 'faith journey'. 'Spiritual matters are neither embarrassing nor taboo here' – a big claim but it feels legitimate. Pupils, though seldom deferential, respect teachers – there is a good working relationship between staff and pupils at all levels. 'They stretch you as far as you can go – but not beyond what you can do,' reflected one sixth former.

Princes and paupers here – all social strata represented and cheerfully interrelate

Pastoral care and discipline: Well-established system of form tutors first resort though pupils able to talk to whichever member of staff they choose. Heads of year back up the tutors and pupils have regular meetings to check on targets, progress, happiness. Chaplaincy team also available. Interaction between ages encouraged – actively by sixth form mentoring of younger pupils and system of form reps. School recently mixed up tutor groups in the sixth form to avoid tutors having particularly strong bonds with the 'home grown' students and less good ties with the newcomers. School council much appreciated – 'It has a lot of power over changes and we can meet the governors,' we were told. Few serious problems – most pupils feeling that offending in school time and on school property 'not worth it' and seemingly a bit immature, though usual crop of minor misdemeanours.

Everyone attends communion service. 'Spiritual matters are neither embarrassing nor taboo here' – a big claim but it feels legitimate

Pupils and parents: As above, huge ethnic mix, Christianity being the unifying principle though 30 places reserved each year for those from 'other world faiths', and Christianity itself taking in Russian/Serbian/Eastern Orthodox along with other denominations. Pupils come from wide geographic area – Brent, Hounslow, all over Ealing and further into town. Most, though, from Christchurch junior school, half a mile away, and nearly 50 other primaries. More boys than girls, though this not generally perceptible. Princes and paupers here – all social strata represented and cheerfully interrelate.

Entrance: Now here's the rub. To get in you not only have to be practising a religious faith but have all the badges and medals to show it too. For year 7, 150 foundation (Christian) and 21 world faith (other religions) places, all based on family's attendance at church/place of worship for at least five years along with home's distance from school. Worth checking this out in detail before losing your heart to the place. No-one is fooled by rapid conversion when your child is in year 6 – though it is still – widely and unsuccessfully – tried. Nineteen music places. Sixth form, hitherto less stringent, now oversubscribed 11:1. They must be getting something right. For external places in the sixth form students must meet individual entry criteria for courses as set out in the sixth form prospectus (minimum usually a B with one or two exceptions) and must be in sympathy with aims and objectives of a C of E school.

Exit: Some 30 per cent leave after GCSEs. Vast and creditable range of courses and universities. They break new records for Oxbridge offers each year – 10 in 2015. The increasing uptake of the extended project has resulted in glowing feedback of pupils' performance in interview and an increasing offer of scholarships.

Remarks: This is an outstanding school. Don't make the mistake of thinking it's anything other than a highly successful inner London comprehensive, however, with all the challenges that entails.

Waldegrave School

Fifth Cross Road, Twickenham, Middlesex TW2 5LH

State • Pupils: 1,280 • Ages: 11–18 • Sixth form pupils: 280 (80 boys)

Tel: 020 8894 3244

Email: info@waldegrave.org.uk
Website: www.waldegrave.richmond.sch.uk

41

Headteacher: Since 2006, Mrs Philippa Nunn, BSc from UCL in zoology, MA in educational management from Greenwich, PGCE and NPQH (40s). Appointed a National Leader of Education in 2011. Married with two daughters at local state schools. Was previously head of the Holt School in Berkshire, an all-girls 11-18 comprehensive. Started teaching science in 1987. Currently teaches ICT.

A calm, glamorous presence. Parents are all big fans. 'She's fantastic. She's a real person. Very approachable. As a mother of two girls she really understands.' Some staff have been teaching here for more than 25 years, which 'adds strength to the ethos of the school'. Introduced a house system to promote a greater sense of loyalty and belonging and to enhance student leadership opportunities.

A keen sports enthusiast, she plays hockey at Teddington, tennis and real tennis are passions. She's also training to become an Ofsted inspector.

Academic matters: Consistently achieves good results in English, maths and science GCSEs. French, history, art, drama, RE always good too. The success rate in A*-C grades is well above the regional and national average; 84 per cent got 5+ A*-C grades including maths and English in 2015 and 50 per cent of grades were A*/A. Top of the Sunday Times Parent Power list for 11 to 16 schools for four years; now has a co-ed sixth form – opened in 2014 – with first students heading for A levels.

We were blown away by the bird sculptures inspired by their sister school in Kenya

Quality of teaching is excellent. 'They're all so dedicated. I can't fault them,' said one parent. Achievements are recognised at assemblies throughout the year and at Celebration Afternoons at the end of the year. High academic standards are expected and some parents say that there is pressure on the students to get good grades. 'My daughter had to do French GSCE when she didn't want to do it as the teachers knew she would get a good grade.' But provision is made within the curriculum for all abilities, and modest acts such as helpfulness to the school or to others are duly acknowledged and rewarded.

Lessons are given in broad ability tutor groups initially, but setting for maths, science and languages occurs early on in the first years. In subsequent years, setting in other subjects if appropriate. All are entered for 6-10 GCSEs; some do up to 13 after discussion with parents and staff. Short course subjects such as ICT and PE well subscribed with good results.

Appointed as one of the first 100 Teaching Schools, and is also a National College for School Leaders National Support School. Designated area in an independent learning centre for gifted and talented girls and those with other special needs. Provides 'enhanced specialist teaching provision' for six girls with speech and languages difficulties/ autism. With an incredible cultural diversity (43 different languages), EAL support is strong, even offering a lunchtime club for all age groups. On the subject of lunchtime, a great deal is compressed into a very short 35 minute break: careers advice, ICT, rehearsals for choirs and bands, puzzle club, homework clubs. Similarly, lots of before and after-school activities. A breakfast club at 8.00am every morning with badminton on offer at the same time for the more energetic. After school up until 4.00pm – choice is much more varied with a high take-up rate.

Games, options, the arts: Good range of sports offered – rounders, tennis, volleyball, athletics, rugby (with the Harlequins). Classes in the fitness suite, cricket, rowing (linked in with Walbrook Rowing Club) and table-tennis. Hidden from view from the road is a huge outdoor green area with tennis courts and marked-out running track. New sixth form block features four court sports hall.

School regularly wins regional netball leagues and was recently the Middlesex hockey champion. Also borough winners at netball and rounders. Running club is popular with 40 girls doing a 5k run twice a week with four teachers before school. (The head attempts to join them once every half term.) Head positively oozes enthusiasm, listing her school's sporting achievements. Another of her aims is to improve participation in sport. Gymnastics is strong – both a multi and traditional gym on site. A dance studio was funded through the National Lottery.

Extra opportunities include bridge, drama (big production every alternate year and an annual joint production with Hampton Boys' School), study skills, chess, art, music theory, ICT, choirs, rock bands and full orchestra. Art and music are both strengths. Year 7s all learn the recorder and in year 8 they get the chance to play the ukulele! When we visited we were blown away by the bird sculptures made in art lessons, inspired by their sister school in Madogo, Kenya.

After-school clubs include extra languages, eg Mandarin GCSE and there's even an astronomy club which parents can also attend. These cost extra but the Pupil Premium funds places for those who qualify.

Background and atmosphere: Original 1930s building has been added to over the years. Science labs are housed in newish block and brand new sixth form building opened in 2014, housing new sports hall and dining room. Outside play area transformed with money from the PTA with an outdoor theatre and landscaped surroundings. Food freshly cooked on site, and a biometric system for payment. Some girls take sandwiches. 'I don't want them having a slice of pizza and a muffin every day,' explained one parent. The girls themselves give this school a buzzy atmosphere. A former pupil remarked that 'all girls is a positive rather than a negative.'

Recent £7 million building programme has provided new sixth form block with library, café, study base, the latest IT and digital resources, specialist laboratories and a Sports England approved sports hall.

Pastoral care and discipline: No real behavioural problems. First years are invited to spend a day in the school to find their way about and practise their journey to and fro – puts a stop to later excuses about buses being late. They also start the term a bit earlier before the older ones arrive. Prefects help out with the younger ones, organise charity events, welcome visitors and play an important leadership role in the school. Each tutor group elects a representative to attend the school council, which in turn represents the school at the Richmond School Student Council. All good training ground for debating and public speaking.

First years are invited to spend a day in the school to find their way about and practise their journey to and fro – puts a stop to excuses about buses being late

School is honest about bullying and admits that, like the poor, it is always with us. However, stringent efforts made to put an end to it. Girls, staff and parents exhorted to report any incident straight away and assured that something will be done.

Pupils and parents: Although the school has no religious affiliation, the majority of the pupils are Christian. More than 25 per cent are from an ethnic minority. All come from the surrounding borough of Richmond, which is known nationally for its high level of professional parents. A local parent declares it to be the sort of school where 'decent folk will be prepared to break all sorts of rules to get their daughters in.' New (co-ed) sixth form is making this school even more desirable.

Entrance: Fully comprehensive intake. It is the only all girls' state school in Richmond so is always oversubscribed. Much to the head's relief, all admissions are dealt with by the local authority. Despite clear and rigid guidelines about admissions policies there are always appeals. Priority to those with special needs and those in public care or who are deemed by the LA to have a particular need, to siblings, daughters of staff and those living in priority areas. Most girls will have attended local primary schools in the borough. Six places are available in total in the school for those with speech and language difficulties or those on the autistic spectrum – invariably very oversubscribed.

Forty out of the 280 places in the sixth form are for boys but majority of girls' places will be taken by Waldegrave students. Five A*-C GCSE grades needed for entry, with Bs in the subjects to be studied at A level.

Exit: In the past students have gone to Richmond Sixth Form College, Esher College, Strodes College or to sixth forms of independent schools. This has changed as the new (oversubscribed) co-ed sixth form enables around 50 per cent of girls to remain at the school to study for A levels. 'We hope to be sending students to Oxbridge and the Russell Group universities,' explains the head.

Remarks: A really buzzy school. 'It felt more dynamic than the other schools we visited,' said one parent. This school has so much going on that you're a lucky girl if you manage to get a place here. Now with the new sixth form you're even luckier.

North

Barnet
Enfield
Harringey

NORTH

An introduction to North London and its state schools

Barnet

Barnet, which stretches from Hampstead Heath to Hertfordshire, is leafy and suburban. It includes Hampstead Garden Suburb, founded in the early 20th century by Henrietta Barnett, whose eponymous grammar school in Central Square is one of the most sought-after in the country. The idea of the Suburb was to have houses for a range of incomes and gardens for every single person. So houses range from tiny to palatial, some Georgian but many Tudorbethan, with flower and tree lined streets. Highgate village is quietly residential with a definitely country atmosphere, Highgate and Hampstead golf courses nearby and Highgate School qv occupying much of the local land and property.

As with Henrietta Barnett School grammar school for girls qv, Queen Elizabeth School qv (boys) also regularly attracts more than 10 applicants per place; the other popular grammar school is St Michael's Catholic Grammar qv. Mill Hill County High qv awards a quarter of its places on aptitude (24 technology, 24 music and 12 dance). Non-selective Ashmole Academy qv, Queen Elizabeth Girls qv, Compton, Copthall qv, Wren Academy qv (50 per cent church places) and Finchley Catholic High also do well, as does Woodhouse sixth form college qv. The newish Archer Academy is attracting increasing numbers of applicants. Hasmonean High is for orthodox Jewish children (boys' and girls' sections on different sites) and JCoSS a cross-communal Jewish school.

Lots of faith primaries here too including Monken Hadley C of E, St Mary's C of E, St Theresa's and Sacred Heart Catholic schools. Wren Academy has opened a primary school on the same site. There are several primary schools for orthodox Jewish families, including the Independent Jewish Day School and Menorah Primary. Popular secular primaries include Brookland , Garden Suburb and Moss Hall Infant and Junior Schools, Foulds, Monkfrith, Manorside and Northside.

Enfield

Enfield is on the northernmost edge of London, with the M25 dividing it from Hertfordshire and Epping Forest to the east. It has over 100km of rivers and waterways, and copious parks and green space. It also houses the Chickenshed theatre, home to the largest youth theatre in Europe.

Its best known school is The Latymer qv, a co-ed grammar school, which attracts over 2000 applicants for 186 year 7 places. It will generally make offers only to those in its 'inner area' postcodes, which include parts of Waltham Forest, Haringey, Hackney and Islington as well as Enfield. Good non-selective secondaries in the borough include Southgate and the rapidly improving Highland School.

Walker primary in Southgate is top of many local parents' primary school lists, as are Chase Side, Eversley and Firs Farm. St George's RC, St Paul's C of E and Our Lady of Lourdes are among the most popular faith schools.

Haringey

Hilly Haringey is bordered by Highgate Golf Club in the west and the Lea Valley in the east. Its westerly wards include some of the most prosperous – Crouch End, Muswell Hill and Highgate – and its easterly wards some of the most deprived. Many young parents move out to the family-friendly areas of Muswell Hill and Crouch End to take advantage of the many popular state schools.

Fortismere qv, at the top of liberal, intellectual Muswell Hill, has long been the comprehensive of choice for those fortunate enough to live close enough. Alexandra Park School qv, its constricted site given an air of greenery by neighbouring Muswell Hill golf club and Durnsford Park, is gaining rapidly in popularity, as is Highgate Woods.

The more westerly areas in particular abound with excellent primary schools: Tetherdown qv, Rhodes Avenue qv,

Coldfall qv, Coleridge, Muswell Hill, St Michael's C of E qv and St James C of E. Several have expanded in recent years to cope with huge demand, but catchments are often rather less than half a mile.

Alexandra Park School

Bidwell Gardens, London N11 2AZ

State • Pupils: 1,430 • Ages: 11–18 • Sixth form pupils: 350

Tel: 020 8826 4880

Email: office@apsch.org.uk
Website: www.apsch.org.uk

21

Headteacher: Since 2008, Mr Michael McKenzie MSc PGCE (early 40s). Educated at a comprehensive in Birmingham, he read chemistry at Nottingham, then did his teacher training at The Institute of Education. Head of year at William Ellis School in Camden, head of sixth form at LaSwap, followed by deputy and associate head at Beal High School in Redbridge. Familiar and comfortable with the school's ethos before he applied, as the founding head had been his teaching mentor. Finds his pupils 'very entertaining, thoroughly enjoyable' and they (and their parents) feel he is a relaxed and positive addition. 'He's always about and knows a lot of the kids by name. He's very on the ball,' said one mother.

Academic matters: Alexandra Park's motto is 'success for all' and the school pulls off the very tricky achievement of being a successful London comprehensive welcoming the full range of abilities and social spectrum. 'Unlike other schools round here, it doesn't pick and choose. It's very inclusive,' said one parent. The intake may be all-encompassing but the academic values remain traditional. 'We don't play any games with the curriculum,' says the head, and the school is notably strong on core

subjects. 2015 results at GCSE: 77 per cent got 5+ A*-C including English and maths, with 40 per cent of grades A*/A. Most pupils take 10, including all three sciences. Spanish, French and Mandarin standard languages with Turkish also an exam option for GCSE and A level. Classics also a popular option with more than 120 pupils studying this at GCSE and A level.

Has specialist status as a science and maths school and an international school. More than 200 students last year had the opportunity of studying in partner schools in France, Spain, South Africa and China. Mandarin on the curriculum here and is more than token – students can spend time on an immersion course in Beijing, with 30 studying the language pre-GCSE, a dozen or so in the sixth form.

A National Teaching School, indicating the importance the school places on appointing the best practitioners and ensuring they receive the latest training.

Some setting from year 7, depending on the department head – so maths and science are setted, English is not. Arts and media studies – unsurprisingly in this heartland of the media classes – are notably good so, to counterbalance the trend, has opted for a specialism in science and maths, with a dramatic upswing in results. Good vocational curriculum, with BTecs in sport, business, art, salon services and catering, some taught at the College of North East London. 'It means children who might have been less engaged have something positive and interesting to do, and those taking academic exams have the space to focus,' said one parent.

Strong gifted and talented programme – pupils take early exams in maths, statistics, astronomy and classics. Also notable SEN support under dynamic head of special needs, with additional support in year 7 for those who've not yet achieved the requisite level in maths and English. Some parents, however, feel the extreme ends attract the bulk of attention: 'I think it would be quite difficult to get support if your kids come in the middle,' said one. 'You have to be very proactive.'

Popular sixth form – in 2015, a creditable 38 per cent A*/A grades and 66 per cent A*-B grades at A level; 32 subjects on offer – strongest include English, French, physics and 'a really happening' history department.

Games, options, the arts: Busy, busy, busy. Specialist music and drama with a media suite and dance on offer. Last year's huge, all-encompassing drama production of The Wiz attracted a cast of 260 kids and staff. Energetic visual arts with A levels in photography, art and product design, plus a creative and

Eclectic range of after-school clubs includes knitting, astronomy, pursuit cycling and cheerleading. 'Kids come up with the ideas,' says the head

media diploma for those wishing to work on large-scale projects. Both BTec and A level music. School choir, with an international schedule. Trips a big feature, with 116 different excursions last year, including a three-week exchange to Beijing, geography in Iceland, French in the south of France, art in Madrid, politics in Washington and design in New York.

Though relatively limited on-site space for sport, games spill over into adjoining Dunsford Park and plenty of variety to suit all tastes. Basketball, football (Newcastle United striker Nile Ranger used to star in the APS team), cricket and netball are main sports, but judo, aerobics, tennis, badminton, wrestling, rugby and golf also part of the offering (aspiring Nick Faldos can daydream their hole-in-ones gazing out from the classroom onto Muswell Hill golf course). Online student newspaper. Eclectic range of after-school clubs includes knitting, astronomy, fashion, pursuit cycling and cheerleading. 'Kids come up with the ideas,' says the head. Good careers advice with visits to universities and higher educational conferences. State-of-the-art sixth form centre, with study centre and purpose-built social space.

Background and atmosphere: Local parents lobbied the local authority to create a new school in the area and APS was eventually founded in 1999 on the site of a former FE college. A relatively constricted site, which feels more spacious due to the surrounding greenery of Muswell Hill golf course and Durnsford Park. The original mix of pleasant brick buildings, some from the 1950s, some from the 1980s, have been joined by a sleek modern extension (winner of a 2006 Civic Trust Award) and the sixth form centre.

Parents unanimous on the remarkably welcoming atmosphere – 'Everyone from the lady on the gate who checks uniform to the school receptionist makes you feel at home'. Even the police officer seeing kids onto after-school buses does it with a smile. Parents also enthuse about the school's multi-culturalism and inclusiveness ('They really try to be for everybody') and genuine concern ('It's far more nurturing than some of the other local comprehensives'). But concern is not cosseting – 'My children came from quite a sheltered primary school, but I feel they've learnt to cope with life here and to cope with London'.

Pastoral care and discipline: Traditional values apply. 'Kids need firm boundaries and it's important for the school to set them,' says the head. 'We expect them to be at school, on time, in uniform, ready to work.' Smart red, grey and black kit is strictly enforced. 'There used to be a gang who wore their uniform in a special way and that's now all ended,' said one parent approvingly. Behaviour in general is good and school hopes to keep it that way by instilling a sense of responsibility. 'We're training pupils to choose to do the right thing.' Misdemeanours promptly and firmly dealt with – 'When my son got into a fight, there was absolutely no messing. They threw the rulebook at him'. Drugs not a notable issue. 'It's bizarre' says the head, 'at a previous school we had an incident every week. Here perhaps they're more savvy – or more mature.' Weapons, too, conspicuously absent.

Year 7 has its own 'transition manager'. Pupils remain in the same tutor groups for five years with a director of studies for each year. Also supported by learning mentors and counsellors. About 40 pupils with statements of special needs have mainly cognitive rather than behavioural difficulties and the school copes well with autism, Asperger's and Down's. Communication between parents and school clearly a strong point – 'All my emails, however trivial, get answered promptly'.

Pupils and parents: Wide social spread, from the comfortable middle-class suburbs near the gates to some of the most deprived kids in the country – 'a high proportion on the cusp of social needs'. Middle classes tend to dominate the PTA, which runs endless jumble sales and bazaars and is strongly involved in the day-to-day running of the school, but the kids themselves mix well. Very supportive parents – 'Parents helped set it up and want to make it work'. The school's popularity has reduced the catchment and the launch of another new school to the east is likely to make the intake more socially homogenous.

Entrance: Around 1500 applications for 216 places. Usual priority to looked-after children, those with statements of special needs and siblings, then distance from the gates, which is now less than a mile. A bulge from adjoining high-achieving primary Rhodes Avenue, as well as from Bounds Green, Our Lady of Muswell, Bowes, Coldfall and Hollickwood.

Majority of existing pupils continue into sixth form. Sixth form of 340; 80 per cent come up from year 11, the rest from other local schools. Open access, provided courses are available and attendance and attitude good enough. External applicants for A levels should have at least five GCSEs A*-C, with Bs in A level subject choice.

Exit: Some 30 per cent leave after GCSEs. In sixth form majority apply to university; popular destinations include Oxbridge, Edinburgh, Bristol, Imperial, King's College London, UCL and Manchester.

Money matters: Training school and academy trust status bring in extra funding.

Remarks: A notably welcoming place for children (and adults) from a large swathe of the borough. Not an academic pressure cooker but a school with high standards for all.

Annemount School

18 Holne Chase, London N2 0QN

Independent · Pupils: 90 · Ages: 2.75–7 · Fees: up to £15,150 pa

Tel: 020 8455 2132

Email: headteacher@annemount.co.uk
Website: www.annemount.co.uk

Headmistress: Since 1993, Ms Geraldine Maidment (50s), previously head of Hilltop Nursery in Hampstead. First teaching experience was as an English teaching assistant in Vienna, during her University College London year abroad, whilst studying German and history of art. Worked at Sotheby's before teaching at Basset House School. A widely travelled linguist (she speaks five languages), she has visited and attended schools in many different countries. During a two-year sabbatical in Colorado, she did a masters in child and family studies at Denver University and joined a school board concerned with social and emotional issues of school age children. Has also been on UK local government committees related to early years and works as an educational consultant for pupils who need schooling advice at any stage.

Has two grown up daughters and five step-grandchildren, who have all attended Annemount. Parents say: 'She's very on the ball and intelligent.'

'She's not going to be your best friend,' commented one (another 'begged to differ'), 'but she's incredible with the children'; 'She's very strict, but in a good way'; 'She's very good at explaining what is going on and how we can help.'

Entrance: Main intakes into the nursery (2.75+ years), kindergarten (3+ years) and reception (4+ years). Both parents are expected to come on the school tour: 'I tell them you're making the biggest decision of your life for your most precious possession. You both need to be involved'. More or less first come first served into the nursery classes, with preference for siblings. Assessments for kindergarten upwards: 'They must be able to fit in socially and behaviour-wise, and they must be able to cope. Our classes are very busy, and the children need energy and stamina'. Discourages applications from families who live further than about four miles away – 'Children shouldn't spend hours a day sitting in a car'.

Exit: Some move at 4 or 5, but most at 7, to local independent schools, eg Habs' Boys' and Girls', Belmont, Highgate, Channing, South Hampstead High, St Margaret's, UCS, North London Collegiate, City of London Girls', St Mary's and Lyndhurst. A few to local state primaries, eg Garden Suburb or Brookland.

Remarks: One of a quiet street of large, brick-built early 20th century houses in the midst of leafy and wealthy Hampstead Garden Suburb. The school, with small but bright and colourful classrooms, was built by grateful parents for the previous ex-governess owner, who was head until she died in

1993 at the age of 93. Large garden, divided into a nursery playground with Wendy house and grassy area and a playground for the older children with a climbing frame, sand table, sports equipment, planting areas and gazebo.

Inevitably, its ultimate raison d'être is to prepare the children for 7+ exams, but this does not overshadow school life – 'People feel we really understand children, their stages of development and their needs'. The early years concentrate on personal and emotional development: learning to listen, developing good social awareness and independent thinking skills – 'We encourage them to be well organised, plan ahead, problem solve'.

A broad curriculum with lots of practical emphasis. Cookery is used to learn maths, debating helps with language, chess with strategy and problem-solving, sports with coordination. Reception had just finished making its own playdough when we visited, another class had taken photos of the other houses in the road and made models of them, and in another were newly-hatched chicks. In year 2 children choose a project they present to the class – which can be on anything from Nelson Mandela to Arsenal. 'By the time they have heard about all the different projects, they know a lot about a lot of things.'

Children are assessed for developmental delays from an early stage and outside help may be recommended for anything from a lack of pencil control to poor social skills. 'We have a good bank of respected practitioners, and interventions work particularly well when they are very young. We recommend them to protect children's self-esteem and help them reach their potential.' Probably not ideal for a very boisterous child, or for one who cannot cope with change. 'We have had fantastic success with one or two Asperger's children, but this is not generally the place for them. We offer places if we feel we can fully meet the child's needs. It is most important that children's school experiences shouldn't be stressful.'

A broad curriculum with lots of practical emphasis. Cookery is used to learn maths, debating helps with language, chess with strategy and problem-solving

Teachers a mix of youth and old hands – 'Some have worked with me for over 20 years, and we're like a family. We're more pedagogues than teachers'. Praise from parents: 'The children really love my daughter's teacher and want to please her', and from the ISI, which talks of the 'high standard of teaching skills across the school'.

Children have plenty of opportunities for, and find great delight in, taking responsibility as head boy, head girl or a member of the school council, which has regular lunches with the head, who also invites birthday children to tea. Many performance opportunities too, in concerts, plays and poetry recitals – 'We like to celebrate the arts'.

Strong emphasis on all matters green: composting, reusing, exercise, healthy eating. Lunch boxes must contain 'real food': nothing processed or ready-wrapped. We saw children tucking in to salmon risotto, sushi, tortillas and pasta salad. 'Seemed annoying at first,' said a parent, 'but my daughter is talking about why certain foods are good for you and why some are not, and how she feels when she eats something too sugary.'

Unusually wide range of extracurricular activities for a pre-prep. Around a third of the children learn the violin at school – 'It gives them zillions of study skills, such as concentration and perseverance, and those who keep it up tend to do exceptionally well academically'. Everyone is offered dance and drama, gym and swimming, French and computing as well as chess and recorder; also a very active and serious co-ed football team. 'When the children leave they have a whole breadth of experiences that stand them in very good stead later on.'

The head brought back with her from the States a belief in strong links with parents and the local community. Parents report lots of emphasis on getting together as families for meals and outdoor activities. The school runs parent education sessions, social events and plenty of whole school initiatives such as sponsored walks. Parents and grandparents come in to lead assemblies, help with topics, accompany school trips to anywhere from Hampstead Heath to the British Museum, talk about their jobs or hobbies. The PTA organises charity events, picnics and parties, and arranges school workshops, visits by theatre groups and farm animals as well as the annual garden fête.

'It's a very warm and friendly place,' said a parent. 'My daughter has thrived here and our experience has been brilliant. They do a nice mix of activities and she's really excited about learning.'

Ashmole Academy

Cecil Road, London N14 5RJ

State • Pupils: 1,485 • Ages: 11–18 • Sixth form pupils: 350

Tel: 020 8361 2703

Email: office@ashmoleacademy.org
Website: www.ashmoleacademy.org

2

Head Teacher: Since 1997, Mr Derrick Brown MA MBA DipEd – degree subjects psychology and business. Formerly a scientist, but changed career when he realised it wasn't all about 'filling pretty liquids into tubes. It was actually quite isolating and I'm a people person.' He was advised at the time to become either a teacher or a prison governor. He opted for the former. Prior to headship at Ashmole, he was vice principal at Leigh City Technology College in Dartford and then senior deputy at Cranford School – both schools much the same size and diversity of Ashmole and in comparable outer London suburbs.

Recently turned 60, but 'nowhere near retiring.. I wouldn't know what to do with myself'. Quietly spoken, serious and tirelessly focused on getting things done, an outstandingly successful head. His drive and determination stem from his own 'not great' secondary school education which prompted him to challenge the state school system – in this case to turn a bog standard local comp into one with all the academic benefits of a private school education, without the fees. As he says: 'Why should only a privileged few have these opportunities? I want to make it available to all kids.'

Mr Brown vowed when he started at Ashmole to make an immediate impact on results; 'It was a fairly averagely performing school with not very high aspirations.' He took a hard look at the areas that were lacking and the following year results were already up by 10 per cent; 'I created partnerships with parents, worked on the discipline and talent scouted good teachers.' His 'football manager's mentality' of never being satisfied, and always something to improve on, has awarded Ashmole the title of 'super state school' according to the Evening Standard.

One gets the feeling that this head has little time or inclination for many hobbies. With two grown up children of his own, any extracurricular activities he may pursue are of the more 'unusual' kind – which currently he says is re-vamping an old wreck he bought (we're presuming he means property). Although there's no resting on laurels for this head, he has already consolidated Ashmole's reputation as a provider of comprehensive education at its best.

Academic matters: This school hasn't been awarded the title of 'super state' for no reason. As the head says: 'Every subject excels here, no subject is weak.' Ofsted outstanding – it has managed to sustain many years of exceptionally high results. Strong value added. Entirely non-selective, so the results are impressive. Way ahead of the other non-selective schools in the area. 'There are no tricks here – all the students come from the local community.' Anyone can do well here, we were told – boys, girls

the less motivated, 'everyone exceeds their personal best.' Classes are setted in main subjects – 'mixed ability doesn't work except in certain areas', says the head.

Drama popular – well-equipped studio and major annual musical production

In 2015, 78 per cent achieved five or more A*-C grades at GCSE, including English and maths, 35 per cent A*/A grades. A levels 33 per cent A*/A and 67 per cent A*-B grades. French is popular and there's a very strong exchange link with the twinned town of Le Raincy, a suburb just outside Paris. Spanish and German are also offered at GCSE and A level, but less popular.

Students are closely monitored and undergo assessments after every half term. The head says: 'If we see underperformance, we can intervene and work with the child individually to make them improve.' However, one parent we spoke to disagreed. 'Ashmole is a great school if you are the academic, studious type. However if, like my daughter, you don't fit the mould, you're going to have more of a struggle there.' Teachers are also closely monitored and parents feel that there is quite a high turnover, although the school says it is similar to most London schools. But if this is the case, it is not an unhealthy state of affairs anyway, according to the head. He says: 'A stable school with no turnover can be a recipe for complacency and disaster.'

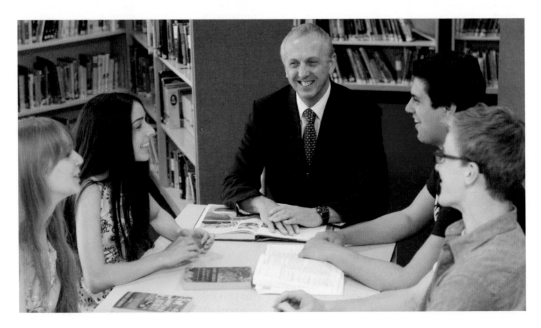

A third of the school has English as an additional language – support in place to make sure they progress, either through extra help or (mostly) in-class intervention. Around a seventh have some kind of SEN – about 1.5 per cent with statements. Learning support is located within its own area, providing adequate space that caters for all needs. The weakest 30 students drop languages after year 8, taking BTec business instead, although this varies every year. These students have extra help with the basics.

Able, gifted and talented pupils – those who have all round ability across the core subjects of English, maths and science (around 1 in 4 students at Ashmole) – have their own programme designed for them. This bespoke Ashmolean programme involves a variety of activities which 'encourage aspiration,' whether this be by visiting higher education institutes or learning through Firefly, the school's virtual learning environment. However, one unhappy parent called it an 'exclusive' club and a very 'rigid' system; 'most students who are on the programme come on it straight from primary school and there seems to be little movement.' She also said that much is made of the G&T students and the privileges offered to them, which makes the other students feel less worthy. Another parent disagreed, saying that her child has been 'on and off the programme many times according to her grades.'

Games, options, the arts: The opportunities are plentiful and the facilities wonderful. Huge floodlit Astroturf court, playing field, sports hall and separate studio for dance, aerobics and net sports, but no pool. Outdoor table tennis on offer, which proves to be a very popular lunchtime activity. Outstandingly successful in both boys' and girls' football; the boys' football team recently won the Barnet Cup and the girls' team reached the semi-final of the Middlesex Cup. Rugby also a biggie and the year 8 rugby team won the Barnet Saracens tournament recently. One parent told us: 'Even if your child is not the academic type, the sports on offer can give them the opportunity to shine.'

Much acclaimed music department. Amy Winehouse was a former student (although head, who was here at the same time, says: 'Amy left us quite early on to join the BRIT school'). Having a music specialism, they are able to employ the very latest technology. Music scholarships on offer to help those with talent develop their skills, and an increasing number of pupils take individual music lessons. A full range of extracurricular music programmes also on offer, including an orchestra, jazz band, chamber string group, junior string group, brass band, senior wind ensemble, Latin rock band, two choirs and show band for the annual school musical.

Drama popular – big, well-equipped studio and major musical production each year. Standards are high – this year saw a 'fantastic' production of Hairspray. Impressive art studios and some astounding individual pieces of art. The school has its own radio station and two recording studios. Plenty of lunchtime and after-school clubs, including film club, debating societies, mad for books club, philosophy, homework clubs and numerous language clubs. Enrichment groups offer a choice of cultural, entrepreneurial and environmental activities. 'The options here are great,' a sixth former told us. 'We're bombarded with courses and clubs which enrich us as people.' He was not wrong.

Background and atmosphere: This is a different school, quite literally, from the Ashmole of yesteryear. It had survived in pretty dire conditions for years but, on his arrival in 1997, the head organised the sale of six acres of school land and began a visionary building programme with the proceeds. Design of new buildings the result of collaboration between the school, a very proactive parent committee and the architect. Rehoming happened in 2004 at a cost of £14m. The result is a bright and spacious, well-mapped-out building, 'which is easy to navigate,' one parent told us. All subjects grouped into their own sections and everything immaculately labelled. No chance of getting lost

Quiet classrooms (with the odd exception), an atmosphere that encourages work and discourages messing around

here. The only confusing things are the different coloured named staircases, like the 'orange staircase,' which in fact is blue. The head told us: 'When we designed the building we wanted to colour group it into sections so, for example, people could meet at the orange staircase, but this wasn't DDA compliant for partially sighted people, so everything has to be kept white and blue.' Lifts are also available for students with disabilities.

Large, wide corridors with beautiful wall displays, seriously impressive artwork and a convivial atmosphere. As we progressed from section to section we witnessed quiet classrooms (with the odd exception), with an atmosphere that encourages work and discourages messing around. 'We have a policy at this school that lessons should be silent, unless they require a discussion. It helps to keep the class focused.' We also noticed a lot of reading going on – by individuals in the canteen and elsewhere. The head told us that he insists every

student carries a book of their choice around with them. 'There is no such thing as doing nothing,' he said. 'One can always read.'

Set in 28 acres of land in quiet, residential Southgate, the outside of the school is none too shabby either, especially for a London comprehensive. Plenty of outdoor space. Remarkably free of litter and immaculately kept lawns, outdoor classroom and environmental area, fully equipped with wooden table and benches. So much excess land that plans are under way to create an Ashmole primary school on the premises. 'There is such a lack of primary schools in the area, it makes sense,' says the head. We say: Start booking your kids in now.

The new sixth form block, kitted out with its own Starbucks, was opened in 2014. This has been many years in the waiting, has taken £1.3 million to raise (through fundraising events and tightening of the old school purse strings), two contractors and various other obstacles. One student told us: 'It's so exciting, I'm just upset I'll only have one year to enjoy it.'

Pastoral care and discipline: Big on discipline. 'Not for the free spirit,' one mother told us. Strict adherence to their uniform code expected – no exceptions or students will be asked to go home and change. Lo and behold: if pupils are caught outside the school premises with a shirt hanging out, they will be seriously reprimanded, sometimes even face a detention. Mobiles, too, are strictly forbidden, except for the sixth form – confiscated immediately if found and, to add to the humiliation, parents have to go in to school and pick them up. While this has been a bone of contention with many of the parents, who like to get hold of their kids after school hours, others feel it is a good thing. 'If nothing else because there have been some phone thefts in the area, but muggers know not to bother with Ashmole kids as they never have phones on them,' one parent told us.

Zero tolerance of drugs, weapons and violence – on or off the premises. Much has been done to combat bullying, which has clearly been a problem at Ashmole in former years (as in many comprehensives of this size). CCTV cameras operate along main corridors 'to monitor any deviant behaviour that may occur' and when the new building was designed head specifically requested wide, open spaces free of 'little cul-de-sacs,' where vulnerable students could be cornered. As Orwellian as this may sound, bullying is now virtually non-existent and parents are very grateful.

Disruptive or abusive pupils are sent to the individual learning room, where they are under supervision, have no contact with their friends and hate it. Two or three days there usually does the trick, but head will exclude for serious offences – roughly five permanent exclusions a year. 'We just can't let a disruptive child continue,' he says. 'They are given community service and various other deterrents, but if they are hell bent on being disruptive, they're out.' The result of this is a school in which pupils feel secure and comfortable and everyone knows the score.

Interaction between year groups encouraged by cultural and charitable activities

Each key stage has its own learning mentors and key stage managers whom pupils know they can go to if they feel the need. Parents aren't so convinced. One parent we spoke to said: 'It's not always made clear who we should be speaking to, or emailing. I have left messages on several occasions and no one has responded. I think the communication between parents and year heads could be improved.' However, for the most part, parents and students we spoke to seemed extremely happy with the school. One sixth former told us: 'I've loved every minute of this school. The sixth form is like a big family, even for external students.'

A large amount of interaction between the year groups, encouraged by the cultural and charitable activities. Pupils feel they have friends in all years. Charity work plays a vital part in the general ethos of the school and every year students and staff raise thousands of pounds for a variety of good causes. Overall, the school has a general sense of self-discipline and a fostering of civilised behaviour.

Pupils and parents: Vast ethnic mix, as you'd expect from the Southgate area, though more Cypriots – Greek and Turkish – than anything else. Main religion is Christianity of all sorts, the second is Islam. Mostly working parents, but a supportive and hard working PTA makes big contribution to the school's development. Pupils are cheery, ambitious, focused and involved. Notable former students include: Amy Winehouse, former S Club 7 member Rachel Stevens, musician Stephen Sidwell, goalie Mark Bunn, Oscar winning producer Mark King, The Feeling lead vocalist Daniel Sells and Channel 5 tsar Sham Sandhu.

Entrance: More than 1,100 apply for the 232 places – of which siblings will take around 80. You'll get in if you have a sibling there, are a looked-after child or live very close – otherwise no chance. 'I wish I had bought on Cecil Road years ago. Houses must be worth a fortune now', one parent sighed. Up to 20 music aptitude places; these pupils, along with others who show talent, are placed on the music scholarship programme.

Exit: Around 30 per cent leave after GCSEs, mostly for vocational courses elsewhere. The rest need to get Bs in the subjects they wish to study for A levels to stay on in the sixth form. Around half of sixth formers to top universities; generally a few to Oxbridge (three in 2015) and several medics; others to places like Durham, Warwick, London universities, Nottingham, Leeds. Science, law and humanities are popular too.

Remarks: Slick, sensible and effective. Check out the housing market.

Belmont Mill Hill Preparatory School

Linked schools: Grimsdell, Mill Hill Pre-Preparatory School, 524; Mill Hill School, 544

The Ridgeway, London NW7 4ED

Independent • Pupils: 470 • Ages: 7–13 • Fees: £16,167 pa

Tel: 020 8906 7270

Email: office@belmontschool.com
Website: www.belmontschool.com

Head: Since September 2015, Mr Leon Roberts MA PGCE. Taught for four years in the state sector, moved to Keble Prep as head of history for the next four years then became deputy head (academic) of Belmont in 2004 before being promoted to senior deputy head (pastoral) in 2010 and finally taking on the headmaster's role. Married with three young daughters, including twins, he enjoys cricket (playing and coaching, both boys and girls), walking and watching Nordic Noir drama.

Down-to-earth, hands on and with the same energetic style as the outgoing head, he approaches the job with the same consultative and open style – in his first year he plans to build on a school which is in great shape (which he's been involved in creating) and adding his own mark.

Entrance: Automatic entry from pre-prep (Grimsdell) to prep (except in some very rare cases). This accounts for two-thirds of the school's intake. For external candidates, there are two main points of entry into the school – 7+ (year 3) and 11+ (year 7). NB part of a group of independent co-ed/boys' schools that coordinate 11+ results, but forbid those who have accepted a place at one school from taking up a subsequent waiting list offer from another. 'Occasional places available in other years (known as 'chance vacancies'). External candidates, so each expected to take reading, creative writing and maths tests together with a reference from their previous school.

Exit: Most, if not all, Belmont students continue on to Mill Hill School, although all have to sit the CE exam (for setting purposes. It is not a qualifying exam for entry). 'Children for whom Mill Hill is not the right school will leave at the end of year 6; once in year 7, the children have a place at Mill Hill at 13+ conditional on continuing good work ethic and good behaviour.' One parent felt that the fact that Belmont goes up to 13 is a massive advantage. 'At 13 they are desperate to make the next jump and are confident to do it. They are not little 11 and 12 year olds floundering around.'

Remarks: Established in 1912 following the success of its senior school Mill Hill, Belmont Junior House opened its gates with one student – Harold Pearse Soundy. By the summer term 1913, it had 12 pupils. Originally a boarding prep for boys, it has been a day school since the 80s and co-ed since 1995.

Situated on the relatively quiet part of Mill Hill's Ridgeway, the school is in an enviable location – set back from the road and flanked by large houses, beautiful greenery and a stone's throw away from the small but popular Belmont Farm. Hard to believe that a 25 minute train ride will take you to the centre of London. Harder still after meandering through some 35 acres of parkland to the rear of the school – taking in the panoramic views of the Totteridge Valley. Undoubtedly the school's selling point, the grounds and its facilities

---

Outdoor facilities include an adventure playground, a variety of games, a giant chessboard, for use during break and lunchtime, and a gardening area

are impressive for a London-based junior school.

For a sporty child, this must be their nirvana. The grounds host seven rugby pitches, 10 football pitches (of various sizes to accommodate different age groups), three cricket pitches, five cricket nets, five rounders pitches, two Astro mini hockey pitches, six Astro tennis courts, six netball courts, a fully equipped gymnasium and a small dance hall. Finally, a 1500 metre woodland cross-country course known as 'The Oti' (in memory of a former student who died of sickle cell anaemia). Pupils also have the use of the brand new 25 metre indoor swimming pool at Mill Hill School for swimming lessons and clubs. As one parent told us, 'Forget this school if your child has absolutely no interest in sport; they'll be unhappy', commenting that it is the most disciplined department in the school.

Outdoor facilities also include a large wooden adventure playground, a variety of large established games including a giant chessboard, for children to use during break and lunchtime, and a gardening area where pupils tend seasonal plants and flowers. We spotted a little recycling area and then learned that Belmont has been awarded the much coveted Eco-Schools Green Flag Award.

After the spectacular exterior, the interior of the school comes somewhat as an anticlimax. The original 18th century house acts as the main entrance to the school and houses the function rooms, main reception area, staff rooms and the head's office. Whilst this has been tastefully refurbished (with the original beautiful winding staircase acting as the centrepiece), several of the classrooms on the upper level seemed on the cramped side and lacking in imagination. The science labs (in the Cloister Block) and the gymnasium particularly struck us as archaic and in need of a refurb.

That said, the Jubilee Hall, which accommodates most of the lower school classrooms, the dining/assembly hall and the head of lower school's office, is modern and airy. The school has a genial vibe, perhaps because it is not as formal as some of the other independent schools we have visited. Colourful and interesting displays of student work adorn the corridors, and the pupils we witnessed, whilst not particularly noisy, were 'spirited'.

A Belmont child is a busy one. School opens at 7.30am and from then on it's a cascade of activities

Belmont pupils 'speak with confidence, whether in a classroom discussion, reading in an assembly or conversing with adults,' said their most recent ISI inspection. This was particularly evident on our tour when we met with school's council members – a bunch of 8+ year old boys and girls who were bright, articulate and bounced off each other like the future spokespeople they may one day become. They were confident, polite and hard pushed to find anything negative to say about the school. One bemoaned the fact that lunch should be better organised, whilst another commented incredulously that 'We've been to play other schools that don't even have their own cricket grounds' – which made him feel very lucky.

A Belmont child is a busy one. School opens at 7.30am for optional breakfast, and from there on in, a cascade of activities barely allows for an oxygen intake. Fifty clubs are on offer during lunchtime and after school, so if elastic or kicking a ball ain't your thing – why not try ancient Greek? Or perhaps origami, Dead Poets Society (we presume without Robin Williams), jazz band, Belle Plates or Bollywood dance, to name but a few. Popular after-school activities include chamber choir and horse riding. Fabulous trips (including a history trip to Venice) are offered from year 6 and above.

Clearly time is set aside for the curricular stuff, as results are well above national expectations. This, we are told, is achieved through 'excellent teaching' (ISI 2012), a broad curriculum that includes French from year 3 and Latin from year 6 and smallish class sizes. Teachers have annual performance reviews and their planning is monitored termly. No sluggards allowed here. A couple of parents we spoke to said that academia across the Foundation has definitely been stepped up a notch over the past few years. One parent told us: 'Belmont was always more of a nurturing school, but the goalposts seem to be constantly changing and you feel like you are kept on your toes the whole time.' In school's view, 'High academic performance is our number one target.'

Sats abolished in favour of continuous assessments from year 3. Most pupils are expected to continue through the Foundation, although places at Mill Hill are not unconditional. Any early problems, academically or behaviourally, are usually flagged up whilst the child is at Grimsdell school (the pre-prep), so there are 'rarely any surprises.' School says that because Belmont is part of a Foundation of three schools, it is important to look at the bigger picture. 'If we didn't feel a child could cope, we wouldn't allow them to progress to year 7.' These cases are few and far between, however.

The school has a small learning support department and is happy to accommodate children with mild cases of dyslexia and dyspraxia. Anything more severe, and 'we're not the school for them.' Small groups of gifted and talented children are arranged across the years, and most are prepared for the 11+ and 13+ scholarship awards.

Belmont is a Christian foundation based upon the principles of 'religious freedom'. Chapel services are obligatory, because if you start pulling pupils out, 'you lose the ability to say we can work together'. However, the school's pupils represent a wide range of faiths and cultures, so chapel services and assemblies are inter-denominational.

During our tour, we noticed the school undergoing building works – six new classrooms, two science labs and an impressive hall. Shortly after our visit, we discovered that Belmont, along with the other two schools in the Mill Hill foundation, was merging with the Mount School for girls in September 2014 (hmmm). The merger came as a great shock for parents who were informed by email, with no prior warning. School insisted that it was not planning a permanent expansion; pupil numbers have increased by some 55 or so, and boy:girl ratio is now more even.

Channing Junior School

Linked school: Channing School, 507

1 Highgate High Street, London N6 5JR	Tel: 020 8342 9862
Independent · Pupils: 245 · Ages: 4–11 · Fees: £15,330 pa	Email: fairseat@channing.co.uk Website: www.channing.co.uk

22

Head: Since 2008, Mrs Louise Lawrance BPrim Ed (30s). She left her native South Africa some 15 years ago and taught at state schools in Burton-on-Trent and Kennington before going to GEMS Hampshire School (now The Hampshire School, Chelsea), where she worked for seven years, the last three as the head of the pre-preparatory school. Clearly immensely proud of her school and her girls, she seems to know each one and they chat to her happily and informally – a pleasure to behold. Also

proud of her staff – 'we're very lucky. We're able to attract fantastic teachers and everyone is hugely talented in one area or another.' Appreciated staff are happy staff and make happy children.

Entrance: Register as soon after birth as you like but 4+ lists don't close till 1 October of the year before entry. Tour round the school with the head and then assessment at rising 4 in groups of 12 to spy out teachability, capacity to listen, collaborate, obey

Music and drama praised – 'they are astounding – I am amazed by what the teachers get out of the girls'

instructions. Wisely, tots are seen in two age-related groups so no panics if EmmyLou is an August baby. Call-back of the most likely – there are only 24 places for a list of 250+ applicants. Offers made on the basis of potential – don't cram them with numbers and letters. A few 7+ places in 2016-2018 only.

Exit: Eighty per cent progress to the senior school. Others opt for boarding, state sector or leave because their families are relocating.

Remarks: Housed opposite the senior school on the other side of Highgate Hill, the junior school occupies Fairseat (formerly the home of the Lord Mayor of London and backing onto the green charms of Waterlow Park, named in honour of said Lord Mayor Sir Sidney, who donated the park to the nation. And a jolly nice house it must once have been – memories linger in fireplaces, cornices, and a sense of gentlemanly solidity. And very fine views too. In 1927, it became part of the school – originally a boarding house – until boarding went in the 1960s. It communicates a relaxed and civilised ethos and this is reflected in the manner and conduct of its girls who are open-faced, relaxed and articulate.

Good displays everywhere and lots of colour. Much into 'thinking', as so many are now and with an encouraging board which poses questions such as 'What colour is Happiness?' Lots of expensive Apple Macs, excellent library in which intent reading was happening when we popped in, and especially pleasing was the thoughtful cross-curricular work we met at all levels. Thinking clearly being done here – and not just by girls. Birds were being studied by year 3 and they make bird boxes in DT, assemble data bases of bird stats (maths), import clips of birdsong (IT) and make pictures (art), write instructions on feeding and caring for birds (English) and look at birds and habitat (biology). (This GSG writer – an English teacher –was once upbraided by a pupil when she cited a Latin derivation. 'You can't know about Latin – you're an English teacher!' No such nonsense at Channing, we can tell.)

Exceptional music – 105 weekly music lessons and all orchestral instruments on offer. Really inviting large music room with ancient beams. Music and drama much praised – 'they are astounding – I am amazed by what the teachers can get out of the girls'. Lively art – we loved year 1's charcoal drawings of bears – each one different, each one full of individuality. Orderly but not obsessively tidy. Smiley faces. Quiet, concentrating classes.

Good outside space – and super outlook. Five courts, tarmac space, fields. Nature walk, bees' nest and fox's den. Good adventure playground with tower, fireman's pole, climbing wall, obstacle course and safe surface – oh to be 7 again. Multi-purpose hall – assemblies, quick turnaround for dining (very yummy food) and PE space.

Parents happy too. 'We're thrilled to have found somewhere that really cares about the girls.' 'The school makes the girls aware of how much they have to offer.' 'I can always go in – the school is very friendly to parents.' 'My daughters love art, reading and music – they are so happy there.' 'It doesn't pressure the girls.' 'It's such a sensible school.'

Channing School

Linked school: Channing Junior School, 506

Highgate, London N6 5HF

Independent • Pupils: 588 • Ages: 11–18 • Sixth form pupils: 130 • Fees: up to £16,800 pa

Tel: 020 8340 2328

Email: admissions@channing.co.uk
Website: www.channing.co.uk

Headmistress: Since 2005, Mrs Barbara Elliott MA PGCE (50s), a Cambridge linguist. Taught previously at St Albans Girls, St Columba's College (boys), East Barnet comprehensive, Aberdeen College of Commerce and Haberdashers' Girls – an impressively varied career. She is relaxed, engaging, sophisticated, capable, retaining a faint Lancastrian directness in her voice; the proud mother of four sons and someone who clearly relishes the charge of so many 'lovely' girls. Has a very level-headed view of her school – 'It's an intellectual place but we're not ferociously competitive. Everyone can try everything – they're not stopped from doing things just because they're not good at them.' 'Mrs Elliott is wonderful' is pupil and parental consensus.

Academic matters: Trad academic curriculum – everyone takes two Englishes, maths, science and a lang at GCSE; popular options are art, business and communications, geography, history and Spanish. Exceptional results in English lang and additional science; more than 87 per cent A*/A grades overall in 2015. Teaching reckoned excellent across the curriculum and nice small classes.

Again, no surprises at A level – 20 options, economics well-established and exceptionally successful; the teachers are examiners and 'they know how to deliver'; 93 per cent A*-B, 71 per cent A*/A in 2015. Apparently, the first girls' school to offer an AS in financial studies. Other popular subjects are English and maths, but no slouches among the disciplines. German, Latin and Greek survive, art flourishes and science numbers are highly respectable – clearly no fitting a mould here.

Staff very much given their head to choose the syllabuses they feel best suit their pupils – IGCSEs now taken in English, sciences and languages – and encouraged to pursue their own continuing education, always a good idea. ICT embraced enthusiastically with suites of Apple Macs and girls produce 'unbelievably sophisticated presentations and assemblies.'

No one with a statement but around 22 girls with an IEP, all supported by additional learning co-ordinator. Most have mild dyslexia or processing difficulties. Everyone screened on entry but 'our classes are so small the staff pick up quickly on any

problems.' No withdrawals and girls 'access guidance and support' in lunchtimes and breaks. Wheelchairs would be difficult here as main school building is on five floors with narrow stairways and no lift. Apparently no-one hitherto with an ASD – 'so far they haven't applied.'

Games, options, the arts: Most done on site – has courts and pitches and new multi-use games area, though the girls also walk to Parliament Hill and Stanhope fields for broader pastures. New sports hall and music school so no deprivation of facilities.

German, Latin and Greek survive, art flourishes and science numbers highly respectable –no fitting a mould here

Lovely relaxed art studios at the top of the building with unique views right across London. Textiles, computer graphics, dark room, printing, drawing and painting – all with a rare freedom and sense of exploration. We saw no prescribed, formulaic work here – much inventive and witty. We liked, especially, the sculptures made out of white straws – a brilliant skeletal snake and a very scary skull. Music reportedly exceptional; lots learn individual instruments and are genuinely enthusiastic – sixth formed their own a capella choir recently, just for fun. 'They have wonderful instrumental teachers,' enthuse parents. 'They fasten onto what an individual child could be good at and nurture it.' Drama a major school preoccupation – good,

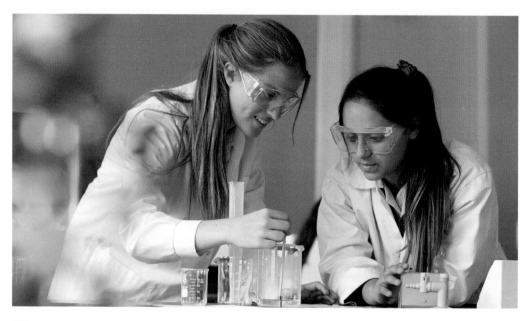

lively productions with mass involvement, also studied eagerly up to GCSE and A levels.

The Highgate location is a dream for luring in visiting speakers – in the week we visited had played host to Carol Ann Duffy and Kazuo Ishiguro. Diane (Kindertransport) Samuels was writer-in-residence at time of our visit and school now appoints its own 'poet laureate' – not, we understand, rewarded with the traditional butt of sack but £200 to spend at High Tea of Highgate: sounds good. Clubs galore, very much following the current enthusiasms of girls or staff. 'It's whatever we've got and,' says head, 'whatever you want. If there's an appetite for something we're very happy to run it.' Sixth form girls would like more opportunities, they told us – once-weekly enrichment classes enliven their studies but, seemingly, they have immense appetites for new things and could take more. Duke of Edinburgh Award pursued with as much gusto as everything else – 14 (out of 38) year 13 girls taking the gold award when we visited. Lots of charity activities which combine do-gooding with fun. 'The school really promotes initiative,' girls told us.

Background and atmosphere: Occupies a considerable frontage along Highgate Hill, yards down from the shops and easy-peasy if you live anywhere in this chic and desirable London village. Founded in 1885 by a Unitarian minister and two of his congregation – daughters of a banker and Egyptologist – for the education of the daughters of Unitarian ministers, it remains the only Unitarian school in the country. Unitarianism, which originated in Hungary, fosters liberalism, religious tolerance and democracy and its tenets still inform the school's atmosphere today, though Unitarians themselves are thin on the ground. The present head of RE is a female Unitarian minister. 'If I come up against a sticky problem, I will sometimes look at what the Unitarians said,' says Mrs Elliott. The school was named after an American – William Ellery Channing – who, Mrs Elliott informed us, 'has a lot of useful things to say about education and women's rights, and the school always listens to extracts from his lectures on our Founder's Day in early July'.

The main building itself is attractive internally, though a rabbit warren away from the few spacious rooms – you go up and down narrow staircases and through little corridors that must take some time to learn. Plenty of remnants of the gentlemen's houses the school buildings once were – good marble fireplaces, elegantly paned windows and cornicing here and there – but it feels cosy and homely and lively displays of girls' art everywhere which warm the heart as one scurries along.

Library is housed in a good, light room overlooking the High Street – modern furniture, airy and well-stocked. We loved the ceramic models of shops on the High Street behind the librarian's desk. Three other buildings on site house the main hall, classrooms, the new sixth form centre with kitchen and separate canteen – we have never seen so many coffee mugs anywhere – IT suite, gym/theatre and sports facilities.

Plenty of remnants of the gentlemen's houses the school buildings once were – good marble fireplaces, elegantly paned windows and cornicing – but it feels cosy

Reasonable amount of outside space given village location, and a rather tragic small garden with a greenhouse and chicken run. But we did visit in late November – 'If you come in the summer it's amazing,' girls assured us. And Mrs Elliott confirms that the organic garden and chickens have fed the real appetite the girls have to become 'greener'.

Pastoral care and discipline: House system recently reintroduced here as elsewhere – always a giggle for this ancient writer, who recalls the abandonment of such things in the 60s when they were seen as reactionary and divisive. 'We love it!' bubble the girls. 'You meet so many girls in other years and it's such a good way to get everyone more friendly' – competitiveness here is clearly less than ruthless.

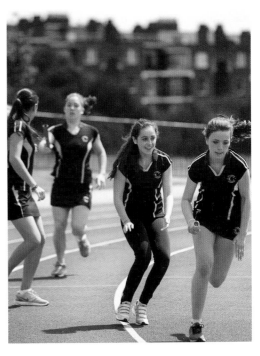

Palpably friendly relations between staff and girls and a relaxed and collaborative feel pervades lessons. Girls evidently glad to be here and seldom rock the boat. 'My daughter had a problem,' a mother told us, 'and the school was magnificent. I cannot speak too highly of how they dealt with it.'

Pupils and parents: Mostly local but they come from all over north and central London as well as Herts and Middlesex. Predominantly white middle class, but a good sprinkling of everyone else too and everyone melts and blends happily together.

Old girls include Baroness Cox, Peggy Vance, Tanya Moseivitch, Harriet Sergeant, Eileen Hulse and Princess Sarvath of Jordan.

Entrance: In addition to the 20-odd who come up from the junior school, takes 60 external candidates at 11+; around 350 apply via the North London Consortium of Schools' entrance exams. About 120 places offered. Joiners from all the local preps and primaries – from around 100 schools. Head or member of senior team meets all prospective parents. At 16+, minimum of six Bs needed including A*/A in A level subjects. Well worth trying for a sixth form place here and many do. Occasional places occur and school keeps a list of hopefuls whom they contact and assess as appropriate.

Exit: The majority stay on for the sixth form but some leave for co-ed or boarding schools, state schools or sixth form colleges. Thereafter, to top universities – four to Oxbridge in 2015, lots of medics, and academic degree courses at Bristol, Durham, Edinburgh and predominantly Russell Group universities. Some to USA and Europe too.

Money matters: Academic and music scholarships up to 10 per cent of tuition. Bursaries up to 100 per cent of fees – means-tested.

Remarks: 'Never forget,' reads the text over the sixth form centre, 'life is expecting much of you and me.' Thus said Miss Matilda Sharpe, one of the founding sisters. Its gentle exhortation characterises this school in which all is relished, much achieved and nothing forced. A parent told us, 'They get their Oxbridge places but in a different way.' Hard to imagine a better start for an outgoing, lively-minded girl.

Coldfall Primary School

Coldfall Avenue, London N10 1HS

State • Pupils: 680 • Ages: 3–11

Tel: 020 8883 0608

Email: office@coldfall.haringey.sch.uk
Website: www.coldfall.haringey.sch.uk

24

Head Teacher: Since 1996, Evelyn Davies (50s). Ms Davies is one of life's 'superheads', a woman who has taken a 'bog-standard' primary and transformed it into a star act with an 'outstanding' Ofsted, three-form entry and very happy parents. Most find her open-minded and approachable. 'I had an idea', commented one, 'and she immediately said "let's have a chat about it."' Hard working and well-organised, she gets things done. 'She's not ticking boxes, she really gets involved in the nitty gritty'. An active opponent of testing, testing, testing, she's even been to parliament to protest, winning the admiration of her local MP ('if I were the minister for education I would grab Evelyn Davies and put her as a key adviser. That way our children would be well educated in every sense of the word').

Entrance: Places given out using the standard local authority formula: children in local authority care, followed by special educational needs, siblings and distance from the gates. Recent expansion means a bit of leeway for those living a few streets away.

Exit: A primary whose catchment fortunately straddles the borough's two highest flying comprehensives. The largest chunk of year 6 proceed to Fortismere, just next door. Sizeable (and growing) slice to Alexandra Park, down the road. Enviable success rate too, in grammar school entrance, then in dribbles to a wide range of local and distant establishments.

Remarks: This meticulously run school has everything going for it. Teaching here is enthusiastic and thorough, with staff constantly looking to improve performance. Academic standards are high and virtually every child reaches the government targets, many far exceeding them. Though the school has an 'unusually high' number of children with special needs, both those who struggle and those who excel are provided with plenty of booster classes.

Not all parents, however, feel difficulties are necessarily dealt with sympathetically. 'Our son has considerable problems', said one, 'and we found the attitude very inflexible'. Behaviour is good and positive performance (particularly regular attendance) rewarded (classes compete enthusiastically for attendance teddies).

Teaching is enthusiastic, with staff constantly looking to improve performance. Academic standards are high and virtually every child reaches the government targets

Facilities here can only be described as exceptional for a London primary. The original, large, low-lying Victorian schoolhouse, once a secondary school, has now been joined by a sleek, modern addition, providing extra classrooms and a new gym. Expansive grounds boast country-like playing fields, as well as two large and notably well-equipped playgrounds kitted out with basketball and netball nets, table-tennis tables and sheltered cabins. Pupils also benefit from the school's own allotments and nature trail, as well as access to nearby Coldfall Woods.

Sport played enthusiastically and successfully. Two hours of PE weekly overseen by a qualified sports coach and training approached with professional efficiency (gymnasts, for example, use flip cameras to study performance). Both boys and girls

triumph in borough-wide competitions, boys winning recent golf and football championships, girls excelling in football and netball. Pupils also qualified for the London Youth Games.

Plenty of enrichment, in lessons and out, including chess (with championship-winning chess teams), French (taught by a native speaker), computer programming and cooking all part of the regular mix. Excellent range of clubs (including geology) and activities. Successful school choir has made appearances at the O2 and Barbican and one enthusiastic parent recently organised an entire week of dance with over 60 workshops and professionals imported from the West End. 'Things don't just happen here', said one mother. 'Everything is well planned and thought through'. Regular trips beyond the school gates include at least one visit to a museum, gallery and musical event for every pupil.

In the main (though not exclusively), parents are comfortably off Muswell Hill locals, so there's a good sprinkling of designer trainers in the playground, but this is low-key prosperity. Almost a third of pupils speak a language other than English at home. Both mothers and fathers (plenty of the latter at pick-up time) involved in making the school a success. 'All parents', said one enthusiast, 'are given an opportunity to contribute, not just non-working mums'. Many arrive at weekends to help with the gardening, and the thriving PTA organises summer and winter fairs, weekly coffee mornings, a Valentine disco, quiz night, fashion show and organic vegetable scheme. Sizeable sums are raised for playground, computer and PE equipment. 'There's a real feeling that everyone matters', said one mother. 'The kids are really blessed'.

Copthall School

Pursley Road, London NW7 2EP

Tel: 020 8959 1937

State • Pupils: 1,045 • Ages: 11–18 • Sixth form pupils: 255

Email: enquiries@copthall.barnet.sch.uk
Website: www.copthallschool.org.uk

Head Teacher: Since 2005, Ms Jane Beaumont BA (Oxford) PGCE (London University's Institute of Education). Started her career at Copthall as an NQT in the early 1990s and has not strayed very far since. Although she came into education 'late', she was assistant head/director of sixth form at Acland Burghley school for 10 years and deputy head at both The Compton and Fortismere schools. 'I live locally and that's very important. I know and understand the local community.' Her husband is head of a Redbridge comprehensive school.

Down to earth, forthright and likeable. Her abiding passion for the job is evident in the way she enthusiastically bounces through our meeting (metaphorically speaking), and is on top of all the facts, figures, statistics, Ofsted reports etc. However, it's not just about making the grade for this head – she also takes a genuine interest in the well-being of her girls. 'Around a lot', is what one of the parents told us. Another said she marvels at her dedication, 'she's always the last one to leave and will wait at the bus stop until every one of her students is safely on the bus.' One pupil told us, 'When she asks you how you are, you know it's because she really cares and it's not just meaningless words'.

The product of a single parent family who went to 'tough schools', but got herself to Oxford University, Ms Beaumont says the experience 'has informed my career and made me passionate about the power of education to improve lives.' She is a firm believer in a strong educational background for a broad spectrum of pupils; 'I love the fact that Copthall is a genuine comprehensive school with children from all backgrounds and abilities. I find it amazing how ambitious most of them are in their learning, and we are here to get them to realise this ambition.'

Academic matters: In the top 20 per cent of schools nationally for student progress recently. All the more admirable when one takes into account that there are 60 different spoken languages at home and 22 per cent of students on free school meals (compared to 16 per cent nationally). Good solid results – in 2014, 56 per cent of pupils got 5+ A*-C at GCSE including English and maths (where value-added is very good), in 2015, 27 per cent A*/A grades. Organises some learning by ability rather than age.

A good range of traditional and non-traditional options, including food tech, ICT, child care, and a City and Guilds level 2 diploma in beauty therapy (equivalent of five GCSE grades A*-C).

Wide range of A levels with maths, biology and chemistry all popular (as elsewhere, few opt for physics); psychology and sociology also get large numbers of takers. Over 30 per cent A*-B grades in 2015, 14 per cent A*/A grades. Non-traditional female subjects like sciences and technology are stronger than in many 'mixed' environments. This is something the head is very proud of – 'the fact that there is such a good uptake across the range of sciences, arts, humanities and technical subjects, allows us to have an unusually wide range of subjects offered at A level for a sixth form of our size.' Has leading practitioners in history, dance and business education.

School analyses who is and isn't taking books out of the library. Encourages parents to read with their children, especially in families where English isn't the first language

Copthall has specialist business and enterprise college status and this is embedded across the curriculum: 'Our mission is that our students will leave Copthall prepared for the constantly changing world of work.' Plenty of opportunities to develop business acumen. These may include raising money for a World Challenge expedition (this year Malaysia), baking and selling biscuits or creating a new children's card game called 'Shuffles', enabling team members to develop production, finance and marketing skills amongst others. PHSE includes modules in personal finance.

The school is 'committed to educational opportunity and inclusion.' It needs to be – approx 32 per cent of students are on the SEN register. The SEN co-ordinator also liaises with outside agencies. One parent said, 'They're really on top of this. My daughter is dyslexic and she is offered a lot of support, including extra reading classes and a scribe for

Strong dance and drama. Students have danced in a programme with English National Ballet

exams.' Reading is a priority here. The school analyses who is and isn't taking books out of the library. Actively encourages parents to read with their children, especially in families where English isn't the first language. Everyone is tested in year 7 – those in need get extra help in class or in small groups. Five teaching assistants manage year 7 and 8 pupils with complex needs who require full-time support. Learning co-ordinators keep an eye on pupils' progression and those who are struggling with work and behaviour may embark on an intensive programme in the inclusion centre, which puts most back on track. The school has converted many parts of the building to make them wheelchair accessible. Two stair lifts and two wheelchair lifts have been installed and a number of classrooms contain height-adjustable furniture.

As with many large comprehensive schools, a healthy amount of self-motivation is required to succeed. One parent expressed concern about her daughter's education at the school: 'I do worry that pupils at the lower end of the spectrum could slip through the net.' However, she continued, 'in many cases the school's GCSE results don't reflect the hard work the teachers put in.'

Games, options, the arts: Plenty to do. A wide range of practical subjects on offer including art, DT and performing arts, with small classes for practical subjects. Good facilities and well-equipped DT and art rooms. Astounding pieces of artwork on display in the art room, although some pieces which deserved to be mounted on feature walls were slightly hidden from view. (One student in particular could've given Dali a run for his money).

Strong on dance and drama. Great success in ballet and selected students have taken part in a programme with the English National Ballet (impressive wall displays of student performances). Drama very popular, too, with lots of performance opportunities in school and regular trips to theatres including the Old Vic, Sadler's Wells and Regent's Park Open Air Theatre. The school runs a summer school for selected year 6 transfer pupils every year. The theme, purpose and pupils differ each summer depending on need, for example literacy and numeracy. Active and diverse music department with extracurricular groups that include rock band, guitar club, a 'glee' choir and a year 11 a capella group.

Big on sports – perhaps inspired by the well-known stadium down the road. GCSE PE is an option and as well as the traditional competitive sports, pupils are offered trampolining, zumba, yoga, rowing, basketball and the option of cheerleading for the Saracens Rugby team, that now uses Copthall Stadium for its games. Own sports hall, netball courts and hockey pitches, with Copthall swimming pool and Power League Football Centre down the road. Links with local sports clubs are used to offer a wider sporting curriculum. Inter-form and inter-school matches, lunch time clubs, and keen sportswomen join Barnet sports clubs. Athlete and commonwealth medal winner Nadia Williams is an alumnus.

Background and atmosphere: Named for Copt Hall, the local 17th century manor house, opened as a grammar school in 1936 and merged with Woodcroft School in 1971. It became a girls' comprehensive in 1973 and operated as a single school on two separate sites, until extensive rebuilding enabled its amalgamation on one site in 1996.

Copthall is situated on the corner of two roads. Page Street is a leafy, pretty road with posh secluded houses and the promise of great things. Indeed, the facade of the school from this perspective is of an imposing brown brick building with a large feature window which sits in a decent forecourt. Turn the corner into Pursley Road and the picture changes. This is a very busy, nondescript road, redeemed slightly by the vast playing fields opposite the school. In the morning, one is faced with a sea of green, as the Copthall girls descend from the buses and make their way into the main entrance.

As well as competitive sports, pupils are offered rowing, yoga or cheerleading for the Saracens

Enter the building from this side and you could be forgiven for thinking you had entered an NHS hospital. The reception area is large and airy, but sterile and very blue, with a large, semicircular reception desk, where we almost expected to pick up our prescriptions. Above the waiting chairs, there is a large television screen with informative bulletins for students and a particular emphasis on healthy eating.

This school is a bit of a hotchpotch of the old and new, and we weren't really sure where one part began and one ended. The original part of the building is fairly dark with narrow corridors and high windows. There was a distinct lack of charm or character in this part of the building, which could partly be rectified by adding some personal touches – more student displays on the wall, a good injection of colour etc. Enter the school hall for a trip down memory lane. It probably hasn't changed since the 50s, which is intentional, the head assures us. This does lend a certain nostalgic charm to it and clearly word has spread as it has become a popular filming venue, which can add Call the Midwife to its recent list of credits.

On the positive side, a cash injection has allowed for some very nice elements. A pretty secluded courtyard where sixth formers can study or have some quiet time, a fully-equipped beauty salon for those taking the beauty course as an option, a superb, fully mirrored dance studio with a sprung floor, a large, well-stocked library and a decent sized (purple) business suite.

Students also took the initiative to design the façade of a new building a couple of years ago. They decided on a 'green vine' motif and had the brainwave of turning each leaf into a national flag using different shades of green – representing the various nationalities in the school. The result is a beautiful variegated pattern.

There is an admirable amount of information for parents, including weekly newsletters and three reports a year. One parent told us, 'we don't lack for information here'

The Copthall School expansion programme is now completed (12 new classrooms including two IT suites), and the school expanded by one form of entry in 2015. One parent expressed concern about this expansion and told us: 'I understand the necessity for creating more school places, but I'm worried how the school will cope with getting even bigger, and how it will impact on the individual.' Indeed, it is hard to imagine how another structure could be cramped into this one site – the only plus side being that they may have to finally remove the demountables in the school's forecourt, which have well passed their sell-by date.

Pastoral care and discipline: Discipline a high priority especially with regards to uniform. One parent said, 'Have you met the head? Even I feel like straightening my skirt when she passes by.' Clearly Ms Beaumont has little time for nonconformists – the school prospectus says it all: 'students will be asked to remove nail varnish at a cost of 20p.. if students opt to have piercings (eg nose studs), this must be done at the beginning of the summer holiday, so they can heal and be removed for the start of school in September.' The result is a well turned out bunch of girls in a smart, dark green tartan uniform (a far cry from this editor's Copthall schoolgirl days). Any desire to out-individualise each other is done beyond the school gates.

Mostly nice, well-behaved girls (a couple of the classes we passed sounded a few decibels louder than possibly acceptable). Permanent exclusion rate is very low, averaging one a year. In most cases it is students who didn't start at the school in year 7. Strict on attendance and punctuality. The education welfare team works closely with the school to highlight the importance of this. An attendance of no less than 95 per cent a year is expected as is a prompt 8.35am start. Early school finish at 2.55pm, but only a 35 min lunch break: 'We have a staggered lunch break to cater for four sittings so that students get a freshly cooked meal.'

Much has also been done to combat bullying, which in a school of 1,200 girls is almost a sad inevitability. Student services situated in the heart of the school is open to any vulnerable student throughout the school day. Peer mediation, buddying and anti-bullying council also help to protect more vulnerable pupils. Learning co-ordinators, many of whom are non-teaching heads of year, are employed specifically for the pastoral needs of students. One parent said, 'I had a child who was bullied when she first started the school, but it was dealt with promptly and sensitively and there are no issues any more.'

What the school lacks aesthetically, it certainly makes up for in its infrastructure. 'Inclusion' is a word used by many of the parents we spoke to. There is an admirable amount of information for parents, including informative weekly newsletters and three reports a year. One parent told us, 'we don't lack for information here.' A conscious effort has been taken to include parents from multi-cultural backgrounds who may find integrating a challenge. Ms Beaumont instigated a group last year for 30 parents which ran for 12 weeks and was completely funded by the school. As a result of its success, the plan is to make it an annual event.

Various incentives for students to perform are given throughout the year. The pièce de résistance is a Celebration Evening held at the end of the school year to recognise exceptional achievements in different subjects. One parent said, 'This is something my daughter really aspires to achieve and it motivates her.' Encouragement is extremely important, the head believes, 'if you get the pastoral stuff right, everything else will fall into place.'

Pupils and parents: A great ethnic and social mix with lots of middle class girls and those from tough estates – 'we don't have large numbers from any particular ethnic minority or social class, which gives us a nice breadth of views.' Parents mostly very supportive; very active PTA and parent governors – strong sense of parental inclusion. One parent told us, 'My daughter had the option of going to a selective school, but when we weighed it up we felt that Copthall provided everything she needed, academically and socially.'

Entrance: Heavily oversubscribed school – some 500 applications for expanded 210 places. Organised by the LA, with looked-after girls and those with particular medical or social needs first on the list, followed by siblings or those with a brother at their partner school Christ's College. Remaining places are offered on a geographical basis – generally less than a mile and a half away. Some 30 to 40 join the sixth form from outside.

Exit: Around 40 per cent of the year leaves after GCSEs, mostly for local colleges, many to follow vocational courses. Over 80 per cent of sixth formers to university (most of the rest to FE colleges), often one a year to Oxbridge. Others to study eg medicine at Manchester, history at Warwick and aerospace systems engineering at Coventry. Good work experience and careers advice.

Money matters: Barnet is officially viewed as leafy suburbia and thus not in need of urgent government cash for, eg, replacing portable classrooms. Stable staff, but turnover not helped by the fact that they can get inner-London weighting just a few miles south. Supportive parents help with raising cash.

Remarks: Good, solid, highly inclusive local school with a strong sense of community. Plenty of scope for developing a bent for science, languages or making a million at business, while picking up performing arts or food technology skills along the way. We hope its expansion will not dilute its ethos.

Dwight School London, Lower School

Linked school: Dwight School London, 517

49 Woodside Avenue, London N12 8SY

Independent • Pupils: 169 • Ages: 2–11 • Fees: up to £14,970 pa

Tel: 020 8920 0600

Email: admissions@dwightlondon.org
Website: www.dwightlondon.org

5

The Lower School Principal: Since 2007, Mr Matt Parkin BEd DipEd. Has taught in the UK, USA and Indonesia. Teaching football and swimming as a teenager helped him find his vocation. Married; likes going running with his labrador dog ('though she is much faster than me').

Overall head of school is David Rose, previously head of Montgomery School in Germany and The British School of Houston, Texas, an ISI inspector, past chair of the London International Schools Association and an accreditation visitor for international schools.

Entrance: Mr Rose likes the phrase that Dwight parents use to describe the school: 'selectively inclusive'. Though most enter in September, expat families join throughout the year, as do children transferring from local state schools. Interview recommended (Mr Rose and Mr Parkin want to get to know all of their students); this and a report from previous school only real requisites.

Exit: Most – around 75 per cent – go on to the upper school to continue with the IB middle years and diploma programmes, but a few trickle elsewhere. Some expat families move on to other foreign assignments.

Good music room and lovely art room. Year 6 has a separate and brand new ecobuilding with easy access to the specialist classrooms

Remarks: The epitome of what an international school should be about. Year groups divided into two parallel classes with an absolute maximum of 20 in each. Lots of child-inspired batiks, pottery and art help create a vibrant atmosphere. IB learner profiles are displayed everywhere. IB primary years programme (IBPYP) well linked with the national curriculum, which keeps inspectorates happy and ensures children are well grounded with an international mind-set. All lessons in each half of term based around one aspect of the curriculum.

Specialist teachers for music, art, PE, French and EAL. Homework important and can be done at after-school club.

Kindergarten and reception based in their own little house, The Lodge, with its own garden for play. Half day and part time options are available and there's a wraparound care programme from 7.30am to 6pm for the lower school.

Door-to-door bus service provided at extra cost extends south to St John's Wood, Belsize Park, Hampstead, Golders Green – ask admissions office about your area. Free shuttle service between campuses

Years 2 to 5 in the main building have good sized, light classrooms with washing lines displaying student work. Each child has own drawer for storage. Computers everywhere. Media resource centres, a small library collection; great gym, which doubles up as the dining hall. Healthy food served from the kitchens next to it (where meals for the kindergarten are also prepared). Photos of all the year 6 student displayed in the passage with their personal blogs. Good music room and lovely art room. Year 6 has a separate and brand new eco-building with easy access to the specialist classrooms and playground; schools has green flag eco-schools status.

Strong emphasis on pastoral care and exceptional provision for special needs, the Quest system, with good screening for dyslexia and related problems. (More needy students are referred to Holmewood School.) As in the upper school, the policy is to accept a controlled number of children with learning difficulties but not those with disruptive behavioural problems. Excellent EAL provision with an enthusiastic and dedicated teacher. Children usually become fluent within a year.

Playground not huge but much use made of local park for cross-country runs and scientific experiments plus compulsory swimming once a week at Trent Park. They also regularly use the school's own playing fields a short bus ride away. Lots of trips, visits and excursions as well. All year 6 students spend a week at an activity centre in Normandy (practising the French that they have been learning since they were 3) and some of them go on exchange to the Dwight School in New York.

About half the families are local north London. The rest are expats representing a mix of professions and embassies. Door-to-door bus service provided at extra cost extends south to St John's Wood, Belsize Park, Hampstead, Golders Green – ask the admissions office about your area. There's a free shuttle service between their two campuses (Friern Barnet and Woodside Park) for parents preferring to drop off at one. Most families have an international background, usually one English-speaking parent. Nationalities include British, then Japanese (10 per cent), and then a complete mix of many nationalities.

Friendly, caring and kind are the adjectives we heard most from Dwight parents we spoke to.

Dwight School London

Linked school: Dwight School London, Lower School, 515

---

6 Friern Barnet Lane, London N11 3LX

Independent • Pupils: 250 • Ages: 11–19 • Sixth form pupils: 70 • Fees: up to £19,290 pa

Tel: 020 8920 0600

Email: admissions@dwightlondon.org
Website: www.dwightlondon.org

Head of School: Since 2005, Mr David Rose (50s) CertEd BA MAEd LPSH. Married, with two adult daughters; his wife Vivienne recently retired as admissions director. Tall and distinguished, he looks the part of head of a serious school. He's had a long career in international schools, with headships in British international schools in Pakistan, Sweden, Cyprus, Germany and Houston. 'Totally approachable,' parents tell us, and by all accounts he knows all of his students.

The benefit brought by the long-term leadership of this confident yet somewhat self-effacing international educator is evident, and noted by longer-term families – notably the strengthening of the three IB programmes, and the improvement to school's culture of discipline. He's overseen renovation of some of the school facilities and the introduction of a new special educational needs partner school, and has raised Dwight's profile on London's international school map. Parents all describe him as a lovely, gentle person; he meets all the students at the time of application, and he regularly drops in to classrooms.

Academic matters: Runs the IB programme at all levels. In 2014, average point score 30 (out of possible 45). One or two students each year opt to take a Dwight High School Diploma, earning IB certificates rather than the full IB diploma. Average class size in upper school not normally more than 15.

Parents receive a chatty weekly newsletter from the head, including updates on extracurricular activities

Mr Rose was proud to announce that Dwight has been designated an IB Open World School – one of only seven worldwide. This means that students from other institutions may register to take IB diploma courses at Dwight through the Pamoja Online courses, which may appeal to local sixth formers who want to combine IB courses with their A levels. By having Pamoja Online courses available to Dwight's students, the course option are much expanded, and it enables students to experience the kind of online learning that is increasingly common at university level.

French is introduced in primary, Spanish added as an option in year 7. Other languages considered on request at additional cost. Computers and interactive whiteboards available throughout the school, yet on the day of our visit we did not see students working on these devices in any of the classes we visited. RE is not an IB subject, though religious and other cultural traditions are addressed through other areas of the curriculum, and parents tell us that there are opportunities to celebrate these in different ways. Photos throughout the the the school buildings depict many school trips, dramatic and music performances and community service activities, suggesting that a lot of learning is regularly extended out and about. After-school homework club for those who want extra help.

Parents receive a chatty weekly newsletter from the head, including updates on extracurricular activities available both to their children and themselves. Helpful and informative website.

Through the QUEST programme (at extra cost) the school can accommodate a range of learning needs, with the support of specialist teachers. The school has a sister school for more significant cases including statemented/EHC plan children.

EAL (also at extra cost) regarded as essential for children with two non-English speaking parents – two to five lessons a week, one to one or in a small group depending on needs. A mother tongue programme is available for Japanese pupils – the

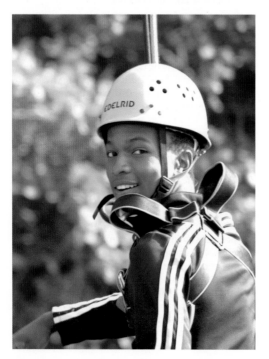

Outings to concerts, theatres and galleries as well as trips home and abroad. Model United Nations Conference is popular

second largest group in the school (about 10 per cent) and some other languages (no extra charge is made if four or more students are in the same group and level). IB diploma students must be completely fluent in English. Language Heritage Day once a year sees everyone speaking their own language. Pupils of over 35 different nationalities, and full-time teachers of 15.

Parents say that what they like about Dwight is that it suits a great variety of children. 'I wanted a school where all of my children would be well served'.

Teachers are international and IB-experienced. They are always willing to help and respond quickly to any parent concerns. One parent tells us her child said that Dwight teachers must go through a 'humour test' – you have to have warm sense of humour to teach at Dwight.

Games, options, the arts: Games obligatory once a week for each year group – the school has its own sports field 10 minutes away by minibus and uses other local sports facilities. They compete not only with local and national schools but also with international overseas schools. Parents say they like the variety of sports on offer – not only the traditional ones but a wider range – rugby, football, basketball, track and field, sailing, ice skating... One Dwight student represented London in the National Schools Swimming Competition.

Lots of after-school clubs. Strong music – about 15 per cent learn an individual instrument; there are rock, jazz and chamber groups. The choir has sung at London's 02 in Young Voices, and on the week of our visit, they were about to jet off to the US to perform with the Dwight New York choir at the Carnegie Hall. There is a music tech lab on a bright upper level that overlooks the music and art rooms below, and soundproofed rooms for individual tuition.

For the last period on Mondays, the pupils do mixed by year group community service projects. This helps to develop relationships across the ages, reinforcing the 'Dwight Family' concept.

Lots of outings to concerts, theatres and galleries as well as trips home and abroad. We saw photos from a science trip to Iceland, the Model United Nations Conference is popular, there's an annual exchange with the year 6 students at Dwight School in New York, and older students have been doing community service helping to build in a Cambodian village. They raise funds, and roughly every three years students, parents and staff travel there to do volunteer work. The drama club was preparing to go to Cuba to study music and dance; while the year before the film club went to Hollywood. India is on the horizon.

Dwight London students are eligible to participate in the Dwight Global Leaders, a summer gathering of high school students from all over who come together at the Dwight Vancouver campus to develop leadership skills and learn about social entrepreneurship. This programme features big name motivational speakers from the world of sport, education and business (for example Monica Seles and Michael Bloomberg) and it receives high praise from the families of students who have participated.

Background and atmosphere: The school was originally founded in 1972 by Dr Stephen Spahn, chancellor of the Dwight School in New York. Previously known as Woodside Park and North London International School, the school recently changed its name in a rebranding exercise to Dwight London School, to heighten awareness of its association with the Dwight family of schools that now has campuses on Vancouver Island, Seoul and Shanghai. 'Dwight family' is a term used by staff and families alike. Dwight London has an advisory board of local parents and others who lend expertise and guidance and serve as a supportive sounding board for Mr Rose in the strategic planning of the school.

The school is on four sites in two locations. The upper school is in the former Friern Barnet Boys' Grammar School and in nearby Jubilee Hall. The main building has recently been refurbished and is clean, bright and welcoming, making very good use of light throughout. The administrative offices and faculty room share the same corridors as the classrooms, which must strengthen the sense of community. Every wall is full of original and creative student art and photographs, and there are posters with quotes from Gandhi, Martin Luther King and Nelson Mandela, who we learned are the role models for the three upper school student houses.

The individualised approach we heard so much about from parents was evident during our visit. One Spanish class had just two students; in a lively drama lesson, students were planning the direction and staging for a Dwight student version of a Chaucer play; art students in a large art room with plenty of natural light were working on sketches and prints as part of a unit on 'celebrations'; and the design technology lab was a hive of activity with students measuring and vigorously sawing away as part of a woodworking project (hopefully

all the fingers survived). A painted wall is a legacy of one student's project on graffiti as an art form. It was easy to see why the parents rave about the quality of the arts programmes.

The Jubilee Hall nearby holds more classrooms, two science labs, the upper school library (closed for a few days when we visited, as the librarian was on a school trip) and a pleasant canteen open throughout the day (there are rave reviews for the new caterers), with a TV tuned into Sky News or the BBC. This looks out onto an outside playground where students engage in a bit of exercise during break or lunch, and a small world garden beyond with picnic tables and benches.

The school admits that conditions are a little crowded, and they are always on the lookout for new property in the area.

Pastoral care and discipline: Head has been credited with an improvement in student behaviour. The IB philosophy and emphasis on tolerance and global understanding are reinforced by the house system in the English tradition, with upper and lower school head boys and girls. Kids look tidy and seem happy, and although there is a uniform there are various options, so they can choose how casual or dressy they want to look. Parents love the small size of the school. 'It's a massive advantage. Everyone is known, everyone can shine and blossom.' It helps build self-confidence, and there's plenty of attention from teachers. As one veteran parent described it, 'The teachers really knew my son.'

Parents repeatedly assured us that they were not aware of any incidents of bullying, and the British ones in particular felt that the huge diversity of student backgrounds is a huge plus, with families inviting students home to share their family traditions during different holidays.

Pupils and parents: Dwight has a larger British student body than most other international schools in London, which seems to make it easier for international families to integrate into the local community. The impression from parents and from our visit is that there is relatively little sense of the 'expat bubble' in this international school. Long term families who joined the school in earlier incarnations (pre-IB) say they have been very pleased with the introduction of the full suite of IB programmes, and the interesting international experiences and friendships that Dwight's growing expat community brings. While they do see the turnover of families as a factor, many of these friendships endure and lead to exciting trips during the holidays to visit old friends who have moved on.

Parent Link works behind the scenes to support the school and organise the social events that are particularly helpful for new families. Parents can also volunteer in the school.

About half of families are local north Londoners. The rest are expats representing a mix of industries and embassies, though most live less than 30 minutes away. Parents appreciate the expansion of the area served by the door-to-door transport provided by the school. There is also a free shuttle service from the local tube stations and the free inter-school shuttle facilitating drop off. Most families have an international background, usually one English-speaking parent. Nationalities primarily British, then Japanese, and then a complete mix of many.

Entrance: Mr Rose likes the phrase that Dwight parents use to describe the school: 'selectively inclusive'. In all of our conversations (with parents and staff), no one emphasised 'academic results'. Though most enter in September, since the school serves expats, there are students entering throughout the year. Interview and report from previous school only real requisites. Many come up from the lower school but others from other local schools or overseas.

Exit: University counselling programme in year 12, but it seems parents often start earlier, commenting they'd like to see a bit more attention to this area. Mainly to university, a lot London based but some overseas – eg recent admissions to Coventry, Goldsmiths, UCL, Durham, Exeter, Hertfordshire, Kent, Nottingham, Colorado and several Japanese universities.

Money matters: Tuition is marginally less than other international schools in London. Extras include school trips and activities such as Model United Nations and some after-school activities. Scholarships are available with testing in the early part of the calendar year.

Remarks: Dwight is a school where the education of the 'whole child' and the learning journey genuinely appear to be as important as exam results. As one parent said, 'When we visited other schools, it was a PR exercise where they told us about their tests, achievements, etc. At Dwight, they asked us about our children.' The school does all it can to provide each student with opportunities to pursue their individual interests, all within the IB context. 'It's a kind school.'

Fortismere School

South Wing, Tetherdown, London N10 1NE

State • Pupils: 1,700 • Ages: 11–19 • Sixth form pupils: 450

Tel: 020 8365 4400

25

Email: office@fortismere.org.uk
Website: www.fortismere.haringey.sch.uk

Head Teacher: Since 2010, Mrs Helen Anthony BA MA PGCE (40s), previously head since 2006 of Central Technology College in Gloucestershire. Studied English at Liverpool and Keele, PGCE at King's College London. Had a number of teaching and leadership roles in London and Gloucestershire before joining Central Technology College, which was then one of the roughest boys' schools in the country. She brought it back from the brink of closure and transformed its rating to 'good' (Ofsted talked of a 'remarkable journey').

She has imported to very middle class Fortismere some of the tactics that had wrought improvements in her previous setting, such as a

'Amazing' preparation for Oxford, said a parent. 'There are several young Oxbridge graduates teaching at the school and they ran workshops and did mock interviews'

hard line on punctuality, attendance and litter. She clearly has a steely determination and is evidently not a head to be trifled with, though on our tour a pupil did not hesitate to buttonhole her to check she had signed a form for him. 'Very hard working and ambitious,' say parents. Mother of two daughters.

Academic matters: A large proportion of bright, motivated pupils and also a greater than average number of pupils with SEN, with a relatively small mid range. In 2015, 43 per cent A*/A grades at A level, with 70 per cent A*/B. Similarly strong at GCSE: 43 per cent A*/A grades, and 80 per cent of pupils got 5+ A*-C grades, including English and maths.

The previous head had introduced setting for every subject from year 7; this has been loosened, but school still sets early for maths and science, whilst English is taught in mixed ability classes. 'I trust my faculty heads on that, but they must show that it works.' Relatively low class size of 24.

Everyone learns French or Spanish in year 7 and promising linguists are offered Mandarin or German in year 8. They are encouraged to take two languages to GCSE; around 80 per cent of pupils

take at least one. The top 60 per cent are encouraged to take triple science GCSE.

Teaching standards mostly very high with the odd exception, say parents. 'They expect of lot of the students – I think they push them very hard. They encourage and extend them, particularly with the personal projects in the sixth form.'

Reporting system to parents 'has improved. They tell you what your child's target is, what level they're performing at now and whether that's okay. I've mostly found teachers very responsive when I've emailed them.'

The sixth form admissions criteria are 'closer to a grammar school', with at least five B grades at GCSE required for A level, and As for certain subjects eg maths. The small number of vocational options, with five C grades at GCSE as a boundary, include music technology, ICT, business, media and sports science. School also teaches classical heritage and global perspectives Pre-U courses.

Maths a very popular A level, alongside history (teaching dubbed 'exceptional' by parents) and English. Respectable numbers pursuing biology and chemistry, and – as one might expect in this liberal, intellectual area – philosophy, psychology, government and politics and sociology, though linguists disappointingly few.

'Amazing' preparation for Oxford, said a parent. 'It was all very low key, but there are several young Oxbridge graduates teaching at the school, and they ran workshops, put on seminars, did mock interviews, and put pupils in touch with other students who'd been through the process recently. It was all there, but it was up to the kids to push themselves that much further.'

With its large, segmented site and high pupil numbers, possibly not the most suitable school for children with learning difficulties, but many choose it nonetheless, 'and we do a very good job with them'. Those with statements/EHC plans – and there are a relatively large proportion of these, mostly with autistic spectrum and behavioural issues – have their own teaching assistant. However, 'we try to keep away from TAs velcroed to children', and they are included in class work as far as possible, with small group sessions to help them develop independent learning skills. Linc team helps those experiencing learning difficulties – temporary or permanent. The secondary department of the Blanche Nevile School for deaf and hearing-impaired children occupies an impressive building on the site. Some of its pupils join in the mainstream school activities.

Games, options, the arts: Fabulous new music block, with recording studios, composing and practice rooms, plus multi-use performance spaces, mirrors the importance of the subject here (though few take it to A level). Symphony orchestra, big band and several choirs; community choirs and orchestras include parents as well as children; hosts Saturday music school. 'We play a key role in the local community.' Head doesn't envisage the abolition of music aptitude places having any effect on the quality of music-making in the school. 'We have always had a lot of hugely musical students – it comes with the parent body.'

Impressive displays of art and fabulous photography coursework around the school on our visit, plus bright papier mâché aliens and rats created by younger year groups. Photography a popular A level and one can see why. Drama also 'massive'. 'We're a very artsy school. It's our natural default

setting.' 'Fantastic' production of Little Shop of Horrors included the actual plant from the West End show; sixth formers regularly take productions to the Edinburgh fringe, and help with GCSE drama performances.

Sports stars used to hone their talents largely outside school, but sport has been bolstered by increased amounts of time in the upper years plus the introduction of Colleges, or houses, which run weekly inter-college competitions and encourage non A team players to get involved. However, parents report that it is possible for the less athletically inclined to avoid breaking into a sweat, and it is fair to say that reports of sports team triumphs do not feature largely in school newsletters. Sports hall, tennis/netball/basketball courts, acres of playing fields and 'very popular' table tennis tables. The head would dearly like the renovation of the 'stagnant' disused swimming pool to be her legacy, but financial constraints seem likely to stymie this ambition.

'I have to remember that parents don't just read the Guardian – quite likely they write for it too,' says the head

Another innovation is whole school enrichment sessions every other Wednesday afternoon, with a choice of 87 activities from yoga to cooking to science. All the staff, including admin staff, are encouraged to join in. An assistant head who was a dancer in a previous life runs a tap dancing club; the head runs a Born to Teach? training course for year 12, which includes planning and teaching lessons in primary, secondary and special schools.

Large range of trips includes 'brilliant and very well organised' week in Beijing for Mandarin speakers, exchange visits to France, Spain, Germany, Senegal and India ('though you do have to queue up at 7am with your cheque to get a place on the popular ones,' commented a parent), D of E, outdoor pursuits in the Brecon Beacons, ski trips, field trips and cultural visits. A steady stream of authors, scientists, politicians etc comes to give talks; librarian organises team of pupils to shadow Carnegie medal deliberations, reading and reviewing shortlisted books; teams enter debating competitions.

Background and atmosphere: Large site amidst leafy Muswell Hill Edwardiana has been the setting for a series of schools of all sorts, including private, state grammar and comprehensive. Fortismere was formed in 1983 by the amalgamation of Creighton and Alexandra Park Schools (another Alexandra Park School has since opened nearby). Site includes a hotch-potch of buildings from its various incarnations. North and South Wings linked by a quarter-mile pathway round the playing fields that can resemble a storm in the North Sea in inclement weather. Accommodation beginning to show its age, but bright and cheerful. Head has encouraged a multitude of notice boards – with college news, photos of trips, information on clubs.

Very much a community comprehensive with a relaxed atmosphere (subject to 'behaviour for learning' sanctions), and pupils strolling around in jeans and tee shirts. 'Proudly non-uniform', though with a veto on revealing too much skin or underwear. 'It's part of the ethos for children to be able to express themselves,' said a parent.

Pastoral care and discipline: Good transition system, with year 6s spending three days at the school in the summer term getting to know the site and teachers. Has recently introduced vertical tutor system, with 18 pupils of different ages from the same college in each group replacing old form tutor system. All staff – including admin staff – are tutors, 'which enables us to have small groups, and also increases student respect for non-teaching staff'. Mixed reviews from parents and pupils, some enthusiastic whilst others feel that the system needs time to bed in and become a tradition, and that they would prefer to spend the time with their peers.

Student leadership team, which includes head boy and girl and their deputies, has a meeting with the head each Monday. 'It has already had a real impact. They really challenge us about why we do things, and it makes me think about structures.'

Head's introduction of zero tolerance for lateness and absenteeism has shocked some families and delighted others, with one parent terming it 'draconian.' 'The behaviour here was good, but I thought it could be better,' says the head. 'If you are disrupting the learning of others, that is not negotiable. Parents complain, but when I tell them their child is stopping other people learning, they find that hard to justify.' She refuses permission for holidays in term time: 'We get a lot of poorly relatives in far flung places towards the end of the Christmas and summer terms.' In response to pupils' requests for carrots as well as sticks, Vivo system gives house points for helpfulness, participation, tidiness etc and is widely reported in the newsletters.

Pupils mostly very happy and have good relationships with staff, but some parents feel that the pastoral system is variable. Some teachers 'do resolve your issues,' said a parent, citing the 'novel and interesting solutions' to stress suggested by her daughter's college head. However, 'I had a very unsympathetic reaction from the school to a family death. I found their policies very inflexible.' 'They didn't seem to be sensitive to the needs of my younger daughter,' said another parent, whose

children had joined from a different education system. 'I really didn't feel she got the support she needed, and I felt that no-one had an overview of the situation. I also had no response to a very carefully worded email about a pastoral issue that had upset her.'

Permanent exclusions rare, and usually for persistent defiance or repeated breaking of behaviour policies. Will swap recalcitrant pupils with other local schools. 'We're good at managed moves – they can be very effective.' Will also use outside providers such as local boxing and football academies for those who clearly need a different approach. 'We prefer to try something different before moving to permanent exclusion.' A parent commented: 'There are some wild and woolly kids, but they don't tend to disrupt classes.'

Pupils and parents: Largely affluent, liberal, middle class families – artists and musicians, writer and actors – plus quite a few looked-after children. 'It is a very political school. I have to remember that parents don't just read the Guardian – quite likely they write for it too,' says the head. These are mostly cool kids, relaxed and confident, proud to be at Haringey's most popular comprehensive. 'My daughters' friends are lovely,' said a parent. 'They meet up to study and all help each other.' Ex-pupils include soul singer Michael Kiwanuka.

Entrance: Takes 243 pupils into year 7. Those with an SEN statement/EHC plan naming the school – and there are many of these – will automatically get a place. Then priority to children in care, those with particular medical, social or emotional needs, and siblings, with the remainder by distance, usually less than half a mile.

Takes 110 or so outside students into the sixth form, from state and independent schools. Requires 5+ A*-C GCSEs for vocational A levels and 5+ A*-Bs for academic A levels, with higher grades for certain subjects eg maths, from internal and external students. Those who don't get at least three D grades at AS are liable to be directed elsewhere.

Exit: Small numbers (around 30 per cent) move on after GCSEs, generally for more vocational courses elsewhere. Nearly all sixth form leavers to university: Sussex, Leeds, Manchester and Bristol the flavour of the moment; usually a good crop to Oxbridge. English, philosophy, psychology, maths, law, geography all popular, plus a few medics and vets.

Money matters: Very active parents' association, the FSA, which underwrote the refurbishment of the sixth form centre.

Remarks: A popular and high-achieving comprehensive that successfully includes those with difficulties as well as extending the most able. Head's vision is for it to have 'an active mind, a finger on the pulse and a big heart.'

Grimsdell, Mill Hill Pre-Preparatory School

Linked schools: Belmont Mill Hill Preparatory School, 503; Mill Hill School, 544

Winterstoke House, Wills Grove, London NW7 1QR

Independent • Pupils: 180 • Ages: 3–7 • Fees: up to £13,305 pa

Tel: 020 8959 6884

Email: office@grimsdell.org.uk
Website: www.grimsdell.org.uk

Head: Since September 2014, Mrs Kate Simon (40s). A current Grimsdell parent, Mrs Simon is no stranger to headship. Between 2002 and 2008 she was head of the junior school of the Royal School, Hampstead (now incorporated into North Bridge Senior) and from 2008 was head of Girls' Upper School at Garden House School in Chelsea.

Entrance: Heavily oversubscribed, due in part to it being non-selective at age 3 or 4. 'I don't feel comfortable with failing children at that age', says the head. Most pupils come from within a five mile radius and there is a 'multi-cultural mix.'

Exit: The majority of pupils continue on to Belmont school. However, if the school feels that a child won't cope there, discussions about alternatives

School states in its prospectus that 'there is no such thing as bad weather, just bad clothing,' so be sure your darlings like outdoor pursuits

take place from year 1. 'We have to be realistic', the school says.

Remarks: Unfortunate name for a very pretty school. On a beautiful autumnal day, Grimsdell was the antithesis of 'grim'. Situated on Mill Hill's Ridgeway, but accessed via a small and very lovely private road, the school occupies the rather grand Winterstoke House. Originally a vicarage for the vicar of St Paul's and sold to Mill Hill School in October 1923, Winterstoke House was purchased to become a school boarding house to host some 42 boys.

The school became Grimsdell in 1995 – a newcomer compared to the other two schools in the Foundation. The reason for its formation was largely due to a Mrs Grimsdell, widow of an Old Millhillian, who bequeathed a large part of her late husband's estate to Mill Hill School. Following a request from the school governors, Mrs Grimsdell agreed that the benefaction be applied to create a 'much required' pre-preparatory school, and Grimsdell opened its gates. The school is situated adjacent to Mill Hill School but has its own grounds – not quite on the scale of the other two schools, but more than adequate for a pre-prep school.

This is a cute, cosy school. Nothing grand and pretentious, despite the impression given by its exterior. We were seated in a colourful and bright reception area with a large aquarium to gaze at while we waited to meet the head. Familiar sounds

of over-excited kids emanated from one or two of the classrooms (and we were particularly struck by one over-zealous music teacher doing something very strange with her arms!)

All classrooms were light, airy and well equipped – particularly the Sunshine Room, which even in its name suggests something warm and nurturing. This is where pupils who need it go for extra one-to-one learning support. Specialist on-site teachers in music, PE and French are on hand and 4 to 7-year-olds have weekly keyboard lessons with a music specialist. The swimming pool at Mill Hill School is a great addition to the PE curriculum. Pupils use the theatre at Mill Hill School for concerts and performances. Cursive handwriting is taught from the start and we were quite amazed with the standard of year 1 handwriting displayed on classroom walls.

As with Belmont and Mill Hill School, Grimsdell's selling point is undoubtedly its idyllic surroundings. Pupils not only have access to 120 acres of beautiful parkland at Mill Hill school with its sports pitches, swimming pool and woodland, but they have their own great adventure playground and science garden to enjoy. A firm believer in the great outdoors, Grimsdell has its own forest school. Each session has a theme and activities can range from mini-beast hunting to fire building and cooking outdoors. With a school that states boldly in its prospectus 'there is no such thing as bad weather, just bad clothing', you had better be sure your little darlings have a healthy interest in outdoor pursuits. Forget this school otherwise – indeed discount the other two schools in the Foundation while you are at it.

Parents appreciate the expertise of the large Foundation, and the lack of pressure to take exams for future schools. One parent told us, 'Grimsdell is a secure and nurturing stepping-stone, which is illustrated by my own excited and eager children.'

The Henrietta Barnett School

Central Square, London NW11 7BN

State • Pupils: 730 girls • Ages: 11–18 • Sixth form pupils: 230

Tel: 020 8458 8999

Email: admissions@hbschool.org.uk
Website: www.hbschool.org.uk

Headteacher: Since September 2014, Mrs Del Cooke BSc MBA NPQH (50s), previously head of Sir William Perkins's School in Surrey. Maths graduate with MBA in educational management, her broad experience covers the comprehensive system, sixth form college, adult education and boarding at Cranleigh,

where she was head of maths, housemistress and finally deputy head. Although relatively new, she is increasingly seen as the embodiment of HBS – smart, quick-witted, friendly and empathetic. 'The girls want to hang out with her. She is like them,' summed up one parent. We found her instantly likeable, not remotely intimidating and surprisingly low-key. Made no dramatic changes so far ('It's such a fantastic school, you'd have to be pretty pompous to come in and turn it upside down,' she says), but is already known as a visible head, particularly interested in getting the girls' views on various aspects of the school, and is clearly keen to focus more heavily on celebrating individual achievements. No bad thing, point out some parents, who say the girls can be 'far too modest, and need reminding how amazing they are'. Has a passion for music, playing a number of instruments, including self-taught bassoon. Married with three sons.

Academic matters: Consistently top or very near the top of both the GCSE and A level league tables. In 2015, 94 per cent A and A* at GCSE, 80 per cent A*/A at A level. Most do 11 GCSEs, four or five AS, three or four A2s. Results strong across all subjects at GCSE, with a bias towards maths and sciences at A level, which around three-quarters of pupils choose, although history and English also have a healthy representation. Languages prioritised, with French and German for all in year 7, Latin and Spanish for all in years 8 and 9. Plus an option of ancient Greek. Setting only for maths at KS4.

Myths about this school being an academic hothouse, where girls are worked like dogs, are prolific, and even the head was initially put off the job because she thought it would be so pressurised. 'I was resistant, assuming the girls would be working in a ridiculously intensive environment. But it's the girls who drive the pace of learning and if anything, the staff sometimes have to tell the girls to slow down!' says the head. Pupils and parents

Competitive learning is frowned upon, making way for a supportive atmosphere and strong sense of co-operation, which everyone agrees is a huge aid to the girls excelling

agree, with one saying her daughter had just been advised to 'take some time out of her revision schedule to do something more relaxing.' Girls are encouraged to be independent, albeit well-supported, learners from day one, with many setting up their own societies and visiting universities for extra lectures. During our visit, we saw one noticeboard with pages from HB Scientist, the sixth-form produced (and very professional looking) science magazine that is sold throughout the school, whilst plenty of posters around the school advertised forthcoming speakers that pupils have organised – Zadie Smith when we visited.

Competitive learning is frowned upon, making way for a supportive atmosphere and strong sense of co-operation, which everyone agrees is a huge aid to the girls excelling academically. Teachers could hardly be considered more dedicated, although many parents say more of them are needed. 'Every one of the teachers would be a good candidate for a head of department in a private school, earning 50-100 per cent more money, but they choose to stay here because of the quality of the school and the commitment of the girls, which makes them very,

very special,' said one parent. Girls love the fact that many of the teachers have had (non-teaching) careers in their subjects, also praising the informal relationships they have with them and level of responsibility the girls are given. Homework is given if and when teachers feel it's required, rather than hours every evening for the sake of it.

Games, options, the arts: Historically sports not brilliant, although improved facilities – large multi-purpose Astroturf court for netball, hockey, football and volleyball – have helped, with the school increasingly winning at both a local and borough level and holding its own against some top private schools. Facilities also include four tennis courts, two average sized gyms, a state-of-the-art fitness suite with a good range of exercise equipment and a variety of pitches available on the nearby Hampstead Heath extension. 'Sport is very much on the up,' insists the head and there's a long list of exercise alternatives, including rock climbing, zumba, fencing, tang soo do, yoga, fitness, indoor rowing, cricket, badminton and dance. Rugby and athletics are also increasingly popular. No swimming due to lack of facilities, which disappoints some.

Thriving music department, with a symphony orchestra that everyone agrees is a joy to listen to, especially at concerts in the nearby ambient St Jude's Church. There are other orchestras and plenty of choirs, along with all manner of bands, including swing and rock. All pupils study music in key stage 3 and many go on to GCSE. Plenty of private tuition in a wide range of instruments, including double bass, bassoon and French horn, and there is an organ scholarship. Great excitement about the new music wing built in 2011. 'Previously, we were taught music in our classroom or temporary huts, so it's a major thing,' said one pupil, who showed us the well-stocked rehearsal room and studio, with several sound-proofed practice rooms. The same wing is home to drama, another lively department with strong facilities, with recent performances including Hamlet (year 9s), a play about Henrietta Barnett (year 7s) and a school-wide Our Country's Good.

Mirroring this wing, on the other side of the main building, is the DT and art block. Downstairs, the spacious DT room is home to all kinds of interesting inventions, including a Batman-style wooden chair and scooter that changes colour when exposed to sunlight. Meanwhile, the upstairs art room is a fantastic space, with some seriously talented work on display across all media. The wrap-around balconies on both wings are both aesthetically pleasing and provide an outside space for students to work during the summer months.

Lots of extracurricular opportunities, including Mandarin, Robotics (year 8 team recently got through to world championships in USA), creative

writing, philosophy society, LAMDA, and many pupil-led activities. For instance, sixth formers currently teach Japanese to younger ones, as well as running a current affairs club, with speakers (invited by pupils themselves) including Melissa Benn and Lucy Holmes.

School trips, through each subject department, take every year group out once a year, with recent examples including Iceland (geography) and Greece (classics). 'It was easily the best holiday I've ever been on, just unbelievably interesting and fun,' said one pupil who went on the latter. French and German exchanges and Spanish trip to Seville. When we visited, 65 students were getting ready to head to the Rhineland for a music tour. Lots of day trips, particularly to theatres, museums and art galleries. Enrichment week, held in the summer, provides an entire week of outings. Own field study centre in Dorset, which every pupil visits for one week during her early years at the school.

Background and atmosphere: Founded in 1911 by formidable social reformer Dame Henrietta Barnett, the school is housed in architecturally stunning Lutyens designed buildings in upmarket Hampstead Garden Suburb. Not unlike the kind of buildings you'd find at Harvard of Stanford, it's also a beautifully landscaped campus. Facilities top-notch, particularly the colour-coded science labs and new swanky new wings for art, DT, music and drama. Floors are polished parquet, classrooms are light and airy and corridors are tastefully decorated with everything from a recent photography competition to huge science-inspired pictures. Dining hall, where food is praised, and all-day café for year 10 upwards. Parts of the interiors could do with a lick of paint and everyone agrees that the plans to turn the relatively small library and separate study-areas into something bigger, brighter and more open-plan can't come soon enough. But overall facilities feel spacious, with excitable students loving their environment, including after school, when something is going on pretty much every evening.

Pastoral care and discipline: 'No bells, no detention, no rules – it's so relaxed that if you came to school in your pyjamas no one would bat an eyelid,' wrote Tatler in its 2015 review, words that are now a source of great pride (not to mention humour) in the school 'simply because they are so true,' explained one pupil. Even a mention of the word 'discipline' will get you a blank look among pupils ('Why would you play up?' one said, genuinely bemused), whilst any occasional quirkiness that's perhaps inevitable among such an academic bunch is accepted as normal and certainly never teased. 'A few weeks ago, a whole class came out of art with painted-on moustaches and top hats from drama – it was so HBS,' laughed one girl. But this is no St Trinian's. Far from it, the girls' behaviour is impeccable and they always do their best, as well as being delightful and friendly. 'If a girl did step out of line, the teacher would just have a chat, adult-to-adult,' says the head, who believes it's the fact that the girls are treated like adults – with all the respect and trust that goes with that – that accounts for the lack of need for rules.

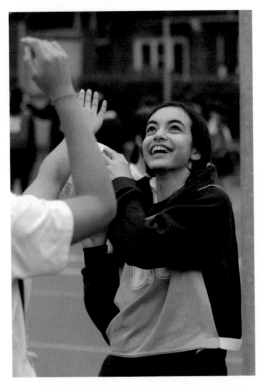

This is no St Trinian's. Far from it, the girls' behaviour is impeccable and they always do their best, as well as being delightful and friendly

Bullying a non-issue, whilst a part-time counsellor is on hand to deal with any problems. Currently a big push on reducing the stigma of mental health issues, with several noticeboards pointing to relevant resources. Strong student council, which is particularly strong in recruitment and currently focusing on raising funds for the new library, plus lunch council.

Pupils and parents: Girls are extremely bright and eager to learn, as well as both interesting and interested. Clear team spirit, where girls in different years bond naturally as well as through schemes like the student-led 'vertical families.' 'Of course, you get friendship groups, but absolutely no cliques,' said one pupil. 'It's a real community where everyone knows you and supports you,' said another. The school has always had a wide catchment area, based as it was on the vision of providing education to bright girls regardless of their means, although since the arrival of league tables, some pupils come in too far for the head's liking. ('I do question whether it's a good thing for some to travel really long distances.') Those in London mostly walk, cycle or get the bus or tube (Golders Green). There's also a parent-organised bus service to cater for those who can't easily get there by public transport.

Great ethnic mix – about a fifth Indian and a fifth white British, the rest from a variety of backgrounds. 'The school is the multicultural, meritocratic face of Britain,' said one parent, proudly. PTA provides refreshments at events, along with the odd quiz night, but not as active as some, particularly for socialising. 'It's inevitable, with families coming from such a wide area and diverse backgrounds,' said one parent, which probably also explains why after-school social life is not as vibrant as elsewhere.

Entrance: It doesn't get more selective than this, with 2000+ applying for 100 places. Some families move house once they have a place, others travel in from as far as Kent. Verbal and numerical reasoning tests in September, then the top 300 are invited back for English and maths tests in January. Pupils come from 50-60 primaries. For sixth form, approximately 600 apply for a further 45-55 places, with six A grades at GCSE minimum requirement, including As in intended A level subjects. Girls already in the school are also expected to achieve this requirement, although in reality most far exceed it.

Exit: Around seven per cent leave after GCSE, mostly to sixth form colleges. Twenty-one to Oxbridge in 2015. Lots of medics and dentists and a good cross-section of all other subject areas. Team of sixth form tutors provide UCAS advice, including raising expectations of what can be achieved. Alumni include Sarah Solemani (actress and television script writer), Ros Altmann (pensions minister) and Debbie Wiseman (composer).

Money matters: Regular fundraising via PTA, pupil-led initiatives and a parental support scheme to which many parents regularly donate.

Remarks: One of the top academic state schools in the country, yet also one of the most liberal and nurturing; it's hard to exaggerate the emotional buy-in from pupils. 'The school becomes part of your DNA in a profound way,' said one. 'I don't know what happens when you get inside those four walls, but it is genuinely unique and stays with you for life.' Producing friendly, fun and delightful girls who come out with academic results that quite literally make the world their oyster, it's no wonder that top universities and employers love it too. 'My only sadness is that I can't see how it will ever be this good again,' said one pupil. A gentle and inspiring education for extremely bright girls, in a fabulous setting.

Highgate Junior School and Pre-Preparatory Department

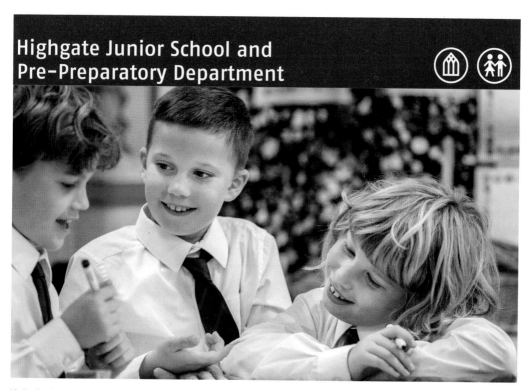

Linked school: Highgate School, 530

3 Bishopswood Road, London N6 4PL

Independent · Pupils: 340 · Ages: 3–11 · Fees: up to £17,160 pa

Tel: 020 8340 9193

Email: jsoffice@highgateschool.org.uk
Website: www.highgateschool.org.uk

Head of Junior School: Since 2002, Mr Mark James BA MA. 'Parents love him,' one fan told us. 'He's involved in everything.' Another said: 'he's fantastic.' You get the idea. He's also head of admissions for the whole school and had the task of transforming the boys' 7-13 prep into a modern mixed 7-11 junior school. Voila! Came from King's Wimbledon Junior where he'd been deputy head. An enthusiast and can-do character, he's just the man to cheer everyone along.

Mrs Diane Hecht DCE (50s) has been head of pre-prep since 2010. Previously deputy head of St Columba's Junior School in Kilmacolm, she came south as two of her grown-up children had settled in London and feels that she has found a wonderfully similar school in Highgate. 'The girls here wear exactly the same tartan skirts as at St Columba's – it was meant to be!' Warm, efficient and enthusiastic.

Entrance: Oversubscribed – 350 try for the 36 places at 3+, 300 again for the 50 places at 7+. Sane and lovely pre-prep head admits that assessing 2 year olds has to be on the arbitrary side, so do not be amazed if your astounding tot just doesn't astound on assessment day. At 3+ teachers observe them at play in groups, look for capacity to listen and follow instructions, general sociability – so don't make them learn their letters the night before. Assessing at 7 is easier – reading, writing and maths – but, again, the odds are not great. Other things count – siblings, school connections, where you live, parental statements on the application forms – but you can't wangle it. So have a Plan B, yes?

Exit: Nearly all go from the pre-prep to the juniors and nearly all go from there to the senior school.

Plenty of warning given to those unlikely to thrive in the higher stages.

Remarks: New junior school building rising apace. Whole school housed in Portakabins until December 2015, when they will take possession of a completely new and wonderful complex – judging by the plans.

Pre-prep separately, delightfully (and permanently) housed. Starts at nursery – 18 morning or afternoon tots in lively spacious space both inside and out with smiley, lively teachers. Whole school theme of colour and light when we visited and lots of attractive work on show. Glorious herd of Elmer elephants made from plastic milk cartons and coloured paper. Lovely singing – the most in-tune bunch of rising 5s we've heard. An orderly, relaxed and friendly school. We saw much warm interaction between staff and small people and just wanted to stay and watch. Juniors have the whole school's fields and facilities to play with – a rare privilege. Excellent approach to emergent special needs – 'it doesn't matter whether they have a label or not, it's how you support them.' Full range of sensitive support, individualised learning, 'management' skills etc brought in when and where needed. Easy to understand why this is possibly the most oversubscribed junior school in London.

Highgate School

Linked school: Highgate Junior School and Pre-Preparatory Department, 529

North Road, London N6 4AY

Independent · Pupils: 1,248 · Ages: 11–18 · Sixth form pupils: 303 · Fees: £18,705 pa

Tel: 020 8347 3564

Email: admissions@highgateschool.org.uk
Website: www.highgateschool.org.uk

27

Head Master: Since 2006, Mr Adam Pettitt MA (40s). Oxford modern and medieval linguist. Taught French and German at Eton, Oundle and Abingdon and was second master at Norwich School, under Jim Hawkins, now head of Harrow – a formidable team. Has French wife and school-age children and is quite the most interesting, eloquent and thought-provoking head this veteran GSG reviewer has met in many a long school visit. Propelled by a sharply focused and incisively articulated moral and educational philosophy, Mr Pettitt is spare, brilliant and energetic. He must be an exacting – though supportive – man to work for. His pupils can only benefit from his firm commitment to outreach to those without their advantages, to placing an

understanding of language at the heart of modern languages, and to educational values rather than exams and results. Parents are unstinting in their praise. The most inspiring head we've met in years.

Academic matters: Head has a refreshing disrespect for the bodies deserving of it: 'You choose the exam board on the basis that it will have the least distorting effect on the way you want to teach' – bingo! IGCSEs now in English x 2, sciences, langs and history and many subjects now opt for the Pre-U as an alternative to A levels. This can only enhance the nature and quality of learning. English and langs the first to head this way. Mr Pettitt the 'de facto head of MFL' at the time of our visit so langs getting the oxygen they needed and number of takers is sure to rise. Mandarin now through to sixth form. Maths much the most popular A level and, with further maths, has impressive results. Also strong are English, art, Latin, all sciences and RS. Tiny numbers take theatre studies, Greek, classics, music – school does not offer music tech nor other popular 'modern' subjects eg textiles, psychology and loses a few post-GCSE on that account. Number of subject options (24) felt by some to be a little limited, given the size of the sixth form, and some sixth formers would like more drama and art. However, good innovations include the 'knowledge curriculum' and 'critical method' courses. In 2015, 90 per cent A*/A at GCSE and 75 per cent at A level. Lively, student-led conferences. Mr Pettitt takes all criticism on the chin and, given that over 70 per cent of the staff are his appointees, this – as everything else – is fast developing.

Head's inclusive approach is just that: 'The quality of the way you learn is critical and every child's experience is equally important. Every day is important – I am most interested in the way each one of us teaches and learns.' IBAC – Independence through Buzz, Aspiration and Collaboration – the new acronym around the place. So this is not the school that was, nor the one people think they know. The fabric – see below – is radically changing and the character equally so. This is encapsulated in the sane and sensitively individualised approach to SEN. The Victorian main building is not good for those with mobility problems though school says 'we will try to make it work by moving our routines and schedules as far as we can.' Director of learning support covers all three schools and is

a renowned expert in autism. The support for all conditions and syndromes as they emerge is individual, tailored, supportive and 'concerned with management rather than labelling.' The very few with EAL needs are usually the very bright.

Games, options, the arts: Blessed with playing fields and space beyond the dreams of other London schools. If the educational philosophy and general zip in the place doesn't inspire you, the sporting facilities will. Girls' sport, some feel – school disputes – still catching up with boys'; football and netball still pre-eminent but plenty more on offer and played hard. Sports hall, pool, weights, Astroturfs, squash courts – it's all here. No country school could offer more.

> *If the educational philosophy and general zip in the place doesn't inspire you, the sporting facilities will*

Interior activities also privileged and currently being transformed by an enormous rolling building project that will add considerably to teaching space but also, it is hoped, to an eventual sixth form and arts campus. Drama and music thrive – many productions, concerts of all kinds and tours – art a little undemonstrative at the time of our visit but some lively colourful work around. Mills Centre provides studio and gallery space. Cultural life better displayed in the admirable school publications – professional-looking periodicals on history, politics, science, theatre and thought written and produced by pupils. Terrific range of clubs (they include 'vinyl and philosophy,' beekeeping, LGBT soc and feminist society), trips, exchanges and tours – extracurricular is praised by many but not fully taken advantage of by all. 'I used to feel that some pupils' cultural references were limited to Arsenal: great though that club is, I want them to see and know so much more,' comments the head, happy to stress to parents that while these opportunities are on offer it is up to pupils to take them up.

Lots of charitable and outreach activities for both staff and pupils – several staff now working at local state schools as part of community partnership work. This very much part of the Pettitt ethos – outreach is not a box ticking necessity here but an essential part of what it is to grow into a valuing and valuable person.

Background and atmosphere: A school with an up and down history. Founded as the Free Grammar School of Sir Roger Cholmeley, Knight at Highgate, in 1565 – former pupils still known as Old Cholmeleians. Became Highgate School in the late 19th century – and no longer free. The chapel, undergoing terrific refurb at time of our visit, 'complete brick by brick restoration, new roof, stained glass windows repaired and cleaned, apse painting restored etc; lighting and heating to render God's work less chilly and gloomy,' in Mr Pettitt's inimitable phrases – and main buildings are 19th century. Some impressive bits – old gothic central hall with Norman arches, leaded lights, wrought iron balcony and cantilevered ceiling and splendid new Sir Martin Gilbert library in old assembly hall. A real library which, unlike so many schools' learning resource centres, actually has books in it, alongside all its rows of PCs, and an atmosphere to encourage concentration and study.

By the 1960s, the school buildings (some considerably less felicitous), including boarding houses, were spread over the heart of Highgate Village – the premier north London suburb whose denizens refer to it as 'the village' and who are, understandably, rather smug about living there. Charter Building adds new subject rooms in a five-storey glass cube. All very high tech – interactive whiteboards and PCs everywhere. The whole site is now a mix of the new, light, glass-bound, airy and stylish, and the old, rather shabby, small passages and dark areas along which school operates a clever one-way system – but all likely to look a great deal smarter and more coherent in the next few years. Much tramping up and down the hill between the main buildings and the Mills Centre, playing fields etc, and each day sees orderly crocodiles with professional chaperones trailing along.

School suffered during the 70s and 80s and took time to recover its reputation. Girls joined the sixth form in 2004 and year 7 in 2006, and the whole school is now fully co-educational and fully rehabilitated. A Christian foundation and an inclusive one, with multi-faith assemblies and speakers from different religions on a weekly basis. House system – 12 houses – but no fanatical exclusive loyalty to these, rather a friendly rivalry in competitions etc and designed to encourage the mixing of year groups. 'It's a family school,' a parent told us. 'Not everyone is terrifically academic, though they really make the scholars work. They are very encouraging to everyone.'

Pastoral care and discipline: We saw only absorbed and concentrating classes with lively teaching. Discipline, as pupils gratefully pointed out, is not dependent on the whims of individual staff but 'whole school,' ie you know what is coming to you at every level should you transgress. Very little transgressing these days and we have seldom seen so few uniform infringements – everyone is smart.

Small classes 'very well-monitored,' say parents. 'It's extremely well-run,' we were told. 'We are kept fully informed and have lots of email contact with staff,' another told us. 'The teaching staff are so enthusiastic and they really care about my children,' another enthused. Occasional loutishness clearly frowned on by majority of pupils, who are a civilised lot. 'We have sent all our children there – they're so different academically and in their characters – but all have been happy.'

Pupils and parents: From a wide area of north and more central London, though most live near, if not within walking distance. 'Not ruthlessly elitist,' as one parent put it but lots of City lawyers, accountants etc with clear idea of what they want from the school. Pupils are friendly, happy and articulate. Most seem proud to be at the school and keen not to jeopardise their futures. Notable OCs include Rt Hons Charles Clarke and Anthony Crosland, Michael Mansfield QC, Johnny Borrell of Razorlight, Ringo Starr's son Zak Starkey of Oasis and The Who, Orlando Weeks of The Maccabees and DJ Yoda, Phil Tufnell, Sir Clive Sinclair, Alex Comfort, Nigel Williams, Sir John Tavener, Barry Norman, Gerard Manley Hopkins and Sir John Betjeman. Doubtless, Old Girl Cholmeleians shortly to make their marks.

Entrance: Wildly oversubscribed at every stage – on a scale we see most commonly with the grammars. Six hundred apply at 11+ for the 70 places available when the junior school pupils have been accommodated. NB part of a group of independent co-ed/boys' schools that coordinate 11+ results, but forbid those who have accepted a place at one school from taking up a subsequent waiting list offer from another. At 13+, 180 compete for 25-30 places; tests and interviews in autumn term of year 7. At 16+, 120 for 30. At 11, around 60 per cent from state primaries and 40 per cent – mainly girls – from local preps. At 13+ mostly boys entering from the obvious preps – Arnold House, Devonshire House, The Hall, Keble etc.

Exit: Around a dozen, mostly boys, leave post GCSE to, mostly, Camden School for Girls, which has boys in the sixth. Around 90 per cent gain places at their first choice university – Bristol, UCL, Durham, Edinburgh and Leeds among most favoured; some now head to top US universities. Good numbers to Oxbridge each year – 23 in 2015. Economics, English and languages are popular subject choices.

Money matters: Scholarships – music and academic – at all usual entry points and now purely honorary. 'Much kudos, but not just to the particularly brainy but to those who exemplify scholarship (persistence, creativity, setting own agenda, leading

learning in the classroom, originality),' stresses head. Bursaries up to the value of 100 per cent fees available each year and most go to those who get all or most of that amount. School makes extensive efforts via primary school visits etc to reach those who need to know.

Remarks: A new school in all but site and name – co-ed, modern, delivering a first rate education to the lively minds and limbs lucky enough to get in.

Keble Prep School

Wades Hill, London N21 1BG

Independent • Pupils: 220 • Ages: 4–13 • Fees: up to £14,010 pa

Tel: 020 8360 3359

Email: office@kebleprep.co.uk
Website: www.kebleprep.co.uk

17

Headmaster: Since 2006, Mr Jed McCarthy (50s). Studied maths and management at Queen Elizabeth College, London, PGCE at the Institute of Education, then worked in state schools in Brent. Left the profession to spend five years in industry, but realised he 'really missed teaching' and returned to Orley Farm, where he remained for 16 years (as head of maths, director of studies and deputy head). A quietly-spoken enthusiast, Mr McCarthy has worked determinedly to build up the esprit de corps of pupils and parents and undoubtedly succeeded. Parents are lavish in their praise.

'He's always waiting at the gate and has a genuine interest in each boy,' said one mother. 'He's a very caring, very nurturing gentleman,' said another. Parents are also grateful for his availability and effectiveness. 'He's always ready to hear you out about any little gripe and he really gets things done.' Two grown-up sons.

Entrance: Register a couple of years before entry at 4 but pressure on places is not intense. The school is non-selective. Some new entrants from the state sector at 11.

Exit: A small exodus at 11 to high-achieving local grammar schools and comprehensives but head hopes to attract parents who understand the benefits of a school that runs to 13. 'I believe in 13 plus,' he says. At that age, Mill Hill and St Albans are historically the two most popular choices, but horizons are expanding – 'we are sending boys to Highgate, City, UCS, Westminster, St Edmund's Ware and St Columba's'. Wherever pupils go, the school does its utmost to ensure the best match between boy and school – 'we know the boys very well and recommend on personality'.

Remarks: A small school, which hovers at around 200 boys in all, so class size is reflectively intimate, ranging from 12-15 in two parallel forms. In the early years the school follows the national curriculum, with add-ons such as French, which starts in year 3. The pace is accelerated and curriculum expanded as boys get older – 'we adapt it to the boys, easing into common entrance after 11,' says the head. Specialist teaching in music and PE in first two years, then further specialisation in art, ICT and French; by year 5, all subjects taught by specialists.

Its aim is to serve the local community – small family businesses rather than City professionals

Enthusiastic teaching and boy-friendly approach. 'We try to make it very hands on,' said one teacher. 'We make models and castles.' Parents praise staff highly. 'My son is motivated, interested and enthused. It's a great credit to the teachers,' said a mother. 'The teachers are incredibly encouraging,' said another. In the past, the school has been criticised for not necessarily stretching the brightest, but the head has spent time, effort and money rebalancing that equation – 'and we're not finished yet'. A director of studies now has a clear brief and the brightest are given differentiated teaching in class and one-to-one support out

Enthusiastic teaching and boy-friendly approach. Parents praise staff highly. 'My son is motivated, interested and enthused. It's a great credit to the teachers,' said a mother

of it. Boys are setted in English and maths from year 5, with informal setting in science, French and humanities.

The philosophy, however, is very much 'each child is an individual' and the struggling are equally well guided, with the full range of SEN support. The school deals comfortably with dyslexia and dyspraxia, mild autism and Asperger's. 'What I'm trying to do is not be the most academic school,' says the head, 'but to get all boys to expect more of themselves, set themselves higher standards and achieve them.' And parents confirm this is what happens – 'They really understand my son's strengths and weakness and really nourish him. I'm certain they meet all the boys' needs, even those at opposite ends of the spectrum'.

This is a small site and facilities are relatively restricted, though there is a French room and small science lab. Rebuild has brought more classroom space, a new science lab and an art room, allowing for relocation of the library, which had doubled as a music room. Limited space, too, for sports (though an attractive small gym), but games, played twice a week, are taken seriously. Rugby (reintroduced by the head), football, cricket and tennis are the main menu and a school minibus transports players to local and distant pitches. Rugby has put the school back on the prep school circuit. 'We mainly play other small local schools,' says the head. 'We lose more than we win, but we do play – and have tea afterwards.' Parents feel that even the sportiest get sufficient exercise and opportunity. 'A new PE teacher has invited a Tottenham scout to come to the school'. Numerous lunch-time and after-school clubs include puzzle club, movie club, common entrance drop-in club.

Has been going for 80 years, a lone prep school in an affluent suburban area of north London. Its aim now, as always, is to serve the local community, a community of small family businesses rather than City professionals. Many parents are first-time buyers. 'Our parents often want what they didn't have for themselves,' says the head. Many have Mediterranean roots (Turkish, Spanish, Greek, Italian, Cypriot) and a firm belief in family, and the school reflects those values with a strong family atmosphere.

Very much a traditional prep, it retains distinctive black and yellow blazers, formal good manners and neatly knotted ties. Boys still wear shorts in the warmer months and long hair is definitely frowned upon. Pastoral care is equally old school. 'We're looking for grounded, rounded individuals,' says the head. 'We cope well with all manner of children.' The aim is supportive rather than hothouse. 'We don't want to put pressure on ridiculously young. We want them to achieve, but not by testing to the eyeballs'. The mood is friendly and safe: 'If you're stuck on something,' said one boy, 'there's always a teacher to help you,' and the atmosphere is orderly and quiet, with bright noticeboards and well-run classrooms.

A 'big brother, little brother' scheme matches older pupils with younger ones – evident and unaffected warmth stretching across the age divide.

On our visit, a boy at the top of the school, clearly revered by a recent arrival, praised his small friend for being able to tie his tie. Discipline is firm but certainly not draconian. 'Can you do it better?' is the gentle reproach. Pupils thrive on it. 'If I'm honest,' said one undoubtedly honest young man in his final year, 'I love the school and I'm going to miss it when I leave'. Parents are equally positive. 'We chose it because it's very friendly and has a great identity that boys can relate to. I wish I could find a school for my daughter that is as good as this one'. 'We love the school. It's a home from home,' said another. 'My son looks forward to going to school every day.' Keble is not a wealthy or notably well endowed place, but is undoubtedly a happy and safe haven, where all boys are treated with respect and respond in kind. A very secure place to start your school days.

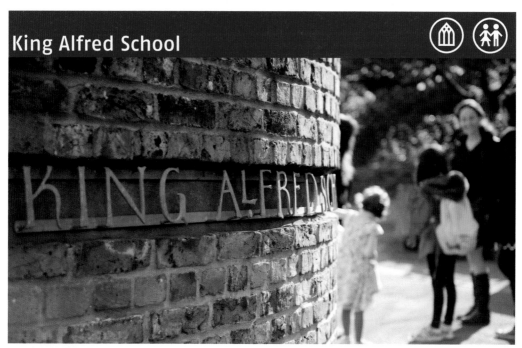

King Alfred School

Manor Wood, 149 North End Road, London NW11 7HY

Independent · Pupils: 625 · Ages: 4–18 · Sixth form pupils: 85 · Fees: up to £16,983 pa

Tel: 020 8457 5200

Email: admissions@kingalfred.org.uk
Website: www.kingalfred.org.uk

Head: Since September 2015, Robert Lobatto, previously head of Barnhill Community High in Hayes. He has an Oxford history degree and has taught in several inner London comprehensives, including Highbury Fields School in Islington.

Head of junior school: Mr David Weale BSc PGCE.

Academic matters: A school where exams are famously not the only priority. Pupils sit no formal exams until year 10, although each subject has its own testing process to ensure students are ready for GCSEs. That said, prides itself on being able to teach to the highest standards – 'if a child can get four or five A*s, we'll get them there'. Pleasing results at GCSE (most pupils take nine), with 48 per cent A*/A grades in 2015; equally so at A level, with 47 per cent A*/A and 76 per cent A*/B. Exams may not be the main focus, but 'personalised learning' definitely is, and parents feel happy that every child is treated as an individual. 'We have no idea who the clever children are,' said one. 'All are special – they're not compared to one another.'

The original ethos – liberal, progressive, egalitarian, child–centred – remains core to school's values

Not a vast range of subject choice at GCSE (curriculum languages French, Spanish and Latin); good variety at A level, with 24 options, and every attempt is made to accommodate any combination. The classroom approach, as with the whole-school approach, is relaxed. 'Teachers are not that strict,' said one senior school pupil. 'It can sometimes take quite a long time for lessons to begin, but you're still motivated to work.' Homework and marking, however, can be a bit too relaxed for some. 'The school believes that children should be children,' said one mother. 'I like the fact that it doesn't force them to do two hours a night, but sometimes I think they could push a little more.'

Sixth form particularly strong in the expressive arts (photography amongst the best in the country) and arts subjects (English, history); scientists generally find themselves in a minority. A few vocational options post-GCSE (business studies and music technology).

Additional support is available for students with mild specific learning difficulties – individually, in groups or in class. Students are monitored throughout their time at the school. Teachers build up a picture of pupils' learning profiles and identify those who might require specific intervention.

Games, options, the arts: Known for its creativity and the strength of its visual arts teaching; all lower school classrooms have ovens for baking and the school has its own forge. Thriving drama, with theatre, 'black box' studio and masterclasses often given by parents who are themselves leading lights in the profession. There are two well-stocked libraries, one for seniors, one for juniors. Music is popular, with orchestras, band and ensembles of all kinds.

Sport played enthusiastically, but 'go, fight, win' is not what this school is about. 'We don't have a 1st XI in each year – often we just have a mixed-ability team.' The spirit, however, is strong, and an eager crowd turns out to support the home team. As well as the usual ball sports, sails three

(school-built) boats on Welsh Harp, the Thames and Norfolk Broads. Games aside, for a London school it is an outdoorsy place. The large central playing field is at the heart of the campus and even on the rainiest day is filled with fresh air enthusiasts. Considerable emphasis on self-sufficiency. Den-building very much part of the experience and whole-year camping trips take place from year 4.

Extracurricular, too, is core. In the senior school, years 7-11 required to make their choice from a wide range of activities, from pottery to golf; sixth form options include screenwriting for films, emotional intelligence and Mandarin. Strong commitment to volunteering throughout, with pupils helping out at the local special school and raising significant sums for international causes (including building a school after the tsunami in Sri Lanka). Good careers advice (which kicks off in year 7) helps with GCSE and A level options and UCAS applications pre- and post-A level. As one might expect, green is high on the agenda – one of the first schools to introduce solar panels and recycling bins. Delicious, exclusively healthy lunches with plenty of fresh salads, yogurt and water.

Background and atmosphere: Founded by parents in Hampstead in 1898, original aim was to provide an education based on what was best for the child and encourage learning for its own sake. Part of the progressive movement, sees its kindred schools as Bedales in Hampshire and St Christopher in Letchworth. Moved to its current site, a leafy patch of north London opposite Golders Hill Park, in 1921, and has recently expanded, with a school building for the infants across the road from the main site at Ivy Wood, once the home of Anna Pavlova. Attractive, if compact, grounds, with a mixture of periods and styles (new fitness studio, music and drama block, lovely arts and crafts dining hall) grouped around a central village-like common. Star attractions include a wooded amphitheatre, an arbour (Squirrel Hall), formed from the sheltering branches of two ancient chestnuts, and a diminutive farm, complete with chickens, ducks and bees.

The original ethos – liberal, progressive, egalitarian, child-centred – remains core to the school's values today. Parents and pupils agree that the needs of each child are foremost. 'They try to act very holistically. They look at the individual and find out what makes them shine'. In many respects, too, operates as a large extended family, without the rigid age divide found elsewhere. 'It's a really friendly school,' said one year 9. 'Older kids look out for younger ones and you'll see sixth formers play with year 7s.' Most children seem to enjoy their time here. 'They skip into school every day,' said one long-time parent. 'Even after the holidays, they can't wait to get back.'

New Fives Court lower school building includes auditorium, cutting-edge art technology room with kiln and multi-purpose room for food science, rural studies and general science. ICT suite, learning support area and lower school library upstairs.

Pastoral care and discipline: Has always believed in minimal rules and flat hierarchy. Teachers are called by their first name and pupils are expected to be self-disciplined, co-operative and self-motivated. The mutual respect between teachers and pupils seen as one of the key strengths of the school. 'We trust them to be sensible'. The expectation, too, is that wrongdoing is likely to be an accident. 'We enable children to learn from their mistakes. There are no quick sanctions. It has to be worked through. Equally there are few reoffenders'. Those who cross the line between liberty and licence – 'being irresponsible in the science labs' or 'putting others in danger' – are given a 'blue form' and sent to the head. Children can be devastated. 'I've seen 16-year-old boys cry,' said a member of staff. Offences too serious to talk through – inappropriate behaviour towards their peers, bullying – can result in suspension. Expulsion for drugs on the premises, but can't remember the last incident, and the school has a 'huge' drugs education programme. 'The kids are pretty mature about sex and drugs,' said one parent. No uniform or dress code, but pupils tend not to push the boundaries, preferring standard-issue jeans and jumpers.

Teachers are called by their first name and pupils are expected to be self-disciplined, co-operative, self-motivated

Four counsellors. 'We know what's out there and make it our business to be proactive'. Help, too, from other pupils – peer mentoring, school 'Cits', pupils' council. The end result is a happy bunch of kids. 'I've seen other parents go through miserable teens,' said one mother with two teenage children at the school. 'King Alfred teaches them a lot of confidence.' Non-denom – pupils of every faith and none.

Pupils and parents: An arts and media favourite, parents often choose it for its informality and creativity. 'They come from both ends of the spectrum. There are those who are so liberal they think we're conservative and those who are conservative with a small "c".' Popular, too, with former pupils. New converts are often those who disliked their own, more traditional school days: 'I'd have

killed to go to a school like this,' said one. 'They make it such fun.' Pupils, mainly from the wealthier suburbs of north London (Hampstead, Golders Green, Highgate, Muswell Hill), are confident and articulate and expect to be given equal weight as adults. Quite a large international contingent – Americans, South Africans, Israelis, Swedish, Germans, Spanish, Italians.

Entrance: For entry into reception at 4+, names are put down from birth. Date of registration in relation to the child's date of birth (over 200 apply for 40 places in reception) decides visit order. 'We go down the list'. Prospective students come for a two-hour visit and are observed by teachers to assess children's readiness for the next stage of their education and 'whether the child is able to fully participate in and take advantage of the education offered by KAS'. Parents meet with the head and senior staff at the same time.

Entry for occasional places is also by waiting list order and the visits are half, full or two days, depending on age.

Over 100 apply for a handful of places at 11. 'A lot of thought goes into the mix of classes'. Not highly selective at A level – four GCSEs minimum for those already in the school; at least five at grade B or above for 10 to 15 or so newcomers, with A*-B in chosen subjects. All candidates, however, interviewed to ensure they'll fit into the school culture.

Exit: Majority of juniors pass seamlessly on to the senior school. Around a quarter or so leave post-GCSE. 'Some children have been here since they were 4 and it's quite a long time to spend at one school.' About 98 per cent to further education, a good chunk (8-12 each year) to art foundation, then to the full spectrum of universities. One to Oxford in 2015, others to eg Birmingham, Bristol, Manchester, Sussex, York, LSE and Warwick.

Money matters: Though not particularly well endowed, attempts to keep fees as stable as possible while keeping facilities up to date. No scholarships, a small number (about four) of means-tested bursaries in year 7 and sixth form.

Remarks: A kind, liberal, creative school that suits the self-starter, the sophisticated and the artistic (pupils and parents). Will get the best out of most children, but possibly not ideal for those who require competition in the classroom or on the games field. Good, too, for the square peg and those who might find a more traditional environment oppressive. Not a school for parents obsessed with league-table position or those looking for children who jump to attention when an adult enters the room.

The Latymer School

Haselbury Road, London N9 9TN

Tel: 020 8807 4037

State • Pupils: 1,365 • Ages: 11–18 • Sixth form pupils: 448

Email: office@latymer.co.uk
Website: www.latymer.co.uk

Headteacher: Since September 2015, Maureen Cobbett (50s), previously head of All Saints' Catholic Voluntary Academy in Mansfield, Nottinghamshire.

Academic matters: Good GCSE results, making it the top performing school in Enfield borough and within the top six per cent in London, with 85 per cent A*/A grades in 2015. Pupils must choose a MFL from French, German (both very popular), Russian or Latin (not so popular) plus a humanity subject or religious education. ICT is not taught as a separate subject but incorporated across the whole curriculum.

Years ago a decision was made to reduce the number of GCSEs to nine to ease the stress on pupils and so that 'school life can be enjoyed for itself'. The recent introduction of triple GCSE science increases the number to 10 but head still thinks it important that academic success is not at the expense of 'a life outside school'.

At sixth form the school offers 'nothing apart from an unashamedly academic programme', so no vocational subjects here. The majority stay on at sixth form but another 50 join from other schools, so exam rates at 63 per cent A*/A and 81 per cent A*/B grades in 2015 are commendable. are commendable. Having a larger than normal sixth form

means the school 'can teach a big range of subjects, which smaller sixth forms struggle to offer'.

Parents agree that the school is 'very good academically' and it certainly makes plenty of effort to award academic achievement across all years. Year 13s are awarded in specialist subjects too, such as mechanics, statistics and government and politics. Pupils who do not gain a subject prize have the opportunity to be awarded either a Latymer Lodge or school prize for gaining a high aggregate at A level. There are also open awards for special achievements in spoken English, creative work, instrumental performance, music composition and fieldwork. Prizes are awarded for service to the school in music, debating and service to the community, thus plenty of motivation to strive and to win here. 'They will take your child through the process and your child will pass the exams,' one parent stated confidently. Another said, 'I believe that both my children have been encouraged and guided to fulfil their academic potential. Classroom teaching is supported with a range of visits and activities to inspire as well as stretch.'

Where pupils have a special learning need, they will find help through one of the two SEN teachers, one of whom focuses on those who need extra support and the other on gifted and talented pupils.

Around 350 pupils have EAL requirements and of the 29 pupils identified as having a special educational need just three have a statement.

Games, options, the arts: More than 17 different sporting activities offered (from athletics and badminton to volleyball and ultimate Frisbee). Notable achievements include winners of Enfield Schools Hockey Champions and Enfield Football Cup, alongside a number of other firsts, seconds and thirds in regional finals for netball, tennis and cricket. In year 10, when pupils have the opportunity to specialise, and at sixth form, they can also take squash, golf, swimming, orienteering and dry-slope skiing in addition to the normal range of sports on offer. The school encourages active lifestyles and rewards pupils' enthusiasm for sport with a number of awards that recognise outstanding achievement both in and outside of school. These include hockey, football (for girls, not boys), netball, cross-country, rounders, tennis and cricket. All pupils have the opportunity to spend a week at Ysgol Latymer (the school's outdoor sports centre in Snowdonia National Park in Wales) for activities such as hill walking, orienteering, climbing, abseiling and canoeing.

Pupils get the opportunity to spend a week at the school's outdoor sports centre in Snowdonia National Park for activities like hill walking, orienteering, climbing, abseiling and canoeing

Latymer once had an art specialism and so the subject has a strong presence outside the department, with work on display around the school and contributing to cross-curricular subjects (for example, year 9s painted the background scenery for senior drama productions of My Fair Lady and Hairspray). Experts visit to do talks and run special workshops in oil painting and sculpture, and the department runs visits to the London Institute, Tate Modern and Tate Britain as well as to Barcelona and Paris. As a result, examiners have commented on the good grasp pupils have on contemporary artists.

Drama is supported by trips out and really plays out hugely in the big theatre productions that take place at the school each year: a main school production in November, a junior production in July, and the house drama competition every other year. The language and drama curriculums are supported by school journeys and exchanges through links with Russia, France and Germany; there have also been exchange visits with the Mwambisi school in Tanzania; other trips include geographers to Iceland, classicists to Italy, artists to New York, skiers to the French Alps, canoeists to the Ardêche, music to Austria, Belgium, Germany, the Czech Republic and other places in Europe; sports to Holland and Italy. Other destinations have included Nepal, India and Malawi, and every other year there is a sports trip to Barbados.

A quarter of the pupils learn a musical instrument at standards ranging from beginners to beyond grade 8. As pupils advance through key stage 3 they focus on 'practical music-making wherever possible', covering projects on classical, jazz, pop and world music, with regular assessment every half term. There are five orchestras ranged from grade 3 to post grade 8, a concert band and several choirs. They perform at school concerts and many are invited elsewhere, such as the National Festival for Music.

Latymerians enjoy a rich range of extracurricular activities that shape life at the school; parents value its contribution to their personal and social development. House theatre and music productions; over 60 different clubs and teams run before, during and after school, and at weekends. Clubs cover art, gardening, chess and more. There is a Young Enterprise group, an economics society, a Christian union and clubs whose sole purpose is to raise funds for less fortunate children in developing nations while pupils learn more about their lives. We are told that the school's Amnesty International group is 'the largest and most active school group in the country'. The LAFTA (Latymer Awards in Film, Television and Advertising) is a fun and creative play on the Oscar-style awards ceremony.

Background and atmosphere: Tradition creates the atmosphere at Latymer. It was established in nearby Church Street in 1624 at the direction of Edward Latymer, a City merchant, who bequeathed certain property to trustees on condition that they were to clothe and educate 'eight poore boies of Edmonton'. His, and the 'generosity of the many others since', are remembered each year on the school's Foundation Day. Pupils are proud of this tradition and seem enthusiastic about the events that keep it alive. The school's motto – Qui Patitur Vincit (Who Endures Wins) – aptly sums up the spirit of the school, and is the title of the annual talk to the school (head's given it seven times so far and says it's a 'feat to bring a new twist to it'). The school moved to its present location in 1910.

On the day of our visit it seemed very quiet, apart from the hum and beat of instrumental practice (including drums) in the music department and a flurry of students preparing for the school's major production in the Seward Theatre downstairs. Built on three acres of land and flanked by 12 acres of playing fields, which separate the school from the main A10 road, it looks deceptively small from the front. There are a number of outbuildings around the main one, added at various times over the school's life and capturing its spirit of progress: the great hall (1928), which seats over 1000; the gymnasia and technical labs (1966); a performing arts centre (2000) and a sports/dining hall complex (2006). In 2010 the high-tech multi-purpose Seward Theatre (performance space, auditorium, media studio, art gallery and drama theatre) was opened. The school also has a number of rooms dedicated to specialist teaching, for example a suite of 12 science laboratories, six fully-equipped technology rooms, and specialist ICT rooms with wireless networks, an intranet and access to remote access learning. There is a large library, with separate learning

There is a rich sense of celebration of the past: each year a whole school assembly is held in honour of Latymerians who died in the two world wars

resource and careers centres. Sixth formers have a large common room and quiet study area.

The school's traditional atmosphere is maintained by the old students' association (there is an old boys' football club and old students' badminton club). Ex-students are very much involved in school life, participating in school events, contributing to lessons, presenting school awards and setting up special funds. There is a rich sense of celebration of the past: each year a whole school assembly is organised for the 'grand Act of Remembrance' in honour of Latymerians who died in the two world wars. They sing the national anthem, read from the Bible, listen to a talk about war life and have a 'blessing suited to a multi-faith audience' pronounced by a local reverend. There is a book listing war casualties in the library, which pupils proudly pointed out.

Pastoral care and discipline: The 186 pupils in each year are organised into six form groups, and each form group belongs to one of the six house groups. They remain in these groups throughout their school lives, meeting daily for registration and form periods, including, in the lower years, PSHE lessons delivered by the form tutor. Each year group also has a head of learning (first port of contact for parents concerned about progress) who, along with the deputy head of learning, also acts as mentor.

House culture is strong. Each has a senior pupil to lead, democratically elected. Activities are organised by senior pupils and used to inject a sense of comradeship and teamwork across all year groups, and to make new year 7s feel fully inducted into life at Latymer. They do this via sports tournaments and various competitions such as cake-making, drama and music. 'Equally importantly', houses also 'operate non-competitively' to organise community service activities and to help raise funds for charity (one house group raised over £80 in 20 minutes for Water Aid by taping water bottles to themselves). Together, this creates 'a strong sense of coherence and team working' among pupils at the school.

Pupils are expected to abide by the school rules and the home school agreement they signed with their parents on joining the school, but the school views 'self discipline resulting from wanting to learn' as more important as a deterrent for poor behaviour. Although behavourial problems are rare and 'dealt with swiftly by the head of learning or form tutor', one parent did say she thinks the pastoral care side of things 'is not as strong as the focus is on the academic side'. However, other parents say pastoral care is excellent: 'Not only do my daughters experience excellent teaching, they also benefit from being at a school with a firm commitment to pastoral care. They feel safe, secure, confident and happy. While the academic side is challenging, it is not to the exclusion of everything else.' Another said she has 'always felt comfortable emailing teachers direct if I have a concern or question'.

Pupils and parents: Anyone and everyone who is 'very clever', though the school wisely lists acceptable postcodes in its admission criteria. This includes half from Enfield, plus some in Haringey, Islington, Hackney and Waltham Forest.

Entrance: Only those 'deemed capable of achieving higher grades of GCSE are considered' at this highly oversubscribed, selective school. Selection is by the NVR test as well as literacy and numeracy. A parent said 'it used to be harder to get into', but 1,900 typically apply for the 186 places, so many are still disappointed. Priority is given to looked-after children and those who live in designated postcode areas in the boroughs of Hackney, Islington, Waltham Forest, Haringey and Enfield. Offers also made to around 20 students who live in these areas and show 'exceptional musical talent and achievement' akin to grade 5. For entry in 2016, a further 20 places awarded to those on Pupil Premium.

At sixth form, 90 per cent stay on. An additional 50 places are allocated to pupils from other schools, bringing the size of the sixth form to 234. Sixth form is also oversubscribed with around 442 applications for these 50 places. Places are offered to students who achieve at least six GCSE grade As, including the subjects they wish to study at AS level; they must also pass the Latymer test and live in one of the designated postcode areas.

Exit: Around 95 per cent go on to university or other forms of higher education in music and art. The school does not 'push Oxford or Cambridge though plenty apply, and plenty get offers' (20 places in 2015). UCL, Bristol and Nottingham also popular; courses include aerospace engineering, medicine, law, Chinese, Russian and Egyptology. Very few – one or two – leave to go straight into employment.

Money matters: The Latymer Foundation offers some financial assistance to pupils experiencing hardship.

Remarks: A peek back in time shows that some well-known former pupils like Baroness Claire Tyler (chair of CAFCASS and president of the National Children's Bureau), footballer Johnny Haynes and Sir Bruce Forsyth CBE all did well here. Pupils clearly still do. This is a zealously traditional school with a highly likeable yet firm-handed head and pupils who show a healthy balance between hard work and play. There is some effort to keep with the times but the school's view is that 'If it ain't broke don't fix it'. Ofsted has a similar attitude and in its last report described the school as outstanding.

Mill Hill County High School

Worcester Crescent, London NW7 4LL

State • Pupils: 1,720 • Ages: 11–19 • Sixth form pupils: 480

Tel: 0844 477 2424

10

Email: admin@mhchs.org.uk
Website: www.mhchs.org.uk

Headteacher: Since 2004, Geoffrey Thompson MA MBA (Ed) FCMI (50s). Formerly head of Duchess's Community High School in Alnwick, Northumberland. Educated at Campbell College, Belfast, then at St Catharine's College, Cambridge, where he read music. Started his teaching career at Langley Park School for Boys in Bromley, where he worked for 18 years, before moving to Norfolk as deputy head, then on to Northumberland. Though Mill Hill County has always been a school with high standards, his decade in charge has improved it significantly. 'Having a vision and a blueprint is not my way,' he says. 'You have a set of principles and good judgement, you make decisions with other people and the place grows organically.'

A dapper soul, whose own tie is always immaculately knotted, he has a dry sense of humour and a delightfully precise command of the English language. Married to a teacher (who also works in the school), he has two daughters and a son. Out of hours, he enjoys reading, particularly modern history, travelling and music.

Academic matters: Mill Hill County is one of the country's highest performing comprehensives. With 63 per cent A*-B grades at A level in 2015, and 29 per cent A*/A at GCSE, including English and maths, and 36 per cent A*/A grades, this is a school which believes in an academic focus. Apart from a handful of vocational qualifications in ICT and media, the curriculum is traditional, with a good range of modern languages (Spanish, French, German, Latin) and a quarter of pupils taking all three sciences at GCSE. In the sixth form – the largest in the borough – the 33 subjects on offer include sociology, psychology, economics and dance. Maths and science, however, are the most popular options (with 10 groups for maths). Most sixth formers take four AS levels ('a few do five, but we don't encourage it,' says the head).

Teaching strong throughout (with regular awards for science, geography and maths) and most subjects provide plenty of enrichment. In English, for example, there are Shakespeare and poetry workshops, in DT, direct links with industry. An undoubted strength of the school is the focused attention it offers for all. 'Every child is taught to their own individual abilities,' commented one parent. For those at the top of the spectrum, there are two members of staff to encourage A level students to aim for A*s and Russell Group universities, while those who struggle to make the A*-C benchmark at GCSE are offered a one-year course in which to resit. At this juncture, too, the school participates in a Barnet-wide scheme which sandwiches vocational college training with English, maths and employment skills. Largest number of SEN pupils in Barnet with a department reflective of their very

An undoubted strength of the school is the focused attention it offers for all. 'Each child is taught to their individual abilities,' commented a parent

varied needs (including provision for the blind). A raft of teaching assistants provides in-class aid and specialist staff oversee classes and support students beyond. 'It's quite an operation,' says the head.

Games, options, the arts: The school prides itself on its extracurricular offering, but there's little doubt that music is the jewel in the crown. 'There are few local schools that can hold a candle to us,' says the head with legitimate pride. He himself rehearses all year 7s to appear in the Christmas concert and from time to time plays the piano at assembly or a duet alongside a visiting professional. Standards throughout are exceptionally high. Recently, for the fourth year in a row, the orchestra is performing a joint concert with the Royal Philharmonic ('you have to be quite good for the RPO to come and play with you,' says the head). Meanwhile the school band will feature alongside that of the Royal Air Force at the Watford Colosseum. Regular lunchtime concerts, major concerts twice a term, large-scale musical in the Easter term, plus an annual European tour for concert and jazz bands. A full range of other sounds, including gospel, African drum and steel drum. Boys participate as enthusiastically as girls – 'unheard of,' says the head – and one talented former pupil performs regularly at Ronnie Scott's.

In sport too, the school has become a 'force to be reckoned with,' particularly in boys' football and girls' netball. Basketball and rugby also on offer and table tennis played enthusiastically by all. Excellent facilities for sport include a range of pitches, three playgrounds, gym, sports hall and in summer, six-lane track and three tennis courts. Art thriving, with a weekly art club and life drawing workshop run by the Royal Academy for A level pupils. Numerous guest speakers and in-demand trips (languages to Barcelona and Normandy, politics to the US, annual ski trip) to inspire and raise aspirations. Good range of clubs run early morning and after school (which can be difficult for those who live at a distance), plus D of E, World Challenge and CCF (shared with nearby independent Mill Hill).

Background and atmosphere: Originally opened in 1931 as Orange Hill Boys' Grammar School, which then combined with matching girls' grammar in the 1970s. Merged again with Moat Mount School in 1984 to create Mill Hill County High School. The school, fringed by a good expanse of playing fields and forest, now sits on a hilly site with panoramic London views. There, however, the picturesque ends, with well-used buildings crammed together in an intricate hotchpotch to accommodate more students than ever. 'It is overcrowded,' said one parent. 'They're the victims of their own success.' Older parts of the fabric include some fairly basic Portakabins (which house dance and drama), but recent additions have provided modern labs, a sixth form centre, computer suites, seven new classrooms and an air-conditioned assembly hall.

> *The school, fringed by a good expanse of playing fields and forest, sits on a hilly site with panoramic London views*

The lack of elbow room doesn't seem to detract from the upbeat mood, with friendly and positive staff (on the day the Guide visited a member of the office team was ringing up a local primary school to ensure a forgotten jumper was returned to its owner) and parents praise the general sense of well-being. 'The school is very good at communicating,' said one. 'They keep us informed and I have the email addresses of all my child's teachers.' Another was grateful for the empathy shown at a difficult time. 'They were understanding and supportive when we had family problems.'

Not the easiest school to get to. No tube nearby, which contributes to the mood of semi-rural calm but can be difficult for those wanting to arrive early or stay late for clubs or games. Mill Hill became an academy in 2011, but still works closely with Barnet Council, particularly in its responsibilities for Oak Hill, a successful facility for 32 emotionally and behaviourally disturbed children, four and a half miles away.

Pastoral care and discipline: One of the first things parents tend to mention is the uniform policy. 'They're very strict on uniform,' said one. 'Everyone looks very smart.' The head sees uniform as a means of setting the expectation bar. 'We're very clear about what we say and insist that what we say is done. We aren't repressive, but you'd be unlikely to see anyone with their shirt tails not tucked in or their ties not tied.'

The head also spends one lesson a week making surprise visits to a range of classrooms. 'That way, you see what's happening. You chat to the children, look at their books. It's a co-operative relationship, but you could potentially see those same children in another context behaving badly.' The insistent focus on behaviour, attitude and good manners undoubtedly pays off. 'Most people who come across our students have positive things to say.'

Pupils and parents: About half the school's intake comes from the leafy and prosperous suburb of Mill Hill, with its high concentration of professionals and business families, but the intake is certainly not uniform. 'There are quite a lot of deprived children, and the ethnic mix is huge,' says the head. It includes significant numbers of families who originate from the Indian sub-continent, Asia and Africa. Only a few, however, 'don't speak excellent English.'

Entrance: Mill Hill has entrance criteria guaranteed to drive north London parents into a neurotic frenzy, with 240 places at 11 sliced up into small print sub-sections. Lucky locals can benefit from one of the 90 guaranteed 'geography' places. But distance from the gates is frighteningly close (rather less than a mile). Siblings, too, are ensured a desk. After that the 60 places awarded on aptitude are split into: 24 for technology, 24 for music and 12 for dance. Technology is tested in two stages – a reasoning test in the summer term of year 5 whittles down about 1500 to 240, the second round (in abstract reasoning and maths) held in September cherry picks the rest ('it's harder than getting into Oxford,' jokes the head). Music equally competitive, with up to 400 auditioning, in two sections: listening and performance. 'You can, however, play a snappy piece on the classroom xylophone and come

out higher than a carefully coached grade 4 violinist.' Dance candidates are selected by audition.

The large (and heavily over-subscribed) sixth form admits a further 40 to 60 pupils out of 600 applicants, with minimum entry requirements of six grade Bs at GCSE, including English and maths. Those wishing to study science and maths need As in their chosen subjects though, and most come garlanded with a string of A*s and As.

Exit: No one is ever asked to leave (except for disciplinary matters), but a fair few move on after GCSE to local sixth form colleges, independent and grammar schools. More than 70 per cent to university, the majority to Russell Group (the school has one of the highest representations here of any comprehensive in the UK). Three to Cambridge in 2015. Quite a number to drama and art-related degrees. A consistent trickle to the US.

Money matters: The transformation to academy status has released additional funds and these are now being used for building projects. Otherwise not rich, but not poor either.

Remarks: A cheerful, well-run school producing highly motivated, high achieving students. Exceptional music.

Mill Hill School

Linked schools: Belmont Mill Hill Preparatory School, 503; Grimsdell, Mill Hill Pre-Preparatory School, 524

The Ridgeway, London NW7 1QS

Tel: 020 8959 1176

Independent · Pupils: 660; 150 boarders · Ages: 13–18 · Sixth form pupils: 240 · Fees: Day £18,885 pa; Boarding up to £29,835

Email: registrations@millhill.org.uk
Website: www.millhill.org.uk

Head: From January 2016, Mrs Frances King (50s), who will also be chief executive of the Mill Hill Foundation and the first woman to lead the school. She is currently principal of Collège Alpin Beau Soleil, a coeducational school in Switzerland. BA in theology from Oxford, PGCE from the Institute of Education, MA in philosophy and religion from Heythrop College, London and MBA in school management from Hull. She became deputy head of St Mary's School, Ascot in 2000, head of Heathfield School in 2003 and head of Roedean School in 2008. She is married to Tim.

Head since 2007, Dr Dominic Luckett BA DPhil FRSA (40s). Educated at the University of Leicester and Magdalen College, Oxford, where he did his

doctorate in Tudor history. Taught at Harrow, where he became both head of history and an assistant housemaster, then at Worth, where he was deputy head. He is a serving inspector with the ISI and on the council of the University of Leicester. Attracted to Mill Hill because it mixes day with boarding and because of its location in north London. Married to Cara, a barrister, and has two young daughters.

A tall, softly spoken and sincere man who pauses before giving a considered response – a likeable head. 'He's very focused,' one parent said. He is under no illusion that the school still has a way to go academically before it can pit itself against other north London rivals, but says the foundations are there to make it a truly 'phenomenal school.' 'My

'We're never going to be the top academic school in the country but we want to make teaching accessible and enjoyable and give children high expectations'

job is to realise some of the potential this school has,' he told us. 'And I think we're getting there – we've already achieved the best A level results we've ever had this year. We're never going to be the most massively selective school, but we pride ourselves on having students with really lovely values, who may bring other things to the table.' That's why, he says, they interview potential candidates before seeing their exam results. 'If someone comes along for an interview and demonstrates they have extra strings to their bow – great at sport or drama for example – we may be a bit more lenient if they're borderline in their CE exam.' Moving on in January 2016 to head Sherborne School.

Academic matters: In 2015, 47 per cent A*/A and 76 per cent A*-B grades at A level. School's aim is to achieve each child's full potential while working in a way that makes them feel comfortable – 'for some, three Bs at A level is a real achievement, but others here get three, four or five As.' Some children, too, require a lot of pressure to achieve and others buckle under pressure.

Twenty-four subjects on offer at A level, including Chinese, business studies and government and politics. One parent criticised the subjects on offer as limiting compared to other schools. 'My friend removed her child from the school to go to another sixth form as they didn't offer psychology as an A level,' she told us. Good spread of languages offered at GCSE: French, Spanish, German, Greek and Latin, plus Portuguese and Chinese as extras. In 2015, 54 per cent A*/A grades overall.

Two of the learning resources on the campus are worth noting. The library (an 'innovative conversion' of the school squash courts) is a two-tiered, large, bright space, incredibly well stocked with books and a gallery for magnificent artwork by students. The stunning and contemporary Favell building has a glass atrium – providing a light and airy home for seven departments, including modern languages, history and geography. Also used for exhibitions and entertainment. Startlingly quiet classrooms (we had to check to see if there were students inside) surround the atrium on three floors. Well presented but scant student displays and artwork adorn the walls, encased in glass frames.

New science block is under way to replace the rather old-fashioned labs where Nobel-winning scientist Francis Crick once studied. (This doesn't seem to hold pupils back since Imperial College is a popular university destination).

Mill Hill takes in a reasonably broad spread of academic ability and aims to get the best out of each child by helping them to learn effectively. 'We're not a hothouse,' says the head. 'We're never going to be the top academic school in the country, but we want to make teaching accessible and

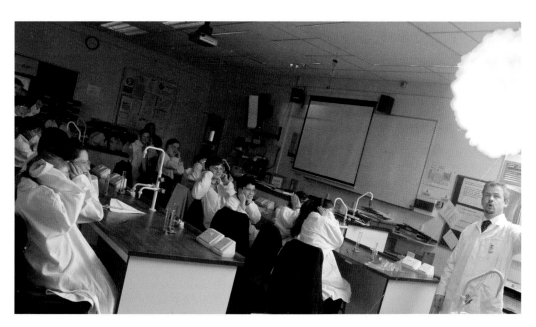

enjoyable and give children high expectations. That said, we have some very bright children. It's a question of identifying what each child is capable of and providing what each child needs.'

The school has limited facilities for SEN. Head is sympathetic but pragmatic. 'We have facilities in place to deal with mild to moderate dyslexia, but for anything more severe, we just don't have the resources in place.' All new entrants are screened for dyslexia and dyspraxia and are given extra time in the CE exam. One parent whose child is moderately dyslexic said the school was 'helpful to a point,' but she had to fight for most things.

Games, options, the arts: Sport, sport, sport. A clincher for pupils and parents alike when choosing this school over others. Competitive and recreational sport has always played a big role at Mill Hill and with its expansive site it's easy to see why. Rugby and cricket are the two biggies here. As one parent told us: 'My son only agreed to come here because of the rugby.' The school established a reputation as a rugby playing school from the outset, and has produced a large number of international rugby players. Great facilities in which to play.

The school's cricket arena has been called 'one of the most beautiful grounds to play cricket in the London area.' To add to this, they have the services of a professional coach. Players (boys and girls) are regularly selected to represent Middlesex and Hertfordshire and occasionally England.

Golf is another major sport here and is even incorporated into the timetable. This is the only school in London to boast a golf academy (although ironically no golf course – pupils play at nearby Hendon). One girl has been selected for the England U16 girls' golf team. Tennis is very strong – one of the strongest schools in the south east.

> *The school's cricket arena has been called 'one of the most beautiful grounds in the London area'*

Soccer, netball, hockey, cross-country and swimming (the school boasts a beautiful, new 25m pool) on offer. More adventurous pupils can try their hand at sailing, skiing/snowboarding, riding, clay pigeon shooting and taekwondo (these incur extra cost). Mill Hill is also one of the few remaining independent schools to have an Eton fives court. The shape of the court is modelled on the chapel at Eton (we thought it looked like a Roman gladiator chamber).

For non-sporty types (and they are seemingly few and far between), drama is very popular and taken by many at both GCSE and A level. With drama studio, theatre and large school stage, it is rare for a production not to be in rehearsal. House arts festival takes place every two years (alternating with a house music competition), with 10 plays performed over three nights. Many ex-students have become thesps of stage and screen. Art is strong and some of the art displayed around the school is amongst the best we've seen. This year saw the first inflatable sculpture floating around the studios. Good music facilities (specialised equipment for composition and recording) and in addition to curricular music, lots of opportunities to participate in a wide range of musical activities (chapel choir, string orchestra, jazz band and chamber music). Well-equipped on the DT side with 30 top-end computers and industry standard 3D printers.

A series of monthly lectures on a variety of topics – from classical history to journalism and politics (presenters include Jonathan Dimbleby and Terry Jones) are a popular and successful addition to the already crammed Mill Hill diary.

Thriving charitable work and partnership trips every summer; lower sixth form pupils have the opportunity to work for two to three weeks in a variety of educational projects with partners in Zambia, India and Nicaragua. Those taking part often talk about them being a 'life-changing experience.' As one parent told us: 'The school does exactly what it says on the box – there's something there for everyone.'

Background and atmosphere: Founded in 1807 by a group of non-conformist Christian ministers and city merchants, who placed their school outside London because of the 'dangers, both physical and moral, awaiting youth while passing through the streets of a large, crowded city.' Once peaceful and rural, The Ridgeway, where the school is situated, has become a busy and frustrating road (to be avoided like the plague at school pick-up). Nonetheless, it is still a very pretty part of the old Mill Hill village, laced with ponds and rambling cottages.

The school itself doesn't disappoint, with its handsome, neoclassical, pillared façade (BBC News website often uses a picture of Mill Hill School for articles about boarding schools). This is more like a stately home than a school, with pale yellow walls, marbled floors, pillars, plaques and elaborately framed portraits (most notably that of Mill Hill's former member of staff, James Murray, the third editor of the Oxford English Dictionary).

Our tour began at the top terrace, with sweeping views across parkland (undoubtedly the school's selling point) and 120 acres of green belt. The panorama is one of immaculately kept lawns, gravelled walkways, ponds and a smorgasbord of varying architecture which marry beautifully from arts and crafts buildings to the glass exterior of the new Favell building. The previous head, we are told, wanted to 'massively transform' the school for its bicentenary. We poked our heads into the beautiful, basilica-style chapel, designed by architect Basil Champney (best known for his work at Oxford and Winchester College). For students it means a compulsory weekly chapel visit, although the school is officially a non-conformist foundation.

Very much a campus school with little access to urban reality, some distance from the gates. It's a vast space for seemingly few pupils (nearly 650 in total) and indeed the walk to the furthest boarding house is so far that we were going to suggest adding Nordic walking to the syllabus. Around a quarter board, many on a weekly basis. No longer has Saturday morning school – full boarders (and many board weekly) are offered a Saturday morning programme of academic workshops and other activities. One full boarder from Africa told us that his houseparents 'became like a surrogate family to me'. Day pupils stay on site during the academic day and are members of one of seven day houses. Pupils can hang out in their houses between classes.

Although a fully co-ed school since 1997, it is still very male-centric – around 70 per cent boys and 30 per cent girls. This has put some prospective parents off sending their daughters there. One parent told us: 'Any school which is not balanced worries me slightly. You wonder if it is as well geared around girls as it so clearly is for boys.' However, a girl we spoke to disagreed. 'The diversity here makes it a really unique place where everyone is accepted,' she said. Indeed the girls we met on our tour didn't appear to be the shy, retiring types who would worry about being outnumbered. Pupils generally seemed a happy and spirited bunch.

Has now merged with The Mount School, and opened an international school on that site, offering courses with a focus on English for overseas students who are not ready to join mainstream schools. Pupils have their own boarding house on the Mill Hill site.

Pastoral care and discipline: Uniform is their thing – 'extremely strict,' one parent told us, and the deputy head is often seen reprimanding students for this reason outside the school gates. The result is an extremely well turned out (and good-looking), bunch of teenagers in traditional dark blazers adorned with the school motto and a myriad of ties denoting their houses. Sixth formers wear their own suits.

Considered to be a kind and gentle school, consistently praised by parents and officials for its outstanding pastoral care – 'very good at giving children their freedom,' one parent told us. Another parent said you can spot a Mill Hill child in a crowd. 'They always seem to be the most social and well rounded.' One pupil told us: 'It's like being part of a big family.' His only criticism was that 'you can't do an extra year.' This 'freedom' has led some parents to feel that the school is fairly slack in some areas, though. One criticised the fact that pupils get the same detention for smoking behind the bike shed as for chewing gum. She added that the head has improved the standard of the school greatly and praises him for not having double standards or being swayed by money or influence. She said: 'It seems to have been a problem with heads before, that it was one rule for one, and another if you had money.'

Formal exclusions are few and far between. Unlike some other schools, with their zero policy on drugs, this head is realistic, but not lax. 'If you are found with drugs once, it's a suspension, twice, you're out.' He says it nearly 'broke his heart' to permanently exclude a very bright and promising student for bringing drugs onto the premises. But 'you can't start making exceptions,' he told us. 'It blurs the line.'

Pupils and parents: No typical Mill Hill pupil. Quite a lot live locally, even boarders, though in the sixth form there's a significant influx from China, Africa, Germany, France and Russia. Diverse ethnic and religious mix – Catholic, Jewish and Greek possibly the most prominent. Strong entrepreneurial element and urban professionals among the parents, together with 'the seriously rich.' The odd celebrity parent has also been known to grace the hallowed halls. Former pupils include Richard Dimbleby, Francis Crick, Simon Jenkins, Timothy Mo, Denis Thatcher, Katharine Whitehorn and Norman Hartnell.

Entrance: Total of 140 places in year 9, with about 70 or 80 going to pupils from the junior school (Belmont) and a handful of other feeder schools. No place is guaranteed, though – 'the school will politely tell you if they don't think your child is up to it.' Approx 20 places reserved for boarders. Sets its own exams in January before entrance in English,

maths, French and science and uses the CE pass mark for setting. Oversubscribed, so 'we want to know what a child will bring. It's partly personality, and partly other factors like sport, music or drama.'

Entry to the sixth form requires two As and three Bs at GCSE, a requirement that applies both externally and internally. These requirements have not always been strictly adhered to, but one of the head's first acts was to enforce it, involving about 15 pupils leaving. 'We've always had a minimum grade requirement, now we're insisting it's met,' he said. One parent grumbled: 'The school is always moving the bar. It used to be automatic entrance into the sixth form.'

Exit: Most leavers to good universities, from Leeds to Oxford Brookes to Swansea. Business popular, otherwise a great range of subjects including medics, linguists and thespians.

Money matters: Middle to higher end of fee-paying schools in London. A selection of scholarships in academic subjects, the arts and sports. Fully-funded bursaries awarded each year and a range of other bursaries up to 90 per cent of the fees, on a carefully graded system of finance. The head's intention is that by 2020, 20 students a year will be offered full bursaries.

Remarks: Suits a busy, engaged child happy to try out a wide range of activities and use all the facilities and range of opportunities. A well-balanced school, determined to put the academic underpinning firmly in place.

Palmers Green Lower School

Linked school: Palmers Green High School, 551

104 Hoppers Road, London N21 3LJ

Independent · Pupils: 160 · Ages: 3–11 · Fees: up to £10,905 pa

Tel: 020 8886 1135

Email: office@palmersgreen.enfield.sch.uk
Website: www.pghs.co.uk

19

Headmistress: Since 2002, Mrs Christine Edmundson, also head of the senior school. She will often work with specialists that she 'may have heard at a conference or on radio'. One of these was a specialist in early years from Homerton College in Cambridge who helped when the early years foundation stage was just being introduced. 'It was great as she was working at the forefront of what was happening, so the staff had her expertise. Where other schools were thinking, "well, how do

you do that?" here teachers had a specialist to tell them how.'

Entrance: Most pupils join the school from the linked Alice Nursery, situated about a mile and a half away. Others come from nearby nursery schools such as Start Right Montessori, Leapfrog, Cedar Park, Bumble Bees Montessori and Leading Strings. Entrance to the prep department at age 4 and the junior department at age 7 is by assessment of ability and potential by one of the primary school teachers. This involves a timed test for children in years 5 and 6 but is less formal for those in year 4 and below. The school welcomes 'pupils with special educational needs, providing that our individual needs department can offer them the support they require'.

Exit: Around 70 per cent go on to Palmers Green High School, others to other independent or selective state schools in the area. Some parents would like 'a greater focus on preparing children for 11+ exams in the same way some other schools do'.

Remarks: Single form entry school with a maximum class size of 24 and a teacher pupil ratio of 1:9. Most children are working above the national average and a few are at level 6 in English, reading and maths. They are taught by mature (average age is 45) and well-qualified teachers. The small classes, say parents, are 'why we chose this school'. They also like the fact that specialist teaching in art, DT, drama, PE and music is introduced to children from as early as year 1 and in some subjects from reception. While core subjects such as English, maths, science and humanities are taught by form tutors, from year 3 girls have specialist French tuition and year 5s have taster courses in a range of languages, including Latin. Year 6 girls receive specialist DT teaching. 'DT is really fun,' remarked one year 6 girl. 'We've been doing models of playground rides and we solder too.' Her classmate showed us some prototypes but admitted that the teacher helped her with the soldering part as 'I was a bit scared' – then again, she had only joined the school

in year 5 and said, 'In my old school we didn't do any DT, they didn't trust us.' Parents comment on the 'teaching with substance'. Early introduction to subjects such as Latin and DT helps to develop the children's reasoning skills and their understanding of a wide variety of topics.

The small classes, say parents, are 'why we chose this school'. They also like the fact that specialist teaching in art, DT, drama, PE and music is introduced to children from year 1 and in some subjects from reception

It is a very friendly school where teachers insist you come in and have a look around the classrooms and the children appear wholly interested in what they are learning and readily talk about their work. A year 4 science class shared with us what they were learning about the comparison of light and dark. Another class showed off their work on historical toys, including specimens they had brought in from home. Learning is supported by visits to places like the British Schools Museum, Hatfield House, Whipsnade Zoo and the year 5 residential trip to Flatford Mill where they develop their skills in navigation, using a compass, and trekking. The school magazine shows off impressive artwork and writing. About half the girls learn one or more instruments at school. Specialist music teachers come in to teach instrument lessons and pupils' skills range from beginners to grade 4 and even 5.

There are no sports fields or courts on site and the main hall was, until recently when the new gymnasium was completed, being used for assemblies, indoor games, gym, dance and drama. Despite the shortage of on-site sports facilities, opportunity and enthusiasm for PE across ages is evident. Pupils travel to the nearby Walker Ground for games and to Southgate pool for swimming lessons. Gymnastics is popular, and now takes place in the new gym/dance studio. Pupils from year 2 upwards compete successfully in the week long Enfield Primary Schools Gymnastics Festival and Enfield netball tournament; there is an inter-house netball tournament for years 5 and 6, and there is a school swimming gala. Gymnastics and dance are taught on half term rotation. Drama is popular too, and year 3 to 6 girls perform at the local theatre. Year 6s take the lead roles in the annual summer play (which includes pupils from year 3 upwards) – 'we put on a play, we sing and dance and dress up in nice costumes'. Titles are adapted and new characters are introduced to popular productions to ensure everyone has the opportunity to take part. One year they 'did the 12 dancing princesses and 10 of their cousins because there were 22 of us'. Some girls played 'the jury in Goldilocks Goes to Court... she is charged with breaking in, and there are witnesses, the three ugly sisters, the bad wolf,

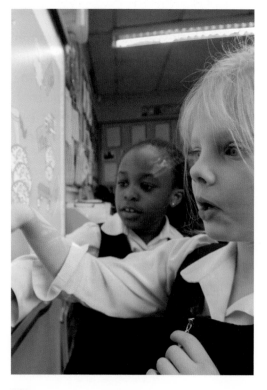

'Doing library' involves learning about how the library works, but pupils say the most exciting part is the badge they get to wear

the three bears, the bad fairy. Goldilocks won in the end. Everyone joins in and helps'.

As Christmas approaches the lower school and seniors come together to practise songs and to make decorations for the carol service. The younger children make stars, sheep and angels whilst years 3 to 6 prepare to recite two poems. The school has close links with the local churches, although 'we have pupils of all faiths and none,' head says.

The prep and junior departments are located on the ground and middle floor of a building shared with the senior school. This supports the close knit pastoral environment where the younger pupils benefit from keen mentoring by the older pupils upstairs – 'during fire drills an older girl must grab a younger one,' said the head, 'and can get upset as there aren't enough little ones to go around'. She says the school believes in teaching children 'to work smart, not hard and long, but smart'. Good peer-to-peer relationships are a key part of this. Children are encouraged to 'play to strengths, to support their friends and learn from them as well as the staff'. There is 'good support for all children ... with girls in higher years being a mentor to younger girls,' said a parent. 'My daughter is really happy and we are really happy.'

All junior pupils learn to be responsible by taking on roles like helping out in the prep school or library, or as head and deputy head girls. These roles – called 'duties' – alongside the range of extra-curricular activities on offer, give pupils plenty to do and they both enjoy and thrive from the responsibility despite their busy schedules: 'I find it amazing that I'm a head girl,' said one pupil. 'I have prep duties two days a week; orchestra on Wednesdays, Thursdays is choir and on Friday we do library.'

'Doing library' involves acting 'as librarians, recommending books and putting them away, and learning about how the library works,' but pupils say the most exciting part is the badge they get to wear. They share the library with the senior school so there is a tight rota in place. Adjacent to the library is the main school hall – called Avondale – which is, in effect, the original school building. They relocated here in 1918, 13 years after the school was founded by a Quaker called Alice Hum. Since then a number of extensions have been added to Avondale Hall, including classrooms, a dining room and more recently the newly built Elizabeth Smith Hall and purpose-built medical room. This is expected to make things a lot easier for the girls, especially in drama and indoor PE, as previously everything took place in the main hall and its use was restricted during exam times.

Extracurricular activities range from sewing, junior orchestra, violin club and several choirs to art and maths puzzle club, speech and drama, netball and gym. The junior choir performs regularly at local events such as the N21 summer festival and Christmas festival. In the speech and drama club, 'we write our own mini plays and act them out', say pupils. 'We get certificates. They're displayed upstairs in the corridor.' There is 'something for

everybody, whether you're arty, sporty, or not ...' said a parent, 'we encourage our daughter to do as much as possible'.

Head says, 'We expect them to work hard and to be involved in things so that if something goes wrong (eg, a girl appears to be struggling or is behaving out of character) we pick it up.'

Parents certainly think highly of the school and most agree that their daughters are being adequately stretched academically. However, if they could wave a magic wand it would be to have more breakfast and after-school clubs to support working parents.

Palmers Green High School

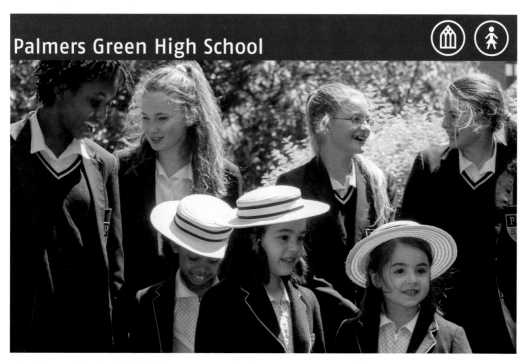

Linked school: Palmers Green Lower School, 548

104 Hoppers Road, London N21 3LJ

Independent • Pupils: 120 • Ages: 11–16 • Fees: £14,340 pa

Tel: 020 8886 1135

Email: office@palmersgreen.enfield.sch.uk
Website: www.pghs.co.uk

20

Headmistress: Since 2002, Mrs Christine Edmundson BMus MBA LRAM ARCM PGCE (Cantab) (50s). Came to London from the Isle of Man to study music at Royal Holloway, University of London, where she was a choral scholar undergraduate and a postgraduate, and entered teaching after a bizarre twist of events. 'Someone from New Zealand working at the British Museum had published his doctoral thesis on my unpublished manuscript, so I

changed course.' This launched her teaching career at a day school for girls in Warwick, which, with its link to a local boys' school 'was great for co-educational productions'. She went on to become director of music at a co-educational day and boarding school in Ascot and then deputy head at a girls' day and boarding school in Bath.

She is a chirpy and warm character with a great sense of humour, a sort of mother figure, which fits well in a school where the atmosphere is like one big family. Parents say she is 'approachable, you can talk to her,' and that 'it's good to see her at the gates in the mornings rather than like some [heads] tucked up in the office'. Interestingly, in the head's view, her presence helps to see off 'parents who are naughty and park on the zigzag lines'. She is known for getting to the bottom of things when parents complain but is no pushover for those who try to pull the wool over her eyes and ask for things like days off to 'go to a family wedding in Scotland'.

Parents say head is chirpy and warm with a great sense of humour, a sort of mother figure. 'It's good to see her at the gates in the mornings rather than tucked up in the office'

She has been here long enough to see a whole generation of children come through, which is 'nice... just one or two left that weren't my generation'. She still teaches, not music but ICT, RE, and general studies. 'I don't get involved in music except through general studies or for Founder's Day and the carol service.' She is vocal about changes in education, and because she talks about these issues during general studies, the girls are also clued up on current debates – 'Oh good,' she says, 'general studies is working'. She says her speeches at the annual prize giving ceremony are not the norm – she uses them to remind parents of changes afoot in education, eg the debacle around GCSE exams and competition for university places.

Academic matters: Consistently high GCSE results: 77 per cent A*/A grades in 2015. Relationships between pupils and teachers are strong; class sizes are small, between 10 and 16. 'That's why we chose this school,' said a parent. 'It was pretty tough to see how overstretched the teachers were at our previous state primary school.' With a teacher pupil ratio of 1:9, 'we get the attention we need', say pupils.

The school offers IGCSE French and Spanish and girls can choose either or both. A few girls study additional maths; firm favourites when choosing options are history, geography and ICT. Parents will be pleased to know, however, that the school is flexible towards subject choice catering to, for example, those who study a language outside school or who have taken a GCSE/IGCSE early (frequently in a modern foreign language spoken at home), allowing them to continue to study the subject at school.

Head believes in teaching 'children to work smart and play to strengths'. She sees the school as moving more toward IGCSE because GCSE 'doesn't stretch the brightest of students'. Parents agree: 'Ms Edmundson made no bones about the school being selective,' said a parent. 'I wanted my daughter to be in that environment.'

Majority of pupils do D of E bronze level and the UK Maths Challenge. There are visiting teachers, educational trips and residential stays to enhance learning – eg year 8 geography trip to Dorset to prepare pupils for their GCSE fieldwork, trips to Poland and Berlin for GCSE history and to the Isle of Wight where pupils study the impact of the festival. 'We've just returned from a trip to Spain,' said a pupil. 'Every morning we had Spanish lessons with a native speaker; even if we asked what a word meant they would explain it in Spanish.'

Pupils say the trips aid what they learn in the classroom: 'it's so amazing to go and see everything expanded... it is all very well learning from a text book...' They particularly look forward to the annual year 9 visit to the Guardian newspaper office as part of the English curriculum, where 'you get to see how everything is put into action, you choose the stories, you choose a name and print the papers'. They bring the papers back to school and stick the front pages up on the walls.

School introduces specialist teaching in subjects such as Latin and DT much earlier than most (in the junior school) and this clearly benefits pupils in the senior school. Older students are able to access AS level course material – this is mainly in modern foreign languages and for those who have already successfully attained an A* in year 9 and year 10. 'The main purpose is to enrich and extend language skills in preparation for taking A levels.' Head says pupils often surprise others with their knowledge due to their early access to specialist teaching or advanced materials: one went for a sixth form interview 'and the interviewer said, "how did you know that? You shouldn't know that at your stage."' However, one parent said that highly able students could be better challenged: 'There have been several instances where the homework has been so basic that my daughter has become demotivated.'

Teachers generally described as friendly; head of history praised by pupils for making the subject one of the most popular. Head of maths also praised: 'In year 7 I didn't like maths and now I'm doing additional maths. They made me enjoy it and that's really good as it's so important. I know that's the case for lots of people in the class.'

No children at present who do not speak fluent English but EAL support can be provided. Around 20 to 25 girls are identified with SEN, mostly dyslexia, and a few pupils have autistic spectrum disorders (ASDs). They can have support in lessons and there is some help for the ASDs in social skills arranged by the individual needs coordinator, who can involve outside agencies if necessary. Extra classes before and after school and one-to-one tuition are also available at an extra charge.

The school helps prepare the girls for moving on to a sixth form elsewhere – 'we want to make sure they have lots of opportunities when they leave because of the opportunities they have had here,' says the head. 'It doesn't matter if they are not strong academically as they will have other strengths which may help them to get a sixth form place somewhere.'

Games, options, the arts: Although the school no longer offers PE as a short course at GCSE, the opportunity and enthusiasm for sport across the years is evident. This is commendable given the shortage of sporting facilities at the school. Until 2012, the main hall was the only space available for assemblies, gymnastics, drama and exams. The Elizabeth Smith Hall now provides a multi-purpose space for all these activities and leaves the main hall free during exams.

Not much of a playground, just a small yard used by junior pupils, and there are no fields. Girls travel 10 minutes by coach to nearby Walker Grounds for outdoor games and to Southgate for swimming lessons. Year 10 and 11 travel to Southbury Leisure Centre for a range of sports. Still, nothing is lost and time is well managed so that, for example, pupils receive pre-lesson instruction in transit, 'with the added advantage that they don't stand freezing listening' on the fields. Parents certainly don't view this as a problem, since 'it's not that far and they are not in the bus for half an hour'. Another said: 'My daughter isn't particularly sporty but we go and support netball matches.'

Pupil explained that the model of a figure drowning in money showed 'how greed can take over'

Dance and gymnastics are taught on half term rotation, and netball is popular. They have won the Barnet Netball League for four years consecutively, 'playing bigger schools', adds the head, 'who have 200-odd in each year group, where we have only 30 girls to choose from.' She puts it all down to the fact that this is a small school where the girls 'know each other incredibly well', something parents attest to.

Around half choose art and design at GCSE and the self-portraits mounted in the art corridor show there is plenty of talent here, as do pupils' willingness to talk thoughtfully about their work.

Classrooms are well equipped with colour wheels for guidance and artefacts for inspiration, 'to help you make a decision about what you are trying to express through colours, shapes, textures, perspectives... which is helpful if you are not too familiar with art,' said one pupil. Another commented: 'We did 3D art and I found that is my niche'. She showed us the model of a figure drowning in money, explaining that it was to show 'how greed can take over... how too much money is never enough for some people. People always want just a little bit more.' The remedy? 'It depends on the sort of person you are,' she said.

Around a third of the girls choose drama at GCSE. It is also popular as an extracurricular activity, as is dance: pupils have performed in the Nutcracker ballet at the Bloomsbury Theatre in Euston. Not many take music at GCSE (15 per cent). At the time of our visit, there was only one girl studying music in year 11 and five in year 10. The music department offers timetabled lessons in different instruments: sax, trumpet, singing – but pupils say that if you want to learn an instrument not offered, the school will get a teacher in. Around 80 girls across the whole school take lessons inside school and many more take lessons outside school hours. Their music skills range from beginners to above grade 8. There is an open door culture in the music department where 'you can come during break if you want to practice your instrument'. There is a senior school orchestra and and two choirs, plus other instrumental groups.

Plenty on offer in terms of extracurricular clubs, though some (particularly working parents) say they would like to see more after-school provision. The school currently offers netball, choir, music, knitting, drama, debating, swimming and a Christian union, and tries to ensure everyone gets involved in something. As well as lunchtime and after-school activities, there's a gym club at 8am and weekend cross-country competitions, D of E expeditions and training. They also take part in eg inter-school debating competitions.

The girls choose songs on powerful themes – 'war, politics, women in power, the economy'

There is a 'very competitive' annual house choral competition. Pupils describe it as a 'bit like a musical but not'. The girls choose songs on some pretty powerful themes – 'about war, politics, women in power, the economy, green issues'. 'People sing, play instruments, costumes get dragged into that... but most important, you don't want your competitor to know what you're doing so it's very secretive, all covered up.' 'Green house won last year,' another butted in, 'yellow house won year before, and we won year before that. So far we're equal... but we're worried about what will happen this year [after we leave] so we will have to come back and see how they get on without us.' The audience for the house choral competition always includes some recent leavers.

Background and atmosphere: Founded in 1905 by a Christian Quaker called Alice Hum whose motto, 'By Love, Serve One Another', still guides the ethos here. The building was originally located in nearby Osborne Road and opened with 12 pupils. It had grown to 300 when it moved to its present location in Hoppers Road in 1918. The original and main building, Avondale Hall, is still the heart of the school. Classrooms and a dining room were added between the 1960s and 1990s. Over the next decade a new office block was built and more recently the new Elizabeth Smith Hall (with a couple of one bed flats above – which the school says will suit student teachers) and a medical room. The school could do with more space but as the site is on a residential street, neatly tucked between houses, expansion is difficult.

Despite its age, the school has a modern feel. The building is intimate and compact yet the rooms, hallway and stairwells are airy and bright. Most spaces, including the head's office, double up for other uses, and there are well thought out rotas for use of the hall and library resource centre to accommodate the needs of both the junior and senior pupils. The prep department shares the same building, and the linked pre-school (Alice Nursery) is about a mile and half away.

Whatever the school lacks in space it greatly makes up for in friendliness: if there were a prize

for the most welcoming atmosphere this school would be in the running. Teachers invited us into lessons, and pupils showed impeccable manners. A science class in the middle of an experiment gladly redid the combustion exercise just for our visit – or so they claimed. Pupils are keen to talk about their work displayed on classroom walls, like the 'wonder posters' they created about different countries that took part in the Olympics.

Pastoral care and discipline: As a relatively small school contained in one building, it would be hard for any child's problem or unhappiness to go unnoticed – 'it is quite common for a member of staff to take a girl aside if she seems troubled in any way'. Very good staff-parent relations as all share the ethos of: work hard and your reward will be a good career.

Pupils told us that settling into the school was easy. 'If teachers can see you are struggling they introduce you to someone'. Pupils have two induction days before they start plus a three-day team building residential trip within the first few weeks of September, 'so we made friends straight away'.

Small group sizes here mean no-one gets lost. 'We have an open door policy so we can talk to any teacher and get help if we need to,' as 'you can feel closer to one particular teacher'. In such a small school teachers 'can spot if something is wrong', and pupils develop good relationships with their form tutors – two to a form – who sometimes stay with the groups as they move up.

As a relatively small school in one building, it would be hard for problems to go unnoticed

The house system also helps them know and support each other well across the school: during the fire drill 'older girls must each grab a younger child and walk them to the meeting place'. Parents mentioned this 'nurturing environment' with girls 'across different year groups interacting and playing with each other' as one of the appealing characteristics of the school. Senior pupils mentor younger pupils and take up roles as head girls, house captains, form and other types of prefects. Prep prefects help out in the prep school, form prefects help year 7s to settle in and career and public relations prefects help out in their relevant areas. Sometimes they double up on roles to share duties.

This culture of active citizenship means that the girls are consulted on lots of important decisions. They formed a committee to help choose a new catering company for the school – the winner was not only chosen because of its great home made yogurt (which has gone on to become a favourite), but also because it creates menus linked to the curriculum. Pupils also formed a panel to choose a new uniform to mark the school's centenary – they hated the old green one, says the head. We walked into a geography lesson where the girls were being consulted on what colour book to use for a new GCSE unit. They went for green.

Behaviour is good and incidences of bullying are rare: 'I've never had a problem... you would know about it,' said a pupil. 'I've been here since reception and never heard of anything.' Another said, 'The worst is you have an argument with your friend but that happens anywhere.' PSHE includes lessons in study and life skills and careers guidance.

Encouragement to work hard includes a star chart, embraced by even the most senior pupils, with stars awarded for high results in the weekly French and Spanish vocab tests – 'if you get 10 out of 10 you get a star, it's a good way to ensure you learn the vocabulary'. Parents praise the commendation system because it means their daughters are 'stretched in individual subjects... achievement and effort even within the subject gives more to aim for'. Notices on classroom walls include injunctions to 'turn up on time', 'help friends', 'have a good attitude', 'show respect'.

Pupils and parents: Parents are mostly professionals and come from a mixture of cultures and backgrounds. There are no parent governors: 'it avoids problems if there are financial difficulties', says the head. However, the parents' association organises events like theatre trips, quiz nights, the summer fair and other fundraising events and has raised money for benches for the grounds, an audio system for the hall and the school minibus. It also helps new families settle in, 'especially if you have moved to London from outside,' said a parent who moved from Cardiff.

Notable past pupils include Marion Tait CBE, prima ballerina and assistant director of the Birmingham Royal Ballet.

Entrance: Girls joining at 11 sit English, maths, science and reasoning tests, with those who show promise invited for interview. However, the vast majority come up from the lower school.

Exit: 'I always say we have the largest sixth form in London. It just happens to be located in all my colleagues' schools,' says the head. Leavers move on to to a variety of schools, including Henrietta Barnett, Latymer, Dame Alice Owen's, Woodhouse College, Haberdashers' Aske's Girls School, North London Collegiate, City of London School for Girls, St Alban's High School for Girls and Haileybury.

Money matters: Academic scholarships, music awards and means-tested bursaries are available to cover up to 100 per cent of fees at 11+. There are also other internal awards related to progress within the school.

Remarks: A small, cosy and nurturing school that prepares girls well to move on to a wider world at 16.

Queen Elizabeth's Girls' School

High Street, Barnet, Hertfordshire EN5 5RR

State • Pupils: 1,129 • Ages: 11–18 • Sixth form pupils: 150

Tel: 020 8449 2984

Email: office@qegschool.org.uk
Website: www.qegschool.org.uk

12

Headteacher: Since September 2015, Mrs Violet Walker, previously deputy head at Northholt High. Psychology degree from UCL and masters in education from Brunel; she is an advanced skills maths teacher.

Academic matters: 'A love of learning is our priority' says the school, but the recent Ofsted report criticised the school for failing the students on Pupil Premium who are not making good progress. Contrary to this report however, the school's GCSE English results are considerably above the national average, as well as above average for girls. All the more impressive when one takes into account that nearly a quarter of the pupils come from homes where English is not a first language.

The school generally produces commendable results. In 2015, 78 per cent got 5+ A*-C at GCSE (including English and maths); 35 per cent A*/A. Nearly all girls achieve 5+ A*-C grades overall and the vast majority get at least a C in maths. At A level, 45 per cent A*-B and 21 per cent A*/A or A. Biology, chemistry, maths, philosophy and ethics, sociology and psychology are all popular

A level choices, alongside English and geography. Vocational courses in product design and business studies are also offered.

Strong focus on science as well as English, with everyone encouraged to include an expressive art and a technology subject amongst GCSE options; school is quick to point out that while the arts have always been strong, its main priority is to deliver a broad curriculum for everybody: 'We aim to deliver a high calibre of subjects across the board and not get labelled as one thing.'

Spanish taught in year 7 and more able pupils can study French from year 8. Languages set from year 8 but all other subjects taught in mixed ability groups. 'We tried setting for science, but the results didn't improve.' Maths has historically been one of the weaker subjects, 'but we've made lots of progress in key stage 3 and the school now has a high performing specialist school second specialism in mathematics and computing.' This has allowed increased investment and focus on maths, producing strong results at GCSE and A level. Homework club offered every day until 4.30pm with teachers in every subject on tap to help students.

Good SEN support, mostly within the classroom. Split level site unsuitable for children with physical disabilities: 'Because we're on a hill and because of the age of the building, we can't accommodate students with significant mobility issues.' Around 10 per cent of pupils have special educational needs, including specific learning difficulties, dyslexia and dyspraxia. The gifted and talented co-ordinator identifies very able girls, who are encouraged to take on extension research projects – 'but we don't want to be exclusive, others can join in too.' Good careers advice – has Investors in Careers status, recently renewed.

Games, options, the arts: Arts are big here. The QEGS bronze art award has been recently introduced to recognise achievement, focusing on personal progress. Annual arts festival is an opportunity for the school and its community to celebrate the events of the past year and includes drama, song, poetry and music.

Great indoor facilities include a mammoth sports hall, gymnasium and a pristine, Olympic size swimming pool; 'I only learned to swim once I started at QE Girls'

Drama GCSE very popular, involving regular showcases for parents. Christmas production is written and directed by sixth formers and performed to the whole school. At Film Skool (an extracurricular activity) professional film makers and producers work with pupils who write, edit and direct their own films, culminating in a private screening in a West End cinema. SMAKS (Stretch your Media Arts Knowledge and Skills) is a programme of after-school workshops, designed to encourage students (as well as the wider community) to try new media skills, including theatre set design, cartoon caricature, and portrait photography. The school hosts two drama studios and media editing suites.

Music is also strong, though relatively few take it to GCSE or A level, where it is available through Barnet Music Centre. Senior and junior orchestras, a jazz band, and various ensembles depending on the strengths and numbers of the musicians. Links with the ENO.

Several (rather basic) art studios, with some eye-catching art dotted around, including a pop art display. Dance an increasingly popular subject, as is sport – including the less traditional, fencing, boxercise and roller-skating. Great indoor facilities include a mammoth sports hall, gymnasium and a pristine, Olympic size swimming pool; 'I only learned to swim once I started QE Girls', a 13-year-old student told us. Outdoor tennis courts. Girls have competed in county football and cross-country competitions. Girls doing PE GCSE often organise dance and games tournaments for local primary schools.

'There's so much going on, you're never bored to death', one pupil told us. And she wasn't wrong. On top of all the media stuff, other extracurricular activities include karate club, music clubs and debating societies, Portuguese, cheerleading, rock challenge, archery, football, swimming, Young Enterprise etc. Blossoming hacks join the journalism club and can take part in the BBC School Report. Trips abroad include skiing in the Alps, language trip, art/drama trips to New York and history trips to the battlefields of France and Belgium.

Background and atmosphere: First opened in 1888 as a grammar school; has been comprehensive since the 1970s. Hilly site on the edge of London's green belt, and set back from busy Barnet High Street. Buildings range from Victorian to 1960s. Rather tatty round the edges and could do with a major influx of cash for refurbishment – which doesn't look imminent: 'We're often at the back of the queue because our results have been good.' A parent commented that in her opinion, the only weakness of the school is that 'it is very old, with small, sometimes manky classrooms.'

On the plus side, the loos were revamped at a cost of £150,000 at the request of the school council some 15 years ago and have been refurbished regularly since (although many pupils still cited the toilets as a downside of the school). During our tour we noticed that new windows were being installed – something the school believes only happened because of the switch to academy status. 'Apart from that, and our sporting facilities which used to be shared, becoming an academy doesn't make much of a difference in real terms.'

After walking through a myriad of corridors which didn't seem to correlate to one another, over an internal bridge (which linked two buildings), we lost our bearings on several occasions. General impression is of bright, sparse spaces painted pale

blue. Rather Victorian and wanting in imagination, we felt. None of this seemed to bother the pair of perpetually positive students who took us on our tour. So proud they were of their school, 'one big family', that it might as well have been Versailles.

> ## Students on our tour were so proud of the school, 'one big family', that it might as well have been Versailles

Large, well-stocked library that was busy and buzzing (but what caught our eye was a student stuffing a sandwich in her mouth directly in front of a sign which read 'no eating in the library'). The canteen was pretty pukka too, with its mouthwatering and beautifully presented selection of hot food, generous salad bar and divine desserts. Thumb print ID system.

The outside space is a pleasant surprise – beautiful grounds adorned with smart benches and a few small Japanese-style feature bridges. 'It's lovely in the summer for picnics', one pupil told us. Hard to believe we were only a stone's throw from Barnet High Street. Very much a community comprehensive, 'we have students whose grandmothers came to this school', with a relaxed atmosphere and confident, articulate girls, used to speaking up in public.

Pastoral care and discipline: Renowned for making new girls feel at home quickly – 'we want parents and girls to feel confident about their choice of secondary school.' The dedicated head of year 7 spends much time and effort visiting feeder primary schools in the summer term to meet students and staff. Sixth formers are also on tap to help out and plan team-building activities for the year 7s, which encourages each form to work together – 'a crucial part of the friend-making process during the first week of term.'

'One of the hallmarks of the school is that girls find the staff very approachable'. High expectations of good behaviour and discipline do not appear to be unrealistic. Only five permanent exclusions over the past 15 years or so and although 'regrettable', they were left with 'no other choice'. Clear policy on drugs and bullying,'Obviously girls are exposed to drugs outside, but inside it is not an issue. Our PHSE programme is very good and we put a lot of effort into equipping girls to make informed decisions on all aspects of life.' The form tutor or head of year is the first port of call if a girl is troubled, but 'my daughter knows she can go to the head if she really needs to', one parent told us.

Students' progress is closely monitored with regular reports, academic reviews and parents' evenings. Great emphasis is placed on parents' inclusion – 'we are kept very well informed via texts, newsletters and emails.' However, the same parent added: 'Parents' evenings can be a bit shambolic. It often feels like speed dating without the fun. I feel it could be better organised.' 'Time for You' sessions have proved very popular; parents are invited to informal meetings every half term which cover topics from self esteem and friendship to e-safety. Sessions also offered just for dads and daughters. 'My daughter did a Ready Steady Cook

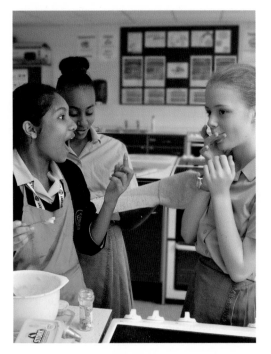

afternoon with her dad. She loved it and it was great bonding,' one parent told us.

Form time and assembly at 8.40am with lessons starting immediately afterwards. 'Students don't like to miss teaching time.'

Outside space is a pleasant surprise – beautiful grounds with smart benches and Japanese-style bridges

Various incentives and rewards schemes are offered to students who work hard and take an active part in school life - anything from an inspired design for a sustainable home to a competition cooking food from around the world.

Pupils and parents: Pupils from across the board. One parent told us: 'You get pupils who come from massive houses in Hadley Wood, and those that come from the local council estate, nature of the beast – you just have to hope they respect each other.' However, higher than average percentage of girls on free school meals. Ethnically diverse – largest share is white British, 40 per cent, the remainder a variety of different ethnicities 'which reflect the population of Barnet as a whole.' Old girls: actress and singer Elaine Paige and actress Stephanie Beacham.

Entrance: Oversubscribed, but not heavily – roughly three applicants for every place. First in line are girls with statement of social or medical needs specifying the school, then siblings, then those living closest ('we moved into the area to get our daughter into the school') – which in practice tends to mean within two miles. Girls entering the sixth form (about 18 each year) need four grades Bs or above at GCSE, and many A level courses specify a B grade in the A level subject.

Exit: About a third leaves after GCSEs for selective sixth forms, co-ed sixth form colleges or FE colleges. Most sixth form leavers go on to higher education, courses including medicine (three in 2015), dentistry and law. One to Cambridge in 2015.

Money matters: Not a rich school – low down in the queue for government cash for refurbishment, but does its best with available funds. Loyal parent body works hard at raising money.

Remarks: A successful comprehensive with high expectations that produces self-assured girls used to discussion and debate.

Queen Elizabeth's School, Barnet

Queen's Road, Barnet, Hertfordshire EN5 4DQ

Tel: 020 8441 4646

State • Pupils: 1,190 • Ages: 11–18 • Sixth form pupils: 145

Email: enquries@qebarnet.co.uk
Website: www.qebarnet.co.uk

Headmaster: Since 2011, Neil Enright MA (Oxon) MBA NPQH FRSA (30s). Educated at St John's College, Oxford, and has worked here since 2002, rising to become head of department (humanities – a geographer), head of year, deputy head. MBA in 2010 from the University of London Institute of Education, which focused on aspects of leadership, management and systems of effective learning.

Sees himself as 'an experienced educational leader committed to safeguarding the academic, pastoral and spiritual interests of able boys, irrespective of their ethnic, religious or socio-economic background'. Aim is to preserve and build upon the reputation of Queen Elizabeth's as a school where able boys who have entered on academic merit will become well-rounded and responsible young men with unbounded opportunities to succeed at university and their chosen careers beyond.

Academic matters: Consistently top of the academic league tables, rivalling most schools, independent or state, in its exam results. Definitely not a school for slackers. You work hard here and you work consistently hard, which can be stressful for some, particularly in the early years. Testing is very much part of the modus operandi. Baseline assessment in year 7, then setting in all subjects, with half-termly tests thereafter. 'It's quite nerve-racking at the beginning,' said one sixth former, 'but it does mean by the time we get to GCSEs we don't find exams a problem.' Certainly not. A*s the norm at GCSE (average 10 A*s). In 2015, 92 per cent A*/A grades. All take French and Latin from year 7 and German from year 8, continuing at least one

---

Consistently top of academic league, rivalling most schools in exam results. Not a school for slackers

---

to GCSE, with Mandarin and Spanish offered as extras. A level choices are decided by tests in years 10 and 11 designed 'to tease out' aptitude. 'GCSE grades are not a good indicator,' says the head. 'Of 180 boys here, 165 will get A*s in maths, but not all will be good enough to do maths.' Seventy per cent of boys do four A levels, most get four A*/A grades (84 per cent of grades were A*/A in 2015); 60 per cent take maths, two-thirds some science, many do a mix. No fluffy options whatsoever. 'We don't want to dilute the curriculum,' says the head.

Most departments and most teaching very strong – 'so many departments get all A*/As'. Boys enthuse particularly about geography and history. Homework load is strenuous (one and a half hours in year 7, one hour per subject per night at A level), but few problems with hungry dogs here. 'We don't need to whine and cajole, it's a culture of achievement.' The school has recently extended its extracurricular enrichment with the Williams Society's weekly tutorials in informal logic, literary theory and analysis of concepts. 'We talk to them about the social sciences and concepts such as liberty,' no doubt helping to up the school's Oxbridge success rate.

All the latest gewgaws throughout with up-to-the minute ICT and all labs refurbished in the last 10 years. 'Special needs' at this school tends to be on the gifted-and-talented end of the spectrum, but every department runs a clinic to support the struggling and challenge the most able. School says it can accommodate mild autism, Asperger's and dyslexia.

Games, options, the arts: This is a school where competing is important and a big part of the competition takes place on the sports field. All play rugby in year 7. 'Rugby serves boys so well,' says the head. 'It has a gentlemanly ethos, of which I enormously approve.' England under-16 head coach coaches the rugby squad and the school fields up to D teams on a regular basis. (Sport, however, is setted from year 7, and it can be difficult to move up the scrum, according to one pupil). Swimming, water polo, Eton Fives, tennis, cross-country and fencing also popular. Plenty of county and national representation in sport, bridge, chess. (Old Boy

A big part of the competition takes place on the sports field. All play rugby in year 7. 'Rugby serves boys well,' says the head. 'It has a gentlemanly ethos, of which I enormously approve'

Tom Aggar recently won a gold medal for rowing in the Paralympics.) Eight-lane swimming pool, all-weather tennis courts, multi-gym and plenty of neatly trimmed green fields for team sports.

School has three full-time music teachers, 12 peripatetic teachers and a music suite where boys can study A level music technology with all the latest recording equipment. Big band, jazz quartet, north and south Indian collection ensemble. 'We are in the vanguard of international music development. It epitomises a strength of the world, the dialectic between different cultures. It's beautiful to listen to a group which includes the sitar, the sax and the violin.' Visual arts take place in open-plan, light-filled art rooms but plenty going on elsewhere, with a daily art club held in the lunch hour, an exhibition space for displays of work and field trips to arty destinations like St Ives and Paris for A level candidates. Growing national reputation for chess. Outside the classroom, the school has invested heavily in infrastructure. In recent years, the school has seen the launch of a dramatic, architect-designed new hall, which, as well as drama productions and debating competitions, hosts recording sessions for professional orchestras. New food technology facility; DT also focuses on product design and ICT.

As one might expect, careers advice taken very seriously. From year 7, pupils have half-termly meeting on their future. 'We want them to ask early on: What do I want to do in life? After the age of 14, they won't do it for their parents or teachers; they do it because they believe it themselves.' Decision making is aided by extensive work experience from year 10. Loyal Old Boys, too, come back for an organised meeting with sixth formers to chat about university and subject choice. Some act as Oxbridge buddies for the next generation. Boys also do voluntary work related to their career aspirations.

Background and atmosphere: Founded in 1573 by Robert, Earl of Leicester, with a charter from Elizabeth I, the school was rebuilt in 1931-32 by Hertfordshire County Council in a noble civic style with terrazzo flooring, parquet and panelling, all kept in spick-and-span condition. Still relatively well endowed with land held in perpetuity and its own Foundation Trustees, QE went comprehensive in the '60s, reverted to grant-maintained status in

1989 and became a grammar school once more in 1994. Difficult to imagine a more orderly and focused environment. Even in traditional chatty art, boys work with heads down, quiet as mice. Significant increases in responsibility from year 11, when own suits are allowed. Ninety prefects voted for by staff and students, monitor lunch (fresh food produced daily), playgrounds and classrooms. 'They lead the school in so many ways.' School captain and house captains appointed from on high.

Pastoral care and discipline: Boys motivated by reward and praise with loads of 'celebratory occasions'. (Homework diaries with merit stickers for every subject in the early years; hand-written notes home later on.) Certainly not a school where misbehaviour is the norm. 'I will expel a boy for violence on the premises aimed at staff, consciously creating racial disharmony or bringing drugs into school, but no boy has been expelled in over 14 years,' says the head. Occasional fixed-term exclusions, however, for persistent 'failure to carry out school protocols' or misbehaving in lessons. Registration twice a day and homework diaries are also monitored for extracurricular activities. 'If a boy is not sufficiently engaged in extracurricular activities, that's often the first warning sign.' If concern is felt, the year head will be involved, then, depending on the issues, parents, special needs or an ed psych.

'Our boys come from very ordinary backgrounds,' says the head. 'In our last Oxbridge intake, many had parents who hadn't gone to university. One was a refugee from Rwanda'

Pupils and parents: Defies the traditional middle class grammar school profile in its diverse student body. Over 80 per cent of boys come from ethnic minorities, predominantly Asian. Most are first generation, most speak English as a second language. 'Our boys come from very ordinary backgrounds,' says the head. 'In our last Oxbridge intake, many boys had parents who hadn't gone to university, and in recent years one was a refugee from Rwanda.' The head feels the school 'contributes massively to social mobility and social cohesion. Here, they have to interact across the divides, whether they're scrumming down on the rugger field or playing chess.'

Entrance: More than 2,000 boys apply for 180 places. Tests now take place in September, and boys are told whether or not they have met the 'standard required' before they have to make their choice of

Difficult to imagine a more orderly environment. In art, boys work with heads down, quiet as mice

schools, so they have nothing to lose by taking the test. NB Meeting the 'standard required' does not guarantee a place. Pupils come from around 90 primary schools, but the ability range is narrow; most are in the top 10 per cent nationally. Head is against the 'industry of preparation' that leaves children trembling in the exam queue. 'It's a waste of time stressing children out.' Parents, however, wouldn't necessarily agree. Occasional vacancies between years 7 and 10, offered to those on the waiting list. No sixth form entry for external candidates. 'This is a seven-year education and I don't want to tread on any of my colleagues' toes.' Automatic transfer to sixth form for virtually all but pupils have to be recommended for individual subjects. Further maths is particularly hard to gain access to.

Exit: UP to 15 per cent of boys leave after GCSE. Some prefer mixed sixth forms, are looking for subjects the school doesn't teach (law, psychology, media studies) or are not offered the subjects they want to take. Some win scholarships to independent schools. Other just prefer a more relaxed environment. Others don't make the grade. Virtually all who stay go on to top universities. In 2015, 26 Oxbridge places. Otherwise primarily to eg Nottingham, Imperial, UCL and Warwick. Economics most popular degree, 20 plus to medicine and medical-related degrees. History and law also popular. The school gives excellent UCAS guidance.

Money matters: State aid is minimal and the head has to put up with the fact he gets less money than many local comps. Gaps are filled with funds from the Foundation and with carefully husbanded donations from parents, old boys and friends, which underwrite school trips and new buildings. Most parents contribute £60 a month, though this is entirely voluntary. 'We say to them, if you want to have a sound education and provide the polish for boys to go to the best universities, you can't do it on state funding.'

Remarks: An extraordinary school that offers the able, the diligent and the aspiring, whatever their social or ethnic origins, an education hard to rival in the state or private sector. You do, however, have to be the right boy. Not a good option for those who would struggle with the workload, rebel against the discipline or dislike competition.

Rhodes Avenue Primary School

Rhodes Avenue, London N22 7UT

State • Pupils: 595 • Ages: 3–11

Tel: 020 8888 2859

Email: admin@rhodes.haringey.sch.uk
Website: www.rhodes.haringey.sch.uk

28

Headteacher: Since September 2015, Adrian Hall, previously headteacher at Churchfield Primary School in Enfield.

Entrance: Recently moved to three-form entry of 90. Admission by means of the local authority criteria, which means that, on the whole, first come siblings and then those living as near as possible. With four applications for every place, this has meant within a quarter of a mile. The success of the school – and its neighbouring comprehensive – has undoubtedly had an impact on local property prices.

Exit: The school backs directly on to Alexandra Park, one of the borough's best secondaries, and the majority of pupils proceed there. Others to Fortismere, Channing and Dame Alice Owen's and a few to eg Henrietta Barnett, JCoSS, Latymer, North London Collegiate, Park View Academy, Queen Elizabeth School for Boys and Ashmole.

Remarks: Has for some years consistently dominated the local authority league tables and Ofsted can barely think of a word of criticism. Sats results here are truly outstanding, with the majority reaching the highest levels – results that would put

a smile on the face of most prep school heads. 'There's a good mix of the thoroughly experienced and young and enthusiastic teachers,' said one mother, and the pupils agree: 'The teaching is really great,' said a boy. Though the pupils are of above average ability on entry, the school gives everyone that little bit more, particularly in the later years.

An extensive enrichment programme in art, drama and creative writing (in which teachers receive regular training) includes workshops and specials events, such as book week. A string of well-known children's authors pitch up to entertain, but the highlight of the week is The Bedtime Story evening, when, accompanied by teddies, children are given hot chocolate and gripping fiction. Hardly surprising, then, that a recent nationwide writing competition saw nine Rhodes Avenue finalists.

Academic progress is charted minutely and parents kept well informed, with three parents' evenings and three reports a year. Strong support, too, for the struggling. 'My son has a special literacy person and she's fantastic,' said one parent. 'He gets taken out during the literacy hour and taught in a small group to ensure he'll cope at secondary school.' French taught from year 3 and 'parlez-vous'

Parents' Association is buzzing, organising a hectic cycle of events including a summer and Christmas fair, fireworks and Burns supper

is supplemented with fun activities like a French breakfast, croissants included.

Music and sport are as high up the agenda as the three Rs. All year 4s learn cello, violin, trumpet or clarinet and specialist teachers, provided by the local authority, offer individual tuition during the school day. Sport is taken seriously – tends to sweep the board in local competitions, whether it's athletics or tennis, football or netball. 'There's an exceptionally good PE teacher,' said one mother, adding that in-school provision is also often supplemented with private coaching. Loads of trips, clubs and workshops, with outings to the cinema, theatre and museums and a regular stream of visiting artists, actors and dancers. Plenty of activity on the pupils' parts, too, with impressive assemblies and regular performances and concerts. 'A lot is done around creativity,' said one parent. After-school clubs include cross-country, orchestra, cricket, recorder, choir, Bollywood dance, Spanish, French, pottery, drama, yoga, computer, netball and badminton. Lots of competitions entered and usually

won, whether that's for the school's abundant and much-loved vegetable garden or for pupils' Christmas card designs. After-school play centre on site 3.30-6pm.

A local primary school and most families live within feet of the gates, giving a strong community feel, though whether increased numbers will dilute this remains to be seen. Major rebuilding programme to incorporate increased numbers now complete. Strong pupil involvement. School council, with two elections a year, debates hot topics like school uniform, sustainability and healthy eating. Peer mediators protect against playground perils. Plenty of praise is the recipe for good behaviour and the naughty are given focused 'reflection' on wrong doing. Despite the friendly upbeat mood, some feel the school places too great an emphasis on obvious winners, whether in the classroom or the sports fields. 'If you are slightly unusual and don't fit in,' said one parent, 'you can slip under the wire a bit.'

Parents, who are increasingly prosperous and professional, are heavily involved. Those with interesting jobs – like astronauts or newspaper editors – come in to share their expertise with the kids. Needless to say, the Parents' Association is buzzing, organising a hectic cycle of events including a summer and Christmas fair, school raffle, jumble sale, fireworks and Burns supper. Class reps are required to stage two cake sales a year. Oodles of extra funds raised.

St Michael's Catholic Grammar School

Nether Street, London N12 7NJ

Tel: 020 8446 2256

State · Pupils: 760 · Ages: 11–18 · Sixth form pupils: 275 (60 boys) · RC

Email: office@st-michaels.barnet.sch.uk
Website: www.st-michaels.barnet.sch.uk

14

Headmaster: Since 2012, Julian Ward BA PGCE MBA (60s). Born in Lancashire and educated at the Pilgrim School, Bedford, and Manchester University, where he read modern history and economics. Then went on to study for an MBA at Bradford, before deciding that 'business was not my cup of tea' and training to be a teacher at Christ's College, Liverpool. ('I enjoyed every minute.') Has spent his entire professional career in London, where he started out teaching economics in 'front-line' local authority schools (Bishop Challoner in Tower Hamlets, John Paul II in Wandsworth, Sir John Cass's Foundation and Redcoat in Stepney), before moving to St Michael's in 1988.

Became sole deputy head in 1995, and his close working relationship with his predecessor, Ursula Morrisey, means he sees his current role more as evolution than revolution. Throughout his time at the school, has been a driving force in setting the highest academic targets, helping move the school from a middle-of-the road grammar to one that consistently sits at the top of the league tables. Since becoming head, has put particular emphasis on improving the percentage of A*s at A level, developing the gifted and talented programme and improving the school-parent partnership. A measured presence with a firm vision of what the school is about. 'Girls like him,' said one mother.'They think he's strict, but fair.' 'Very dedicated,' said another. Married with three adult children, he continues to teach citizenship and RE.

Academic matters: St Michael's has won numerous awards (including Sunday Times State Secondary School of the Year 2013) for providing an outstanding education and is now one of the country's leading secondary schools, always sitting within the top 20 grammar schools (often in the top 10) nationally at A level, usually in the top five at GCSE. 2015 saw 89 per cent A*-B and 39 per cent A*/A grades at A level. At GCSE, 87 per cent A*/A. Teaching is undoubtedly a strength ('There are very clever teachers who provide very good teaching,' said one parent) and the school works hard to maximize both pupils' and parents' aspirations. 'We give a great deal of time to thinking about it,' says the head.

All the girls accepted here are bright, but St Michael's still offers significant added value, with a packed, fast-paced curriculum ('You need to enjoy academic work and want to find out about things,' says the head). Almost all take 11 GCSEs, including a large compulsory core, which includes English, maths, history and/or geography, RS, a science (about a third take all three) and a modern foreign language (large numbers take two). Language offering particularly vibrant, with French, German, Spanish, Latin, classical Greek and Italian all on the timetable, and Japanese and Mandarin offered outside it. Italian and Spanish particularly popular A levels (as well as psychology, RS and maths). Sixth form has its own building ('St Michael's is really two schools, with two distinct regimes,' says the head, 'a girls'- only school in years 7-11, and a co-ed sixth form college.') Only small numbers with

Headmaster is a measured presence with a firm vision of what the school is about.

special needs, but strugglers are provided with generous support. Homework is pushed hard. 'If you're ill you have to catch up on what you've missed,' said one mother.

Games, options, the arts: No playing fields and only a handful of courts, so team games not a forte (no hockey, for example), but a spacious new-ish sports hall (the largest school gym in Barnet) is used to the full to deliver high standard athletics, netball, volleyball, gymnastics, table tennis and badminton. Professional basketball and netball coaches bring out the best in nascent stars and the school is successful at local and regional level in a number of sports. The top performing school in the borough's inter-sports competitions for girls.

Academic music is excellent, with dedicated practice rooms and a recording suite, though the head is pushing for higher standards of extracurricular involvement. 'Lots of girls participate in choir and orchestra, but I would like us to have greater opportunities for high quality performance.' Large, well-equipped art and DT studio (offering material technology, food technology and graphics) with plenty of enthusiastic participants.

Good range of clubs (mainly in the lunch hour rather than after school as many pupils live far away) and trips (including skiing, modern languages and faith-centred activities, such as retreats and a visit to Lourdes).

Background and atmosphere: Founded by the Congregation of the Sisters of the Poor Child Jesus in 1908 as a prep school in the grounds of its convent. In 1958, a girls' grammar school was launched to share the site, and eventually the prep school was closed to allow the grammar school to expand.

Still quite a compact school housed in a motley collection of periods and styles. The Grange, which now accommodates the sixth form, was once a 19th century private house, and has the elegant proportions reflective of this history. The main school was built in the 1950s and comes with large windows and bright views. Modernisation is a constant theme (and drain on finances), but recent additions include an air-conditioned media suite and sixth form study centre. Classrooms remain a mix of old and new, but all are equipped with interactive whiteboards. Attractive gardens, once the convent orchard, are graced by a monkey puzzle tree, large redwood and shrine to the Virgin Mary.

The school, which is voluntary aided, is conducted by its governing body as part of the Catholic church and the Catholic ethos remains fundamental. Prayers are said daily and every pupil attends a weekly religious assembly, as well as mass on Feast days. But this is contemporary Catholicism. 'They go to mass, but they don't expect them to be cleaning the vestry floors,' said one parent. Attractive chapel with superior stained glass windows by Patrick Reyntiens, a master craftsman whose work also features at Liverpool and Coventry cathedrals. Girls put their faith into practice with charity work, helping in the community and giving food to homeless. Generally, the atmosphere is kind, warm and supportive. 'Academically, they push them to their limits, but they do look after them,' said one parent.'There's a very nice feeling to the school.' 'No one gets lost,' says another.'It feels very safe.'

'Academically, they push them to their limits, but they look after them. There's a very nice feeling to the school'

Pastoral care and discipline: The primary aim here is the formation of responsible and committed Catholic citizens. 'We try to create a relaxed and happy atmosphere,' says the head, 'but we expect high standards of behaviour, self-discipline and responsibility.' Those from bohemian families are advised to think carefully about their choice. Even those who aren't acknowledge that the regime is firm. 'There is very strong discipline, which can irritate the girls,' says a parent. 'They will stamp on anything – possibly too hard.'

The pre-GCSE years have a slightly old-fashioned air. 'There's no talk of drugs,' said one mother. 'They do go to parties, but there's no big modern teenage culture.' Girls leap to attention if Mr Ward is spotted in the corridor and pupil pressure as much as teacher pressure patrols the classroom. 'My daughter said to me in astonishment, "a new girl in the school keeps answering the teacher back. Nobody will be friends with her. We like our teachers. They're on our side; we're on theirs".'

In the pre-GCSE years, uniform strictly enforced, with purple skirts at the knee or close to it, no jewellery or make-up. In the sixth form, mufti is permitted and the dress code becomes 'decency'.

Pupils remain accountable for what happens outside the gates if in uniform. Few problems, however. 'Most people who come here are impressed by the behaviour and friendliness of the pupils.'

Pupils and parents: Cradle Catholics from all over London and the world, with increasing numbers of Eastern Europeans, particularly Poles. Not as skewed to the professional middle classes as some other grammar schools, with more new immigrants (33 per cent do not speak English as their first language at home).

Entrance: Not perhaps as tricky to get into academically as some of the other North London grammar schools (390 apply for 96 places), simply because of its single-sex faith criteria. That said, the Catholic hurdle is not for slackers. Applicants at 11 plus must provide proof of First Holy Communion and at least one parent must also be a Catholic with a written reference from their parish priest stating they attend mass on Sunday with the applicant. There is no catchment ('you can come from Sheffield if you want') but only girls who meet the religious criteria are allowed to sit the admissions tests (in verbal and non-verbal reasoning, English and maths). Sixth-form applicants are not required to be Catholic (about 20 per cent come from other faiths) but 'must subscribe to the Catholic ethos'. At this stage, there are a further 60 places (open to boys and girls with at least six GCSE passes at A* to A, with at least an A in the subjects they wish to study and no lower than a B in English and maths). Boys in this relatively large sixth form remain in the minority, with about 30 a year. 'The boys have to be quite brave,' said one parent.

Exit: Roughly 15 girls leave post-GCSE, to nearby sixth form colleges, like Woodhouse, or larger co-ed selective schools. Most sixth formers go onto the older universities. A handful each year to Oxbridge (10 in 2015), guided by the school's own Oxbridge specialist.

Money matters: St Michael's is a voluntary-aided school and parents are expected to contribute towards the cost of the buildings and facilities. 'The school would fall down otherwise,' says the head. An annual contribution of £275 a year is asked for and 90 per cent of parents contribute something. 'We don't go chasing the other 10 per cent.'

Remarks: A happy school, with firm discipline, high expectations and outstanding results.

St Michael's CofE Primary School

North Road, London N6 4BG

State · Pupils: 465 · Ages: 3–11 C of E

Tel: 020 8340 7441

Email: admin@stmichaelsn6.com
Website: www.stmichaelsn6.com

29

Head Teacher: Since 2013, Geraldine Gallagher (40s), BEd Liverpool University. Was NQT in a 'semi-rural' primary school with a mixed catchment, then went inner city to work in a primary school in Hackney, an experience she called 'very good although challenging at times.' She left after a year to teach at St John Evangelist School in Islington where she worked her way up to becoming deputy head. Sixteen years later she was ready to embrace the demands of becoming a head and saw the post advertised for St Michael's CofE: 'I grew up in Islington so had heard of the school and it had always had a pretty good reputation, so decided to go for it.'

Focused, 'I've wanted to be a teacher since I was 14', grounded, and knows the score. Ms Gallagher is only too aware that this was not an easy school to take on, with its prominent milieu of extremely hands-on parents (a positive in many ways but could arguably marginalise the power of a new head). She says: 'In the main the parents here are very supportive, but like most people if things go out of kilter, they will let you know.' However, judging by the feedback we've had, she need not worry. One parent told us that Ms Gallagher has already turned things around for the better in so many ways since starting: 'Parents now know where they stand with her and with the school as she has clear rules and guidelines.' Another said: 'She is a fantastic head. Before she came there was a lot of discontent and the school was in quite a bit of turmoil. The school was operating on the ethos of an old head and it became a situation of us and them between parents and teachers. Ms Gallagher has brought consistency to the school and moved it forward.'

Ms Gallagher aware that this was not an easy school to take on, with its extremely hands–on parents (a positive but could marginalise the power of a new head)

With three of her own children at the school, this head undoubtedly has a vested interest in its success, both academically and pastorally. As one parent pointed out, 'The ethos here is very much that you get out what you put in.' Married for 14 years, any extracurricular time that Ms Gallagher has is spent with her family on days out and the odd swim or two.

Entrance: Heavily oversubscribed at nursery and reception. Around 100 apply for 52 nursery places. The 60 reception places are allocated on a points system, 14 points being the maximum. (Four points for church attendance at St Michael's Church, three for living in N6. Thereafter, local Christians, siblings, other faiths.) Christianity very much part of the ethos. Open days every term and, if a vacancy is available, parents are welcome to look round. Places do arise, particularly in the higher years when some pupils leave for the private sector.

With three of her own children at the school, this head undoubtedly has a vested interest in its success, both academically and pastorally

Exit: On the border of three boroughs – Haringey, Islington and Camden – St Michael's sends its leavers to as many as 30 secondary schools. About half to independent schools (many with scholarships), particularly Highgate, with which the school has a close association, and City of London, but also Channing, UCS, Westminster, North London Collegiate, Haberdashers' Aske's and South Hampstead, plus top grammars Henrietta Barnett, Latymer, St Michael's Catholic Girls and Queen Elizabeth's Boys. A considerable chunk each year to Fortismere School, the popular local comprehensive in Muswell Hill.

Remarks: One of north London's most sought-after primary schools, St Michael's has high academic standards and a high proportion of pupils who reach well beyond the government's expectations at 7 and 11. This partly reflects the intake (largely middle class Highgate), but is also due to strong teaching – recently boosted by an overhaul of the teaching structure. 'Much more academic,' one parent told us; another said, 'the school is now back on track and on its way to becoming very successful again.'

The shift in the teaching structure came about following a period of upheaval at the time when Ms Gallagher was appointed head over two years ago. She says, 'I don't believe in old style leadership and pointing the finger. I knew the school had been though a difficult time, but I believe in working together to achieve the best teaching model.' This included bringing in several new members of staff and making some of the existing ones non-teaching heads of phases, which freed them up to oversee the efficient running of the year groups. While some parents were initially resistant, others feel their children are really reaping the rewards. One told us: 'There is a huge difference in what my son gets for homework to what my older daughter got at that age. It was a bit haphazard before, now it's more structured – not hothousing, just wanting each child to reach their potential.'

This is a school that doesn't rest on its laurels – which it probably could do quite comfortably by virtue of its catchment. A dedicated teacher/parent partnership ensures that even the least engaged child will derive something because of the constantly stimulating and original methods of teaching. Pupils will still enthuse a year later about how 'a spaceship landed in their grounds', which they were allowed to explore – after which they were encouraged to write a story about the experience. This was courtesy of some very innovative parents, who together with the English leader spent hours creating the spaceship, and Troy, the 'legendary' school manager who ran into each classroom shouting that a spaceship had landed, amidst loud noises and flashing lights.

Pupils still enthuse a year later about how 'a spaceship landed in their grounds', which they explored

This year saw a camper-van book bus parked in the grounds to encourage pupils to go in and read during break times (a cool spin on the old mobile library). Other stimulating learning tools include a charming open reading shed in the grounds funded by parents, a play pod with an assortment of recycled goods to encourage imaginative play and an allotment run by parent volunteers. We also loved the idea of a 'kindness wall', which we spotted in a couple of the classrooms, and which, we are told by one pupil, 'encourages us to write nice things about each other.' The pupils we chatted to were an astute bunch, happy and friendly. We even got treated to one spectacular card trick by a pupil who said he loved the school because the teachers 'let me do magic.' Another pupil told us that as a Muslim he liked how a Christian school 'embraces other cultures.'

Parents are an unusually energetic bunch – the school's Parents' Association (SMSA) is possibly the most committed we have come across. Last year alone they raised an astonishing £61,000, through events such as a bonfire night, battle of the bands, fun run and, the pièce de résistance, the annual parents' pantomime. This, we are told, can rival anything seen in the West End and is the highlight of the school calendar. One parent told us: 'What makes this school so special is the dedication of parents. Because we are a church school with no funding we can only get the extras we want if we raise the money ourselves. It does create a lovely community atmosphere, but forget it if you want a school where you can just drop your kids off and not get involved.' For this year's production of Dick Whittington, it was not unusual to see parents rehearsing or building sets until midnight, on top of the jobs they do during the day. Luckily for the school, parents include actors, musicians and set designers.

Excellent drama, with two or three plays annually, plus a nativity play and annual summer concert. A good range of sport – gymnastics, football, tag rugby, tennis, cricket, netball and basketball – taught in lesson time. Swimming, taught in years 5 and 6, is particularly strong.

Fantastic and varied extracurricular programme provides a wonderful resource for working parents. Breakfast clubs start as early as 7.45am and for the particularly energetic early bird fencing and gymnastics are offered. The quieter soul can indulge in a bit of Latin or creative writing, and an early morning maths club is also offered for 'invited pupils.' After-school activities include football, netball, dance, drama (led by the school's celebrated drama teacher, Bob Williams CBE), orchestra, French, chess and fortnightly film club (pupils have won several awards for film reviewing as part of the National Film Club).

Charity a big part of the school's ethos. On the day we visited parents were arriving with hampers to distribute to the local community and a bus-load of senior citizens arrived for their annual Christmas party. At this much anticipated event, year 6s dress up as waiters and waitresses to serve food and give out individually handmade cards and wrapped presents.

Good SEN department. Specific programmes designed for pupils who are classified as SEN or statemented (roughly 16 per cent), and access to regular sessions with art, occupational, and speech and language therapists. Each classroom has an adjoining intervention room for those who need extra help with maths, English etc.

For the particularly energetic, early bird fencing and gymnastics are offered

The school is a couple of hundred yards down from pretty Highgate village – barely visible from the road, but as you approach the main gates the beauty of this building and its grounds can be appreciated. Founded in the mid-19th century as a school to train young locals to go into service, by 1852 it was on its current three-and-a-half acre site with the intention of not only providing an academic education, but also cultivating the spacious grounds as a farm. The green fields and listed Victorian buildings have since been joined by a block built in the 1970s, two large, well-equipped playgrounds and a large, new all-weather court. Both building and grounds are extensive and it is easy to lose one's bearings. The only gripe we heard from parents was about improving the concrete play area. One parent told us: 'I appreciate it is all about funding, and it's definitely better than it was previously, when it looked like a camp site, but there has been just talk for a long time.'

Tetherdown Primary School

Grand Avenue, London N10 3BP

State · Pupils: 420 · Ages: 4–11

Tel: 020 8883 3412

Email: admin@tetherdownschool.org
Website: www.tetherdownschool.org

30

Headteacher: Since September 2013, Tony Woodward, previously head of Warren Mead Junior School in Surrey. Keen on music (plays piano and clarinet), art and gymnastics (trampolining is his speciality – came second in the European Championships). Has worked in Surrey as a local leader in education, supporting the leaders of struggling local schools, and as an additional Ofsted inspector.

Entrance: The school admits 60 pupils in reception, but there's still fierce competition to get in. In the past it was only siblings and those living feet from the gates who stood a chance, now at least an address in the same street might reasonably be expected to do the trick. (Needless to say property prices nearby have their own exotic micro-climate.) Parents can view the school in the autumn term prior to entry, kids visit in the summer term before they start.

Exit: Not only is Tetherdown one of the country's top-performing primary schools, if you're clever enough to have got your child in here you're also pretty much guaranteed a smooth transition to one of the capital's best comprehensives. Smug parents, who've sorted it all by the age of 4, tend to assume their children will proceed to Fortismere and the vast majority go on here. The rest to north London grammar schools or leading independents ('This is Muswell Hill,' said one mother, 'parents tutor without hesitation.')

Remarks: This is a school which regularly sits near the top of the local authority league tables and, even in an average year, over 50 per cent of pupils reach level 5 in English and maths. 'Teaching is consistently good, with some that is outstanding,' says Ofsted, which demoted it from outstanding to good in the latest inspection, partly because 'A few high-attaining pupils are not always sufficiently challenged'. With meticulous monitoring, a dollop of regular homework ('there's not a lot of pressure') and dedicated parents willing to supervise nightly reading from reception to year 6, and you get some idea how these results happen. The school follows the national curriculum but adds its own flourishes.

Fun is very much part of the academic recipe, both in the classroom and outside, whether that's learning fractions in history by means of tricky Tudor recipes, studying maths with the help of a visiting Maths Clown or sharpening up those multiplication tables in Beat the Parents at Mental Maths. 'The children have a lovely education,' said one parent. Pupils are grouped, extended and supported according to ability. 'If they're struggling, it gets noticed. My son was given extra spelling and extra handwriting.' Special needs are caught early by a dedicated special needs coordinator, who works with classroom teachers and outside specialists to set appropriate targets. The recent requirement for the inclusion of modern language teaching is provided (courtesy of the Italian consulate) by weekly Italian lessons, and French is also offered as an after-school club.

Fun is very much part of the academic recipe, whether that's learning fractions in history by means of tricky Tudor recipes or studying maths with the help of a visiting Maths Clown

Plenty of stretching and thinking in all directions, whether in an opera workshop or an after-school street dance club. Plenty of creative parents, too, who come in to share their expertise. All children learn to play the recorder and read music in year 3 and individual instrumental tuition, subsidised by the local authority, is provided during the working day. Sport is perhaps the school's weakest link: 'There isn't much and what there is isn't competitive,' said one mother of boys. In recent years, this has been partially due to a rebuild. Now the outdoor space is both more expansive and better equipped. In year 6, all children learn swimming and travel outside the school for specialist coaching. School's meals are nutritious – parents have their own tasting to ensure their experience matches their kids' – and naughty sweets, chocolates and fizzy drinks are banned from the premises. Plenty of after-school clubs – football, drama, etc – and while there's no after-school care on site, those who want it can be collected from the playground and taken to a nearby club. Regular school trips include an annual outing to the seaside for years 2 and 5, where the deputy head sets a good example by leading the troops into the bracing waves.

Virtually all parents and pupils live within a few surrounding streets and the school has always offered an exceptionally tight-knit community. Expansion has marginally diluted the atmosphere, but has brought advantages. 'It used to be very much like a village school, where everyone knew each other and older pupils looked out for the younger ones,' said one mother with children at both ends of the spectrum. 'That was comforting, but sometimes your child didn't have a particularly wide choice of friends. Now there's plenty of scope.'

Until 2009, Tetherdown was a square and solid Victorian board school, but an exciting £6.5 million redesign has provided lots of lovely light interiors and well-planned playgrounds for infants and juniors. The make-over has also brought up-to-the-minute wireless IT, with interactive whiteboards in every classroom and two computer suites.

The school has no uniform and rules are kept to a minimum. 'We have just two rules. Respect yourself, and respect others. If you respect yourself you are going to work hard to become the best you can.' Parents admire the way these principles are implemented. Those demonstrating behavioural difficulties are given the same support as those with academic problems, with intervention and targets. Children are encouraged to get involved: with the school council; with each other's welfare (by becoming play leaders and buddies); and with the broader community (for example, running a soup kitchen at harvest time). They are also lavished with praise. Regular 'Achievements Assemblies' recognise work, effort and attitude.

Tetherdown is located in north London's prosperous, professional Muswell Hill and the parent body is a mirror of the locality, with plenty of engaged parents who devote the same attention to reading rotas and library duty as they give to successful careers. Parents, too, provide support in a very concrete fashion and the enthusiastic Parent School Association generously underwrites school trips and playground extras. Parents know each other well in and out of school, are ambitious for their kids and for the school.

Woodhouse College

Woodhouse Road, London N12 9EY

State · Pupils: 1,336 · Ages: 16–19

Tel: 020 8445 1210

Email: enquiries@woodhouse.ac.uk
Website: www.woodhouse.ac.uk

15

Principal: Since September 2013, John Rubinstein BSc (50s). Has been a teacher for over 25 years and still teaches A level maths, 'because it keeps me in touch with students, with the experience of colleagues, but most of all, because I love it.' His wife is also a teacher and they have three children, two of whom attended Woodhouse and are now at university. Mr Rubinstein is also a part-time Ofsted inspector. Enjoys running and takes part in 10K and half marathon races, 'four or five times a year.'

Academic matters: Woodhouse is one of the country's leading sixth form colleges, always in the top five nationally, usually in the top three. This is essentially an academic place, whose main focus is on A levels. In 2015, 30 per of grades were A*/A and 65 per cent A*-B.

Undoubtedly a key part of the success is enthusiastic, experienced and focused teaching. 'I've become much better at teaching A levels here,' said

one department head. 'In the comprehensive where I taught before, I was always worried about my year 9s.' Parents are very positive. 'Most of the teachers seem very, very good,' said one, whose son transferred from an independent school. 'They're excellent at monitoring and keep their finger on the pulse.' Results are certainly not achieved by hothousing or editing, and all students who pass AS level can continue to A2s.

A wide range of options on offer, with 32 subjects in almost any combination. Maths is the most popular A level choice (with 45 per cent taking it) and results are notably strong. One of London's largest providers of A level science, with many going on to science-related degrees. Four languages, including Italian, and an abundance of 'ologies', from sociology to music technology and the extended project also available. The extended project programme is taken by over 100 students annually and yields high grades.

Though the majority at Woodhouse tend to favour professional courses at university, social science and arts-based studies are strong, with thriving theatre studies, economics, English literature and geography. 'Independent learning' is high on the agenda. 'We want students to prepare for lessons, using the teacher and their fellow students as a resource,' says the head. Motivated students respond well to this approach. 'Teachers assume if you're interested in your subjects, you will want to read around them,' said one. 'They don't force you to work, but they'll give you the resources and make themselves available to you,' said another.

Woodhouse prides itself on 'a broad and civilising education' and all are expected to participate in at least two six-week courses of 'enrichment', the majority on Wednesday afternoons

All students have access to two learning mentors – one for humanities, the other, science and maths – to sort out any day-to-day tangles. One full-time SENCo, plus two part-time specialists, providing individual support for those with dyslexia and dyspraxia, as well as study skills aid for those who need it. The buildings are 99 per cent adapted for those with physical disabilities.

Games, options, the arts: Woodhouse prides itself on providing 'a broad and civilising education'

and all are expected to participate in at least two six-week courses of 'enrichment', the majority of which take place on Wednesdays afternoons, when there are no lessons. Most relish the opportunities to develop new skills in everything from observational drawing to street dance. Duke of Edinburgh and Amnesty International also on offer.

Art and dance are strong curricular subjects here, with excellent A level results, and the college has a lovely bright dance studio and art department. Sports facilities, too, are good, with a new sports hall and floodlit all-weather pitch. Official team sports include football (girls' and boys'), netball and basketball, but individualists can also enjoy cross-country, squash, trampolining and kick boxing. 'If there isn't a club that you'd like to do,' said one student, 'the sports department are happy to try and set something up.'

Woodhouse students like to get involved and there's an active college council, which has recently helped introduce a daily loan system for netbooks. Plenty of outside speakers and activities including art trips, foreign exchanges, a ski trip and the opportunity to undertake voluntary work abroad.

Background and atmosphere: Located in a pleasant leafy suburb, Woodhouse began its educational life as Woodhouse Grammar School in 1925, but became one of the capital's rare sixth form colleges in the 1980s. Today all pupils are aged between 16 and 18 and all are studying A levels. With 660 new pupils a year, the college is significantly larger than a traditional school sixth form, but smaller than a FE college.

The original stately Victorian façade (deriving from its former incarnation as the home of ornamental plasterer Thomas Collins) has now been joined by a motley timeline of newer buildings, leaving it today with well-equipped facilities. The state-of-the art Learning Zone is one of the most recent innovations, offering space to work in solitary silence as well as in small groups, and supervised open-access IT. In 2014 the college added a two-story, purpose built mathematics facility.'Quite a lot of students here can't work in silence at home and don't have the facility to do the "hard hours",' says the head. 'We wanted to create learners who can work on their own.'

Values here are traditional. 'We believe in honesty, hard work, mutual respect and taking responsibility for your own learning.' The atmosphere is generally enthusiastic, as much for work as for play. 'Here it's cool to work, cool to be involved,' said one student. 'The atmosphere is incredible,' said another. 'There's a massive sense of community. There are always things happening.'

Pastoral care and discipline: Not every 16-year-old is ideally suited to the self-motivation required by an academic sixth form college, but here high expectations are supported by a well-thought-out tutorial system and plenty of individual guidance. Every student has their own tutor, 'My son sees a guy two or three times a week, whom he likes and respects,' said one mother. 'When he was having trouble at home, they really kept an eye on him.'

'Everyone makes friends ridiculously fast because there are so many people in the same position,' said one boy

The college sees itself as a bridge between school and university, and new students are eased into this more adult world with an induction day in the summer before they start. The enrichment programme helps aid new friendships beyond the classroom. 'Everyone makes friends ridiculously fast because there are so many people in the same position,' said one boy. Boundaries are firm and there's zero tolerance on punctuality. 'It's an issue they have to grasp,' says the head. 'If they're not making the effort, why should other students suffer?'

In lessons, students are attentive. 'If a teacher leaves the room, people get on with their work,' said one boy, 'They want to do well.' One recent arrival, who'd left a successful local comprehensive, said, 'I came here because I felt I would be made to work. I've really grown up quickly into a different person. The change is on a biblical scale.' Few significant discipline problems. 'Issues found elsewhere are not even on the radar here,' notes the head gratefully. Standard formula of oral and written warnings, with a code of conduct signed by all parents and pupils, but exclusion is a rarity. 'We have pupils from quite challenged backgrounds, but I have thrown out just one student,' says the head. 'My predecessor excluded two.' Parents agree that discipline is firm but reasonable. 'They run quite a tight ship, but it makes them responsible,' said one father. 'When my son's attendance was only 90 per cent, he had to see the senior tutor every week. As his attendance improved, he went less frequently.' There's no dress code, but pupils don't push it. Relaxed but neat is the general rule.

Pupils and parents: An eclectic mix – 'some nerdy kids, some cool kids, all sorts, colours and creeds.' The core is probably typical of the reasonably prosperous 'squeezed middle' of north London, but with a far higher ethnic intake than you'd assume from the location, and a far higher proportion of those who require some type of financial support. 'Last year, we did a survey and were surprised to find that over a third of pupils were on the full EMA [now abolished],' says the principal.

Parents tend to be involved and supportive, students upbeat, mature, outgoing and energetic. They clearly enjoy the school – more than half volunteered on the annual open day held on a Saturday. 'They want to do well and they want to enjoy themselves,' says the principal. 'They're trying to get the balance right of working hard and having a good social life.' A parent agreed: 'My son is so happy. He really appreciates the fact that people are there because they want to learn, not because their parents are pushing them. Most students here are trying to better themselves and work really, really hard.' Past students include journalist Johann Hari, comedian Michael McIntyre and actress Naomie Harris.

Entrance: Priority is given to applicants from one local secondary school, Friern Barnet. After that, it's predicted grades and/or interview. Competition is ferocious (about 4,500 apply for 660 places), particularly for in-demand subjects. 'We can afford to be choosy,' says the head, 'but we're looking for a range.' All applicants with minimum predicted grade requirements (evaluated on a point system, with specific grades for individual subjects) are given a 20-30 minute interview (with optional parental accompaniment) in the February/March prior to entry. 'We're looking for maturity,' said one teacher. 'We want them to demonstrate that they are committed to A levels and really want to work, but we also want people who will get involved on a wider basis.' The interview is frequently of as much benefit to the student as to the college. 'We often spend it giving careers advice,' says the head.

Travel time is also taken into consideration. 'We generally consider an hour and a quarter by bus the maximum desirable distance.' Applications available from the time of the open day in November until the closing deadline in January. All candidates require a confidential report from their current school and must be between 16 and 18 when starting at the college. The college operates a waiting list for the reshuffle that often takes place after results day in August.

Exit: Over 95 per cent to university with the most popular destinations being London universities, Warwick, Manchester, Kent and Sussex. Most popular subject choices are economics, law, engineering, business and psychology. Twelve to Oxbridge and 13 medics in 2015. Good advice about careers and courses, including a full time careers co-ordinator. Regular tutorials on university admissions and interview practice for those who require it.

Money matters: Parents are asked for £100 contribution for the two-year stint, enabling the college to keep up to date with books and underwrite the enrichment programme and facilities (those who can't afford it, don't pay). A £50 refundable deposit also required for text books. The college has attempted to replace some money lost through EMA cuts with bursaries.

Remarks: An upbeat environment, with strong teaching and results. A firm stepping stone between school and university.

Wren Academy

Hilton Avenue, London N12 9HB

State · Pupils: 1,200 · Ages: 11–18 (plus new primary school reception class) · Sixth form pupils: 220 · C of E

Tel: 020 8492 6000

16

Email: firstcontact@wrenacademy.org
Website: www.wrenacademy.org

Executive Principal: Since June 2007, some 15 months before the academy opened, Mr Michael Whitworth (40s). Previously head of Kelmscott School in Walthamstow. Born and brought up in Northumberland, he graduated as a historian and has recently taught history and religious studies. After working in both private industry and the civil service, he entered teaching and has worked in schools in London, Hertfordshire and Essex. He was attracted by the 'unusual opportunity to create a brand new school from scratch', and built up the school's reputation very rapidly. 'I think the governors recognised my capacity to stick to a task and see it through.' Understated but extremely caring, say parents, very driven and with sights set very high. Married with two young children.

Principal of the secondary school is Gavin Smith.

Academic matters: This is a comprehensive, but the nature of the students in this leafy area means it is primarily an academic one. The biggest initial challenge was achieving a truly comprehensive intake: the previous school on the site had a very poor reputation and Barnet has a variety of popular state schools, including three grammars. However, within a short space of time Ofsted stated that 'the teaching at Wren is stunning', and this is not something you read very often. 'As well as maximising achievement – because children need that currency to move on – we teach learning skills and aptitudes,' says the head. 'Children need the capacity to think for themselves. They are encouraged to seek out their own answers, to be flexible and take risks.' GCSE results in 2015 saw 83 percent of pupils achieving 5+ A*-C grades including English and maths with 37 per cent A*/A grades. The first cohort of sixth formers achieved 27 per cent A*/A grades, 56 per cent A*-B in their A level exams.

Parents are enthusiastic. 'The teachers are very wisely chosen.' 'They're great at finding and encouraging talents.' 'They really encourage them to aim high.' Newsletters all include brainteasers for parents and pupils to solve, and articles on ways of building learning power.

Enrichment activities from Latin and knitting to debating. Staff and students learn together and either can win Excellent Learner awards

English, maths and science are taught in single sex classes. 'This gives us opportunities to stretch children in gender-specific ways. For example, in English boys can look at their powers of reflectiveness and empathy, whilst in girls' maths classes we can encourage them to take risks and concentrate on answering quickly. It helps to broaden their skill sets, and they enjoy it.' Research suggests that girls taught in single sex groups are more likely to continue with maths and science, and a good percentage of girls is choosing single science GCSEs.

The school sets for English, maths, science and foreign languages from part of the way through year 7. 'We like to get data of our own rather than relying on Sats results.' Everyone studies a language (generally French, though some take Japanese or Spanish) and most are expected to take it to GCSE. Regular language days involve a range of linguistic activities. GCSE courses start in year 9.

The specialism of design and the built environment enhances rather than dominates the curriculum, says the head. 'It influences our culture and our ways of thinking about tasks. We have a high emphasis on creativity, and each task has a creative phase, a planning phase and an evaluation phase. But we also have the opportunity to plan projects in architecture and civil engineering.'

Those who need extra help are identified at the beginning of year 7 and follow a six week key skills programme to help bring them up to speed. There are also after-school support groups that help with spelling and comprehension. Although some get one-to-one help from teaching assistants, 'the aim is for everyone to be unsupported in lessons eventually. We do what helps them to access the curriculum in the appropriate lesson.'

Games, options, the arts: The school week includes three extended days, with compulsory enrichment activities from 3-4pm. These range from samba band, Latin and knitting to debating. Staff and students learn together and either can win Excellent Learner of the Week awards.

Houses – named for Wren churches – give the main opportunities for sporting rivalry, but football, netball, basketball, badminton and athletics teams also take part in borough and regional competitions with increasing success. There's a sports hall, netball courts and a football pitch. Opponents have commented on Wren teams' good sportsmanship. Pupils can take sports GCSE or BTec, and enrichment options include rugby, trampolining and table tennis.

Art, design and technology very strong and creative – as one would expect in a school with a design specialism. Projects include designing sculptures of dream ice cream sundaes, creating a piece of artwork inspired by the River Thames and designing an Olympic stadium.

Music is keen – there's an orchestra, samba band, gospel choir, Indian drumming club – and increasing in quality as musicians move up the school and hone their skills. Drama also finding its feet; eagerly awaited annual school musical – eg Bugsy Malone and Hairspray. Wren's Got Talent showcases singers, magicians and musicians.

Background and atmosphere: Named for Sir Christopher Wren, designer of St Paul's Cathedral, which reflects its C of E status and specialism in design and the built environment. Opened in 2008 on the site of a failed school next door to Woodhouse College. Partly refurbished but mostly newly built, it has an open plan feel, with roof lights and large north windows, grey carpets and aluminium cladding. Steps leading down from the entrance hall to the library, 'the heart of the school', are lined by ledges where children can sit and chat, under treble-height rooflights, giving an amphitheatre-like atmosphere. There is a feeling of space and airiness throughout. Corridor walls are decorated with graphics of the footprint of St Paul's Cathedral, and with murals quoting inspiring biblical texts eg 'Be

willing and available to provide support and guidance to others'.

The school is sponsored by the London Diocesan Board for Schools, hence its Christian character, and by Berkhamsted School, which provides some of the governors. The schools work together on areas such as curriculum development, Wren students go over to Berkhamsted for activities, including a year 7 residential retreat, and Berkhamsted sixth formers visited Wren to give their views on appointing a new head of sixth form. 'It's a partnership, and we hope that both schools will get an equal amount from it.'

Primary school on the same site adjacent to the existing school opened in September 2015; will eventually become a complete all-through school.

Pastoral care and discipline: 'The teachers don't tolerate any bad behaviour,' say parents. 'It is a lovely, safe environment for learning'; and indeed the school had a supremely ordered feel during our visit. Three different breaks and lunchtimes help. So does the design of the building: staff and pupils share uni-sex toilets, and there is no staff room, so everyone socialises in the restaurant. 'It's a philosophy that when staff and students share the same space there is passive supervision, and students feel secure. They're encouraged to sit in here and chat – it's part of the curriculum.' 'Focus days' concentrate on matters ranging from sexual health to university choices.

Much emphasis on good manners and courtesy. Common sanctions include litter duty and community service. There's a Reflection Room for 'those who would benefit from time on their own'. Pupils have a high degree of autonomy, with plenty of opportunities to get involved in the way the school is run, from becoming prefects to interviewing potential teachers to taking part in curriculum reviews. 'In return, they generally play their part. There's a high level of buy-in.'

The chaplain, who plays a counsellor-like role, is generally considered a good egg. The only parental criticism is that some feel the school doesn't take their views on board. 'When you start a new school you have to put in place structures that will work. We opened with a very clear idea of what we wanted. We've always listened and explained to parents, but we haven't always amended our ways as a result.'

Pupils and parents: A diverse range, about 25 per cent white British, and characteristic of this leafy outer-London suburb; mostly 'ambitious people who want to do well'. Pupils have taken GCSEs in 13 different home languages. Active PTA which organises quiz nights and festivals, organises second hand uniform sales and has raised funds for the gazebo, which offers a shady outdoor place to socialise.

Entrance: Takes 180 into year 7, with 90 foundation (church) places and 90 community places. First priority for community places to looked after children, those with SEN statements or exceptional medical or social need. Points for having a sibling at the school and for attending a Barnet primary school, then by distance – generally within about half a mile. For foundation places, points for siblings and for regular church attendance, with distance as a tie-break. Has waiting lists for occasional places in other years. Internal and external sixth form applicants need at least five B grades at GCSE including maths, English, and the subjects they want to study at A level; prospective maths, further maths, science and French students need A grades in these subjects. At least 25 external sixth form places.

Becoming an 'all through' school: first cohort of children joined the primary reception class in September 2015. The primary will grow one year at a time until school has children from 4–18 (in 2022).

Exit: Some 50 per cent stay on post-GCSE. Around 50 per cent of first year 13 leavers to top universities; one to Oxbridge and one medic in 2015.

Remarks: This young school has already established a reputation for high teaching standards, courteous students and excellent enrichment activities. Likely to go from strength to strength.

East

Barking & Dagenham
Havering
Newham
Redbridge
Tower Hamlets
Waltham Forest

EAST

An introduction to East London and its state schools

Barking & Dagenham

Barking and Dagenham, with the Thames as its southern boundary, stretches north to encompass the green belt area of Chadwell Heath. Once, companies such as the Ford Motor Company provided settled blue collar employment (and the setting for Made in Dagenham, a dramatisation of the ground-breaking 1968 strike where female workers campaigned for equal pay). Now, most of the employment is in low-paid service industries. A large proportion of the population lives in the vast Becontree estate. Robert Clack qv is a top secondary: this once-failing school was captained to success by Sir Paul Grant, who took the helm in the late 90s, and is now massively over-subscribed. The Sydney Russell School is rated outstanding; Barking Abbey, Jo Richardson and All Saints Catholic School are all popular.

William Ford Junior School – linked with Village Infants on the same site – was founded in 1841, when Dagenham was a village surrounded by fields. Manor Infants/Manor Longbridge are also rated outstanding, as is Warren Junior School. Most Barking and Dagenham primary schools are large, with only a couple of faith schools having one form entry, and many with four or more forms in a year group.

Havering

Havering is the most easterly of the London boroughs. Its main town is Romford, a major metropolitan area, but it also includes large areas of green belt land. Coopers Company and Coburn school qv in Upminster is one of the most popular secondaries and has a 'religious character': it will only consider regular worshippers from any of the major faiths. Admissions arrangements are convoluted: it gives preference to children of staff and former students; a certain percentage of places to those living in specific areas; 10 sport and nine music places. Other high performing secondary schools are both Catholic and both in Upminster: Sacred Heart of Mary girls' school The Campion boys' school. Both give preference to practising Catholic families living in specific local parishes.

Ardleigh Green Junior and Scott's Primary, both in Hornchurch, are rated outstanding, as is Engayne primary in Upminster. Several Catholic primaries do well: St Peter's in Romford, St Joseph's in Upminster and La Salette in Rainham.

Newham

Newham – home of most of the Olympic Park, including the fabulous Zaha Hadid-designed Aquatic Centre – is also one of the most deprived boroughs in the country. It does however have rapidly improving public transport, including Stratford Station, Docklands Light Railway and – in future – several Crossrail stations. Plashet School in East Ham is very well thought of, as are St Bonaventure RC school for boys and St Angela's Ursuline Convent school for girls (these two have a joint sixth form). The newish selective sixth college, the London Academy of Excellence, is in Stratford; it was the brainchild of the heads of the local Kingsford Community School and independent Brighton College, one of its backers.

Elmhurst Primary ranks highly, as do Vicarage, Central Park, St Stephen's Primary, St Edward's Catholic Primary and Upton Cross (which is expanding to five form entry on a new site and will have some 1,200 pupils by 2016). Tollgate in Plaistow is also rated outstanding, as is St Luke's C of E in Canning Town.

Redbridge

Redbridge is one of the greenest boroughs, with plentiful parks and open spaces. Woodford County High for girls qv and Ilford County High for boys qv are the local selective grammar schools, with results to match (priority to high achievers who live within the school catchment areas). But there is a also a high proportion of non-selective schools rated as outstanding, including Seven Kings High qv, Loxford School, Valentines High, Beal High, Oaks Park High, Chadwell Heath Academy and Trinity Catholic High. Understandably, a large proportion of pupils go on to university.

The primary schools are good too. Christchurch Primary, a secular school in spite of its name, is one of the largest in the country with five forms in each year group. St Bede's RC primary and Our Lady of Lourdes RC primary are high-achieving, as are Redbridge, Nightingale, Churchfields and Gearies.

Tower Hamlets

Tower Hamlets, one of the oldest parts of London (tribal, pre-Roman, silted and swampy at the time), was in more recent times home to most of London's Cockney dock workers. Wapping and the areas along that length of the river were lined with docks and warehouses for the thousands of ships and workers in London's port, characterised as well by Dickensian levels of poverty and crime. Those same docks, winding streets and riverside warehouses now contain very high end flats, served by the best butcher in east London and lively cafés and trendy restaurants (one, for example, in a converted power hydraulic station), but some areas still have high levels of poverty.

This is a vibrantly multi-ethnic borough – successive waves of immigrants, including Huguenot refugees, Irish weavers, Askanazi Jews and most recently Bangladeshis have congregated here. As well as the largest city farm in the country – the 32 acre Mudchute Park and Farm in the middle of the Isle of Dogs – it has the oldest surviving music hall in the world, Wilton's.

In the 90s it had some of the worst performing schools in the country; now it has some of the best. It reduced absences, set ambitious targets and used its extra funding as a deprived area to attract some high quality teaching staff and heads.

Sir John Cass's Foundation and Redcoat School qv is one of the most popular secondary schools. Although a C of E school, only a small minority of places is for committed Christians, and the vast majority of pupils, mirroring the ethnic make-up of the area, are Bangladeshi. In 2014 it was caught up in the controversy about Islamic extremism in schools, and downgraded by Ofsted from outstanding to inadequate, primarily over segregation of boys and girls and some sixth form Facebook activity. Mulberry School for Girls, with a similar demographic, is rated as outstanding, as are Morpeth School and Swanlea School. St Paul's Way Trust, undersubscribed and rated as 'satisfactory' a few years ago, is now, in a new building with greatly improved reports, another of the most sought-after schools in the borough.

Amongst many popular primary schools are Sir William Burrough qv with its international primary curriculum, Old Palace, Bygrove, Bonner, Old Ford and Clara Grant – interesting that many of the top-performing primaries in this area are secular. A controversial free school, Canary Wharf College (a primary in spite of its name) has hit the news for having only two per cent of pupils on free school meals in an area where most schools have 50 per cent, and limiting class sizes to 20. A second College opened in September 2014, again with 50 per cent of places for Christian church goers.

Waltham Forest

Waltham Forest is a borough of contrasts: the area south of the North Circular Road is mostly built-up and urban, with the socially and ethnically mixed population characteristic of inner cities. The northern area encompasses lots of open space, including parts of Epping Forest, and several reservoirs, and has a suburban feel. Walthamstow School for

Girls is a flagship secondary; Highams Park is also popular.

St Mary's Catholic Primary in Chingford in the leafy northern part is highly rated, as are Henry Maynard, Hillyfield on the Hill and Greenleaf, Handsworth and Dawlish Road.

If you're moving to London from abroad, Living in London: a Practical Guide might help explain the nitty-gritty. It's written by volunteers from the Junior League of London who have hundreds of years of expat experience between them. We appreciate their permission to draw on some of their descriptions of London districts.

Bancroft's Preparatory School

Linked school: Bancroft's School, 586

611–627 High Road, Woodford Green, Essex IG8 0RF

Tel: 020 8506 6751

Independent • Pupils: 260 • Ages: 7–11 • C of E
• Fees: £12,684 pa

Email: prep.office@bancrofts.org
Website: www.bancrofts.org

Headmaster: Since September 2012, Mr Joe Layburn MA, previously acting head. MA in German literature from University College London, followed by a 15-year career as investigative journalist and TV reporter, primarily for Channel 4. Retrained as a teacher and joined Bancroft's Prep in 2004. Author of a trilogy of children's books. Married with three sons, two at Bancroft's and one at a special needs school. Keen on running, cycling and West Ham United.

Entrance: At 7+ – over-subscribed by about three to one. Testing in English – reading and writing – and maths for year 3 entry takes place on beanbags. Children seen (and offered doughnuts) in small groups with head and deputy – it's 'as informal and low key as possible'. Around 70-75 places offered – Bancroft's will be first choice for most applicants.

Exit: Vast majority – around 90 per cent – to senior school; a few to local grammars, including Woodford County High, KEGS and Latymer. Others to local schools like West Hatch, Valentines. Other pupils move because families are moving out of the area.

Remarks: Two conjoined, inviting-looking, modern red-brick buildings at the lower right hand side of the main school playing fields – two-storeyed and with big windows. From the main school they appear small and modest; the main school, viewed from the prep, looks imposing and a little awe-inspiring, but the prep children spend time in the main school, so that 'It's a bit scary as it's so big and the students are so big, but we had a meeting with Mrs Ireland [senior school head] so we know much more about it now and I'm not really scared any more'. Quite! And senior pupils trot over to visit their junior siblings in break too. However the prep is its own world and, as you descend the slope to its entrance, between the playing field and the tennis court, a gentleness and palpable sense of fun envelops you.

The prep has splendid new rooms which have greatly enhanced its overall space and provision. New science, drama, music and DT rooms, a good-sized hall with flexible seating – lots of IT and new laptops. Around 23 children in a class, but the rooms are big and airy enough not to feel crowded – we did not feel the need to open windows, as

We liked the alternatives to 'said' and loved the paper collages showing variations on the Arcimboldo fruity face and the glittery, sparkly, firework ones

one so often does. The library, recently refurbished, is well-stocked and a good mix of fact and fiction. Outside space good and super all-weather surface for littlies with monster chess set and apparatus – not surprisingly, 'Everyone loves coming out here'.

Classrooms busy, not over-orderly and relaxed – we wanted to look at the displays, all of which seemed interesting and not as predictable as they so often are. We liked the alternatives to 'said' and loved the paper collages showing variations on the Arcimboldo fruity face and the glittery, sparkly,

firework ones. We also approved some of the interesting work in progress, especially the lesson on moulds – 'We had to throw them away as they were beginning to smell,' was a rueful observation. Year 6 has critical thinking lessons – 'to expand our minds, to think out of the box, to widen our imagination,' we were told, earnestly. We were impressed by the sensible 'traffic light' system whereby pupils assess their grasp of what they have learnt and where they need help. All entrants assessed for SpLD at 7 and SENCo-led help laid on where needed – mostly mild dyslexia.

Exuberant sports, music and drama and lots of inspiring extracurricular stuff. Outgoing, relaxed and confident children from a vast range of local backgrounds, as you'd expect.

A true preparatory school, what goes on here is sound, sensible and confidence-building for what is to follow. But is not just preparatory for senior school – four happy years here are a solid foundation for life. Apply early – and cross your fingers.

Bancroft's School

Linked school: Bancroft's Preparatory School, 585

611–627 High Road, Woodford Green, Essex IG8 0RF

Tel: 020 8505 4821

Independent • Pupils: 870 • Ages: 11–18 • Sixth form pupils: 236 • C of E • Fees: £15,576 pa

Email: stephanie.wallis@bancrofts.org
Website: www.bancrofts.org

Head: Since January 2008, Mrs Mary Ireland BSc DipEd Member Soc of Biologists, chartered biologist (50s). Career began with Proctor and Gamble, but light dawned, she took her teaching qualification and has taught all three sciences and maths in both state and independent schools. Prior to Bancroft's, she was deputy head of Christ's Hospital, before which she had been housemistress at Ardingly and head of science at King's Hall.

Married, with a grown-up musician son, brisk, open, energetic, easy to talk to, attractive Scots intonation. True, professional head, clear about her modernising agenda – lost no time in implementing changes – and as clear about the values upon which Bancroft's was founded and which still inform its ethos. She has clearly been won over by the school and its community. 'The buildings have a wow factor – though I tell parents that they are not what the school is about – but the thing that really appealed to me was the children. They are London children who tell it how it is, multi-racial, striving children who want to do well – they are incredibly competitive. They do everything here

that we did at Christ's Hospital, only they cram it into a school day'.

A safe pair of hands – and not hands that mind getting dirty: she cleared up a lunch that slid off a pupil's plate onto the floor when we visited. She is involved, busy and available. Some of her changes not immediately understood by school community, restructuring of the school council and the popular Stars in their Eyes extravaganza being two. Introduction of new virtual learning environment – internet school-home communications system – hit by predictable teething troubles and much groused about, but now a useful asset. She manages to teach some GCSE biology – we applaud. Bancroft's has continued to thrive under her eager eye and hands-on regime.

Retiring in July 2016.

Academic matters: Notable results across the board (in 2015, 93 per cent A*/A grades at GCSE) but maths is a star performer by any standards. English more of a spread, despite reports of some brilliantly inspirational teaching. Modern langs getting a boost – all year 7s learn German and Spanish; Russian is an option from year 9; Mandarin recently introduced. Greek and Latin have healthy numbers. Remarkable science results – especially in chemistry. History and geography also impressive. Few takers for art, music and DT – surprising, given the facilities – but a school which takes its academics seriously. No trendy subjects, though drama has seduced its way into the timetable and options list. A particular, enlightened feature is that subjects can be chosen not, as elsewhere, from 'blocks' but from the whole curriculum. If they can manage it at Bancroft's, why not everywhere?

A safe pair of hands – and not hands that mind getting dirty: she cleared up a lunch that slid off a pupil's plate onto the floor

A level results similarly impressive – 92 per cent A*-B, 72 per cent A*/A in 2015. Maths and chemistry popular and successful. Demand for maths and sciences has led to creation of new maths room and science lab. Economics and geography good and, at this level, English also impresses. Greek and Latin survive, though the numbers taking modern langs are, we would suggest, a cause for concern, though may reflect the immense diversity of backgrounds here.

A place where serious learning happens and in which learning is taken seriously. The library,

revamped with a stylish mezzanine floor beautifully integrated into the whole, is a proper scholarly resource – not something you see everywhere these days, when for 'library' you can so often read 'IT suite'. Pupils appreciate the library and its staff – 'they are fantastic – they get in anything you need'. Sixth form has a dedicated library and quiet study area plus university-type lecture theatre – used for societies, debates and visiting speakers. IT everywhere – lots of rooms with new PCs, including a tiptop language lab, which should give the languages a deserved boost.

Learning support department screens all at 11+ (the prep also screens at 7+). Mrs Ireland appointed the school's first SENCo and has also ensured that all new staff get some training in SpLD. All on the LS register (mostly mild dyslexics) have an IEP and get some kind of individual support – the younger ones come out of different lessons each term and older ones get one-to-one. A TA in class helps those who are happy to be helped in that way. Lower sixth get help to 'develop individual learning skills'. 'They are wonderfully flexible over special needs,' says a parent.

Games, options, the arts: Sports are 'big' and well-resourced. Large playing fields on site plus vast sports hall with 25m pool. Five minutes away is school's own West Grove with pitches, courts, tracks etc. Achievement to match – triumphs in netball, rugby and cricket as well as tours in these and hockey to, eg, New Zealand, Australia, South Africa and Sri Lanka. Heart-felt pupil and parental complaints that sport is too elitist – 'if you're not in a squad, they don't give a monkey's' – seen by Mrs

Twisty, brick staircases and leaded lights which grab eager 10 year olds immediately – 'I chose it because it was like Hogwarts': a unique selling point in Essex

Ireland as a priority and B and C teams now being developed, along with soccer. 'We are encouraging more staff to help so we can run more teams. It's something we need to work on.'

CCF is huge, very popular and enthusiastically pursued by those who surprise themselves by how much they get out of it, girls as well as boys – 'It's taught me how to get on with people I'd never mix with normally'; 'It's good that the sixth form help with it – you can have a bit of a laugh with them': not common in what is still, more or less, a London school. Thriving D of E and Sea Scout group with cubs, scouts and explorer sections.

Equally, Mrs Ireland was determined to boost time for arts across the school and has steadily increased provision. Music and drama enthusiastic and popular – annual concert in Drapers' Hall the big annual event, with bands, solo performances and musical mix the main features. Vast range of instruments studied – music maybe more pop and jazz than classical, though we are told around eight classical concerts each year. Drama had a fillip with conversion of old gym to good, large studio and subject now on the curriculum at all levels. Not all musicals here, either – The Caucasian Chalk Circle and Macbeth among recent productions; year 9 and 10 performers taught to fence for their production of The Three Musketeers. Productions at Edinburgh Fringe Festival.

Art, electronics and DT departments produce lively work – we liked the clever clocks, mobiles and the remote control cars and, within the remit of the task, pupils are given their head to be creative with the actual design. Art, exceptionally well-displayed throughout school, originates in one of two brand new studios with kilns and exhibition space – light, spacious and full of quiet artists. Nice ceramics. Art could and should be bigger here – perhaps textiles and photography (on the way), as more than a club?

Tons of trips and tours – though some parental gripes about not enough places on trips for eager applicants. Extracurricular stuff is good, though some cries for more from the inexhaustible.

Background and atmosphere: Founded in 1737 by the Drapers' Company on behalf of Francis Bancroft as a school for poor boys; moved to Woodford from Mile End in 1889 into the present large and imposing red-brick Victorian gothic revival building – clearly designed to impress, with serious scholarly credentials by architect, Sir Arthur Blomfield, also responsible for Selwyn College, Cambridge, The RCM, much of Charterhouse, The Bank of England, Wellington, Eton Lower Chapel etc etc, as well as an astounding number of parish churches. This is one of his more benign and attractive buildings, with towers, crenellations and oriel windows, a splendid central quad and admirably generous corridors which, though originally intended for 200 boys, still feel spacious for today's quadrupled numbers.

A truly impressive school with twisty, brick staircases and leaded lights which grab eager 10 year olds immediately – 'I chose it because it was like Hogwarts': a unique selling point in Essex, to be sure. Large Great Hall – typical of date and type. Excellent Courtyard Building with colonnaded atrium and sitting area, dining room (all eat together; good food, though popular vegetarian option can run out too fast for true veggie latecomers, we're told), servery and sixth form common room and café: large and well-used. Some typically dismal 1960s add-ons but much better later additions (such as enormous multi-purpose sports hall) and adjoining buildings, eg vast head's house now used for admin and offices too, with head's garden open to everyone for quiet time and 'well-respected'. Very recent physics labs and modern language rooms and DT suite.

Integral chapel one of the best bits (complete with much-loved chaplain who is 'lovely, a wonderful person for a chat, a laugh and advice – he takes Salsa club'), into which everyone comes once weekly for an ecumenical service. Brass plaques to former heads and a vast stained glass east window set the tone for the services, which are inclusive in all ways, given the mix of pupils. Chapel also used for arts events – words and music etc, a classy extra-curricular feature here.

Integral chapel one of the best bits (complete with much-loved chaplain who is 'lovely, a wonderful person for a chat, a laugh and advice – he takes Salsa club')

Parental tributes to general efficiency of school and its communications. Sense of order, purposeful activity and common sense all-pervasive.

Pastoral care and discipline: When asked what was good about the school, all the parents and pupils we spoke to – lots – said, as with one voice, 'the pastoral care' – we can't recall such unanimity on any other school feature anywhere. Tributes to the teaching staff, overall friendliness, care and attention given to individuals pour from everyone and are a delight to hear: 'My teacher is amazing – he's given me extra lessons every week. He's ordered in around 30 extra books just to help me. They'll help with anyone – not just the Oxbridge candidates'; 'The teacher gave my daughter as much time as she needed when she was struggling'; 'The staff commitment is excellent; pastoral care couldn't be better'; 'My children love it – they look forward to every day.'

Pupils and parents: From as far away as Potter's Bar, Winchmore Hill and Cheshunt, though most from between 10 and 20 minutes' drive away. Transport from local tube station to encourage pupils to look out of town towards green space for schooling. Vast ethnic and social intake – 'very well-handled by school,' say parents: around 30-35 per cent South Asian, 10-15 per cent Jewish, 40 per cent white. Most parents first-time buyers who 'work very hard to pay fees'.

OB notables include Dennis Quilley, Sir Frederick Warner, Sir Neil McFarlane, Hari Kunzru, Adam Foulds, Yolanda Browne, Andrew Saul, Anita Anand, Lord Pannick QC, Samantha Spiro and Mike Lynch.

Entrance: At 11, 50 come up from the school's own prep. Around 400 apply for 60 additional places. Tests in maths and English plus interviews. In practice around a third of those whose first choice is Bancroft's will get in. Umpteen feeders, though several from St Aubyn's, Loyola and Woodford Green Prep. Around a quarter from state primaries.

Candidates for the sixth form sit the school's own entrance exam in two proposed AS subjects, need six As at GCSE plus the usual references. Around 20 places at this level – very few (around 10 per cent) leave.

Exit: Ten to Oxbridge in 2015 and 21 to study medicine (including dentistry, vet studies). Other popular choices Durham, UCL, Exeter.

Money matters: Fifteen Drapers' scholarships offered annually at 11+ worth a quarter to a half of fees. No means-testing – based solely on performance at entrance exams. Also music scholarships worth half or quarter fees plus free tuition in one instrument. Several Francis Bancroft scholarship awards – means-tested but with a generous financial threshold, worth up to full fees, based on a sliding scale dependent on family income. Bancroft's Foundation set up in 2012 to mark 275th anniversary has already raised significant amounts to increase means-tested provision – enough to fund six Foundation scholars.

Remarks: A splendid school, catering for bright children and those who will seize opportunities. Deservedly over-subscribed. Brings glory to Essex well beyond its immediate catchment.

The Coopers' Company and Coborn School

St Mary's Lane, Upminster, Essex RM14 3HS

Tel: 01708 250500

State • Pupils: 1,391 • Ages: 11–18 • Sixth form pupils: 230

Email: info@cooperscoborn.org.uk
Website: jjn@cooperscoborn.co.uk

Headteacher: Since May 2013, Dr David Parry; had been deputy of the school since 2005, including a stint as acting headteacher. Was involved in setting up the school's link with Canterbury Christ Church University and also works with the University of London as a visiting research associate.

Academic matters: You 'can expect to do well', said Ofsted in its most recent response to pupils, and so they do. Learning takes place in a culture of success led by passionate and well-qualified teachers, who clearly benefit from the school's third and most recently awarded specialist status, as a teacher training school (the other two are sport and humanities). School has therefore consistently achieved near top GCSE results nationally and the proportion of pupils achieving the highest grades is significantly above the national average – 77 per cent of candidates gained five or more A*-C passes including English and maths in 2015, and 33 per cent of grades were A*/A. They are especially strong in English lang, English lit, mathematics and art and design, but pupils do exceptionally well in RS, DT, textiles technology and music.

At sixth form pupils are offered a wide curriculum of traditional subjects but are also introduced to new courses – media studies, psychology and politics. Popular choices are the sciences, especially biology, business studies, history, maths and psychology. In 2015, 65 per cent A*-B and nearly 34 per cent A*/A grades.

Curriculum options are as standard, with years 7 and 8 studying all 10 subjects but a second MFL introduced in year 8. Work on careers is introduced for year 9s. Popular GCSE choices are history, German, geography and sport/PE but fair numbers also choose Spanish and French.

Pupils are setted only for maths, at the end of year 7. From year 7 to sixth form, homework is considered an essential part of shaping pupils' academic experience, particularly in relation to independent learning and thinking skills. School says 'regular homework would be equivalent to an extra year of education with consequent benefits', so expects parental support. Parents are informed of what is expected at the beginning of each school year.

Despite high results and a NACE award for its gifted and talented programme, the school is working on improving grades. Although all achieve the nationally expected levels, Ofsted noted that even better progress is possible. Having recognised this, the school introduced TRIPS – a Tracking, Reporting, Intervention and Planning System to monitor progress – and 'early indications' of change look successful. Parents receive regular TRIPS reports (at least every half term) showing an academic target grade, pupils' present attainment grade and an effort grade, enabling all three parties to monitor progress and make any necessary interventions to keep grades on track. Underachieving pupils receive support from either the SEN department, LSAs or learning mentors. Just six per cent currently receive some type of extra support and less than one per cent of these have been statemented.

Games, options, the arts: Games and PSHE remain compulsory throughout the school years, even at sixth form. PE is outstanding with pupils winning many national competitions: 'There have been many times when we were behind and looked unlikely to win, but we won', observed former head, capturing pupils' exceptional achievement, resilience and aptitude for sport and learning in general.

Pupils enjoy a rich curriculum ranging from circuit gym training to trampolining, cricket and netball to indoor rowing. Coopers Cats has received natural recognition as an outstanding star programme for athletes, so lots of opportunity to be stretched. Sports and athletics have been so successful at the school that several teams often represent the school at national and international events and pupils took part in the opening ceremony for the 2012 Olympics.

'They match you really well so you have lots in common and make real friends'

Well-equipped art studios, arranged as individual cubicles where pupils have their own designated area in which to work. Its 'open house' policy approach encourages independent work and, along with the clearly outstanding levels of work on display, creates a wonderful 'art school' atmosphere. Pupils consistently have work displayed in exhibitions around the country.

Music and drama are also both strong here. Pupils take part in several national ensembles and theatrical events. Connection to the Worshipful Company of Coopers means there are various concerts and events throughout the year. Around 250 pupils have instrumental lessons in school and at least another 50 have lessons outside school. Standard is high, up to grade 8, and students with exceptional achievement attend the Guildhall and Trinity Saturday College.

Several teams often represent the school at international events and pupils took part in the Olympic opening ceremony

Huge range of extracurricular choice. Pupils are expected to get involved in music, drama and sport as well as the academic curriculum, since school feels this has a great impact on the sense of culture and engagement. 'There is something for everyone,' said a year 11 pupil. Clubs – before and after school and at lunch time – cover almost every conceivable area, from chess to fishing (under music alone there are 28 weekly activities including four wind bands, two orchestras, four jazz bands, a swing and brass band, five choirs and numerous rock bands). Several clubs have been instigated and are run by pupils.

Overseas trips are important. Language trips (year 8) and exchange trips (year 10) support Spanish, German and French but there are many others eg a rugby trip to New Zealand and a tennis trip to Florida, plus other trips to explore interesting places such as Namibia and Botswana. Year 12 and 13 pupils visited Madagascar to build a secondary school block. The school is developing links with China. Pupils praised the language exchange programme: 'They match you really well so you have lots in common and are able to make real friends, which is a good motivation for wanting to actually have a conversation'.

Background and atmosphere: A rich history dating to 1536 when it was first established as a free school for boys. Its name came in 1552 when the Coopers' Company was asked to take over the running of the school. It was then located in Stepney, Tower Hamlets. In 1891, it joined foundations with the Coborn school for boys and girls and remained at sites at Mile End and Bow until it moved to Upminster in 1971.

At its present location, situated a good distance from the main road amid 25 acres of greenery, and home to a pond visited by ducks and geese, the school very much resembles an independent school. Modernisation and development have seen new buildings regularly erected since the 80s, the latest being a sixth form block. Other smaller but notable modern developments include a solar panel roof, i-desks (with computers that pop up) and a laser cutter, with which, pupils confessed, 'we have gone to town'. The outcome of their efforts is the various metal placards signposting the DT, textile technology and design and art departments. 'The best way to protect the future is to design it,' says the laser-cut sign on the front of the main DT building, as if to help create an atmosphere of vitality and aspiration for future success.

Pastoral care and discipline: Organised by heads of year. Year 7-11 form tutors are responsible for about 30 pupils, who remain in the same form group throughout the five years. Sixth form tutors look after about 20 students each. School tries to create a good mix with external entrants to the sixth form easily assimilated. Two forms allocated to each of three houses, a system which helps create vertical links as well as the horizontal year groupings. The school also selects school captains from year 12 pupils, who must apply for the position. These are prestigious positions and the selection process includes interviews by the head. The one boy and one girl selected hold office throughout their final year. Whole school council plays a key role in the decision-making processes – including the appointment of senior staff. Pupils are given a sense of importance and are consulted on important developments, 'because it won't work if the students don't like it'.

The word on the street blames it for increased house prices in Upminster

Peer to peer mentoring, and around 150 sixth formers work with younger pupils. Very high expectations of conduct. Parents and students report an effective response to the few incidents of bullying and racism; they are dealt with quickly by form tutors and heads of years. The school's approach to remedying problems is to get those concerned to accept responsibility and consequences for their actions. Bad behaviour is just simply 'uncool'. Instead pupils exhibit very positive attitudes to learning and life. 'We do try to look after each other, standards are high, it's tough love and there is a genuine sense of commitment.'

Pupils and parents: Mainly white middle class and clearly aspirational. A 'Christian school with an eclectic mix from all recognised world religions'. Pupils seem proud of their school and very contented. In a day when many young people seem to take what they have for granted, it was refreshing to meet a group of pupils who seemed extremely appreciative. They clearly thrive on their many opportunities for responsibility – 'you have these free periods and you soon learn that you need to work independently, so you use it to complete essays and extra research'.

Everyone is welcoming – greeting visitors with smiles and hellos, saying thank you, holding doors open and even singing to themselves as they pass by. Many parents are supportive of the school and help out at school events. Active PTA of about 30 members, very good for a secondary state school. They arrange various fundraising events including a monthly sale of supermarket vouchers to parents and staff which enables school to raise over £10,000 per year to buy eg a minibus.

Entrance: Unusually large number of feeder schools (around 100); admissions rules complicated due to the school's historic links to east London and wish to preserve the principles of the Coopers' Company and Coborn Educational Foundation.

No doubt this helps intensify competition for places – over 800 applications for just 180 places and a fair number go to appeal. Ten sport and nine music places. All other applicants must be actively connected to one of the main world faiths. Some places for children of staff and former students; others by promixity; others to those who live in specific areas including Havering, Brentwood and Billericay.

Most stay on to the sixth form after GCSE. Around 50 places for students from outside but, again, massively popular with over 300 applications. Applicants need at least eight A*-C grades to be considered for a place, to be sympathetic to the school's Christian character and be willing to uphold its 'Love as Brethren' ethos by giving time to serve the school. Oversubscription criteria prioritise looked after children, highest predicted grades and then availability in specific sets.

Exit: Around 30 per cent leave after GCSE. Some three-quarters of sixth formers to university (two to Oxbridge in 2015). School provides a range of opportunities to prepare for post school eg science pupils attend conferences, workshops, competitions and special events at Nottingham and Cambridge. Many go on to study pure science subjects or vocational courses such as medicine, veterinary science and dentistry. Other popular subjects include psychology, economics, architecture, art history, journalism, politics and theatre design.

Money matters: The school allocates £10k to assist pupils that need help and also provides music and sports grants of up to £500.

Remarks: An impressive and dynamic school that prepares pupils for success. Dazzling reputation in the local community and the word on the street blames it for increased house prices in the Upminster area. World class in true sense of the word.

Forest Preparatory School

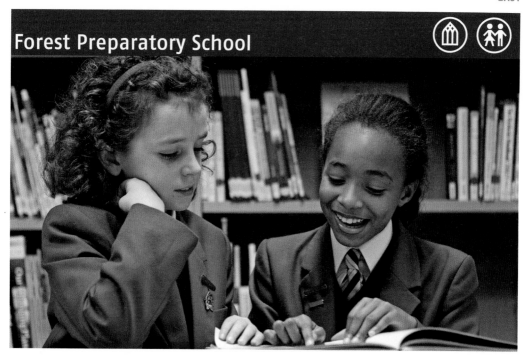

Linked school: Forest School, 594

College Place, London E17 3PY

Independent • Pupils: 270 • Ages: 4–11 • C of E • Fees: up to £12,813 pa

Tel: 020 8520 1744

Email: prep@forest.org.uk
Website: www.forest.org.uk

Head: Since 2012, Mr Andrew Noakes MA education, Open University (30s). Previously head of Northampton Junior School. Studied at Reed's, Surrey, then De Montfort, where he read European studies and French. He trained at St George's College; has also been director of studies at Bedford Modern Junior School. Described as 'calm and unflappable', he is married to a teacher and has two daughters.

Entrance: Main entries at 4 and 7 via play-based or literacy/numeracy assessments. Most pupils come from the local area and there is a good mix of ethnic backgrounds.

Exit: Prep pupils are automatically offered a place at either the boys' or girls' sections of Forest School and majority – over 90 per cent – take up the offer.

Remarks: Tucked away from the main roads, surrounded by the ancient Epping Forest, and accessible by what resembles a narrow dirt track lane, the school stands as a closely hidden secret in its inner city surroundings. However, once we had cleared the highly secure, gated reception area to enter the school grounds, the bustle of life at the school immediately greeted us. We heard string and brass instruments sounding out from one of the many lunchtime concerts at the chapel, and saw brightly clad prep pupils at play or through their open classroom windows, merrily chanting foreign words in rote-like fashion. Pupils seem to be busy, happy and oblivious. They are taught in buildings alive with a heritage dating back to the school's foundation in 1834. Even with its Georgian buildings, this school has a distinctively bright, spacious and airy feel. Expect to see lively but small groups of pupils actively involved in learning, lots of writing and artwork displays in and outside of the classrooms, and tiny, well-behaved pupils following behind their teacher in duckling-like fashion from one part of the school to another.

In the pre-prep (4 to 7), children are taught in co-ed classes and follow the EYFS; in the prep they begin to experience single-sex teaching preparation for their later move to the boys' and girls' senior schools. Class sizes 16 in the pre-prep and 22 in the prep school. Teaching based on national

The school stands as a closely hidden secret

curriculum with specialists brought in for art, PE, drama, foreign languages and, in particular, music.

All of the children have the opportunity to learn an instrument here for at least a year. The prep school music department is led by a teacher prized for her ability to spot the 'differences between concert and worship' voices, as well as knowing how hard to push the youngest of performers to discover their best. Each May, the school organises Composition Week, where year 5 pupils are transformed into a team of songwriters, singers and composers to produce, for example, a signature melody inspired by the retelling of the legend of Arachne. The experience is 'demanding but rewarding' for the pupils, and this spirit is one of the prized characteristics of the school: even the youngest of pupils is stretched and pushed to learn.

There is plenty else to do aside from music-making – pupils are also actively involved in dance, drama and sports. The prep school sits between the main school buildings and senior pupils behave like older siblings to the younger ones. The prep children use senior school facilities, including the sports fields, theatre and a modern leisure centre with swimming pool and gymnasium.

Many trips organised – to 'help us to learn', say the children – some local to eg Strawberry Hill Ponds and the Suntrap Centre, others further afield eg Paradise Park, the Europa Centre and the Royal Observatory in Greenwich, others even as far as Berlin.

None of the pupils here have a statement of special educational need but about 16 receive some kind of learning support. They all speak English as their main language, so no EAL needs here either; the ISI describes them as highly articulate and well above average ability. Many win academic, sport or music scholarships, to Forest senior school and elsewhere, but only a few move away.

The chapel and chaplaincy are central to learning here. The chapel is where pupils begin and end each term with events such as breakfasts for parents followed by a welcome service. Last year all new pupils brought in a cardboard brick to build a 'prayer wall' showing their aspirations for the term. These included learning to read, wishing to play football for the school, becoming a monitor, making lots of friends and, simply, 'I want to make my teacher and parents proud.'

Pupils make respectable contributions to a very lively school diary of events, such as the pre-prep nativity play, a dramatised festival service and an idiom recital day to mark the 400-year anniversary of the King James version of the Bible. They also have house competitions in eg acting, singing and rounders, and charity fundraising events. They compete in the UK chess championships and have hosted a prep-level junior science competition involving over 20 schools. They won a school prize in a wildlife foundation global art competition, with 10 year 4 and 5 pupils selected among entrants from around the world, including Hong Kong, Nigeria and Arabia. Cricket is popular but football is 'something special', and there are several teams and matches played in and outside the borough.

Parents describe it as a school where 'teaching is good but not too pushy', teachers 'know your child well' and 'there is a very active PTA'. In fact, the majority of the parents involved in the parents' association are from the prep school. They are kept up to speed via a newsletter and the school website.

Forest School

Linked school: Forest Preparatory School, 593

College Place, Snaresbrook, London E17 3PY

Independent • Pupils: 1,077 • Ages: 11–18 • Sixth form pupils: 260 • C of E • Fees: £16,335 pa

Tel: 020 8520 1744

Email: info@forest.org.uk
Website: www.forest.org.uk

12

Warden: Since September 2015, Mr Antony Faccinello (40s), previously senior deputy head of Alleyn's School. English degree from Oxford and PGCE. Has also taught at Cheltenham College, Haberdashers' Aske's Boys' School in Elstree and RGS Guildford. Loyal supporter of Manchester City football club. He is married with two children.

Academic matters: 'Both of my daughters are scholars,' said one very pleased parent. Single-sex teaching in this co-educational environment 'creates a study environment that boys and girls feel comfortable with and which enables them to achieve their best', says school. Teachers are committed; about a third have been here more than 10 years and all are specialists in their subjects; also large number part-time eg music, drama and dance specialists. Most pupils are of above average ability. They do well across the board, notably in English, history, geography, maths and the sciences. From year 8, some setting occurs for maths, English, MFLs and science. There is a free choice from French, German and Spanish. Latin is taught to all pupils during the first two years, then it becomes a GCSE option along with ancient Greek.

In 2015, 68 per cent A*/A at GCSE and 48 per cent at A level. Extended projects, which allow GCSE and A level students to flex their academic muscles beyond the norm, are popular. With topics and titles such as 'A legal definition of torture' and 'Love and the Adversary' (a treatise on the representation of Satan in English literature), pupils demonstrate their capacity for critical thought.

Courses in both the boys' and girls' schools run broadly in line with the national curriculum. This leads some parents to make the same complaint heard of state schools, that lessons can have 'too much focus on the sometimes dull GCSE syllabus rather than wider lateral thought.. but I think this is what happens everywhere'. Hence, by and large, parents also prize the school for its 'good academic expectations but not [being] too pushy'. As one parent echoed, 'I don't consider that [my daughters] are always adequately stretched, but the humanities and arts subjects appear to be particularly well taught', adding that they had turned down places at more academic schools in favour of Forest's 'more balanced experience'.

The number of academic challenges, competitions, tournaments and Olympiads these pupils enter is dizzying: maths challenges, chemistry masterminds, physics Olympiads, and even the informatics Olympiad – where pupils have competed in Thailand against the best young computer scientists in the world. Trips to eg the Battlefields, Munich (history), Devon (geography), China, Russia, Japan and the USA.

It is close to the bustling City of London and yet surrounded by the quietness of ancient forest

Majority of pupils stay on at sixth form where courses include classical civilisation, government and politics (with visits to key places in London, Washington DC and New York, and supported by guest speakers such as Iain Duncan Smith, John Bercow, George Galloway and Nigel Farage), philosophy (a popular university choice) and economics. The A level economics department has links with the City of London, the Economics Association and Institute of Economic Affairs.

Extra support for those who need it; school publishes an excellent guide to independent study to help struggling pupils find their own answers or at the very least to formulate thoughtful and clear questions before asking for help.

Games, options, the arts: You will find them all here: aerobics, basketball, cricket, even fencing. Extensive playing fields, netball and tennis courts, various pitches, a sports centre housing two heated swimming pools, cricket nets and a fitness suite. At sixth form, PE covers sports psychology, history and exercise physiology. Pupils can try out other sports eg karate, cross-country and golf during activities afternoons and house matches. Several record achievements gained at county, regional and national level in netball, rounders, hockey, tennis, badminton and athletics.

A large (one of the largest in London) and busy music department with over 700 instrumental and vocal lessons a week. Every pupil has the opportunity to try out an instrument free of charge and pupils are encouraged to take the lead in musical activities, often leading to specialisms. With seven orchestras, 10 bands, 14 choirs and more than 40 specialist teachers, numerous opportunities to perform. School is extensively equipped with practice, recital and technology rooms. On the day of our visit one of the bands was preparing for a lunch time concert in the chapel, the norm at this school that presents more than 80 concerts and other performances a year both in and out of the school. Tours take place in the UK, Spain, Italy, Netherlands and France and the school regularly sends pupils to major conservatoires. Regular choral and organ scholarships to Oxford and Cambridge.

Drama and art also taken seriously. The purpose-built Deaton Theatre seats 350 and has excellent lighting and sound equipment. Pupils act in large-scale productions and learn design or technical skills. As part of the house drama competition, they can select, cast and direct their own productions. A long tradition of excellence in drama with present and past pupils making successful careers

One of the bands was preparing for a lunch time concert in the chapel, the norm at this school that regularly sends pupils to major conservatoires

in this area (the West End show Stomp was founded by former pupils) and pupils have been involved in many well-known television and theatre productions, including East Enders and The Bleak Old Shop of Stuff for the BBC, and a West End production of Oliver! Art and design studios are well-resourced and pupils allowed to develop their passion outside classroom learning hours.

Co-curricular opportunities in sport, music, drama, dance and visual arts. CCF linked to the

Royal Green Jackets offers field days, annual camps and weekly training. The Duke of Edinburgh Award is popular. Other opportunities include student-led societies, video production, languages, musical theatre, and journalism. Pupils also take part in raising money for charity, in public speaking competitions, and community work such as visiting the elderly and riding for the disabled.

Background and atmosphere: Old and new exist side by side here. It is close to the bustling City of London and yet surrounded by the quietness of ancient forest. The St John the Baptist chapel, where pupils regularly congregate for services and other events, is at the heart of the school and reminiscent of a history that goes back to 1834 when it began with just 22 pupils. Although Anglican in tradition, the outlook is ecumenical to cater to the broad range of backgrounds, faiths and cultures. Pupils enjoy this and say, 'It is good to have the school come together and talk about different faiths.' Alongside the old, are new buildings like the Sylvestrian Leisure Centre – built with the aid of a 'buy a brick' fundraiser organised by the parents' association, used by the public at weekends and as a quiet camp for Team GB during the 2012 London Olympics – and the Martin Centre for Innovation, with digital teaching and learning facilities for the whole school.

Pastoral care and discipline: Form and house groups, headed by a housemistress or master, provide a sense of belonging and stability. Because classes are small, community atmosphere is strong; 'pupils are well known individually by the staff,' say parents. Pastoral care gives each child 'the support they need to progress socially, morally and academically'. Housemasters and mistresses stay with a child through his or her time at the school and are there to advise on any aspect of school life. This continues at sixth form. Pupils are allocated a tutor who oversees academic progress, helps with university applications, and advises on careers.

There is heavy emphasis on the code of conduct in the school prospectus: 'all observed behaviour, which indicates a lack of mutual regard, will be fully investigated', 'the school stands firmly against any form of verbal or physical bullying or any behaviour which is intended to cause distress to pupils', and the 'warden may require the permanent exclusion of a pupil if.. it is in the interest of the pupil or of the school community'. Approach is good lines of communication. 'Children are encouraged to talk and are listened to' and to report incidents of bullying to an appropriate person, says school. 'Where bullying is detected, we acknowledge our responsibility to support both the bully and the victim'.

Parents say, 'Bullying – the school deals with this very well' and 'We hear mixed things about how long it takes the school to home in and deal with these issues; but no direct experience'. Most say their children learn 'in a secure, supportive and encouraging environment'. 'The children know they are lucky but they don't see themselves as special', says school. 'If children are not happy they won't learn; get that right and the grades will come.'

The best thing about being at the school, said a pupil, is the 'diversity. I like the mix, staff are kind, they encourage you to do the best you can do.'

Pupils and parents: A diverse ethnic mix. They come from the surrounding east and north London and Essex areas. Most are the children of professional parents and no-one speaks English as a second language. Past pupils include actor Ian Beale and cricketer Nasser Hussain.

Entrance: Most from the prep move to the senior school at 11, joined by a large number from other state and private schools (English and maths tests). Variable numbers admitted at 13+ depending on spaces.

Exit: Virtually all to university; nine to Oxbridge in 2015, eight to medical schools. Good mix of subjects across the range.

Money matters: Academic and music awards at 11+, academic, music and sports at 13, academic, art, music, drama and sports at 16. Means-tested bursaries only awarded as scholarship add-ons.

Remarks: A happy school with committed staff, and pupils who display a strong sense of independence and enjoyment of school life. While remaining true to its traditional roots, this is a forward-thinking school, humane and open-minded, with both feet on the ground. Its clear grasp of the rich inter-relationship between the curricular, the co-curricular and the pastoral ensures children do well.

Ilford County High School

Fremantle Road, Ilford, Essex IG6 2JB

Tel: 020 8551 6496

State · Pupils: 930 · Ages: 11–18 · Sixth form pupils: 340

Email: enquiries@ichs.org.uk
Website: www.ichs.org.uk

5

Headteacher: Since April 2015, Mrs Rebecca Drysdale, previously deputy and then acting head. She joined Ilford in 2012 from Edmonton County School.

Academic matters: In 2015, 65 per cent A*/A grades at GCSE, with strongest results shown in the sciences and mathematics. French in year 7 and in year 8 pupils take up either German or Spanish as well. Everyone takes one language at GCSE, though few take two or continue languages to A level, despite European trips and work experience opportunities. The school is developing partnerships with schools and colleges in Germany, Spain, Switzerland and Denmark and has British Council International School status. It has historic links with Southern Africa and is seeking to develop links with India and China and explore alternative learning styles. School has introduced enquiry-based learning to develop critical thinking skills.

At A level popular subjects are biology, chemistry, economics, mathematics and physics; most stick to academic rather than creative subjects. In 2015, 67 per cent A*/B and 42 per cent A*A grades. Subject-based reviews help to monitor each subject and data tracking to monitor pupil progress helps spot and tackle underperformance; not that there is much of that here, according to parents. The school was rated outstanding by Ofsted at the last full inspection. Maximum class sizes, at 30 (and 22 in the sixth form), are at the higher end. Some 560 pupils with EAL requirements plus 30 or so who need SEN support.

Games, options, the arts: Sporting trophies for cricket and swimming, and a Sportsman of the Year award, all point to an environment where sport is taken seriously and given plenty of room for expression. Pupils enjoy taking part in swimming galas and pointed out to us the 'basketball court where we play football'. They explained, 'There is space for both but the football is the most popular though cricket is what we are best at, we tend to do well at cricket.' At the entrance to the sports hall is a notice board invitation to follow the PE department on Twitter to keep up with fixtures, lessons, inter-house competitions and results. There is plenty to report on, given the substantial provision, from ultimate frisbie to indoor rowing and rugby. On-site facilities include an artificial cricket strip, two football pitches and a 400m running track. The sports hall itself houses a heated swimming pool. There are also four badminton courts, a full size basketball court, with two small courts and provision for volleyball, five-a-side football, and tennis.

For those wishing to stick to the academic, there are clubs to deepen awareness of astronomy, philosophy or physics

Upstairs there is a fitness/weights room, an aerobics area and a viewing gallery and a 'theory room for people taking GCSE or A level' – currently about 31 at GCSE and three at A level.

Drama is compulsory for year 7s as part of the English curriculum, and they all take part in an annual production, but after that it disappears from the curriculum.

Those few students who do choose art produce rich, bold and inspiring work, much of it on display in corridors throughout the school. It includes drawings, paintings, photography and sculpting. Curriculum is enriched by visits to national museums and art galleries.

Provision for music is as rich as sport, though it is not so popular as an option. Over 60 pupils have timetabled music lessons and some exceptional talent can be found here. Some lessons take place at the Redbridge Music School and specialist music teachers visit to teach. Pupils have plenty of opportunity to develop their gifts on piano, violin, cello, double bass, saxophone, drum, voice and more through orchestra, jazz ensemble, choirs and various bands. There are concerts and performances in London and abroad. Few pupils take art or music A level.

Extracurricular provision across the school is rich, with clubs, groups and ensembles covering every interest. There are debating societies, rugby, sailing and indoor rowing clubs and, for those wishing to stick to the academic, clubs to deepen awareness of astronomy, philosophy or physics.

Background and atmosphere: The school was founded in 1901 as Park High Grade School. It was a boys' and girls' school back then and located in Balfour Road. The boys' school split in 1929 and moved to its present location in Freemantle Road in 1935. This is a built-up residential area but the school has a secluded feel. The building is traditional, with beautiful oak stairwells, large wooden boards with lists of past notables – headteachers, year captains and the like – and display cabinets. The cabinets line either side as you enter the reception area and show off a big collection of plaques and trophies, a reminder of the sort of school this is. They include awards for the Bank of England and Times Interest Rate Challenge, an Acknowledgement of Educational Excellence in Academic A Levels from Edexcel, an award from Help the Aged for helping to unite generations, and, most impressive of all, an award for best A level results achieved by boys taking critical thinking at an English grammar school, from the Good Schools Guide.

The school layout resembles two adjacent squares, with two stories of classrooms organised around these in circular fashion. This makes it very easy for new pupils to learn their way round as where you start is usually where you will finish. Near the front is 'the hall where assemblies happen – we have them in the afternoon,' a pupil explains, 'and variety nights where students and teachers perform'.

The atmosphere is bustling and lively, especially in the music department where boys frequently practice and experiment. A new learning resource centre and library was opened by the author Chris Ryan and has remained true to the celebration of literature with regular live and video conference talks by visiting authors. Other talks also take place there, including, for example, one for students interested in medicine, organised by York University. The school is planning further expansion, including an enlarged sixth form, which will increase funding. Building work will provide more independent study space for the sixth form.

Pastoral care and discipline: Parents comment on being drawn to the school by its 'ethos of competitiveness and success... it nurtures the boys and prepares them for the future'. Sometimes it is just the small things, like planners 'to ensure their homework is completed on time and all timescales are met' and the even distribution of that homework across the week. A parent said this allows his son time to complete and hand in work. This helps because 'he has music and drama lessons outside school in the evening and on weekends, which he enjoys. He also does sports two days a week.'

Noticeboards for each house, year and department keep pupils updated... 'notices on helping out, tours, linguist of the month..' Department specific news is also tweeted and there is a Facebook page for prefects.

Pastoral care arrangements at the school have moved from a horizontal year-based one to a vertical house system. There is a head of house and a team of five form tutors who work with and support pupils as they progress through the school. Form tutors are generally responsible for pupil welfare and progress. The new system provides greater opportunity for the boys to develop stronger skills in leadership, mentorship and responsibility, plus opportunities to develop relationships across year groups, right to sixth form. Pupils report that keenly-contested form sports competitions have been replaced by equally high-spirited house competitions.

Year 7s receive peer mentoring from older pupils in year 9, 10 and sixth form. 'They're a bit of a role model for the younger kids, someone to look up to...' and 'if you have any problems settling in you [can] go to see them.' For one pupil, who joined at sixth form, this was 'one of the things I liked when I came, people always willing to help'. He told us that bullying, or rather the lack of it, was another nice surprise for him, as at his previous school 'fights were a common occurrence. It was a radical change for me; since I've been here I haven't seen one'. 'The school has a strict anti-bullying policy,' said another sixth form pupil who has been at the school since year 7. 'I haven't really come across many cases of bullying in the school. I think most boys are fairly clued up on that it's wrong.'

It is this reputation for strict discipline that was given by several parents as one of the school's strong points. They said, 'The boys are well behaved', the school has 'a good approach to bullying' and 'I do not hear of any violent incidents at the school.' Evidently there is the occasional event, but 'in that one experience the head of house got in touch quickly to explain the situation; it was quickly settled. Thankfully my son has not had any further incidents and we hope it remains that way.'

Pupils and parents: Overall, pupils come across as happy and well-adjusted. They come from a wide mix of ethnic backgrounds, and from the borough of Redbridge and surrounding areas Waltham Forest, Newham, Barking and Dagenham. They range from bubbly, stumbling and oblivious year 7s making their way between lessons, to the year 11s

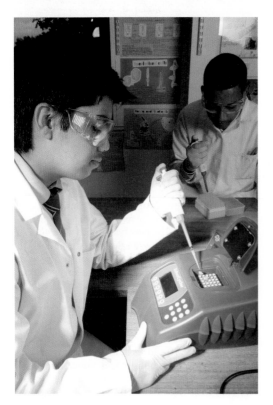

who showed us around and were articulate, mature and friendly. One told us about the cooking lessons the school organises for sixth formers to help them prepare for university. He said: 'I think I am fairly confident for a boy of my age.' He then added, with honesty, 'I can't fault it and I have achieved as good grades as I can. I didn't motivate myself as well as I could have before, but now I've put my foot down.'

The majority of parents believe their children

'If a boy's real interest and passion is for humanities and not science, fine, as that it is where they will get real satisfaction and achievement'

---

are being well taught and that all round provision at the school is good, although one mentioned that it would be nice to see pupils involved in more volunteer work and fundraising and more 'events such as leadership conferences, etc' to stimulate boys' minds. There is an enormous sense of relief at having got a place at the school, which is unsurprising given that it is the only boys' grammar in the borough. One parent said that the school 'has lived up to our expectations'. They appreciate the 'emphasis on all-round development and not just academics'.

There is a parents' association that helps to raise money for resources at the school but, like many senior schools, it dreams of more getting involved. 'The general trend here is that parents do not get involved,' said an active parent. 'They feel that once their child is in the school that is all they need to do. The school is not greatly funded and some parental support could help pay for things that are needed. It's not only about the fundraising but the community spirit, which I am afraid is very lacking.' School understands that 'parents have busy lives' but says 'in some cases parent don't get involved enough; we still have parents you never see other than at parents' evenings'.

School is more anxious about boys whose parents 'have unrealistic aspirations for them'. Main message to parents is that it is about the education, not just the grades, 'about the breadth of roundness'. It is not just pupils that need to learn to think outside of the box, parents do too. 'If a boy's real interest and passion is for humanities and not science, fine, as that it is where they will get real satisfaction and achievement.' School tries to instil into both parents and pupils that, 'If you want to do engineering at university you can't just concentrate on maths and physics, your GCSE profile needs to be high quality across all 10 subjects, you can't afford to have A*, A*, A*,..., A, C. It is the quickest route to an admissions tutor's waste paper basket.' Most parents get this and some have little sympathy for those that do not. One said, 'There are always a few parents who do not take this on board, despite the school's best efforts, and end up disappointed when their sons fail to get into their chosen university.'

Notable former pupils include Raymond Baxter, TV personality (Tomorrow's World), Sir Trevor Brooking, footballer, and David Miller, Deputy Chief Inspector of Air Accidents.

Entrance: More than 850 boys in the borough of Redbridge and nearby compete for the 120 places available each year by sitting the 11+ examination. The test is administered by the borough. School manages its own admissions to the sixth form, with places offered dependent on predicted GCSE grades.

Exit: Almost all (some 95 per cent) stay on to sixth form. Leavers go on to study subjects such economics, architecture, dentistry, medicine, law, physics and engineering. Majority choose to study in London at eg King's College and UCL. Four to Oxbridge in 2015.

Remarks: A school that delivers a high standard of education and produces young men who seem well prepared for the wider world. Somehow seems to be a victim of its own success, constantly having to grapple with the challenge of how to progress and maintain its impressive record and position among high performing secondary schools.

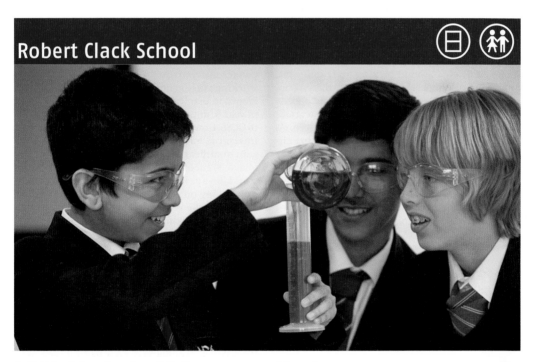

Robert Clack School

Gosfield Road, Dagenham, Essex RM8 1JU

State • Pupils: 2,069 • Ages: 11–18 • Sixth form pupils: 500

Tel: 020 8270 4200

Email: office@robert–clack.bardaglea.org.uk
Website: www.robertclack.co.uk

Headteacher: Since 1997, Sir Paul Grant MA PGCE (60s), famously promoted from head of humanities when the school was at its lowest ebb and has since transformed it into an outstanding success story. He is the eldest of seven children from a working-class Liverpudlian family. A keen football fan, he once hoped to turn professional. He went to the Salesian Grammar School in Bootle,

where an influential teacher inspired him to study history at Hull University. He completed a PGCE at Durham and an MA at London University, and taught in north Yorkshire, Australia and Newham before joining Robert Clack in 1990.

At this point the school was sliding downhill. Weak leadership meant a lack of support for those teachers who did try to keep order and behaviour was deteriorating rapidly. There was a serious gang culture, children smoked in the corridors and caused chaos in the community at lunchtime. Pupils rode bicycles inside and it was commonplace to set off fireworks indoors. In 1996, only 17 per cent of pupils gained five or more A–C grades at GCSE and the school was on the verge of special measures. The humanities department, however, was going from strength to strength. Sir Paul was appointed headteacher with an emergency plan of action which included a tough, transparent code for bad behaviour and a new system of rewards. He suspended 300 troublemakers in his first week.

'He led by example,' says a deputy, who had then just left the school as a pupil. 'I saw him stopping a bus outside the school and talking to passengers about how the school was going to change and inviting them to phone the school if they had any problems with Robert Clack pupils.' Most teachers were delighted by the new regime but some parents were outraged. Sir Paul insisted on meeting every one and gradually won them round. Changing behaviour was a gradual process which included driving around picking up truants and talking to local shopkeepers, local councillors, council employees such as housing officers, and police.

Sir Paul was knighted for services to education, a few weeks after the school received an Evening Standard award for excellence in challenging circumstances. Larger than life in build and character and described by Ofsted as 'tireless', he is married with three daughters. The school has been his life's work, he says. 'I wanted to prove that the children in this school could be excellent and my colleagues could be excellent. I'm incredibly proud of the children, parents and staff.'

The school is a specialist science, maths and computing college and has added a modern languages specialism

Pupils are proud too. 'He always works hard to make us succeed in life.' 'He's strict but fair. You know not to get on his wrong side but he always congratulates you when you do well.'

Academic matters: The school is one of 12 outstanding secondary schools fêted by Ofsted for excelling against the odds. Some 40 per cent of pupils are on the special needs register and 40 per cent have free school meals, but results have improved steadily from the 1996 nadir: in 2015, 65 per cent of pupils got five or more good GCSEs including maths and English. At A level, nearly 77 per cent A*/C and 20 per cent A*/A grades.

The girls' and boys' choirs performed movingly in assembly during our visit – the boys' choir was recently voted best in the borough and one pupil has starred in a West End musical

Alongside a strict disciplinary procedure, high quality teaching from a mostly young staff has helped the school achieve outstanding status. The 'Robert Clack good lesson' is a template devised by staff which involves explaining to pupils the objective, content and process of each lesson. We met one teacher who was off to Suffolk, appointed to help a school there achieve 'outstanding' status by using his experience at Robert Clack.

The school is a specialist science, maths and computing college and has added a modern languages specialism – a bold move in a strongly working-class school. Although everyone takes French in year 7 and talented linguists add Spanish in year 8, at present only 15–20 per cent continue to GCSE. However, the department plans to increase this considerably over the next few years, and many gain qualifications in their own community language. French and Spanish A level available, but tiny take-up. Everyone takes core science, with some going on to take additional science, others opting for the vocational applied science option and 100 or so taking three separate sciences. Other vocational options include health and social care, business studies, catering, beauty and ICT.

'We have got where we are because all the children feel there is a pathway for them. They're not finding themselves stranded in set 11 for everything.' The school sets right from the start for English, maths, science and languages. 'We're auditing progress all the time and a significant number have worked their way right up through the sets'. Other subjects, such as history, geography and RE, are taught in mixed ability groups from year 10 onwards. The ability range is massive, from those aiming at A*s to those who joined the school with a reading age of 5 or 6. 'Teaching a huge range is possible if the behaviour is excellent and class sizes are small, so we make sure that they are'.

Learning support and mentor rooms where children can come to catch up on literacy and numeracy, perhaps because they have had time off sick or are middle of the road and tend to be overlooked in class. Or they may come here because they are upset because of family problems and can't cope amongst their peers – 'if children are in the wrong place they will disrupt the lesson. We want to be proactive and avoid problems if possible'. But the 40 per cent on the SEN register – including partially sighted and deaf children – are mostly integrated into the classrooms. We saw a boy with cerebral palsy putting his views across forcefully to the class, despite speech problems. 'The children are very protective of each other'.

The sixth form is part of the North East Consortium with three other local schools, offering more than 40 courses at different levels. Over 800 sixth formers in the consortium, including some 450 at Robert Clack. No minimum entry requirements, as courses range from a certificate in motor vehicle servicing to further maths, though students who want to take A levels must have at least five grade Cs at GCSE – 'many of these students are the first in their families to stay on at school after 16. We don't want to set the benchmark too high, despite the risk of being marked down by Ofsted, because we want to give these children a chance'. Media studies and general studies are the most popular A level courses; maths, further maths, physics and chemistry the most successful. BTecs in business, IT and sport are popular too, as is beauty therapy, taught in an on-site beauty salon – 'we give everyone the opportunity to be successful here'.

Games, options, the arts: Sport is hugely important here and the school is frequently borough champion at athletics, swimming, rugby and cross-country. It has also been county champion at rugby and netball, a huge achievement against the Essex selective schools. A rugby academy attracts talented players to the sixth form. Pupils have competed nationally at sports ranging from netball to skiing and their team shirts are displayed proudly alongside photos and trophies. 'If you're good at something we'll encourage you and give you recognition,' said a deputy. 'Paul is very good at reinforcing our successes and using them to motivate pupils.'

A plush leisure centre includes a sports hall and fitness suite, open to the local community outside school hours. There are also tennis and netball courts and a large playing field which includes an all-weather pitch. Numerous sports clubs before, during and after school, and even on Saturday mornings, range from hockey to dance to girls' boxing.

The girls' and boys' choirs performed movingly in assembly during our visit – the boys' choir was recently voted best in the borough and one pupil has starred in a West End musical. Instrumental lessons are free, and there's an orchestra and a jazz group. Sixty pupils are studying for music GCSE and a few each year move on to music technology A level. The school puts on major performances of eg Oliver! and High School Musical. Plenty of high-quality art displayed around the school and DT is

another popular option at GCSE. The school debating team recently won 'best delegation' at a Model UN conference.

School trips range from French exchanges to sports trips to Canada and Barbados and a conservation expedition to Egypt. Few parents could afford to pay for these trips, so the school raises funds from eg the Worshipful Company of Chartered Surveyors, and children fundraise enthusiastically too. 'We believe these trips are vitally important to our children's development, and our wonderful staff will always go the extra mile to make sure they happen.'

Background and atmosphere: This is a huge, split-site school, named after local legend Bob Clack, who was mayor from 1940 to 1942. The lower school site, which houses years 7 and 8 and most of year 9, opened in 1935, the upper school buildings, half a mile away, in 1953. The tower blocks of the Becontree Estate – one of the largest in England – bear down on the school like a fortress. It is one of the most deprived areas of the country and has been a BNP stronghold. Staff and pupils alike express delight that the BNP was routed in a recent and credit the school with considerable influence. 'The school is the centre of the community.' 'You can't be racist here.'

The buildings range from shabby prefabs put up 'temporarily' in the '40s to the bright new science block and the media block with facilities for drama, music and media studies, as well as the pristine beauty salon. There are plentiful computers and whiteboards, but the planned rebuild now seems to be receding into the far distance as government funds are cut. However, a £3 million expansion of the lower school site has seen 18 new classrooms.

The school was the highest placed education establishment in a Sunday Times Best Hundred Companies to Work For list and winner in the medium-sized company section. It also came first for the quality of its leadership, for personal growth and for its employees' pride in working there.

Pastoral care and discipline: This is one of the smartest and most ordered schools we have ever visited. Children are immaculate in blazers and ties, orderly in corridors and attentive in lessons. 'People know not to mess about,' say pupils. 'But it's all fair – punishments are fair. The rules are good ones.' The school works on a combination of iron discipline and plenty of praise. There are colours for sport, music and performing arts. During the assembly we attended large numbers of children lined up to receive merit awards. They approve of their uniform. 'It makes you feel proud to wear our uniform, when you see pupils from other schools prancing around in polo shirts and trainers.'

Children feel very safe here. 'If something happens here they get straight on top of it. This school really does hate bullying – they don't tolerate it.' There's a close bond between pupils and teachers. 'They're always really cheerful. They'll make a joke out of things if they can. And they treat us like grown-ups. They respect our feelings.' Staff are stationed in corridors between lessons and outside the school when pupils leave at the end of the day. No-one below sixth form is allowed out at lunchtime. Sir Paul tours classrooms daily, greeting pupils with words of praise or good-natured censure.

The pupil referral unit handles children who have disrupted lessons, breached the uniform code, started a fight or played truant. 'We get in quickly – we're proactive – and so we've only had two permanent exclusions in the last 10 years.'

Pupils and parents: Largely from the surrounding estates, though proximity to the school puts a premium on the prices of the few houses for sale in the area. Large numbers of single parent families and those with several generations of unemployment. The school employs a parental adviser who visits families under stress and helps with housing, clothing and food allowances. Around 20 per cent Afro-Caribbean families, the rest mostly white working class: Robert Clack was the only London school on Ofsted's 'excelling against the odds' list with a preponderance of children from such typically under-achieving backgrounds

Entrance: Takes 300 children into year 7 but there are over 200 appeals every year, so the intake invariably increases. Looked-after children get priority, as do those with special educational needs, then by distance from the upper school site – generally within a mile or so. Some 2,000 applications for the 300 places. Large numbers from other schools join the sixth form.

Exit: About 70 per cent of pupils move up to the sixth form, up from around 20 per cent 10 years ago. Two students off with scholarships to study for A levels at Eton recently. Excellent careers advice and encouragement to aim high. The school has links with Oxford, Cambridge, Essex, York and east London universities, with visiting speakers, university visits and summer schools. One to Oxbridge, one to Princeton in 2015.

Remarks: Outstandingly successful comprehensive in one of the most deprived areas of the country. Excellent leadership by a tireless head has transformed a failing school into one that is a source of pride for staff, parents and pupils. 'This school gets you ready for the future,' said a pupil.

Seven Kings High School

Ley Street, Ilford, Essex IG2 7BT

State • Pupils: 1,400 pupils • Ages: 11–18 • Sixth form pupils: 480

Tel: 020 8554 8935

Email: enquiries@skhs.net
Website: www.skhs.net

6

Head Teacher: Since 2008, Ms Tracy Smith BA PGCE (40s). Educated at St Martin's School, Brentwood. Read history and sociology at Warwick, PGCE at Goldsmith's College, London, then taught at Barking Abbey School for seven years. Moved to Seven Kings as head of sixth form in 1995, then deputy to former head Sir Alan Steer, and a key player in the team which transformed this east London school into one of the country's most successful comprehensives. Before taking over the headship, she led a project on Assessment for Learning carried out by King's College, Cambridge and the Institute of Education and continues to sit on a number of influential committees, including the SSAT London Headteachers' Steering Group. Energetic, level-headed and good-humoured, she's undoubtedly a safe pair of hands to keep this school top of the form. Married with two teenage children. A keen West Ham supporter, she spends down time watching football, going to the theatre, hill walking and travelling.

Academic matters: If academic matters are uppermost in your schooling choice, then you have very little to fret about at Seven Kings. Despite its 'very average' intake, Seven Kings seems to sail effortlessly to the top of the league tables. Seventy-two

per cent of GCSE candidates in 2015 achieved 5+ A*-C grades including English and maths; over 29 per cent of grades were A*/A. The hugely oversubscribed sixth form produced equally dazzling results – 66 per cent A*/B grades and nearly 37 per cent A*/A. Teaching is vibrant and committed – 'the quality of the teaching manages to challenge every student,' said one parent – and teacher-pupil relationships strong. 'Teachers know you well and know how you are feeling,' said one boy. 'You can ask them anything.'

'Students now say science is their favourite subject,' says the head. 'There are about 50 experiments going on a day'

Success is down to monitoring, tracking and a can-do approach, and certainly no one here gets lost at the back. 'You won't find a pupil we haven't spoken to in the past three weeks about their learning,' says the head. 'They don't give us grades, they give us comments,' said one student. 'They tell you what you can do to improve and what you've already done well. They know what you need to do to get better.' Every student is also given two one-to-one interviews about academic progress. 'We track, interview and talk.' 'This isn't an exam factory,' says the head, 'but we do know the syllabus and the exam requirements.' And not only can they distinguish their Pre-Us from their A levels, they know how to prioritise a UCAS form, with a large chunk of the high-powered sixth form going on to top universities.

Three languages on offer – French, Spanish and Mandarin – with well over half the students studying at least one language to GCSE. Science newly energised by a 'skills-based' approach, and bangs and smells part of the fabric of school life. 'Students now say science is their favourite subject,' says the head. 'There are about 50 experiments going on a day.' After-school clubs include the academic as well as the just for fun, providing support with homework and coursework.

Games, options, the arts: Art, DT and PE all highly valued and popular. 'Our kids do two hours PE a week and even on days when they don't have sport, we make sure they get off their bottoms,' says the deputy. Football, cricket, netball, rugby, running and athletics all core to the curriculum. One basketball superstar recently won a scholarship to a top US university. Music and drama are popular options with plenty on offer for aspiring performers. Plenty of other extracurricular activities are available for spiritual, social and cultural nourishment such as Amnesty International, chess, model airplanes, astronomy and a film club.

Background and atmosphere: The school began life as a girls' grammar in the 1930s, and some remaining original features give a feel of the inter-war years, with an expansive spread of low rise brick buildings and a Betjemanesque assembly hall ideal for listening to the clock ticking away the exam minutes. Inside the tall-windowed classrooms, the focus is on learning, helped by full range of thoroughly modern additions, from a new lecture theatre and a spacious, glass entrance hall to a wheelchair park and interactive whiteboards. The motto is 'friendship, excellence, opportunity,' which most pupils and parents believe the school more than delivers. 'The kids know we really care about them,' says the head. Seven Kings is particularly noted for its SEN provision and has a national reputation as a centre of excellence for disabled children. As well as the specially adapted entrance and well-equipped medical centre, classrooms are accessible by wheelchair and there is well-staffed highly-skilled SEN department.

Pastoral care and discipline: Seven Kings serves a neighbourhood that is certainly on the less affluent side of the rich-poor divide, with the social problems and deprivation typical of many parts of urban London. But despite its relatively stark surrounding streets, the school itself is a haven of purposeful calm. Discipline is assumed, corridors are quiet, classes orderly. That's not to say, of course, that every child's an angel. 'We have 1,500 hormonal kids,' says the head. 'Of course we have discipline problems.' But few that aren't sorted out rapidly. 'We haven't excluded anyone permanently since I've been head.' Short sharp shocks for fighting or cheeking the teacher. 'Expectations are very clear, as are sanctions, but we try to apply them sensitively. This isn't a zero-tolerance environment.' Positive peer pressure is a definite help keeping potential bad boys on the straight and narrow. 'Some kids are definitely from challenging homes and we do our best to keep them going.' No-one from years 7-11 let off-site at breaks or lunchtimes. Proactive pastoral care and timetabling used constructively. 'How you timetable the school day has a massive impact on behaviour,' says the deputy.

Pupils and parents: This is a neighbourhood comprehensive and more than three-quarters of the pupils come from Indian, Pakistani or Bangladeshi backgrounds. Parents here want their children to do well and give their full backing to the education on offer, with nearly all seats filled at parents' evenings. They aren't, however, a cake-baking, raffle-holding crowd and the school has no PTA. The kids themselves support their parents' aspirations, work hard and behave well. 'The kids are bright and ambitious,' says the head.

Entrance: The school is extremely popular and oversubscribed with 1,800 eager candidates queuing for the 180 year 7 places and a waiting list well into the hundreds. 'Fortunately, that's all done by the local authority,' says the head. Strict catchment rules apply, though those with statements automatically go to the top of the admissions ladder. Around 80 per cent go through to the sixth form, which attracts a massive number of outside applications every year – those successful have predicted GCSE grades that meet the entrance criteria for their chosen A level subjects.

The Seven Kings Primary School opened in September 2015 with 120 reception children. The school will gradually become an all through school.

Exit: Around half to Russell Group universities; rest to other good universities or destinations such as internships in the City.

Remarks: An inspiring place, where any parent could feel confident that their child's needs will be met and where every child will reach or exceed expectations.

Sir John Cass Foundation and Redcoat Church of England Secondary School

Stepney Way, London E1 0RH

State • Pupils: 1,582 • Ages: 11–19 • Sixth form pupils: 605 • C of E

Tel: 020 7790 6712

Email: info@sjcr.net
Website: www.sjcr.net

9

Headteacher: Since 1995, Mr Haydn Evans (60s), who arrived in Stepney after deputy headships in Tonbridge and, briefly, Bridgend. His then school-age children failed to settle in Wales, and he returned happily to commute in from Kent to the headship of this inner-city church school. Praised as a strong, determined, strategic thinker and very successful head ('exemplary', said Ofsted), he has overseen the opening of the sixth form and the upward trajectory of the whole school, transforming it from an under-subscribed comprehensive with exam results on the minimal side to one with over 1,200 applicants for 180 places.

A hands-on head, he teaches chemistry to A level and is frequently out and about in the school with other senior managers, helping to police the comings and goings between lessons as 1,600 pupils move round a school built for 800. 'We act as an unobtrusive presence – we rarely have to say or do anything.'

Awarded a CBE for services to education in the 2014 New Years Honours List.

Academic matters: Consistently near the top of the value-added tables and has three times been ranked the most improved school in the country. Most pupils come in with lower than average achievement, but in 2015, 83 per cent got 5+ A*-C grades at GCSE including English and maths (31 per cent A*/A). They come from a huge range of primaries and many have difficult home lives. 'Our first focus is on behaviour, on creating a climate for learning. Then we engage them with exciting teaching.'

A recent Ofsted report, which rated the school 'outstanding', praised its very high expectations of all pupils. However, it has recently been downgraded to inadequate, largely over concerns about a sixth form Islamic society, with fears of students becoming radicalised online. New year 7s are tested and placed in sets for maths, English, science and RE. These are fluid and there's plenty of scope to move up as one's English improves or down should the maths start to prove tricky. There are vocational as well as academic courses at KS4, for example in science and IT. The school keeps a close eye on pupils' progress, targeting those who need extra help to ensure that everyone gets the grades they need to move on to the next stage. 'They have very high aspirations for my daughter,' said a parent. 'They push the children very hard to succeed.'

It is a specialist language college and everyone studies two languages for the first three years, from a choice of French, Spanish and Bengali, continuing at least one to GCSE. There is also a choice of 11 languages in twilight classes (for parents as well as pupils), and many pupils take a GCSE in their own native language before year 11. Many go on French or Spanish exchanges. The school has links with an instituto in rural Spain, and children who have rarely left the East End of London have found themselves travelling to school by horse and cart.

It also has a business and enterprise specialism and good links with Canary Wharf and City firms, with some offering work placements, scholarships to cover university fees and jobs after graduation to talented students. Sixth form business studies students can have mentoring from business partners, visits and seminars, lectures and summer internships. One pupil recently spent the summer in America, having won a coveted place on a student leadership programme.

The large sixth form, with some 600 pupils, has its own new centre, including a library, IT suite, common rooms and a popular café. It offers

The school has links with an instituto in rural Spain, and children who have rarely left the East End of London have found themselves travelling to school by horse and cart

a variety of vocational courses alongside A levels and GCSE retakes. Many students come in from elsewhere to join those moving up, and quite a few have relatively low qualifications. Some start with intermediate level courses then move up to higher levels en route to university. Science and maths A levels are particularly popular and successful, alongside psychology, RE and sociology. In 2015, 40 per cent A*-B; 17 per cent A*/A.

About 10 per cent of pupils have some kind of special need. 'We have an elaborate academic support team. The governors have decided to invest heavily in this and it is a very worthwhile investment.' Gifted and talented pupils are also identified for extra support. Learning mentors and assistants work through teachers and directly with pupils, helping to track their progress and ensure they know what they need to do to improve. There are regular extension and catch-up classes. Staff recruitment is not a problem, with over 60 applicants for a recent RE vacancy. 'We have a high profile and we attract high quality applicants.'

Games, options, the arts: Sports facilities include a swimming pool (everyone learns to swim by the end of their first term) and a sports hall with space for basketball, badminton, football and cricket. Football and basketball teams play enthusiastic and successful matches against other schools. Table tennis, boxing and fencing are also on the agenda. A level sports science students coach younger pupils.

Actors perform at the Mile End Theatre and the steel band has played at the Albert Hall. Guitar club and a gospel choir, and many pupils have individual music lessons. Trips to operas and musicals. A school ski trip in the Easter holidays, D of E, ice skating, rock climbing and canoeing trips. Sixth formers organise societies, including Christian Union and Muslim Students' Society.

Background and atmosphere: Formed in 1964 by the governing body of Red Coat School (established in 1714 for boys born within Mile End Old Town) and the governors of the Sir John Cass Foundation (a charity set up in 1710 by Sir John Cass for poor children in the East End of London). The school is owned by the Foundation, one of London's oldest educational charities, and Founder's Day in St Botolph-without-Aldgate church is one of the

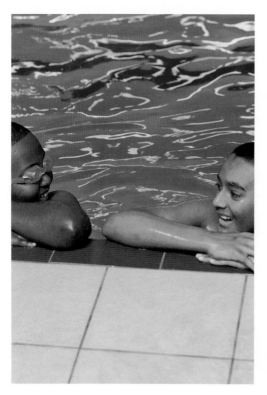

highlights of the school year. Its present site, with its pleasant red-brick buildings, dates from 1965. It is right in the middle of the East End but in a deceptively rural-seeming setting with a city farm opposite, a park next door and the school church and its tranquil graveyard beyond.

The school has been refurbished to include up-to-date science labs and learning centres stocked with computers. These are open before and after school and on Saturday mornings, with learning mentors around to help. Many pupils have no computer at home, nor quiet space in which to do homework. The great hall with stage and balcony doubles as a lecture theatre and can accommodate the entire school for assemblies. 'These are important for setting the behaviour tone for the school.' Lower school pupils wear a traditional uniform including a blazer, which becomes more informal higher up the school. Honours boards line the reception area. Although this is a C of E school, the vast majority of pupils are Muslims and they have their own prayer room.

Pastoral care and discipline: An orderly atmosphere is central to the ethos of the school. 'Security and mutual respect are very high priority. First of all we make them feel secure and safe, then we start to cultivate respect for all. A feeder primary school may be less traditional than we are but we're confident that when they come here we'll get them into our ethos by the end of the first half term.' The atmosphere is indeed calm and orderly, with some exuberance in the corridors between lessons but quiet concentration in the classrooms. There are CCTV cameras throughout, which, say staff, discourage vandalism and add to students' sense of security. Staff check on the destinations of those wandering the corridors between lessons.

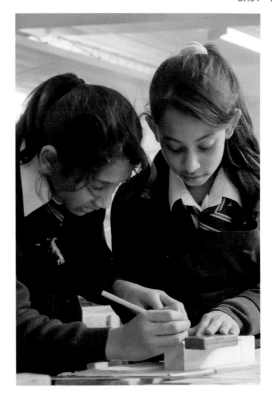

Lower school pupils wear a traditional uniform including a blazer, which becomes more informal higher up the school

By all accounts very little racial tension and very few exclusions. 'We do very occasionally have some challenging behaviour but it does not threaten the learning environment. We try hard not to exclude if we can possibly avoid it.' Two qualified counsellors on the staff. 'It's a very happy school,' said a parent, 'but the kids are expected to knuckle down and achieve.'

The most recent Ofsted visit resulted in a downgrade to inadequate, largely due the school's failure to monitor a sixth form Islamic society. In particular, it was criticised over a Facebook site set up by the society that contained links to hardline Islamist preachers — a move that could have made pupils vulnerable to radicalisation, it is claimed. The report also criticised separate entrances, playground and common rooms for boys and girls. Local educators accused Ofsted of over-reacting. After an interim visit Ofsted said: 'School leaders have taken rapid action to address the concerns raised'.

Pupils and parents: About two-thirds of the pupils are Bangladeshi, the rest from a variety of ethnic minorities, including many Somali refugees. Parents mostly very supportive of the school and its high expectations for their children. They join in maths workshops and twilight language classes and become involved in the numerous community projects. Pupils form strong peer groups. 'There's a very strong ethos of care for one another,' said a parent.

Entrance: Some 1,200 applicants for 180 places. Everyone is placed in one of four ability bands, assessed by the standard Tower Hamlets primary school test, with equal numbers of places offered from each band. This is a C of E school, so it does allocate a minority of places to committed Christians. Thirty-six places go to worshippers in a recognised Christian church, with looked-after children, social and medical needs, living in one of the listed parishes and then siblings in order of priority. The other 144 places have a similar priority order, but 20 are offered to first-born children. Families in the area tend to be large and siblings would otherwise monopolise the intake. Distance from the school is the tie-break.

The sixth form is also highly over-subscribed, with over 1,000 applicants for 300 outside places. Most advanced level courses require five or more A*-C grades at GCSE including English and maths, with some higher stipulations eg an A in maths for maths or further maths A level. But those with lesser qualifications can take lower level courses, and the majority of pupils from year 11 go through to the sixth form.

Exit: Those who leave after GCSEs – about 10 per cent of year 11s – mostly go on to another sixth form or straight into a job. All year 13 leavers for the past three years – and some of these may have spent several years in the sixth form improving

their qualifications – have gone straight to university. For social and cultural reasons, the vast majority choose London universities, but some venture further afield. Has had several successful Oxbridge candidates. 'I am confident that once they start coming back to tell our students about it we'll have more applicants.' Some students return to the school as teachers or learning mentors.

Remarks: A beacon of excellence in a deprived area of London, which takes in students with low levels of attainment and sends the majority off to university with commendable exam results. A strong head and committed staff insist on good behaviour, provide expert teaching and inspire high aspirations. 'It's gone from strength to strength,' said a parent. 'It's a great school.'

The Ofsted report revealed some serious shortcomings, particularly in monitoring, but we believe that the school is capable of and willing to set things right rapidly.

Sir William Burrough Primary School

Salmon Lane, London E14 7PQ

State • Pupils: 375 • Ages: 3–11

Tel: 020 7987 2147

Email: admin@sirwilliamburrough.
towerhamlets.sch.uk
Website: sirwilliamburrough.net

10

Headteacher: Since 1995, Mrs Avril Newman BEd (60s), who was educated at Hendon County Grammar School and has a first class degree in

education from Goldsmith's. She has spent her entire career in east London primary schools and is a National Leader of Education and a JP. A slight

This is an oasis of colour and calm. Inside the tall Victorian building, brightly painted walls form a background to swathes of fabric, flowers, displays of work and photos of outings

and engaging lady, married with two grown-up children, she is viewed by Ofsted as 'inspirational' and an 'outstandingly good leader.'

Together with her highly experienced leadership team, she is evidently the driving force behind the school's immense success. She believes that every child must aspire to read, write and calculate to the highest possible standards and insists on formal skills-based programmes for the three Rs.

Entrance: The usual priorities: special needs, siblings, then distance, which is not very far. This is a massively oversubscribed school in a highly populated urban area.

Exit: To a variety of local state secondaries; occasionally children go off to eg City Boys or Girls, sometimes on scholarships.

Remarks: Not far off the A13 Commercial Road, overshadowed by building sites, this is an oasis of colour and calm. Inside the tall Victorian building, brightly painted walls form a background to swathes of fabric, flowers, displays of work and photos of outings, with children in red, blue, green or yellow sweatshirts.

The school has an excellent mix of cultures and ethnicities. Small majority of the pupils are of Bangladeshi heritage, others are of Somalian, Eastern European and indigenous white British background. All are expected to do well, and they do. 'We do not wish to take deprivation, culture, class or gender into account,' says the school. 'We're in the business of teaching and learning and the children do that for seven years here. We're ferocious about them learning to read, write and calculate – no-one falls through the net. Unless they have serious problems, we guarantee that they will meet or exceed government expectations.'

The school uses synthetic phonics to teach reading – 'they all learn very quickly and early.' As children become more proficient, they use an online accelerated reader system which monitors their progress, suggests books to read, sets quizzes and awards prizes. Maths is also taught by an online system: 'they always know what they need to learn next. They're not waiting for the teacher to hand out the next bit of learning.' Children requested, and received, a system that allows them to assess themselves and take time to fill in any gaps. They can also compete against children from other countries. As a result, over 90 per cent reach the expected level 4 in year 6 Sats, and a large proportion – more than half – reach level 5. A small number reach level 6.

However, this emphasis on the basics does not preclude an exciting, creative curriculum with a global dimension. Sir William Burrough was one of the first state primaries in the country to adopt the International Primary Curriculum (IPC). Originally developed for international schools run by petrol giant Shell, the IPC focuses on cross-curricular topics such as fashion, chocolate or treasure. There's an emphasis on hands-on learning with huge numbers of trips out: children studying treasure start with a treasure hunt round the school then go off to the Tower of London to see the crown jewels. Year 6s learning about WW2 have an interactive show about an evacuee, delivered by an actor, and visit the Britain at War Experience at nearby London Bridge. Children Skype their peers in South Korea – 'they want our creativity, we want their maths results' – and some have travelled to Rome and Washington on exchange trips. The IPC and the British Council send many foreign visitors, and staff travel all over the world to see how other IPC schools operate. 'We're always scanning the horizon for better ideas.'

The children's experiences are well-documented: they make iMovies, animations and multi-media presentations as well as printing books of photos. 'Even the year 3s can edit their own presentations.' A room full of Apple Mac computers, plus plenty of laptops, are testimony to the school's profitable partnerships with several City firms, which also send in reading partners and chess mentors. The school business manager is a skilled fundraiser, providing welcome extra funding for playground equipment, sports coaches, visiting artists, actors and storytellers.

There's an emphasis on hands-on learning with huge numbers of trips out: children studying treasure start with a treasure hunt round the school then go off to the Tower of London to see the crown jewels

The school's catch-phrase is 'you can do it'. 'If you can't do something you always keep trying,' say pupils. 'We're very independent and we never give up.' Pupils help to staff the reception desk and show round international visitors. The debating team has won competitions across London, and many pupils get merit or distinction in English Speaking Board assessments. When we visited, year 6 were rehearsing for a performance of Joseph and the Amazing Technicolour Dreamcoat. Assembly, which involves plenty of vigorous singing, happens at the end of the day. 'It harnesses their collective energy and sends them home feeling good about the day.'

The choreographer-in-residence organises spectacular dance displays; the 70-strong choir makes many public performances. Everyone plays the recorder. The three playgrounds include a wooded area where the children build camps and play on the jungle gym, and an all-purpose sports pitch. There are not many opportunities for inter-school matches, but plenty of sport: the cricket team has played at

Lords, they swim at Mile End Leisure Centre and skate at Canary Wharf, play handball, baseball, hockey and rounders. Year 5 has a challenging outdoor pursuits week. After-school clubs include wide variety of sports, yoga, street dance, animation, cookery, chess, sailing, Spanish and lots more.

The school has a strong relationship with the local community. 'We never stop asking the question: how can we do things better? We have regular parents' forums, and listen and act on their excellent suggestions. Parents help run the toddlers' group, and organise an opening doors programme of families meeting in each other's homes which creates strong bonds across different ethnic groups.' The children are doing this from the moment they start. 'We all get along with each other,' they say. 'We have brilliant friendships.' 'If Martin Luther King came along to our school today he would think to himself: my dream has come true.'

Snaresbrook Preparatory School

75 Woodford Road, South Woodford, London E18 2EA

Tel: 020 8989 2394

Independent • Pupils: 165 • Ages: 3–11 • Fees: up to £10,410 pa

Email: office@snaresbrookprep.org
Website: www.snaresbrookprep.org

Head: Since 2013, Mr Christopher Curl MA BEd TEFL, studied English and drama at Exeter. Taught in a mixture of prep and senior schools, including his own, King's Canterbury. Has been boarding housemaster, head of English and drama, i/c co-curricular activities. Third headship – chose this

school because of its size, family atmosphere and autonomy. Active and involved governors – including some of the original founding family – give him scope to shape the school. They also give lots of practical support, from HR to decorating. 'On some other boards you see some three times a year for large lunches and no one knows who they are,' says the head.

He aims to 'make learning more interesting' while 'trying not to fiddle with everything', especially since the school already has an outstanding report. Parents think he strikes a good balance, especially in the difficult role of following 'a much-loved, very long-standing incumbent'. One said, 'He is doing a great job of listening to parents and making positive changes.' Parents describe him as a 'very visible', 'open, approachable', and a 'supremely capable steward' who 'genuinely cares about the school'.

He is hands on, helping with drama and musical productions, at the gate before and after school, and teaching. Every Monday he starts with year 6 and works his way down to the nursery, teaching the older ones current affairs and conducting story time sessions with younger pupils. He likes to avoid being 'this remote head who sits in an office'.

Head also provides weekly lunch time cover for his secretary, so he 'gets to see the front of the organisation, what she is dealing with, what's happening, who comes in, what people are saying'. He thinks that 'if as a head you stop doing the kinds of things other members of staff are asked to do, you become out of touch'.

Entrance: Most come in at nursery and go though to year 6. There is a low-key family interview with the head; sibling priority. Places higher up subject to a family interview and in-class assessment. Pupils come from various nurseries in the local area, from Canary Wharf and Stratford out to Epping, Woodford Green, Romford and Loughton, and beyond.

Exit: Many go on to win scholarships to eg City of London, Forest, Chigwell, St Edmund's Ware and Bancroft's. Others go off to grammars like Woodford County High and Ilford County High.

There is a huge blackboard where they chalk to their heart's content and above it a huge, colourful mural painted by year 6s

Remarks: Small size and family atmosphere mean pupils settle in quickly. 'You don't have to be scared to talk to a year 6 because everyone knows each other,' a pupil said. One parent said that during her son's first year at the school he has 'waved to and greeted any older pupil we met in the street. And the bigger kids have invariably waved back.'

The main school is set in a 1930s Victorian house and was managed by the same family for 50 years. Its small, quaint classrooms are close together and the corridors are dainty, but it is an intimate rather than cramped feel. The nursery and reception are housed in a separate, purpose-built building overlooking a small playground, with the hall and a multi-purpose library room on the other side of the playground. Beyond that is a covered sensory garden, designed and constructed by an architect governor. The children grow plants here, and experiment with different climates and seasons. There is a huge blackboard where they chalk to their heart's content and above it a huge, colourful mural painted by year 6s.

The governors, as mentioned, are very much involved in everyday school life, often to be seen popping in and out. They are helping to extend the hall to create more storage space, they have helped decorate the staff room and to build the new canopied decking area outside the nursery so pupils can enjoy year round outdoor play free of leaves and rain. 'They are very sensitive to the needs of the staff and children,' said the head.

Single form entry, with class sizes of roughly 24 in the infants and 18 in the juniors, and plenty of classroom assistants. 'It is mixed ability here,' says the head. 'What is exciting is seeing children who didn't come in as high fliers leave having made massive progress.' Most extra support for those with learning difficulties is provided in class, with a part-time specialist available as required.

French from nursery, optional German and Spanish, year 6 learn Latin and also embark on self-directed projects. Lots of investment in IT. We saw year 5 listening to a live commentary on an Arsenal v Southampton match and learning how to extract key information from a database to write up their news reports.

The school adventure service challenge is 'like a mini Duke of Edinburgh... we do camping, rowing, bird watching, cooking and it's lots of fun,' say pupils. Years 4 and 5 are excited about the annual trip to France where they visit a chocolate factory in Boulogne (they like this better than the snail farm). Whilst in France they spend time with penfriends and complete a shopping task in French, although some confess they have found ways around this: 'Luckily the lady that was serving us knew English'. Year 5 has a history trip to York and year 6 an end of year trip to Shropshire.

Before and after-school clubs include the usual range of sports plus country and maypole dancing, scooter club, creative writing, art club and knitting. Popular sports are football and netball, and considering how small the school is, they do well: 'Once we played in a tournament and there were two Snaresbrook teams in the football play-off and they ended up playing each other,' a pupil said with pride. There are no fields here so pupils take a minibus to Redbridge Sports Centre and Ashton playing fields.

One parent commented: 'I feel the school works hard to optimise the use of space available.' At breaktimes a daily games timetable saves the tiny playground from being dominated by football (football still an option at lunchtime when playtimes are staggered) and the children can try out a different game each day. 'Our new games teacher

Years 4 and 5 are excited about the annual trip to France where they visit a chocolate factory in Boulogne (they like this better than the snail farm). Whilst in France they spend time with penfriends and complete a shopping task in French

came up with the idea,' said a pupil. It was inspired by Olympics sports such as handball, dodgeball and basketball. Most of the children take part and girls and boys play together. Other activities are on offer, too – they can read, do art, play table tennis. The head says: 'In my last school we had acres and

acres of green grass and the children didn't use it as well. Here they are much more appreciative, and the lack of space can be an advantage rather than a disadvantage.'

When we visited, years 1 and 2 were in the hall preparing for a dress rehearsal of Rise and Shine.

Pupils help inside school too. A year 6 pupil said of the nursery: 'We come in our free time and help the children and teachers with projects. It's also fun for us'

'All have a part to play in the production,' said their teacher. The school tries to offer a taste of a wide range of drama and music, and each class gets a chance to perform. 'Lots of parents come to see the productions whether they have children in that year group or not.' Around 20 per cent of children learn to play the recorder, violin or flute.

House system gives everyone a chance to shine in different areas. 'Browns usually win on sports day, blues dominate swimming, yellows are good at choir singing and pancake races,' a pupil told us, 'so we each have our fair share of glory'. The many charitable and fundraising activities include readathons, movie nights to raise funds for Redbridge Night Shelter, sports events for the NSPCC and Great Ormond Street and harvest collections for the British Red Cross. Year 4 girls created a magazine, 'packed with quizzes, gossip and pictures. They made £61 by selling it to everyone'.

Pupils help inside school too. A year 6 pupil said of the nursery: 'We come in our free time and help the children and teachers with projects. It's also fun for us as this was our room when we were in the nursery.' It invokes a sense of service: 'This morning I was holding the door for a parent and I heard one of the year 4s say, "Dad, when I'm in year 6 I will be able to hold the door, I will say good morning to everyone".'

Support is good, say parents, with teachers always willing to discuss and address problems. Plenty of incentives and rewards for doing well, including Good Marks assemblies and commendation awards. The merit board includes an award to teachers for 'making a good start on the return after holidays'.

A new system of online live reports, with up-to-date comments from teachers that parents can access at any time, has replaced yearly written reports. The plan is to produce a detailed picture of how each child learns and how they are progressing.

Very active parents' association – '40 donations for the bake sale the other day', said a member – with an impressive participation rate considering that many, if not most, families have two working parents. Hotly-contested annual pancake race involves children, staff and parents. After examining video evidence following one race, the head sent out an urgent email saying parents had in fact lost and parents retorted: 'Mr Curl, wait till next year.'

Woodford County High School

High Road, Woodford Green, Essex IG8 9LA

State • Pupils: 887 • Ages: 11–18 • Sixth form pupils: 280

Tel: 020 8504 0611

Email: head@woodford.redbridge.sch.uk
Website: www.woodford.redbridge.sch.uk

8

Headteacher: Since 2010, Ms Jo Pomeroy (40s), MA in English language and literature (St Andrews), BEd (Open), NPQH. Spent two years in a comprehensive in rural Scotland before going to work in France at a mixed grammar school for three years. It was at this high achieving international school that she became aware of 'what can be achieved', 'what is possible' and 'what bright students are capable of if they are given enough challenge,' she says. So the aim here 'is for students always to be working just beyond what they are comfortable with'. Back in the UK she spent another three years working in a comprehensive school with strong bias towards European languages and at that point 'got interested in management, in getting into position where you could make a bigger change'. Sure enough, at her next appointment at a girls' grammar in Surrey, where she spent 16 years, she eventually became deputy head. 'There is enormous satisfaction in seeing incrementally what can be achieved in one place,' she says. Academic life at Woodford is very much influenced by this passion for great leadership as well as head's English teaching background. 'What excites me the most is working from what you may be able to stimulate in your own life and career and then being able to share that with students so that they can enjoy challenges themselves.'

Academic matters: Best results in Redbridge. These are bright girls taught by committed teachers, a third of whom have been here for over 10 years. As a selective school (there are only some four students with SEN), it has maintained an outstanding record

These days the girls focus their design skills in technology, where they recently emerged winners of the National Technology Design Prize

of achievement, with 75 per cent A*/A grades at GCSE in 2015. And these stats despite most students – in fact well over half of the school population – speaking English as a second language. 'The joy of being in a school like this is that it is self-propagating: when students come in and they see other students valuing learning and success, and working hard on collaborative projects, it really affects everything else they do.'

This school models leadership extremely well. It has an impressive mentoring structure in place where older pupils mentor younger ones. There are literacy mentors who provide targeted additional support for year 7s where needed, and this 'sustained focus on academic literacy across the curriculum has been highly successful'. Head says, 'I have an interest in a great many subjects and I think the joy of English being my subject is that it takes you into everything, history, philosophy, art and music, and it is wonderful being able to investigate and enjoy literature and other languages as well.' These pupils have the opportunity to be mentored in other subjects as well, by sixth formers who relish the opportunity to 'give something back', though 'teachers still keep a close eye...'

In some classrooms desks are arranged to encourage interaction between students, not only with teachers. In the English department, year 7s are introduced to Shakespeare texts usually reserved for later years and invited to write an essay

on what they have learnt. They also have lots of opportunity to visit theatres. Pupils take two languages from year 7 (French and either German or Latin). English, languages and science are all strong here and around 87 per cent of girls take triple science GCSE. Lots of information and support provided to both students and parents on choosing options. GCSE computing now offered.

In the sixth form, where roughly a quarter of students come from other schools, Woodford maintains good A level results with 76 per cent A*/B grades, 49 per cent A*/A, in 2015, with students off to Oxford and Cambridge and on to medical careers. Academic mentoring and university preparation at sixth form, and guidance to final transition here is second to none, or in one parent's words, 'really very strong'.

Games, options, the arts: Head's commitment to leading a school that offers plenty of opportunity to be stretched is evident across the whole curriculum. Reasonable range of games on offer – badminton, athletics, netball, rounders, gymnastics and dance – and girls can pursue their interest in multi-cultural dance options such as Bhangra, African and street dance. Games either take place outside on the field and tennis courts or indoors in the newly built Lottery funded sports hall, which looks gorgeously fresh next to the main school building, already well over 100 years old when it opened as a school in 1919. Outdoor Greek theatre recently restored. The girls do well at games; they recently reached the UK badminton national finals, and they seem willing to try their best at everything, keen or not: 'Sport, I'm not good at, but it's a popular subject.'

Pupils speak highly of the sports leadership qualification offered in years 10 and 11: 'It gives you skills in being responsible, listening skills and classroom theory. We learn to create lesson plans.' Another said it 'opens us up to new areas; we realise there is more to our skill set and that motivates and opens us up to aim higher'. D of E also offered.

School does well at art and has had pupils featured in a Saatchi Exhibition. Major drama event each term as well as an annual musical (most recently, Oliver!) plus a summer production run by teachers and a spring production organised by students. A beautiful patchwork tapestry displayed under glass in the technology department harks back to the days when the school offered textiles. These days the girls focus their design skills in technology, where they recently emerged winners of the National Technology Design Prize.

Instrumental and vocal lessons at all levels on offer, though most who learn do so out of school. Many are involved in one of a large number of ensembles and clubs: guitar, singing, Carnatic music. There is a large junior choir and band, a folk group, a brass project (all year 8 pupils learn a brass instrument), woodwind ensemble, and a staff choir too. Girls have also participated in Redbridge Choral Festival at the Royal Albert Hall.

Lots of trips to support lessons and extracurricular activities, including expeditions to eg Ghana, Morocco, Indonesia, China, Cambodia. Annual geography trip to Iceland.

Sixth form enrichment programme includes dance, cookery, computing, BSL sign language, art, sports and an extended period of voluntary service. Girls have the opportunity to complete the advanced extension award. Older students preside over all manner of different extracurricular opportunities, such as talks, clubs and charity events, and there is a society for everything – even to discuss current affairs. 'We have house competitions,' head says, 'and sometimes there can be more drama off stage than on stage.' But because there is no adult intervention the girls learn to work together and develop great teamwork skills – 'a real success and selling point of the school.' All comes good in the end, as evidenced by the year 11-led assembly held on the morning of our visit. In their well-structured presentation the girls demonstrated what they had learnt about self, learning and approaching life, showing extraordinary wisdom and the ability to work together. Head says, 'They listen to each other very well, and coming up the school younger students see this and that sets their aspirations.'

'We have house competitions,' head says, 'and sometimes there can be more drama off stage than on stage'

Background and atmosphere: Main building dates from 1768 when it was built as the country manor home of the Highams; school opened here in 1919, and its venerable features lend an atmosphere of tradition – from the beautiful open air Greek theatre that stands in the grounds near to the tennis courts, to the hymnals still used in assemblies – 'I'm not a Christian but I enjoy it', a pupil remarked.

With its small classrooms, narrow stairwells and corridors, the school has an intimate feel. The lack of space noted at our last visit has been remedied by using Portakabins for some lessons. Population is not that large, with just 600 in the main school, but there is a larger than average sixth form of 280 students. Still, the girls lack nothing in terms of modern resources, thanks to a very active PFTA.

Pastoral care and discipline: Pupils receive support from their form tutors and also have prefects to help school life run smoothly. 'Teachers are approachable, and there are some small classes so you get to know everyone.' When issues of bullying come up, 'once staff are aware of it the response is immediate and caring'.

Lots of careful thought has gone into ensuring peer support is strong. 'Our greatest glory is not in never failing but in rising up every time we fail' says a poster on the PSHCE board in the corridor. The board provides information about the peer support service run by older pupils. 'So important,' said a pupil; 'petty things getting out of hand is rare.' Pupils say they 'can't imagine peer support not being there. It's natural.' Also, 'Form prefects develop close relationships so you stay in contact even after leaving, like on Facebook.' House groups are active and help mobilise the girls to get involved in drama performances and fundraising events for the chosen recipient of charity week. Events like the five-penny race are popular and encourage heated competition, raising as much £2000 in one hour.

Career support is good. There is a university success board to inspire the girls and year 11s have a review day including one-to-one meetings with teachers. Year 12s spend two hours per week in voluntary service, often working with children or the elderly or the disabled. 'It's a steep learning curve and you find yourself going back for several months.'

Pupils and parents: Multi-ethnic population: over 40 languages spoken here and there is a significant Tamil and Indian population. One parent said, 'My daughter benefits from being with children from many different ethnic backgrounds'. Parents support the PFTA as an opportunity to solve many of the school's cash problems (£25,000 raised for digital language lab, a minibus and external lighting).

Girls seem confident, resilient and creative. Former pupils here include Lucy Kirkwood, playwright (RSC, National Theatre), Sarah Winman, best-selling novelist (When God was a Rabbit) and Peggy Reynolds, Radio 4 broadcaster in the arts.

Entrance: Massively oversubscribed, with some 900 applying for 120 years 7 places – will expand from four forms of entry to six in 2016. The verbal and non-verbal reasoning tests are written exclusively for the borough's only two grammar schools (the other being the brother school, Ilford County for Boys). It is one of just three all-girls schools in the area (the other two are independent and Catholic). Common catchment area with boys' grammar school. Head says the girls are tested on 'wit rather than what's been studied in the classroom'. Nearly all girls stay on to the sixth form, joined by 30 or so from other schools.

Exit: A few (around 10 per cent) leave post-GCSE but nearly all that stay go on to university. Subject choices are academic but varied: physics, law, medicine, languages (most likely French), mathematics, geography, English or economics. A few go on to study business or architecture. Some success in applications to top universities and competitive courses with four Oxbridge places in 2015. Other destinations include UCL, Queen Mary's, Kent, King's College London, Birmingham, Nottingham.

Remarks: With the great pastoral and peer support in place and strong academic atmosphere there is no reason why a pupil should not do well here. The message from pupils to any year 6s considering the school is: 'If you love academic study, close relationships with teachers, clubs and societies, and you want to get involved, this is the place for you.'

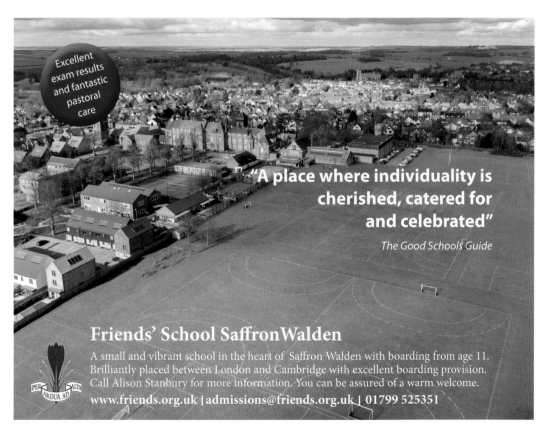

Children with special educational needs

Whether you are moving to London or already live here, the process of choosing a school is fraught with difficulties; throw into the mix a child with special needs and the challenges increase. You want your child to have an unparalleled education, but what are your options, and how do you work out what really is best?

What counts as a special need?

If your child has a difficulty that makes learning harder for them than for most children of the same age – whether the difficulty is social, emotional, intellectual, behavioural, physical, sensory or a mixture – then they may well have a special need. The most complex needs are generally diagnosed at birth or soon after, but other conditions, such as mild autistic spectrum disorders or specific learning difficulties such as dyslexia, may not be identified until well into their schooling. Indeed, you may well have to work hard to have your child's need recognised as 'special'. These needs may be transitory or permanent, but what matters is getting good help and support as soon as possible.

State schools – your choices

All state schools are in theory open to children with special needs – though for grammar schools they will need to pass the entrance exams. If your child has a Statement or, since September 2014, an Education Health and Social Care plan (EHC plan – next page) then it may be possible to add special schools to the list.

Independent schools – their choice

Independent schools choose the pupils they want to teach – if they don't want your child there is not a lot you can do about it. Some, such as Finton House in Wandsworth, keep a handful of places especially for children with special needs, others have a healthy, helpful attitude and will look at each child on merit.

London is blessed with some very good SEN specialist schools but the number and type of places available are limited. They tend to be expensive, too. Occasionally, an LA may agree to fund a place at an independent school (even if it is not in their own borough) but such places and funding are increasingly rare.

If a special or specialist school catches your eye, approach the school and ask them if they think your child might fit. They are likely to ask you to send reports, visit, even pay for an assessment. If they subsequently think they can help, they may offer assistance with the knotty process of securing LA funding, but be prepared for a long, fraught, frustrating fight with no guarantees.

SEN: a state of flux

Since September 2014 any new assessment for the two per cent or so of children with greatest needs is via an EHC plan rather than a Statement. Many of the finer details of EHC plans have yet to be worked out, but they are intended to cover both education and health needs, giving greater flexibility and greater autonomy for the child and their family. The picture is less clear for those whose needs are less severe, but most likely schools will have to provide help for them with no extra funding.

School admissions

If your child has an EHC plan or Statement you can, with the help of your LA, name the school you would like them to attend. Mainstream or special state schools, and independent special schools, must in theory admit your child unless the governing body thinks doing so would be 'unsuitable for the age, ability, aptitude or SEN of the child or young person;

or the attendance of the child or young person there would be incompatible with the efficient education of others; or the efficient use of resources'. If the school says no, you can appeal to the SEND tribunal.

Evaluating schools for children with SEN

Before signing on the dotted line, check out inspection reports, school policies, school websites and any independent reviews such as those by The Good Schools Guide – do they reflect a positive approach to SEN?

Once you've done the virtual work, arrange to visit schools, request a tour and ask to meet with the head and SENCo. Do they have a flexible and positive approach to SEN? Is support an integral part of school life? How is individual progress monitored? Is there a widespread celebration of achievement? Is the school generally geared up for diverse needs?

Try to visit two or more schools so you can compare them and make the best choice possible. Keep an eye on entry requirements and deadlines; rules and timings can and do change. Finally, remember to look beyond your child's special needs to ensure their strengths, talents and interests will be well catered for too.

For more information, visit www.goodschoolsguide.co.uk/sen

SEN schools in North London

The following schools offer specialist, targeted help for specific learning difficulties such as dyslexia, dyspraxia and ADHD. Some of their pupils may be able to return to mainstream school after a period of specialist teaching, but all will benefit from teaching methods and therapies specifically designed for these difficulties.

Abingdon House School

Broadley Terrace, London NW1 6LG
0845 2300426
www.abingdonhouseschool.co.uk

Head: Since 2014, Mr Roy English MA PGCE Adv Dip SEN (early 50s). Stepped up to the post after six years as deputy, following a stint as senior teacher and head of maths at Fairley House School. Popular with parents.

Entry: All children have learning difficulties, often with a diagnosis: ASD, Asperger's, dyspraxia, dyslexia, ADD, speech and language or social communication problems. Many arrive with poor self-esteem and social anxiety from mainstream schools. Children are taken after a two-day multi disciplinary assessment with teachers and therapists, which includes a try-out within the classroom. 'We take our admissions on the individual, not on any particular difficulty.' As a consequence the classes are both mixed ability and mixed socially. Many children are privately funded and some by LA, from both north and south of the river; 25 per cent from overseas.

Exit: 'We don't see it as a through school,' remarks the head. 'The majority we plan to get back to other schools.' He estimated a school career at Abingdon House for most children of between one and three years. Some go on to nurturing independents like The Moat, Portland Place, Wetherby and St Augustine's Priory while others go to mainstream secondaries.

Remarks: Age groups are mixed to create a social and academic blend and the emphasis is on flexibility. Teachers are supported in class by therapists (three speech and language; also music and play therapist) as well as frequent input from physio and OT. The school's enlightened understanding of the importance of speech and language support in building a child's confidence is palpable; parents can opt for extra one-to-one after school too. Physio and OT (known as 'Cosmo') is invisibly woven into lessons two or three times a week, perhaps as beanbags or climbing the apparatus.

The national curriculum is adapted to a thematic approach, so children who attend nurture groups or extra therapy sessions don't miss out on vital stages. We witnessed a group of the youngest children unaware it was a numeracy lesson, as they sang and jumped to 20. ICT is the head's passion so laptops and iPads are available for each child as well as a designated ICT room with a cluster of desktops.

A new sports specialist teacher oversees taekwondo, yoga and games. Team sports are difficult for this population and in such an urban setting, but the children get to visit a neighbouring playground and swim at a local leisure centre. On the top floor, music, DT, art and drama are synthesised in a whitewashed garret known affectionately as 'creative central.' The children are encouraged to try out the instruments on show: ukulele, guitar, keyboard, trumpet as well as lots of percussion. A magnificent big game trophy sculpted in paper sits outside the art room, still life drawings and textiles adorn the walls.

Boys outnumber girls six to one. Being in the heart of the city gives the teachers plenty of choice when it comes to day trips: Kensington museums, Imperial War Museum, London

Aquarium and Kew Gardens to name a few. For a London child with specific learning difficulties, this is a thoughtful and nurturing find.

Fairley House

30 Causton Street, London SW1 4AU
020 7976 5456
www.fairleyhouse.org.uk

Head: Since September 2013, Mr Michael Taylor BA PGCE FRGS (40s). A geographer, he came here from four years as deputy head at More House near Farnham, another good specialist school. Parents say 'boyish', 'deals with problems well', 'has a laugh with the pupils but keeps their respect', 'hands shaken, greeted by name, knows if they have been away.'

Entry: Children are invited to spend two days here, where they will have a transdisciplinary all-round assessment to ensure that the school will be able to meet their needs. After the assessment, parents are provided with reports from an educational psychologist, speech therapist and occupational therapist and then invited for a conference to discuss how the school can help and support their child. Assessments cost £290–£890.

Exit: The average stay for pupils at Fairley House is approximately two/three years. Depending on when a child arrives at the school, there is a tendency for the Fairley programme to end at odd ages (from an entrance point of view) like 12 or 14, which some potential next schools get stuffy about. Some parents clearly feel that the school could have been more helpful in the search for where to go to next. Top destinations are Bedales (senior and junior), DLD College, Hall School (Wimbledon), Kingham Hill, Millfield (senior and junior), Milton Abbey, Portland Place, Bedes (senior and junior), St Christopher and

Windlesham House – but there are a wide range of others who welcome Fairley pupils.

Remarks: Regularly inspected and accredited by CReSTeD, the register for specialist schools with provision for dyslexia and SpLDs. The main emphasis being on numeracy and literacy, everyone is put into a small group to match their ability and skills for maths and English and rejoins their class for other subjects. Children are taught to understand their own learning styles and shown strategies to overcome barriers to learning to achieve their targets.

Every child has an IEP which is regularly reviewed by the trans-disciplinary team to monitor progress and ensure that individual needs are being catered for. The trans-disciplinary approach is used across the curriculum, helpfully allowing therapy delivery to be linked to specific subjects and development. Depending on the individual needs of the pupil, speech therapy and occupational therapy are incorporated into classroom learning, art, drama and sports.

The children enjoy a great variety of artistic activities including textiles, fashion, design and technology, sewing and puppet-making. A range of sports - all the traditional ones, alongside canoeing, fencing and yoga. Although doesn't have its own playing fields, they make good use of local facilities at Battersea Park and the Queen Mother sports centre. Everyone is encouraged to learn a musical instrument and the school runs its own acting awards and music medals scheme.

Families scattered all over London, and a few from the edges of the home counties – requires an effort to get to know other families. A remarkable school for its holistic, multi-sensory and transdisciplinary approach. A beacon for children with learning and processing differences and parents who have been tearing their hair out trying to cope in other situations.

The Moat School

Bishops Avenue, London SW6 6EG
020 7610 9018
www.moatschool.org.uk

Head: Since February 2013, Miss Clare King (30s). Has only taught at The Moat, where she started as an NQT and received accelerated promotion. Previously director of studies and deputy head.

Entry: Entrance by way of careful review of a pupil's reports. The head will also take a view when the child comes in for an 'acquaint' day, and if the school feels they can support the child they will take them in even if reports are poor. Primarily a school for a child with dyslexia or dyspraxia, many also have expressive language difficulties. Many more interviewed than taken on because a good match needed in such small classes. Most mainstream primary schools, but also we met several from Blossom House and some from Fairley House in year 9, though late entry to the school a real disadvantage since the preparatory learning that takes place from year 7 all builds towards good learning skills for GCSE.

Exit: The school ends at GCSE; some parents and pupils expressed the desire for the school to continue to sixth form, but at present 75 per cent of pupils go into mainstream sixth form colleges or schools rather than supported placements and so the need is not there for this provision. It's a credit to the school that they are able to wean the pupils off special support. No data re where every child goes after sixth form but school suggests that about a third go on to higher education.

Remarks: Education is broad - pupils taught lots of communication and study skills alongside literacy and maths.

They are weaned off the extra help during the two year GCSE syllabus but by then class sizes get even smaller. Each pupil is issued with a laptop and helped to manage this responsibility by having convenient lockers to store them in between lessons (an example of the practical solutions to problems of organisation for dyslexics).

'A good range of subjects,' according to pupils, who all aim to leave with at least five GCSEs, though no language or classics teaching. All sit maths, English and science (many sitting additional science), but creativity high on school's and pupils' agenda since popular subjects are business communication, design technology, drama and media studies. Everything taught as kinaesthetically as possible – we saw a paper ball being thrown from teacher to pupil and back while being questioned – to help keep focus, keep energy levels high and pupils on their toes.

An integrated Skills for Learning programme takes the form of small, cross-age range groups, who are mentored in literacy skills three times a week throughout their school life, working on specific areas of weakness. Occupational therapist available and two speech therapists work with individual children but also teach language and communication skills throughout year 7.

Practical subjects predictably popular – science, media studies, music, art, PE. Drama a large part of the school curriculum with all children taking part in productions in one form or another. Sport encouraged but it is definitely not a competitive school and sport is 'more about keeping fit than winning'. Music for GCSE but also plenty of individual music lessons – drums, saxophone, guitar, piano etc. Gorgeous art all over the school includes collaborative and fine art (and lots of visits to galleries) but also wider design technology and resistant materials, and even film making. On our visit we saw very practical wood turning and food technology lessons – skill-based practical activities. Each day ends with an hour of a chosen extension activity such as quilting, drama, cricket, debate, sport.

Clear boundaries and sanctions intended to assist with the teenage problem of organisation and lost property that is exacerbated by dyslexia and dyspraxia. Understanding their own thinking and learning styles and self-reflection are encouraged and a school counsellor is available for children who are referred or who ask for time to talk. Eighty per cent have statements/EHC plans and are paid for by local authorities from all over London. They are all dyslexic but come from a wide range of backgrounds and there's no one type – sporty, academic, shy, drama queens – all sorts sharing a common tolerance.

This special school is remarkably conventional in many ways – discipline, high behavioural expectations, solid learning leading to GCSEs in usual range of subjects. What is unusual is such innovative and integrated teaching.

"If everyone is thinking alike, then no one is thinking."
Benjamin Franklin

At Frensham Heights, we are proud to think differently. We know every child is an individual and we treat them as such. That's why you'll continue to find Old Frenshamians leading in everything from medicine to opera and from the boardroom to the stage.

Come and see for yourself what makes Frensham so successfully individual. Visit www.frensham.org or call 01252 792561 to order a prospectus or arrange a visit.

Frensham Heights | Think, Create, Explore

Frensham Heights, Rowledge, Farnham, Surrey GU10 4EA Tel. 01252 792561 Charity No. 31205

Are two languages better than one?

Bilingualism remains, for monolingual parents, an impossibly glamorous idea. One language is good, two languages even better. Three languages? Why, the world's your oyster, huître or – depending, of course, on what those languages are.

London's linguistic make-up is becoming increasingly complex. Almost eight in 10 pupils in Newham primary schools, for example, speak English as an additional language. And as the capital becomes ever more culturally diverse, the number of schools offering a bilingual education is also increasing.

The French have been particularly energetic in working with local authorities to offer a small (very small) number of children a bilingual, French and English education in state schools. Danish and Italian bilingual schools, amongst others, are cropping up too. Given that the French make up one of the largest expat groups in the country, their enthusiasm is understandable. But if you're a really ambitious family, French may not be enough.

Bilingual nurseries

A new nursery in east London is tapping into the growing demand for families convinced that early exposure to Mandarin is a sure fire path to academic career success. Their statistics are an exercise in appetite whetting and there are plenty more out there, showing how a bilingual education can contribute to everything from improved concentration to better exam results.

Bringing up baby in more than one language isn't, however, always problem-free. Nor is it an easy way of guaranteeing top results. As one international school expert points out, it's not bilingual crèches that put Singapore at the top of the education achievement tables.

Exposure to a language and immersion are two very different things, while the simultaneous bilingualism that can occur naturally when the family is bilingual is a far cry from the bilingual crèche approach. Regardless of how many languages parents would like their child to speak, it is crucial that they develop a firm foundation in at least one to get the most out of their education.

The reason? It can take between five and seven years to develop the full literacy in a second language necessary to be a fully functioning bilingual. To be truly successful at school, children need fluent academic English. Being able to chat just isn't enough.

Lacking foundations

Too many students speak and function in two, three or more languages without having developed full literacy skills in any single one, something that is particularly likely to happen if they have not had proper EAL foundations provided in primary school.

If this doesn't happen, problems may not show up until children start to fail at Common Entrance or the 11+, missing out on offers for selective independent secondary schools because their higher-level cognitive thinking skills have not developed. For other students, the crunch point comes at 16, when IB diploma choices loom, with the need to be able to write critical literary analyses in their first language whilst also studying a second. It becomes clear that they do not have sufficient proficiency in any language to cope with this demanding course.

'Behind closed doors, we refer to these children as the 'bi-illiterates' – illiterate in two languages,' says one international schools expert.

In addition to ensuring children become truly proficient in at least one language, it is also important to understand that some children with learning needs will be worse off with a multilingual education. Speech and language processing problems, for example, can be magnified. A child struggling in one language can find it doubly hard to cope with two.

Mandarin or Martian

Any language, French, Mandarin or Martian, could end up holding back your child unless their school is also able to ensure that they acquire full literacy skills in the mother tongue or first language.

That said, pupils who achieve a good fluency and form a strong foundation in a first language can successfully go on to learn many more. But the bottom line is that parents who want their children to be educated in an English-speaking school need to ensure that their children have a sound foundation in their first language, otherwise the subtleties and complexities of higher order language processing will always elude them.

Wonderful though it is to be able to converse in and understand other languages, children need at least one they can learn in – and this generally means the one they think in. Speaking one language at home and another at school must therefore always be carefully thought through so children do not feel excluded or become disenfranchised.

City slippers – boarding for Londoners

Boarding, like sheep herding, polytunnelling and plume scrumpling, is something many Londoners assume to be an exclusively rural activity. Not too rural, of course. These days, families are increasingly selective about just how countrified they want the boarding experience to be. Greenery, yes. Day-long hikes to sports day, on the whole, not.

It's no coincidence that boarding schools whose yield per hectare, if not quite a match for top cash crops, comes close, hit greatest density levels within easy reach of London's top postcodes – no more than a sonic boom's echo from Heathrow or Gatwick.

Most famous of the lot are Eton and Harrow. While other schools have not just rolled over in response to parental requests for part-time boarding but also offered to juggle a couple of hoops with their front paws, there are no such concessions here. When boys' only full boarding for all has worked for centuries, you can't really blame them.

It's the same story for the girls at St Mary's Ascot, which held its nerve through the dark days of the recession and has been rewarded with record demand. Parents who don't buy in to the idea of boarding the traditional way are gently – but firmly – urged to look elsewhere.

Some city slickers don't buy into boarding, full stop. Others start to wonder whether the bracing two hour trek across London to and from that excellent day school and in the dark both ways during winter really is as character-forming as they'd hoped.

For these families, boarding can seem life-enhancing, making it possible to start early and stay late with food and friends provided – and without a punitive journey at the beginning and end of the day.

B&B

Many schools make a virtue – and success – of combining education with what can feel like a large-scale bed and breakfast operation: some pupils day only, some there pretty much full time, others opting for in-school sleepovers because of parental commitments, exam revision, late night games or early morning training.

Girls'-only establishments offering boarding and day places within or close to M25 range from Woldingham in Surrey, Marymount in Kingston-upon-Thames and St George's Ascot to the south and south west, while the Royal Masonic School for Girls and St Margaret's fill a similar niche north of the river. Boy boarders, meanwhile, can opt for Reed's School in Cobham, Surrey (girls are admitted in the sixth form) or Dulwich College, though day pupils dominate at both.

Those in search of a co-ed environment are, if not spoiled for choice close to London, far from being deprived, with Epsom College in Surrey and LVS in Ascot among those giving their accommodation eye-popping makeovers, from colour-coordinated furnishings (it's hard to spot a cushion that isn't tonally related to the curtains) to unlimited fresh fruit to snack on. Further north, there's Mill Hill School, with 100 weekly and full boarders.

Boarding, like every other aspect of education, has its fair share of curiosities. Like the ravens at the Tower of London, boarders at the City of Freemen's School in Ashtead, Surrey, specified by statute, must always be part of the community (though, unlike the ravens, wing-clipping isn't required to keep them there).

Schools for skills

Then there are the specialists – such as the Yehudi Menuhin School (music) and Tring Park (performing arts) – where boarding helps the super talented to hone their skills in and out of hours, free from tube strike blues and similar aesthetic lows; the different (eg St Christopher in Letchworth, set up by the Theosophists) and the new (flushed with the success of its first boarding house, Whitgift School, in the non-plush territory of South Croydon, is already mulling over a second).

Even costs don't necessarily need to be sky high if you opt for a state boarding school such as Cranbook (selective) and Gordon's (all-comers) where parents pay for accommodation while teaching comes courtesy of the ever-generous taxpayer.

For any dyed in the wool Londoners who come over all faint at the prospect of breathing air outside the congestion zone, no longer enhanced with flavoursome carcinogens, it's hard to beat boarding, literally, on your doorstep.

Westminster School, with 185 or so boarders (including girls, admitted in the sixth form), is pretty much as close as you can get to total immersion in the beating heart of the city without squatting in Big Ben. 'You get that sense of community,' says a former Westminster parent. 'You have more time to get involved and people tend to stay late anyway.'

For some London parents, day places will always be the educational black, the only goal worth pursuing, with boarding the reserve choice when all other options have been exhausted. Others, relishing the out of hours opportunities, from extra tuition to drama, debate, music and sport, feel very differently. Costs permitting (and boarding is, undeniably, costly) it could well be worth taking a look at both.

HURTWOOD HOUSE

THE BOARDING SCHOOL FOR THE CREATIVE & PERFORMING ARTS

www.hurtwoodhouse.com

Gumley House School FCJ

Gumley House School FCJ provides a Catholic Education for girls, including boys in the sixth form. (Open policy with no faith requirement for sixth form)

The Gumley Journey: Our students benefit from a strong academic learning environment, whole person development, extensive extracurricular provision, pastoral support, diverse international opportunities and abundant grounds and green spaces.

Top Performing State School: Academic results reflect our tradition of achievement; the students' high levels of ambition and expectation and the teaching and dedication of our staff.

Latest results:

- A Level: Continued success with 100% pass rate and Oxbridge entrance. Results exceed by far the national average. Our A* results of 15% are the highest in the borough.
- From Year 7, students can study Mandarin, one of 4 languages taught. Almost 90% of GCSE students taking a language regularly achieve A*- C grades. **(Gumley is one of only 8% of state schools teaching Mandarin)**

Sixth form results

Please do contact us anytime directly on general@gumley.hounslow.sch.uk

Shower Gel to Start Up Business! Imperial College Science & Enterprise project.

For our review visit www.goodschoolsguide.co.uk/schools/100540/gumley-house-school-fcj

www.gumley.hounslow.sch.uk

Get set for the school run

Between 6.45am and 8.00am every day in term time, a rash of buses appears on London's streets. Some are vast, in-your-face coaches, school destination flagged in big, flashing letters; others smaller, anonymous white minibuses. Big or small, their purpose is the same - to ferry hundreds of children, some as young as four and five, to and from school each day.

Many parents are understandably opposed to bolting on transport arrangements that segregate their children from others and make their educational experience even more rarified.

But the experience isn't all bad. One leading headmaster was recently quoted as saying that pupils look forward to their daily commute because, in such a pressurised environment, it's just about the only chance they have to relax.

And as the race for places at desirable schools, both state and independent, hots up, a longer home to school commute seems to be an additional price that increasing numbers of desperate families are willing for their child to pay to secure the best possible education – making anything that eases the stress of the journey an understandable bonus.

There are other factors, too. Traffic and children aren't a natural mix. For the truly worried, there's even a website that lets you search accidents by postcode. Though overall figures are down, injuries or worse for the young would give even well-adjusted parents the jitters, with a third of incidents involving 11 and 12-year-olds, coinciding with a longer commute to senior school and possibly not unconnected with a rise in smart phone ownership.

Then there's crime. One leading boys' school has become notably relaxed about its pupils shedding uniform for their homeward journey after its distinctive blazers - as good an indication of quality merchandise as a Harrod's label - made them easy pickings for muggers. Instead, pupils are advised to don hoodies (sensible) or 'overcoats' (a Crombie a day keeps the robbers away? Well, perhaps).

Add in ex-pat families trying to get to grips with a new city and it's not hard to see why roughing it on local transport, however worthy, can have limited appeal.

Whatever the reasons, the number of school bus routes has climbed. NW3, where rush hour traffic is epically awful and parents perhaps correspondingly eager to avoid it, should probably get the prize for the most buses packed into a single postcode.

A lot is down to a parent-led firm, Transport4schools, which through grit and, presumably, a phenomenal appetite for red tape, now runs bus routes to over 30 schools. The vast majority are in NW3 and include Devonshire House, South Hampstead and just about all the saints (Mary, Anthony and Christopher) as well as some local state primaries.

Its buses also reach out to Hammersmith (Latymer Upper School), as well as City of London School for Girls in EC2, on a route that follows the path of the Northern Line, 'which seems barking to me,' thought a former parent. (City of London School for boys, in contrast, cheerfully lists local public bus and train stops and leaves it at that.)

The firm hopes its buses will replace 1,400 private cars on local roads. You have to admire their prosletysing zeal, with a website that includes the costs of car use (an estimated £20 a day for a return journey to a school nine miles from home, if you include depreciation and finance costs) while its site tells of the 'immiserating' impact of the school run.

Other companies are getting in on the act and there's a whiff of competition in the air, with offers of refunds for non-use - and the clincher: 'the more children ... the cheaper it gets...' from one. Pile 'em high, bus 'em cheap?

Some schools even attract more than one operator. One leading girls' school, for example, has two, serving broadly similar routes, though there's no sign so far (fun though it would be to witness) of punch ups between rival firms at going home time.

Around the capital, the route permutations are sufficiently varied to keep an anoraks' convention happy for days. Some are as small and exclusive as the school they serve, one small prep doing most of its ferrying in Chelsea, St John's Wood and Mayfair.

There are buses that will whisk your child from Bayswater and Canary Wharf to Dulwich College and from Golders Green and St John's Wood to St Paul's, while North London Collegiate School's routes currently extend to Kensington in the west and Potters Bar in the north.

It's worth noting that, unlike formal school trips where everything, from teacher to pupil ratios, is set in stone, morning and afternoon bus commutes are less regulated.

Similarly, the age your child can travel to and from school isn't fixed in stone. At one leading girls' school, pupils are welcomed on board from reception age onwards with an older pupil acting as a chaperone on the morning journey, though there's adult supervision on the way home to ensure that the afternoon collection from the bus stop is problem free.

Operating companies, too, vary in what they can and can't do. Routes shouldn't generally be than 15 miles in London to avoid going above a maximum journey length of around 75 minutes for older children and 45 minutes for little ones.

The strictest rules apply to firms registered as licensed operators, where drivers and the buses themselves are allowed on the road only after they've shown themselves to be fit for purpose and even non-driving directors have to pass exams to show they know what they're doing.

But when it comes to the increasing numbers of minicab firms offering door to door school pickups round London in smaller vehicles – up to eight passengers, plus the driver - there's rather less officialdom. Checking who your driver will be, whether you'll have the same one each day and their experience, background and checks, is definitely worth doing.

Finally, for families who have had enough of the whole London education experience, several schools offer what they (inevitably) describe as the best of both worlds – home in the big smoke, education far, far away.

Some, (such as Woldingham) meet, greet and sweep up from the local station – handily it's on a direct route from Clapham Junction, and just happens to border their extensive grounds. Others like Caldicott and Papplewick (both boys' prep schools) run their own daily return bus service from assorted West London destinations (Brook Green, twixt Hammersmith and Shepherd's Bush, is the minibus equivalent of platform 9 at King's Cross).

Routes can, of course, change, as families' postcodes differ and bus services that were over-booked one year empty out in the next. But whether through the school itself, parent-organised services or independent companies, it's more than likely that however esoteric the journey your child needs to take, from the shortest cross-borough hop to a cross-Capital marathon, someone will be able to help. And if all else fails, there's always London Transport. We've heard it's quite good these days...

Tutors and tutoring in London

Tutoring is endemic in the UK these days, and nowhere more so than in the capital, where top agencies have parents queueing to pay £70+ an hour to buy 3 year olds an advantage in the selection stakes. But keep your head, even if your child's already turned 2. Remember, an anxious mother and her money are soon parted, and the race has only just begun.

Two is too early

Seriously, there are folks out there offering to tutor children as young as 2, but it's all snake oil. Don't be taken in. Spend the money at one of London's wonderful bookshops and read to your child instead. What pre-school-age children need is not tutoring and angst, but time and love from the grown-ups who care for them. If you're reading this article, you are by default an educated, thinking parent who wants the best for your child, so give her the treasures of your mind, your vocabulary, your tastes; they will far out-class anything a paid charlatan can provide.

When do you need a tutor?

Put simply, when there is a clear and specific reason for using one. Your child may need help with the 11+ or 13+ entry to an academically selective senior school. Or perhaps he's struggling with a particular GCSE/A level subject. Or she may be falling behind at school. Or he may have missed school through illness or some other crisis. Where there is a known goal to work towards, or a genuine problem to address, tutoring comes into its own.

For a shy child who's under-performing, a friendly tutor can be a godsend. Free from the distractions of the classroom and other pupils, he or she can sit quietly with your child and concentrate solely on whatever's confusing her, filling in gaps in her knowledge and building up her confidence. Grades start to improve, and the child becomes a happier learner, keener to put her hand up in class and more relaxed about going to school. For a teenager who's struggling with maths, demoralised by always coming last in his set and stressed about approaching exams, quality one-to-one teaching from someone with no preconceptions about him can make the difference between failure and success; between giving up and keeping on.

It could be that you're putting your child through the state system to begin with while you save up for the independent senior school you hope he'll attend. If this is the case, he will need help with exam preparation. You may feel confident going through maths and English 11+ preparation books and past papers with him, but if not, tutoring is pretty much essential. No matter how bright your child, he'll be up against other children who have been intensively coached. If he's to stay in the game, you'll have to do likewise.

But tutoring is one of those things parents usually do in secret, either because they don't choose to tell it around that their child struggles at school, or because they've no wish to increase the opposition's chances in the race for places. Perhaps you feel your child needs a tutor even though he's already at a good preparatory school. Well, maybe. Be very sure, though, that the need is real. Depending on where he is, a year's tutoring in the run-up to common entrance may make sense, if only because it'll bring you peace of mind. But to have your tutored 7-year-old win a place at a high-achieving prep and then immediately start having him tutored some more just because everyone else is doing it, will only exhaust him and your bank account. Wave him off to St Brainiac's with a proud smile, and let the school do its work.

No matter now bright your child, he'll be up against other children who have been intensively coached. If he's to stay in the game, you'll have to do likewise

On the other hand, if you've just relocated to the UK from overseas, using a tutor is an excellent way to get your kids up to speed with the English system and help them to feel more assured and comfortable in lessons. This in turn will help them to make friends, and the whole settling-in process will be smoother. For a child in a new country, confidence is key.

If a person's replies to your messages are semi-literate, don't engage them as an English tutor

If you want a tutor for your child, how do you find one? The best way should be word of mouth, of course. But tutoring is one of those things parents usually do in secret, either because they don't choose to tell it around that their child struggles at school, or because they've no wish to increase the opposition's chances in the race for places. Try asking a friend with an older child, who won't begrudge your using what they no longer need. If this doesn't bring results, don't worry. This is London, and you have plenty of options.

Tutor companies

We review many of the best tutor companies on the Good Schools Guide website, and using them has a number of benefits. They'll be skilled at matching your child to the right person, and will give you redress if you're not happy. This is the most expensive way of employing a tutor, however. Almost all companies charge a registration fee, anything from a few quid to a hair-raising £180, and the hourly rate for tuition is high (be prepared for at least £45), because the company takes a cut before paying the teacher. Some of the really big tutorial companies cover too wide a geographical area to interview all their tutors in person, but they will have interviewed them by phone, and checked their references and DBS record.

Tutor websites

A cheaper option is finding a tutor online. There are a number of websites on which tutors can advertise, and whose contact details you buy, usually for around £20, after you've had an exchange of messages with your selected tutor to see if they're the right fit. Tuition rates vary from £16 ph – probably an undergraduate trying to earn a bit of extra cash – to £45+ ph for an experienced and qualified teacher. The website companies run checks to ascertain whether the tutor advertising is who they claim to be, but otherwise it's down to you to judge people's suitability. Websites like these can be very useful and we regularly hear reports from satisfied parents, ourselves included. Again, use your common sense. If a person's replies to your messages are semi-literate, don't engage them as an English tutor.

Don't believe them when they say they can get from Wood Green to Putney in half an hour, they absolutely can't

Do your homework

Self-employed individuals are unlikely to be DBS-checked, because the law prevents them from running a check on themselves, so ask to see references or to speak to previous clients. In fact, do this even if they are DBS-checked. Interview the tutor on the phone before fixing a first date, and don't feel pressured into accepting someone who doesn't sound right. Don't be afraid to sit in on the first lesson, and afterwards ask your child what she thought. If the tutor is travelling to you, check that they can get there easily. Don't believe them when they say they can get from Wood Green to Putney in half an hour, they absolutely can't. Lastly – and this wisdom comes from years of weary experience – insist on punctuality. A tutor who is routinely late will soon drive you up the wall.

With careful preparation, your child's tutoring experiences should be happy, productive and affordable. Good luck.

Child protection

If you are preparing to entrust your child to a school – whether day or boarding – you will most likely assume that your child will be safe and that all members of the school's staff will take the greatest care to ensure that this is always the case. The chances are that your expectations will be fulfilled. Unfortunately, in a sad minority of cases that is not what happens.

What can you do?
Parents can warn their children – gently but seriously – of the dangers, however remote these may be, so they feel that it is easy to speak to you should they meet them. It is worth pointing out that abuse can come from anyone – including a teacher or an adult they know well.

At any school you may be considering, inquire about the steps taken to safeguard children in the same way you might ask about bullying or learning support. As always, much can be gleaned from the head's attitude when questions about child protection are asked. Openness is what you're looking for.

For those who want to probe further:
Where can I find the school's child protection policy?
Every school is required to have a child protection policy that is made available to staff, volunteers and parents on request.

Where can I and my children find out who the child protection officers are?
Ideally, a school should have more than one designated person and they should be named on a public notice board, so that everyone knows who to talk to.

What training do staff receive in child protection?
Training is mandatory every two years for designated officers, and every three years for all staff who work with children.

Is it the school's written policy to report child protection allegations to the Local Authority Designated Officer ('LADO')?
A good head will have a good working relationship with their LADO, so that both can have confidence that incidents will be well managed.

How many 'referrals' have been made to the Department of Education in the past three years and for what reasons?
A referral means a member of staff has left the school in circumstances which indicate they were unfit to work with children. Do not rule out a school because a case of abuse has been brought to light there. Tabloid coverage can be the price the school has to pay for handling a case of abuse or bullying openly.

Dwight School London
Igniting the spark of genius in every child

Personalised Learning · Community · Global Vision

Dwight is an IB World School for students aged 2-18, representing over 40 nationalities; ***no two students are alike.*** Our aim is to foster the development of the whole child, whatever their talent or passion. Dwight is committed to realising every student's full potential.

For details of our International Baccalaureate Programmes for students of all ages contact:

admissions@dwightlondon.org
6 Friern Barnet Lane N11 3LX
020 8920 0600
www.dwightlondon.org

CollegeBoard

ecis

Dwight Global Campuses and Programmes: London | New York | Seoul | Shanghai | Canada

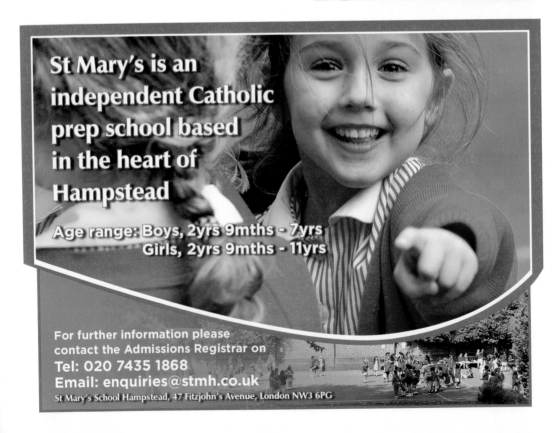

St Mary's is an independent Catholic prep school based in the heart of Hampstead

Age range: Boys, 2yrs 9mths - 7yrs
Girls, 2yrs 9mths - 11yrs

For further information please contact the Admissions Registrar on
Tel: 020 7435 1868
Email: enquiries@stmh.co.uk
St Mary's School Hampstead, 47 Fitzjohn's Avenue, London NW3 6PG

Further reading

The Good Schools Guide 20th edition
Features independent and unbiased views of over 1,200 state and independent schools throughout Britain, written by parents for parents.

The Good Schools Guide online subscription
Read all our reviews plus exam data, catchment maps, university entrance information, and advice on choosing a school, tutors, SEN, talented children and much more.

Uni in the USA
Written by students who have been through the US system, features in-depth descriptions of 65 US universities, plus the inside track on getting in and preparing for life across the pond.

Uni in the USA and Beyond online subscription and ebook
Also includes unis in Europe and the East, from Alberta to Abu Dhabi, and advice from SATS to visas.

The Good Schools Guide International online subscription
The one-stop educational shop for ex-pats, it reviews the best state and independent schools round the globe, plus insider knowledge on life overseas.

All available via www.goodschoolsguide.co.uk/shop-online

BERKHAMSTED

The School that grows with you

BERKHAMSTED
day nursery

PRE-PREP

PREP

GIRLS

BOYS

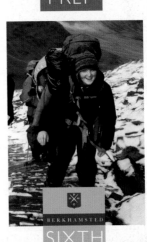

SIXTH

- 30 minutes direct by train from Euston
- Situated in an historic market town with easy links to Heathrow
- Consistently high academic results, achieved alongside a broad co-curricular timetable
- Diamond School, Co-education (3-11) (16-18) and Single Sex (11-16)
- Supporting working parents through extended hours and holiday care

For more information on admissions and scholarships call
01442 358001 or visit our website www.berkhamstedschool.org

A member of the Berkhamsted Schools Group Registered Company No. 622349 Registered Charity No. 310630

London North school index

London North districts index

List of advertisers

Advertisers (Website)

Notes

Notes

Notes